By the late JAMES D. DANA

SYSTEM OF MINERALOGY. *Seventh Edition.*

Rewritten and enlarged by Charles Palache,
the late Harry Berman, and Clifford Frondel.

VOL. I. 1944.
VOL. II. 1951.
VOL. III. In preparation.

MANUAL OF MINERALOGY. *Sixteenth Edition.*
Revised by Cornelius S. Hurlbut, Jr.

By the late EDWARD S. DANA

A TEXTBOOK OF MINERALOGY. *Fourth Edition.*
Revised by the late William E. Ford. 1932.

MINERALS AND HOW TO STUDY THEM. *Third Edition*
Revised by Cornelius S. Hurlbut, Jr. 1949.

THE SYSTEM OF

MINERALOGY

of James Dwight Dana and Edward Salisbury Dana
Yale University 1837–1892

SEVENTH EDITION
Entirely Rewritten and Greatly Enlarged

By

CHARLES PALACHE

the late HARRY BERMAN

and CLIFFORD FRONDEL

Harvard University

VOLUME I

ELEMENTS, SULFIDES, SULFOSALTS,

OXIDES

JOHN WILEY AND SONS, INC.
NEW YORK   *LONDON*

PRINTED IN THE UNITED STATES OF AMERICA

Dedicated to the Memory

of

Richard Alexander Fullerton Penrose, Jr. (1863–1931)

and

Albert Fairchild Holden (1866–1913)
whose bequests to the Geological Society of
America and to Harvard University made this
volume possible

PREFACE

In 1892 Edward S. Dana published the sixth edition of his father's *System of Mineralogy*, dating from 1837. In the preface to the work, followed as it is by excerpts from the prefaces of the preceding editions, Dana gave in briefest outline the history of the successive changes that the development of the science had brought about. This book soon became and still is a recognized authority, used wherever mineralogy is studied.

During the half century which has elapsed since that edition appeared, vast changes have affected the science of mineralogy. In undertaking a new edition, the authors began with the definite intention of preserving the long-familiar form so far as should prove possible. But after a few years spent in the attempt to incorporate in the pages of the sixth edition the accumulated new data, this proved to be impracticable and in its present form the book will be found to be essentially a new work.

The principal changes found necessary in the seventh edition may be briefly tabulated.

a. A new mineral classification, based on crystal chemistry.

b. A new elastic series of classification numbers for species.

c. Revised morphological elements based on the structural unit cell.

d. A new form of presentation of the crystallographic data.

e. Introduction of data derived from x-ray crystallography.

f. Revision of specific gravities, based on new observations.

g. Introduction of the optical characters of the opaque minerals.

h. A new chemical treatment of species, with generalized formulas for types, discussion of group relations, and a sharper definition of varieties.

i. A new method of treating minerals that form a so-called series, that is, describing a series as if it were a single-species description.

j. Expansion and annotation of the reference section to include sources of data, transformation formulas, lists of rare forms, general literature, and a statement of controversial questions requiring elucidation.

These changes are treated at some length in the introduction. Many of them are clearly due to the wider knowledge we now have of the nature of crystals made possible by x-ray analysis of their structure. Upon this basis is founded the science of crystal chemistry. The crystallographic data are also based on existing knowledge of the structural cell and this leads not infrequently to change in the choice, position, or relative dimensions of the morphological elements employed.

The form of presentation of crystallographic data is wholly new. It is based on position angles as obtained by measurement of crystals with the two-circle goniometer and on the gnomonic projection made from those angles. This change involves a new tabulation form and the recalculation of all the angles presented. Interfacial angles are included to facilitate comparison with older tabulations of crystal measurement. All the crystal figures have been redrawn and many of them are new to the *System*.

The x-ray data presented are few. They include the unit cell and its axial ratio, the space group, and the atomic contents of the cell so far as they are known. The theoretical specific gravity has also been calculated where data suffice.

The optical data given are based largely on the tables of Larsen and Berman, published during the progress of this work. Data on the optical characters of the opaque minerals are taken largely from the work of Schneiderhöhn and Ramdohr.

For the chemical treatment, reference must be made to the introduction. It is believed that a great gain in the sharpness of definition of varieties has been obtained by the introduction of the uniform adjectival prefix for chemical varieties as proposed by Schaller.

The general statement of types of occurrence given for each of the common species is new to the *System*. It is based chiefly on the classification and description in Lindgren's *Mineral Deposits*. No attempt has been made to list all known localities.

Nomenclature and synonymy follow the older editions of the *System* with minor exceptions, and here there is less change than in any other part of the work. It is hoped that the new system of classification numbers adopted will meet the needs of the many who have requested the retention of some form of numeration of species. The older number series is, of course, completely disrupted by the new classification.

In justice to the many men and institutions who have contributed to bring the first volume of this work to completion, a brief history of the undertaking is needed.

In 1915, a few months after the publication of the Third Appendix to the sixth edition of the *System*, E. S. Dana asked Professor W. E. Ford of Yale University to prepare a seventh edition of the book. Shortly afterwards Professor Dana legally relinquished all rights in the book, giving full authority to Ford and the publishers to proceed in the matter as seemed wise to them. Professor Ford realized at once that the task was too large for him to undertake alone, and he sought and obtained the assistance of Professors Palache and Larsen of Harvard University for crystallography and optical mineralogy. He also sought aid in the chemical side of the work, reserving for himself the section dealing with the occurrence of minerals. In 1927 a definite contract was entered into with the publishers by the three men named. Professor Ford, aided by the Sterling Fund of Yale University, secured the assistance of Dr. J. F. Schairer and then of Dr. M. Fleischer to collect and to discuss chemical data. Professor Palache, with funds subscribed by Mr. G. S. Holden and the publishers, had as assistants Dr. L. LaForge and later Dr. M. A. Peacock. Professor Larsen, with Dr. Berman, completed the preparation of optical data in the form of their tables (1934). Work advanced slowly and, although a large amount of data, especially that relating to species new after 1892, was collected, no actual beginning was made in writing the revised edition. After some years had passed, Professor Ford's health broke down so that he felt obliged to give up the task.

At this point it became evident that real progress would not be made until properly equipped men were able to devote their whole time to the work. Backed by a large number of their geological and mineralogical associates, Professors Ford and Palache in 1936 applied to the Geological Society of America for a grant from the Penrose Fund to enable the work to be completed. Still underestimating the task, they asked for $6,000 a year for four years to pay the salary of two men and a stenographer to work under the direction of Dr. Palache at Harvard. The grant was made in December, 1937. Dr. Berman and Dr. Peacock were engaged to carry out this project. They spent many months deciding on the final form of the presentation. Ford continued to supply occurrence data up to the time of his death in 1939. Dr. Palache sought crystallographic data where they were lacking. Dr. Peacock left to take a position elsewhere after a year had elapsed. Dr. Berman carried on, at first alone, later with the efficient full-time help of Dr. Frondel.

Others gave part-time assistance. Dr. C. W. Wolfe did most of the angle computations and some of the crystal drawings, and prepared the statement of crystallographic procedure contained in the introduction. Miss A. M. Dowse for a time, then Mr. H. T. Evans, Jr., made drawings, the latter by far the larger number. Dr. J. D. H. Donnay assisted one summer in discussing the form of presentation of the material. To Dr. Berman and Dr. Frondel fell the task of writing the final text and in the summer of 1941, the grant from the Penrose Fund just at an end, the first of three volumes was completed.

The preparation of the second volume was begun at once, the continued services of Dr. Frondel being provided for by a grant made to Professor Palache and Professor Berman from the Penrose Fund of the American Philosophical Society in 1941 for the Dana work. This work was interrupted in 1942 by the war, but there seems to be no reason to doubt that it will be resumed and brought to ultimate completion as soon as conditions of peace make it practicable.

Certain printed works have been indispensable to our progress. Without Dr. Spencer's *Mineralogical Abstracts* at hand we would have been often at a loss. Goldschmidt's *Atlas* was taken as a point of departure for compilation of form lists and for the selection of typical crystals for drawings. His *Winkeltabellen* often gave a welcome check on the accuracy of our new angles.

New mineralogical data have been accumulated during the progress of this work, some of them not yet published elsewhere. Most notable are the accurate specific gravity determinations made on authentic small crystals with the Berman microbalance. These are scattered through the whole text. Reexamination of the morphology of many of the more complexly crystallized sulfosalts, based on x-ray cell determination, has also been carried out in this laboratory. Some new chemical analyses by Mr. F. A. Gonyer are also included. In short, the resources of the Harvard laboratories and collections, which owe so much to the Holden Endowment Fund, have been employed at every opportunity. Many problems of classification and morphology remain unsolved, but at least the necessity of research upon them has been pointed out. Miss M. B. Fitz, Secretary-Librarian of the Harvard Department of Mineralogy gave devoted assistance in all stages of the preparation of the final manuscript.

The Dana staff is indebted in various ways to others for voluntary assistance. Dr. W. T. Schaller of the U. S. Geological Survey and Dr. H. E. Merwin of the Geophysical Laboratory have sent valuable data; Dr. M. J. Buerger of Massachusetts Institute of Technology and Dr G. Tunell of the Geophysical Laboratory have made studies on incompletely described species as have Dr. Peacock and his students at the University of Toronto; Dr. J. P. Marble of the U. S. National Museum prepared a statement on the radioactivity of uraninite; Professor L. C. Graton of Harvard University gave wise counsel and read and added much to the text; The U. S. National Museum through Dr. W. F. Foshag and The American Museum of Natural History through Mr. H. P. Whitlock and Dr. F. H. Pough loaned valuable material for study. The staff of the mineralogical section of the British Museum of Natural History, especially Mr. F. A. Bannister and Dr. M. H. Hey, carried out x-ray studies at our request. Professor Larsen and Professor Hurlbut of the Harvard Staff have also contributed much in counsel and research. To Dr. Hunt, Editor of *The American Mineralogist*, thanks are due for permission to use cuts which have appeared in that journal.

The authors desire to express their great obligations to the publishers, Messrs. John Wiley & Sons, Inc., whose association with the Dana Mineralogies dates back to 1844, when they published the second edition of the *System*. Members of their staff have given patient and indispensable aid in the preparation of the text and figures for the press. It has already been stated that the firm advanced money to be used in the collection of data for the book. But it did much more. When the application of Professors Ford and Palache was made to the Geological Society of America for a grant of funds for the preparation of the book, the firm supported the application by guaranteeing, as the authors had already done, to take no profit from the sale of the book until the grant had been repaid. It is not too much to say that this guarantee did much to determine the award of the grant. To Mr. W. O. Wiley, Chairman of the

Board, the publication of this new edition of the *System* has been from the beginning of the enterprise a matter of personal interest and pride in the continuation of the firm's long association with the Dana Mineralogies, quite apart from the probable financial returns.   The stimulation of such personal support has been of inestimable value to the authors.

Despite every care in checking, errors are bound to occur where so much concentrated detail is presented.   Readers will confer a favor by pointing out any that they discern.

CHARLES PALACHE

Harvard University,
   April, 1944

CONTENTS

xiii

INTRODUCTION

1. Classification

Nearly all minerals are solid and crystalline and as such their chemistry is embraced within the new science of crystal chemistry.[1] Because many mineral species furnish excellent crystals much of the early work leading to important crystallochemical conclusions has been done with minerals.[2] Although crystal chemistry is formally a new branch of chemistry, the mineralogists early recognized the importance of crystallography in a consideration of the relations between minerals, and their classifications were based in a large measure on both crystallography and chemistry. These are essentially the bases of the new classifications of crystalline substances. The external crystallography (morphology) is only an expression of the internal structure, as deduced from x-ray crystallographic studies, and the internal structure is in turn an expression of the interrelations of the atoms of the substance. Crystal chemistry is concerned with these correlations.

Most minerals have the ionic type of bonding, that is, the interatomic binding force consists of an electrostatic attracting force between oppositely charged ions. A small portion of the total number of minerals has a metallic type of bonding, that is, the positive ions are enmeshed in a field of electrons. The native elements (of the metallic type) and perhaps certain of the sulfides are the only minerals having this kind of bonding. Diamond, sphalerite, and a number of the sulfides have the homopolar type of bonding; that is, the atoms are held together by the sharing of electrons from their outer shell.[3] With the exception of the metals and a few sulfides, then, all minerals are predominantly ionic. These latter have been subdivided on the basis of the variation in the strength of the binding force into (1) isodesmic, (2) mesodesmic, and (3) anisodesmic compounds. Most of the minerals (with the exception of the metals and homopolar compounds) in this volume are isodesmic compounds, that is, the strength of the bondings of the cations with the anion are qualitatively the same, and no discrete units are formed by particular cation-anion groups. In the silicates, which are to be described in Volume III, the silicon-oxygen bond is stronger than that between oxygen and the other cations, and they fall, therefore, into the second division of the crystallochemical classification (mesodesmic). The phosphates, sulfates, arsenates, etc., are in the third

---

[1] C. W. Stillwell, *Crystal Chemistry*, McGraw-Hill Book Co., New York, 1938. R. C. Evans, *An Introduction to Crystal Chemistry*, University Press, Cambridge, England, 1939.

[2] W. L. Bragg, *Atomic Structure of Minerals*, Cornell University Press, Ithaca, New York, 1937.

[3] An account of different bonding types is given in Stillwell (1938) and Evans (1939).

division (anisodesmic) because the PO_4, SO_4, AsO_4 groups are discrete units in the structure. All these are grouped in Volume II. The classification as given in the previous edition is, therefore, in essential agreement with the demands of a modern treatment, and it is only within these broad groupings that important changes have been made in this edition.

The minerals of the first volume are divided into eight classes as follows: (1) native elements, (2) sulfides, (3) sulfosalts, (4) simple oxides, (5) oxides containing uranium, thorium, and zirconium, (6) hydroxides, (7) multiple oxides, (8) multiple oxides containing columbium, tantalum, and titanium. Within each class the further divisions are according to types, i.e., the $A : X$ ratio, where A stands for positive ions (cations) or electropositive atoms, and X for negative ions (anions) or electronegative atoms. The types, comparatively few in number, are arranged according to the decreasing ratio $A : X$; thus the most metallic sulfides come at the beginning of the sulfide class, and cuprite is the first of the simple oxides. In the multiple oxides (such as spinel) or multiple sulfides (here called sulfosalts) the arrangement is by the ratio $A + B : X$ primarily, and then according to the decreasing $A : B$ ratio.

In many of the simple A_mX_n and $A_mB_nX_p$ minerals the structural control is largely geometrical, that is, the so-called *radius ratio* of $R_A : R_X$ is the determining factor in the structure. These ratios are related to the number of atoms of one kind which are packed around atoms of the other, that is, the coordination number. The following is a tabulation of coordination number and radius ratio limits.[4]

TABLE 1

COORDINATION NUMBER AROUND A	$R_A : R_X$
2	to 0.15
3	0.15–0.22
4	0.22–0.41
6	0.41–0.73
8	0.73 and up

Other factors such as polarizability of the atoms also play a part in the structure. However, these cannot be considered in detail here. The books by Stillwell and Evans, previously referred to, consider the problems of crystal chemistry, and these should be consulted for details.

The A_mX_n types in the various classes often show geometric and structural similarities when the $A : X$ ratio is the same. Thus, halite, where $A = Na$ and $X = Cl$ is similar in structure with galena, where $A = Pb$ and $X = S$, or with periclase, where $A = Mg$ and $X = O$. However, from a mineralogical point of view, it is not desirable to place such dissimilar minerals together in the classification, and it is for this reason that the divisions are first made by classes rather than by structure type. The $A_mB_nX_p$ classes also show similarities when the ratio $A + B : X$ is the same as the ratio $A : X$ in the simple classes. For example, rutile, TiO_2, is

[4] Stillwell (1938).

closely related in structure and geometric properties to tapiolite, $FeTa_2O_6$, $(A + B : X = 1 : 2)$.

Since the ionic radii are important in a consideration of the relations of mineral species and groups, and also play an important role in the classification, a tabulation is given here, together with the atomic weights and atomic numbers.

Most types contain a number of groups, and these usually are minerals of closely similar structure. Thus, the *galena group* contains *galena*, PbS, *altaite*, PbTe, and *clausthalite*, PbSe. *Alabandite*, MnS, and *oldhamite*, CaS, are less closely related to galena than are the others mentioned, but they are included. In the same AX type, minerals closely related in structure to *sphalerite* form another group. Groups, however, are not here restricted to minerals having similar structures. Chemical similarities or close physical similarities are sometimes a basis for grouping minerals. When the characteristics of a number of minerals within a type can profitably be discussed together they form a group.

Minerals showing a continuous variation in their properties with change in composition are called *series*, and they are described here in the same way as *species*. In such instances, the natural mineralogical unit is the *series*, and an arbitrary segmentation does not give an adequate picture of any part of the series. The plagioclases and the spinels are examples of series.

CLASSIFICATION NUMBERS

The species numbers adopted here are intended to conform to the classification principles explained in the previous section. Each class has a number; within the class each type also receives a number; the groups within a type are likewise numbered; the species in a group or series are further designated by the final number. Thus galena, by this numbering system, is 2611, cuprite is 411. It is unlikely that any number for a species will have more than five digits. The first two numbers always refer to the class and type, respectively, and the last number to the species; if the species is a member of a group, then the group number precedes the species number. This method, it is hoped, will eliminate the inelasticity of the numbering in the previous edition and help to place new minerals in their proper position in the classification. Minerals of doubtful validity are not given a number.

2. Morphological Crystallography

a. Choice of Unit Form. The choice of the unit form upon which the morphological description is based is often ambiguous when only the external crystallography is known. Only when the form series is extensive, or, if limited, when all the important planes indicate the same unit, can one be reasonably certain that the most suitable unit has been found. If the x-ray unit is determined, the problem of the morphological unit is solved,

TABLE 2

ATOMIC WEIGHTS AND IONIC RADII

	Symbol	Atomic Number	Atomic Weight*	Ionic Radius† C.N. 6
Aluminum	Al	13	26.97	0.57
Antimony	Sb	51	121.76	0.62 (Sb^{5+}), 0.90 (Sb^{3+})
Argon	A	18	39.944	....
Arsenic	As	33	74.91	0.40 (As^{5+}), 0.69 (As^{3+})
Barium	Ba	56	137.36	1.36
Beryllium	Be	4	9.02	0.34
Bismuth	Bi	83	209.00	0.74 (Bi^{5+}), 1.20 (Bi^{3+})
Boron	B	5	10.82	0.22
Bromine	Br	35	79.916	1.96
Cadmium	Cd	48	112.41	1.00
Calcium	Ca	20	40.08	1.01
Carbon	C	6	12.010	0.18
Cerium	Ce	58	140.13	1.18
Cesium	Cs	55	132.91	1.67
Chlorine	Cl	17	35.457	1.81
Chromium	Cr	24	52.01	0.65 (Cr^{3+})
Cobalt	Co	27	58.94	0.77 (Co^{2+}), 0.65 (Co^{3+})
Columbium	Cb	41	92.91	0.70
Copper	Cu	29	63.57	0.96 (Cu^{1+})
Dysprosium	Dy	66	162.46	....
Erbium	Er	68	167.2	1.04
Europium	Eu	63	152.0	1.13
Fluorine	F	9	19.00	1.33
Gadolinium	Gd	64	156.9	1.11
Gallium	Ga	31	69.72	0.62
Germanium	Ge	32	72.60	0.48
Gold	Au	79	197.2	1.37
Hafnium	Hf	72	178.6	0.84
Helium	He	2	4.003	....
Holmium	Ho	67	164.94	1.05
Hydrogen	H	1	1.0080	....
Indium	In	49	114.76	0.87
Iodine	I	53	126.92	2.19 (I^{-1})
Iridium	Ir	77	193.1	....
Iron	Fe	26	55.85	0.79 (Fe^{2+}), 0.67 (Fe^{3+})
Krypton	Kr	36	83.7	....
Lanthanum	La	57	138.92	1.14
Lead	Pb	82	207.21	1.32
Lithium	Li	3	6.940	0.69
Lutecium	Lu	71	174.99	0.99
Magnesium	Mg	12	24.32	0.75
Manganese	Mn	25	54.93	0.91 (Mn^{2+}), 0.52 (Mn^{4+})
Mercury	Hg	80	200.61	1.11

because the two units are identical in ratio, in most instances, and it is only in special cases that it is wise to depart from the x-ray unit cell ratio.

Various rules have been proposed for selecting the proper *morphological unit cell.* A simple, and often adequate, rule is that of *lowest total of indices,* developed by Ungemach[5] from the law of Haüy. By this method each possible unit is tested by a summation of the indices of all the forms, and the one finally chosen gives the lowest summation. But Friedel and others

[5] *Zs. Kr.,* **58.** 150 (1923).

TABLE 2 (*Continued*)

	Symbol	Atomic Number	Atomic Weight*	Ionic Radius† C.N. 6
Molybdenum	Mo	42	95.95	0.67 (Mo⁴⁺)
Neodymium	Nd	60	144.27	1.08
Neon	Ne	10	20.183	....
Nickel	Ni	28	58.69	0.74
Nitrogen	N	7	14.008	....
Osmium	Os	76	190.2	....
Oxygen	O	8	16.0000	1.32
Palladium	Pd	46	106.7	....
Phosphorus	P	15	30.98	0.34
Platinum	Pt	78	195.23	....
Potassium	K	19	39.096	1.33
Praseodymium	Pr	59	140.92	1.16
Protactinium	Pa	91	231	....
Radium	Ra	88	226.05	....
Radon	Rn	86	222	....
Rhenium	Re	75	186.31	....
Rhodium	Rh	45	102.91	0.69
Rubidium	Rb	37	85.48	1.48
Ruthenium	Ru	44	101.7	....
Samarium	Sm	62	150.43	....
Scandium	Sc	21	45.10	0.81
Selenium	Se	34	78.96	1.95 (Se⁻²)
Silicon	Si	14	28.06	0.41
Silver	Ag	47	107.880	1.20
Sodium	Na	11	22.997	0.98
Strontium	Sr	38	87.63	1.18
Sulfur	S	16	32.06	1.81 (S⁻²)
Tantalum	Ta	73	180.88	0.68
Tellurium	Te	52	127.61	0.85
Terbium	Tb	65	159.2	....
Thallium	Tl	81	204.39	1.47
Thorium	Th	90	232.12	1.06
Thulium	Tm	69	169.4	....
Tin	Sn	50	118.70	0.73 (Sn⁴⁺)
Titanium	Ti	22	47.90	0.65 (Ti⁴⁺)
Tungsten	W	74	183.92	0.67
Uranium	U	92	238.07	1.01 (U⁴⁺)
Vanadium	V	23	50.95	0.59
Xenon	Xe	54	131.3	....
Ytterbium	Yb	70	173.04	....
Yttrium	Y	39	88.92	0.87
Zinc	Zn	30	65.38	0.79
Zirconium	Zr	40	91.22	0.82

* International atomic weights, 1941.
† Ionic radii taken mainly from Stillwell (1938) and averaged with other values; for coordination 6.

have shown that this simple rule does not take into account the Bravais lattice type which certainly has an influence on form development. The *Bravais rule* (or " Law of Bravais ") states that the faces which occur most frequently and which are the best developed conform to the lattice planes with the highest reticular density. Donnay and Harker[6] have extended this concept to include the effect not only of the lattice type but also of the space group. The Donnay method consists essentially of a study of syste-

[6] *Am. Min.*, **22**, 446 (1937).

matic omissions in the principal zones of the crystal as well as an evaluation of the relative importance of the faces developed. Details of this useful morphological method are to be found in a number of his papers.[7] The method is admittedly purely geometrical, for it makes no provision for habit variation or the effect of structural controls.

The designation of the crystallographic axes in the chosen unit, that is, the orientation, is a matter of choice, except in the cases where certain symmetry axes conventionally coincide with axial elements. The usual rule is that $c < a < b$. In the triclinic system the (001) face is taken in the front right quadrant of the gnomonic projection of the faces of the crystal, with the emergence of [001] at the center of projection. This is the " normal triclinic setting " of Peacock.[8]

The orientation rule of $c < a < b$ is not always observed. Exceptions due to symmetry requirements, already mentioned, and some others are here enumerated:

(1) In the tetragonal and hexagonal systems c is fixed.

(2) In the monoclinic system b is the symmetry axis.

(3) In invariably acicular or long prismatic crystals the elongation axis is taken as c (but rules 1 and 2 above cannot be violated).

(4) If the crystal belongs in a group with other minerals, the orientation most suitable to the entire group is used.

(5) In the tetragonal system the body-centered lattice is preferred over the face-centered one, if the lattice is centered.

(6) In centered monoclinic lattices the unit is usually chosen so that the lattice is base-centered rather than body-centered, regardless of the rule $c < a$. However, if a cleavage direction or other prominent crystallographic feature coincides with the {001} of a body-centered lattice, then that orientation may be taken.

b. **Symmetry.** The class names used here are those of Groth modified by Rogers; the Hermann-Mauguin symbol is also given because it indicates the symmetry characteristics. The following brief explanation of the Hermann-Mauguin symbols is taken from the more detailed treatment in the *International Tables for the Determination of Crystal Structures.*

(1) Symmetry axes are denoted by numbers, and axes of rotary inversion by numbers with a line above, i.e., $\bar{6}, \bar{4}, \bar{3}$. Symmetry planes are indicated by m. An axis of symmetry with symmetry plane normal thereto is given as a number over m, for example, $\dfrac{2}{m}$, $\dfrac{4}{m}$ or $2/m$, $4/m$.

(2) In the hexagonal, tetragonal, isometric, and monoclinic systems, the first part of the symbol refers to the principal axis of symmetry.

(3) In the isometric system the second and third parts of the symbol refer, respectively, to the trigonal and twofold symmetry elements.

---

[7] *Ac. Belgique, Bull.* [5] **23**, 749 (1937); *Mém. soc. russe min.* [2] **67**, 31 (1938); *Soc. géol. Belgique, Ann.*, **61**, B260 (1938); Extrait du *Nat. canadien*, **67**, 33 (1940).

[8] *Am. Min.*, **22**, 588 (1937).

(4) In the tetragonal system the second and third symbols refer to the axial and diagonal symmetry elements.

(5) In the hexagonal system the second and third symbols refer to the axial and alternate axial symmetry elements.

(6) In the orthorhombic system the symbols refer to the symmetry elements in the order a, b, c.

Table 3 lists the 32 symmetry classes giving the corresponding notations in common use.

c. Elements. The elements include the direct, or linear, ratio $a : b : c$ and the reciprocal, or polar, ratio $p_0 : q_0 : r_0$, together with interaxial angles for each (when necessary) and gnomonic projection constants (when these differ from the polar values).

These elements are calculated from measurements by methods which are modifications of those first extensively used by Goldschmidt, Palache, Peacock, and Wolfe. The basis of all the calculations is the gnomonic projection, and all the calculations, therefore, begin with these projection elements, derived from two-circle goniometer angles.

The calculated elements should be given only to the accuracy attained in the measurements. Often this has not been carefully followed with the result that many crystallographic angle tables are misleading. Few of the multiple oxides containing columbium and tantalum (the so-called columbates and tantalates) occur in crystals suitable for measurement with an optical goniometer; the measurements are consequently no better than $\pm 1°$. Yet the elements given indicate measurements accurate to less than a minute. The one who makes the measurement is best fitted to judge the accuracy thereof; therefore, the elements as given by the investigator are generally used here, but a note of caution is in order.

In succeeding sections calculation methods for each crystal system are given in detail. These are the methods used in preparing the crystallographic data of this volume, and they are reprinted here from a recently published paper originally prepared for this section by Dr. Wolfe.

d. Tabulation of Forms and Angles. The table of forms and angles following the elements includes all the common forms with letters and important angles. The less common forms and letters are listed below the angle table. Rare and uncertain forms are given in the references.

Few general rules for the order of form listing can be given for all crystal systems, since each possesses restrictive peculiarities. The general order is first, forms cutting but one crystal axis; second, those cutting two axes; third, those cutting three axes. In the hexagonal system, with four axes, a similar order is employed.

Tabulations will be found in the following pages for each crystal system, giving the order in which all possible forms in each symmetry class are listed. Complementary (or correlative) forms are grouped with their holohedral equivalents and are listed in the same order as though holohedral. If the vertical axis is polar, the headings " lower " and " upper " are used beneath the Hermann-Mauguin symmetry class symbol. Only

TABLE 3
SYMMETRY CLASS NOTATION

System	Groth, modified by Rogers (1937)	Hermann-Mauguin	Schoenflies	Dana-Ford (1932)
Triclinic	1. Pedial	1	C_1	32
	2. Pinacoidal	$\bar{1}$	C_i	31
Monoclinic	3. Domatic	m	C_s	30
	4. Sphenoidal	2	C_2	29
	5. Prismatic	$\dfrac{2}{m}$	C_{2h}	28
Orthorhombic	6. Rhombic-pyramidal	$m\ \ m\ \ 2$	C_{2v}	26
	7. Rhombic-disphenoidal	$2\ \ 2\ \ 2$	D_2	27
	8. Rhombic-dipyramidal	$\dfrac{2}{m}\ \dfrac{2}{m}\ \dfrac{2}{m}$	D_{2h}	25
Tetragonal	9. Tetragonal-disphenoidal	$\bar{4}$	S_4	12
	10. Tetragonal-pyramidal	4	C_4	9
	11. Tetragonal-dipyramidal	$\dfrac{4}{m}$	C_{4h}	8
	12. Tetragonal-scalenohedral	$\bar{4}\ \ 2\ \ m$	D_{2d}	10
	13. Ditetragonal-pyramidal	$4\ \ m\ \ m$	C_{4v}	7
	14. Tetragonal-trapezohedral	$4\ \ 2\ \ 2$	D_4	11
	15. Ditetragonal-dipyramidal	$\dfrac{4}{m}\ \dfrac{2}{m}\ \dfrac{2}{m}$	D_{4h}	6
Hexagonal P or R*	16. Trigonal-pyramidal	3	C_3	24
	17. Rhombohedral	$\bar{3}$	C_{3i}	22
	18. Ditrigonal-pyramidal	$3\ \ m$	C_{3v}	21
	19. Trigonal-trapezohedral	$3\ \ 2$	D_3	23
	20. Hexagonal-scalenohedral	$\bar{3}\ \ \dfrac{2}{m}$	D_{3d}	20
Hexagonal P*	21. Trigonal-dipyramidal	$\bar{6}$	C_{3h}	19
	22. Hexagonal-pyramidal	6	C_6	16
	23. Hexagonal-dipyramidal	$\dfrac{6}{m}$	C_{6h}	15
	24. Ditrigonal-dipyramidal	$\bar{6}\ \ m\ \ 2$	D_{3h}	18
	25. Dihexagonal-pyramidal	$6\ \ m\ \ m$	C_{6v}	14
	26. Hexagonal trapezohedral	$6\ \ 2\ \ 2$	D_6	17
	27. Dihexagonal-dipyramidal	$\dfrac{6}{m}\ \dfrac{2}{m}\ \dfrac{2}{m}$	D_{6h}	13
Isometric	28. Tetartoidal	$2\ \ 3$	T	5
	29. Diploidal	$\dfrac{2}{m}\ \ \bar{3}$	T_h	2
	30. Hextetrahedral	$\bar{4}\ \ 3\ \ m$	T_d	3
	31. Gyroidal	$4\ \ 3\ \ 2$	O	4
	32. Hexoctahedral	$\dfrac{4}{m}\ \ \bar{3}\ \dfrac{2}{m}$	O_h	1

* In the hexagonal system the lattice mode in classes 16 to 20 may be either primitive hexagonal (P) or rhombohedral (R); in classes 21 to 27 only the primitive mode is possible.

upper form indices are given, and an x in the column headed " lower " indicates that the form may occur as a lower one. In specific tabulations of the forms of such crystals the same letter is given for the lower as for the upper form, but a minus sign is placed over it ($\bar{c}$ for example). If the form is observed only as a lower one, its letter appears only in that column, but the indices are always those of the upper merohedral equivalent. Plus or minus signs before a form letter indicate the sign of phi of the form. Prime marks (') to the right or left of a form letter indicate whether the form occurs to the right or left of some defined meridian. The general order for plus and minus, right and left forms is plus right $(+')$, plus left $('+)$, minus left $('-)$, minus right $(-')$.

The angles given in the table for the representative face of each form include the azimuth *phi* (ϕ) and polar distance *rho* (ρ), angular coordinates, as well as interfacial angles to two or more fundamental faces. The angles given and their meanings will be shown in figures included in the discussion of each system.

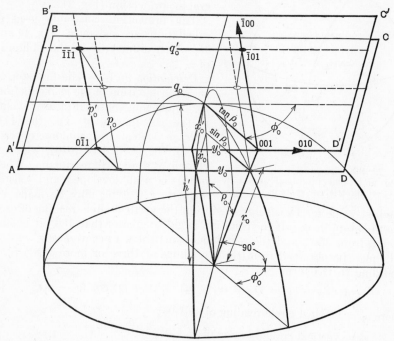

Fig. 1. Relation of gnomonic projection elements to polar elements in the triclinic system.

The Triclinic System

Elements. The elements in the triclinic system include: the linear axial ratio $a : b : c$ ($b = 1$) and interaxial angles α, β, γ; the polar axial ratio $p_0 : q_0 : r_0$ ($r_0 = 1$) and interaxial angles λ, μ, ν; and the gnomonic projection constants p_0', q_0', x_0', y_0'. In the triclinic system the gnomonic projection values are greater than the polar values, since r_0 of the polar ratio, which is taken as unity and normal to $c(001)$, is inclined to the center of the projection. The plane of projection of the polar elements thus drops an amount which is a function of the rho value of $c(001)$. The gnomonic projection plane $A'B'C'D'$ (Fig. 1) drops to the position $ABCD$ of the polar elements, both parallel to the equatorial plane. The position of $ABCD$ is determined by the point of emergence on the sphere of projection of the normal to $c(001)$.

The linear interaxial angles α, β, γ are defined as follows.

$$\alpha = [010] \wedge [001], \quad \beta = [001] \wedge [100], \quad \gamma = [100] \wedge [010] \qquad [1]$$

The polar axial angles λ, μ, ν are the following interfacial angles:

$$\lambda = (010) \wedge (001), \quad \mu = (001) \wedge (100), \quad \nu = (100) \wedge (010) \qquad [2]$$

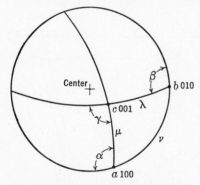

FIG. 2. Stereographic projection of linear and polar interaxial angles in the triclinic system.

The six angles are shown in stereographic projection (Fig. 2).

The projection constants used in calculations are shown in Figs. 4a and 4b, which differ only in the obliquity of ν.

Calculation of V_0. The first step in the determination of the elements from two-circle goniometrical measurements is the calculation of V_0, the best average vertical circle goniometer reading for the normal to (010), which is chosen as the zero meridian. When $b(010)$ is well developed and reflects well, its ν reading may be made V_0.

The best value for V_0 is subtracted from the vertical circle reading of each face to obtain its ϕ. If the resulting angle be greater than 180°, it is subtracted from 360°, and the remainder constitutes a negative ϕ.

V_0 may be obtained from the ν readings of three or more $(hk0)$ faces according to the formula:

$$\cot (V_0 - v_2) = Q \cot (v_3 - v_2) - (1 - Q) \cot (v_2 - v_1) \qquad [3]$$

where v_1 = vertical circle reading of (h_1k_10);

v_2 = vertical circle reading of (h_2k_20);

v_3 = vertical circle reading of (h_3k_30);

$$Q = \frac{\dfrac{k_3}{h_3} - \dfrac{k_2}{h_2}}{\dfrac{k_3}{h_3} - \dfrac{k_1}{h_1}}$$

V_0 is also calculated from measurements of various pairs of terminal faces, each pair having the same h/l value, according to the following formula.

$$\tan V_0 = \frac{(\sin v_2 \tan \rho_2) - (\sin v_1 \tan \rho_1)}{(\cos v_2 \tan \rho_2) - (\cos v_1 \tan \rho_1)} \qquad [4]$$

where v_1, ρ_1; v_2, ρ_2 are the angular readings of the two faces (Fig. 3). This calculation is repeated for several pairs of such faces, and the results

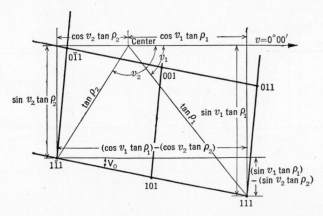

FIG. 3. Gnomonic projection to illustrate calculation of V_0 from the angular readings of two terminal forms with the same h/l value.

averaged. Due attention must be given to the signs of the trigonometric functions.

Extended demonstrations and illustrations of the use of equations 3 and 4 are given by Dreyer and Goldschmidt,[9] by Borgström and Goldschmidt,[10] and by Parsons.[11]

Calculation of Projection Elements. The following formulas are useful in the calculation of the projection elements p_0', q_0', x_0', y_0', from two-circle goniometric measurements (see Fig. 4).

From Fig. 4

$$x' = \sin \phi \tan \rho = x_0' + \frac{h}{l} p_0' \sin v \qquad [5]$$

$$y' = \cos \phi \tan \rho = y_0' + \frac{k}{l} q_0' + \frac{h}{l} p_0' \cos v \qquad [6]$$

If x_1', x_2', ... x_n' are the ordinates and y_1', y_2', ... y_n' the abscissas of the

[9] *Medd. Grønland,* **34,** 29 (1907).
[10] *Zs. Kr.,* **41,** 75 (1905).
[11] *Am. Min.,* **5,** 193 (1920).

gnomonic poles $(h_1k_1l_1)$, $(h_2k_2l_2)$, ... $(h_nk_nl_n)$, then from equation 5

$$p_0' \sin \nu = \frac{l_1 l_2 (x_1' - x_2')}{h_1 l_2 - h_2 l_1} \tag{7}$$

$$x_0' = x' - \frac{h}{l} p_0' \sin \nu \text{ from (5)} \tag{8}$$

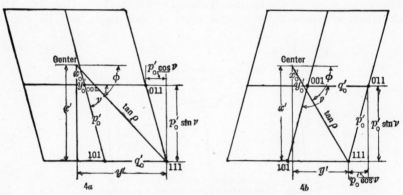

FIG. 4.　Gnomonic projection constants in the triclinic system with ν less than 90° 00′ (a), and greater than 90° 00′ (b).

From equation 6

$$p_0' \cos \nu = \frac{l_1 l_2 (y_1' - y_2')(k_2 l_3 - k_3 l_2) - l_2 l_3 (y_2' - y_3') k_1 l_2 - k_2 l_1}{(h_1 l_2 - h_2 l_1)(k_2 l_3 - k_3 l_2) - (h_2 l_3 - h_3 l_2)(k_1 l_2 - k_2 l_1)} \tag{9}$$

$$q_0' = \frac{p_0' \cos \nu (h_2 l_1 - h_1 l_2) + l_1 l_2 (y_1' - y_2')}{k_1 l_2 - k_2 l_1} \tag{10}$$

$$y_0' = y' - \frac{k}{l} q_0' - \frac{h}{l} p_0' \cos \nu \tag{11}$$

and

$$\tan \nu = \frac{p_0' \sin \nu}{p_0' \cos \nu} \tag{12}$$

$$p_0' = \frac{p_0' \sin \nu}{\sin \nu} = \frac{p_0' \cos \nu}{\cos \nu} \tag{13}$$

Relation of Projection Elements to Polar Elements. ϕ_0 and ρ_0 are the azimuth and the polar distance of $c(001)$, the rectangular coordinates of which are x_0' and y_0' (Fig. 5).

From Fig. 5

$$\tan \phi_0 = \frac{x_0'}{y_0'} \tag{14}$$

and from Figs. 1 and 5

$$\tan \phi_0 = \frac{x_0}{y_0}$$

(Projection values are primed, and polar values are unprimed.)

From Fig. 5

$$\tan \rho_0 = \frac{x_0'}{\sin \phi_0} = \frac{y_0'}{\cos \phi_0} \qquad [15]$$

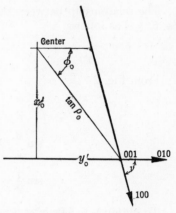

From Fig. 1

$$\sin \rho_0 = \frac{x_0}{\sin \phi_0} = \frac{y_0}{\cos \phi_0} \qquad [16]$$

FIG. 5. Angular and rectangular coordinates of $c(001)$ in the triclinic system.

Therefore

$$x_0 = \sin \rho_0 \sin \phi_0 \qquad [17]$$

$$y_0 = \sin \rho_0 \cos \phi_0 \qquad [18]$$

From Fig. 1

$$p_0 = p_0' \cos \rho_0 \qquad [19]$$

$$q_0 = q_0' \cos \rho_0 \qquad [20]$$

From Fig. 2

$$\cos \lambda = y_0 \qquad [21]$$

$$\cos \mu = y_0 \cos \nu + x_0 \sin \nu \qquad [22]$$

The linear and polar elements are related as follows.

$$a : b(= 1) : c :: \frac{\sin \alpha}{p_0} : \frac{\sin \beta}{q_0} : \frac{\sin \gamma}{r_0(= 1)} :: \frac{\sin \lambda}{p_0} : \frac{\sin \mu}{q_0} : \frac{\sin \nu}{r_0(= 1)} \qquad [23]$$

From equations 19, 20, and 23

$$a = \frac{q_0' \sin \lambda}{p_0' \sin \mu} \qquad [24]$$

and from (20) and (23)

$$c = \frac{q_0' \cos \rho_0 \sin \nu}{\sin \mu} \qquad [25]$$

From (23)

$$p_0 = \frac{c \sin \alpha}{a \sin \gamma} \qquad [26]$$

$$q_0 = \frac{c \sin \beta}{\sin \gamma} \qquad [27]$$

The relationship between the polar angles λ, μ, ν and the linear angles α, β, γ is as follows.

$$\sigma = \frac{\lambda + \mu + \nu}{2}$$

From Fig. 2

$$\sin \frac{\alpha}{2} = \sqrt{\frac{\sin \sigma \sin (\sigma - \lambda)}{\sin \mu \sin \nu}} \qquad [28]$$

$$\sin \frac{\beta}{2} = \sqrt{\frac{\sin \sigma \sin (\sigma - \mu)}{\sin \nu \sin \lambda}}$$

$$\sin \frac{\gamma}{2} = \sqrt{\frac{\sin \sigma \sin (\sigma - \nu)}{\sin \lambda \sin \mu}}$$

To obtain λ, μ, ν from α, β, γ, substitute the latter group for the former, respectively, in (28).

Order of Form Listing. The following order of listing (Table 4) is used in the triclinic system. The letters c, b, a, m, M are reserved for the faces (001), (010), (100), (110), ($1\bar{1}0$), respectively.

TABLE 4

ORDER OF FORM LISTING IN THE TRICLINIC SYSTEM

Class 1			$\bar{1}$
Lower	Upper		
$\bar{c}$	c	001	001
	b	010	010
	$-b$	$0\bar{1}0$	
	a	100	100
	$-a$	$\bar{1}00$	
	d	$hk0$	$hk0$ in order of increasing h/k
	$-d$	$h\bar{k}0$	
	D	$h\bar{k}0$	$h\bar{k}0$ in order of decreasing h/k
	$-D$	$\bar{h}k0$	
$\bar{w}$	w	$0kl$	$0kl$ in order of increasing k/l
$\overline{W}$	W	$0\bar{k}l$	$0\bar{k}l$ in order of increasing k/l
$\bar{e}$	e	$h0l$	$h0l$ in order of increasing h/l
$\overline{E}$	E	$\bar{h}0l$	$\bar{h}0l$ in order of increasing h/l
x	x^*	hhl	hhl in order of increasing h/l
x	x	$h\bar{h}l$	$h\bar{h}l$ in order of increasing h/l
x	x	$\bar{h}hl$	$\bar{h}hl$ in order of increasing h/l
x	x	$\bar{h}\bar{h}l$	$\bar{h}\bar{h}l$ in order of increasing h/l
x	x	hkl	hkl in order of increasing h/l
x	x	$h\bar{k}l$	$h\bar{k}l$ in groups of equal h/l, list
x	x	$\bar{h}kl$	$\bar{h}kl$ in order of increasing k/l
x	x	$\bar{h}\bar{k}l$	$\bar{h}\bar{k}l$

* x indicates possible occurrence of form.

Triclinic Angles. The angles given in triclinic tables are: ϕ, ρ, A, B, C. Figure 6 is a stereographic projection showing these angles.

$$\tan \phi_{hkl} = \frac{x'}{y'} = \frac{x'_0 + \dfrac{h}{l} p'_0 \sin \nu}{y'_0 + \dfrac{k}{l} q'_0 + \dfrac{h}{l} p'_0 \cos \nu} \qquad [29]$$

From Fig. 4 and equation 29

$$\tan \rho_{hkl} = \frac{x'}{\sin \phi} = \frac{y'}{\cos \phi} \qquad [30]$$

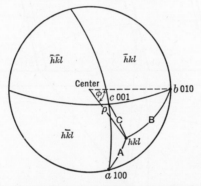

FIG. 6. Stereographic projection of angles given for forms in the triclinic system.

The angles A, B, C are the angles which the face makes with $a(100)$, $b(010)$, $c(001)$, respectively. These angles are calculated by means of the general formula for the interfacial angle Δ:

$$\cos \Delta = \cos \rho_1 \cos \rho_2 + \sin \rho_1 \sin \rho_2 \cos (\phi_2 - \phi_1) \qquad [31]$$

where ϕ_1, ρ_1 and ϕ_2, ρ_2 are the angular coordinates of the two faces. For the specific cases of the calculations of the angles A, B, C, formula 31 becomes

$$\cos A = \sin \rho_{hkl} \cos (\phi_{100} - \phi_{hkl}) \qquad [32]$$

$$\cos B = \sin \rho_{hkl} \cos \phi_{hkl} \qquad [33]$$

$$\cos C = \cos \rho_{hkl} \cos \rho_0 + \sin \rho_{hkl} \sin \rho_0 \cos (\phi_0 - \phi_{hkl}) \qquad [34]$$

A graphical check is always made to avoid gross errors. The only source of error in the determination of ϕ and ρ is the calculation of the x' and y' coordinates. These may be checked satisfactorily on a gnomonic projection with a unit circle radius of 10 cm., using the projection constants for plotting the faces. The interfacial angles A, B, C are checked on a stereographic net (20-cm. radius), using the calculated ϕ and ρ values for plotting the faces. This check is accurate to ± 15 minutes.

THE MONOCLINIC SYSTEM

Elements. The elements here consist of: the linear axial ratio, $a : b : c$ ($b = 1$), and the axial angle β between the positive ends of the c and a axes; the polar ratio, $p_0 : q_0 : r_0$ ($r_0 = 1$), and the reciprocal axial angle μ

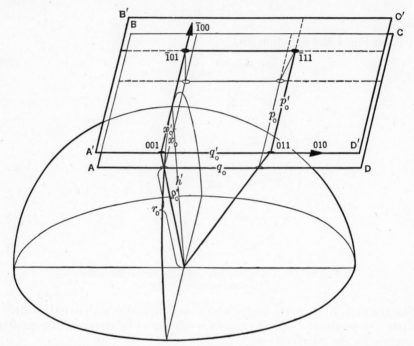

FIG. 7. Relation of gnomonic projection elements to polar elements in the monoclinic system.

(the supplement of β); the polar ratio $r_2 : p_2 : q_2$ ($q_2 = 1$), obtained when $b(010)$ is set in polar position, and the phi of $a(100)$ is $0°00'$; the projection constants p_0', q_0', x_0' (see Fig. 8).

In the monoclinic system, as in the triclinic, the projection elements do not coincide with the polar elements. For $r_0 = 1$ the gnomonic plane $A'B'C'D'$ (Fig. 7) must drop to the position of $ABCD$, the amount of that drop being a function of the ρ angle of $c(001)$, (ρ_0).

Calculation of Projection Elements. The ϕ and ρ angles of the various faces are obtained from measurements. From Fig. 8 are derived the following.

$$x' = x_0' + \frac{h}{l} p_0' = \sin \phi \tan \rho \qquad [35]$$

If x_1' and x_2' are the coordinates of faces $(h_1k_1l_1)$ and $(h_2k_2l_2)$, then, from (35)

$$p_0' = \frac{l_1l_2(x_1' - x_2')}{(h_1l_2 - h_2l_1)} \qquad [36]$$

$$x_0' = x' - \frac{h}{l}\, p_0' \text{ (from 35)} \qquad [37]$$

and from Fig. 8

$$y' = \frac{k}{l}\, q_0' = \cos \phi \tan \rho \qquad [38]$$

From (38)

$$q_0' = \frac{ly'}{k} \qquad [39]$$

$$\cot \mu = x_0' \qquad [40]$$

$$\tan \rho_0 = x_0' \qquad [41]$$

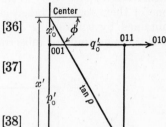

FIG. 8. Gnomonic projection constants in the monoclinic system, conventional orientation.

Calculation of Polar Elements. The polar elements are related to the projection elements as follows. From Fig. 7

$$p_0 = p_0' \cos \rho_0 = p_0' \sin \mu = \frac{c}{a} \qquad [42]$$

$$q_0 = q_0' \cos \rho_0 = q_0' \sin \mu \qquad [43]$$

$$r_0 = 1 \qquad [44]$$

$$r_2 = \frac{1}{q_0} = \frac{1}{q_0' \sin \mu} = \frac{1}{c \sin \mu} \qquad [45]$$

$$p_2 = \frac{p_0}{q_0} = \frac{p_0'}{q_0'} = \frac{1}{a \sin \mu} \qquad [46]$$

$$q_2 = 1 \qquad [47]$$

Calculation of Linear Elements. The linear elements are related as follows to the polar and projection elements. From equation 23

$$a = \frac{q_0}{p_0 \sin \mu} = \frac{q_0'}{p_0' \sin \mu} = \frac{c}{p_0} \qquad [48]$$

$$c = \frac{q_0}{\sin \mu} = q_0' \qquad [49]$$

$$\beta = 180° - \mu \qquad [50]$$

The derivation of the elements of a monoclinic mineral from measurements made with the b-axis vertical is as follows.

V_0 may be obtained as in (3) and (4). If, however, the quality of either $c(001)$ or $a(100)$ is sufficiently good, the vertical circle reading of one of them may be taken as V_0. The ϕ_2 readings for all the faces are obtained by subtracting V_0 from their vertical circle readings (see Peacock[12] for meaning of subscript 2). Ordinarily the elements are calculated

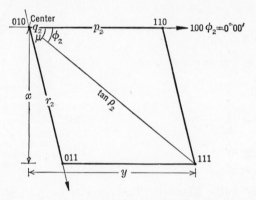

Fig. 9. Gnomonic projection constants in the monoclinic system with b-axis vertical.

with the azimuth ϕ_2 of $(100) = 0°00'$ (Fig. 9), and the angles are given accordingly; but they may be calculated as readily when the azimuth of $(001) = 0°00'$. Two sets of similar formulas are given below for these two cases. Using the measured ϕ_2 and ρ_2 values, the x and y coordinates of each face in this orientation are obtained by (5) and (6). In the formulas below x_1 and x_2 are the ordinates and y_1, y_2 are the abscissas of any two gnomonic poles $(h_1k_1l_1)(h_2k_2l_2)$. Indices obtained from the gnomonic plot in this orientation are listed in the sequence of the intercepts of the gnomonic pole on the polar axes p_2, $q_2 = 1$, and r_2, clearing fractions where necessary. Thus, these indices are identical with those obtained for the same face in the normal position where $r_0 = 1$.

Where ϕ_2 of $a(100) = 0°00'$

$$\tan \mu = \frac{k_1h_2x_1 - k_2h_1x_2}{k_1h_2y_1 - k_2h_1y_2} \tag{51}$$

$$r_2 = \frac{kx}{l \sin \mu} \tag{52}$$

$$p_2 = \frac{ky}{h} - \frac{kx}{h \tan \mu} \tag{53}$$

[12] *Am. J. Sc.*, **28**, 241 (1934).

Where ϕ_2 of $c(001) = 0°00'$

$$\tan \mu = \frac{k_1 l_2 x_1 - k_2 l_1 x_2}{k_1 l_2 y_1 - k_2 l_1 y_2} \qquad [54]$$

$$r_2 = \frac{ky}{l} - \frac{kx}{l \tan \mu} \qquad [55]$$

$$p_2 = \frac{kx}{h \sin \mu} \qquad [56]$$

$$a = \frac{1}{p_2 \sin \mu}, \quad c = \frac{1}{r_2 \sin \mu} \qquad [57]$$

$$p_0' = \frac{p_2}{r_2 \sin \mu}, \quad q_0' = \frac{1}{r_2 \sin \mu}, \quad x_0' = \cot \mu \qquad [58]$$

Order of Form Listing. The order of listing in the monoclinic system is shown in Table 5. The letters c, b, a, m are conventionally used for (001), (010), (100), (110), respectively.

Monoclinic Angles. The angles given in the monoclinic system are ϕ, $\rho, \phi_2, \rho_2 = B, C, A$ (Fig. 10). ϕ_2 and ρ_2 are the phi and rho values obtained when $b(010)$ is set in polar position and the azimuth of $a(100)$ is $0°00'$ (in this position the $r_2 : p_2 : q_2$ polar ratio is obtained). C and A represent the angles which a face makes with $c(001)$ and $a(100)$, respectively.

From Fig. 8

$$\tan \phi = \frac{x'}{y'} \qquad [59]$$

$$\tan \rho = \frac{x'}{\sin \phi} = \frac{y'}{\cos \phi} \qquad [60]$$

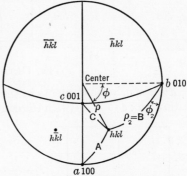

FIG. 10. Stereographic projection of angles given in the monoclinic system.

From equation 35 and Figs. 9 and 10

$$\cot \phi_2 = x' = \sin \phi \tan \rho \qquad [61]$$

From Figs. 9 and 10

$$\cos \rho_2 = \cos B = \sin \rho \cos \phi \qquad [62]$$

From Fig. 10

$$\cos C = \sin (\phi_2 + \rho_0) \sin B \qquad [63]$$

$$\cos A = \sin \rho \sin \phi \qquad [64]$$

TABLE 5

ORDER OF FORM LISTING IN THE MONOCLINIC SYSTEM

Class m			2		$\dfrac{2}{m}$
Lower	Upper				
x	c	001		001	001
	b	010		010	010
			$-b$	0$\bar{1}$0	
	a	100		100	100
	$-a$	$\bar{1}$00			
	k	hk0	k'	hk0	hk0 in order of increasing phi
	$-k$	$\bar{h}k$0	$'k$	$h\bar{k}$0	
x	w	0kl	w'	0kl	0kl in order of increasing rho
			$'w$	0$\bar{k}l$	
x	d	h0l		h0l	h0l in order of increasing h/l
x	D	$\bar{h}$0l		$\bar{h}$0l	$\bar{h}$0l in order of increasing h/l
x	q	hhl		hhl	hhl in order of increasing h/l
x	Q	$\bar{h}hl$		$\bar{h}hl$	$\bar{h}hl$ in order of increasing h/l
x	r	hkl	r'	hkl	hkl in order of increasing h/l;
			$'r$	$h\bar{k}l$	in groups of equal h/l,
					list in order of increasing k/l
x	R	$\bar{h}\bar{k}l$	R'	$\bar{h}kl$	$\bar{h}kl$ same as for hkl
			$'R$	$\bar{h}\bar{k}l$	

THE ORTHORHOMBIC SYSTEM

Elements. The elements in the orthorhombic system include: the axial ratio $a : b : c$ ($b = 1$) (with the convention usually adopted that $c < a < b$);

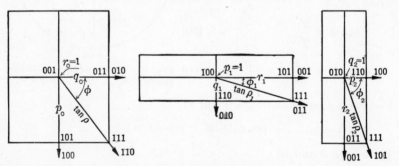

FIG. 11. Gnomonic projections of cyclic permutations of polar elements in the orthorhombic system.

the polar ratio $p_0 : q_0 : r_0$ ($r_0 = 1$); the polar ratio $q_1 : r_1 : p_1$ ($p_1 = 1$); the polar ratio $r_2 : p_2 : q_2$ ($q_2 = 1$) (See Peacock[13] and also Fig. 11.) Cyclic

[13] *Am. J. Sc.*, **28**, 241 (1934).

permutations of the polar ratio are given because an orthorhombic crystal may be measured with any one of the three axes vertical, and the ensuing gnomonic plot would change accordingly.

Calculation of Elements. The angular measurements, ϕ and ρ, are related to the linear and polar elements as follows. From Fig. 11

$$a = \frac{q_0}{p_0} = \frac{h \cot \phi}{k} \qquad [65]$$

$$p_0 = \frac{l \sin \phi \tan \rho}{h} \qquad [66]$$

$$q_0 = c = \frac{l \cos \phi \tan \rho}{k} \qquad [67]$$

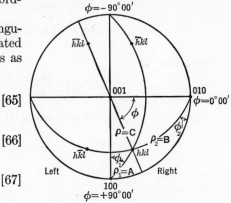

FIG. 12.   Stereographic projection showing form designation and angles in the orthorhombic system.

Order of Form Listing.   The order of listing in Table 6 is followed in the orthorhombic system.   The letters c, b, a, m, are reserved for the faces (001), (010), (100), (110), respectively.   The 90° meridian defines right and left forms (Fig. 12).

TABLE 6

ORDER OF FORM LISTING IN THE ORTHORHOMBIC SYSTEM

Class $m\ m\ 2$		$2\quad 2\quad 2$		$\dfrac{2}{m}\ \dfrac{2}{m}\ \dfrac{2}{m}$
Lower	Upper			
x	c 001		001	001
	b 010		010	010
	a 100		100	100
	k $hk0$		$hk0$	$hk0$ in order of increasing h/k
x	w $0kl$		$0kl$	$0kl$ in order of increasing k/l
x	d $h0l$		$h0l$	$h0l$ in order of increasing h/l
x	q hhl	q'	hhl	hhl in order of increasing h/l
		$'q$	$h\bar{h}l$	
x	r hkl	r'	hkl	hkl in order of increasing h/l;
		$'r$	$h\bar{k}l$	in groups of equal h/l,
				list in order of increasing k/l

Orthorhombic Angles.   Six angles for each form are given in the orthorhombic system.   These are: ϕ and ρ in the conventional orientation $(c < a < b)$; ϕ_1 and $\rho_1 = A$, with $a(100)$ in polar position and the ϕ of $c(001)$ equal to $0°00'$; and ϕ_2 and $\rho_2 = B$, with $b(010)$ in polar position and the ϕ of $a(100)$ equal to $0°0'$ (see Fig. 12).   Not only do these angles give important interfacial angles, but they also provide a ready check on measured angles regardless of which axis is made vertical. From Fig. 11

$$\tan \phi = \frac{h p_0}{k q_0} \tag{68}$$

$$\tan \rho = \tan C = \frac{h p_0}{l \sin \phi} = \frac{k q_0}{l \cos \phi} \tag{69}$$

From Fig. 12

$$\tan \phi_1 = \frac{k q_0}{l} \tag{70}$$

$$\cos \rho_1 = \cos A = \sin \rho \sin \phi \tag{71}$$

$$\cot \phi_2 = \frac{h p_0}{l} \tag{72}$$

$$\cos \rho_2 = \cos B = \sin \rho \cos \phi \tag{73}$$

Tetragonal System

Elements. The elements in this system include the linear ratio, $a : c$ ($a = 1$), and the polar ratio $p_0 : r_0$ ($r_0 = 1$). In these ratios c and p_0 are equal and may be obtained from the ϕ and ρ readings of the various types of forms as follows.

From $(0kl)$ or $(k0l)$

$$c = p_0 = \frac{l \tan \rho}{k} \tag{74}$$

From (hhl)

$$c = p_0 = \frac{l \tan \rho \sin 45°}{h} \tag{75}$$

From (hkl)

$$c = p_0 = \frac{l \tan \rho \sin \phi}{h} = \frac{l \tan \rho \cos \phi}{k} \tag{76}$$

Order of Form Listing. Table 7 shows the order in the tetragonal system. The letters c, a, m, are reserved for the faces (001), (010), (110), respectively. The plus 45° and minus 45° meridians define right and left forms (Fig. 13).

Tetragonal Angles. The angles given in the tetragonal system are: ϕ; ρ; A, the angle to $a(100)$; $\overline{M}$, the angle to $-m(1\overline{1}0)$, given for plus forms only; M, the angle to $m(110)$, given for minus forms only. These yield useful interfacial angles as is seen in Fig. 13. The formulas for calculation of these angles are, from Fig. 13,

$$\tan \phi = \frac{h}{k} \tag{77}$$

$$\tan \rho = \frac{h p_0}{l \sin \phi} = \frac{k p_0}{l \cos \phi} \tag{78}$$

TABLE 7

Order of Form Listing in the Tetragonal System

Class $\bar{4}$		4 Lower	4 Upper	$\frac{4}{m}$	$\bar{4}\ 2m$	4 m m Lower	4 m m Upper	4 2 2	$\frac{4}{m}\frac{2}{m}\frac{2}{m}$
c	001	x	001	001	001	x	001	001	001
a	010		010	010	010		010	010	010
m	110		110	110	110		110	110	110
d −d	$hk0$ $\bar{h}k0$		$hk0$ $\bar{h}k0$	$hk0$ $\bar{h}k0$	$hk0$		$hk0$	$hk0$	$hk0$ in order of increasing h/k
i′ ′i	$0kl$ $k0l$	x	$0kl$	$0kl$	$0kl$	x	$0kl$	$0kl$	$0kl$ in order of increasing k/l
o −o	hhl $\bar{h}hl$	x	hhl	hhl	hhl $\bar{h}hl$	x	hhl	hhl	hhl in order of increasing h/l
u′	hkl	x	hkl	hkl	hkl	x	hkl	hkl	hkl in order of increasing h/l;
′u	khl	x	khl	khl				khl	in groups of equal h/l,
−′u −u′	$\bar{h}kl$ $\bar{k}hl$				$\bar{h}kl$				list in order of increasing k/l

$\cos A = \sin \rho \sin \phi$; supplement is obtained when ϕ is negative, that is, for $\{\bar{h}kl\}$ and $\{\bar{k}hl\}$ forms [79]

$\cos \bar{M} = \sin \rho \cos (45° + \phi)$; supplement is obtained when form symbol is $\{khl\}$ [80]

$\cos M = \sin \rho \cos (45° - \phi)$; supplement is obtained when form symbol is $\{\bar{k}hl\}$ [81]

Since ϕ is a constant for each h/k value in the tetragonal system, the following table of ϕ angles is given with variations in h and k from 1 to 11. The angles are given according to increasing magnitude to facilitate rapid comparison with measured values. The same angles are valid in the isometric system.

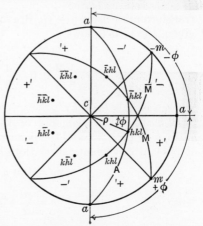

Fig. 13. Stereographic projection showing form designation and angles in the tetragonal system.

Hexagonal System

Introduction. The hexagonal system has caused considerable difficulty, principally because of the introduction of the so-called G_2 position of

V. Goldschmidt. The G_1 position is, however, without ambiguity, as has been pointed out by Peacock[14] if certain changes of the polar axes and prime meridian of Goldschmidt are made. In Goldschmidt's works the G_2 position is sometimes the only one used. It is important, therefore, that the

TABLE 8

PHI ANGLES IN THE TETRAGONAL SYSTEM

$h : k$	ϕ	$h : k$	ϕ	$h : k$	ϕ
1 : 11	5°11'40''	4 : 11	19°58'59''	7 : 10	34°59'31''
1 : 10	5 42 38	3 : 8	20 33 22	5 : 7	35 32 16
1 : 9	6 20 25	2 : 5	21 48 05	8 : 11	36 01 39
1 : 8	7 07 30	3 : 7	23 11 55	3 : 4	36 52 12
1 : 7	8 07 48	4 : 9	23 57 43	7 : 9	37 52 30
1 : 6	9 27 44	5 : 11	24 26 38	4 : 5	38 39 35
2 : 11	10 18 17	1 : 2	26 33 54	9 : 11	39 17 22
1 : 5	11 18 36	6 : 11	28 36 38	5 : 6	39 48 20
2 : 9	12 31 44	5 : 9	29 03 17	6 : 7	40 36 05
1 : 4	14 02 10	4 : 7	29 44 42	7 : 8	41 11 09
3 : 11	15 15 18	3 : 5	30 57 50	8 : 9	41 37 37
2 : 7	15 56 44	5 : 8	32 00 19	9 : 10	41 59 14
3 : 10	16 41 57	7 : 11	32 28 16	10 : 11	42 16 25
1 : 3	18 26 06	2 : 3	33 41 24	1 : 1	45 00 00

transformation from the G_2 Bravais symbol to the G_1 Bravais symbol be given. It is as follows.

$$\overset{h}{\frac{1}{3}} \overset{k}{\frac{2}{3}} 0\ 0\ /\ \frac{1}{3} \frac{\bar{1}}{3} 0\ 0\ /\ \overset{\bar{\imath}}{\bar{\imath}}\ /\ \overset{l}{0001} \qquad [82]$$

where i equals $(h + k)$.

Elements. The elements of the hexagonal system include the axial ratio, $a : c$ $(a = 1)$, and the polar ratio, $p_0 : r_0$ $(r_0 = 1)$. Some of the more important mathematical relations here involved are as follows.

$$p_0 = \tan \rho \ (10\bar{1}1) \qquad [83]$$

$$c = \frac{p_0}{2} \sqrt{3} = \tan \rho \ (11\bar{2}2) \qquad [84]$$

The elements p_0 or c may be obtained from the ϕ and ρ angles of faces intersecting three axes or more, one of which must be the c-axis, by the following formulas.

From $(h0\bar{h}l)$ or its equivalents,

$$p_0 = \frac{l \tan \rho}{h} \ ; \ c = \frac{l\sqrt{3} \tan \rho}{2h} \qquad [85]$$

14 *Am. Min.*, 23, 314 (1938).

From $(hh\,2\bar{h}\,l)$ or equivalents,

$$p_0 = \frac{l\tan\rho}{h\sqrt{3}}\;; \quad c = \frac{l\tan\rho}{2h} \tag{86}$$

From $(hk\bar{\imath}l)$ or equivalents,

$$p_0 = \frac{l\tan\rho}{\sqrt{h^2 + k^2 + hk}}\;; \quad c = \frac{l\sqrt{3}\tan\rho}{2\sqrt{h^2 + k^2 + hk}} \tag{87}$$

Form Symbols. The four-index Bravais symbols are used throughout. When the lattice mode is rhombohedral, Millerian three-index symbols are also given. Bravais $hk\bar{\imath}l$ symbols may be transformed to Millerian hkl symbols by the use of the following formula.

$$\text{Bravais to Miller:} \quad \frac{1}{3}\,0\,\frac{\bar{1}}{3}\,\frac{1}{3} \,/\, \frac{\bar{1}}{3}\,\frac{1}{3}\,0\,\frac{1}{3} \,/\, 0\,\frac{\bar{1}}{3}\,\frac{1}{3}\,\frac{1}{3} \tag{88}$$

The reverse transformation is as follows.

$$\text{Miller to Bravais:} \quad 1\,\bar{1}\,0 \,/\, 0\,1\,\bar{1} \,/\, \bar{1}\,0\,1 \,/\, 1\,1\,1 \tag{89}$$

Indexing of Forms. In the indexing of forms in the hexagonal system, two coordinate axes, P_1 and P_2 (Fig. 14), are used which are normal to $(10\bar{1}0)$ and $(01\bar{1}0)$, respectively (see also Fig. 15). The positive unit lengths along these coordinate axes extend from the center of projection to the gnomonic poles of $(10\bar{1}1)$ and $(01\bar{1}1)$. The Bravais indices $(hk\bar{\imath}l)$ are found as follows (clearing fractions, if necessary).

$$h = P_1 \text{ coordinate}$$
$$k = P_2 \text{ coordinate}$$
$$\bar{\imath} = (h + k)$$
$$l = 1$$

In Fig. 14 the faces for which P_1 and P_2 coordinates are given receive the following indices.

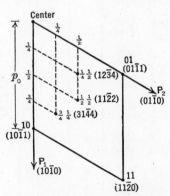

$$\frac{1}{4}\,\frac{1}{2} = \left(\frac{1}{4}\cdot\frac{2}{4}\cdot\frac{\bar{3}}{4}\cdot 1\right) = (12\bar{3}4)$$

$$\frac{1}{2}\,\frac{1}{2} = \left(\frac{1}{2}\cdot\frac{1}{2}\cdot\bar{1}\cdot 1\right) = (11\bar{2}2)$$

$$\frac{3}{4}\,\frac{1}{4} = \left(\frac{3}{4}\cdot\frac{1}{4}\cdot\bar{1}\cdot 1\right) = (31\bar{4}4)$$

FIG. 14. Determination of Bravais form indices from the gnomonic projection in the hexagonal system.

To calculate Bravais indices from coordinate angles phi (ϕ) and rho (ρ), Fig. 14:

$$\frac{h}{l} = \frac{2 \sin (30° + \phi) \tan \rho}{p_0 \sqrt{3}}$$

$$\frac{k}{l} = \frac{2 \sin (30° - \phi) \tan \rho}{p_0 \sqrt{3}}$$

Order of Form Listing. The order of listing in the hexagonal system is given in Tables 9, 10, and 11. Table 9 includes those symmetry classes in which the lattice mode is necessarily primitive hexagonal (P). Table 10 is the order of listing for the remaining classes if their lattice mode is primitive hexagonal. If, however, the lattice mode is rhombohedral (R), the order of listing for these same classes is given in Table 11. The division into three tables is necessary since certain forms which are complementary (or correlative) merohedral forms in the primitive lattice mode are actually holohedral in the rhombohedral lattice mode. For example, $0h\bar{h}l$ forms must be listed with their complementary $h0\bar{h}l$ forms if the

TABLE 9

ORDER OF FORM LISTING IN CLASSES WITH LATTICE MODE UNIQUELY HEXAGONAL — P

Class $\bar{6}$		6 Lower	6 Upper	$\frac{6}{m}$	$\bar{6} \ m \ 2$	$6 \ m \ m$ Lower	$6 \ m \ m$ Upper	$6 \ 2 \ 2$	$\frac{6}{m} \frac{2}{m} \frac{2}{m}$
c	0001	x	x	x	x	x	x	x	x
m	$10\bar{1}0$		x	x	x		x	x	x
$-m$	$01\bar{1}0$				x				
a'	$11\bar{2}0$		x	x	x		x	x	x
$'a$	$2\bar{1}\bar{1}0$								$(i > h > k)$
j'	$hk\bar{i}0$		x	x	x		x	x	x in order of increasing h/k
$'j$	$i\bar{k}\bar{h}0$		x	x					
$-'j$	$kh\bar{i}0$				x				
$-i'$	$\bar{k}ih0$								
q	$h0\bar{h}l$	x	x	x	x	x	x	x	x in order of increasing h/l
$-q$	$0h\bar{h}l$				x				
e'	$hh \, 2\bar{h} \, l$	x	x	x	x	x	x	x	x in order of increasing h/l
$'e$	$2h \, \bar{h}\bar{h} \, l$								
s'	$hk\bar{i}l$	x	x	x	x	x	x	x	x in order of increasing h/k; in groups of equal h/k, list in order of increasing h/l
$'s$	$i\bar{k}\bar{h}l$	x	x					x	
$-'s$	$kh\bar{i}l$				x				
$-s'$	$\bar{k}i\bar{h}l$								

TABLE 10

ORDER OF FORM LISTING IN CLASSES WITH LATTICE
MODE NOT UNIQUELY HEXAGONAL — P

Class 3 Lower	Class 3 Upper		$\bar{3}$	3 m Lower	3 m Upper	3 2	$\bar{3}\,\dfrac{2}{m}$
x	c	0001	x	x	x	x	x
	m	$10\bar{1}0$	x		x	x	x
	$-m$	$01\bar{1}0$			x		
	a'	$11\bar{2}0$	x		x	x	x
	$'a$	$2\bar{1}\bar{1}0$			x		$(i > h > k)$
	j'	$hk\bar{i}0$	x		x	x	x in order of increasing h/k
	$'j$	$i\bar{k}h0$	x			x	
	$-'j$	$kh\bar{i}0$	x		x		
	$-j'$	$\bar{k}ih0$	x				
x	q	$h0\bar{h}l$	x	x	x	x	x in order of increasing h/l
x	$-q$	$0h\bar{h}l$	x	x	x	x	x
x	e'	$hh\,2\bar{h}\,l$	x	x	x	x	x same as for $h0\bar{h}l$
x	$'e$	$2h\,\bar{h}\bar{h}\,l$	x			x	x
x	s'	$hk\bar{i}l$	x	x	x	x	x in order of increasing h/k;
x	$'s$	$i\bar{k}hl$	x			x	in groups of equal h/k,
x	$-'s$	$kh\bar{i}l$	x		x	x	x list in order of increasing h/l
x	$-s'$	$\bar{k}ihl$	x				x

lattice is primitive; but they are listed separately if the lattice is rhombohedral. The letters c, m, a are reserved for the faces (0001), (10$\bar{1}$0), (11$\bar{2}$0), respectively. The plus and minus 30° meridians define right and left forms (Fig. 15).

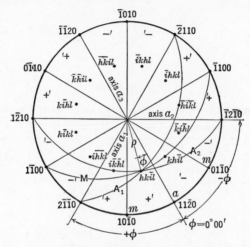

FIG. 15. Stereographic projection showing designation and angles in the hexagonal system.

Hexagonal System Angles. The angles given in the hexagonal system are: (Fig. 15) the azimuth angle ϕ with ϕ of (11$\bar{2}$0) 0°00′; the polar angle ρ, equal to the interfacial angle to c(0001); M, the interfacial angle to (1$\bar{1}$00), given for crystals of the primitive mode only; A_1, the interfacial angle to (2$\bar{1}\bar{1}$0), given for crystals of the rhombohedral mode only; and A_2, the interfacial angle to ($\bar{1}$2$\bar{1}$0). The following formulas are useful in calculating these angles.

$$\tan \phi = \frac{h - k}{h + k} \cdot \frac{1}{\sqrt{3}} \quad \text{or} \quad \cot \phi = \frac{h + k}{h - k} \cdot \sqrt{3} \qquad [90]$$

For $(hk\bar{i}l)$

$$\tan \rho = \frac{p_0}{l} \sqrt{h^2 + k^2 + hk}$$

For $(h0\bar{h}l)$ and $(0h\bar{h}l)$

$$\tan \rho = \frac{p_0 h}{l} \qquad [91]$$

For $(hh\,2\bar{h}\,l)$

$$\tan \rho = \frac{p_0 h \sqrt{3}}{l}$$

TABLE 11

Order of Form Listing in Classes with Lattice
Mode Not Uniquely Hexagonal — R

Class 3 Lower	Class 3 Upper	$\bar{3}$	3 m Lower	3 m Upper	3 2	$\bar{3}\,\dfrac{2}{m}$
x c	$000\bar{1}$	x	x	x	x	x
m	$10\bar{1}0$	x		x	x	x
$-m$	$01\bar{1}0$			x		
a'	$11\bar{2}0$	x		x	x	x
$'a$	$2\bar{1}\bar{1}0$				x	$(i > h > k)$
j'	$hk\bar{i}0$	x		x	x	x in order of increasing h/k
$'j$	$i\bar{k}h0$	x			x	
$-'j$	$kh\bar{i}0$	x		x		
$-j'$	$\bar{k}ih0$	x				
x q	$h0\bar{h}l$	x	x	x	x	x in order of increasing h/l
x Q	$0h\bar{h}l$	x	x	x	x	x same as for $h0\bar{h}l$
x e'	$hh\,2\bar{h}\,l$	x	x	x	x	x same as for $h0\bar{h}l$
x $'e$	$2h\,\bar{h}\bar{h}\,l$	x			x	
x s'	$hk\bar{i}l$	x	x	x	x	x in order of increasing h/k; in groups of equal h/k,
x $'s$	$i\bar{k}hl$	x			x	list in order of increasing h/l
x $-'s$	$kh\bar{i}l$	x	x	x	x	x same as for $hk\bar{i}l$
x $-s'$	$\bar{k}ihl$	x			x	

TABLE 12

Calculation of Interfacial Angles* in the Hexagonal System (Fig. 15)

Form	M	A_1	A_2
$h0\bar{h}l$	$\cos M = \dfrac{\sin \rho}{2}$	$\cos A_1 = \dfrac{\sqrt{3}}{2}\sin \rho$	$90°00'$
$0h\bar{h}l$	$\cos (180° - M) = \dfrac{\sin \rho}{2}$	$90°00'$	$\cos A_2 = \dfrac{\sqrt{3}}{2}\sin \rho$
$hh\,2\bar{h}\,l$	$90°00'$	$\cos A_1 = \dfrac{\sin \rho}{2}$	$\cos A_2 = \dfrac{\sin \rho}{2}$
$2h\,\bar{h}\bar{h}\,l$	$\cos M = \dfrac{\sqrt{3}}{2}\sin \rho$	$A_1 = 90°00' - \rho$	$\cos (180° - A_2) = \dfrac{\sin \rho}{2}$
$hk\bar{i}l$	$\cos M = \sin \rho \sin \phi$	$\cos A_1 = \sin \rho \cos (60° - \phi)$	$\cos A_2 = \sin \rho \cos (60° + \phi)$
$i\bar{k}hl$	$\cos M = \sin \rho \cos (30° + \phi)$	$\cos A_1 = \sin \rho \cos \phi$	$\cos (180° - A_2) = \sin \rho \cos (60° + \phi)$
$kh\bar{i}l$	$\cos (180° - M) = \sin \rho \sin \phi$	$\cos A_1 = \sin \rho \cos (60° + \phi)$	$\cos A_2 = \sin \rho \cos (60° - \phi)$
$\bar{k}ihl$	$\cos (180° - M) = \sin \rho \cos (30° + \phi)$	$\cos (180° - A_1) = \sin \rho \cos (60° + \phi)$	$\cos A_2 = \sin \rho \cos \phi$

* ϕ in this table is always that of the equivalent $hk\bar{i}l$ form.

Since ϕ is a constant for each h/k value in the hexagonal system, the following table of ϕ angles is given with variations in h and k from 1 to 11. The angles are given according to increasing magnitude to facilitate rapid comparison with measured values.

TABLE 13

PHI ANGLES IN THE HEXAGONAL SYSTEM

$h : k$	ϕ	$h : k$	ϕ	$h : k$	ϕ
1 : 1	0°00′00″	3 : 2	6°35′12″	3 : 1	16°06′08″
11 : 10	1 34 29	11 : 7	7 18 40	10 : 3	17 16 10
10 : 9	1 44 26	8 : 5	7 35 21	7 : 2	17 47 01
9 : 8	1 56 42	5 : 3	8 12 48	11 : 3	18 15 30
8 : 7	2 12 15	7 : 4	8 56 54	4 : 1	19 06 24
7 : 6	2 32 35	9 : 5	9 22 01	9 : 2	20 10 25
6 : 5	3 00 16	11 : 6	9 38 15	5 : 1	21 03 06
11 : 9	3 18 16	2 : 1	10 53 36	11 : 2	21 47 12
5 : 4	3 40 14	11 : 5	12 12 59	6 : 1	22 24 23
9 : 7	4 07 40	9 : 4	12 31 11	7 : 1	23 24 48
4 : 3	4 42 54	7 : 3	13 00 14	8 : 1	24 10 57
11 : 8	5 12 31	5 : 2	13 53 52	9 : 1	24 47 29
7 : 5	5 29 47	8 : 3	14 42 17	10 : 1	25 17 06
10 : 7	5 49 03	11 : 4	15 04 45	11 : 1	25 41 36

Special Relations in Rhombohedral Lattices. In crystals with a rhombohedral lattice mode there are generally given, in addition to the regular hexagonal elements, the following constants.

a_{rh} = absolute length of the rhombohedral edge, derived from x-ray measurements.

α = interaxial angle of the direct rhombohedral lattice.

λ = interaxial angle of the reciprocal rhombohedral lattice.

Some formulas relating the hexagonal and rhombohedral lattice modes follow (Fig. 16). If

a_0 = absolute length along a-axis of hexagonal lattice;

c_0 = absolute length along c-axis of hexagonal lattice;

$\rho_1 = \rho$ of $(10\bar{1}1) = (0001) \wedge (10\bar{1}1)$;

$\rho_2 = \rho$ of $(01\bar{1}2) = (0001) \wedge (01\bar{1}2)$.

Then

$$\sin\frac{\lambda}{2} = \frac{\sqrt{3}}{2}\sin\rho_1 = \sqrt{3}\sin\rho_2 \qquad [92]$$

$$\cot \frac{\alpha'}{2} = \sqrt{3} \cos \rho_1 \tag{93}$$

$$\left.\begin{array}{l} \end{array}\right\} \text{Primed values are supplements of unprimed}$$

$$\cos \frac{\alpha'}{2} = \frac{\sqrt{3}}{2} \cos \rho_2 \tag{94}$$

$$\sin \frac{\alpha}{2} = \frac{a_0}{2a_{rh}} = \frac{3a_0}{2\sqrt{3a_0^2 + c_0^2}} = \frac{3}{2\sqrt{3 + \left(\dfrac{c}{a}\right)^2}} \tag{95}$$

$$a_{rh} = \frac{1}{3}\sqrt{3a_0^2 + c_0^2} \tag{96}$$

$$\frac{c_0}{a_0} = \sqrt{\left(\frac{3}{2 \sin \dfrac{\alpha}{2}}\right)^2 - 3} \tag{97}$$

Volume rhombohedral cell $\quad \dfrac{a_0^2 c_0 \sqrt{3}}{6} \tag{98}$

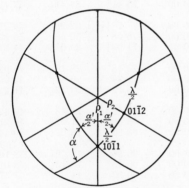

FIG. 16. Stereographic projection of linear and polar interaxial angles in the rhombohedral lattice mode.

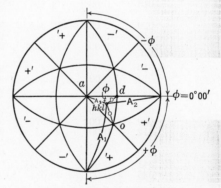

FIG. 17. Stereographic projection showing form designation and angles in the isometric system.

ϕ = azimuth angle measured from (010), zero meridian.
$\rho = A_3$ = interfacial angle with (001).
A_1 = interfacial angle with (100).
A_2 = interfacial angle with (010).
D = interfacial angle with (011).
O = interfacial angle with (111).

ISOMETRIC SYSTEM

Elements and angle tables are not given for isometric minerals, since the same angular relations hold for all. Angles for commonly found isometric forms are listed in Table 14. The meaning of the angles given is shown in Fig. 17.

Forms for which the same letters are used in all species are given letters in Table 14. In order that there may be sufficient remaining letters to designate the form assemblage of any one species, no convention has been adopted for the lettering of other forms.

TABLE 14

Isometric Angle Table

	Form	ϕ	$\rho = A_3$	A_1	A_2	D	O
a	001	......	0°00'	90°00'	90°00'	45°00'	54°44'
d	011	0°00'	45 00	90 00	45 00	0 00	35 16
o	111	45 00	54 44	54 44	54 44	35 16	0 00
	0·1·15	0 00	3 49	90 00	86 11	41 11	52 05
	0·1·10	0 00	5 42½	90 00	84 17½	39 17½	50 48½
	018	0 00	7 07½	90 00	82 52½	37 52½	49 52½
	017	0 00	8 08	90 00	81 52	36 52	49 13
δ	016	0 00	9 27½	90 00	80 32½	35 32½	48 22
η	015	0 00	11 18½	90 00	78 41½	33 41½	47 12½
	029	0 00	12 31½	90 00	77 28½	32 28½	46 27½
h	014	0 00	14 02	90 00	75 58	30 58	45 33½
	072	0 00	15 56½	90 00	74 03½	29 03½	44 27½
	0·3·10	0 00	16 42	90 00	73 18	28 18	44 02
f	013	0 00	18 26	90 00	71 34	26 34	43 05½
k	025	0 00	21 48	90 00	68 12	23 12	41 22
	037	0 00	23 12	90 00	66 48	21 48	40 42
	049	0 00	23 57½	90 00	66 02½	21 02½	40 21
e	012	0 00	26 34	90 00	63 26	18 27	39 14½
	059	0 00	29 03½	90 00	60 56½	15 56½	38 16½
	047	0 00	29 44½	90 00	60 15½	15 15½	38 01½
l	035	0 00	30 58	90 00	59 02	14 02	37 37
g	023	0 00	33 41½	90 00	56 18½	11 18½	36 48½
	057	0 00	35 32½	90 00	54 27½	9 27½	36 21
θ	034	0 00	36 52	90 00	53 08	8 08	36 04
ζ	045	0 00	38 39½	90 00	51 20½	6 20½	35 45½
ν	056	0 00	39 48½	90 00	50 11½	5 11½	35 35½
	078	0 00	41 11	90 00	48 49	3 49	35 26½
	1·1·12	45 00	6 43½	85 15	85 15	40 28	48 00½
	1·1·11	45 00	7 19½	84 49½	84 49½	41 14½	47 24½
	1·1·10	45 00	8 03	84 19	84 19	39 38	46 41
	119	45 00	8 56	83 42	83 42	39 05½	45 48
	118	45 00	10 01½	82 56	82 56	38 26	44 42½
	117	45 00	11 25½	81 57	81 57	37 37	43 18½
ϕ	116	45 00	13 16	80 40	80 40	36 35	41 28

TABLE 14 (*Continued*)

Form	ϕ	$\rho = A_3$	A_1	A_2	D	O
ω	115	45°00′	15°47½′	78°54½′	78°54½′	35°16′	38°56½′
ψ	229	45 00	17 26½	77 45½	77 45½	34 28	37 17½
μ	114	45 00	19 28½	76 22	76 22	33 33½	35 15½
τ	227	45 00	22 00	74 38½	74 38½	32 33	32 44
m	113	45 00	25 14½	72 27	72 27	31 29	29 29½
	338	45 00	27 56½	70 39	70 39	30 48	26 47½
γ	225	45 00	29 30	69 37½	69 37½	30 30	25 14
λ	337	45 00	31 13	68 33	68 33	30 15	23 31
n	112	45 00	35 16	65 54½	65 54½	30 00	19 28
	447	45 00	38 56½	63 36½	63 36½	30 12	15 47½
σ	335	45 00	40 19	62 46½	62 46½	30 23	14 25
β	223	45 00	43 19	60 59	60 59	30 58	11 25
χ	334	45 00	46 41	59 02½	59 02½	31 54½	8 03
	556	45 00	49 41	57 22½	57 22½	32 59½	5 03
	188	7 07½	45 13½	84 56	45 13½	5 04	30 12
	177	8 08	45 17½	84 14	45 17½	5 46	29 30
	166	9 27½	45 23½	83 16½	45 23½	6 43½	28 32½
ξ	155	11 18½	45 33½	81 57	45 33½	8 03	27 13
ρ	144	14 02	45 52	79 58½	45 52	10 01½	25 14½
	277	15 56½	46 07½	78 34½	46 07½	11 25½	23 50½
q	133	18 26	46 30½	76 44	46 30½	13 16	22 00
Γ	255	21 48	47 07½	74 12½	47 07½	15 47½	19 28½
p	122	26 34	48 11½	70 31½	48 11½	19 28½	15 47½
Δ	477	29 44½	49 02	68 00	49 02	22 00	13 15½
	355	30 58	49 23	67 00½	49 23	22 59½	12 16½
r	233	33 41½	50 14½	64 45½	50 14½	25 14½	10 01½
	344	36 52	51 20½	62 03½	51 20½	27 56½	7 19½
	455	38 39½	52 01	60 30	52 01	29 30	5 46
x	1·10·18	5 42½	29 10½	87 13½	60 59	16 11	35 41½
	1·6·12	9 27½	26 53	85 44	63 31	18 54½	35 22½
	1·6·11	9 27½	28 56½	85 26	61 29½	17 00½	34 14
	1·5·10	11 18½	27 01	84 53½	63 33	19 06½	34 37
	1·6·10	9 27½	31 18½	85 06	59 09½	14 51	33 01
	179	8 08	38 09½	84 59½	52 17½	8 42	30 57½
	128	26 34	15 37	83 05	76 04	31 39	40 08
	138	18 26	21 34	83 19½	69 35½	25 17	36 21

TABLE 14 (*Continued*)

Form	ϕ	$\rho = A_3$	A_1	A_2	D	O
	148	14°02′	27°16′	83°37′	63°36½′	19°28½′	33°29½′
	158	11 18½	32 31	83 57	58 11½	14 18½	31 34½
	127	26 34	17 43	82 10½	74 12½	30 00	38 13
u	137	18 26	24 18½	82 31	67 00½	22 59½	34 13½
	157	11 18½	36 04	83 22	54 44	11 32	29 56
	2·3·12	33 41½	16 43½	80 49	76 09	32 10	38 26
w	136	18 26	27 47½	81 31½	63 45	20 14	31 39
	156	11 18½	40 21½	82 42	50 35	8 57	28 22½
	2·5·11	21 48	26 05	80 36	65 54½	22 31	31 57
Y	125	26 34	24 05½	79 29	68 35	25 21	32 35½
X	2·5·10	21 48	28 18	79 51½	63 53	20 57½	30 12½
V	135	18 26	32 18½	80 16	59 32	17 01½	28 33½
	145	14 02	39 30½	81 07½	51 53	10 54	27 01
	239	33 41½	21 50	78 05½	71 58½	28 56	33 31
T	249	26 34	26 25½	78 31½	66 33	23 50½	30 29½
	269	18 26	35 06	79 31½	56 56½	15 22	26 50½
	238	33 41½	24 15½	76 49½	70 00½	27 34½	31 12
t	124	26 34	29 12½	77 23½	64 07½	22 12½	28 07½
	134	18 26	38 19½	78 41½	53 57½	13 54	25 04
	3·5·11	30 58	27 55½	76 03½	66 19½	24 40	28 13½
y	5·10·18	26 34	31 50½	76 21	61 50½	20 52½	25 57
	237	33 41½	27 15	75 17	67 36½	26 06	28 22½
	247	26 34	32 34½	76 04	61 13	20 33	25 22
	3·4·10	36 52	26 34	74 26	69 02	27 41½	28 37
	3·5·10	30 58	30 15	74 59	64 24½	23 37	26 08
	3·7·10	23 12	37 17½	76 11½	56 09½	17 00	23 16½
	236	33 41½	31 00	73 24	64 37½	24 37	24 52
s	123	26 34	36 42	74 30	57 41½	19 06½	22 12½
	358	30 58	36 05	72 21½	59 40	21 47	21 04
U	235	33 41½	35 47½	71 04	60 52½	23 24½	20 31
D	245	26 34	41 48½	72 39	53 24	18 26	18 47
Z	357	30 58	39 47½	70 46½	56 43	21 21	18 05
	458	38 39½	38 40½	67 01½	60 47½	26 12	16 42
	346	36 52	39 48½	67 24½	59 11½	25 07½	16 03½
z	234	33 41½	42 02	68 12	56 08½	23 12	15 13½
E	467	33 41½	45 51	66 33	53 20½	23 50½	12 24½
	345	36 52	45 00	64 54	55 33	25 50½	11 33½
	578	35 32½	47 04½	64 48½	53 25½	25 27½	10 36
	456	38 39½	46 47½	62 54½	55 18½	27 33½	9 19½
F	689	36 52	48 01	63 31	53 31	26 41	9 14½
G	10·12·13	39 48½	50 14	60 31½	53 48½	29 33½	6 06

Calculation of Angles.   The angles in Table 14 are calculated as follows.

$$\tan \phi = \frac{h}{k} \text{ (see Table 8)} \tag{99}$$

$$\tan \rho = \frac{h}{l \sin \phi} = \frac{k}{l \cos \phi} \tag{100}$$

$$\cos A_1 = \sin \rho \sin \phi \tag{101}$$

$$\cos A_2 = \sin \rho \cos \phi \tag{102}$$

$$\cos D = \frac{\sqrt{2}}{2}(\cos \rho + \sin \rho \cos \phi) \tag{103}$$

$$\cos O = \cos \rho \cos 54°44' + \sin \rho \sin 54°44' \cos (45° - \phi) \tag{104}$$

The order of form listing is given in Table 15 for the five isometric symmetry classes.

TABLE 15

ORDER OF FORM LISTING IN THE ISOMETRIC SYSTEM

Class 2 3		$\dfrac{2}{m}\bar{3}$	$\bar{4}\ 3\ m$	4 3 2	$\dfrac{4}{m}\ \bar{3}\ \dfrac{2}{m}$
a	001	x	x	x	x
d	011	x	x	x	x
o	111	x	x	x	x ($h < k < l$)
$-o$	$\bar{1}11$		x		
e'	$0kl$	x	x	x	x in order of increasing k/l
$'e$	$k0l$	x			
j	hhl	x	x	x	x in order of increasing h/l
$-j$	$\bar{h}hl$		x		
n	hll	x	x	x	x in order of increasing h/l
$-n$	$\bar{h}ll$		x		
s'	hkl	x	x	x	x in order of increasing h/l;
$'s$	khl	x			in groups of equal h/l,
$-'s$	$\bar{h}kl$		x	x	list in order of increasing k/l
$-s'$	$\bar{k}hl$				

e. Transformation Formulas.   In the transformation of elements and indices from one set to another (old to new) the transformation matrix is written in the linear form (Barker, 1930): $u_1v_1w_1/u_2v_2w_2/u_3v_3w_3$, where $(u_1u_2u_3)$,[15] $(v_1v_2v_3)$, and $(w_1w_2w_3)$ are the indices, multiple if need be, in the

[15] The usage of brackets followed here is: ( ) = face symbol; { } = form symbol; [ ] = zone or axis symbol.

new orientation of the old axial planes (100), (010), and (001), respectively; and where $[u_1v_1w_1]$, $[u_2v_2w_2]$, and $[u_3v_3w_3]$ in the old orientation represent the new axial lengths [100], [010], and [001], respectively.

To obtain such a formula, then, it is necessary to determine the new indices of the old axial planes (100), (010), and (001) and to write them in that order in vertical columns as shown below. It is further necessary to determine the new indices of any general face (hkl) or of a pair of special faces of $(hk0)$, $(0kl)$, and $(h0l)$. This requirement arises because it is impossible to determine from a projection whether the new indices of the old axial planes are correct, or whether they are but the simplest expression of the actual multiple indices of the plane, as is demonstrated later. Any face symbol (hkl) in the old orientation may be transformed to the new equivalent $(h'k'l')$ by the formula $u_1v_1w_1/u_2v_2w_2/u_3v_3w_3$ as follows.

$$h' = u_1h + v_1k + w_1l; \quad k' = u_2h + v_2k + w_2l; \quad l' = u_3h + v_3k + w_3l$$

The following example will serve to indicate the procedure followed to obtain a transformation formula.

Old Orientation	New Orientation	
(100) =	$(\bar{1}01) = (u_1u_2u_3)$	
(010) =	$(0\bar{1}0) = (v_1v_2v_3)$	[105]
(001) =	$(011) = (w_1w_2w_3)$	
(121) =	$(\bar{1}03)$	

By writing the given relations in the linear form $u_1v_1w_1/u_2v_2w_2/u_3v_3w_3$ $\bar{1}00/0\bar{1}1/101$ is obtained. This formula must be checked by transforming (121) to obtain the new symbol. This is done graphically below.

$$
\begin{array}{ccccccccc}
1 & 2 & 1 & 1 & 2 & 1 & 1 & 2 & 1 \\
\times & \times & \times & \times & \times & \times & \times & \times & \times \\
\bar{1} & 0 & 0 / 0 & & \bar{1} & 1 / 1 & & 0 & 1 \\
\hline
\bar{1}+0+0 & & 0+\bar{2}+1 & & & 1+0+1 & & & \\
= \bar{1} & & = \bar{1} & & & = 2 & & &
\end{array}
$$

[106]

The new indices obtained are $(\bar{1}\bar{1}2)$ instead of the correct $(\bar{1}03)$, showing the need of adjusting the terms of the formula. By a simple cut-and-try process various multiple indices are substituted in the second column of equation 105. When (011) of equation 105 is changed to (022), the other equivalences remaining unchanged, the correct formula results.

Old	New	
(100) =	$(\bar{1}01)$	
(010) =	$(0\bar{1}0)$ or $\bar{1}00/0\bar{1}2/102$	[107]
(001) =	(022)	

By transforming (121) as in equation 106 $(\bar{1}03)$ is obtained which validates formula [107].

As was indicated earlier, this type of formula not only facilitates the transformation of indices, but it also permits the determination of the new axial directions, lengths, and angles from their identity in the old lattice. $[u_1v_1w_1]$ $[u_2v_2w_2]$, and $[u_3v_3w_3]$ in the old lattice orientation are the new [100], [010], and [001], respectively. Thus, in the transformation example just given one sees that:[16]

Old Orientation		New Orientation	
$[u_1v_1w_1] = [\bar{1}00]$		$\equiv [100]$	
$[u_2v_2w_2] = [0\bar{1}2]$		$\equiv [010]$	[108]
$[u_3v_3w_3] = [102]$		$\equiv [001]$	

Conventionally, the new interaxial angles are defined as follows.

$$\text{New} \qquad \text{Old}$$
$$\alpha' = [010] \wedge [001] \equiv [0\bar{1}2] \wedge [102]$$
$$\beta' = [001] \wedge [100] \equiv [102] \wedge [\bar{1}00]$$
$$\gamma' = [100] \wedge [010] \equiv [\bar{1}00] \wedge [0\bar{1}2]$$

The length, T, of any $[uvw]$, in this case of $[\bar{1}00]$, $[0\bar{1}2]$, or $[102]$ in the old lattice, is calculated as follows.

$$T_{uvw}^2 = a^2u^2 + b^2v^2 + c^2w^2 + 2bcvw\cos\alpha + 2cawu\cos\beta + 2abuv\cos\gamma \quad [109]$$

(a, b, c, α, β, γ are the linear elements of the old lattice). If τ is the angle between the directions $[u_1v_1w_1]$ and $[u_2v_2w_2]$ in the old lattice, the new axial angles are computed by the general formula,

$$\cos\tau = [a^2u_1u_2 + b^2v_1v_2 + c^2w_1w_2 + bc(v_1w_2 + w_1v_2)\cos\alpha$$
$$+ ca(w_1u_2 + u_1w_2)\cos\beta + ab(u_1v_2 + v_1u_2)\cos\gamma]/T_{u_1v_1w_1} \cdot T_{u_2v_2w_2} \quad [110]$$

For a fuller discussion of transformations the reader is referred to more extensive treatments.[17]

3. X-Ray Crystallography

The unit cell and its axial ratio, the space group, and the atomic contents of the cell are given under **Structure Cell** in the species description. In *group* and *type* discussions general statements concerning the structure are often mentioned, but further details are not included because many books are now available where these data are given in considerable detail. In the references, original papers on the structure are cited.

[16] The sign $\equiv$ is read " equals after transformation."
[17] W. J. Lewis, *Crystallography*, 104, 1899.
T. V. Barker, *Systematic Crystallography*, 32, 1930.
J. D. H. Donnay, *Am. Min.*, **22**, 621 (1937).
M. A. Peacock, *Am. Min.*, **22**, 588 (1937).
W. E. Richmond, *Am. Min.*, **22**, 630 (1937).
C. W. Wolfe, *Am. Min.*, **22**, 736 (1937).
Int. Tables Det. Cryst. Struct., **1**, 73 (1935).

The space group symbols used here are in the Hermann-Mauguin notation as given in the *International Tables for the Determination of Crystal Structures*. These are used in preference to earlier notations because they express the geometric and symmetry characteristics of the space group, and are in conformity with the symmetry class notation. The following brief explanation of the Hermann-Mauguin symbols is taken from the more detailed treatment referred to above.

a. The first letter of the symbol indicates the lattice mode or translation group. The letters so used are:

P = primitive	A = *a*-face-centered
C = *c*-face-centered	I = body-centered
B = *b*-face-centered	F = all-face-centered
	R = rhombohedral-centered

b. After the translation group symbol the symmetry elements of the space group are symbolized in the same way as in the crystal class, except that in some instances screw axes and glide planes now replace the simple rotation axes and symmetry planes. In the various crystal systems the order of the symbols given is:

Triclinic	none		
Monoclinic	[010]		
Orthorhombic	[100]	[010]	[001]
Tetragonal	[001]	[010]	[110]
Hexagonal	[0001]	[1000]	[10$\bar{1}$0]
Isometric	[001]	[111]	[011]

c. Rotation symmetry axes are given according to their multiplicity as 1, 2, 3, 4, 6, with 1 indicating absence of symmetry. The screw axes of symmetry are as follows: 2_1, 3_1, 3_2, 4_1, 4_2, 4_3, 6_1, 6_2, 6_3, 6_4, 6_6, where the translation along the screw axis is indicated by the subscript. Thus, 4_1 indicates that there is a 1/4 translation along the four-fold screw axis; 6_3 indicates 3/6 or 1/2 translation along the sixfold screw axis. A bar over the symmetry axis symbol shows that it is a rotary inversion axis (as in the crystal class notation).

d. Reflection planes are denoted by the following symbols.

m = simple reflection plane.

a, b, c = reflection planes with glide components of $\frac{1}{2}a$[100], $\frac{1}{2}b$[010], $\frac{1}{2}c$[001], respectively.

n = reflection planes with glide component of $\frac{1}{2}$[011], $\frac{1}{2}$[101] or $\frac{1}{2}$[110].

d = reflection planes with glide components of $\frac{1}{4}$[011], $\frac{1}{4}$[101], $\frac{1}{4}$[110], or $\frac{1}{4}$[hhl] (in the tetragonal and isometric systems).

e. As in the crystal class notation, a number over a letter symbolizing a reflection plane indicates that the plane is perpendicular to an axis of a given multiplicity. Thus $\dfrac{6}{m}$ is a sixfold rotation axis with a plane of simple reflection perpendicular thereto.

4. Habit

Crystals are described as *prismatic, long prismatic, acicular,* as an indication of their characteristic elongation. *Short prismatic* to *tabular* to *platy* to *scaly* (*micaceous*) indicates varying habits of crystals. Since elongation is usually in a prominent zonal direction, this habit is usually indicated by the zone axis of the elongation. Tabular and platy habits are best indicated by face symbols, thus: tabular (001). Characteristic striae are given in terms of direction, i.e., the zone axis, on a given face. The general appearance and shape of twins are also given. For crystals in the isometric system and others where the habit is characteristic, such terms as *octahedral, cubic, pyramidal, steep pyramidal* are employed.

Crystalline aggregates of various kinds are described under **Habit** rather than under **Varieties** as has been done sometimes in previous editions. Few habit varieties are retained here.

Twinning. Under this heading are recorded the various twin laws observed and a brief statement of the general appearance of the aggregate. The twinning is referred to either a plane or an axis. Where a further geometrical study in the manner of Friedel is made, the *index* of the twin is given. In some few species the relation of twinning to the structure has been studied, and references to these works are made.

Mechanical twinning, or twin gliding, is mentioned under twinning, and the notation used by the original investigator is given since no universally acceptable notation is yet available, and the different notations are often not transformable.

Intergrowths. The intergrowth relations of two species are given in the descriptions of each. The position of mutual orientation is given by a statement of the planes and of the zone axes in those planes which correspond in the two species.

5. Physical Properties

The physical properties given in this edition are much the same as those in previous editions, except that in some instances they are more precise. Crystal structure results have given an impetus to attempts at quantitative expression of such properties as hardness, cleavage, refractive index, and specific gravity. These attempts have been only partially successful because of the mathematical complexities, on the one hand, and crystal imperfections, which have a great effect, on the other. Cleavage has been treated quantitatively by Shappell [18] as a problem of bond strength across planes in the crystal.

[18] *Am. Min.,* **21**, 75 (1936).

Cleavage is a fracture yielding a more or less smooth surface in the crystal, usually along one of the principal planes of the lattice. The cleavage is characterized by the plane, the ease of production and the character of the surface.

Parting is applied to a separation which is not produced along a plane of minimum cohesion in the lattice but is produced by lamellar twinning, by directed pressure exerted on the crystal, or by oriented inclusions which develop planes of weakness. Parting, in some instances, does not conform to the symmetry requirements of the crystal.

Fracture is designated here as hackly, even, uneven, conchoidal, etc. It is a purely qualitative character, and its terms may merge into those expressing cleavage of an inferior kind.

Tenacity is designated by the terms brittle, sectile, malleable, flexible, or elastic. These properties can be given quantitative expression; but, to date, few quantitative data of this kind are available even for the common minerals.

Hardness is given in this edition, as in the last, in terms of the old Mohs scale. Numerous precise hardness testing devices have been employed, but a general application to minerals other than ore minerals has not been made. The various methods of measuring hardness depend on the depth of indentation of a point (sphere or wedge)[19] or on ease of scratching to a given depth.[20] These two methods do not necessarily lead to parallel results. Where such quantitative values are available the results are given here. A qualitative correlation between hardness and bond strength in known ionic crystal structures has been made. As the A to X distance in AX ionic crystals increases, the hardness, in general, decreases.[21]

Specific gravity (density compared with water at 4° C.) is an important physical constant of a mineral, and it is especially so since the advent of x-ray methods. With a knowledge of the unit cell volume it is possible to calculate the atomic contents of the unit cell, if the density is carefully determined. The density is therefore a correlating property between the composition of the mineral and its crystallography. Conversely, if the composition is well established, and the unit cell is determined, one can calculate the density. The calculated value is given in this volume in every instance where the unit cell is known.

Many of the specific gravity values given are between wide limits. This may be due to inaccurate determinations or to actual variations due to compositional changes in the mineral. Many new values have been determined (using the microbalance for small samples) and are published for the first time in this edition. Where the variation is due to compositional changes, an attempt is made to correlate particular values with specified analyses. Satisfactory specific gravity values are

[19] Knoop, Peters, and Emerson, *J. Res. Bur. Standards*, **23**, 39 (1939).
[20] Talmadge, *Econ. Geol.*, **20**, 531 (1925).
[21] See Evans (21, 1939).

an excellent means of identification of minerals, especially the heavy opaque minerals.

Physical properties such as *compressibility, mechanical deformation, thermal expansion, elasticity,* and *dielectric constants* have received little attention from mineralogists. However, these properties, among others, are of increasing importance to the problems of geophysics and as such should be included in a mineralogical description. It is hoped that these properties will be available for succeeding editions of this work.

6. Optical Properties

Such optical properties as are not observed under the microscope are given in the species descriptions under **P h y s.**, i.e., physical properties. They include *color, streak, luster,* and *diaphaneity.* Variations in color are listed, and if the pigmenting agent or cause of the color has been the subject of a special investigation references are given. *Streak* is recorded since it is perhaps a more diagnostic property than color. The kinds and intensity of *luster* are described in the following way.

a. Metallic, the luster of metals.
b. Submetallic, imperfect metallic.
c. Adamantine, like diamond.
d. Vitreous, like broken glass.
e. Resinous, luster of yellow resins.
f. Greasy, like nepheline or cerargyrite.
g. Pearly, like pearl.
h. Silky, fibrous gypsum and other fibrous minerals.

The degrees of intensity are:
(1) Dull.
(2) Splendent.
(3) Shining.
(4) Glistening.

Diaphaneity, or degree of transparency, is indicated by the terms *opaque* and *transparent,* and less often by *translucent.* If a mineral transmits no light of the visible spectrum, even under the microscope, it is called opaque. All others are transparent to some degree, and the degree of transparency is indicated where known. For most oxides of deep color only thin splinters when seen under the microscope will transmit light. Minerals which are not transparent in large pieces because of the scattering of light within the crystal are not called translucent because this is not characteristic of the substance. Most small crystals are either transparent or opaque.

For *isotropic minerals* the refractive index n is given for specified wavelengths together with the characteristic color under the microscope. Anomalous optical behavior (as in diamond) is noted.

For *uniaxial minerals* the refractive indices for the ordinary ray, O, and for the extraordinary ray, E, are given at specified wavelengths. Dichroism and the optic sign are included. The sign is positive or negative according to the relation $E - O$; that is, when $E - O$ is a positive value, the sign is said to be positive. Since the orientation between the crystal and indicatrix is fixed, no further data are required.

In biaxial crystals a tabulation of data is made which includes the following:

X, Y, Z indicate, respectively, in the indicatrix, the *directions* of the low, intermediate, and high refractive indices. The *orientation* of the indicatrix in the crystal is given in the second column by indicating the crystal axes or angular relations to the axes, corresponding to the three elements of the indicatrix. In the third column the refractive indices, n, for the various indicatrix directions are given for various wavelengths. The last column gives the characteristics of differential absorption. In addition, the optic sign, size of axial angle and kind of dispersion are also tabulated. Certain optical studies pertaining to changes of optical character on heating, or dispersion of the refractive indices, or detailed studies of anomalies, are not suitable for tabulation. These are discussed separately.

The triclinic system involves a special statement of the orientation. The position of the indicatrix is given by the phi (ϕ) and rho (ρ) positions of X, Y, and Z on the stereographic projection of the crystal in normal position, i.e., with the c[001] axis in the center of projection and the face b(010) to the right with a phi (ϕ) of 0° and a rho (ρ) of 90°.

Details of optical mineralogy are not included in this introduction because many works in this special field have appeared since the last edition of the *System*.

Observations of the opaque (and some nonopaque) minerals by reflected light, in polished section, are included. The color, behavior in polarized light, and reflection percentages are listed. The latter values, taken from a recent work,[22] are admittedly not of a high order of accuracy, but they are at least an attempt at quantitative data for the ore minerals. Etch reactions are not included. Several good books specializing in this work are now available in this country.[23]

7. Chemistry

The formula, representing the composition, and showing the relation to other minerals, is given at the beginning of the chemistry section. The dualistic formulas and alternate interpretations are omitted or placed in the reference section. Often when the necessary formula is very long, because of many substituting elements, as in a series, the type formula, $A_m B_n X_p$, is given, with the designation of the elements belonging to A, B, and X. The limits of substitution, *as observed in the actual analyses*, are stated. When sufficient data are at hand, an evaluation of the role of

[22] H. Schneiderhöhn and P. Ramdohr, *Erzmikroskopische Bestimmungstafeln*, vol. 2, Berlin, 1931.
[23] The most recent work is: M. N. Short, "Microscopic Determination of the Ore Minerals," (second edition) *U. S. Geol. Sur., Bull. 914*, 1940.

minor constituents is presented, that is, whether they are due to admixed impurities or substitution. Chemical relations concerned with a group are usually not discussed in the species description, but the *group* discussion (and *type* discussion) preceding the first mineral of the group (or type) contains the general chemical statement. Older chemical theories concerning the constitution of minerals are, for the most part, omitted from this work, because they may be found in great detail elsewhere, and are generally inconsistent with present-day crystallochemical developments.

Analyses are presented in tabulated form with the computed composition for the formula at the beginning of the table. For those minerals which have many published analyses only those recently made and those which give important chemical deviations are listed. Poor analyses or analytical data on impure samples are omitted unless no others are available. Analyses have in every instance possible been taken directly from the original work, and any deviation from this procedure is noted.

Tests are given in much the same way as in the Brush and Penfield tables, since no systematic revision of these has appeared.

Varieties are listed according to a new system recently proposed and here adopted.[24] Varieties are due essentially to relatively minor chemical variations. In some special instances (as in quartz and corundum), however, long usage has established varietal terms for physical or genetic variations, which are usefully retained. Since varieties are chemical deviations from the principal composition, the above-mentioned system of nomenclature can replace all the old varietal names. These old names are considered in this work as synonyms, and it is hoped that this procedure will generally be followed. The mineral name, for example, *freibergite* is here considered a synonym for *argentian tetrahedrite*. *Hatchettolite, uranpyrochlor*, and *ellsworthite* are all considered as synonyms for the varietal term *uranian pyrochlore*. The general rule for designating varieties is as follows. The adjectival prefix is determined by the constituent next most abundant after the principal constituents of the species.

The following table of adjectival endings for the chemical suffixes is taken from the original paper by Schaller.

Aluminum — aluminian
Antimony — antimonian
Argon — argonian
Arsenic — arsenoan, arsenian
Barium — barian
Beryllium — beryllian
Bismuth — bismuthian
Boron — borian
Bromine — bromian
Cadmium — cadmian
Calcium — calcian
Carbon — carbonian
Cerium — cerian
Cesium — cesian
Chlorine — chlorian

Chromium — chromian
Cobalt — cobaltian
Columbium — columbian
Copper — cuproan, cuprian
Dysprosium — dysprosian
Erbium — erbian
Europium — europian
Fluorine — fluorian
Gadolinium — gadolinian
Gallium — gallian
Germanium — germanian
Gold — aurian
Hafnium — hafnian
Helium — helian
Holmium — holmian

[24] Schaller, *Am. Min.*, **15**, 566 (1930).

Hydrogen — hydrogenian
Indium — indian
Iodine — iodian
Iridium — iridian
Iron — ferroan, ferrian
Krypton — kryptonian
Lanthanum — lanthanian
Lead — plumbian
Lithium — lithian
Lutecium — lutecian
Magnesium — magnesian
Manganese — manganoan, manganian
Mercury — mercuroan, mercurian
Molybdenum — molybdenian
Neodymium — neodymian
Neon — neonian
Nickel — nickelian
Nitrogen — nitrogenian
Osmium — osmian
Oxygen — oxygenian
Palladium — palladian
Phosphorus — phosphorian
Platinum — platinian
Potassium — potassian
Praseodymium — praseodymian
Radium — radian
Radon — radonian

Rhenium — rhenian
Rhodium — rhodian
Rubidium — rubidian
Ruthenium — ruthenian
Samarium — samarian
Scandium — scandian
Selenium — selenian
Silicon — silician
Silver — argentian
Sodium — sodian
Strontium — strontian
Sulfur — sulfurian
Tantalum — tantalian
Tellurium — tellurian
Terbium — terbian
Thallium — thallian
Thorium — thorian
Thulium — thulian
Tin — stannian
Titanium — titanian
Tungsten — tungstenian
Uranium — uranoan, uranian
Vanadium — vanadian
Xenon — xenonian
Ytterbium — ytterbian
Yttrium — yttrian
Zinc — zincian
Zirconium — zirconian

Where an element shows more than two valencies, the proper form can easily be made. Thus, for vanadium:

For vanadous vanadium, valency of 3, use vanadoan.
For vanadyl vanadium, valency of 4, use vanadylian.
For vanadic vanadium, valency of 5, use vanadian.

8. Occurrences

A general statement of the various types of occurrence is given for each species. This includes a brief paragenetic discussion, where necessary, and an enumeration of localities demonstrating the various types. With common minerals it is impractical to list all the known localities. In this work are listed only well-known localities where the mineral occurs in abundance, or in some special association, or in exceptional crystallization. Localities for the less common and rare minerals are given as completely as possible. If there is some doubt about the authenticity of an occurrence of a given mineral, that doubt is usually expressed by a qualifying phrase, " reported from." If the occurrence is very doubtful, the qualifying phrase is, " said to occur at." In general, references are not given to original works in which the occurrence is first mentioned.

Locality names and spellings, especially for those in Central Europe, present many difficulties. In these times one rarely knows from week to week the political status of European mineral localities. In this work, therefore, such regional names as *Bohemia, Banat, Tirol,* and *Poland* are used without special regard for changes in frontiers. The spelling of central European locality names offers as many difficulties as the regional designation, especially since these names are very different for different language groups.[25] The name and spelling used here are those which seemed most familiar to mineralogists. Thus the Magyar name Felsö-bánya is preferred to Baia Sprie, the Roumanian name for the same place; and the region or country is Roumania.

9. Alteration

In the section under alteration (A l t e r.), the character of the alteration products and the minerals which alter to the described mineral are discussed. Further, any inversions noted from one modification to another are mentioned. A record of pseudomorphs is given. When available, data for artificial alterations are included. Changes involved in the process of exsolution are often discussed elsewhere, as under *chemistry* or *oriented growths*.

10. Synthesis

Under the section Artificial (A r t i f.) are listed some of the more important ways in which the substance may be reproduced in the laboratory. Unless clear proof is at hand that the artificial substance is identical with the natural mineral, not too much reliance can be placed on the supposed synthesis. This proof must be not only with respect to chemical composition, but also with respect to structural identity for many natural systems do not conform with the phases obtained in the laboratory. This is particularly true in some sulfide and sulfosalt syntheses carried out from melts. Present-day x-ray methods furnish a rapid and simple method of comparing artificial compounds with minerals and, unless this is done, the work must be considered incomplete.

11. Name

The derivation of the name is given, usually without further reference than that of the sixth edition of the *System* or other well-known works where these derivations are recorded.[26] When a choice is made between a number of names current in the literature for the same mineral, an explanation of the choice is given. Preference is given to names after persons. (See further under " Nomenclature " in the next section.)

12. Nomenclature

For an account of the historical development of mineral nomenclature and of some early accepted principles in naming minerals the reader is

[25] See Spencer and Slavík, *Min. Mag.*, **21**, 441 (1928).
[26] Dr. Paul J. Alexander of Harvard University has rechecked the Greek derivations.

referred to the Introduction to the fifth and sixth editions of the *System*. Another account is in Chester's work[27] on mineral names.

The Mineralogical Society of America, through the Committee on Nomenclature and Classification of Minerals, has recommended a number of rules and principles to be followed in the naming of minerals.[28] These are enumerated below and with most of them the authors of this work are in full agreement. With a few of them, however, we are not in sympathy.

a. As far as practicable, names of mineral species should terminate uniformly in *ite* (or *lite*) and proposers of new names are urged to follow this rule. A list is given of thirty-eight names not so ending which are recognized as so well fixed in the literature that no attempt to change them should be made.

b. An additional list of nine names of minerals, largely group names or rock names, which do not end in *ite* is also regarded as not to be changed.

With these two proposals the authors are in agreement.

c. A list of thirty names well established in the literature is given and it is proposed to add to each the termination *ite*, since, it is claimed, the change can be made without obscuring the derivation or euphony of the name.

This proposal met with widespread opposition in the Society and is not acceptable to the authors.

d. Certain changes in the spelling of mineral names were recommended by the Committee, as follows.

(1) Substitution of " f " for " ph " in " sulphur," and names derived from it.

(2) The diphthongs " ae " and " oe " simplified to " e."

(3) The Umlaut (¨) in German names to be replaced by " e," as is often done by the Germans.

(4) The majority of the Committee agree that the Swedish letter " å " should be reduced to " a " in mineral names. The Norwegian " å " should be given in names as " aa."

(5) Double word names should be combined into single ones.

(6) When letters in a name are brought together in a manner not customary in English a change should be made.

(7) In translating Russian words the rules of the Library of Congress should be followed.

A list of names showing the effects of these proposed changes in spelling is given by the Committee; the usage adopted by the authors is in essential agreement with the recommendation.

e. The Committee recommended the adoption of Schaller's proposal for adjectival endings for the names of chemical elements used as varietal

[27] A. H. Chester, *A Dictionary of the Names of Minerals including their History and Etymology*, John Wiley and Sons, New York, 1896.
[28] *Am. Min.*, 8, 50 (1923); 9, 60 (1924); 21, 188 (1936).

modifiers of mineral names. This proposal has been adopted, as already explained, under the heading " Chemistry."

f. The following abbreviations are recommended and agree with our usage.

(1) For *specific gravity* or *density* use " G."

(2) For dispersion data use *r* and *v.*

(3) For the crystal systems use Isometric, Tetragonal, Hexagonal, Orthorhombic, Monoclinic, Triclinic.

g. A list of thirty-six minerals for which two or more names have been used is given with a preferred choice for each. This choice we shall, in general, follow.

h. The Committee proposed that the letters alpha (α), beta (β), and gamma (γ) be used to indicate both vibration directions and the values of the refractive indices in those directions. This proposal we have not followed. We have adopted the vibration direction X, Y, and Z in preference to α, β, γ; further, we have tabulated the optical data so that these same Greek letters are not used to designate the refractive indices. The choice is made largely for typographical reasons and because the Greek letters α, β, and γ are much overworked as designations for physical constants.

13. Synonymy

At the beginning of each species description a complete synonymy is given which includes (*a*) old synonyms taken from previous editions and corrected when necessary; (*b*) old names now considered to be synonyms but not so treated in the last edition; (*c*) old mineral names discredited in the sixth edition; (*d*) recently discredited species, (*e*) variety names now discarded (see section under " Varieties " in this " Introduction ").

Minerals which have been discredited since the last edition are described briefly at the end of the main species discussion, but before the references. Species of doubtful validity or relatively incomplete description are described after the species to which they are most closely related, and their names do not appear in the synonymy.

14. Bibliography

An attempt has been made to record the original references for all measurements and all observations of importance. Some well-established data simply repeated from the older editions do not have references. In general, references and data from the older editions have been reexamined in the original. All references cited have been actually consulted unless otherwise noted. Thus a reference given as follows: Fermor, *Nat. Inst. Sc., India,* 4, 253 (1938) — *Min. Abs.,* 7, 169 (1938) means that the reference was found in *Mineralogical Abstracts* and was not seen in the original. Special compilations of data in particular subjects have often been cited instead of the original, or in addition to the original papers. This type of reference is followed particularly for the crystallographic form listings, where the large and critical compilation of V. Goldschmidt is better than any individual work which could be cited. The Strukturbericht of the *Zeitschrift für Kristallographie* and the recent book of Bragg on the structure of minerals[29] or the books of Stillwell[30] and Evans[31] on crystal chemistry are all useful books of reference for structure data when the original paper is inaccessible to those using mineralogical libraries.

References to books are given as follows: Goldschmidt (3, 22, 1916). The full title of the book is given in the list appearing in this introductory section under the name Goldschmidt, and all books by the author are arranged chronologically. In the catalogue of books this reference appears as: Goldschmidt (1913–1923). *Atlas der Krystallformen.* 9 vols. text; 9 vols. atlas by Victor Goldschmidt. Heidelberg, vol. 3–1916.

Where books are cited which have no general application, and are unlikely to appear often in the references, the whole title and place of publication are given in the reference.

Repeated references in the same species description are given as follows: Goldschmidt (1929), which means that a previous reference was to a work by Goldschmidt in 1929. Reference numbers in the text are often different for the same work, because the annotation to the reference for one part of the text may be different from that for another. In the spinel description, for example, the reference numbers 7, 9, 16, and 20 refer to the same paper by Rinne, but each reference is annotated differently and the reference numbers refer to other works in addition to that of Rinne.

The references are not merely the citations of works pertaining to the subject, but contain comments and various annotations. All data not well established but pertinent are included in the annotation. Opinions of the authors of this work, when they are not in agreement with the published data, are likewise included here. Alternate and less likely interpretations than those in the text are placed in this section. Finally, theories concerned with parts of the text referred to are stated in the reference section.

The following catalogue of periodicals and their abbreviations as used in the references contains all those cited in the first volume. It is believed that this list will serve as well for subsequent volumes, since most periodicals in which mineralogical papers customarily appear are contained in the list.

Ac. Belgique, Bull./Mém. Académie royale des sciences, des lettres et des beaux arts de Belgique, Brussels. Bulletin 1–23, 1832–56; ser. 2, vols. 1–50, 1857–80; ser. 3, vols. 1–36, 1881–98. Continued in classes: Classe des sciences, vol. 1, 1899–date. Index: 1899–1910; 1911–14. Mémoires couronnés et mémoires des savants étrangers. Collection in 4vo, 1–62, 1817–1904. Continued in classes: Classe des sciences, ser. 2, vol. 1, 1904–date. Mémoires couronnés et autre

[29] W. L. Bragg, *Atomic Structure of Minerals*, 1937.
[30] C. W. Stillwell, *Crystal Chemistry*, 1938.
[31] R. C. Evans, *An Introduction to Crystal Chemistry*, 1939.

mémoires. Collection in 8vo. 1–66, 1840–1904. Continued in classes: Classe des sciences, ser. 2, vol. 1, 1904–date.

Ac. Imp. Japan, Proc. Imperial Academy, Tokyo. Proceedings: vol. 1, 1912–date; 1879 as Tokyo Academy.

Ac. roy Belgique, Cl. sc., Bull. *See* **Aç. Belgique, Bull.**

Ac. sc. Bohême, Bull. *See under* **Ak. Česká, Bull.**

Ac. sc. Leningrad, Bull./C.r. (from 1917). Académie des sciences de l'Union des Républiques Soviétiques Socialistes. Previous to 1917 as Académie imperiale des sciences, St. Petersburg. Latest form of name in Russian: Akademiia nauk S. S. S. R., Leningrad. Bulletin: ser. 1 as Bulletin scientifique, 1–10, 1836–42; ser. 2 in classes: Classe physico-mathématique. Bulletin: 1–17, 1843–59; ser. 3, vol. 1–32, 1860–88; ser. 4, vol. 1–4, 1890–94; ser. 5, vol. 1–25, 1894–1906; ser. 6, vol. 1–21, 1907–27. Continued as: Izvestiia, ser. 7, 1928–date; ser. 4, vol. 1–4 also as ser. 3, vol. 33/36; ser. 7, 1928–date published in sections. Comptes rendus (Doklady) 1922–25 as Doklady Rossiĭskoĭ Akamdeiia Nauk. In 2 series: ser. A, 1–158, 1922–33. Superseded by Comptes rendus de l'académie des sciences de l'U.R.S.S., n.s., vol. 1, 1933–date. Published in 2 editions: Russian with German, French, or English summaries, and German, French, or English edition. Ser. B, 1924–31.

Ac. Sc. Philadelphia, J./Proc./Sp. Pap./Not. Academy of Natural Science of Philadelphia, journal: 1–8, 1817–42; ser. 2, vol. 1–16, 1847–1918. Index: 1817–1910 in " An index to the scientific contents of the Journal and Proceedings," 1913. Proceedings: vol. 1, 1841–date. Index with that for Journal. Special Papers: no. 1, 1922–date. Notulae Naturae, no. 1, 1939–date.

Ac. sc. St. Pétersbourg, Bull. (to 1917). *See* **Ac. sc. Leningrad, Bull.**

Ac. sc. St. Pétersbourg, Trav. Mus. géol. Académie imperiale des sciences St. Pétersbourg. Musée géologique, Travaux. Latest name and title in Russian: Akademiiâ nauk, S.S.S.R. Leningrad, Geologicheskiĭ Muzei Trudy, vol. 1–8, 1926–31.

Acc. Catania, Att. Accademia gioenia di scienze naturali, Catania. Atti: vol. 1–3, 1824–29. Continued by: Atti, vol. 1–20, 1834–43: ser. 2, vol. 1–20, 1844–65; ser. 3, vol. 1–20, 1865–88; ser. 4, vol. 1–20, 1888–1907; ser. 5, vol. 1, 1908–date.

Acc. Linc., Att./Trans./Mem./Rend. Reale accademia nazionale dei Lincei, Rome. 1870–1920 as Reale accademia dei Lincei. Index: 1876–1930. Atti: 24–26, 1870–73; ser. 2, vol. 1–8, 1873–76. Continued in part the Accademia pontificia dei nuovi Lincei. Atti: 1–23, 1847–70. Continued in 3 sections: Classe di scienze fisiche, matematiche e naturali. Memorie: ser. 3, vol. 1–19, 1876–84; ser. 4, vol. 1–7, 1884–90; ser. 5, vol. 1–14, 1894–1924; ser. 6, vol. 1, 1925–date. Atti: Classe di scienze morali — Transiunte. Ser. 3, vol. 1–8, 1876–84. Superseded by Rendiconte, ser. 4, vol. 1–7, 1884–91.

Acc. Napoli, Att./Rend. Reale accademia delle scienze fisiche e matematiche, Naples. Supersedes Reale accademia delle scienze, Naples. Atti: 1–9, 1861–82; ser. 2, vol. 1, 1888–date. Suspended 1917–26. Rendiconti: 1–25, 1862–86; ser. 2, vol. 1–8, 1887–94; ser. 3, 1–36, 1895–1930; ser. 4, vol. 1, 1931–date.

Acc. Padova, Att. Reale accademia di scienze, lettere ed arti in Padova. Through 1825 as Cesario-regia accademia di scienze, lettere ed arti di Padova. Atti e memorie; n.s., vol. 1, 1885–date; ser. 1, 1817–47 as Nuovi saggi; n.s., vol. 1–14 numbered as anno 286–99; n.s., vol. 15–18 numbered as anno 358–61. Index: " Indice generale . . . ," 1779–1900.

Acc. Torino, Att./Mem. Reale accademia delle scienze di Torino. Through 1873 as Societas privata taurinensis. 1802–12 as Académie des sciences littérature et beaux-arts. Atti: 1–62, 1865–1926/27. Continued in sections: Classe di scienze morali, and Classe di scienze fisiche, matematiche e naturali. Atti: vol. 63, 1927/28–date. Index: each tenth volume includes index to preceding volumes. Memorie: 1–40, 1759–1838; ser. 2, vol. 1, 1839–date. Vol. 1 as Miscellanea philosophio-mathematica; 2–5, Mélanges de philosophie et de mathématique. Index: vol. 1–22 in 22; 23–32 in 32; 33–40. Ser. 2, each tenth volume includes index to preceding volumes.

Act. Soc. Fenn. *See under* **Finska Vet.–Soc.**

Afhandl. Fys. Kem. Min. Afhandlingar i Fysik, Kemi och Mineralogi, Stockholm. 1–6, 1806–18.

Ak. Berlin, Abh./Ber./Monatsber./Mem. Sitzungsberichte der Akademie der Wissenschaften, Berlin. Title varies: Societät der Wissenschaften; Koenigliche Societät der Wissenschaften; Churfürstlich brandenburgische Societät der Wissenschaften. Preussiche Akademie der Wissenschaften. Index: 1710–1870. Abhandlungen: 1804–date; 1908–date as Abhandlungen under separate classes: Philosophisch-historische Klasse; Physikalisch-mathematische Klasse. Bericht., 1–20, 1836–55. Superseded by its Monatsberichte, 1856–81, which is superseded by its Sitzungsberichte, 1882–1921. This continued in classes: Philosophisch-historische Klasse and Physikalisch-mathematische Klasse, 1922–date. Memoires: 1786–1804. Supersedes its Nouveaux Mémoires, 1770–86.

Ak. Česká, Bull. Česká Akademie véd a uměně u Praze. 1890–1920 as Česká Akademie Césaře Františka Josefa provédy slovesnost a uměni u Praze. French name: Académie des sciences de l'Empereur François Joseph I, Prague. Bulletin international: 1, 1895–date; 1–8, 1895–1904 in 2 parallel series: Sciences, Mathématiques et Naturelles and Médicine.

Ak. Česká, Roz. Česká Akademie véd a uměně u Praze. (French title: Académie des sciences de l'Empereur François Joseph I, Prague. Rozpravy: Třída I: Pro vedy filosické . . . 1, 1891–date. Trida II: Mathematicko-přírodnickár. Třida III: Filologická, 1, 1892–date.

Ak. Krakau. Akademija umiejetności, Krakow. Wydzial filologiczny. Bulletin international, 1901–date. Second title in German: Anzeiger der Akademie der Wissenschaften in Krakau.

Ak. Leipzig, Ber. Akademie der Wissenschaften, Leipzig, 1846–1918, as K. saechsischen Gesellschaft der Wissenschaften. Mathematisch-physische Klasse: Berichte 1, 1849–date. Index: 1846–95.

Ak. Magyar, Értes. Magyar Tudományos Akadémia, Budapest. Matematikai és Természettudományi osztaly. Mathematikai és Természettudományi értesíto: 1, 1882/83–date.

Ak. München, Ber./Gel. Anz. Akademie der Wissenschaften, Munich. Title varies: Churfürstlich-Baierische Akademie der Wissenschaften; Baierische Akademie der Wissenschaften; Koeniglich bayerische Akademie der Wissenschaften. Index: 1807–1913. Berichte über du arbeiten, 1–10, 1824–26. Gelehrte anzeigen, 1–50, 1835–60. Superseded by its Sitzungsberichte. Index: 1–50.

Ak. Stockholm, Handl./Öfv./Bihang. Svenska Vetenskapsakademien, Stockholm. Handlingar: 1–40, 1739–79; ser. 2, vol. 1–33, 1780–1812; ser. 3, vol. 1–42, 1813–54; n.s. (ser. 4), vol. 1–63, 1855–1923; n.s. (ser. 5), vol. 1, 1924–date; ser. 2, vol. 1–33, 1780–1812 as its Nya handlingar. Index: 1–15; 16–30; 31–40. Bihang til Handlingar: 1–28, 1872–1903; 12–28, 1886–1903 in 4 series. Öfversigt af Sv. Vet. Akad. Forhandlingar: 1–59, 1844–1902.

Ak. Wien, Anz./Ber./Denkschr. K. Akademie der Wissenschaften, Vienna. Mathematisch — naturwissenschaftliche Klasse. Anzeiger: 1, 1864–date. Denkschriften: 1, 1850–date; Index: 1–25 in 26, 26–40 in 40, 41–60 in 61. Sitzungsberichte: 1, 1848–date. Index: 1–120; 43–64 in ser. 2; 65–96 in ser. 3; 97–date in ser. 4.

Allg. J. Chem. Allgemeines Journal der Chemie, Berlin; Leipzig. 1–10, 1798–1803. Also known as Scherer's Journal. Superseded by Neues allgemeines Journal der Chemie.

Am. Ac. Arts Sc. Mem./Proc. American Academy of Arts and Sciences Boston. Memoirs: 1–4, 1780–1821; n.s., vol. 1, 1826–date. Proceedings: 1, 1846–date; 9–31 also as n.s., vol. 1–23.

Am. Assoc., Proc. American Association for the Advancement of Science. 8vo. Vol. 1, meeting at Philadelphia in 1848; 2, at Cambridge, 1849; 3, at Charleston, 1850; 4, at New Haven, 1850; 5, at Cincinnati, 1851; 6, at Albany, 1852; 7, at Cleveland, 1853; 8, at Washington, 1854; 9, at Providence, 1855; 10, at Albany, 1856; 11, at Montreal 1857; 12, at Baltimore, 1858; 13, at Springfield 1859; 14, at Newport, 1860; 15, at Buffalo, 1866; 16, at Burlington, 1867; and annually since then; 40, at Washington, 1891. Since 1901 most of the Papers have been published in *Science*, the volumes of the Proceedings being reserved for the Constitution, list of members, papers, etc.

Am. Assoc. Pet. Geol., Bull. American Association of Petroleum Geologists. 1917 as Southwestern Association of Petroleum Geologists. Bulletin: 1, 1917–date. Index: 1–10, 1917–26.

Am. Chem. J. American Chemical Journal. Vol. 1–50, No. 6, 1879–1913, Baltimore. Edited by Ira Remsen (Johns Hopkins University). Merged into American Chemical Society, Journal. Index: 1–10, 1879–88; 11–20, 1889–98; 21–50, 1899–1913.

Am. Chem. Soc., J./Proc./Chem. Abs. But **Chem. Abs.** without Am. Chem. Soc. American Chemical Society. Journal: 1, 1879–date. Index: 1–20, 1879–98; 1879–date in its Journal. Proceedings; 1–2, 1876–78; 1879–date in the Journal.

Am. Geol. American Geologist, Minneapolis. Vol. 1–36, 1888–1905. Index: 1–36 in 36.

Am. Inst. Min. Met. Engr./Tech. Pub./Inst. Met. Div. American Institute of Mining and Metallurgical Engineers. Through February, 1918 as the American Institute of Mining Engineers. Technical Publications: no. 1, 1927–date. Institute of Metals division: Transactions: 1, 1926/27–date. Title varies: Proceedings; Papers and discussions.

Am. J. Sc. American Journal of Science, New Haven. 1, 1818–date. Known also as Silliman's Journal of Science. 1820–79 as American Journal of Science and Arts. 51–100 also numbered ser. 2, vol. 1–50; 101–150 as ser. 3, vol. 1–50; 151–200 as ser. 4, vol. 1–50; 201–date as ser. 5, vol. 1–date. Index: vol 1–49 in 50. Beginning with ser. 2 every tenth volume includes index covering preceding 10 volumes.

Am. Min. American Mineralogist (Mineralogical Society of America), Lancaster, Pa., etc. Vol. 1, 1916–date. Index: 1–10, 1916–25; 1–20, 1916–35.

Am. Min. J. American Mineralogical Journal: "being a collection of facts and observations tending to elucidate the mineralogy and geology of the United States of America." Edited by Archibald Bruce, New York. Vol. 1, 1810–14.

Am. Mus. Nov./Bull. American Museum of Natural History, New York. Bulletin: 1, 1881–date. Index: 1–16 in 19. American Museum Novitates: 1, 1921–date.

Am. Nat. American Naturalist, Boston, New York, etc. 1, 1867–date.

Am. Phil. Soc., Mem./Proc./Trans. American Philosophical Society, Philadelphia. Memoirs: 1, 1935–date. Proceedings: 1, 1838–date. Index: 1–50, 1838–1911; 51–75, 1912–35.

Am. Phys. Soc., Bull. American Physical Society, Bulletin, Ithaca. Vol. 1–3, no. 1, 1899–1902. Bulletin: Menasha, Wis., 1, 1925–date.

An. soc. españ. fis. quím. Sociedad española de física y química, Madrid Anales: 1, 1903–date.

An. soc. españ. hist. nat. *See under* **R. soc. española hist. nat.**, Boletin.

Ann. Chemie. Justus Liebig's Annalen der Chemie, Leipzig, etc. Vol. 1, 1832–date. 1–32, 1832–39, as Annalen der Pharmacie; 11–168, 1840–73, as Annalen der Chemie und Pharmacie; 169–172, 1873–74, Justus Liebig's Annalen der Chemie, und Pharmacie; 77–172 also as n.s., vol. 1–96. Index: 1–100; 101–116; 117–164; 165–220; 221–276; 277–328; 329–380; 381–430; 431–500.

Ann. Chem. Pharm. Liebig's Annalen. **Annalen der Chemie und Pharmacie.** *See* Justus Liebig's **Annalen der Chemie.**

Ann. chim. Annales de chimie, Paris. Ser. 9, vol. 1–20, 1914–23; ser. 10, vol. 1–20, 1924–33; ser. 11, vol. 1, 1933–date. Index: ser. 10, vol. 1–20, 1924–33. Continues the chemical section of Annales de chimie et de physique.

Ann. chim. phys. Annales de chimie et de physique, Paris. Vol. 1–96. 1789–1815; ser. 2, vol. 1–75, 1816–40; ser. 3, vol. 1–69, 1841–63; ser. 4 to ser. 8, vol. 1–30 each, 1864–1913. 1–96 as Annales de chimie. Continued in 2 sections: Annales de chimie; Annales de physique. Index: ser. 1–8.

Ann. mines. Annales des mines. (France, Ministère des travaux publiques, des postes et des telegraphes) Paris. Vol. 1–13, 1816–26; ser. 2, vol. 1–8, 1827–30; ser. 3, vol. 1–20, 1832–41; ser. 4, vol. 1–20, 1842–51; ser. 5, in 2 parts; Partie administrative, ser. 5–11, vol. 1–10 each, 1852–1921; partie scientifique, ser. 5–10, vol. 1–20 each, 1852–1911; ser. 11, vol. 1–12, 1912–21; ser. 12, vol. 1, 1922–date. Index: each series has index covering both parts.

Ann. mus. Congo belge. Musée du Congo belge, Tervueren, Belgium. Annales: issued in 5 sections: Botanique 1, 1898–date; Ethnographie et anthropologie 1, 1899–date; Zoologie 1, 1898–date; Miscellanées 1, 1924–date; Géologie, géographie, physique, minéralogie et paléontologie 1, 1908–date.

Ann. mus. d'hist. nat. Muséum national d'histoire naturelle, Paris. Annales: 1–21, 1802–13. Index: 1–20, as vol. 21.

Ann. Mus. Wien. Annalen des naturhistorischen Staats-Museum. 1, 1886–date. 1886–1918 as K. K. Naturhistorisches Hof Museum. Index: 1–10 in 10; 11–27 in 28.

Ann. Phil. Annals of Philosophy, London. Vol. 1–28, 1813–26. 1–16 as Annals of Philosophy; or Magazine of chemistry, mineralogy, mechanics, natural history, agriculture and the arts. 17–28 also as n.s., vol. 1–12.

Ann. Phys. Annalen der Physik, Halle, Leipzig. Vol. 1–76, 1799–1824; ser. 2, vol. 1–160, 1824–76; n.s., vol. 1–69, 1877–99; ser. 4, vol. 1–87, 1900–28; ser. 5, vol. 1, 1929–date. 1819–24 as Annalen der Physik und der physikalischen Chemie. 1824–99, Annalen der Physik und Chemie. Index: 1799–1842; ser. 2, vol. 1–160; n.s, vol. 1–69; ser. 4, vol. 1–30; ser. 4, vol. 31–78. Also known as Gilbert's, Poggendorf's, or Wiedemann's Journal.

Arch. Math. Nat. Archiv för Mathematik ag Naturvidenskab, Oslo, 1, 1876–date. Index: 1–25 in 25.

Arch. Min. Archiv für Mineralogie, Geognosie, Bergbau und Hüttenkunde, Berlin. 1–26, 1829–55. Supersedes Archiv für Bergbau und Hüttenwesen. Index: 1–26 in 26. 1–10 edited by C. J. B. Karsten and 11–26 by Karsten and H. von Dechen.

Arch. Min. Soc. Warsaw. Archiwum Mineralogiczne 1, 1925–date. French title: Archives de minéralogie. (Towarzystwo Naukowe Warszawskie, French name: Société scientifique de Varsovie.)

Arch. Mus. Paris. Muséum national d'histoire naturelle. Archives: 1–10, 1839—61; 1–10, 1865–74; ser. 2, vol. 1–10, 1875–88; ser. 3, vol. 1–10, 1889–98; ser. 4, vol. 1–10, 1899–1908; ser. 5, vol. 1–6, 1909–14; ser. 6, vol. 1, 1926–date. 1865–1914 as Nouvelles archives. Index: 1839–88 in ser. 2, vol. 10; 1889–98 in ser. 3, vol. 10; ser. 4, 1899–1908 in ser. 4, vol. 10.

Arch. Mus. Rio de Janeiro. Museu Nacional do Rio de Janeiro. Archivos: 1, 1876–date; 1–9 as its Revista. Index: 1–22, 1876–1919 in 22.

Arch. Nat. Archiv für die gesamte Naturlehre, Nüremberg. 1–27, 1824–35. Added title page in vol. 19–27: Archiv für chemie und meteorologie, vol. 1–9. Also known as Kastner's Archiv. Index: 1–9 in 9; 10–18 in 18.

Arch. sc. phys. nat. See Bibl. Univ.

Arch. wiss. Kunde Russland. Archiv für wissenschaftliche Kunde von Russland, Berlin. 1–25, 1841–67. Index: 1–10 in 10; 11–20 in 20; 21–25 in 25. Also known as Erman's Archiv.

Ark. Kemi. Arkiv för Kemi, Mineralogi och Geologi. (K. Svenska Vetenskaps-akademien), Stockholm. Vol. 1, 1903–date.

Att. soc. tosc., Mem./Proc. Società toscana di scienze naturali di Pisa. Atti. Memorie: vol. 1, 1875–date. Processi verbali: vol. 1, 1878–date.

Australasian Assoc. Adv. Sc., Rep. Australian and New Zealand Association for the Advancement of Science, Sydney. Through 1926 as Australasian Association for the Advancement of Science. Reports: vol. 1, 1888–date. Index: vol. 1–16, 1888–1923.

Australasian Inst. Mining Met., Proc. Australasian Institute of Mining and Metallurgy, Melbourne. 1897–1919 as Australasian Institute of Mining Engineers. Proceedings: 1897–1903; n.s., vol. 1–8, 1904–11; (ser. 3) no. 1, 1917–date. Index: 1897–1914; 1915–23.

Australian Mus., Mem./Misc. Publ./Rec./Rep. Australian Museum, Sydney. Memoirs: vol. 1–4, 1851–1914; Miscellaneous series: no. 1–10, 1890–1916; Records: vol. 1, 1890–date; Report: vol. 1, 1853/54–date.

Baumgartner's Zs. See Zs. Phys. Math.

Beitr. Kr. Min. Beiträge zur Krystallographie und Mineralogie, Heidelberg. Vol. 1–3, 1914–34.

Beitr. Min. Japan. Beiträge zur Mineralogie von Japan, Tokyo. Vol. 1–5, 1905–15; n.s., vol. 1, 1935–date.

Ber. deutsche chemische Gesellschaft. Berichte: vol. 1, 1868–date. Index: vol. 1–40, 1868–1907; 41–54, 1908–21.

Ber. Mitt. Freund. Wiss. Wien. Berichte über die Mitteilungen von Freunden der Naturwissenschaften in Wien, Vienna. Vol. 1–7, 1846–50. Index: 1–7 in 7.

Ber. Niederrhein. Ges. Niederrheinische Gesellschaft für Natur und Heilkunde, Bonn. Sitzungsberichte: 1851/54–1905. 1851/54–94 in Naturhistorischer Verein der preussischen Rheinlande und Westfalens. Verhandlungen, (later Decheniana), with separate paging. 1869–1905 issued also separately.

Ber. Ungarn. Mathematische und Naturwissenschaftliche Berichte aus Ungarn, Berlin, Budapest, Leipzig. Vol. 1–38, 1882–1931.

Berg.- u. hütten. Jb. Berg.- und hüttenmännisches Jahrbuch, Vienna. Vol. 1, 1851–date.

Bergm. J. Bergmaennisches Journal, Freiberg. Vol. 1–6, 1788–93. Superseded by Neues Bergmannische Journal.

Berzelius' Jahresber. See Jahresber. Chem. Min.

B. H. Ztg. Berg- und hüttenmännische Zeitung, Freiberg, Leipzig. Vol. 1–63, 1842–1904. Merged into Glueckauf. Index: vol. 1–10.

Bibl. Univ. Bibliothèque Universelle de Genève. Begun 1816. In 1846, the scientific section commenced publishing separately and takes the subtitle, Archives des Sciences physique et naturelles. Vol. 1–36, 1846–59; n.s., vol. 1–64, 1858–78; ser. 3, vol. 1–34, 1878–95; ser. 4, vol. 1–46, 1896–1918; ser. 5, vol. 1, 1919–date. Index: 1–36; n.s. vol. 1–64; 1879–1910.

Böhm. Ges., Ber. K. boehmische Gesellschaft der Wissenschaften, Prague. Jahresbericht: vol. 1, 1875–date. 1864–74 in its Sitzungsberichte. Sitzungsberichte: 1859–84. Continued in classes: (1) Třída filosofecko historicko-jazykozpytna. (2) Třída mathematicko-přírodovedecka Vestnik. Vol. 1, 1885–date. 1885 as its Zpravy. 1885–1917 have added title page, Sitzungsberichte; 1918–date as Memoires. The Society varies in its use of languages, sometimes having titles for same numbers in several languages. Czech name: Česká Společnost Nauk. French name: Société des lettres et des sciences de Bohême.

Boll. com. geol. Ital. R. comitato geologico d'Italia, Rome. Bollettino: 1870–date.

Boston J. Nat. Hist. Boston Journal of Natural History, containing papers and communications, read to the Boston Society of Natural History, Boston. Vol. 1–7, 1834–63. Later name of Boston Society, New England Museum of Natural History.

Boston Soc. Nat. Hist., Proc. Boston Society of Natural History. In 1936 the Society's museum became New England Museum of Natural History. Proceedings: vol. 1, 1841–date.

British Assoc., Rep. British Association for the Advancement of Science, London. Reports: vol. 1–108, 1831–1938. No meetings held 1917–18, reports of committees inserted between 86–87. Index: 1831–60; 1861–90.

Bruce's Am. Min. J. *See* **Am. Min. J.**

Bull. ac. sc. Russie. *See* **Ac. sc. Leningrad, Bull.**

Bull. Geol. Inst. Upsala. University of Upsala. Geological Institution. Bulletin: vol. 1, 1892–date. Index: 1–10, 1892–1910 in 10; 11–20, 1911–27 in 20.

Bull. soc. belge géol. Société belge de Géologie, de paléontologie et d'hydrologie, Brussels. Bulletin: vol. 29, 1919–date. Vol. 1–28, 1887–1914 issued in 2 sections: Procès-verbaux and Mémoires.

　Bull. soc. min. Société française de minéralogie, Paris. Bulletin: vol. 1, 1878–date. 1878–85 as Société minéralogique de France. Index: 1–10; 11–20; 21–30; 31–40.

Bull. soc. nat. Moscou. Société impériale des naturalistes de Moscou. Bulletin: 1–62, 1829–97; n.s., vol. 1–30, 1887–1916. Index: 1–56, 1829–81. Continued in sections: Section géologique. n.s., vol. 31, 1917–22–date. Section biologique. n.s., vol. 31, 1917–22–date. Russian titles also given: Moskovskoe Obshchestvo Ispytateleĭ Prirody. (Through 1930 as Moskovskoe Obshchestvo Luĭbitelei Prirody.) Otdel biologicheskiĭ and Otdel geologicheskii.

Cambridge Phil. Soc./Proc. Cambridge Philosophical Society, Cambridge, England. Proceedings: vol. 1, 1843–date. For Proceedings 1923–25 see its Biological Reviews and Biological Proceedings, 1923–25.

Can. J. Canadian Journal of Science, Literature and History, Toronto. 1–3, 1852–1855; n.s., vol. 1–15, 1856–1878. Vol. 1–3 as Canadian Journal: a repertory of industry, science and art; n.s., vol. 1–11 as Canadian Journal of Industry, Science and Art.

Can. Nat. Canadian Naturalist and Quarterly Journal of Science, with proceedings of the Natural History Society of Montreal, Montreal, vol. 1–8, 1856–1863; n.s., vol. 1–10; no. 8, 1864–83. 1–8 and n.s., vol 1–3 as Canadian Naturalist and Geologist. Subtitle varies. Index: 1856–83 in 10.

Cbl. Min. Centralblatt für Mineralogie, Geologie und Paleontologie, Stuttgart. Vol. 1, 1900–date. Supplement to Neues Jahrbuch für Mineralogie, Geologie und Paleontologie. After 1934 as **Zbl. Min.**

Chem. Abs. Chemical Abstracts. Easton, Pa. Vol. 1, 1907–date. Published by American Chemical Society. Supersedes Review of American Chemical Research. Index: 1–10, 1907–16; 11–20, 1917–26; 21–30, 1927–36.

Chem. Ann. Chemische Annalen für die Freunde der Naturlehre, Arzneygelahrtheit, Haushaltungskunst und Manufacturen, Helmstädt, Leipzig. Vol. 1–40, 1784–1803. Index: 1784–91; 1792–99; 1800–03.

Chem. Erde. Chemie der Erde, Jena. Vol. 1, 1914–date.

Chem. Gaz. Chemical Gazette or Journal of Practical Chemistry, London, Vol. 1–17, 1842–1859.

Chem. Ges. Ber. Deutsche chemische Gesellschaft, Berlin. Berichte: vol. 1, 1868–date. Index: vol. 1–40, 1868–1907; 41–54, 1908–21.

Chem. Met. Mining Soc. South Africa, J./Proc. Chemical, Metallurgical and Mining Society of South Africa, Johannesburg. 1894–1903 as Chemical and Metallurgical Society of South Africa. Journal: vol. 1, 1894–date. Suspended October, 1899–May, 1902. Proceedings: 1–4, 1894–1904.

Chem. News. Chemical News and Journal of Industrial Science, London. Vol. 1–145 (no. 1–3781), 1859–1932. Supersedes Chemical Gazette. Vol. 1–2, as " Chemical News with which is incorporated the Chemical Gazette "; vol. 3–122 as Chemical News and Journal of Physical Science. Index: 1–100, 1859–1909. American reprint. Vol. 1–6, no. 6, 1867–70, consists of parts of vol. 15–21.

Chem. Soc. Japan., J. Chemical Society of Japan, Tokyo. Journal, published monthly: vol. 57 in 1936. Japanese title: Nippon Kwagaku Kwaishi.

Chem.–Ztg. Chemiker-Zeitung, Cöthen. Vol. 1, 1877–date. 1–2 as Allgemeine Chemiker-Zeitung.

Colorado Sc. Soc., Proc. Colorado Scientific Society. Proceedings, Denver: vol. 1, 1883–date; vol. 10, no. 4, not issued.

Com. géol. St. Pétersbourg, Mém. Comité géologique, St. Pétersbourg, Mémoires. Vol. 1, 1883–date. Title also in Russian: Geologicheskiĭ komitet, Trudy.

Comm. géol. Finlande, Bull. Commission géologique de Finlande, Bulletin. Vol. 1, 1895–date. Also Finnish name: Geologiska Kommissioneni Finland, Bulletin.

C. R. Académie des sciences, Paris, 1795–1815 as Institut de France. Classe des sciences mathématiques et physiques. Comptes rendus hebdomadaires des séances: vol. 1, 1835–date. Index: vol. 1–31, 1835–50; 32–61, 1851–65; 62–91, 1866–80; 92–121, 1881–95.

C. r. ac. sc. U.R.S.S. *See* **Ac. sc. Leningrad, Comptes rendus.**

Crell's Ann. Crell's Chemical Journal, London. Vol. 1–3, 1791–93. English edition of Chemische Annalen für die Freunde der Naturlehre.

Cryst. Soc., Proc. Proceedings of the Crystallological Society, London. Part I, 1877; II, 1882.

DanskeVidensk Selsk.,/Overs./Skr./Nat. — Mat. Afd./Mat. — fys. Medd. K. Danske Videnskabernes Selskab, Copenhagen. Oversigt oner det kongelige danske videnskabernes selskab forhandlinger: 1814–date. 1917–date the Scientific Notes are continued in 4 series, one of which is the Mathematisk — fysiske Meddelelser, vol. 1, 1917–date. Skrifter: vol. 1, 1743–date. 1781–99 as Nye samling af der … selskabs skrifter: vol. 1–6, 1800–1812. Continued in 2 series: (ser. 2) Naturvidenskabelig og mathematisk Afdeling. Ser. 4-Ser. 8 of 12 volumes each. Ser. 9, vol. 1, 1928–date.

Dingler J. Dinglers Polytechnisches Journal, Berlin, Stuttgart. Vol. 1–346, 1820–1931. 1–211, 1820–74 as " Polytechnisches Journal." Also numbered in series of 50 volumes each. Index: vol. 1–78; 79–118; 119–58; 159–98.

Dublin Q. J. Sc. Dublin Quarterly Journal of Science, Dublin. 6 volumes, 8vo, 1861–66.

Dublin Soc., Proc. Royal Dublin Society. Scientific Proceedings: n.s., vol. 1, 1877–date. Index: 1–8, 9–11. Also Proceedings issued. No dates, earlier, around 1845–55.

Econ. Geol. Economic Geology, Lancaster, Pa., etc. Vol. 1, 1905–date. Supersedes American Geologist. Supplement: Annotated bibliography: vol. 1, 1929–date.

Econ. Geol. (Annot. Bibl.). *See under* **Econ. Geol.**

Edinburgh J. Sc. Edinburgh Journal of Science, Edinburgh. Vol. 1–10, 1824–1829; n.s., vol. 1–6, 1829–1832. Subtitle varies. Merged into Philosophical Magazine, later London, Edinburgh, and Dublin Philosophical Magazine and Journal of Science.

Edinburgh N. Phil. J. Edinburgh New Philosophical Journal, Edinburgh. Vol. 1–57, 1826–1854; n.s., vol. 1–19, 1855–64. Supersedes Edinburgh Philosophical Journal. Superseded by Quarterly Journal of Science, later Journal of Science.

Edinburgh Phil. J. Edinburgh Philosophical Journal, Edinburgh. Vol. 1–14, 1819–1926. Superseded by Edinburgh New Philosophical Journal.

Efem. Berg.–Hütt. Efemeriden der Berg.- und Hüttenkunde. As vol. 4–8, 1805–09, of Annalen der Berg- und Hüttenkunde.

Enc. Brit. Encyclopædia Britannica, London. First edition in 1771; fourteenth edition in 1929.

Eng. Mining J. Engineering and Mining Journal, New York. Vol. 1, 1866–date; vol. 1–7, 1866–1869 as American Journal of Mining; 8–113, 1869–1922 as Engineering and Mining Journal; 114–21, 1922–26 as Engineering and Mining Journal-Press.

Erman's Arch. See **Arch. wiss. Kunde Russland.**

Field Mus. Chicago, Pub. Field Museum of Natural History, Chicago. 1894–1908 as Field Columbian Museum. Publications: vol. 1, 1894–date, issued in sections.

Finska Vet.-Soc.,/Act. Soc. Fenn./Öfv. Acta Societatis Scientiarum Fennicae. Vol. 1–50, 1842–1926. Nova Series A: Vol. 1, 1927–date. Nova Series B: vol. 1, 1931–date. Finska Vetenskaps-Societeten, Helsingfors. Finnish name: Suomen Tiedesura. Latin name: Societas Scientiarum Fennica. Oversigt av Förhandlingar: vol. 1–64, 1838–1922. Vol. 51–64 in 3 series: A. Matematik och Naturvetenskaper; B. Humanistiska vetenskaper; C. Redogörelger och Förhandlingar.

Földt. Közl. Földtani Közlöny. (Magyarhone Földtani Torsulat), Budapest. Vol. 1, 1872–date.

Fortschr. Min. Fortschritte der Mineralogie, Kristallographie und Petrographie, Jena. Vol. 1, 1911–date. Published by Deutsche mineralogische Gesellschaft.

Franklin Inst., J. Franklin Institute, Philadelphia. Journal: vol. 1, 1826–date. Supersedes American Mechanics Magazine. Vol. 1–6, 1826–28 as Franklin Journal, and American Mechanics Magazine. Also numbered in series. Index: vol. 1–120, 1826–85; 121–40, 1886–95; 141–160, 1896–1905; 161–180, 1906–15.

Gazz. chim. ital. Gazzetta chimica italiana, Rome. Vol. 1, 1871–date. Published by the Societa chimica italiana. Index: vol. 1–20, 1871–90; 21–40, 1891–1910.

Gehlen's J. See **Allg. J. Chem.**

Geol. Bundesanst., Wein, Jb./Abh./Vh. Geologische Bundesanstalt, Vienna. To 1920 as K. K. Geologische Reichsanstalt. 1920–21 as Geologische Staatsanstalt Abhandlungen. Vol. 1, 1852–date. Jahrbuch: vol. 1, 1850–date. Index: every tenth volume has an index. Supplement: Mineralogische und petrographische mitteilungen. Verhandlungen: 1867–date. To 1867 in its Jahrbuch.

Geol. För. Förh. Geologiska Föreningens i Stockholm. Förhandlingar, Stockholm: vol. 1, 1872–date. Index: vol. 1–5; 6–10; 11–21; 22–31; 32–41; 42–50.

Geol. Landesanst., Elsass-Löthringen, Mitt. Elsass-Löthringen. Geologische Landesanstalt. Mitteilungen: vol. 1, 1886–88. Herausgegeben von der Direktion der geologischen Landes-Untersuchung von Elsass-Löthringen, Strassburg.

Geol. Mag. Geological Magazine or Monthly Journal of Geology, London. Vol. 1, 1864–date. Also in series of 10 volumes each. Supersedes Geologist. Index: 1–40, 1864–1903.

Geol. Reichsanst., Jb./Abh./Vh. See **Geol. Bundesanst, Wien.**

Geol. Soc. Am., Bull./Mem./Sp. Pap. Geological Society of America. Bulletin: vol. 1, 1888–date. Index: vol. 1–10; 11–20; 21–30; 31–40. Memoir: New York. Vol. 1, 1934–date. Formerly in the Bulletin. Special Papers: New York, no. 1, 1934–date.

Geol. Soc. London, Trans./Proc./Q. J. Geological Society of London. Transactions: ser. 1, 1–5, 1811–21; ser. 2, 1–7, 1824–56. Proceedings: vol. 1–2, 1826–38. Quarterly Journal 1, 1845–date. Index: 1–50, 1845–94. General Index: 1811–68; 1869–75; 1876–82; 1883–89.

Geol. Soc. South Africa, Trans./Proc. Geological Society of South Africa, Johannesburg. Transactions: vol. 1, 1896–date. Index: vol. 1–13. Proceedings: 1904–date, with vol. 7 to date of Transactions.

Geol. Soc. Tokyo, J. Geological Society of Tokyo. Journal: vol. 1, 1893–date. 2–5 as Geological Magazine. In Japanese. Index: vol. 1–33, 1893–1927.

Geol. Sur. Canada, Rep. Prog./Ann. Rep./Sum. Rep./Mem. Geological Survey of Canada. Report of Progress: *See* Annual Report. Annual Report, 1843–date; 1843–1884 as Report of Progress; 1885–date as new series. Index: 1863–84, 1885–1906. Summary Report, Ottawa, vol. 1, 1869–date; 1870–82 published only in Reports of Progress. Earlier reports also in Reports of Progress. 1883–85 in Annual Reports for those years. Memoirs: Ottawa, No. 1, 1910–date. Published under Dept. of Mines.

Geol. Sur. India, Mem./Rec. Geological Survey of India, Calcutta. Memoirs: vol. 1, 1859–date. Index: vol. 1–54, 1859–1929. Records: vol. 1, 1868–date. Index: vol. 1–65, 1868–1932.

Geol. Sur. South Africa, Mem. South Africa, Geological Survey, Pretoria. Memoir: no. 1, 1905–date; no. 1–5 issued by Transvaal Geological Survey.

Ges. Mus. Böhmen, Verh. Gesellschaft des vaterlandischen Museums in Böhmen, Prague. Verhandlungen: 1823–55/56. Name of Museum varies; latest name, Národní Museum. Verhandlungen for 1827–29 issued also in Museums Monatschrift.

Ges. nat. Freunde Berlin, Besch./Schr./N. Schr./Mag./Vh./Mitth./Ber. Schriften der Gesellschaft naturforschender Freunde in Berlin. 11 volumes, 8vo. Vol. 1 ann.: 1780; 5, 1884; 8, 1886–87; 8, 1888; 9, 1889; 10, 1892; 11, 1894 (vol. 7–11, also as 1–5 of Beobachtungen und Entdeckungen, etc.). Next, Neue Schriften, etc., 4 volumes 4to: 1, 1795; 2, 1799; 3, 1801; 4, 1803–4. Afterward Magazin, etc. Ber. Sitzungsberichte: vol. 1, 1839–date. 1839–59 issued in one volume in 1912. Index: 1839–59; 1860–64.

Ges. Wiss. Göttingen, Abh./Nachr. Gesellschaft der Wissenschaften zu Göttingen. Abhandlungen: vol. 1–40, 1838–95. Continued in series: Mathematisch-physikalische Klasse, vol. 1–16, 1897–1931; ser. 3 no. 1, 1932–date. Nachrichten: 1845–93; 1894–date, continued in series. *See* **Nach. Ges. Göttingen.**

Gilbert's Ann. *See* **Ann. Phys.**

Giorn. Min. Giornale di mineralogia, cristallografia e petrografia, Milan. Vol. 1–5, 1890–94.

Göttingen gel. Anz. Göttingische gelehrte Anzeigen, Göttingen. Vol. 1, 1739–date. Published by Gesellschaft der Wissenschaften zu Göttingen. 1739–52 as Goettingische Zeitungen von gelehrten Sachen; 1753–1801 Goettingische Anzeigen von gelehrten Sachen. Index: 1753–82; 1783–1822.

Groth's Zs. *See* **Zs. Kr.**

Haidinger's Ber. *See* **Ber. Mitth. Freund. Wiss. Wien.**

Haidinger's Nat. Abh. *See* **Naturwiss. Abh. Wien.**

Hercyn. Archiv. Hercynisches Archiv oder Beiträge zur Kunde des Harzes und seiner Nachbarländer, Halle. Vol. 1, no. 1–4, 1805.

Hokkaidô Univ., J. Fac. Sc. Hokkaidô Imperial University Faculty of Science. Journal 1, 1930–date. Issued in 6 sections.

L'Institut. L'Institut, Paris. Vol. 1–44, 1833–36. Subtitle varies. Vol. 4–40 in 2 sections; vol. 41–44 also as n.s., vol. 1–4.

Int. Geol. Cong. XVI Sess., Rep. International Geological Congress, Washington, D. C. Report of the sixteenth session, 1933.

Ist. Geogr. Catania. Catania, Universita. Istituto di Geografia Fisica e Vulcanologia. Publicazioni, Rome. No. 1–4, 1914–15.

Ist. Lombardo, Rend. R. Istituto Lombardo di Scienze e Lettere, Milan. Supersedes I. R. Istituto del Regno Lombardo-Veneto. Index: 1803–88; 1889–1900. Rendiconti: vol. 1–4, 1864–67; ser. 2, vol. 1, 1868–date. 1864–67 in two classes. Classes united in ser. 2: ser. 2, vol. 7, 1937–date; also as ser. 3, vol. 1–date.

Ist. Veneto, Att. R. Istituto Veneto di Scienze, Lettere Arti, Venice. Atti:

vol. 1–7, 1840–48; ser. 2, vol. 1–6, 1850–55; ser. 3, vol. 1–16, 1856–71; ser. 4, vol. 1–3, 1871–74; ser. 5, vol. 1–8, 1874–82; ser. 6, vol. 1–7, 1883–89; ser. 7, vol. 1–10, 1890–98; ser. 8, vol. 1–18, 1898–1916; ser. 9, vol. 1, 1917–date. Index: 1840–94.

J. Am. Chem. Soc. *See* **Am. Chem. Soc. J.**

J. Chemie u. Phys. Journal für Chemie und Physik, Nuremberg. Vol. 1–69, 1811–33. Supersedes Journal für die Chemie, Physik und Mineralogie. Vol. 1–30 as Beiträge zur Chemie und Physik. Vol. 31–60 also as Jahrbuch der Chemie und Physik. Vol. 61–69 also as Neues Jahrbuch der Chemie und Physik. United with Journal für technische und ökonomische Chemie to form Journal für praktische Chemie. Edited by J. S. C. Schweigger. Index: Vol. 1–69. Also known as Schweigger's Journal.

J. Chem. Phys. Journal of Chemical Physics, Lancaster, Pa. Vol. 1, 1933–date. Published by the American Institute of Physics.

J. Chem. Phys. Min. Journal für die Chemie, Physik und Mineralogie, Berlin. Vol. 1–9, 1806–09. Supersedes Neues allegemeines Journal der Chemie. Superseded by Journal für Chemie und Physik.

J. Chem. Soc. London. Chemical Society, London. Journal. Vol. 1–127, 1847–1926; 1927–date; vol. 1–14 as Quarterly Journal; vol. 16–29 also as n.s., vol. 1–14; vol. 33–124, 1878–1923 in two parts, Transactions and Abstracts. Index: 1848–72; 1872–82; 1883–92; 1893–1902; 1903–12; 1913–22.

J. Geol. Journal of Geology, Chicago. Vol. 1, 1893–date. Published by the University of Chicago, Department of Geology. Index: vol. 1–35, 1893–1927.

J. Geol. Soc., Tokyo. Geological Society of Tokyo. Journal: vol. 1, 1893–date; vol. 2–5 as Geological Magazine; vol. 42, 1925–date as Journal of the Geological Society of Japan. Index: vol. 1–33, 1893–1927.

J. Ind. Eng. Chem. Industrial and Engineering Chemistry, Washington; Easton, Pa. Vol. 1, 1909–date. Vol. 1–14, 1909–22 as Journal of Industrial and Engineering Chemistry. Published by the American Chemical Society. Two editions: Analytical edition, vol. 1, 1929–date; News edition, vol. 1, 1923–date.

J. Inst. Met. Institute of Metals, London. Journal: vol. 1, 1909–date. Index: 1–25, 1909–21.

J. Iron Steel Inst. Iron and Steel Institute, London. Journal: vol. 1, 1871–date; vol. 43, 1893 first numbered volume. Index: 1869–81; 1882–89; 1890–1900; 1901–10; 1911–21.

J. mines. Journal des mines; ou Recueil de mémoires sur l'exploitation des mines, et sur les sciences et les arts qui s'y rapportent, Paris. Vol. 1–38 (no. 1–228), 1794–1815. Suspended February, 1799–April, 1801. Superseded by Annales des mines. Index: vol. 1–28, 1794–1809; vol. 29–38, 1810–15.

J. Phil. Chem. Arts. Journal of Natural Philosophy, n.s., Chemistry and the Arts, London. Vol. 1–5, 1917–1801; n.s., vol. 1–36, 1802–1813. Merged into Philosophical Magazine. Later London, Edinburgh, and Dublin Philosophical Magazine.

J. phys. Le Journal de physique et le radium, Paris. Vol. 1–10, 1872–81; ser. 2, vol. 1–10, 1882–91; ser. 3, vol. 1–10, 1892–1901; ser. 4, vol. 1–9, 1902–10; ser. 5, vol. 1–9, 1911–19; ser. 6, vol. 1–10, 1920–29; ser. 7, vol. 1, 1930–date. Ser. 1–5, 1872–1919 as Journal de physique théorique et appliquée. Index: 1872–1901.

J. Phys. Chem. The Journal of Physical Chemistry. Vol. 1, 1896–date. Cornell University, Ithaca, N. Y. Since 1933 published under auspices of the American Chemical Society and the Faraday Society, Baltimore, Md.

J. Phys. chim. Journal de physique, de chimie, d'histoire naturelle et des arts, Paris. Vol. 1–96, 1773–1823. Supersedes Introduction aux observations sur la physique. Index: vol. 1–10 in 10; 11–29 in 29; 30–56.

J. pr. Chem. Journal für praktische Chemie, Leipzig. Vol. 1, 1834–date; vol. 109, 1870, also as n.s., vol. 1–date. Index: vol. 1–30, 1834–43; 31–60, 1844–

53; 61–90, 1854–63; 91–108, 1864–69; n.s., vol. 1–50, 1870–94; n.s., vol. 51–100, 1895–1920; n.s., vol. 101–150, 1921–37.

J. Res. Nat. Bur. Stand. Journal of Research of the National Bureau of Standards, Washington. Vol. 1, 1928–date. Published by the U. S. National Bureau of Standards. Supersedes the Bureau's Scientific Papers and its Technologic Papers. Vol. 1–12, 1928–1934, as Bureau of Standards Journal of Research.

J. Sed. Petrol. Journal of Sedimentary Petrology, Tulsa, Okla. Vol. 1, 1931–date.

Jahresber. Chem. Jahresbericht über die Fortschritte der Chemie und verwandter Theile anderer Wissenschaften. Unter Mitwerkung von Th. Engelbach, Al. Naumann, W. Städel, herausgegeban von Adolph Strecker. Giessen, J. Ricker'sche Buchhandlung.

Jahresber. Chem. Min. Jahresbericht über die Fortschritte der Chemie und Mineralogie, Tübingen. Vol. 1–30, 1822–51. Edited by Berzelius. 1822–41 as Jahresbericht über die Fortschritte der physischen Wissenschaften. Translation of Svenska Vetenskaps-Akademien. Årsberättelser: section 3, Index: 1–25.

Jb. Min./Ref./Beil.-Bd./Sonderb. Neues Jahrbuch für Mineralogie, Geologie und Paleontologie, Heidelberg, Stuttgart. Vol. 1, 1830–date. Vol. 1–3, 1830–32 as Jahrbuch für Mineralogie Geognosie, Geologie und Petrefaktenkunde. Other title changes. 1925–27 in 2 sections. 1928–date in 3 sections: Beilage, vol. 1, 1881–date; Sonderband, vol. 1, 1–5, 1922–26. Referate.

Jb. preuss, Landesanst. *See* **Preuss. geol. Landesanst., Jb.**

Karsten's Arch. *See* **Arch. Min.**

Kastner's Arch. *See* **Arch. Nat.**

Koll.-Zs. Kolloid-Zeitschrift, Dresden, Leipzig. Vol. 1, 1906–date; vol. 1–12, 1906–13, as Zeitschrift für Chemie und Industrie der Kolloide. Index: vol. 1–50, 1906–30.

Kyoto Univ., Mem. Coll. Sc. Kyoto Imperial University. Department of Science. Through 1918 as College of Science. Memoirs: in 2 series; ser. A, vol. 1, 1914–date; ser. B, vol. 1, 1924–date.

Lempe's Mag. *See* **Mag. Bergbauk.**

Lyc. Nat. Hist. New York, Ann. Lyceum of Natural History of New York. Annals: vol. 1–11, 1824–1876. Continued as New York Academy of Sciences, Annals.

Mag. Bergbauk. Magazin für die Bergbaukunde, Dresden. Vol. 1–13, 1785–99. Also known as Lempe's Mag.

Mag. Nat. Helvet. Magazin für die Naturkunde Helvetiens, Zurich. Vol. 1–4, 1787–89. Superseded by allgemeines Helvetisches Magazin zur beförderung der inländischen Naturkunde.

Magyar Chem. Foly. Magyar Chemiai Folyóirat, Budapest. Vol. 1, 1895–date.

Mat. Termés. Ért. *See* **Ak. Magyar, Értes.**

Medd. Grønland. Meddelelser om Gronland, Copenhagen. Vol. 1, 1881–date. Published by the Kommissionem för Videnskabelige Undersøgelser i Grønland. Before 1931 entitled " Commissionem för Ledelsen af de Geol. og Geogr. Undersogelser i Grønland."

Mem. soc. russe min. Mineralogicheskoe Obshchestvo, Leningrad. Zapiski (Memoirs): 1842–63; ser. 2, vol. 1, 1866–date. Supersedes Schriften: vol. 1, no. 1–2, 1842; 1842–58 as Verhandlungen der russisch-kaiserlichen mineralogischen gesellschaft zu St. Petersburg; 1866–date as Zapiski I St. Petersburgskago Mineralogicheskago Obshchestva; 1842–63 text in German; 1866–date in Russian and German. Index: 1866–84; 1885–95.

Met. Erz. Metall und Erz. Halle a.S.: n.s., vol. 1, 1912–date. Published by the Gesellschaft deutschen Metallhütten-und Bergleute. Supersedes, in part, Metallurgie.

Metall. Ferrum. Zeitschrift für theoretische eisenhüttenkunde und allgemeine

Materialkunde. Halle a.S.: vol. 1–14, no. 12, 1904–17; vol. 1–9 as Metallurgie.

Min. Abs. *See* **Min. Mag.**

Min. Mag. Mineralogical Magazine and Journal of the Mineralogical Society, London. Vol. 1, 1876–date. Index: vol. 1–10, 1876–94; vol. 11–20, 1895–1925. Mineralogical Abstracts: vol. 1, 1920–date as Supplement.

Min. Mitt./Ref./Ergänzungsbd. Mineralogische und petrographische Mitteilungen, Vienna. Vol. 1–7, 1871–77; n.s., vol. 1, 1878–date. 1871–77 as Mineralogische Mitteilungen; n.s., vol. 1–10, as Mineralogische und petrographische Mitteilungen; n.s., vol. 11–38, 1889–1925 as Tschermak's mineralogische und petrographische Mitteilungen. Vol. 40, 1929–date also called Zeitschrift für Kristallographie, Mineralogie und Petrographie. Abteilung B. Index: 1871–77 in 1877; n.s., vol. 1–10, 1878–89; n.s., vol. 11–25, 1889–1907; n.s., vol. 26–40, 1908–30. Ergänzungsband: *See* **Zs. Kr.** Referatenteil: vol. 1, 1931–date.

Min. Soc. Warsaw, Arch. *See* **Arch. Min. Soc. Warsaw.**

Mus. Belgique, Ann./Bull./Mém. Musée royale d'histoire naturelle de Belgique. Annales: vol. 1–14, 1877–87. Bulletin: vol. 1, 1882–date. Mémoires: no. 1, 1900–date; no. 1–37, 1900–21, also as vol. 1–8, no. 4.

Nach. Ges. Göttingen. Gesellschaft der Wissenschaften zu Göttingen, Berlin. Mathematisch-physikalische Klasse. Nachrichten: vol. 1, 1894–date.

N. allg. J. Chem. Neues allgemeines Journal der Chemie, Leipzig. Vol. 1–6, 1803–06. Edited by Gehlen. Supersedes Allgemeines Journal der Chemie. Superseded by Journal für die Chemie, Physik und Mineralogie.

Nat. canadien. Naturaliste canadien; bulletin de recherches, observations et découvertes se rapportant à l'histoire naturelle du Canada, Quebec; etc. Vol. 1, 1868–date; vol. 21–date also as ser. 2; vol. 6, no. 4 omitted in numbering. Index: vol. 1–20, 1868–91.

Nat. Ges. Basel, Vh. Naturforschende Gesellschaft, Basel. Verhandlungen: vol. 1, 1852–date. Index: vol. 1–40, 1852–1929.

Nat. Ver. Hamburg. Naturwissenschaftlicher Verein, Hamburg. Abhandlungen und Verhandlungen: n.s., vol. 1, 1937–date. Formed by the union of its Abhandlungen aus dem Gebiete der Naturwissenschaften; vol. 1–23, no. 1, 1846–1931, and its Verhandlungen, n.s., vol. 1–6, 1875–81; ser. 3, vol. 1–29, 1893–1921; ser. 4, vol. 1–5, 1922–35.

Nat. Ver. Rheinland. Naturhistorischer Verein der Rheinlande und Westfalens, Bonn. Sitzungsberichte: 1906–32/33. Verhandlungen: 1844–date.

Naturaleza. Naturaleza, Mexico. Vol. 1–7, 1869–86; ser. 2, vol. 1–3, 1887–1909; ser. 3, vol. 1, no. 1–4, 1910–12. Published by the Museo Nacional de Historia Natural; Sociedad Mexicana de Historia Natural.

Nature. London. Vol. 1, 1869–date.

Naturwiss. Die Naturwissenschaften, Berlin. Vol. 1, 1913–date. Supersedes Naturwissenschaftliche Rundschau. Index: vol. 1–15, 1913–27.

Naturwiss. Abh. Wien. Naturwissenschaftliche Abhandlungen, Vienna. Vol. 1–4, 1847–51.

Natuurw. Tijdschr. Natuurkundig Tijdschrift voor Nederlandsch-Indie. (Natuurkundige vereeniging in Nederlandsch-Indië) Batavia, Weltevreden. Vol. 1, 1850–date. Also numbered in series. Index: vol. 1–60.

New South Wales Geol. Sur., Rec. New South Wales, Geological Survey, Sydney. Records: Vol. 1, 1899–date. At head of title of vol. 1–2: Department of Mines. At head of title of vol. 3: Department of Mines and Agriculture, Sydney.

New York Ac. Sc., Ann. New York Academy of Sciences. Annals: vol. 1, 1877–date. Supersedes its Annals of the Lyceum of Natural History of New York.

New York State Mus., Bull. New York State Museum. Museum Bulletin: no. 1, 1887–date. No. 1 issued in 1892. Index to publications: 1847–1902, in Museum Bulletin 66.

New Zealand Inst., Trans. Royal Society of New Zealand, Wellington.

To 1933 as New Zealand Institute. Transactions and Proceedings: vol. 1, 1868–date; vol. 18–40 also as n.s., vol. 1–22; vol. 41–57 as new issue; vol. 58–date as quarterly issue. Index: vol. 1–40, 1868–1907; vol. 41–51, 1908–19.

Nicholson's J. *See* **J. Phil. Chem. Arts.**

Nordd. Beitr. Berg- u. Hüttenk. Norddeutsche Beiträge zur Berg- und Hüttenkunde, Brunswick. Vol. 1, 1806.

Norsk. Ak., Forh./Avh./Skr. Norske Videnskaps-Akademi, Oslo. 1857–1911 as Videnskaps-Selskabet i Kristiania. Forhandlinger: 1858–1924. Index: 1858–1924. (Matematisk-Naturvidenskapelig Klasse) Avhandlinger: vol. 1, 1925–date. Skrifter: vol. 1, 1894–date.

Norsk Geol. Tidsskr. Norsk Geologisk Tidsskrift, Oslo. Vol. 1, 1905–date. Published by Norsk Geologisk Morening.

Nuovo Cimento. Nuovo Cimento, Pisa. Vol. 1–28, 1855–68; ser. 2, vol. 1–16, 1869–76; ser. 3, vol. 1–36, 1877–94; ser. 4, vol. 1–12, 1895–1900; ser. 5, vol. 1–20, 1901–10; ser. 6, vol. 1–24, 1911–22; ser. 7, vol. 25–26, 1923; n.s. (ser. 8), vol. 1, 1924–date. Published by the Società Italiana di Fisica. Supersedes Cimento. Index: 1843–1900.

Nytt Mag. Nytt Magazin for Naturvidenskaberne, Oslo. Vol. 1–20, 1836–74; ser. 2, vol. 1–6, 1875–81; ser. 3, vol. 1, 1882–date. Published by Physiographisk Forening. Supersedes Magazin for Naturvidenskaberne. Index: vol. 1–62, 1836–1925 in vol. 62.

Off. Gaz. British Guiana. Official Gazette of British Guiana, Georgetown. N.S., vol. 12, 1900–date.

Ontario Bur. Mines, Rep. Ontario Department of Mines, Toronto. Annual Report: vol. 1, 1891–date; 1891–1919 as Bureau of Mines. General index: vol. 1–25, 1891–1916.

Per. Min. Periodico de Mineralogia, Rome. Vol. 1, 1930–date.

Phil. Mag. London, Edinburgh and Dublin Philosophical Magazine and Journal of Science, London. Vol. 1–68, 1798–1826; n.s., vol. 1–11, 1827–1832; ser. 3, vol. 1–37, 1832–1850; ser. 4, vol. 1–50, 1851–1875; ser. 5, vol. 1–50, 1876–1900; ser. 6, vol. 1–50, 1901–25; ser. 7, vol. 1, 1926–date. 1798–1813 as Philosophical Magazine; 1814–26 as Philosophical Magazine and Journal; 1827–32 as Philosophical Magazine, or Annals of Chemistry, Mathematics, Astronomy, Natural History and General Science; 1832–40 as London and Edinburgh Philosophical Magazine and Journal of Science. Index: n.s.; ser. 3.

Phys. Arb. Wien. Physikalische Arbeiten der einträchtigen Freunde in Wien, Vienna. Vol. 1–2, no. 3., 1783–86.

Physica. Physica, The Hague. Vol. 1, 1933–date. Published by Hollandsche Maatschappij der Wetenschappen, Haarlem. A continuation in part of Physica; Nederlandsch Tijdschrift voor Natuurkunde.

Physica. Physica; Nederlandsch Tijdschrift voor Natuurkunde, The Hague, etc. Vol. 1–13, 1921–33. Superseded by Physica (1933–date) and Nederlandsch Tijdschrift voor Natuurkunde.

Phys. Rev. Physical Review, a Journal of Experimental and Theoretical Physics. New York; Lancaster, Pa.; etc. Vol. 1–35, 1893–1912; ser. 2, vol. 1, 1913–date. Published by the American Physical Society. Index: 1893–1920.

Poggendorff's Ann. *See* **Ann. Phys.**

Preuss. geol. Landesanst., Jb. Königlich preussische geologische Landesanstalt und Bergakademie, Berlin. Jahrbuch: vol. 1, 1880–date.

Proc. Nat. Ac. Sc. National Academy of Sciences, Washington. Proceedings: vol. 1, pt. 1–3. 1863–1894; n.s., vol. 1–, 1915–date.

Publ. Congo belg. Publications relatives au Congo belge et aux regions voisines, Liége. 1910/11–date. As Supplement to Société géologique de Belgique, Annales. Vol. 38–date.

Q. J. Sc. Quarterly Journal of Science, Literature, and Art, London. Vol. 1–22, 1816–26; n.s., vol. 1–7, 1827–30. Published by the Royal Institution of Great

Britain. Superseded by the Institution's Journal. Index: vol. 1–20. Title varies.

Rec. Gen. Sc. Records of General Science, London. Vol. 1–4, 1835–36.

Rec. Geol. Sur. New South Wales. Geological Survey of New South Wales, Sydney. Records: 1889–1922.

Rec. trav. chim. Pays-Bas. Recueil des travaux chimiques des Pays-Bas et de la Belgique, Leyden. Vol. 1, 1882–date. Published by Nederlandsche Chemische Vereeniging. Vol. 16–30 also as ser. 2, vol. 1–15; vol. 31–38 as ser. 3, vol. 1–8; vol. 39–date as ser. 4, vol. 1–date. Index: vol. 1–50, 1882–1931.

Rev. géol. Revue de géologie et des sciences connexes, Liége. Vol. 1, 1920–date. Published by the Société géologique de Belgique.

Rev. min. Revista minera, metalúrgica y de ingenieria, Madrid. Vol. 1, 1850–date. Vol. 1–33 as Revista minera; vol. 34–36 as Revista minera y metalúrgica. Index: vol. 1–25, 1850–74.

Rhodesia Sc. Ass., Proc. Rhodesia Scientific Association, Bulawayo. Proceedings: vol. 1, 1899/1900–date.

Riv. min. Rivista di mineralogia e cristallografia italiana, Padua. Vol. 1–50, 1887–1918.

Riv. studi, Trentino. Studi Trentini. Ser. 2: Scienze naturali ed economiche, Trento; vol. 1, 1926–date.

R. soc. española hist. nat., Anales/Bolet. Sociedad española de historia natural, Madrid. Anales: vol. 1–30, 1872–1901; vol. 21–30 also as ser. 2, vol. 1–10. Continued in 2 parts: Memorias: vol. 1, 1903–date. Boletin: vol. 1, 1901–date. Index: to Anales, vol. 1–30; to Boletin, vol. 1–15; to Memorias, vol. 1–9.

Roy. Soc. Canada, Trans. Royal Society of Canada. French name: Société royale du Canada, Ottawa, Montreal. Transactions: Vol. 1, 1882–date; vol. 1 to ser. 3, vol. 20, 1882–1926 as Proceedings and Transactions; vol. 13–24, 1895–1906 also as ser. 2, vol. 1–12; vol. 25, 1907 to date as ser. 3, vol. 1 to date. Index: ser. 1–2, 1882–1906.

Roy. Soc. Edinburgh, Trans. Royal Society of Edinburgh. Transactions: vol. 1, 1783–date; vol. 1–4 in 3 sections. Index: vol. 1–34, 1783–1888; vol. 35–46, 1889–1908.

Roy. Soc. London, Phil. Trans./Proc. Royal Society of London. Philosophical Transactions: vol. 1–177, 1665–1886; vol. 178, 1887–date in 2 series: ser. A, containing papers of a mathematical or physical character; ser. B, containing papers of a biological character. Index: vol. 1–70; vol. 71–110; vol. 111–120.

Roy. Soc. New South Wales., Proc. Royal Society of New South Wales, Sydney. Supersedes Philosophical Society of New South Wales. Journal and Proceedings: vol. 1, 1867–date; vol. 1–8, 1867–74 as its Transactions; vol. 9, 1875 as its Proceedings.

Roy. Soc. South Africa, Trans. Royal Society of South Africa, Cape Town. Transactions: vol. 1, 1908–date.

Roy. Soc. Western Australia, J. Royal Society of Western Australia. Supersedes Natural History and Science Society of Western Australia. Journal: vol. 1, 1914–date; vol. 1–10 as its Journal and Proceedings.

Russ. Ges. Min., Mat. Geol./Schr./Vh. Mineralogicheskoe Obshchestvo, Leningrad. Materialien zur Geologie Russlands. Vol. 1, 1869–date. Vol. 1–15 have title in Russian; Vol. 16–date in Russian and German. Text in Russian. For Schriften and Verhandlungen *see* **Mem. soc. russe min.**

Sachs. Ak. Wiss., Abh./Ber. Akademie der Wissenschaften, Leipzig. Founded 1846. 1846–1918 as Königliche saechsische Gesellschaft der Wissenschaften. Index; 1846–95. Berichte über die Verhandlungen: vol. 1–2, 1846–48. Continued in classes: Mathematisch-physische Klasse. Abhandlungen: vol. 1, 1849–date. Berichte: vol. 1, 1849–date.

Scherer's J. *See* **Allg. J. Chem.**

Sch. Mines Q. School of Mines Quarterly; a journal of applied science, New York. Vol. 1–36, 1879–1915. Published by Columbia University. Index: vol. 1–10; vol. 11–20; vol. 21–30.

Schweigger's J. *See* **J. Chemie u. Phys.**

Schweiz. min. Mitt. Schweizerische mineralogische und petrographische Mitteilungen, Frauenfeld. Vol. 1, 1920–date. Index: vol. 1–10, 1920–30 in vol. 10.

Science. Science, Cambridge, Mass; New York, etc. Vol. 1–23, 1883–1894; n.s., vol. 1, 1895–date. Subtitle varies.

Senck. Ges. Frankfurt, Abh. Senckenbergische Naturforschende Gesellschaft, Frankfurt a.M. Index: 1826–97 in Bericht. 1896/97. Abhandlungen: vol. 1–43, no. 3 (no. 1–427), 1854–1933; no. 428, 1934–date.

Smithson. Inst. Misc. Coll. Smithsonian Institution. Smithsonian Miscellaneous Collections: vol. 1, 1862–date. Also a quarterly issue of same name which is composed of vol. 45, 47–48, 50, 52 of the above set.

Soc. chim., Bull. Société chimique de France. 1858–1907 as Société chimique de Paris. Bulletin: vol. 1–5, 1858–63; n.s., vol. 1–50, 1864–88; ser. 3, vol. 1–36, 1889–1906; ser. 4, vol. 1–54, 1907–33. Continued in 2 series: Documentation; no. 1, 1933–date; Memoires: ser. 5, no. 1, 1934–date. 1858–72 as Bulletin Mensuel. Issued in two parts: Mémoires, and Travaux étrangères.

Soc. géol. Belgique, Ann./Bull./Mém. Société géologique de Belgique, Liége. Annales: vol. 1, 1874–date. In three separately paged sections: Bulletin; Mémoires; Bibliographie. Index: vol. 1–10 in vol. 10; vol. 11–20 in vol 20; vol. 21–30 in vol. 30. Mémoires: vol. 1, 1898–date.

Soc. géol. France., Bull. Société géologique de France, Paris. Bulletin: vol. 1–14, 1830–43; ser. 2, vol. 1–29, 1844–72; ser. 3, vol. 1–28, 1872–1900; ser. 4, vol. 1, 1901–date. 1912–21 as its Compte rendu sommaire et bulletin. Index: ser. 1; ser. 2, vol. 1–20; ser. 2, vol. 21–29; ser. 3, vol. 1–20.

Soc. geol. ital., Boll. Società geologica italiana, Rome. Bollettino: vol. 1, 1882–date. Index: vol. 1–20, 1882–1901.

Soc. nat. Moscou, Bull. Société des naturalistes de Moscou. Russian name: Moskovskoe Obshchestvo Liûbiteleĭ Priordy, Moscow. Bulletin: vol. 1–62, 1829–86; n.s., vol. 1, 1887–date. Index: vol. 1–56, 1829–81.

Soc. sc. Bohême, Mém. Société royale des sciences de Bohême, Prague. Classe des Sciences. Czech name: K. Česká Společnost nauk; Třída Matematicko-Přírodověděcká, Prague. Memoires (Věstnik): vol. 1, 1885–date.

Strukturber. Strukturbericht, Leipzig. Vol. 1, 1913/28–date. Vol. 1 as Zeitschrift für Kristallographie, Ergänzungsband; vol. 2–date as its Abt. A.

Svensk Kem. Tidskr. Svensk Kemisk Tidskrift, Stockholm. Vol. 1, 1889–date. Supersedes Kemiska Notiser.

Taschenb. Min. Taschenbuch für die Gesammte Mineralogie, mit hinsicht auf die neuesten entdeckungen, Frankfurt a.M., Heidelberg. Vol. 1–23, 1807–29. Each part has special title page: vol. 12–18, 1818–24 as Mineralogisches Taschenbuch; 1825–29 as Zeitschrift für Mineralogie, superseded by Jahrbuch für Mineralogie, later Neues Jahrbuch. . . .

Tech. Q. Technology Quarterly and Proceedings of the Society of Arts, Boston. Vol. 1–21, no. 4, 1887–1908. Published by Massachusetts Institute of Technology.

Tokyo Univ., J. Coll. Sc. Tokyo Imperial University, College of Science. Journal: vol. 1–45, 1887–1925. Index: vol. 1–25, 1887–1908. Supersedes the University's Science Department. Memoirs: Continued by the University's Faculty of Science. Journal: vol. 1, 1925–date. Issued in 5 sections.

Tomsk Univ., Bull. Tomsk University. Bulletin. (Izvestiîâ): vol. 1, 1889–date.

Trans. Am. Inst. Mining Eng. American Institute of Mining and Metallurgical Engineers. Through 1918 as American Institute of Mining Engineers.

Transactions: vol. 1–76, 1871–1928. 1928–date issued as Transactions of various sections. Index: vol. 1–35, 1871–1904; vol. 36–55, 1905–16; vol. 56–72, 1917–25; vol. 73–117, 1926–date.

Trans. Faraday Soc. Faraday Society, London. Transactions: vol. 1, 1905–date.

Tschermak's Min. Mitt. *See* **Min. Mitt.**

Univ. California Dept. Geol., Bull. University of California, Department of Geology. Bulletin: vol. 1, 1893–date.

Univ. Toronto Stud., Geol. Ser. University of Toronto, Toronto. Studies: Geological Series: no. 1, 1900–date.

U. S. Geol. Sur., Prof. Pap./Bull./Monog./Atlas. United States Geological Survey. Professional Papers: vol. 1, 1902–date. Bulletin: vol. 1, 1883–date. Monographs: vol. 1–55, 1890–1929. Geologic Atlas: folio 1, 1894–date.

U. S. Nat. Mus., Bull./Proc. United States National Museum. Index: 1875–1900 in its Bulletin 51. Bulletin: vol. 1, 1875–date; no. 1–16 also in Smithsonian Miscellaneous Collections, vol. 13, 23–24. Proceedings: vol. 1, 1878–date; vol. 1–4, 1878–81 also in Smithsonian Miscellaneous Collections, vol. 19, 22.

Vh. Min. Ges. *See* **Mem. soc. russe min.**

Vidensk. Skr. Oslo., Mat-Nat. Kl. *See* **Norsk. Ak.**

Washington Ac. Sc., Proc./J. Washington Academy of Sciences, Washington, D. C. Proceedings: vol. 1–13, 1899–1911. Superseded by its Journal.

Wern. Soc. Mem. Wernerian Natural History Society. Edinburgh. Memoirs: vol. 1–8, pt. 1, 1808–38.

Western Australia Geol. Sur. Bull. Western Australia, Geological Survey. Bulletin: no. 1, 1898–date.

Wett. Ges. Hanau. Wetterauische Gesellschaft für die Gesammte Naturkunde zu Hanau. Annalen: vol. 1–4, 1809–19. Bericht: 1843–1921; 1843–63 as its Jahresbericht. Naturhistorische Abhandlungen: vol. 1, 1858.

Wiedemann's Ann. *See* **Ann. Phys.**

Zbl. Min. *See* **Cbl. Min.**

Zs. anorg. Chem. Zeitschrift für anorganische und allgemeine Chemie, Hamburg, Leipzig. Vol. 1, 1892–date; vol. 1–91, 1892–1915 as Zeitschrift für anorganische Chemie. Index: vol. 1–50, 1892–1906; vol. 51–100, 1906–17; vol. 101–150, 1917–25.

Zs. deutsche geol. Ges. Deutsche geologische Gesellschaft, Berlin. Zeitschrift: vol. 1, 1848–date. Index: vol. 1–50, 1848–98 in vol. 50.

Zs. Elektrochem. Zeitschrift für Elektrochemie und angewandte physikalische Chemie, Halle a.S. Vol. 1, 1894–date. Published by Deutsche Bunsen-Gesellschaft für angewandte physikalische Chemie. Vol. 1, 1894–March 1895 as Zeitschrift für Elektrotechnik und Elektrochemie. Index: vol. 1–10, 1894–1904; vol. 11–30, 1905–24.

Zs. geol. Ges. *See* **Zs. deutsche geol. Ges.**

Zs. Kr., Ref./Strukturber. Zeitschrift für Kristallographie, Mineralogie und Petrographie, Leipzig. Vol. 1, 1877–date; vol. 1–55, 1877–1920 as Zeitschrift für Krystallographie und Mineralogie. Index: vol. 1–50, 1877–1912; vol. 51–75, 1912–30. Also indexes for every 10 volumes 1–40. Referatenteil, Leipzig: vol. 1, 1928–date. For Strukturbericht see under that title. Ergänzungsband: vol. 1, 1931–date; also as Mineralogische und petrographische Mitteilungen.

Zs. Nat. Halle. Zeitschrift für Naturwissenschaften, Halle, etc. Vol. 1, 1853–date. Published by Naturwissenschaftlicher Verein für Sachsen und Thüringen. Vol. 1–54, 1853–81 as Zeitschrift für die Gesammten Naturwissenschaften. Also numbered in series. Index: vol. 1–20, 1853–62 in vol. 20.

Zs. Phys. Zeitschrift für Physik, Brunswick, Berlin. Vol. 1, 1920–date. Published by Deutsche physikalische Gesellschaft. Vol. 1–3 as Supplement to the Society's Verhandlungen. Index: vol. 1–50, 1920–28; vol. 51–100, 1928–36.

Zs. phys. Chem. Zeitschrift für physikalische Chemie, Leipzig, Berlin. Vol. 1–

136, 1887–1928 as Zeitschrift für physikalische Chemie, Stöchiometrie und Verwandtschaftslehre. Vol. 137, 1928–date in 2 series. Abt. A, Chemische Thermodynamik, Kinetik, Elektrochemie, Eigenschaftslehre: vol. 1, 1887–date. Abt. B, Chemie der Elementarprozesse: vol. 1, 1928–date.

Zs. Phys. Math. Zeitschrift für Physik und Mathematik, Vienna. Vol. 1–10, 1826–32. Superseded by Zeitschrift für Physik und Verwandte Wissenschaften. Index: vol. 1–5 in vol. 5; vol. 6–10 in vol. 10.

Zs. pr. Geol. Zeitschrift für praktische Geologie, Berlin, Halle a.S. Vol. 1, 1893–date. Index: vol. 1–10; vol. 11–17.

The following is a list of independent works consulted in the preparation of this volume, and cited in the references. In addition, some old works listed in the bibliography of previous editions but not cited here (except in the synonymy) are also included. Some recent works of general interest also have been included. Often references to new editions have replaced the older works cited in previous editions. Some works here given have appeared as special bulletins of societies, or research institutions, and some have appeared in periodicals. They are listed here, however, because reference to them is frequent and it is therefore more convenient to cite them simply under the author's name and date. If more than one work appears under the author's name, the sequence is chronological.

Adam (1869). *Tableau minéralogique*, by M. Adam. 4to, Paris, 1869.

Agricola (1529). *Bermannus, sive De re metallica Diallogus*, by Georgius Agricola. Basel.

────── **(1543).** *De ortu et causis subterraneorum.*

────── **(1546).** *De natura fossilium* and *De veteribus et novis metallis.*

────── **(1546).** *Interpretatio Germanica vocum rei metallicae.*

────── **(1550).** *De re metallica*, 502 pp., Basel.

Agricola-Lehmann (1809). *Georg Agrikola's mineralogische Schriften, Übersetzt und mit erlauternden Anmerkungen Begleitet*, by Ernst Lehmann. 2 volumes, containing the *Oryktognosie* (*De Natura fossilium*). 342, 335 pp., Freyberg, Craz, and Gerlach, 1809–1810.

Ahlfeld and Reyes (1938). *Mineralogie von Bolivien*, by Fr. Ahlfeld and J. Muñoz Reyes. 89 pp., Berlin, 1938.

Aikin (1814, 1815) *Manual of Mineralogy*, by A. Aikin. First edition, 1814; second edition, 1815. 8vo, London.

Albertus Magnus (1262). *De Mineralibus*, by Albertus Magnus. Written after 1262.

Allan (1814). *Mineralogical Nomenclature*, by T. Allan. 8vo, Edinburgh, 1814.

Allan (1834). *Manual of Mineralogy*, by R. Allan. 8vo. Edinburgh, 1834. *See also* **Phillips — Alger.**

Argenville (1755). *L'Histoire Naturelle, etc.*, by D. d'Argenville, 4to, Paris, 1755.

Aristotle. Aristotle's works: particularly the Μετεωρολογικα, or "*Meteorology*" and Περι Θαυμασιων ακουμτων, or "*Wonderful Things Heard of.*" Works written about the middle of the fourth century B.C., Aristotle born about 384 B.C. and died 322 B.C.

Arppe (1855–61). *Analyser af Finska Mineralier*, by A. E. Arppe. Published in parts I, II, and III in *Act. Soc. Fenn*, 4, 1855; 5, 1857; 6, 1859/61.

Artini (1914). *I Minerali*, by E. Artini. 422 pp., Milan, 1914; second edition, 518 pp., Milan, 1921.

Astbury and Yardley (1924). "Tabulated Data for the Examination of the

230 Space-Groups by Homogeneous X-Rays," by W. T. Astbury and Kathleen Yardley. In *Phil. Trans. Roy. Soc. London*, [A] **224**, 221, (1924).

Barker (1922). *Graphical and Tabular Methods in Crystallography as the Foundation of a New System of Practice*, by Thomas Vipond Barker. 152 pp., London, 1922.

—— **(1930).** *Systematic Crystallography.* 115 pp., London, 1930.

—— **(1930).** *The Study of Crystals.* 136 pp., London, 1930.

Bauer (1886). *Lehrbuch der Mineralogie*, by Max Bauer. First edition, 562 pp. 8vo, Berlin and Leipzig. A second edition, Stuttgart, 1904.

—— **(1896, 1932).** *Edelsteinkunde*, by Max Bauer. 711 pp., with col. plates, Leipzig, 1896. A third edition by K. Schlossmacher, 871 pp., Leipzig, 1932.

Bauer-Spencer (1904). *Precious Stones.* Translated with additions, by L. J. Spencer, from the first edition of Bauer's *Edelsteinkunde.* 627 pp., with col. plates, London, 1904.

Bauerman (1881). *Text-Book of Systematic Mineralogy*, by Hilary Bauerman. 367 pp., 12 mo, London, 1881.

—— **(1884).** *Text-Book of Descriptive Mineralogy.* 399 pp., London, 1884.

Baumhauer (1889). *Das Reich der Krystalle für jeden Freund der Natur, insbesondere für Mineraliensammler, leichtfässlich dargestellt*, by Heinrich Adolf Baumhauer. 364 pp., 8vo, Leipzig, 1889.

—— **(1894).** *Die Resultate der Aetzmethode in der krystallographischen Forschung.* 131 pp., 4to, Leipzig, 1894.

Beck (1842). *Report on the Mineralogy of the State of New York*, by L. C. Beck. 534 pp., 4to, Albany, 1842.

Beckenkamp (1913). *Statische und kinetische Kristalltheoren*, by Jakob Beckenkamp. vol. 1, 206 pp.; vol. 2, 670 pp.; Berlin, 1913.

Becker (1903). *Krystalloptik*, by A. Becker. 362 pp., Stuttgart, 1903.

Bergmann (1780). *Opuscula of Tobernus Bergmann*, 1780.

—— **(1782).** *Sciagraphia regni mineralis.* 8vo, 1782. *See* **Withering.**

Berzelius (1816). *Neues System der Mineralogie*, by J. J. Berzelius. Translated from the Swedish by Gmelin and Pfaff. Nürnberg, 1816.

—— **(1819).** *Nouveau système de Minéralogie.* Translated from the Swedish. 8vo, Paris, 1819.

Beudant (1824). *Traité élémentaire de Minéralogie*, by F. S. Beudant. 8vo, Paris, 1824; second edition, 2 volumes, 1832.

Birch (1942). *Handbook of Physical Constants*, edited by Francis Birch, Chairman, J. F. Schairer, and H. Cecil Spicer. Geol. Soc. Am. Sp. Pap. 36, New York, 1942.

Bischoff (1847–1854). *Lehrbuch der chemischen und physikalischen Geologie*, by G. Bischoff. 2 volumes, 8vo, Bonn, 1847–54. Also an English edition published by the Cavendish Society. Second edition, 3 volumes, 8vo, Bonn, 1863/66.

Blum (1833–1874). *Lehrbuch der Mineralogie*, by J. R. Blum. First edition, 1833; second edition, 1845; third edition, 1854; fourth edition, 1874; Heidelberg and Stuttgart.

—— **(1843–1879).** *Die Pseudomorphosen des Mineralreichs.* Stuttgart, 1843. With Nachträge, 1, 1847; 2, 1852, Heidelberg; 3, 1863, Erlangen; 4, 1879, Heidelberg.

Blumenbach (1807). *Handbuch der Naturgeschichte*, by Johann Friedrich Blumenbach. Eighth edition, 8vo, Göttingen, 1807.

Boeke (1911). *Die Anwendung der stereographischen Projektion bei kristallographischen Untersuchung.* 58 pp., Berlin, 1911.

—— **(1913).** *Die gnomonische Projecktion in ihrer Anwendung auf kristallogrophische Aufgaben.* 54 pp., Berlin, 1913.

Boetius de Boot (1647). *Lap. gemmarum et lapidum historia*, by Anselmus Boetius de Boot. 4to, Jena, 1647. First edition published at Jena in 1609; second edition enlarged by Andr. Toll, Lugduni Bat. 8vo. 1636.

Bøggild (1905). *Mineralogia groenlandica,* by Ove Balthasar Bøggild. 625 pp., Kjøbenhavn, 1905. (Meddelelser om Grønland, XXXII.)

Boldyrev (1928). *Kurs opisatelnoi Mineralogii,* by A. K. Boldyrev. Leningrad, 1928.

Bombicci (1862). *Corso di Mineralogia,* by L. Bombicci. First edition, Bologna, 1862; second edition, 2 volumes, Bologna, 1873–75.

Born (1773). *Briefe von Wälschland* (Italy), by Ignatius von Born. 8vo, Prague, 1773.

———— (1772–75). *Lythophylacium Bornianum; Index fossiliumquae colligit, etc.,* Prague; pt. 1, 1772; pt. 2, 1775.

———— (1790). *Catalogue méthodique et raisonné de la collection des fossiles de Mlle. Eleonore de Raab.* 4 volumes, 8vo, Vienna, 1790.

Bouasse (1929). *Cristallographie géométrique: groups de déplacements,* by Henri Bouasse. 354 pp., 8vo, Paris, 1929.

Bourgeois (1884). *Reproduction artificielle des minéraux,* by Léon Bourgeois. 240 pp., 8vo, Paris, 1884. (*Encycl. chimique* by Frémy, vol. 2, app. 1).

Bournon (1808). *Traité de Minéralogie,* by Comte de Bournon. 3 volumes, 4to, 1808.

———— (1817). *Catalogue de la collection minéralogique particulière du roi.* 8vo, with atlas in fol., Paris, 1817.

Bragg and Bragg (1915). *X-Rays and Crystal Structure,* by W. H. Bragg and W. L. Bragg. 228 pp., London, 1915.

Bragg (1934). *The Crystalline State.* Vol. 1: *A General Survey,* by W. L. Bragg. 352 pp., New York, 1934.

———— (1937). *Atomic Structure of Minerals,* 292 pp., Ithaca, 1937.

Brauns (1903). *Das Mineralreich,* by R. A. Brauns. Text and Atlas of col. plates. 440 pp., 4to, Stuttgart, 1903–1904. Also an English translation by L. J. Spencer, 432 pp., London, 1908–12.

———— (1922). *Die Mineralien der niederrheinischen Vulkangebiete.* 225 pp., 4to, Stuttgart, 1922.

Bravais (1866). *Études cristallographiques,* by Auguste Bravais. 290 pp., Paris, 1866.

Breithaupt (1820). *Kurze Charakteristik des Mineral-System's,* by A. Breithaupt. 8vo, Freiberg, 1820.

———— (1823, 1832, 1852) *Vollständige Characteristik etc.* First edition, 1823; second edition, 1832; third edition, 1852. Dresden.

———— (1830). *Übersicht des Mineral-System's.* 8vo, Freiberg, 1830.

———— (1836–47). *Vollständiges Handbuch der Mineralogie.* Vol. 1, 1836; 2, 1841; 3, 1847; Dresden and Leipzig.

Brendler (1908–12). *Mineralien-Sammlungen; ein Hand- und Hilfsbuch für anlage und instandhaltung mineralogischer Sammlungen,* by Wolfgang Brendler. Vol. 1, 220 pp., 1908; vol. 2, 699 pp., 1912; Leipzig, 1908–12.

Brezina (1896). *Die Meteoritensammlung des K. K. naturhistorischen Hofmuseums am 1. mai 1895,* by Aristides Brezina. Vienna, 1896.

Brezina and Cohen (1886). *Die Structur und Zusammensetzung der meteoreisen erläutert durch photographische Abbildungen geätzter Schnittflächen,* by Aristides Brezina and E. Cohen. 5 volumes, Stuttgart, 1886–1906.

Brochant (1808). *Traité de minéralogie,* by A. J. M. Brochant. 2 volumes, 8vo. First edition, 1800; second edition, Paris, 1808.

Brögger (1890). *Die Mineralien der Syenitpegmatitgänge der sudnorwegischen Augit- und Nephelinsyenit,* by W. C. Brögger. 235, 663 pp., Leipzig, 1890. (Zeitschrift für Krystallographie, vol. 16, 1890.)

———— (1906). *Die Mineralien der sudnorwegischen Granitpegmatitgänge.* Pt. 1, "Niobate, Tantalate, Titanate und Titanoniobate." Videnskabs-Selskabets Skrifter, Math.-Naturv. Klasse, 1906, no. 6. 162 pp., Kristiania, 1906.

———— (1922). Pt. 2, Silikate der Seltenen Erden (Y-Reihe und Ce-Reihe), by

W. C. Brögger, Th. Vogt and J. Schetelig. ibid., 1922, no. 1, 150 pp., Kristiania, 1922.

Bromell (1730, 1739). *Herr Magni von Bromells Mineralogia.* First edition, Stockholm, 1730; second edition, 16mo, Stockholm, 1739.

Brongniart (1807). *Traité élémentaire de minéralogie,* by A. Brongniart. 2 volumes, 8vo, Paris, 1807.

—— **(1833).** *Tableau des espèces minérales.* 48 pp., 8vo, Paris, 1833.

Brooke (1823). *Familiar Introduction to Crystallography,* by H. J. Brooke. 8vo, London, 1823.

Brooke and Miller (1852). *Introduction to Mineralogy,* by Wm. Phillips, London, 1823. New edition by H. J. Brooke and W. H. Miller. 8vo, London, 1852.

Bruckmann (1727, 1730). *Magnalia dei in locis subterraneis.* 2 parts, fol.; Pt. 1, 1727; Pt. 2, 1730.

Bruhns (1902). *Elemente der Krystallographie,* by W. Bruhns. 211 pp., Leipzig and Vienna, 1902.

Brush-Penfield (1898). *Manual of Determinative Mineralogy,* by George Jarvis Brush, revised and enlarged by Samuel L. Penfield. Fifteenth edition, 312 pp., New York, 1898; first edition, New York, 1875.

Buerger (1942). *X-Ray Crystallography,* an introduction to the investigation of crystals by their diffraction of monochromatic x-radiation, by Martin Julian Buerger. 531 pp., New York, 1942.

Buttgenbach (1918). *Tableaux des constantes géométriques des minéraux,* by H. Buttgenbach. 83 pp., Bruxelles, 1918.

—— **(1925).** *Minéralogie du Congo belge.* 183 pp., Bruxelles, 1925.

—— **(1935).** *Les minéraux et les roches; études pratiques de cristallographie petrographie et minéralogie.* Sixth edition, 730 pp., Paris, 1935.

Caesalpinus (1596). *De metallicis,* by Andreas Caesalpinus. 1596.

Caesius (1636). *De Mineralibus,* by Bernardius Caesius. 656 pp., fol., Lugduni, 1636.

Cahen and Wootton (1920). *The Mineralogy of the Rarer Metals,* by Edward Cahen and William Ord Wootton. Second edition, rev. by Edward Cahen. 246 pp., London, 1920.

Calderón (1910). *Los minerales de España,* by Salvador Calderón y Arana. 2 volumes: vol. 1, 414 pp.; vol. 2, 561 pp., Madrid, 1910.

Cat. de Drée (1811). *Catalogue des huit collections qui composent le Musée Minéralogique de Et. de Drée.* 4to, Paris, 1811. Dufrénoy speaks of it as the work of M. Leman.

Cavallo (1786). " Mineralogical table 1, containing the classes, orders, genera, species, and varieties of mineral substances." " Mineralogical table 2, containing the principal properties of mineral substances," by Tiberius Cavallo. (Two charts), London, 1786.

Chapman (1843). *Practical Mineralogy,* by Edward J. Chapman. 8vo, London, Paris, and Leipzig.

—— **(1844).** *Brief Description of the Characters of Minerals.* 12mo., London, 1844.

Chester (1896). *A Dictionary of the Names of Minerals including Their History and Etymology,* by Albert Huntington Chester. 320 pp., New York, 1896.

Church (1883). *Precious Stones Considered in Their Scientific and Artistic Relations,* with a catalogue of the Townshend Collection of gems in the South Kensington Museum, by A. H. Church. 111 pp., London, 1883.

Clarke (1924). " The Data of Geochemistry," by Frank Wigglesworth Clarke. Fifth edition, *U. S. Geol. Sur., Bull. 770,* 841 pp., Washington, 1924. (First edition, *Bull. 330,* 1908.)

Cleaveland (1816, 1822). *Treatise on Mineralogy and Geology,* by Parker

Cleaveland. First edition, 8vo, Boston, 1816; second edition, 2 volumes, 8vo, Boston, 1822.

Cohen (1894, 1903, 1905). *Meteoritenkunde,* by E. Cohen. Vol. 1, 340 pp., 1894; 2, 301 pp., 1903; 3, 419 pp., 1905; Stuttgart.

Collins (1871). *A Handbook to the Mineralogy of Cornwall and Devon,* by Joseph Henry Collins. 108 pp., London, 1871.

Cronstedt (1758, 1781). *Mineralogie; eller Mineral-Rikets Upstallning,* by A. Cronstedt (issued anonymously). 12mo, Stockholm, 1758; Brünnich's edition in Danish, 8vo, Copenhagen, 1770. 2d. Swedish edition, Stockholm, 1781; Magellan's edition in English, 2 volumes, 8vo, London, 1788.

D'Achiardi (1873). *Mineralogia della Toscana,* by A. D'Achiardi. Vol. 1, 276 pp.; vol. 2, 402 pp.; 8vo, Pisa, 1872–73.

―――― **(1883).** *I Metalli loro Minerali e Miniere.* Vol. 1, 402 pp.; vol. 2, 635 pp.; 8vo, Milan, 1883.

Dana (1837). *System of Mineralogy,* by J. D. Dana. First edition, New Haven; second edition, New York, 1844; third edition, New York, 1850; fourth edition, New York, 1854, with supplements 1–10 in *Am. J. Sc.,* 1855/62, 8–10, by G. J. Brush; fifth edition, New York, 1868, aided by G. J. Brush — Appendix 1, by G. J. Brush, 1872; 2, 1875; 3, 1882, by E. S. Dana; sixth edition, by E. S. Dana, New York, 1892 — Appendix 1, 1899; 2, 1909, by E. S. Dana and W. E. Ford; 3, 1915, by W. E. Ford.

Dana-Ford (1932). *A Textbook of Mineralogy,* by Edward Salisbury Dana, revised and enlarged by William E. Ford. Fourth edition, 851 pp., New York, 1932.

Daubenton (1784). *Tableaux méthodiques des Minéraux,* by Daubenton. Paris, 1784. Only a classified catalogue. Several subsequent editions were issued, the sixth in 1799.

Daubrée (1868). *Substances minérales,* by Auguste Daubrée. 340 pp., Paris, 1868.

Davey (1934). *A Study of Crystal Structure and Its Applications,* by Wheeler Pedlar Davey. 695 pp., New York and London, 1934.

Davila (1767). *Catalogue syst. et raisonné des curiosités de la nature et de l'art qui composent de cabinet de M. Davila.* 3 volumes, 8vo, Paris, 1767.

Davy and Farnham (1920). *Microscopic Examination of the Ore Minerals,* by W. M. Davy and C. M. Farnham. First edition, 154 pp., New York, 1920.

Delamétherie (1792). *New Edition of Mongez's Sciagraphie,* (French transl. of Bergmann's *Sciagraphia,* with additions), by J. C. Delamethérie. 2 volumes, 8vo, Paris, 1792.

―――― **(1797).** *Théorie de la Terre.* Second edition, 5 volumes, Paris, 1797; vol. 1 and 2 of this edition contain his Mineralogy.

―――― **(1811).** Leçons de minéralogie. 8vo, vol. 1, 1811; vol. 2, 1812; Paris.

de Lisle (1772). *Essai de cristallographie,* by Romé de Lisle. 8vo, Paris, 1772.

―――― **(1783).** *Cristallographie, ou description des formes propres à tous les corps du regne minéral.* Called second edition of preceding. 4 volumes, 8vo, Paris, 1783.

Des Cloizeaux (1862–1893). *Manuel de minéralogie,* by A. Des Cloizeaux. 2 volumes and Atlas; vol. 1, 572 pp., 1862; vol. 2, 1 Fasc., 208 pp., 1874; 2 Fasc., pp. 209–544, 1874/93; Paris.

―――― **(1867).** *Nouvelles recherches sur les propriétés optique des cristaux, naturels ou artificiels, et sur les variations que ces propriétés éprouvent sous l'influence de la chaleur.* 222 pp., 4to, Paris, 1867, Institut impérial de France, Mémoires 18.

―――― **(1857, 1858).** *De l'emploi des propriétés optiques biréfringentes en minéralogie* (in *Ann. mines,* 11, 261–342 [1857]. Also (2e Mémoire) in *Ann. mines,* 11, 339–420 (1858). The third memoir of this series is the Nouvelles recherches cited above under 1867.

d'Halloy (1833). *Introduction à la géologie,* by Omalius d'Halloy. 8vo, Paris, 1833.

Dioscorides (A.D. 50). περι ὕλης ιατρικῆς (*Materia Medica*), written about A.D. 50. The mineral part treats especially of the medical virtues of minerals but often gives also short descriptions.

Doelter (1890). *Allgemeine chemische Mineralogie,* by Cornelio Doelter. 277 pp., 8vo, Leipzig, 1890.

───── **(1911–1931).** *Handbuch der Mineral-chemie,* by C. Doelter, with the collaboration of many others. In 4 volumes, divided into parts: vol. 1, 1912 (sep. printed sections dated 1911–1912); vol. 2, pt. 1, 1914 (1912–1914), pt. 2, 1917 (1914–1917), pt. 3, 1921 (1919–1921); vol. 3, pt. 1, 1918 (1913–1918), pt. 2, 1926 (1919–1926); vol. 4, pt. 1, 1926 (1925–1926), pt. 2, 1929 (1926–1929), pt. 3, 1931 (1929–1931) with general index.

───── **(1915).** *Die Farben der Mineralien.* 96 pp., Braunschweig, 1915.

Domeyko (1845, 1860, 1879, 1883). *Elementos de Mineralogia,* by Ignacio Domeyko. First edition, Serena, 1845; second edition, Santiago, 1860, with appendices 1–6; third edition, 1879, with appendix 1, 1881, 2, 1883.

───── **(1858).** *Tratado de Ensayes.* Second edition, 8vo, Valparaiso, 1858.

Dufrénoy (1844–1847). *Traité de minéralogie,* by A. Dufrénoy. First edition, 8vo; vol. 1, 1844, vol. 2, 1845, vol. 3, 4, 1847.

───── **(1856–1859).** Second edition, vol. 1, 2, 3, 5, 1856; vol. 4, 1859, Paris.

Duparc and Tikonovitch (1920). *Le platine et les gîtes platinifères de l'Oural et du monde,* by Louis Duparc and Marguerite N. Tikonovitch. 542 pp., Geneva, 1920.

Egleston (1889–1891). " Catalogue of Minerals and Synonyms " alphabetically arranged, by Thomas Egleston. (*U. S. National Museum, Bull. 33,* 1889.) Also republished, enlarged, 378 pp., New York, 1891.

Emmanuel (1867). *Diamonds and Precious Stones; Their History, Value, and Distinguishing Characteristics,* by Harry Emmanuel. 266 pp., London, 1867.

Emmerling (1793–1799). *Lehrbuch der Mineralogie,* by L. A. Emmerling. 8vo, first edition, 1793–97; second edition, 1799, 1802; Giessen.

English (1939). *Descriptive List of the New Minerals 1892-1938,* by George Letchworth English. 257 pp., New York and London, 1939.

Eppler-Eppler (1934). *Edelsteine und Schmucksteine,* by Alfred Eppler. Second edition, by W. Fr. Eppler, 554 pp., Leipzig, 1934.

Ercker (1574). *Aula subterranea* (on Ores, Mining, and Metallurgy), by L. Ercker. Written in 1574, published in 1595.

Erdmann (1853). *Lärobok i Mineralogien,* by A. Erdmann. 8vo, Stockholm, 1853.

Escard (1914). *Les pierres précieuses, propriétés caractéristiques et procédés de détermination,* by Jean Georges Escard. 520 pp., Paris, 1914.

Estner (1794). *Versuch einer Mineralogie für Anfänger u. Liebhaber, etc.,* by F. J. A. Estner. 3 volumes in 5 parts, 8vo, Vienna, 1794–1804.

Evans (1939). *An Introduction to Crystal Chemistry,* by R. C. Evans. 388 pp., Cambridge (England), 1939.

Fabricius (1566). *De rebus metallicis ac nominibus observationes variae, etc.,* ex schedis Georgii Fabricii. Tiguri, 1566. Issued with an edition of Gesner's *Fossilium.*

Farrington (1915). *Meteorites; Their Structure, Composition, and Terrestrial Relations,* by O. C. Farrington. 233 pp., Chicago, 1915.

Faujas (1778). *Recherches sur les volcans éteints du Vivarais et du Velay,* by Faujas de St. Fond. Fol., Grenoble and Paris, 1778.

───── **(1784).** *Minéralogie des volcans.* 8vo., Paris, 1784.

Fedorov (1920). *Das Krystallreich; Tabellen zur krystallo-chemischen Analyse,* by E. von Fedorov. Publ. in *Mem. Acad. Sc. U.S.S.R.,* Cl. Phys.-Math., Petrograd, ser. 8, vol. 36, 1920, 1050 pp., 4to. Written in German.

Ferraz (1929). *Compendio dos Mineraes do Brazil en forma de Diccionario,* by L. C. Ferraz. 645 pp., Rio de Janeiro, 1929.

Fersmann (1929). *Geochemische Migration der Elemente,* by A. Fersmann. Parts 1 and 2: "Abhandlungen zur praktischen Geologie und Bergwirtschaftslehre," vol. 18 and 19, Halle, 1929.

Fersmann and Goldschmidt (1911). *Der Diamant,* by A. von Fersmann and V. Goldschmidt. 274 pp. and atlas, Heidelberg, 1911.

Fichtel (1791). *Mineralogische Bemerken von die Karpathen,* by Johann Ehrenreich von Fichtel. Wien, 1791.

———— **(1794).** *Mineralogische Aufsätze.* Wien, 1794.

Fischer (1939). *Mineralogie in Sächsen von Agricola bis Werner. Die ältere Geschichte des staatlichen Museums für Mineralogie und Geologie zu Dresden (1560–1820),* by Walther Fischer. 347 pp., Dresden, 1939.

Fletcher (1892). *The Optical Indicatrix and the Transmission of Light in Crystals,* by L. Fletcher. 112 pp., London, 1892.

Fock (1888). *Einleitung in die chemische Krystallographie,* by Andreas Fock. 126 pp., Leipzig. 1888.

Forsius (1643). *Minerographia,* by Sigfrid Avon Forsius. 16mo, Stockholm, 1643.

Forster (1768). *An Introduction to Mineralogy, or an Accurate Classification of Fossils and Minerals, etc.,* by Johann Reinhold Forster. 8vo, London, 1768.

———— **(1772).** *An Easy Method of Classing Mineral Substance.* 8vo, London, 1772.

Fouqué and Lévy (1882). *Synthèse des minéraux et des roches,* by F. Fouqué and A. Michel-Lévy. 423 pp., 8vo, Paris, 1882.

Freiesleben (1807–1818). *Geognostischer Arbeiten,* by Johann Karl Freiesleben. 6 volumes, Freiberg, 1807–18.

———— **(1822).** *Systemtische Uebersicht der Litteratur für Mineralogie, Berg- und Hüttenkunde von Jahr 1800 bis mit 1820.* 350 pp., Freiberg, Graz, and Gerlach, 1822.

Frenzel (1874). *Mineralogisches Lexicon für das Königreich Sächsen,* by August Frenzel. 380 pp., 12mo, Leipzig, 1874.

Friedel (1893). *Cours de minéralogie. Minéralogie genérale,* by Charles Friedel. 416 pp., Paris, 1893.

Friedel (1904). *Étude sur les groupements cristallins,* by Georges Friedel. In *Bulletin de la société de l'industrie minérale,* ser. 4, vol. 3 and 4, pp. 1–485, Saint Étienne, 1904.

———— **(1911).** *Leçon de cristallographie,* by Georges Friedel. 310 pp., Paris, 1911.

Fröbel (1843). *Grundzüge eines Systems der Krystallographie,* by Julius Fröbel. Zurich, 1843. A second edition in 1847, Leipzig.

Fuchs (1872). *Die künstlich dargestellten Mineralien, etc.,* by C. W. C. Fuchs. 174 pp., 8vo, Haarlem, 1872.

Gallitzin (1801). *Recueil de noms par ordre alphabétique apropriés en minéralogie,* by D. de Gallitzin. Small 4to, Brunswick, 1801.

Gaubert (1907). *Minéralogie de la France,* by Paul Gaubert. 210 pp., Paris, 1907.

Genth (1875). *Preliminary Report on the Mineralogy of Pennsylvania,* by F. A. Genth. With an appendix on the Hydrocarbon Compounds, by Samuel P. Sadtler. Second Geological Survey of Pennsylvania, 1874. Harrisburg, 1875.

———— **(1891).** "The Minerals of North Carolina," *U. S. Geol. Sur., Bull. 74,* 119 pp., 1891. Also, earlier, Minerals and Mineral Localities of North Carolina. 122 pp., Raleigh, 1881.

Gesner (1565). *De omni rerum fossilium genere, gemmis, lapidibus, metallis, etc.,* by Conrad Gesner. Tiguri, 1565.

Gimma (1730). *Della storia naturale delle gemme, delle pietre, e di tutti i min-*

erali, ovvero della fisica sotterranea, by Giacinto Gimma. 2 volumes, Naples, 1730.

Glocker (1831, 1839). *Handbuch der Mineralogie,* by E. F. Glocker. 8vo, Nürnberg, 1831; second edition, 1839.

—— **(1847).** *Generum et specierum mineralium secundum ordines naturales digestorum synopsis.* 8vo, Halle, 1847.

Glocker (1896). *Grundriss der physikalischen Krystallographie,* by Theodor Glocker. Leipzig, 1896.

Gmelin (1780). *Einleitung in die Mineralogie,* by J. F. Gmelin. 8vo, Nürnberg, 1780.

—— **(1790).** *Grundriss einer Mineralogie.* 8vo, Göttingen, 1790.

Gobet (1779). *Les anciens minéralogistes du royaume de France,* by Nicolas Gobet. 2 volumes, 908 pp., Paris, 1779.

Goldschmidt (1886–1891). *Index der Krystallformen der Mineralien,* by Victor Goldschmidt. 3 volumes: vol. 1, 601 pp., 1886; vol. 2, 542 pp., 1890; vol. 3, 420 pp., 1891; Berlin.

—— **(1913–1923).** *Atlas der Krystallformen.* 9 volumes, atlas, and text: vol. 1, 1913; 2, 1913; 3, 1916; 4, 1918; 5, 1918; 6, 1920; 7, 1922; 8, 1922; 9, 1923. Heidelberg.

—— **(1934).** *Kursus der Kristallometrie.* Berlin, 1934.

Goldschmidt and Gordon (1928). *Crystallographic Tables for the Determination of Minerals,* by Victor Goldschmidt and Samuel G. Gordon. Special Publication No. 2, Ac. Sc. Philadelphia, 70 pp., 1928.

Goldschmidt (1923–1926). *Geochemische Verteilungsgesetze der Elemente,* by Victor Moritz Goldschmidt (and others). In 9 parts, 1923–26, published in Skrifter utgit av Det Norske Videnskaps-Akademi, Oslo. Matem.-Naturvid. Klasse. Pt. 1, 1923, no. 3; pt. 2, 1924, no. 4; pt. 3, 1924, no. 5; pt. 4, 1925, no. 5; pt. 5, 1925, no. 7; pt. 6, 1926, no. 1; pt. 7, 1926, no. 2; pt. 8, 1926, no. 8; pt. 9, 1938, no. 4.

Gordon (1922). *The Mineralogy of Pennsylvania,* by Samuel G. Gordon. 255 pp., Philadelphia, 1922.

Greg and Lettsom (1858). *Manual of the Mineralogy of Great Britain and Ireland,* by R. P. Greg and W. G. Lettsom. 483 pp., 8vo, London, 1858.

Groth (1874). *Tabellarische Übersicht der Mineralien nach ihren krystallographish-chemischen Beziehungen,* by Paul Groth. First edition, 1874; second edition, 1882; third edition, 1889; fourth edition, 1898; Braunschweig.

—— **(1878).** *Die Mineraliensammlung der K. W. Universität Strassburg.* Small 4to, 271 pp., Strassburg and London, 1878.

—— **(1904).** *Einleitung in die chemische Krystallographie.* 80 pp., Leipzig, 1904. Also an English translation, by H. Marshall, New York, 1906.

—— **(1905).** *Physikalische Krystallographie und Einleitung in die krystallographische Kenntniss der wichtigsten Substanzen.* Fourth edition, 820 pp., Leipzig, 1905.

—— **(1906–1919).** *Chemische Krystallographie.* 5 volumes: vol. 1, 1906; 2, 1908; 3, 1910; 4, 1917; 5, 1919; Leipzig.

—— **(1926).** *Entwicklungsgeschichte der mineralogischen Wissenschaften.* 261 pp., Berlin, 1926.

Groth and Mieleitner (1921). *Mineralogische Tabellen,* by P. Groth and K. Mieleitner. 8vo, 176 pp., München and Berlin, 1921.

Haan (1932). *Kristallometrische determineerings-Methoden,* by Jan Hendrik Haan. 177 pp., Groningen, 1932.

Haidinger (1825). *Treatise on Mineralogy,* by F. Mohs; translation with considerable additions by Wm. Haidinger. 3 volumes, Edinburgh, 1825.

—— **(1829).** *Anfangsgründe der Mineralien.* 8vo, Leipzig, 1829.

—— **(1845)A.** *Handbuch der bestimmenden Mineralogie.* 8vo, Vienna, **1845**; second edition, 1850.

—— (1845)B. *Übersicht der Resultate mineralogischen Forschungen im Jahre 1843.* Erlangen, 1845.

Hanawalt (1938). " Chemical Analysis by X-Ray Diffraction, Classification and Use of X-Ray Diffraction Patterns," by J. D. Hanawalt, H. W. Rinn, and L. K. Frevel. Published in *Ind. Eng. Chem., Anal. Ed.,* **10** [9], 456–512 (Sept. 15, 1938).

Hansen (1936). *Der Aufbau der Zweistofflegierungen. Eine Kritische Zusammenfassung,* by M. Hansen. 110 pp., Berlin, 1936.

Harada (1936). *Chemische Analysenresultate von japanischen Mineralien,* by Zyunpei Harada. Reprinted from the *J. Faculty Sci.,* Hokkaido Imperial University, Series IV, **3** [3–4], 221–362 (December, 1936), Sapporo, Japan.

Hardy and Perrin (1932). *The Principles of Optics,* by Arthur C. Hardy and Fred H. Perrin. First edition, 632 pp., New York and London, 1932.

Hassel (1934). *Kristallchemie,* by O. Hassel. 114 pp., Dresden and Leipzig, 1934. Also an English translation by R. C. Evans, London, 1935.

Hatle (1885). *Die Minerale des Herzogthums Steiermark,* by Edward Hatle, 212 pp., Graz, 1885.

Hausmann (1805, 1809). *Versuch eines Entwurfs zu einer Einleitung in die Oryktognosie,* by J. F. L Hausmann. 8vo, Braunschweig, 1805; Cassel, 1809.

—— (1813). *Handbuch der Mineralogie.* 3 volumes, 12mo, Göttingen, 1813; second edition, 12mo:

—— vol. 1, introductory, 1828; vol. 2, in two parts, 1847.

Haüy (1801, 1822). *Traité de minéralogie,* by R. J. Haüy. First edition: 4to in 4 volumes with atlas in fol.; also 8vo, 1801, Paris; second edition, 4 volumes, 8vo, with fol. atlas, 1822.

—— (1822)B. *Traité de cristallographie,* 2 volumes, 8vo, 1822.

—— (1809). *Tableau comparatif des résultats de la cristallographie et de l'analyse chimique relativement à la classification des minéraux.* 8vo, Paris, 1809.

Heddle (1901, 1923). *The Mineralogy of Scotland,* by Matthew Forster Heddle. 2 volumes, 8vo, Edinburgh, 1901; second edition, 2 volumes, 8vo, 1923–24, edited by J. G. Goodchild.

Heide (1934). *Kleine Meteoritenkunde,* by Fritz Heide. 120 pp., Berlin, 1934.

Henckel (1725) *Pyritologia oder Kiess-Historie,* by J. Fr. Henckel. 8vo, Leipzig, 1725. Also French and English translations.

Hessel (1897). *Kristallometrie,* by Johann F. C. Hessel. 2 volumes, 192. 165 pp., Leipzig, 1897. (Ostwald's Klassiker, no. 88, 89.)

Hiärne (1694). *Kort Anledning till atskillige Malm och Bergart,* by Hiärne. Stockholm, 1694.

Hill (1771). *Fossils Arranged According to Their Obvious Characters,* by John Hill. 8vo, London, 1771. (de Lisle says it was not issued until 1772.)

Hilton (1903). *Mathematical Crystallography, and the Theory of Groups of Movements,* by Harold Hilton. 262 pp., Oxford, 1903.

Hintze (1889–1939). *Handbuch der Mineralogie,* by Carl Hintze. 6 volumes: vol. 1, pt. 1, no. 1–8 (Elements-Sulfides) pp. 1–1208, 1898–1904; vol. 1, pt. 2, no. 9–17 (Oxides-Haloids) pp. 1209–2674, 1904–1915; vol. 1, pt. 3, first half, no. 18, 23–27 (part) (Nitrates-Manganates) pp. 2677–3656, 1916–1929; vol. 1, pt. 3, second half, no. 27–33 (Sulfates-Uranates) pp. 3657–4565, 1929–1930; vol. 1, pt. 4, first half, no. 19–22, 34 (part) (Borates-Phosphates) pp. 1–720, 1921–1931; vol. 1, pt. 4, second half, no. 34–38 (Phosphates-Organic) pp. 721–1454, 1931–1933; vol. 2, no. 1–12 (Silicates-Titanates) pp. 1–1842, 1889–1897; also an Ergänzungsband, 760 pp., 1936–1937, and a general index, 71 pp., 1939; Berlin and Leipzig. After the death of Hintze in 1916 the work was carried on by G. Linck with the help of contributors.

Hisinger (1808). *Mineralogisk Geografi Ofver Sverige,* by W. Hisinger. 8vo, Stockholm, 1808.

—— **(1826).** *Versuch einer mineralogischen Geographie von Schweden.* Translated by F. Wöhler. 8vo, Leipzig, 1826.

—— **(1843).** *Handbok för Mineraloger under Resor i Sverige.* 8vo, Stockholm, 1843.

Höfer (1870). *Die Mineralien Kärnthens,* by A. Höfer. 84 pp., 8vo, Klagenfurt, 1870.

Hoff (1801). *Magazin für die gesammte Mineralogie, etc.,* by K. E. A. von Hoff. 1 volume, 8vo, Leipzig, 1801.

Hoffmann (1811–1819). *Handbuch der Mineralogie,* by C. A. S. Hoffmann. Vol. 1, 1811; 2A, 1812; 2B, 1815; 3A and B, 1816; 4A, 1817; 4B, 1818. Work after vol. 2A issued by Breithaupt, Hoffmann having died, March, 1813. Vol. 4B consists of notes and additions by Breithaupt, and also the Letztes Min. Sys. of Werner (1817).

Honess (1927). *The Nature, Origin and Interpretation of the Etch Figures on Crystals,* by Arthur P. Honess 8vo, 171 pp., New York, 1927.

Hume-Rothery (1936). *The Structure of Metals and Alloys,* by William Hume-Rothery. Institute of Metals, Mon. and Rep. Ser., no. 1, 120 pp., 1936, London.

Hunt (1886). *Mineral Physiology and Physiography,* by Thomas Sterry Hunt. 710 pp., 8vo, Boston, 1886.

—— **(1891).** *Systematic Mineralogy Based on a Natural Classification.* 391 pp., 8vo, New York, 1891.

Huot (1841). *Manuel de Minéralogie,* by J. J. Huot. 2 volumes, 16mo, Paris, 1841.

Iddings (1906, 1911). *Rock Minerals,* by Joseph Paxson Iddings. First edition, 548 pp., 1906; second edition, 617 pp., 4to, 1911; New York.

Int. Crit. Tab. *International Critical Tables of Numerical Data, Physics, Chemistry and Technology.* Prepared by National Research Council, U. S. A. Editor; in-Chief, Edward W. Washburn. 7 volumes and index: vol. 1, 1926; 2, 1927; 3, 1928; 4, 1928; 5, 1929; 6, 1929; 7, 1930; index, 1933.

Int. Tables Det. Cryst. Struct. (1935). *International Tables for the Determination of Crystal Structures.* Vol. 1, Tables on the Theory of Groups; vol. 2, Mathematical and Physical Tables; Berlin, 1935.

Ito, T. *Japanese Minerals in Pictures.* Vol 1, 1937. Tokyo. In Japanese.

Jameson (1804–1820). *A System of Mineralogy,* by Robert Jameson. First edition, 2 volumes, 8vo, Edinburgh, 1804; second edition, 3 volumes, 1816; third edition, 3 volumes, 1820.

—— **(1805).** *Treatise on the External Characters of Minerals.* 8vo, Edinburgh, 1805; second edition, 1816.

Jasche (1817). *Kleine min. Schriften,* by C. F. Jasche. 12mo, Sondershausen, 1817.

Ježek (1932). *Mineralogie,* by Bohuslav Ježek. 2 volumes, 1368 pp., Praha, 1932.

Karsten (1789). *Museum Leskeanum, Regnum minerale,* by D. L. G. Karsten. 2 volumes, 8vo, Leipzig, 1789.

—— **(1791).** *Tabellarische Übersicht der mineralogisch-einfachen Fossilien.* Berlin, 1791.

—— **(1793).** *Über Herrn Werners Verbesserungen in der Mineralogie auf veranlassung der freimüthigen Gedanken, etc., des Herrn Abbé Estner.* 80 pp., 12mo, Berlin, 1793.

—— **(1800, 1808).** *Mineralogische Tabellen.* Fol., first edition, 1800; second edition, 1808; Berlin.

Kenngott (1849, 1850). *Mineralogische Untersuchungen,* by G. A. Kenngott, Breslau. 8vo, Pt. 1, 1849; 2, 1850.

—— **(1852–1868).** *Ubersichte der Resultate mineralogischer Forschungen.* For the years 1844–49, Vienna, 1852; for years 1850–51, Vienna, 1853; for 1852, Vienna, 1854; for 1853, Leipzig, 1855; for 1854, Leipzig, 1856; for 1855,

Leipzig, 1856; for 1856–57, Leipzig, 1859; for 1858, Leipzig, 1860; for 1859, Leipzig, 1860; for 1860, Leipzig, 1862; for 1861, Leipzig, 1862; for 1862–65, Leipzig, 1868.

———— (1853)B. *Das Mohs'sche Mineralsystem.* 8vo, Vienna, 1853.

———— (1866). *Die Minerale der Schweiz.* 460 pp., Leipzig, 1866.

Kirwan (1784–1810). *Elements of Mineralogy*, by R. Kirwan. First edition, 8vo, London, 1784; second edition, 1794–96; third edition, 2 volumes, 452, 459 pp., 1810.

Klaproth (1795–1815). *Beiträge zur chemischen Kenntniss der Mineralkörpers*, by M. H. Klaproth. Vol. 1, 1795; vol. 2, 1797; vol. 3, 1802; vol. 4, 1807; vol. 5, 1810; vol. 6, 1815; 8vo, Berlin and Posen.

Klockmann-Ramdohr (1936). *Lehrbuch der Mineralogie*, by Friedrich Klockmann, revised by Paul Ramdohr. Eleventh edition, 625 pp. Stuttgart, 1936. First edition in 1892.

Knop (1876). *System der Anorgraphie*, by A. Knop. 8vo, Leipzig, 1876.

Kobell (1830, 1831). *Charakteristik der Mineralien*, by Fr. von Kobell. Pt. 1, 1830; 2, 1831; 8vo, Nürnberg.

———— (1838). *Grundzüge der Mineralogie.* 8vo, Nürnberg, 1838.

———— (1853)A. *Tafeln zur Bestimmung der Mineralien.* Fifth edition, 1853; eighth edition, 1864; eleventh edition, 1878. München.

———— (1853)B. *Die Mineral-Namen.* 8vo, München, 1853.

———— (1864). *Geschichte der Mineralien.* 703 pp., 8vo, München, 1864.

Koksharov (1853–1891). *Materialien zur Mineralogie Russlands*, by Nikolai von Koksharov, 11 volumes with atlas: vol. 1, 1853; 2, 1854–57; 3, 1858; 4, 1862; 5, 1866; 6, 1870; 7, 1875; 8, 1878; 9, 1884; 10, 1888; 11, 1891.

———— (1865). *Vorlesungen über Mineralogie.* 4to, St. Petersburg, 1865.

Kopp (1849). *Einleitung in die Krystallographie und in die krystallographische Kenntniss die wichtigeren Substanzen*, by Hermann Kopp. 2 volumes, text, and atlas, 8vo, Braunschweig, 1849.

Kraus (1906). *Essentials of Crystallography*, by Edward Henry Kraus. Ann Arbor, 1906.

———— (1911). *Descriptive Mineralogy.* 344 pp., 4to, Ann Arbor, 1911.

Kraus, Hunt, and Ramsdell (1936). *Mineralogy; an Introduction to the Study of Minerals and Crystals*, by Edward Henry Kraus, W. F. Hunt, and L. S. Ramsdell. Third edition (of the Mineralogy of Kraus and Hunt, 1920), 638 pp., New York, 1936.

Kraus and Slawson (1939). *Gems and Gem Materials*, by Edward Henry Kraus and Chester Baker Slawson. Third edition, 287 pp., 8vo, New York and London, 1939; first edition by Kraus and Holden, 1925.

Kreutz (1915). *Elemente der Theorie der Krystallstruktur*, by Stefan Kreutz. With an atlas of stereograms. 174 pp., Leipzig, 1815.

Kunz (1895). *Gems and Precious Stones of North America*, by George Frederick Kunz. First edition, 1890; second edition, 367 pp., New York, 1892.

Lacroix (1893–1913). *Minéralogie de la France et des ses colonies*, by A. Lacroix. 5 volumes: vol. 1, 1893–95; 2, 1897; 3, 1901; 4, 1910; 5, 1913; Paris.

———— (1922–1923). *Minéralogie de Madagascar.* 3 volumes: vols. 1, 2, 1922; 3, 1923; Paris.

Lampadius (1795–1800). *Sammlung practisch-chemisches Abhandlungen*, by W. A. Lampadius. Vol. 1, 1795; vol. 2, 1797; vol. 3, 1800; Dresden.

———— (1816). *Neue Erfahrungen im Gebiete der Chemie und Hüttenkunde.* 2 volumes, 8vo, Weimar, 1816–17.

Landero (1888–1891). *Sinopsis Mineralógica ó catálogo descriptivo de los Minerales*, by Carlos F. De Landero. 528 pp., Mexico, 1888–91.

Lapparent (1884). *Cours de Minéralogie*, by A. de Lapparent. 560 pp., Paris, 1884.

———— (1907). *Précis de minéralogie.* Fifth edition, 424 pp., Paris, 1907.

Larsen (1921). " The Microscopic Determination of the Nonopaque Minerals." First edition by E. S. Larsen, *U. S. Geol. Sur., Bull. 679*, 1921; second edition by E. S. Larsen and H. Berman, *U. S. Geol. Sur., Bull. 848*, 1934.

Lehman (1904). *Flüssige Kristalle sowie plastizität von Kristallen in allgemeinen, molekulare Umlagerungen, und Aggregatzustandsänderungen*, by Otto Lehman. 4to, 267 pp., Leipzig, 1904.

Lenz (1791–1822). *Versuch einer vollständigen Anleitung zur Kenntniss der Mineralien*, by D. G. Lenz. 2 volumes, Leipzig, 1794; also Tabellen, 1781; Handbuch, 1791; Grundriss, 1793; Mustertafeln, 1794; Tabellen fol., 1806; System, 1800, 1809; Handbuch, 1822.

Leonhard (1806). *Systematisch-tabellarische Übersicht und Charakteristik der Mineralkörper*, by C. C. Leonhard, K. F. Merz, and J. H. Kopp. Fol., 125 pp., Frankfurt a.M., 1806.

Leonhard (1843). *Handwörterbuch der topographischen Mineralogie*, by G. Leonhard. Heidelberg, 1843.

———— **(1860).** *Grundzüge der Mineralogie.* 404 pp., 4vo, Leipzig and Heidelberg, 1860.

Leonhard (1821, 1826). *Handbuch der Oryktognosie*, by K. C. Leonhard. First edition, 1821; second edition, 1826; Heidelberg.

Lévy (1837). *Description d'une collection de minéraux, formée par M. Henri Heuland, et appartenant à M. Ch. H. Turner, de Rooksnest, dans le comté de Surrey en Angleterre*, by A. Lévy. 3 volumes, 8vo, and atlas of 85 plates, London, 1837.

Lévy and Lacroix (1888). *Les minéraux des roches*, by A. Michel-Lévy and Alfred Lacroix. 334 pp., Paris, 1888.

Lewis (1931). *A Manual of Determinative Mineralogy with Tables*, by Joseph Volney Lewis. Fourth edition by A. C. Hawkins, 230 pp., New York, 1931.

Lewis (1899). *A Treatise on Crystallography*, by William James Lewis. 612 pp., Cambridge (England), 1899.

Leymérie (1859, 1880) *Cours de minéralogie*, by A. F. G. A. Leymérie. 8vo, Toulouse, 1859; third edition, 2 volumes, 8vo, 1880.

———— **(1861).** *Éléments de minéralogie et de lithologie.* Toulouse, 1861; fourth edition, 2 volumes, 1879.

Libavius (1597). *Alchemia*, by A. Libavius. Frankfurt, 1597.

Liebisch (1881). *Geometrische Krystallographie*, by Th. Liebisch. Leipzig, 464 pp., 8vo, 1881.

———— **(1891).** *Physikalische Krystallographie.* 614 pp., 8vo, Leipzig, 1891.

Linck (1896). *Grundriss der Krystallographie*, by G. Linck. 252 pp., Jena, 1896.

Lindgren (1933). *Mineral Deposits*, by Waldemar Lindgren. First edition, 883 pp., 1913; second edition, 957 pp., 1919; third edition, 1049 pp., 1928; fourth edition, 930 pp., 1933; New York.

Linnaeus (1735–1770). *Systema Naturae of Linnaeus.* First edition, 1735; tenth edition, 1770.

Liversidge (1874, 1882, 1888). *The Minerals of New South Wales*, by Archibald Liversidge. First published in *Trans. Royal Soc. New South Wales*, December, 1874. Second edition, 137 pp., Sydney, 1882; third edition, 326 pp., 8vo, London, 1888.

Lucas (1806, 1813). *Tableau méthodique des espèces minéraux*, by J. A. H. Lucas. Pt. 1, 8vo., 1806; pt. 2, 1813; Paris.

Ludwig (1803–1804) or Ludwig's Werner. *Handbuch der Mineralogie nach A. G. Werner*, by C. F. Ludwig. 2 volumes, 8vo, Leipzig, 1803, 1804.

Luedecke (1896). *Die Minerale des Harzes*, by Otto Luedecke. 643 pp., Berlin, 1896.

Mallard (1879–84). *Traité de cristallographie géométrique et physique*, by Ernest Mallard. Vol. 1, 372 pp., Paris, 1879; vol. 2, 599 pp., 1884.

Marx (1825). *Geschichte der Crystallkunde*, by C. M. Marx. 8vo, Carlsruhe and Baden, 1825.

Matthesius (1562). *Berg Postilla, oder Sarepta*, by Matthesius. Fol., Nürnberg, 1562.

Mellor (1922–1937). *A Comprehensive Treatise on Inorganic and Theoretical Chemistry*, by J. W. Mellor, 16 volumes, London, 1927: vol. 1, 1922; 2, 1922; 3, 1923; 4, 1923; 5, 1924; 6, 1925; 7, 1927; 8, 1928; 9, 1929; 10, 1930; 11, 1931; 12, 1932; 13, 1934; 14, 1935; 15, 1936; 16, 1937 (with general index).

Merrill (1904, 1910). *The Non-Metallic Minerals; Their Occurrence and Uses*, by George P. Merrill. First edition, 414 pp., New York, 1904; second edition, 432 pp., 1910.

Meunier (1891). *Les méthodes de synthèse en minéralogie*, by Stanislaus Meunier. 359 pp., 8vo, Paris, 1891.

Miers (1902). *Mineralogy: An Introduction to the Scientific Study of Minerals*, by Henry Alexander Miers. 584 pp., London and New York, 1902; second edition revised by H. L. Bowman. London, 1929.

Miller (1839). *A Treatise on Crystallography*, by William Hallows Miller. 139 pp., 8vo, Cambridge (England), 1839. Also a German translation by J. Grailich, 328 pp., Vienna, 1856.

——— **(1863).** *A Tract on Crystallography.* 8vo., 86 pp. Cambridge, England, 1863.

Mohs (1804). *Des Herrn J. F. Null Mineralien-Kabinet, nach einem, durchaus auf aussere Kennzeichnen gegründeten Systeme geordnet*, by F. Mohs. 3 abthl., 8vo, Vienna, 1804.

——— **(1820).** *Characteristic of the Natural History System of Mineralogy.* 8vo, Edinburgh, 1820.

——— **(1822).** *Grundriss der Mineralogie.* 2 volumes, 8vo, Dresden, 1822, 1824. (Translated into English by Haidinger.)

——— **(1839).** *Aufangsgründe der Naturgeschichte des Mineralreichs.* Pt. 1, introductory, published in 1836; pt. 2, by F. X. M. Zippe, 8vo, 1839. An earlier edition of this work in 1832.

Monticelli and Covelli (1825). *Prodromo della mineralogia vesuviana*, by T. Monticelli and N. Covelli. Vol. 1, *Orittognosia*, Naples, 1825.

Moore (1859). *Ancient Mineralogy, or an Inquiry Respecting Mineral Substances Mentioned by the Ancients*, by N. F. Moore. Second edition, 250 pp., New York, 1859.

Morey (1938). *The Properties of Glass*, by George W. Morey. *American Chem. Soc. Mon. Ser. 77*, 561 pp., New York, 1938.

Moses and Parsons (1916). *Elements of Mineralogy, Crystallography and Blowpipe Analysis*, by Alfred J. Moses and Charles Lathrop Parsons. Fifth edition, 631 pp., New York, 1916; first edition in 1865.

Mügge (1903). *Die regelmässigen Verwachsungen von mineralen verschiedener Art*, by O. Mügge. *Jb. Min. Beil. Bd.* 16, 335–475 (1903).

Murdoch (1916). *Microscopical Determination of the Opaque Minerals*, by Joseph Murdoch. 165 pp., New York, 1916.

Napione (1770). *Elementi di Mineralogia*, by C. A. G. Napione. 8vo, Turin, 1770. A later edition in 1797.

Naumann (1829). *Lehrbuch der Krystallographie*, by C. F. Naumann. 2 volumes, 8vo, Leipzig, 1829. Naumann also published *Lehrbuch der Mineralogie*, 8vo, Berlin, 1828; *Anfangsgründe der Kryst.*, 8vo, 1854; *Elemente der theor. Kryst.* 8vo, 1856.

——— **(1846–1873).** *Elemente der Mineralogie.* 9 editions: 1846, 1850, 1852, 1855, 1859, 1864, 1868, 1870, 1873; 3 editions revised by F. Zirkel: 1877, 1881, 1885; Leipzig.

Necker (1835). *Le règne minéral ramené aux méthodes de l'histoire naturelle*, by L. A. Necker. 2 volumes, 8vo, Paris, 1835.

Neumann (1823). *Beiträge zur Krystallonomie,* by F. C. Neumann. Vol. 1, 154 pp., 8vo., Berlin and Posen, 1823.

Nicol (1849). *Manual of Mineralogy,* by J. Nicol. 8vo, Edinburgh, 1849.

Niggli (1919). *Geometrische Kristallographie des Diskontinuums,* by Paul Niggli. 576 pp., Leipzig, 1919.

———— (1920). *Lehrbuch der Mineralogie.* 694 pp., 8vo, Berlin, 1920; second edition: vol. 1 (Spezielle) 697 pp.; vol. 2 (Allgem.) 712 pp.; Berlin, 1924–26.

———— (1927). *Tabellen zur allgemein und speziellen Mineralogie.* 300 pp., Berlin, 1927.

Niggli, Koenigsberger, and Parker (1940). *Die Mineralien der Schweizeralpen,* by P. Niggli, J. Koenigsberger, and R. L. Parker. 661 pp., 2 volumes, Basel, 1940.

Nordenskiöld (1820). *Bidrag till närmare Kännedom af Finlands Mineralier och Geognosie,* by Nils G. Nordenskiöld. 8vo, Stockholm, 1820.

Nordenskiöld (1855, 1863). *Beskrifning öfver de i Finland funna Mineralier,* by N.A.E. Nordenskiöld. Helsingfors, 1855; second edition, 1863.

Orcel (1934). *L'étude microscopique des minerais métalliques.* Paris, 1934.

Osann (1927). *Die Mineralien Badens,* by Alfred Osann (completed by his widow, Dr. Gertraud Heffter). 238 pp., Stuttgart, 1927.

Pabst (1938). "Minerals of California," by Adolf Pabst. California Dept. of Natural Resources, *Division of Mines, Geologic Branch, Bull. 113* (revision of A. S. Eakle, *idem,* 1914). 338 pp., Sacramento, 1938.

Palache (1935). "The Minerals of Franklin and Sterling Hill, Sussex County, New Jersey," by Charles Palache. *U. S. Geol. Sur. Prof. Paper 180,* 1935.

Parker (1929). *Kristallzeichnen,* by Robert Lüling Parker. Berlin, 1929.

Petterd (1910). *Catalogue of the Minerals of Tasmania,* by W. F. Petterd. 221 pp., Hobart, 1910.

Petzholdt (1843). *Beiträge zur Geognosie von Tyrol, etc.* 8vo, Leipzig, 1843.

Phillips (1912). *Mineralogy, an Introduction to the Theoretical and Practical Study of Minerals,* by Alexander Hamilton Phillips. 699 pp., New York, 1912.

Phillips (1816–1823). *Elementary Introduction to Mineralogy,* by William Phillips. First edition, London, 1816; third edition, 406 pp., 8vo, London, 1823. The first edition was republished in New York with notes and additions by Samuel L. Mitchill, 1818.

Phillips-Alger (1844). A fifth edition of Phillips' *Mineralogy* (from the fourth London edition by R. Allan) with numerous additions by Francis Alger. 662 pp. 8vo, Boston, 1844.

Phillips-Allan (1837). A fourth edition of Phillips' *Mineralogy,* considerably augmented by Robert Allan. 8vo, London, 1837.

Phillips-Brooke and Miller (1852). *See* **Brooke and Miller (1852).**

Pisani (1883). *Traité élémentaire de minéralogie,* by F. Pisani. First edition, 415 pp., 8vo, Paris, 1875; second edition, 421 pp., 1883.

Pliny (A.D. 77). *Historia naturalis C. Plinii Secundi.* First published A.D. 77. Latin edition consulted, Silligs, in 8 volumes, 1851–58; and English, that of Bostock and Riley, 5 volumes, London, 1855. Pliny's *Natural History* is divided into XXXVII books, and these into short chapters. The numbering of the chapters differs somewhat in different editions; that stated in the references is from the English edition. The last five books are those that particularly treat of metals, ores, stones, and gems.

Pockels (1906). *Lehrbuch der Kristalloptik,* by Friedrich Pockels. 519 pp., Leipzig and Berlin, 1906.

Prior (1923, 1927). *Catalogue of Meteorites with Special Reference to Those Represented in the Collection of the British Museum,* by G. T. Prior. 196 pp., London, 1923. With an appendix, 48 pp., London, 1927.

Pryce (1778). *Mineralogia cornubiensis,* by W. Pryce. 331 pp., London, 1778.

Quenstedt (1873). *Grundriss der bestimmenden und rechnenden Krystallo-*

graphie nebst einer historischen Einleitung, by Fr. Aug. Quenstedt. 443 pp., Tübingen, 1873.

——— **(1853–1877).** *Handbuch der Mineralogie.* First edition, 8vo, Tübingen, 1853; second edition, 1863; third edition, 1877.

Raaz and Tertsch (1939). *Geometrische Kristallographie und Kristalloptik und deren Arbeitsmethoden*, by Franz Raaz and Hermann Tertsch. 215 pp., Vienna, 1939.

Raimondi (1878). *Minéraux du Pérou: Catalogue raisonné d'une collection des principaux types minéraux de la République*, by A. Raimondi. Translated from the Spanish by J. B. H. Martinet. 336 pp., 8vo, Paris, 1878.

Rammelsberg (1841–1853). *Handwörterbuch des chemischen Theils der Mineralogie*, by C. F. Rammelsberg. Berlin, 1841. Supplement 1, 1843; 2, 1845; 3, 1847; 4, 1849; 5, 1853.

——— **(1847).** *J. J. Berzelius's neues chemisches Mineralsystem.* Nürnberg.

——— **(1860, 1875, 1886).** *Handbuch der Mineralchemie.* First edition, Leipzig, 1860; second edition, 1875; Ergänzungsheft, 1886.

——— **(1881, 1882).** *Handbuch der krystallographish-physikalischen Chemie.* Leipzig. Pt. 1, 1881; pt. 2, 1882.

Rashleigh (1797, 1802). *Specimens of British Minerals Selected from the Cabinet of Phillip Rashleigh.* (Descriptions and col. plates.) 4to, London. Pt. 1, 1797; pt. 2, 1802.

Read (1936). *Rutley's Elements of Mineralogy.* Twenty-third edition by H. H. Read, 490 pp., London, 1936. First edition appeared in 1874.

Reuss (1801–1806). *Lehrbuch der Mineralogie*, by F. A. Reuss. 8vo, Leipzig, 1801–1806. Divided into parts and the parts into volumes. Pt. 1 and pt. 2, vol. 1, 1801; vol. 2, 1802; vol. 3, 4, 1803; pt. 3, vol. 1, 2, 1805; pt. 4, including index, 1806.

Ridgway (1912). *Color Standards and Color Nomenclature*, by Robert Ridgway. With 53 col. plates and 1115 named colors. Washington, 1912.

Rio (1795). *Elementos de Oryktognosia, ó del Conocimiento de los Fóssiles, despuestos según los principios de A. G. Werner*, by A. M. del Rio. 4to, Mexico, 1795.

——— **(1804).** *Tablos mineralogicos*, by D. L. G. Karsten. 4to, Mexico, 1804.

——— **(1827).** *Nuevo Sistema Minerale.* Mexico, 1827.

Robinson (1825). *Catalogue of American Minerals with Their Localities*, by S. Robinson. 8vo, Boston, 1825.

Rogers (1937). *Introduction to the Study of Minerals*, by Austin Flint Rogers. Third edition, 626 pp., New York and London, 1937. First edition, 522 pp., New York, 1912.

Rose (1837, 1842). *Reise nach dem Ural, dem Altai, und dem kaspischen Meere*, by G. Rose. 8vo, vol. 1, 1837; vol. 2, 1842; Berlin.

——— **(1838).** *Elemente der krystallographie, nebst ein tabellarischen Uebersicht der Mineralien nach den Krystallformen*, by Gustav Rose. Second edition, 175 pp., 8vo, Berlin, 1838.

——— **(1852).** *Das krystallo-chemischen Mineral-System.* 8vo, Leipzig, 1852.

Rosenholtz and Smith (1931). *Tables and Charts of Specific Gravity and Hardness for Use in the Determination of Minerals*, by Joseph L. Rosenholtz and Dudley T. Smith. 83 pp., Troy, N. Y., 1931.

Roth (1879). *Allgemeine und chemische Geologie*, by Justus Roth. Vol. 1, *Bildung und Umbildung der Mineralien*, etc., 633 pp., Berlin, 1879; vol. 2, *Petrographie*, 695 pp., 1887; vol. 3, *Verwitterung . . . der Gesteine*, and *Nachträge*, 530 pp., 1893.

Sadebeck (1876). *Angewandte Krystallographie (Ausbildung der Krystalle, Zwillingsbildung, Krystallotektonic) nebst einem Anhang uber Zonenlehre*, by Alexander Sadebeck. (Rose's Elemente der Krystallographie, Bd. II.) 284 pp., 8vo, Berlin, 1876.

Sage (1772, 1777). *Eléméns de minéralogie docimastique*, by B. G. Sage.   First edition, 1772; second edition, 2 volumes, 1777.

Sandberger (1882–85). *Untersuchungen über Erzgänge*, von Fridolin Sandberger. 430 pp., 8vo, Wiesbaden, 1882–85.

Saussure (1779–1796). *Voyages dans les Alpes*, by H. B. Saussure. 4 volumes: vol. 1, 2, 1779, 1780; vol. 3, 4, 1796.

Scacchi (1841). *Memorie mineralogiche e geologiche*, by A. Scacchi. 8vo, Napoli, 1841.

────── (1842). *Quadri Cristallografici, e Distribuzione sistematica dei minerale.* 8vo, Napoli, 1842.

────── (1864). *Polisimmetria dei Cristalli.* 4to, Napoli, 1864.

────── (1872, 1887). *Contribuzioni mineralogiche per servire all Storia dell' Incendio Vesuviano, del mese di Aprile*, 1872. Pt. 1, Naples, 1872; pt. 2, 1874. Catalogo dei Minerali Vesuviani, Naples, 1887.

Schairer (1931). " The Minerals of Connecticut," by John Frank Schairer. *Connecticut State Geological and Natural Hist. Survey Bull. 51*, 121 pp., Hartford, 1931.

Schiebold (1932). *Methoden der Kristallstructurbestimmung mit Röntgenstrahlen*, by Ernst Schiebold. Vol. 1, *Die Lauemethode*, 183 pp., Leipzig, 1932.

Schmeisser (1794–1795). *A System of Mineralogy, Formed Chiefly in the Plan of Cronstedt*, by Johann Gottfried Schmeisser. 2 volumes, 8vo, London, 1794–1795.

Schmidt and Baier (1935). *Lehrbuch der Mineralogie*, by Walter Schmidt and E. Baier. 320 pp., Berlin, 1935.

Schneiderhöhn (1922). *Anleitung zur mikroskopischen Bestimmung von Erzen und Aufbereitungsprodukten, besonders im auffallenden Licht*, by Hans Schneiderhöhn. 292 pp., 8vo, Berlin, 1922.

Schneiderhöhn and Ramdohr (1931). *Lehrbuch der Erzmikroskopie*, by Hans Schneiderhöhn and Paul Ramdohr. 2 volumes: vol. 1, 312 pp. (general); vol. 2, 714 pp., 1931 (descriptive). With sep. bound determinative tables. Berlin.

Schoenflies (1923). *Theorie der Kristallstruktur; ein Lehrbuch*, by Artur Schoenflies. 555 pp., Berlin, 1923.

Schrauf (1864). *Atlas der Krystall-Formen des Mineralreiches*, by Albrecht Schrauf. 4to, with 50 tables, Vienna, 1864.

────── (1866, 1868). *Lehrbuch der physikalischen Mineralogie.* Vol. 1, 253 pp., 8vo 1866; vol. 2, 426 pp., 1868; Vienna.

Schulze (1895). *Lithia Hercynica. Verzeichnis der Minerale des Harzes und seines Vorlandes*, by E. Schulze. 192 pp., Leipzig, 1896.

Schütz (1791). *Beschreibung einiger nordamerikanischen Fossilien*, by A. G. Schütz. 16mo, Leipzig, 1791.

Scopoli (1776). *Crystallographia Hungarica.* Pars I, " Exhibens crystallos indolis terrae cum figuris rariorum," by Giovanni Antonio Scopoli. 139 pp., Prague, 1776.

Sella (1856). *Studii sulla Mineralogia Sarda*, by Quintino Sella. 4to, Turin, 1856.

Selle (1878). *Cours de minéralogie et de géologie*, by Albert de Selle. Vol. 1, *Minéralogie*, 589 pp., 8vo, Paris, 1878.

Senft (1875). *Synopsis der Mineralogie und Geognosie*, by F. Senft. Pt. 1, " Mineralogie," 931 pp., 8vo, Hannover, 1875.

Shannon (1926). " The Minerals of Idaho," by Earl V. Shannon. *U. S. Nat. Mus., Bull. 131*, 1926.

Shepard (1832–1857). *Treatise on Mineralogy*, by C. U. Shepard. First edition: vol. 1, New Haven, 1832, vol. 2, 3, 1835; second edition, 1844; third edition: vol. 1, 1852, vol. 2, 1857.

────── (1837). *Report on the Geological Survey of Connecticut.* 8vo, New Haven.

Short (1931). " Microscopic Determination of the Ore Minerals," by Max N. Short. First edition, *U. S. Geol. Sur. Bull. 825*, 1931. A mimeographed revision of the determinative tables appeared in 1934. Second edition, *U. S. Geol. Sur., Bull.* 914, 1940.

Simpson (1932). *A Key to Mineral Groups, Species and Varieties,* by Edward Sydney Simpson. 84 pp., London, 1932.

Smith (1940). *Gemstones,* by George Frederick Herbert Smith. Ninth edition, 443 pp., London, 1940. First edition in 1912.

Sohncke (1879). *Entwickelung einer Theorie der Krystallstruktur,* by L. Sohncke. 247 pp., 8vo, Leipzig, 1879.

Sommerfeldt (1906). *Geometrische Kristallographie,* by Ernst Sommerfeldt. 139 pp., Leipzig, 1906.

———— **(1907).** *Physikalische Kristallographie.* 131 pp., Leipzig, 1907.

———— **(1911).** *Die Kristallgruppen, nebst ihren Beziehungen zu den Raumgittern.* 79 pp., Dresden, 1911.

Sosman (1927). *The Properties of Silica,* by Robert Browning Sosman. 856 pp., New York, 1927.

Souza-Brandão (1906). *Elementos de mineralogia e geologia,* by Vincente Souza-Brandão. 209 pp., Lisbon, 1906.

Sowerby (1850). *Popular Mineralogy,* by Henry Sowerby. 344 pp., London, 1850.

Sowerby (1804–17). *British Mineralogy, or Coloured Figures Intended to Elucidate the Mineralogy of Great Britain,* by J. Sowerby. 5 volumes, London, 1804–17.

Spencer (1911). *The World's Minerals,* by Leonard James Spencer. 272 pp., New York, 1911. *See also* **Bauer** and **Brauns.**

———— **(1936).** *A Key to Precious Stones.* 237 pp., London, 1936.

Steffens (1811–1819). *Handbuch der Oryktognosie,* by H. Steffens. 3 volumes, 18mo: vol. 1, 1811; vol. 2, 1815; vol. 3, 1819; Halle.

Stelzner-Bergeat (1904–06). *Die Erzlagerstätten,* by Alfred Wilhelm Stelzner. Edited by Bergeat. 2 volumes, 1330 pp., Leipzig, 1904–06.

Stillwell (1938). *Crystal Chemistry,* by Charles W. Stillwell. 431 pp., New York, 1938.

Story-Maskelyne (1895). *Crystallography.* A treatise on the morphology of crystals, by Nevil Story-Maskelyne. 521 pp., Oxford, 1895.

Stromeyer (1821). *Untersuchung über die Mischung der Mineralkörper, etc.,* by Fr. Stromeyer. 8vo, Göttingen, 1821.

Strukturber. *Strukturbericht (Ergänzungsband der Zeitschrift für Kristallographie).* Vol. 1, 818 pp., for 1913–1928 (1931), by P. Niggli, P. P. Ewald, K. Fajans, M. von Laue; vol. 2, 963 pp., for 1928–1932 (1937), by C. Hermann, O. Lohrmann, H. Phillip; vol. 3, 901 pp., for 1933–1935 (1937), by C. Gottfried and F. Schlossberger; vol. 4, for 1936 (1938), by C. Gottfried; vol. 5, for 1937 (1940), by C. Gottfried.

Stutzer (1911–1938). *Die wichtigsten Lagerstätten der "Nicht-erze,"* by Otto Stutzer. 6 volumes, Berlin, 1911–1938.

Sutton (1928). *Diamond,* a descriptive treatise, by J. R. Sutton. 114 pp., London, 1928.

Tchirvinsky (1903–06). *Réproduction artificielle de minéraux au XIXème siècle,* by Peter Tchirvinsky. 638 + LXXXVIII, Kieff, 1903–1906. In Russian.

Terpstra (1927). *Leerboek der geometrische Kristallografie,* by Pieter Terpstra. 302 pp., Groningen, 1927.

Tertsch (1926). *Trachten der Kristalle,* by Hermann Tertsch. 222 pp., Berlin, 1926.

———— **(1935).** *Das Kristallenzeichnen auf Grundlage der stereographischen Projektion.* Vienna, 1935.

Theophrastus (circa 315 B.C.). περι λιθων (on Stones). Written about 315 B.C. Only a portion of the whole work is extant.

Thomson (1836). *Outlines of Mineralogy, Geology, and Mineral Analysis,* by

T. Thomson, 2 volumes, London, 1836. A treatise on mineralogy was published also with preceding editions of his work on chemistry, the earliest in 1802.

Traube (1888). *Die Minerale Schlesiens*, by H. Traube. 285 pp., 8vo, Breslau, 1888.

Tschermak (1885–1921). *Lehrbuch der Mineralogie*, by Gustav Tschermak. Second edition, 597 pp., 8vo, Vienna, 1885; eighth edition by F. Becke, 751 pp., Vienna and Leipzig, 1921.

Tutton (1911). *Crystals*, by A. E. H. Tutton. 301 pp., London, 1911.

——— **(1911)A.** *Crystallography and Practical Crystal Measurement.* 946 pp., London, 1911; second edition: vol. 1 (Form and Structure), vol. 2 (Physical and Chemical), 1446 pp., London, 1922.

——— **(1924).** *The Natural History of Crystals.* 287 pp., London and New York, 1924.

——— **(1926).** *Crystalline Form and Chemical Constitution.* 252 pp., New York, 1926.

Ullmann (1814). *Systematisch-Tabellarische Uebersicht der min.-einfachen Fossilien*, by J. C. Ullmann. Small 4to, Cassel and Marburg, 1814.

Ulrich (1870). *Contributions to the Mineralogy of Victoria*, by G. H. F. Ulrich. 32 pp., 8vo, Melbourne, 1870.

Van der Veen (1925). *Mineragraphy and Ore Deposition*, by Rudolf Willem van der Veen. 168 pp., The Hague 1925.

Vernadsky (1908–1918). *Descriptive Mineralogy*, by W. Vernadsky. Vol. 1 (Native Elements), 839 pp., 1908–1914; vol. 2, (S and Se compounds), 1918.

Viola (1904). *Grundzüge der Kristallographie*, by Carlo Maria Viola. 389 pp., Leipsig, 1904.

Vogt (1903–1904). *Die Silikatschmelzlösungen mit besonderer Rücksicht auf die Mineralbildung und die Schmelzpunkterniedrigung*, by J. H. L. Vogt. Kristiania, 1903–1904. (Videnskabs-Selskabets Skrifter, Math.-Nat. Kl.: no. 8, 161 pp., 1903; no. 1, 235 pp., 1904.)

——— **(1924–1931).** *The Physical Chemistry of the Magmatic Differentiation of Igneous Rocks.* Oslo, 1924–31. (Videnskapsselskapets Skrifter, Math.-Nat. Kl.: no. 15, 132 pp. 1924; no. 4, 101 pp., 1926; no. 6, 131 pp. 1929; no. 3, 242 pp., 1930.)

Voigt (1928). *Lehrbuch der Kristallphysik*, by Woldemar Voigt. 978 pp., Leipzig, 1928.

Volger (1854). *Studien zur Entwicklungsgeschichte der Mineralien*, by G. H. O. Volger. 8vo, Zurich, 1854.

Wada (1904, 1905–1915, 1935). *Minerals of Japan*, by Tsunashiro Wada. 144 pp., Tokyo, 1904. A supplement (*Beiträge zur Mineralogie von Japan*, no. 1–5), 1905–15, Tokyo (1915?). Also a new series (*Beiträge . . . Japan*), edited by T. Ito, Tokyo; I, 1935; II, 1937.

Wadsworth (1909). *Crystallography*, by M. E. Wadsworth. 299 pp., Philadelphia, 1909.

Wagner (1929). *The Platinum Deposits and Mines of South Africa*, by Percy A. Wagner. With a chapter on the " Mineragraphy and Spectrography of the Sulphidic Platinum Ores of the Bushveld Complex," by H. Schneiderhöhn. 326 pp., Edinburgh, 1929.

Walker (1914). *Crystallography, an Outline of the Geometrical Properties of Crystals*, by Thomas Leonard Walker. 204 pp., New York, 1914.

Wallerant (1891). *Traité de minéralogie*, by Frederic Wallerant. 459 pp., Paris, 1891.

——— **(1909).** *Cristallographie.* 523 pp., Paris, 1909.

Wallerius (1747). *Mineralogia, eller Mineralriket*, by J. G. Wallerius. 12mo, Stockholm, 1747.

——— **(1753).** French edition of the foregoing work. 2 volumes, 8vo, Paris, 1753.

—— (1772, 1775). *Systema mineralogicum.* 8vo, Holmiae; vol. 1, 1772; vol. 2, 1775.

—— (1778). *Systema mineralogicum.* 2 volumes, 8vo, Vienna, 1778.

—— (1779). *Brevis introductio in historiam litterariam mineralogicam atque methodum systemata mineralogica.* Holmiae, 1779.

Weisbach (1875–1884). *Synopsis mineralogica, systematische Übersicht des Mineralreiches,* by Albin Weisbach. 78 pp., 8vo, Freiberg, 1875; second edition, 1884.

—— (1880). *Characteristik d. Classen etc. d. Mineralreiches.* 57 pp., 8vo, Freiberg, 1880.

—— (1892). *Tabellen zur Bestimmung der mineralien Mittels ausserer Kennzeichen.* Fourth edition, 106 pp., Leipzig, 1892.

Weiser (1933, 1935, 1938). *Inorganic Colloid Chemistry,* by Harry Boyer Weiser. 3 volumes: vol. 1, *The Colloidal Elements,* 389 pp., 1933; vol. 2, *The Hydrous Oxides and Hydroxides,* 429 pp., 1935; vol. 3, *The Colloidal Salts,* 473 pp., 1938. New York.

Wells (1937). *Analyses of Rocks and Minerals from the Laboratory of the U. S. Geol. Sur.,* 1914–1936. Tabulated by Roger C. Wells, *U. S. Geol. Sur., Bull.* 878, 1937.

Werner (1774). *Von d. äusserlichen Kennzeichen d. Fossilien,* by A. G. Werner. Leipzig.

—— (1780). *Cronstedt's Versuch einer Mineralogie, Übersetzt und Vermehrt.* Vol. 1, pt. 1, Leipzig, 1780.

—— (1791, 1793). *Verzeichness des Mineralien-Kabinets des Herrn K. E. Pabst von Ohain.* 2 volumes, Freiberg, 1791, 1793.

—— (1817). *Letztes Mineral-System.* Freiberg and Vienna. A catalogue with notes. Werner and his scholars issued from time to time a tabular synopsis of his Mineral System revised to the time of publication, on folio sheets, or published them in other works. The earliest after that of Werner's Cronstedt was issued by Hoffmann in *Bergm. J.,* **1,** 369 (1789). Emmerling's *Lehrbuch der Mineralogie,* vol. 1, 1799, contains the synopsis of 1798 and Ludwig's *Handbuch der Mineralogie* contains that of 1800 and 1803. Leonhard's *Tasch.,* vol. 3, p. 261, that of 1809.

Whewell (1828). *An Essay on Mineralogical Classification and Nomenclature; with Tables of the Orders and Species of Minerals,* by William Whewell. 71 pp., Cambridge, 1828.

Wiik (1881). *Mineral-Karakteristik. En Handlednung vid Bestämmandet af Mineralier och Bergarter,* by F. J. Wiik. 218 pp., 12mo, Helsingfors, 1881.

Williams (1932). *The Genesis of the Diamond,* by Alpheus F. Williams. 2 volumes, 636 pp., London, 1932.

Williams (1892). *Elements of Crystallography for Students of Chemistry, Physics and Mineralogy,* by George Huntington Williams. Third edition, 270 pp., New York, 1892.

Winchell (1929–1937). *Elements of Optical Mineralogy,* by Alexander Winchell. Pt. 1, " Principles and Methods," fifth edition, 305 pp., 1937; pt. 2, " Descriptions of Minerals," third edition, 459 pp., 1933; pt. 3, " Determinative Tables," first edition, 204 pp., 1929. New York.

—— (1931). *The Microscopic Characters of Artificial Inorganic Solid Substances or Artificial Minerals.* Second edition, 403 pp., New York and London, 1931.

Withering (1783). *Outlines of Mineralogy.* A translation of Bergmann's *Sciagraphia* by Wm. Withering. 8vo, London, 1783.

Woodward (1714). *Naturalis historia telluris illustrata et aucta,* by J. Woodward. 8vo, London, 1714. Also German (Erfurt, 1744) and French (Paris, 1753) translations.

—— (1728). *Fossils of All Kinds Digested into a Method Suitable to Their Mutual Relation and Affinity.* 8vo, London, 1728.

—————— **(1729).** *An Attempt towards a Natural History of the Fossils of England.* 2 volumes, London, 1728–29 (posthumous).

Wooster (1938). *A Textbook on Crystal Physics,* by W. A. Wooster. 295 pp., Cambridge (England), 1938.

Wright (1911). *The Methods of Petrographic-Microscopic Research, Their Relative Accuracy and Range of Application,* by Frederic Eugene Wright. *Carnegie Institution of Washington, Pub. 158,* 204 pp., Washington, 1911.

Wyckoff (1930). *The Analytical Expression of the Results of the Theory of Space Groups,* by Ralph W. G. Wyckoff. *Carnegie Institution of Washington, Pub., 318,* 239 pp., second edition, Washington, 1930.

—————— **(1931–1935).** *The Structure of Crystals. Am. Chem. Soc. Mon. Series,* first edition, 462 pp., 1924; second edition, 497 pp., 1931. Supplement to second edition, 240 pp., 1935.

Wyrouboff (1889). *Manuel pratique de crystallographie,* by Grégoire Wyrouboff. 344 pp., Paris, 1889.

Zambonini (1910). *Mineralogia Vesuviana,* by Ferruccio Zambonini. 368 pp., 4to, Naples, 1910; with an appendix, 51 pp., 1912; second edition with Quercigh, 463 pp., 4to, Naples, 1935.

Zepharovich (1859, 1873). *Mineralogisches Lexicon fur das Kaiserthum Oesterreich,* by V. R. von Zepharovich. Vol. 1, 8vo, Vienna, 1859; vol. 2, 1873.

Zippe (1839). *Physiographie des Mineralreichs,* by F. X. M. Zippe. Vienna, 1839.

—————— **(1859).** *Lehrbuch der Mineralogie.* 435 pp., 8vo, Vienna, 1859.

15. Abbreviations

Å	Ångstrom units (10^{-8} cm.)
a_{rh}	Rhombohedral cell edge
Alter.	Alteration
Anal.	Analyses or analyst
Artif.	Artificial
Ax. pl.	Optic axial plane
B. B.	Before the blowpipe
B. P.	Boiling point
Bx_a	Acute bisectrix
Bx. or Biax.	Biaxial
Calc.	Calculated
Chem.	Chemistry
F.	Fusibility
G.	Specific gravity
H.	Hardness
M. P.	Melting point
n	Refractive index
O. F.	Oxidizing flame
priv. comm.	Private communication
pt.	Part, in part
Ref.	Reference
R. F.	Reducing flame
Var.	Varieties
a, b, c	Linear crystallographic axes
a_0, b_0, c_0	Absolute unit cell axes
p_0, q_0, r_0	Polar crystallographic axes
p_0', q_0', r_0'	Gnomonic projection elements
α, β, γ	Crystallographic axial angles
$2E, 2V$	Optic axial angle in air, and in the mineral respectively
$m\mu$	Millimicrons = 10^{-7} cm. = 10Å
O	Ordinary ray, refractive index
E	Extraordinary ray, refractive index
λ	Wavelength
X, Y, Z	Indicatrix directions

DESCRIPTIVE MINERALOGY
GENERAL CLASSIFICATION

CLASS 1. Native elements

Type
1. Metals
2. Non-metals and semi-metals

CLASS 2. Sulfides, including selenides, tellurides

Type
1. $A_m X_n$ where $m : n > 3 : 1$ 6. AX
2. A_3X 7. A_3X_4
3. A_2X 8. A_2X_3
4. A_3X_2 9. AX_2
5. A_4X_3 10. AX_3

CLASS 3. Sulfosalts

Type
1. $A_m B_n X_p$ where $m + n : p > 4 : 3$ 6. $A_2B_2X_5$
2. A_3BX_3 7. $A_2B_3X_6$
3. A_3BX_4 8. AB_2X_4
4. A_2BX_3 9. AB_4X_7
5. ABX_2

CLASS 4. Simple oxides

Type
1. A_2X 4. A_2X_3
2. AX 5. AX_2
3. A_3X_4 6. $A_m X_n$ Miscellaneous

CLASS 5. Oxides containing uranium, thorium, and zirconium

Type
1. AX_2 2. $AX_3 \cdot nH_2O$ 3. Miscellaneous

CLASS 6. Hydroxides and oxides containing hydroxyl

Type
1. AX_2
2. AX_3

CLASS 7. Multiple oxides

Type
1. ABX_2 5. A_2BX_5
2. AB_2X_4 6. AB_2X_5
3. AB_4X_7 7. AB_3X_7
4. ABX_3

CLASS 8. Multiple oxides containing columbium, tantalum, and titanium

1 NATIVE ELEMENTS

11 METALS

111   GOLD GROUP

1111   Gold
1112   Maldonite
1113   Silver
1114   Copper
1115   Lead

112   Mercury
113   Moschellandsbergite
114   Gold amalgam
115   Potarite

116   PLATINUM GROUP

1161   Platinum
1162   Palladium
1163   Platiniridium ·
1164   Aurosmiridium
1165   Iridosmine
1166   Siserskite
1167   Allopalladium

117   IRON GROUP AND METEORITES

1171   Iron
1172   Nickel-iron
1173   Cohenite
1174   Moissanite
1175   Osbornite
1176   Schreibersite
1177   Siderazot
118   Tantalum
119   Tin
11·10   Zinc

12 SEMI-METALS AND NON-METALS

121   ARSENIC GROUP

1211   Arsenic
1212   Arsenolamprite
1213   Allemontite
1214   Antimony
1215   Bismuth ·

122   TELLURIUM GROUP

1221   Selenium
1222   Selen-tellurium
1223   Tellurium

123	SULFUR GROUP	
1231	Sulfur	
1232	β-Sulfur	
1233	γ-Sulfur	

124	CARBON GROUP	
1241	Diamond	
1242	Graphite	

111 GOLD GROUP

1111	Gold	Au
1112	Maldonite	Au_2Bi
1113	Silver	Ag
1114	Copper	Cu
1115	Lead	Pb

These native metals are isometric, hexoctahedral — $4/m\,\bar{3}\,2/m$. They are alike in structure (copper type), the atoms lying at the points of a face-centered cubic lattice. This structure conforms to the space group $Fm3m$; the unit cell contains 4 atoms. The cubic cell edges for the pure metals compare as follows.

	Cu	Au	Ag	Pb
a_0	3.6077	4.0699	4.0772	4.9396

Although differing somewhat in crystal habit, all the members of the group show twinning on {111} and a strong tendency to form dendritic and arborescent crystal groups. They are also similar in their physical properties (hardness, malleability, ductility, and conductivity of heat and electricity.)

The variations in the compositions of the native metals correspond in a measure to the different degrees of mutual solubility of the end members in the artificial binary systems. Gold and silver are most nearly alike; they form a continuous series with a minimum cell edge at 20 per cent Ag[1] (electrum). Gold and copper show complete mutual solubility.[2] Silver and copper, on the other hand, are practically mutually insoluble.[3] Gold and silver form continuous series with palladium,[4] the gold-palladium series being represented by porpezite. Gold will take some rhodium into solid solution, much less than the reported rhodium content of rhodite; silver will not hold rhodium in solid solution.[5] Gold takes mercury up to 16.5 per cent at 90° (mercurian gold); silver will dissolve up to 45 per cent of mercury[6] (mercurian silver). Gold dissolves less than 0.2 per cent of bismuth;[7] some of the reported natural bismuthian gold appears to be an intermetallic compound, Au_2Bi (maldonite). Silver will dissolve about 5 per cent of antimony[8] (antimonian silver), and about 7 per cent of arsenic[9] (arsenian silver). Copper takes about 4 per cent of arsenic.[10]

Ref.

1. Sachs and Weerts, Zs. Phys., **60**, 481 (1930).
2. Vegard and Kloster, Zs. Kr., **89**, 560 (1934); Strukturber., 504, 1913–28 and 615, 1928–32.

3. Owen and Rogers, *J. Inst. Met.*, **57**, 257 (1935).
4. McKeehan, *Phys. Rev.*, **20**, 424 (1922); Holgersson and Sedström, *Ann. Phys.*, **75**, 143 (1924).
5. Drier and Walker, *Phil. Mag.*, **16**, 294 (1933).
6. Stenbeck, *Zs. anorg. Chem.*, **214**, 16 (1933); Murphy, *J. Inst. Met., Proc.*, **46**, 507 (1931).
7. Jurriaanse, *Zs. Kr.*, **90**, 322 (1935).
8. Guertler, *Metallographie*, **1**, 769 (1912, Berlin); Peacock, *Univ. Toronto Stud., Geol. Ser.*, **44**, 31 (1940); Broderick and Ehret, *J. Phys. Chem.*, **35**, 3322 (1931).
9. Broderick and Ehret (1931).
10. Ramsdell, *Am. Min.*, **14**, 188 (1929).

1111 **GOLD** [Au]. Sol *Alchem.* Gediegen Gold *Germ.* Gediget Guld *Swed.* Or natif *Fr.* Oro nativo *Ital., Span.* Electrum *Pliny* (33, 23, A.D. 77). Porpezite *Fröbel* (in Dana [15, 1892]). Rhodite *Adam* (83, 1869).

C r y s t. Isometric; hexoctahedral — $4/m\,\bar{3}\,2/m$.

Forms:[1]

$a\{001\}$ $d\{011\}$ $o\{111\}$ $e\{012\}$ $m\{113\}$ $x\{1\cdot10\cdot18\}$ $t\{124\}$

Structure cell.[2] Space group $Fm3m$; a_0 4.0699 ± 0.0003 (18°); contains 4Au.

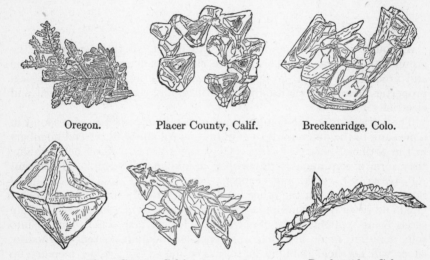

Oregon.   Placer County, Calif.   Breckenridge, Colo.

Placer County, Calif.   Breckenridge, Colo.

Habit. Octahedral; dodecahedral; cubic. Common forms: *o d a m.* Often elongated with [111]; flattened on {111}. In parallel groups and twinned aggregates branching at 60° parallel to the edges or the diagonals of the faces of {111}. Commonly reticulated, dendritic, arborescent, filiform, spongy. Also massive, in rounded fragments, flattened grains, scales.

Twinning. On {111}, common, usually repeated to give reticulated and dendritic aggregates.

P h y s. Cleavage none. Fracture hackly. Very malleable and ductile. H. 2½–3. G. 19.3; 19.309 (calc., 0°). M.P. 1062.4° ± 0.8.[3] Color and streak gold-yellow when pure; silver-white to orange-red in impure varieties. Luster metallic. Opaque in all but thinnest folia which transmit blue and green light. Polished surfaces brilliant gold-yellow, varying with silver content; isotropic; highly reflecting. Percentage reflection in air,[4] green, 47.0; orange, 82.5; red, 86.

m(113) Oregon.

C h e m. Gold, Au, with varying amounts of silver; also copper, iron; rarely bismuth, tin, lead, zinc, platinum, palladium, iridium, rhodium (?).

Anal.[5]

	1	2	3	4	5	6
Au	99.91	90.99	94.22	74.33	85.21	73.54
Ag	[0.09]	3.53	2.84	4.49	14.71	20.92
Cu	......	5.32	0.11	20.39	.....	4.27
Fe	......	0.07	......	.....	.....	.....
Bi	......	......	2.92	.....	.....	.....
Sn	......	......	......	.....	.....	0.28
Pb	......	......	......	.....	.....	0.20
Zn	......	......	......	.....	.....	0.77
Insol.	......	......	......	0.26	.....	.....
Total	100.00	99.91	100.09	99.47	99.92	99.98
G.		17.587	18.22	15.17	16.90	

1. Sponge gold, Kalgoorlie.[6] 2. Borneo.[7] 3. SchilowoÏssetsky mine, R. Issét, Schilowa, W. of Kamenskij Zavod, Russia.[8] 4. Mt. Karabasch, E. of Sojmanowschen Valley, Urals.[9] 5. Ostrig Bugöz, W. Nagolnij Krajsch, Don basin, Russia.[10] 6. Electrum, West Africa.[11]

Var. *Argentian.* Electrum *Pliny* (33, 23, A.D. 77).

Ag substitutes for Au and a complete series[12] extends through aurian silver to silver. Ordinarily gold carries up to 10–15 per cent of Ag. The color ranges from deep gold-yellow to pale yellow and yellowish white with increase in silver content. The name electrum (from ἤλεκτρον, *amber,* in allusion to the color) has been applied to gold with 20 per cent or more of silver (Pliny).

Palladian. Porpezite *Fröbel* (in Dana [53, 1892]). Gold containing 5 to 10 weight per cent Pd in solid solution has been reported from " Porpez " (Pompeo ?), Taguaril and other localities in Minas Geraes and Goyaz, Brazil.[13]

Rhodian. Rhodite *Adam* (83, 1869); *del Rio* (*Ann. chim. phys.*, **29**, 137, 1825). Gold containing 34 to 43 weight per cent Rh has been reported from Colombia and Mexico. G. 15.5–16.8. Brittle. Not confirmed.[14]

Cuprian. Possibly contains Cu in substitution for Au to at least 20 per cent (anal. 4).[15]

Bismuthian. Gold containing several per cent of Bi, possibly in solid solution,[16] has been reported (anal. 3). Maldonite (which see) is not here included.

Tests. B.B. fuses easily (1100°). Not acted on by fluxes. Insoluble in acids except aqua regia, the separation not being complete if more than 20 per cent of silver is present.

O c c u r.[17] Gold in common with other elements is widely distributed in small amounts in all igneous rocks and in sea water. The order of concentration is 6 parts in a hundred million. The element is combined in nature only with tellurium (and possibly with selenium and bismuth, as in some of the seleniferous gold deposits [Boliden, Sweden]). The small amount of gold in the igneous rocks is therefore in the native state. In auriferous sulfides the gold is not in chemical combination. Gold occurs in notable amounts in three main types of deposit: in veins of hydrothermal and related origin, in consolidated placer deposits, in unconsolidated placer deposits. The last two types are derived from the first by degradational geologic processes.

Most vein gold is associated with quartz and pyrite. In pegmatites gold is reported with typical granite pegmatite minerals together with scheelite (Natas mine, South-West Africa); in contact metamorphic deposits with pyrite, pyrrhotite, chalcopyrite and other sulfides in a quartz-calcite-garnet gangue (Cable, Montana); in the so-called hypothermal deposits, which include many of the important mines of the world, with pyrite or pyrrhotite and other sulfides, sylvanite, krennerite, calaverite, altaite, scheelite, ankerite, tourmaline. In quartz veins (Porcupine, Ontario; Homestake mine, Lead, South Dakota; Morro Velho, Minas Geraes); in less deep-seated deposits of quartz veins, with ankerite, sericite (Mother Lode; Bendigo); in shallow vein deposits with tellurides, pyrite, bismuthinite (Goldfield; Cripple Creek).

In placer deposits gold is found as rounded or flattened grains and nuggets associated with the other heavy resistant minerals of the concentrates. In buried consolidated placers the same association holds. Most of the early gold workings were of the placer type and only within recent times have vein deposits become of greater importance as a source of the metal.

Europe. The gold districts are the Urals, the Balkans, and the less important Alpine region reaching from Carinthia through the Austrian Tirol and the Italian Alps to the Pyrenees. The most important European district is in Transylvania, in the southeast portion of the Bihar Mountains. The important centers are Verespátak (Rosa Montană), Nagyág (Săcărâmb), Botés, Brad, Baita, where the gold is in veins or pipes in or near volcanic vents, and is associated with sylvanite, nagyagite, petzite in quartz.

Asia. In Siberia gold is found on the eastern slope of the Ural Mountains for a distance of 500 miles. The important districts are Bogoslovsk, Nizhne Tagilsk, Beresovsk, and other localities near Ekaterinburg,

Syssertsk, and Kyshtymsk, and Miask district including Slatoust and Mount Ilmen, Kotchkar, and, at the southern limit of the fields, Orsk. Siberia also has the important placer districts in Tomsk, which includes Altai and Marinsk, and in Yeniseisk, the Achinsk, Minusinsk, and the north and south Yenisei districts. Farther east there are deposits in Transbaikalia and the Lena district in Yakutsk. In India the chief districts are the Kolar field near Bangalore in Mysore and the Gadag and Hutti districts to the northwest. Gold has been mined in China in Chihli, Shantung, Weihaiwei, Szechwan, and Fukien. In Manchuria on the Liaotung Peninsula. In Korea principally at Un-San. Gold-quartz veins, many of which have been worked for a long time, occur on a number of the Japanese islands.

Australasia. The most important districts in New Zealand lie on the Hauraki Peninsula with the Waihi mine as the most famous. Other districts are the West Coast area on the western slopes of the Alps of the South Island and the Otago area. In Queensland the districts of Charters Towers and the Mount Morgan mine are important. There are many gold districts in New South Wales among which are Hillgrove, Mount Boppy, and Hill End. Rich districts in Victoria are the Bendigo and Ballarat. The principal gold fields of Tasmania are Beaconsfield, Mathinna, and the copper deposits of Mount Lyell. The chief gold field in Western Australia is near Kalgoorlie where the ores are largely tellurides. Large nuggets have been reported from Australia; one found in 1858 weighed 184 lb., another found in 1869 weighed 190 lb. Masses of over 200 lb. have been reported in quartz veins from Hill End, New South Wales.

Africa. Gold is found in Egypt in the section between the Nile and the Red Sea. Some of these deposits were worked in very early days. Gold has been produced for a long time from the Gold Coast district on the Gulf of Guinea. Important deposits are found in Matabeleland and Mashonaland in Southern Rhodesia. The most important gold district in the world is that of the Witwatersrand in the Transvaal. The mines occur in an east and west belt, some 60 miles in length, near Johannesburg. The gold is found scattered in small amounts, with pyrite through a series of steeply dipping quartz conglomerate rocks.

South America. Colombia has in the past produced large amounts of gold. The chief districts today are in the states of Antioquia and Cauca. Comparatively small amounts are produced in the other northern countries. The important deposits of Brazil lie 200 miles to the northwest of Rio de Janeiro in Minas Geraes along the Sierra do Espinhaço. The gold deposits of Chile lie chiefly in the coast ranges in the northern and central parts of the country.

Mexico. While Mexico is chiefly noteworthy for its silver output it also produces considerable gold. Important districts are as follows: Altar, Magdalena, and Arizpe in Sonora; various places in Chihuahua, especially about Parral and the Dolores mine on the western border of the state; the El Oro mines in the state of Mexico; the Pachuca district in Hidalgo; also various places in Guanajuato and Zacatecas.

Canada. The three important placer districts of Canada are the Klondike in Yukon Territory and the Atlin and Cariboo in British Columbia. One of the most productive regions of the world lies in eastern Ontario in the Porcupine district, with the Hollinger, McIntyre, and Dome mines as the most important of the region, and many others scattered throughout the Canadian Shield. Here the gold occurs in the veins and adjacent wall rock, associated with sulfides, tellurides, scheelite, quartz, ankerite, albite, tourmaline, and chlorite.

United States. Gold occurs in the United States chiefly along the mountain ranges in the western states. Smaller amounts have been found along the Appalachians in the states of Virginia, North and South Carolina, and Georgia. The more important localities in the western states are given below, the states being arranged approximately in the order of their importance. In California at the present time about two-thirds of the state's output comes from the lode mines and one-third from placer deposits. The quartz veins are chiefly found in what is known as the Mother-Lode belt that lies on the western slope of the Sierra Nevada and stretches from Mariposa County for more than 100 miles toward the north. The veins occur chiefly in a belt of slates. The mines are found chiefly in Amador, Calaveras, Eldorado, Kern, Nevada, Shasta, Sierra, and Tuolumne counties. Crystals have been noted at localities in Amador, Eldorado, and Trinity counties. About 90 per cent of the placer gold is obtained by the use of dredges. In South Dakota the output is chiefly from the Homestake mine at Lead in Lawrence County. In Alaska the most important lode mines are in the Juneau district, while the chief placer deposits are those of Fairbanks and Iditarod in the Yukon basin and the now nearly exhausted Nome district on the Seward Peninsula. In Colorado gold is mined in various districts in Gilpin County, from the Leadville district and others in Lake County, in the region of the San Juan Mountains in the Sneffels, Silverton, and Telluride districts, Cripple Creek district (telluride ores) in Teller County, placer deposits in the Breckenridge district in Summit County. In Utah gold is chiefly produced from the Bingham and Tintic districts in Salt Lake County and from Juab County. In Nevada the most important districts are those of Goldfield in Esmeralda County and Tonapah in Nye County. In Arizona much of the gold output comes from the copper ores of the state, also from placer deposits. The important counties are Mohave and Cochise. In Idaho gold is produced from various lead deposits and from dredging of placer deposits. Important districts are found in Elmore, Idaho, and Valley counties. In Montana the greater part of the gold output comes from the district about Butte, Silver Bow County. Other deposits are located in Beaverhead, Madison, and Broadwater counties.

Alter. Native gold has been found as spongy alteration pseudomorphs after calaverite (Cripple Creek, Colorado).

Artif.[18] Obtained in crystals by the action of heat or acids on gold amalgam, and variously by the reduction of solutions of gold salts.

Ref.

1. Goldschmidt (4, 75, 1918); Ungemach, *Bull. soc. min.*, **39**, 5 (1916). Rare or uncertain: 014, 013, 025, 118, 114, 112, 223, 3·5·11, 237, 123, 345.
2. Owen and Yates, *Phil. Mag.*, **15**, 472 (1933), on spectroscopically pure gold.
3. Day and Sosman, *Am. J. Sc.*, **29**, 93 (1910).
4. Schneiderhöhn and Ramdohr, **2**, 64 (1931).
5. For additional analyses see Doelter, **3** [2], 187 (1922).
6. Simpson anal. in Krusch, *Zs. pr. Geol.*, **11**, 331 (1903).
7. Chernik, *Ac. sc. St. Pétersbourg, Trav. Mus. géol.*, **6**, 78 (1912).
8. Nenadkewitsch, *Ac. sc. St. Pétersbourg, Trav. Mus. géol.*, **1**, 81 (1907).
9. Nenadkewitsch, *Zs. Kr.*, **53**, 609 (1914).
10. Samojloff, *Zs. Kr.*, **46**, 286 (1909).
11. Wibel, *Nat. Ver. Hamburg*, **2**, 87 (1852).
12. See Weiss, *Roy. Soc. London, Proc.*, **108**, 643 (1925), on artificial Au-Ag alloys.
13. See Ferraz (326, 1929). A complete series exists between Au and Pd in the artificial system; see Holgersson and Sedström, *Ann. Phys.*, **75**, 143 (1924).
14. Drier and Walker, *Phil. Mag.*, **16**, 294 (1933) report a maximum solubility of about 4.1 atomic per cent Rh in Au in the artificial system.
15. A complete series exists between Au and Cu in the artificial system; see *Strukturber.*, 504, 1913–26; 615, 1928–32.
16. Jurriaanse, *Zs. Kr.*, **90**, 322 (1935), reports the solubility of Bi in Au to be less than 0.2 atomic per cent, in the artificial system.
17. See Emmons (*Gold Deposits of the World*, New York, 1937); Lindgren (1933); Lincoln, *Econ. Geol.*, **6**, 247 (1911).
18. Doelter (1922).

1112 **Maldonite** [Au_2Bi]. Bismuthic gold ? *Shepard* (*Am. J. Sc.*, 4, 280, 1847); Bismuthaurite ? *Shepard* (*Am. J. Sc.*, **24**, 112, 281, 1857). Maldonite *Ulrich* (4, 1870). Bismuth-gold. Black-gold.

Cryst.[3] Isometric; hexoctahedral — $4/m\,\bar{3}\,2/m$ (?) (artif.)

Structure cell.[3] Space group probably $Fd3m$; a_0 7.942 ± 0.002; contains $Au_{16}Bi_8$.

Habit. Massive granular, and in thin coatings. Also as octahedral crystals (artif.).

Phys. Cleavage {001} distinct.[4] Malleable and sectile.[5] H. $1\frac{1}{2}$–2. G. 15.46 (artif.);[6] 15.70 (calc.). M.P. 373°.[6] Luster metallic. Color pinkish silver-white on fresh fracture, tarnishing copper-red to black.

Chem. An intermetallic compound, Au_2Bi.
Anal.

	1	2	3
Au	65.36	64.5	65.12
Bi	34.64	35.5	34.88
Total	100.00	100.0	100.00

1. Au_2Bi. 2. Nuggety Reef.[1] 3. Nuggety Reef.[2]

Tests. On charcoal easily fusible giving a white bismuth sublimate and leaving a gold button. Soluble in aqua regia.

O c c u r. At Nuggety Reef, Maldon, Victoria, Australia, with native gold in a greisen-like zone or vein in granite. Also in the Eagle Hawk mine, Union Reef, Maldon, with scheelite and apatite. A bismuth-gold mineral (*bismuthaurite*) has been said to occur in Rutherford County, North Carolina, but has not been verified.

A r t i f. Observed in the system Au-Bi.

N a m e. From the locality at Maldon, Victoria. The natural material is not certainly the same as the described artificial compound.

Ref.

1. Newberry anal. in Ulrich (1870).
2. McIvor, *Chem. News*, **55**, 191 (1887).
3. From x-ray study by Jurriaanse, *Zs. Kr.*, **90**, 322 (1935), on artificial material.
4. Ulrich (1870). vom Rath (Niederrhein. Ges. Bonn, *Sitzber.*, **34**, 73 [1877]) states that the cleavage of the natural mineral is not cubic but rhombohedral.
5. Artificial Au_2Bi is stated by Jurriaanse (1935) to be very brittle.
6. Jurriaanse (1935) on artificial material.

1113   S I L V E R [Ag]. Luna *Alchem.* Gediegen Silber *Germ.* Gediget Silfver *Swed.* Argent natif *Fr.* Argento nativo *Ital.* Plata nativa *Span.*

Güldisch-Silber *Hausmann* (104, 1813). Küstelite *Breithaupt* (*B. H. Ztg.*, **25**, 169, 1866). Arquerite *Domeyko* (*Ann. mines*, **20**, 268, 1841). Kongsbergite *Pisani* (*C. R.*, **75**, 1274, 1872). Bordosite *Domeyko* (362, 1879). Arseniksilber *Klaproth* (**1**, 183, 1795). Pyritolamprite *Adam* (39, 1869). Chanarcillite *Domeyko* (in Dana [36, 1868]). Arsenargentite *Hannay* (*Min. Mag.*, **1**, 149, 1877). Huntilite *Wurtz* (*Eng. Mining J.*, **27**, 55, 1879). Animikite *Wurtz* (*Eng. Mining J.*, **27**, 55, 1879). Dyscrasite pt. Macfarlanite *Sibley* (*Am. Inst. Min. Eng., Trans.*, **8**, 236, 1880).

C r y s t. Isometric; hexoctahedral — $4/m\,\bar{3}\,2/m$.

Forms:[1]

    $a\{001\}$ $d\{011\}$ $o\{111\}$ $h\{014\}$ $e\{012\}$ $m\{113\}$

Structure.[2] Space group $Fm3m$; a_0 4.0772 ± 0.0002 (18°); contains 4Ag.

Habit. Cubic; octahedral; dodecahedral. Common forms: *a o d m.* In groups of parallel cubic or octahedral individuals. Commonly in variously elongated, reticulated, arborescent and wiry forms.[3] Also massive, in scales, as a coating. The habit is, in general, similar to that of copper and gold.

Twinning. On {111}, common; sometimes in simple pairs; commonly repeated in aggregates radiating along the axes [111]; also in reticulated and dendritic aggregates flattened on {111} and branching at 60°. In fivelings.

P h y s. Cleavage none. Ductile and malleable. Fracture hackly. H. $2\frac{1}{2}$–3. G. 10.1–11.1; 10.5 (pure); 10.497 (calc.). M.P. 960.6°.[4] Luster metallic. Color and streak silver-white; often gray to black due to tarnish. Opaque. In polished section[5] brilliant silver-white, with greatest known reflectivity. Isotropic. Reflection percentages: green 95.5, orange 94, red 93.

Chem. Silver, Ag. Often with much Au or Hg and, less commonly, As, Sb, Bi, Pt, Cu in solid solution.

Anal.

	1	2	3	4	5	6
Ag	98.450	[73.1]	[50.0]	94.94	86.5	69.21
Au	0.004	26.9	50.0	......	.....	.....
Cu	0.011	.....	.....	......	.....	.....
Fe	0.024	.....	.....	......	.....	.....
Sb	0.581	.....	.....	......	.....	.....
Hg	1.130	.....	.....	[5.06]	[13.5]	30.76
Total	100.200	100.0	100.0	100.00	100.0	99.97

1. Kongsberg.[6] 2, 3. Kongsberg.[7] 4. Kongsberg (kongsbergite).[8] 5. Arqueros (arquerite.)[9] 6. Chili (bordosite).[10]

Var. *Aurian.* Güldisch-Silber *Hausmann* (104, 1813). Küstelite *Breithaupt* (*B. H. Ztg.*, 25, 169, 1866). Au substitutes for Ag, and a complete series extends through argentian gold (electrum) to gold. The color inclines to brass-yellow with increasing substitution of Au.

Mercurian. Arquerite *Domeyko* (*Ann. mines*, 20, 268, 1841). Kongsbergite *Pisani* (*C. R.*, 75, 1274, 1872). Bordosite *Domeyko* (362, 1879). Silver-Amalgam. Amalgam. Quicksilfwer amalgameradt med gediget Silfwer *Cronstedt* (189, 1758). Natürlich Amalgam, Silberamalgam *Germ.* Amalgam natif *de Lisle* (1, 420, 1783). Mercure argental *Haüy* (3, 307, 1822). Pella natural *Del Rio.* Amalgama *Ital., Span.* Hg often occurs[11] in substitution for Ag, up to at least Hg : Ag = 1 : 4.2 (anal. 6).[12] (Moschellandsbergite [which see] is not here included.)

Cuprian. Highly cuprian material has been reported[13] but evidence of homogeneity is lacking.

Arsenian. Arseniksilber *Klaproth,* (1, 183, 1795). Pyritolamprite *Adam* (39, 1869). Chanarcillite *Domeyko* (in Dana [36, 1868]). Arsenargentite *Hannay* (*Min. Mag.*, 1, 149, 1877). Huntilite *Wurtz* (*Eng. Mining J.*, 27, 55, 1879). Arsenical silver ores of uncertain composition, perhaps including definite intermetallic compounds.[14]

Antimonian. Animikite *Wurtz* (*Eng. Mining J.*, 27, 55, 1879). Dyscrasite pt. Sb substitutes for Ag up to a probable limit of about 5 atomic per cent Sb.[15] The antimonian material is somewhat harder and tougher than pure silver. Antimonian silver is commonly intergrown with dyscrasite. The so-called dyscrasite which is isotropic in polished section is presumably antimonian silver.[16]

Tests. B.B. fuses easily to a silver-white globule which in O.F. gives a faint dark red coating of silver oxide. Soluble in HNO_3.

Occur.[17] Native silver is widely distributed in small amounts, principally in the oxidized zone of ore deposits. The larger deposits of native silver, however, are probably the result of deposition of silver from hydrothermal solutions of primary origin. Deposits of this kind are of three main types: silver associated with various silver minerals, sulfides and zeolites in a gangue of calcite, barite, fluorite, and quartz (Kongsberg); silver with arsenides[18] and sulfides of nickel and cobalt and other silver minerals in a calcite or barite gangue (Cobalt); with uraninite and nickel-cobalt minerals (Joachimstal; Great Bear Lake).

The mines of Kongsberg, Norway, worked for several hundred years, have afforded magnificent specimens of crystallized and wire silver. Other century-old mines are those at Freiberg, Schneeberg, and Johanngeorgenstadt in Saxony, Přibram, Schemnitz, and Joachimstal in Bohemia, Andreasberg in the Harz Mountains, Wittichen in Baden. In France at Ste. Marie aux Mines in Alsace and at the mine of Chalanches, near Allemont, Isère. In Asiatic Russia at Zmeinogorsk, Altai, Tomsk. In Sardinia in the mines of Monte Narba near Sarrabus. In New South Wales at Broken Hill. In Chile at Copiapó and Chañarcillo, Atacama. In Mexico, long the most important producer of silver, the native metal is found especially at Batopilas, Chihuahua, and Guanajuato; also at various places in the states of Sonora, Durango, and Zacatecas.

In the United States silver occurs associated with native copper on the Keweenaw Peninsula, Michigan. In Montana at Butte and at Elkhorn, Jefferson County. In Idaho large amounts were obtained at the Poorman mine, Silver City district, Owyhee County; also in the Coeur d'Alene district. In Colorado especially at Aspen, Pitkin County. In Arizona at the Silver King mine, Pinal County, and in the Globe district, Gila County. In Canada large amounts of native silver have been mined at Cobalt, Ontario, where slabs of great size have been found; one of these, weighing 1640 lb., is now in the Parliament building in Toronto. In the Thunder Bay district on the north shore of Lake Superior, at Silver Islet. Associated with pitchblende at Great Bear Lake, Mackenzie.

A l t e r. Pseudomorphs of cerargyrite, iodembolite, ruby silver, argentite, and stephanite after silver are known. Silver has been observed as an alteration of ruby silver, stephanite, and other silver minerals.

A r t i f.[19] Readily obtained in crystals by electrolysis of silver solutions, and from melts.

N a m e. The ultimate origin of the name silver is not known.

MACFARLANITE. *Sibley* (*Am. Inst. Min. Eng., Trans.*, **8**, 236, 1880). A mixture essentially of native silver, galena, and niccolite.[20]

Ref.

1. Goldschmidt (**8**, 38, 1923). Rare forms: {013}, {025}, {047}, {112}, {133}, {255}, {233}, {157}.

2. Vegard, *Phil. Mag.*, **31**, 83 (1916). Cell edge from Owen and Yates, *Phil. Mag.*, **7**, 472 (1933), on silver 99.9 per cent fine. Hultgren (priv. comm., 1938) measured 4.0783 on spectroscopically pure silver.

3. On the origin of wire silver see Beutell, *Cbl. Min.*, 14, 1919, and Doelter (3 [2], 112, 1919). The direction of elongation of some wire silver is [110] (Montoro, *Per. Min.*, **9**, 55 [1938]).

4. Weidner and Burgess, *U. S. Bur. Standards Bull.*, **7**, 1 (1910).

5. Schneiderhöhn and Ramdohr (**2**, 58, 1931). On the reflectivity see Orcel, *Bull. soc. min.*, **53**, 301 (1930), and Doelter (1919).

6. Münster anal. in Krusch, *Zs. pr. Geol.*, **93**, 1896.
7. Sammelesen and Hjordtdahl in Rath, *Jb. Min.*, 443, 1869.
8. Pisani, *C. R.*, **75**, 1274 (1872).
9. Domeyko, *Ann. mines.*, **20**, 268 (1841).
10. Domeyko in Dana (23, 1892).
11. See Newhouse, *Am. Min.*, **18**, 295 (1933), on the occurrence of mercurian silver.
12. See Murphy, *J. Inst. Met.*, **46**, 507 (1931), on the artificial system Ag–Hg, who finds Hg to substitute for Ag to the extent of about 45 weight per cent with an attendant increase in the cell edge from 4.077 to 4.175.
13. See Pilipenko, *Tomsk Univ., Bull.*, **63**, 1915. Only a limited solid solution (up to 6.5 atomic per cent Cu) has been found in the artificial system Ag–Cu by Erdal, *Zs. Kr.* 65, 69 (1927).
14. Broderick and Ehret, *J. Phys. Chem.*, **35**, 3322 (1931) report a limit of 7 atomic per cent substitution of As in Ag in the artificial system Ag–As, with a concomitant variation in cell edge from 4.076 to 4.080 Å. Heide and Leroux, *Zs. anorg. Chem.*, **92**, 119 (1915), report only the compound Ag_9As in this system. The composition Ag_3As has been attributed to arsenargentite but without real evidence.
15. See Broderick and Ehret (1931) on the artificial system Ag–Sb, and Peacock, *Univ. Toronto Stud., Geol. Ser.*, **44**, 31 (1940), on natural antimonian silver.
16. See Schwartz, *Am. Min.*, **13**, 495 (1928), Schneiderhöhn and Ramdohr (**2**, 236, 1931). See further under dyscrasite.
17. On the paragenesis of silver, see Lindgren (600, 1933).
18. See Dadson, *Univ. Toronto Stud., Geol. Ser.*, **38**, 51 (1935), and Palmer, *Econ. Geol.*, **12**, 207 (1917), on the action of Co–Ni arsenides on solutions of silver salts.
19. Hintze (1 [1], 234, 1898).
20. Parsons and Thomson, *Univ. Toronto Stud., Geol. Ser.*, 23, 1921.

1114   C O P P E R [Cu].   Aes Cyprium *Pliny* (*Hist. Nat.*, A.D. 77).   Venus *Alchem.*
Gediegen Kupfer *Germ.*   Gediget Koppar *Swed.*   Cuivre natif *Fr.*   Rame nativo *Ital.*
Cobre nativo *Span.*   Cuprocuprite pt. *Vernadsky* (1 [3], 416, 1910).

C r y s t.   Isometric; hexoctahedral — $4/m\,\bar{3}\,2/m$.

Forms:[1]

| a | 001 | o | 111 | f | 013 | e | 012 | m | 113 | y | 5·10·18 |
| d | 011 | h | 014 | k | 025 | l | 035 | n | 112 | | |

Structure cell.[2]   Space group *Fm3m*; a_0 3.6077 ± 0.0002 (18°); contains 4Cu.

Habit.   Cubic; dodecahedral; tetrahexahedral {012}, {035}; rarely octahedral.   Common forms: *a d h e l o*.   Often flattened {111}, elongated [001], or otherwise malformed; also irregularly distorted, in twisted bands of indistinct form, or in wirelike forms.   Filiform and arborescent; massive; as a coarse powder.

Twinning.   On the plane {111}, very common, giving simple contact twins usually flattened on the twin plane, penetration twins, cyclic groups of five individuals, and complex groups branching at 60°.

P h y s.   Cleavage none.   Fracture hackly.   Highly ductile and malleable.   H. $2\frac{1}{2}$–3.   G. 8.95; 8.94 (calc.).   M.P. 1083°.[3]   An excellent conductor of heat and electricity.   Color on fresh fracture surface, light rose, quickly changing to copper-red, then to brown.   Luster metallic.   Streak metallic, shining.   Opaque.   In polished section[4] rose-white, isotropic, and strongly reflecting.   Percentage reflection: green, 61; orange, 83; red, 89.

C h e m.   Copper, Cu, often with small amounts or traces of silver, arsenic, iron, bismuth, antimony, mercury, germanium.[5]

Var. *Arsenian.* Whitneyite *Genth* (*Am. J. Sc.*, **27**, 400, 1859). Contains up to $11\frac{1}{2}$ per cent As, but part of this belongs to algodonite.

Tests. F. 3.   B.B. fuses readily; on cooling becomes coated with black oxide. Dissolves readily in HNO_3.

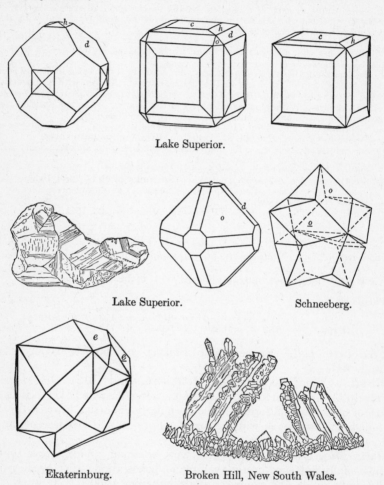

Lake Superior.

Lake Superior.   Schneeberg.

Ekaterinburg.   Broken Hill, New South Wales.

O c c u r.[6] Most commonly associated with basic extrusive rocks in
which copper has formed by the reaction of copper solutions with hematite
or other iron minerals (Lake Superior).   In this type of deposit copper is
associated with native silver in small amounts, chalcocite, bornite, epidote,
calcite, prehnite, datolite, chlorite and zeolites, indicating that the temperature of formation was not high.   May form through the reduction of copper
solutions by carbonaceous material, as in the action of wood on mine waters.

Found in Russia, in fine crystals at Turinsk, near Bogoslovsk, Perm; near Ekaterinburg and near Nizhne Tagilsk. In Germany at Rheinbreitbach in the Rhineland, at Friedrichssegen, near Ems, Hesse-Nassau. In Italy at Montecatini near Volterra, Tuscany, in basic flows. In Great Britain in Cornwall and at Stirling, Scotland. In the basalts of the Faeroes. In South Australia at Wallaroo and nearby on Yorke Peninsula; at Broken Hill, New South Wales. In Chile at Andacollo, near Coquimbo. In Bolivia there is a noted occurrence at Corococo, southwest of La Paz. Found in Mexico at Cananea, Sonora, and at Mapimi, Durango.

Copper is found in the United States in small amounts in many localities in the east in Triassic traps or in red sandstone (Massachusetts, Connecticut, New Jersey, Virginia, and Pennsylvania). Near New Haven, Connecticut, masses have been found in the glacial drift, one weighing 200 lb. At Franklin, New Jersey, copper is sometimes found in the zinc ores. The greatest known deposit of native copper is in the Lake Superior district on the Keweenaw Peninsula of northern Michigan, where it is found in a narrow belt over 200 miles in length. The rocks of this district are a series of interbedded basic lavas, sandstones, and conglomerates in which the copper occurs either in the interstices of the sediments, or replacing the grains and pebbles, or filling the cavities in the amygdaloidal lavas, or in veins cutting all the rocks. The associated minerals are prehnite, datolite, epidote, pumpellyite, chlorite, adularia, calcite, and zeolites, occasionally with native silver. Single masses of copper of great size have been found in this district; the largest, measuring 45 ft. by 22 ft. by 8 ft. and weighing about 420 tons, was discovered in 1857 in the Minnesota mine. Copper occurs in Arizona in the Copper Queen mine, Bisbee, in arborescent groups of small crystals and in the Globe district, Gila County. Also in New Mexico, at Georgetown, Grant County; in Oregon. In Alaska in the Copper River district. In Nova Scotia copper is found as veins in trap rocks at Cap d'Or.

Alter. On oxidation, native copper becomes filmed by cuprite; on continued weathering the metal may afford a variety of secondary copper minerals, including malachite, atacamite, azurite. Copper often has been observed as pseudomorphs after cuprite; also after aragonite (Corocoro, Bolivia), azurite (Grant County, New Mexico), calcite, chalcocite, chalcanthite, fibrous antlerite (Chuquicamata, Chile). Hollow shell-like masses of copper — the so-called "skulls" — are formed by partial replacement of pebbles or cobbles in the conglomerates of the copper district in northern Michigan.

Artif.[7] Readily obtained in crystals by sublimation and by the reduction or electrolysis of solutions of copper salts. Large single crystals without external faces have been produced by withdrawing heat in one direction from molten copper, and by careful annealing of polycrystalline copper wire.

Name. From κυπρος, *Cyprus*, where the metal was early found.

Ref.

1. Goldschmidt (5, 57, 1918); Dana, *Am. J. Sc.*, 32, 413 (1886), for fullest description of Lake Superior crystals, simple, twinned, and symmetrically distorted; Oebike (Inaug. Diss., Münster, 1915 — *Min. Abs.*, 1, 348 [1922]); Hawkins, *Am. Min.*, 14, 309 (1929); Palache (priv. comm., 1941). Rare or uncertain forms: 037, 047, 023, 0·10·11, 116, 115, 114, 227, 223, 1·3·11, 1·6·11, 2·3·12, 124, 245, 459.
2. The structure of copper was determined by Bragg, *Phil. Mag.*, 28, 255 (1914); the cell edge from Owen and Yates, *Phil. Mag.*, 15, 472 (1933), on electrolytic copper of 99.9 per cent purity.
3. Weidner and Burgess, *Bull. U. S. Bur. Standards*, 7, 1 (1910).
4. Schneiderhöhn and Ramdohr (2, 53, 1931).
5. On Ge in native copper see Geilmann and Brünger, *Zs. anorg. Chem.*, 196, 312 (1931), and Papish, *Econ. Geol.*, 23, 660 (1928).
6. Lindgren (514, 1933); for Corocoro, Geier, (*Jb. Min., Beil.-Bd.*, 58, 1 (1928); for the Appalachian region, Watson, *Econ. Geol.*, 18, 732 (1923); for the Lake Superior region, Butler and Burbank, with others, *U. S. Geol. Sur., Prof. Pap. 144*, 1929; in meteorites, Quirke, *Econ. Geol.*, 14, 619 (1919).
7. Doelter (3 [2], 53, 1919); Hughes, *J. Inst. Met.*, 23, 525 (1920).

WHITNEYITE. *Genth* (*Am. J. Sc.*, 27, 400, 1859), and DARWINITE *Forbes* (*Phil. Mag.*, 20, 423, 1860), have been shown to be essentially arsenian copper,[1] with some intimately associated algodonite. The early analyses of whitneyite[2] give an arsenic content of about 11½ per cent, indicating that the mixture may represent a eutectic composition, or possibly a decomposition of a previously homogeneous substance.

Ref.

1. Ramsdell, *Am. Min.*, 14, 188 (1929). Machatschki, *Jb. Min., Beil.-Bd.*, 49, 137 (1929).
2. Dana (45, 1892).

1115 **L E A D** [Pb]. Plumbum nigrum *Pliny* (34, 47, A.D. 77). Saturnus *Alchem.* Gediegen Blei *Germ.* Gediget Bly *Swed.* Plomb natif *Fr.* Piombo nativo *Ital.* Plomo metálico *Span.*

C r y s t. Isometric; hexoctahedral — $4/m \bar{3} 2/m$.

Forms:[1]

| $a\{001\}$ | $d\{011\}$ | $o\{111\}$ | $h\{014\}$ | $m\{113\}$ | $n\{112\}$ | $\xi\{155\}$ |

Structure cell.[2] Space group $Fm3m$; a_0 4.9396 ± 0.0003 (18°); contains 4Pb.

Habit. Octahedral; also dodecahedral, cubic. Crystals rare. Usually in rounded masses and thin plates. Also dendritic; wirelike.

Twinning. On $\{111\}$.

P h y s. Cleavage none. Very malleable; somewhat ductile. H. 1½. G. 11.37; 11.36 (calc. 0°). Color and streak, lead-gray, usually dull; gray-white, metallic, when freshly cut. Opaque. Fresh polished surfaces gray-white, isotropic, with high reflectivity, but quickly dulled.

C h e m. Lead, Pb, sometimes with a little silver, also antimony. Crystals from the Harstig mine gave 99.71 per cent Pb.

Tests. Very easily fusible (330°). Dissolves readily in HNO_3.

O c c u r. Native lead is extremely rare and many of the reported occurrences are doubtful. In Vermland, Sweden, in fine large crystal groups (130 lb.) from Långban; in small crystals, associated with caryopilite, sarkinite, and brandtite, from the Harstig mine, Pajsberg; and in compact dolomitic limestone, with hematite, magnetite, hausmannite, rhodonite, at the iron and manganese mines, Pajsberg. In Russia, in the gold placers of the Urals in the district of Ekaterinburg; on the Kirghese Steppes; and in the Altai, Asiatic Russia. In lava on the island of Madeira. In Mexico near Jalapa, state of Vera Cruz. In the United States at Franklin, New Jersey, and at the Jay Gould mine, Wood River district, Blaine County, Idaho.

Artif. Crystallized lead has been obtained electrolytically from lead nitrate.

Ref.

1. Goldschmidt (**1**, 198, 1913).
2. Vegard, *Phil. Mag.*, **32**, 65 (1916). Cell edge, Owen and Yates, *Phil. Mag.*, **15**, 472 (1933), on lead of 99.9 per cent purity.

112 **M E R C U R Y** [Hg]. χυτός ἄργυρος *Theophrastus* (*Stones*, ca. 315 B.C.). Ὑδράργυρος καθ᾽ ἑαυτὴν [native] *Dioscorides* (*Mat. Med.*, ca. A.D. 50). Argentum vivum, Hydrargyros *Pliny* (33, 32, 20, 41, A.D. 77). Quicksilver. Mercurius *Alchem.* Gediegen Quecksilber *Germ.* Qvicksilfver *Swed.* Mercure natif *Fr.* Mercurio *Ital., Span.*

Phys. Liquid; solidifies at − 39°, forming rhombohedral crystals.[1] G. 13.596; 14.26 (cryst., −46°, calc.). Tin-white, metallic, very brilliant. Opaque.

Chem. Mercury, Hg, sometimes with a little silver or gold.

Tests. B.B. entirely volatile, vaporizing at 350 ± 10°. Dissolves readily in HNO₃.

Occur.[2] Native mercury is rare. It occurs in isolated drops, at times in larger fluid masses, usually associated with cinnabar in volcanic regions or in connection with hot springs. Mercury is found at Idria, in Gorizia, Italy (formerly in Carniola, Austria); at Mount Avala near Belgrad, Yugoslavia; associated with amalgam at Moschellandsberg (Landsberg near Ober-Moschel), Palatinate, Bavaria; in Spain at Almaden, Ciudad Real. In the United States it has been found at Terlingua, Texas, and in California associated with the cinnabar deposits, especially at New Almaden, Santa Clara County, and in Sonoma, Napa and Lake Counties.

Ref.

1. Structure cell: Hexagonal — R; a_{rh} 2.999, α 70°31′42″ (−46°); contains 1Hg. For hexagonal axes: a_0 3.463, c_0 6.706; $a_0 : c_0 = 1 : 1.937$; contains 3Hg (Mehl and Barrett, *Am. Inst. Min. Met. Engr., Tech. Pub. 225*, 1929); Neuburger, *Zs. anorg. Chem.*, **212**, 40 (1933).
2. Becker, *U.S. Geol. Sur., Monog. 13*, 1888; Lindgren (463, 1933).

113 **M O S C H E L L A N D S B E R G I T E** [Ag₂Hg₃]. *Berman* and *Harcourt* (*Am. Min.*, **23**, 761, 1938). Amalgam, pt.

Cryst. Isometric; hexoctahedral — $4/m\,\bar{3}\,2/m$.

Forms:[1]

a{001}   d{011}   o{111}   f{013}   e{012}   n{112}   p{122}   s{123}

Structure cell.[2] Space group $Im3m$ (?); a_0 10.1; contains $Ag_{20}Hg_{30}$.
Habit.[3] Dodecahedral; common forms: $d\,a\,n$. Also massive; granular.

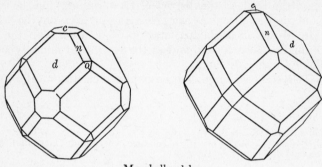

Moschellandsberg.

P h y s. Cleavages $\{011\}$, $\{001\}$, distinct.[2] Fracture conchoidal.
Somewhat brittle. H. $3\frac{1}{2}$. G. 13.48–13.71; 13.5 (calc.). Silver-white
with bright metallic luster. Opaque.

C h e m. A compound of silver and mercury, Ag_2Hg_3.
Anal.[4]

	1	2	3	4
Ag	26.4	27.5	26.48	27.04
Hg	73.6	[72.5]	73.44	72.94
	100.0	100.0	99.92	99.98
G.			13.71	13.48

1. Ag_2Hg_3. 2. Chalanches mine.[5] 3. Sala.[6] 4. Moschellandsberg.[7]

Tests. B.B. on charcoal the mercury volatilizes leaving a globule of silver. Dissolves
in HNO_3.

O c c u r. At Moschellandsberg (Landsberg, near Ober-Moschel),
Bavaria, in fine crystals; at Sala in Sweden; in the Chalanches mine, near
Allemont, Isère, France.

A r t i f. Corresponds to the γ-phase of the artificial system.[8]

Ref.

1. Goldschmidt (**1**, 12, 1913).
2. Berman and Harcourt (1938) on crystals from Moschellandsberg. The lattice
type and cell edge agree with those found for the γ-phase of the artificial system
($Ag_{10}Hg_{13}$) Murphy, *J. Inst. Met.*, **46**, 507 (1931); (Ag_5Hg_8) Stenbeck, *Zs. anorg. Chem.*,
214, 16 (1933).
3. The octahedron in Goldschmidt (**1**, pl. 10, Fig. 13, 1913) represents mercurian
silver (arquerite).
4. The analyses of silver-amalgam in Doelter (3 [2], 365, 1926) represent mercurian
silver (Hg up to 49 per cent), moschellandsbergite (Hg 73.6 per cent) and some doubtful
alloys of intermediate composition.
5. Cordier, *J. mines*, **12**, 1 (1802).
6. Mauzelius anal. in Sjögren, *Geol. För. Förh.*, **22**, 187 (1900).
7. Gonyer anal. in Berman and Harcourt (1938) on crystals centrifugally freed from
adhering mercury.
8. Murphy (1931).

114   Gold-Amalgam [Au_2Hg_3?].   Perhaps isometric in part.   In grains and lumps of white or yellowish color with metallic luster.   Plastic, or brittle (?) with distinctly conchoidal fracture.   G. 15. 47.   Some of the analyses correspond well with the composition Au_2Hg_3, suggesting a compound homologous with the isometric silver compound Ag_2Hg_3 (moschellandsbergite).   Other analyses give (Au, Ag, Hg).

Anal.

	1	2	3	4	5
Ag	....	.....	.....	5.00	4.78
Au	39.6	39.02	41.63	38.39	34.23
Pt	....	......	......	.....	0.12
Hg	60.4	[60.98]	[58.37]	57.40	60.57
Total	100.0	100.00	100.00	100.79	99.79

1. Au_2Hg_3.   2, 3. Mariposa region; material pressed between leather.[1]   4. Columbia; plastic material.[2]   5. Borneo; brittle material.   Includes chromite, 0.09.[3]

Occurs in the Mariposa region, California; in rounded white grains with platinum in Columbia; in the vicinity of Pleiari, Borneo.

Ref.

1. Sonnenschein, *Zs. deutsche geol. Ges.*, **6**, 243 (1854).
2. Schneider anal. in Marchand, *J. pr. Chem.*, **43**, 307 (1848).
3. Chernik, ref. in *Zs. Kr.*, **55**, 190 (1915–20).

115   Potarite [Pd_3Hg_2?].   Palladium-Amalgam, palladium mercuride *Harrison* and *Bourne* (*Off. Gaz. British Guiana*, no. 71, 1925).   Potarite *Harrison* (MS., 1925); *Spencer* (*Min. Mag.*, **21**, 397, 1928).   " Potarite groundmass and potarite inclusions," *Cissarz* (*Zs. Kr.*, **74**, 501, 1930).

Potarite is apparently isometric,[1] as indicated by octahedral points on the surfaces of nuggets with indistinct, slightly divergent columnar or fibrous structure.   Cleavage doubtful.   Brittle.   Color and streak silver-white with bright metallic luster.   H. $3\frac{1}{2}$.   G. 13.48–16.11.   Composition PdHg = Pd 34.7, Hg 65.3; anal., Hg 64.1, 65.2.   Perhaps Pd_3Hg_2 = Pd 44.4, Hg 55.6; anal., Hg 54.4, 54.9.   B.B. spurts on heating with loss of part of the mercury.   Gives a brown solution in HNO_3.   Occurs in scattered grains and nuggets in the diamond washings, Potaro River region, British Guiana.   Named after the locality.

In polished section,[2] potarite has been found to consist of two components, " potarite groundmass " and small irregular " potarite inclusions." The groundmass is pure white, isotropic, with high reflecting power; soft; without cleavage; quickly attacked by HNO_3.   The inclusions are light gray, distinctly anisotropic; with less reflecting power and softer than the groundmass; without cleavage; unattacked by HNO_3 or aqua regia.   Both components presumably consist of palladium and mercury.

Ref.

1. Harrison and Bourne (1925) and Spencer (1928).
2. Cissarz (1930).

116 PLATINUM GROUP

1161	Platinum	Pt
1162	Palladium	Pd
1163	Platiniridium	Pt, Ir
1164	Aurosmiridium	Ir, Os, Au
1165	Iridosmine	Ir, Os
1166	Siserskite	Os, Ir
1167	Allopalladium	Pd

Platinum, palladium, and iridium are isometric with the copper type of structure. The edges of the face-centered cubic lattices of the pure metals compare as follows.

	Pt	Pd	Ir
a_0	3.9158	3.8824	3.8312

Osmium, the alloys of iridium and osmium, and allopalladium are hexagonal.

Analyses of native *platinum* give most of the other platinum metals (Pd, Ir, Os, Rh), metals of the structurally related gold group (Au, Cu), and the iron group (Fe, Ni). Of these, Fe is the most abundant foreign constituent. Notable quantities of foreign elements have given rise to the numerous varietal names. The existence of relatively pure native *palladium*, isometric or hexagonal, requires confirmation. Iridium is known only in *platiniridium* (formerly accepted as native iridium) and in *iridosmine*. Nearly pure osmium is likewise unknown.

This mutual association of the platinum metals with metals of the gold and iron groups is in keeping with the considerable mutual solubility shown by the components of the binary artificial systems.

1161   **PLATINUM** [Pt].   Platina *Ulloa* (1748 [in Dana, 25, 1892]); *Brownrigg* (*Roy. Soc. London, Phil. Trans.*, 584, 1750).   Platina del Pinto *Scheffer* (*Ak. Stockholm, Handl.*, 269, 1752).   Polyxen *Hausmann* (97, 1813).   Siderisches Platin, Eisen-Platin *Breithaupt* (256, 1832).   Iron-platinum *Dana* (1854).   Ferroplatinum *Doelter* (3 [2] 980, 1926).   Cuproplatinum, Palladic platinum, Rhodic platinum *Wagner* (11, 1929).

C r y s t.[1]   Isometric; hexoctahedral — $4/m\,\bar{3}\,2/m$.

Forms:

$a\{001\}$ $d\{011\}$ $o\{111\}$ $f\{013\}$ $e\{012\}$ $l\{035\}$ $g\{023\}$

Structure cell.[2]   Space group $Fm3m$; a_0 3.9158 ± 0.0003   (18°); contains 4Pt.

Habit.   Cubic; often distorted.   Usually in grains or scales; occasionally in nuggets or lumps up to 20 lb. in weight.

Twinning.   On {111}.

P h y s.   Cleavage, none.   Fracture hackly.   Malleable and ductile. H. 4–4½, increasing with iron content.   G. 14–19; 21.46 (calc. Pt, 0°). Nonmagnetic to distinctly magnetic, often with polarity, when rich in iron. Whitish steel-gray to dark gray.   Luster metallic.   Opaque.   In polished section[3] white, isotropic. Percentage reflection in air: green, 70; orange, 73; red, 70.

C h e m. Platinum, Pt, always with iridium, iridosmine, rhodium, palladium; iron in considerable amounts; also copper, gold, nickel.

Anal.[4]

	1	2	3	4	5
Pt	90.16	87.47	86.34	80.30	73.02
Ir	0.33	1.24	1.30	5.26	1.68
Os	.....	0.48	.....	.....	.....
Ir-Os	0.18	.....	0.95	8.76	1.57
Rh	1.32	0.25	0.53	0.50	0.98
Pd	1.18	0.85	0.54	0.30	0.51
Au	.....	0.02	.....	.....	.....
Cu	0.38	0.71	0.55	2.05	3.20
Fe	6.26	7.41	9.10	2.63	16.42
Ni	.....	0.10	0.06	.....	1.05
Gangue	.....	1.04	.....	.....	.....
Total	99.81	99.57	99.37	99.80	98.43
G.		19.0	17.11		

1. Katchkanar River, Goussewi Kamen, Urals.[5] 2. Solwa River, Deneschkin Kamen, Perm.[6] 3. Serlich River, Urjanchai district, Urals.[7] 4. Omoutnaïa River, Urals.[8] 5. Bolchaïa Bonrovka River, Urals.[9]

	6	7	8	9
Pt	86.20	79.48	84.75	59.9
Ir	0.85	0.82	.....	.....
Os	.....	.....	.....	.....
Ir-Os	0.95	1.41	0.95	.....
Rh	1.40	0.75	.....	.....
Pd	0.50	0.49	0.53	37.1
Au	1.00	0.49	.....	3.0
Cu	0.60	.....	1.28	.....
Fe	7.80	16.50	11.98	.....
Ni	.....	.....	0.48	.....
Gangue	0.95	.....	.....	.....
Total	100.25	99.94	99.97	100.0

6. Chocó, Colombia.[10] 7. Birbir River, Abyssinia.[11] 8. Onverwacht mine, Lydenburg district, Transvaal.[12] 9. Rietfontein, Waterberg district, central Transvaal.[13]

Var. Ordinary. Polyxene. Polyxen *Hausmann* (97, 1813). Non-magnetic or slightly magnetic, light steel-gray to silver-white in color, with 80-90 per cent Pt and 3-11 per cent Fe.

Ferrian. Siderisches Platin. Eisen-Platin *Breithaupt* (256, 1832). Iron-platinum *Dana* (1854). Ferroplatinum *Doelter* (3 [2], 980, 1926). Magnetic platinum. Dark gray to almost black in color. Magnetic, often with polarity. Contains up to 28 per cent Fe.

Cuprian. Cuproplatinum *Wagner* (11, 1929). A variety containing 8-13 per cent Cu, found as thin shells around grains of ferrian platinum in dunite from the Nizhne Tagilsk region, Urals. Readily etched by aqua regia. Ordinary platinum often contains a few per cent of Cu.

Palladian. Palladic platinum *Wagner* (13, 1929). Contains up to 37 per cent Pd.

Rhodian. Rhodic platinum *Wagner* (13, 1929). Contains up to 4.6 per cent Rh.

Iridian. Contains Ir up to at least 7.5 per cent.

Tests. B.B. infusible. Soluble only in hot aqua regia.

O c c u r.[14] Platinum originates by magmatic differentiation of basic and ultrabasic rocks, olivine-gabbros, pyroxenites (Urals), peridotites, and especially dunites (Urals, Transvaal) in which the greatest concentration occurs. The metal almost invariably contains palladium and minute crystals of iridosmine. The principal associated minerals are olivine, pyroxene, chromite, and magnetite. Platinum has also been found associated with hematite, chlorite, and pyrolusite in quartz veins (Waterberg), and it has been reported in minute amounts in a contact metamorphic deposit with wollastonite and grossularite (Sumatra). The most productive deposits are placers which are usually close to the platinum-bearing igneous rocks from which they were derived.

Platinum was first found in the alluvial deposits of the river Pinto near Papayan in the intendencia of Chocó, department of Cauca, Colombia, whence it was first taken to Europe in 1735. Here it first received its name platina (platina del Pinto) from its resemblance to silver. It was also found at Santa Rosa, department of Antioquia. The world's most important district is in the Ural Mountains, Russia, where it was discovered in 1822. Here it is found over a large area on the upper Tura River, especially on the Iss River, a tributary of the Tura. The region is in the province of Perm, east of the crest of the Urals. This district, of which Nizhne Tagilsk is about the center, extends from Denezhkin-Kamen, north of Bogoslovsk to south of Ekaterinburg. Platinum has also been found in the sand of the Ivalo River, northern Finland; sparingly in the sand of the Rhine; and in county Wicklow, Ireland.

Occurs also in Borneo; from New South Wales it is reported as occurring in place in the Broken Hill district, in a feldspathic rock with iridosmine, also in a gold placer at Platina (Fiefield) and elsewhere. Also from the river Takaka, in New Zealand, in a region of dunite and serpentine; similarly with awaruite in the drift of the Gorge River; also from quartz lodes in the Thames gold field, Auckland. From Brazil and Peru. Found in placers on the east coast of Madagascar from north of Fénérive south to the neighborhood of Vangaindrano. From the Lydenburg district in the Transvaal, in basic rocks derived from the differentiation of norite; also in the Waterberg district. On the river Jaky, Santo Domingo, island of Haiti. Reported in Choluteca and Gracias, Honduras.

Platinum has been reported as found in traces in the gold sands of Rutherford and Burke Counties, North Carolina. Occurs in the black sands of placers of California in a number of districts, especially in Trinity County, and at Oroville, Butte County; similarly in Oregon at Cape Blanco (Port Orford), Curry County, and elsewhere. In Canada it was found in the gold washings of Rivière-du-Loup and Rivière des Plantes, Beauce County,

Quebec. In British Columbia in the sands of a number of streams, especially in the Kamloops mining district along the Fraser and Tranquille rivers; in the Similkameen mining district on Granite, Cedar, and Slate creeks, tributaries of the Tulameen River. It has also been found in this last section in fine grains in the peridotites of Olivine Mountain. In Alberta on the North Saskatchewan River near Edmonton.

Name. From Span. platina, diminutive of plata, silver. Polyxene from πολύξενος, *entertaining many guests*, in allusion to the many elements housed by the native metal.

Ref.
1. Goldschmidt (6, 121, 1920).
2. Hull and Davey *Phys. Rev.*, 17, 571 (1921). Cell edge, Owen and Yates, *Phil. Mag.*, 15, 472 (1933), on spectroscopically pure platinum.
3. Schneiderhöhn and Ramdohr (2, 42, 1931).
4. Numerous analyses are listed by Duparc and Tikonovitch (237, 1920); Doelter (3 [2], 1000–1004, 1926); Žemczužny, *Zs. anorg. Chem.*, 156, 99 (1926); Wagner (1929); Mellor (16, 6, 1937).
5. Karpoff anal. in Doelter (1926).
6. Karpoff anal. in Žemczužny (1926).
7. Karpoff anal. in Žemczužny (1926).
8. Koifmann anal. in Duparc and Tikonovitch (246, 1920).
9. Karpoff anal. in Duparc and Tikonovitch (240, 1920).
10. Deville and Debray, *Ann. chim. phys.*, 56, 449 (1859).
11. Duparc and Molly, *Schweiz. min. Mitt.*, 8, 240 (1928).
12. Cooper, *J. Chem. Met. Mining Soc. South Africa*, 26, 228 (1926) — *Min. Abs.*, 3, 137 (1926).
13. Watson and Cooper anal. in Wagner (260, 1929).
14. Howe and Holtz (Bibliography of the metals of the platinum group, 1748–1917 — *U. S. Geol. Sur.*, *Bull. 694*, 1919); Duparc and Tikonovitch (1920); Wagner (1929).

CANADIUM. *French* (*Chem. News*, 104, 283, 1911).
A supposed new element of the platinum group, found as white metallic grains in placers in the Nelson district, British Columbia. Not confirmed.[1]

Ref.
1. *Ann. Rep. Minister of Mines, British Columbia, 1911–1912*, 157, 165; *Mining J. London*, 101, 344,(1913).

1162 **PALLADIUM** [Pd]. Palladium *Wollaston* (Anon. not., London, 1803; *Phil. Trans.*, 428, 1804).

Cryst. Isometric; hexoctahedral — $4/m \, \bar{3} \, 2/m$. Small octahedrons (?). Commonly in grains. Sometimes with radial fibrous texture.

Structure cell.[1] Space group *Fm3m*; a_0 3.8824 ± 0.0003 (18°); contains 4Pd.

Phys. Cleavage, none. Ductile and malleable. H. $4\frac{1}{2}$–5. G. 11.9; 12.04 (calc., 0°). M.P. 1556 ± 15°. Luster metallic. Color whitish steel-gray. Opaque. In polished section white, with high reflecting power; isotropic. Percentage reflection: green, 69; orange, 70; red, 71.5.

Chem. Palladium, Pd, with a little platinum and iridium.

Tests. The bluish tarnish is removed in the R.F., restored in the O.F. A flattened piece fused with $KHSO_3$ is oxidized and partially dissolved. A crystal of KI added to the portion soluble in water forms a black ppt. of PdI_2 which gives a deep wine-red solution in excess KI. Soluble in HNO_3.

O c c u r.   Rare.   In Colombia, in the Intendencia of Chocó; in Brazil, at Itabira, Minas Geraes.   In the platinum district of the Ural Mountains. In the oxidized zone of the platinum deposits in the Transvaal.

N a m e.   After the planetoid *Pallas* reported in 1802.

Ref.

1. Hull and Davey, *Phys. Rev.*, **17**, 571 (1921).   Cell edge, Owen and Yates, *Phil. Mag.*, **15**, 472 (1933), on spectroscopically pure material.

1163   **P L A T I N I R I D I U M** [Ir, Pt].   Platiniridium *Svanberg* (*Jahresber. Chem.* **15**, 205, 1834).   Gediegen Irid *Breithaupt* (*Ak. Stockholm, Handl.*, 84, 1834).   Iridplatin *Glocker* (340, 1839).   Avaite *Heddle* (*Enc. Brit.*, **16**, 382, 1883).

C r y s t.   Isometric; hexoctahedral — $4/m\,\bar{3}\,2/m$.

Forms:[1] $a\{001\}$ $d\{011\}$ $o\{111\}$ $f\{013\}$ $\theta\{034\}$

Structure cell.[2]   For nearly pure iridium, space group $Fm3m$; a_0 3.8312 ± 0.0005 (18°); contains 4Ir.

Habit.   Generally cubic.   Commonly in rounded or angular grains.

Twinning.   On $\{111\}$, in polysynthetic groups.

P h y s.   Cleavage $\{001\}$, indistinct.   Fracture hackly.   Somewhat malleable.   H. 6–7.   G. 22.65–22.84; 22.66 (calc., 0°).   M.P. 2360°. Luster metallic.   Color silver-white with a yellow tinge; gray on fracture. Opaque.

C h e m.[3]   Iridium, Ir, and platinum, Pt, with some palladium, rhodium, iron, copper.

Anal.

	1	2
Pt	19.64	55.44
Ir	76.85	27.79
Os	.....	trace
Pd	0.89	0.49
Rh	.....	6.86
Fe	.....	4.14
Cu	1.78	3.30
Total	99.16	98.02

1. Nizhne Tagilsk, Newjansk, Ural Mts.[4]   2. Brazil.[4]

Tests.   B.B. infusible.   Unattacked by acids.

O c c u r.   Very rare.   Found in placers associated with platinum of the Ural Mountains; in Brazil; perhaps in northern California; in the gold sands of Ava near Mandalay, Burma.

N a m e.   From the composition.

Ref.

1. Goldschmidt (4, 211, 1918).
2. Hull and Davey, *Phys. Rev.*, **17**, 571 (1921).   Cell edge, Owen and Yates, *Phil. Mag.*, **15**, 472 (1933), on iridium of 99.8 per cent purity.
3. Even tolerably pure iridium is not known with certainty in nature.   Svanberg's name (Platiniridium) is therefore preferred to Breithaupt's name (Gediegen Irid) for the same material.   The early analyses require confirmation and the homogeneity of the

substance needs to be established. Schneiderhöhn and Ramdohr (**2**, 44, 1931) have described a polished section from Nizhne Tagilsk, showing tablets and grains of iridium in a groundmass of platinum.

4. Svanberg (1834).

1164   Aurosmiridium. Aurosmirid *Swjaginzew* (*C.r. ac. sc. U.R.S.S.*, **4**, 176, 1934 — *Min. Abs.*, **6**, 51, 1935).

Isometric; a_0 3.816.   Brittle with irregular fracture.   H. > 7.   G. 20. Silver-white.   A solid solution of gold and osmium in iridium.   Analysis gave: Ir 51.7, Os 25.5, Ru 3.5, Au 19.3, Fe trace.   Insoluble in aqua regia. From the platinum residues of the Urals.

Iridosmine Series

1165   I R I D O S M I N E [Ir, Os].   Ore of Iridium, consisting of Iridium and Osmium *Wollaston* (*Roy. Soc. London, Phil. Trans.*, **95**, 316, 1805).   Alloy of Iridium and Osmium *Phillips* (244, 1819; 326, 1823).   Native Iridium *Jameson* (**3**, 54, 1820); *Hausmann* (**1**, 96, 1813).   Osmiure d'Iridium *Berzelius* (195, 1819).   Iridium Osmié *Haüy* (**3**, 234, 1822).   Osmium-Iridium *Leonhard* (173, 1821).   Iridosmin *Breithaupt* (*Edinburgh Phil. J.*, **3**, 273, 1827; 259, 1832).   Osmiridium *Glocker* (490, 1831; 339, 1839); *Hausmann* (18, 1847).   Lichtes Osmium-Iridium *Rose* (**2**, 390, 1842).   Iridosmine *Beudant* (**2**, 723, 1832).   Newjanskit *Haidinger* (558, 1845).   Nevyanskite. Osmiridium *Hintze* (**1** [1], 133, 1898).   Ruthenosmiridium *Aoyama* (*Sc. Rep. Tôhoku Univ.*, 527, 1936 — *Min. Abs.*, **7**, 315, 1938).   Ruthenium-nevyanskite, Rhodium-nevyanskite, Platinum-nevyanskite *Vernadsky* (**1** [2], 248, 1909).   Irite *Hermann* (*J. pr. Chem.*, **23**, 276, 1841).

1166   S I S E R S K I T E [Os, Ir].   Dunkles Osmium-Iridium *Rose* (**2**, 390, 1842). Sisserskit *Haidinger* (558; 1845).   Sysertskit.   Iridosmium *Hausmann* (18, 1847); *Hintze* (**1**, [1], 133, 1898).   Osmite, Ruthenium-siserskite *Vernadsky* (**1** [2], 248, 1909). Iridosmine pt.

C r y s t.   Hexagonal — P; dihexagonal dipyramidal — $6/m\,2/m\,2/m$.[1]
$$a : c = 1 : 1.5961;[2] \qquad p_0 : r_0 = 1.8430 : 1$$

Forms:[3]

	ϕ	$\rho = C$	M	A_2
c 0001	.....	0°00′	90°00′	90°00′
m 10$\bar{1}$0	30°00′	90 00	60 00	90 00
a 11$\bar{2}$0	0 00	90 00	90 00	60 00
p 10$\bar{1}$1	30 00	61 31	63 56	90 00
r 11$\bar{2}$2	0 00	57 56	90 00	64 56

Structure cell.   For pure osmium,[4] space group $C6/mmc$; a_0 2.714, c_0 4.314; $a_0 : c_0 = 1 : 1.584$; contains 2 Os.   The cells of the various members of the series differ only slightly in their dimensions and axial ratios.[5]

Habit.   Tabular {0001}; rarely short prismatic [0001].   Common forms: $c\,p\,m$.   Usually in cleavage flakes or irregular flattened grains.

Iridosmine.   Urals.

Phys.   Cleavage {0001} perfect, but difficult. Slightly malleable to nearly brittle.   H. 6–7.   G. 19– 21; 22.69 (calc. for pure Os).   Luster metallic.   Color tin-white (iridosmine) to light steel-gray (siserskite).   Streak gray.   Opaque.   In polished section[6] white with a slight yellow tint; weakly anisotropic and pleochroic. Reflection percentages: green 67.5, orange 66, red 67.

C h e m. An alloy containing essentially iridium and osmium, ranging from about 77 per cent Ir to about 80 per cent Os. Ru, Rh, Pt, and, to a less extent, Fe and Cu, substitute for (Ir, Os). Material in the series with Ir > Os is here named *iridosmine* and material with Os > Ir is named *siserskite*.

Anal.[7]

	1	2	3	4	5	6	7
Pt	0.2	7.4	13.6	1.8	10.08	....	0.05
Ir	17.0	24.5	34.7	44.7	55.24	57.80	69.95
Os	67.9	46.0	41.8	35.6	27.32	35.10	17.25
Rh	4.5	....	1.0	1.8	1.51	0.63	11.25
Ru	8.9	18.3	6.2	14.1	5.85	6.37	....
Cu	0.03	trace	....	....	trace	0.06	trace
Fe	0.03	2.6	....	1.6	trace	0.10	trace
Total	98.56	98.8	97.3	99.6	100.00	100.06	98.50
G.	21.16	18.36	17.8	17.6			20.98

1. Borneo.[8] 2. Transbaikalia. With Au trace.[9] 3. Nevyansk, Urals.[9] 4. Nevyansk, Urals.[9] 5. Nizhne Tagilsk, Urals.[9] 6. Colombia.[10] 7. Borneo.[8]

Var.

For iridosmine.

Ruthenian. Ruthenian-nevyanskite *Vernadsky* (1 [2], 248, 1909). Ruthenosmiridium *Aoyama* (*Sc. Rep. Tôhoku Univ.*, 527, 1936). Contains Ru in substitution for (Ir, Os) to at least 14.1 per cent (anal. 4).[11]

Rhodian. Rhodium-nevyanskite *Vernadsky* (1 [2], 248, 1909). Contains Rh in substitution for (Ir, Os) to at least 11.25 per cent (anal. 7).

Platinian. Platinum-nevyanskite *Vernadsky* (1, [2], 248, 1909). Contains Pt in substitution for (Ir, Os) to at least 10 per cent (anal. 5).

For siserskite.

Ruthenian. Ruthenium-siskerskite *Vernadsky* (1 [2], 248, 1909). Contains Ru in substitution for (Os, Ir) to at least 18.3 per cent (anal. 2).

Platinian. Contains Pt in substitution for (Os, Ir) to at least 13.6 per cent (anal. 3).

Rhodian. Contains Rh in substitution for (Os, Ir) to at least 4.5 per cent (anal. 1).

Tests. F.7. Insoluble in aqua regia. Acquires a film of copper when dipped in a $CuSO_4$ solution with zinc forceps. B.B. siserskite loses its luster and blackens, giving off a strong odor (OsO_4; poisonous, attacking the eyes). Nevyanskite is not decomposed and does not give the osmium odor unless fused with KNO_3; the mass so obtained is soluble in water, and addition of HNO_3 gives a precipitate of blue iridium oxide (probably hydrated IrO_2).

O c c u r. With platinum, in the Ural Mountains, in the district of Ekaterinburg, at Syssertsk, near Nizhne Tagilsk, at Nevyansk, and elsewhere; on the Vilui River, Yakutsk, Siberia, and in Transbaikalia. In the gold-bearing conglomerates of the Witwatersrand, South Africa. From

New South Wales. On the islands of Tasmania and Borneo. In South America in Brazil and in Chocó Province, Colombia. In the United States rather abundant in the gold sands of northern California and southern Oregon. In Canada in British Columbia at Dease Lake, Quesnel mining district, on Granite Creek, Similkameen mining district, and at Ruby Creek, Atlin district; also in traces in the gold washings of the Rivière du Loup, Beauce County, Quebec.

N a m e. The name iridosmine, given in allusion to the composition, was originally applied to the iridium-rich alloy from South America. The name was later extended by some authors to include both the iridium- and osmium-rich portions of the series. Iridosmine is here restricted to material in the series with Ir > Os, and the name siserskite is applied in its original sense to material with Os > Ir. Siserskite (sysertskite) and nevyanskite are named from the localities at Syssertsk and Nevyansk in the Urals. Osmium from ὀσμή, *odor*, in allusion to the characteristic smell of its volatile oxide.

Ref.

1. The hexagonal scalenohedral class — 3 2/m, proposed by Rose, *Ann. Phys.*, 77, 149 (1849), and accepted by Zerrenner, *Zs. deutsche geol. Ges.*, 25, 460 (1873), and Groth (13, 1878) on the grounds of trigonal striations on the base, requires confirmation.
2. Angles of Gledhill, *Univ. Toronto Stud., Geol. Ser.*, 12, 40 (1921), on crystals from Ruby Creek, from California and from the Ural Mts.; orientation and unit of Hull, *Phys. Rev.*, 18, 88 (1921). Gledhill retained the lattice of Rose, *Ann. Phys.*, 29, 452 (1833); 77, 149 (1849) adopted by Dana (27, 1892) and Goldschmidt (6, 112, 1920). Transformation: Rose to Hull $0\bar{1}10/10\bar{1}0/\bar{1}100/0002$.
3. Goldschmidt (1920); Gledhill (1921). Uncertain: {1016}, {1012}.
4. Barth and Lunde, *Zs. phys. Chem.*, 121, 78 (1926).
5. Swjaginzew and Brunowski, *Zs. Kr.*, 83, 187 (1932).
6. Schneiderhöhn and Ramdohr (2, 49, 1931).
7. For additional analyses see Hintze (1 [1], 136, 1898), Chernik, *Ac. sc. St. Péters-bourg Trav. geol. Mus.*, 6, 77 (1912), and Swjaginzeff, *Zs. Kr.*, 83, 182 (1932).
8. Chernik (1912).
9. Swjaginzeff, *Zs. Kr.*, 83, 182 (1932).
10. Deville and Debray, *Ann. chim. phys.*, 56, 481 (1859).
11. Aoyama (1936) gives Ir 39.018, Os 38.885, Ru 21.080, Rh 0.986, total, 99.969, G. 18.97, for material from Hokkaido, Japan.

1167 **Allopalladium**. *Dana* (12, 1868). Selenpalladium *Zinken* (*Ann. Phys.*, 16, 496, 1829). Eugenesite *Adam* (82, 1869).

Hexagonal (? rhombohedral), in small hexagonal tables. Cleavage {0001}, good. Nearly silver-white to pale steel-gray. Luster bright. Opaque.

Polished sections,[1] showing occasional twinning and basal cleavage, are white-yellow with a reflecting power which is high but less than that of palladium. Isotropic in hexagonal (basal) sections, distinctly anisotropic in lath-shaped (prismatic) sections. Percentage reflection in air: green, 53; orange, 54; red, 54. Comp. (spectrographic):[2] palladium, Pd, with some mercury, platinum, ruthenium, copper, and traces of iridium, rhodium, silver. Occurs with clausthalite and gold at Tilkerode, and elsewhere in the Harz Mountains; also reported in hortonolite-dunite from Mooihoek, Transvaal.

Ref.

1. Cissarz, *Zs. Kr.*, **74**, 501 (1930), and Schneiderhöhn and Ramdohr (**2**, 50, 1931) on the original material from Tilkerode, confirming the early reported hexagonal form and disproving Spencer's conjecture, *Min. Mag.*, **21**, 397 (1928), that allopalladium is the same as normal isometric palladium.
2. Cissarz (1930).

117 IRON GROUP

1171	Iron	Fe, Ni
1172	Nickel-iron	Ni, Fe

The modification of iron (α-iron) which is stable at ordinary temperatures has the body-centered cubic structure (α-iron type). Nickel has the face-centered cubic structure (copper type). The α-iron lattice will hold nickel in solid solution up to about 30 per cent at ordinary temperatures; the nickel lattice will take up to about 70 per cent of iron under the same conditions. Native irons, which all carry some nickel, may be grouped into these two types: *iron,* with about 2–7 per cent Ni, found both as terrestrial masses and as *kamacite* in meteorites; *nickel-iron* with about 30–75 per cent Ni, also found in terrestrial masses and as *taenite* in meteorites. Structural data on kamacite (Buey Huerto meteorite) and taenite (Cañon Diablo meteorite) compare as follows.

Kamacite (Ni 5.43 per cent) Isometric — I		Taenite (Ni 30.85 per cent) Isometric — F	
a_0	2.859	a_0	3.590
$d_{(110)}$	2.022	$d_{(111)}$	2.073
$p_{[1\bar{1}1]}$	2.476	$p_{[1\bar{1}0]}$	2.538

The similarity of the spacing of $\{110\}$ and the period of $[1\bar{1}1]$ in kamacite to the spacing of $\{111\}$ and the period of $[1\bar{1}0]$ in taenite serves to explain the common mutual orientation of these materials with these planes and rows in parallel position.

1171   I R O N [Fe].   Mars *Alchem.*   Gediegen Eisen *Germ.*   Jern *Swed.*   Fer natif *Fr.* Ferro *Ital.*   Hierro *Span.*   Sideroferrite *Bahr* (Dana, 19, 1854).
Kamacite, Balkeneisen *Reichenbach* (*Ann. Phys.*, 114, 99, 1861).   Wickelkamazit *Brezina* and *Cohen* (1886); *Cohen* (94, 1894).   Ferrite *Vernadsky* (*Cbl. Min.*, 759, 1912).

C r y s t.   Isometric; hexoctahedral — $4/m\,\bar{3}\,2/m.$
Forms:[1]

$$a\{001\} \qquad d\{011\} \qquad o\{111\}$$

Structure cell.[2]   Space group $Im3m$.   For α-iron: a_0 2.8607 ± 0.0002 (18°); contains 2Fe.   For kamacite: a_0 2.859 ± 0.002; contains 2(Fe,Ni).

Habit.   Crystals rare.   Terrestrial: in blebs, sometimes large masses; meteoric: in plates and lamellar masses, and in regular intergrowth with nickel-iron; artificial: in octahedral, rarely cubic crystals, and in dendrites branching at 90°.
Twinning.[3]   On $\{111\}$; composition plane $\{112\}$ in lamellar masses.

P h y s. Cleavage {001}. Parting and perhaps gliding {112}. Fracture hackly. Malleable. H. 4. G. 7.3–7.87; 7.87 (calc., Fe, 0°). Luster metallic. Color steel-gray to iron-black. Magnetic. Opaque. In polished section,[4] white, isotropic. Percentage reflection: green, 64; orange, 59; red, 58.

C h e m. Iron, Fe, with nickel rarely exceeding 7 per cent; also small amounts of cobalt, copper, sulfur, carbon, phosphorus.

Anal.[5]

	1	2	3	4	5	6
Fe	99.16	97.79	93.16	90.17	93.75	93.09
Ni	......	0.11	2.01	6.50	5.43	6.69
Co	......	0.23	0.80	0.79	0.58	0.25
Cu	.....:	0.10	0.12	0.13	0.00	.....
Mn	......	0.57	.....	.....	.....	.....
C	0.065	.....	2.34	.....	.....	0.02
P	0.207	1.07	0.32	.....	0.19	.....
S	......	0.13	0.41	.....	0.08	.....
SiO_2	0.37	.....	.....	1.54	.....	.....
Cl	......	.....	0.02	.....	.....	.....
Total	99.802	100.00	99.18	99.13	100.03	100.05
G.	7.43	6.86	6.42	7.46		

1. Cameron, Mo. (terrestrial).[6] 2. St. Josephs Island (terrestrial).[7] 3, 4. Ovifak (terrestrial).[8] 5. Cerros del Buey Huerto, Chile (meteoric; kamacite from hexahedrite).[9] 6. Welland, Ont. (meteoric; kamacite from octahedrite).[10]

Var. *Terrestrial Iron.* Ferrite *Vernadsky (Cbl. Min.*, 1912, 759) (not the ferrite of Vogelsang or of Heddle). Nearly pure iron, with nickel usually about 2 per cent and rarely more than 3 per cent, is known only in terrestrial occurrences.

Meteoric Iron. *Kamacite*, Balkeneisen *Reichenbach (Ann. Phys.*, **114**, 99, 1861). Wickelkamazite *Brezina* and *Cohen* (1886); *Cohen* (94, 1894). Lamellar meteoric iron containing around 7 per cent of nickel. From κάμαξ, *shaft*, *lath*.

Tests. B.B. infusible. Easily soluble in dilute HCl with evolution of hydrogen. Insoluble in concentrated H_2SO_4; slowly soluble in acetic acid.

O c c u r.[11] Native terrestrial iron is a rarity. It occurs in igneous rocks, especially basalts (Greenland), also in carbonaceous sediments (Missouri) and mixed with limonite and organic matter in petrified wood. Iron in igneous rocks has been regarded as a primary magmatic constituent, or a secondary product because of the reduction of iron compounds by assimilated carbonaceous material. Iron in sedimentary rocks is probably the result of reduction by organic matter.

The most important terrestrial occurrence is on Disko Island, Greenland. Here it is found in masses occasionally of great size (up to 20 tons) as well as in small embedded particles in the basalt, as at Blaafjeld near Ovifak; also at Fortune Bay, Mellemfjord, Asuk, and at other points on the same island and at Niakornak, Disko Bay, and elsewhere on the west coast of

116   NATIVE ELEMENTS

Greenland. The Disko iron was discovered by Nordenskiöld in 1870, although as early as 1819 it was known that iron was used by the natives in the manufacture of various utensils. The iron was at first supposed to be meteoric but its terrestrial origin has since been placed beyond doubt. Some of the iron from Disko exhibits, when etched, a crystalline structure which resembles the common structures in meteoric iron.

Also found in basalt at Bühl near Weimar, northwest of Cassel in Hesse-Nassau; at Mühlhausen, Thuringia, in pyrite nodules in limestone; in Ireland, county Antrim; in Bohemia; near Rouno, Wolyn district, Poland; in France at Auvergne in trachyte. In southern Russia at Grushersk in the Don district associated with iron minerals as a product of their reduction, with pyrite on the Uil River in the southern Urals. In Scotland, with magnetite in the granite at Ben Bhreck. In Canada as minute spherules in feldspar at Cameron Township, Nipissing district, and on the north shore of St. Josephs Island, Lake Huron, Ontario, as a thin crust on quartzite.

In the United States iron has been noted in the coal measures of Missouri, at Cameron, Clinton County, and reported from the shale near New Brunswick, New Jersey.

The low-nickel meteoric iron (kamacite) makes up almost the whole mass of the iron meteorites with hexahedral structure (hexahedrites); it is also the principal constituent of the octahedral irons (octahedrites). Kamacite is likewise the main metallic constituent of the siderolites and the stony meteorites. (See also under Nickel-Iron and Meteorites.)

Alter. Changes readily to ferric oxide on exposure. May disintegrate quickly aided by the presence of ferrous chloride (lawrencite).

Artif. The low-nickel native iron corresponds to the artificial iron-nickel alloys which form a continuous series of solid solutions (Ni, 0 to about 25 per cent) having the body-centered structure of α-iron.

Ref.

1. Goldschmidt (**3**, 85, 1916).
2. Hull, *Phys. Rev.*, **9**, 84 (1917); **10**, 661 (1917); **14**, 540 (1919); *Strukturber.*, **1**, 66 (1913–28). Cell edge for α-iron, Owen and Yates, *Phil. Mag.*, **15**, 472 (1933), on iron with 0.018 per cent impurities; for kamacite (anal. 5), Heide, Herschkowitsch and Preuss, *Chem. Erde*, **7**, 483 (1932).
3. Dana (28, 1892) followed Neumann and Tschermak in accepting {122} as the symbol of the planes of the twin lamellae in meteoric iron. Linck, *Zs. Kr.*, **20**, 209 (1892), found the lamallae to be parallel to {112}, and that the intergrowth is due either to twinning on {112} or twinning on {111} with {112} as the composition plane.
4. Schneiderhöhn and Ramdohr (**2**, 39, 1931).
5. For terrestrial irons: Doelter (**3** [2], 768, 1926); for meteoric irons (kamacite): Cohen (**1**, 96, 1894; **2**, 214, 1903).
6. Allen, *Am. J. Sc.*, **4**, 99 (1897).
7. Hoffmann, *Geol. Sur. Canada, Ann. Rep. 1892 — Zs. Kr.*, **23**, 507 (1894), calculated to 100 per cent after subtracting 9.76 per cent insoluble.
8. Smith, *Ann. chim. phys.*, **16**, 452 (1879) — Dana (29, 1892).
9. Heide, Herschkowitsch, and Preuss (1932).
10. Davidson, *Am. J. Sc.*, **42**, 64 (1891).
11. For terrestrial occurrences: Greenland, Dana (32, 1892); Cameron, Missouri, Allen (1897); Bühl, Irmer, *Senck. Ges. Frankfurt, Abh.*, **37**, 104 (1920) — Doelter (**3** [2], 774, 1926).

1172 **NICKEL-IRON** [Fe, Ni]. Nickeleisen *Germ.*
Taenite, Bandeisen, Plessite, Fülleisen *Reichenbach* (*Ann. Phys.*, 114, 1861). Meteorin *Abel* (in *Zimmermann, Jb. Min.*, 557, 1861). Edmonsonite*Flight* (*Roy. Soc. London, Phil. Trans.*, 888, 1882). Awaruite *Skey* (*New Zealand Inst. Trans.*, 18, 401, 1885). Josephinite *Melville* (*Am. J. Sc.*, 43, 509, 1892). Souesite *Hoffmann* (*Am. J. Sc.*, 19, 319, 1905). Bobrovkite *Wyssotzky* (*Com. géol. St. Pétersbourg, Mém.*, 62, 668, 1913).

C r y s t. Isometric; hexoctahedral — $4/m\,\bar{3}\,2/m$.

Structure cell:[1] Space group $Fm3m$; a_0 3.590; contains 4(Fe, Ni).

Habit: Terrestrial: in pebbles, grains and fine scales. Meteoric: with kamacite, in narrow borders or intimate regular intergrowths.

P h y s. Cleavage none. Malleable; flexible. Luster metallic. Silver white to grayish white. H. 5. G. 7.8–8.22. Opaque. Strongly magnetic.

C h e m. An alloy of nickel and iron (Ni, Fe) with Ni 77 to 24 per cent and small amounts of cobalt, copper, phosphorus, sulfur, carbon.

Anal:[2]

	1	2	3	4	5
Fe	21.45	21.87	22.30	25.24	31.02
Ni	76.60	76.16	76.48	74.17	67.63
Co	1.19	1.37	0.00	0.46	0.70
Cu	0.66	0.49	1.22	.....	.....
P	0.04	0.08	.....	0.04	.....
S	0.06	0.03	.....	0.09	0.22
SiO_2	.....	.....	.....	.....	0.43
Total	100.00	100.00	100.00	100.00	100.00
G.	7.85	7.746	8.215		8.1

1. South Fork (terrestrial; awaruite).[3] 2. Hoole Cañon, Pelly River, Yukon (terrestrial; awaruite).[4] 3. Fraser River (terrestrial; souesite).[5] 4. Josephine Co. (terrestrial; josephinite).[6] 5. Gorge River (terrestrial; awaruite).[7]

	6	7	8	9	10	11
Fe	37.69	61.89	63.69	68.13	70.14	74.78
Ni	59.69	36.95	33.97	30.85	29.74	24.32
Co	0.40	0.36	1.48	0.69	.....	0.33
Cu	0.90	.....	.....	0.33	.....	.....
P	0.10	.....	0.05	.....	.....	.....
S	.....	.....	0.16	.....	.....	.....
C	.....	0.80	0.20	.....	.....	0.50
SiO_2	0.41	.....	0.01	.....	.....	.....
Total	99.19	100.00	99.56	100.00	99.88	99.93
G.	8.54		7.75–7.84			

6. Octibbeha Co. (? terrestrial; octibbehite).[8] 7. Taenite, large flexible tablets from Bischtübe meteorite.[9] 8. Santa Catharina (? terrestrial; catarinite).[10] 9. Taenite from the Cañon Diablo meteorite.[11] 10. Taenite from the Cranbourne meteorite, Victoria.[12] 11. Taenite from the Welland, Ont., meteorite.[13]

Var. Terrestrial Nickel-iron. Awaruite *Skey* (*New Zealand Inst., Trans.*, 18, 401, 1885); from the locality, Awarua Bay, New Zealand. Josephinite *Melville* (*Am. J. Sc.*, 43, 509, 1892). Souesite *Hoffmann* (*Am. J. Soc.*, 19, 319, 1905). Bobrovkite *Wyssotzky* (*Com. géol. St. Pétersbourg, Mém.*, 62, 668, 1913 — *Spencer, Min. Mag.*, 19, 336, 1922).

Alloys of nickel and iron with about 67 to 77 per cent nickel; near a possible compound, $FeNi_2$ = Fe 32.3, Ni 67.7, in composition. Octibbehite (anal. 6) and catarinite (anal. 8), said to be terrestrial, have lower nickel contents according to the analyses.

Meteoric Nickel-iron. Taenite, Bandeisen *Reichenbach* (*Ann. Phys.*, **114**, 1861); from ταινία, *band.* Meteorin *Abel*, in *Zimmermann* (*Jb. Min.*, 557, 1861). Edmonsonite *Flight* (*Roy. Soc. London, Phil. Trans.*, 888, 1882). Alloys of nickel and iron with about 24 to 37 per cent nickel.

Plessite, Fülleisen *Reichenbach* (*Ann. Phys.*, **114**, 1861); from πλῆθος, *filling.* An intimate intergrowth of kamacite and taenite in meteorites (octahedrites).

Tests. Slowly soluble in dilute HCl; only slightly attacked by acetic acid.

O c c u r. Terrestrial nickel-iron was found in small plates and grains in the gold washings of the Gorge River which empties into Awarua Bay, New Zealand. In fine scales in the platinum-bearing sands of the Bobrovka River, Nizhne Tagilsk, Urals. In Italy, on the river Elvo, in the Piedmont. In the United States, in Josephine and Jackson counties, Oregon, as large ellipsoidal masses, exceeding 100 lb.; near South Fork, Smith River, Del Norte County, California. In Canada, in small scales in the gold dredgings on the Fraser River, Lillooet district, British Columbia. The irons Santa Catharina, Brazil, and Octibbeha, Missouri, first thought to be meteoric, were later supposed to be terrestrial.

The meteoric nickel-iron, taenite, is present in all octahedrites, which show the Widmannstätten structure, and in some ataxites in which the structure is ill defined. Plessite is a constituent of the octahedrites. (See also under Iron and Meteorites.)

A l t e r. Oxidizes slowly on exposure.

A r t i f. The natural nickel-irons correspond to the artificial nickel-iron alloys which form a series of solid solutions (Fe, 0 to about 75 per cent), without proved intermetallic compounds. These alloys have the face-centered structure of β-nickel and γ-iron.

Ref.

1. Cell edge, Young, *Roy. Soc. London, Proc.*, **112**, 630 (1926) on taenite in the Cañon Diablo meteorite (anal. 9). For an artificial Ni-Fe alloy with 33.80 atomic per cent Ni, corresponding to some taenites, Jette and Foote, *Am. Inst. Min. Met., Engr., Tech. Pub. 670*, 1936, obtained 3.5862 ± 0.0006 at 25°. The mutual orientation of taenite and kamacite in two meteorites has been determined by Derge and Kommel, *Am. J. Sc.*, **34**, 203 (1937).

2. For taenite, Cohen (**1**, 102, 1894; **2**, 217, 1903).

3. Jamieson, *Zs. Kr.*, **41**, 157 (1906), reduced to 100 per cent after withdrawing the insoluble portion.

4. Johnston, *Geol. Sur. Canada, Sum. Rep. 1910*, 258, 1911, reduced to 100 per cent after withdrawing 1.72 per cent insoluble.

5. Wait, in Hoffmann, *Am. J. Sc.*, **19**, 319 (1905).

6. Jamieson (1906), reduced to 100 per cent after withdrawing 24.15 per cent insoluble.

7. Skey, *New Zealand Inst., Trans.*, **18**, 401 (1885).

8. Genth anal. in Taylor, *Am. J. Sc.*, **24**, 294 (1857).
9. Cohen (**2**, 217, 1903).
10. Damour, *C. R.*, **84**, 478 (1877).
11. Florence anal. in Cohen (**2**, 217, 1903); kamacite removed chemically; reduced to 100 per cent after withdrawing 3.60 per cent nickel-iron phosphide.
12. Flight, *Royal Soc. London, Phil. Trans.*, **888**, 1882; taenite mechanically separated from kamacite.
13. Davidson, *Am. J. Sc.*, **42**, 64 (1891).

METEORITES

Classification. Meteorites[1] are broadly classed according to the relative proportions of their metallic and stony components. The *iron meteorites* or *siderites* are composed almost wholly of iron alloyed with nickel. The *iron-stone meteorites* include the *lithosiderites* in which a continuous cellular matrix of nickel-iron encloses discontinuous bodies of silicate minerals, and the *siderolites* in which a discontinuous meshwork pervades a stony mass. The *stony meteorites* or *aerolites* consist of silicate minerals with dispersed clots, grains, or scales of nickel-iron. To these long-recognized groups may be added the *glassy meteorites* or *tektites* consisting almost wholly of siliceous glass which frequently appears to be of cosmic origin.

Constituent Minerals.[2] Meteorites are composed of minerals most of which are known in terrestrial rocks: iron and nickel as kamacite, taenite and plessite; carbon as graphite, cliftonite and diamond; the carbides, cohenite, and moissanite; the phosphide, schreibersite; the sulfides, troilite (pyrrhotite), daubreelite, oldhamite, and osbornite; the oxides, quartz, tridymite, magnetite, and chromite; the carbonate, breunnerite; the chloride, lawrencite; plagioclase feldspars and the glassy equivalent, maskelynite; the orthopyroxenes, enstatite, bronzite, and hypersthene; the clinopyroxenes, clinoenstatite, clinohypersthene, diopside, hedenbergite, and augite; olivine (chrysolite) and forsterite; weinbergerite; the phosphate apatite; and glassy material. Of these, only schreibersite, daubreelite, oldhamite, moissanite, maskelynite and weinbergerite have not as yet been recognized in terrestrial rocks. The alloys of iron and nickel, olivine, and the pyroxenes are by far the most abundant constituents of meteorites. Cohenite, schreibersite, troilite, and glass are usually present in small amounts; the remaining constituents are rare and sparingly developed. The specific properties of the minerals mentioned are given elsewhere in this work.

Iron Meteorites. These present a variety of forms imposed on the mass during its flight through the atmosphere. The form may approach a flat cone or pyramid; occasionally it is spindle-shaped or annular; often it is irregular. The surface is coated with a thin skin of magnetite which is underlaid by a layer of structureless iron that was strongly heated or melted during flight. The surface is usually more or less pitted. In the oriented irons the head side may be smooth or covered with small elongated pits or radial grooves; on the rear side the pits are shallow and more nearly circular.

The iron meteorites are classed according to the internal structure revealed on polished sections etched with dilute acid. A small group of irons shows one or more systems of fine parallel lines (*Neumann lines*) revealing complex lamellar twinning of the kamacite of which these irons are wholly composed. The planes represented by these lines are referred to {112} of kamacite and the lamellar structure has been explained as due to mechanical twinning caused by the shock of impact on the earth.[3] These irons also show cubic cleavage from which they are named *hexahedrites*.

A larger group of iron meteorites exhibits systems of intersecting bands (*Widmanstetter* or *Widmanstätten figures*, named after Baron Widmanstetter [1753–1849]) corresponding to the traces of the planes of the octahedron in the plane of section. The bands represent plates of kamacite with narrow selvages of taenite in regular structural orientation.[4] The angular interstices are usually occupied with plessite, an intimate intergrowth of kamacite and taenite. From their octahedral structure these irons are known as *octahedrites*.

A third group of meteoric irons reveals no definite structure. These are the *ataxites* whose meteoric origin is sometimes uncertain. A similar structureless aspect can be obtained in an octahedrite by prolonged heating at about 900°.

A great number of analyses of iron meteorites have been made.[5] In general they are remarkably alike; the following averages show the slight but distinct differences corresponding to the three structural types. The hexahedrites, which consist of kamacite, are very constant in composition. In the octahedrites the nickel content is somewhat higher owing to the presence of taenite, and the nickel value increases perceptibly as the grain of the octahedral structure becomes finer. The nickel-poor ataxites are not distinguishable in composition from the coarse octahedrites. The nickel-rich ataxites stand out from the other analyses; they may include irons of terrestrial origin.

Anal.[6]

	1	2	3	4	5	6
Fe	94.03	92.33	88.36	92.99	76.72	90.57
Ni	5.05	6.01	10.42	6.21	21.98	8.71
Co	0.65	0.55	0.68	0.59	1.01	0.69
Cu	0.05	0.05	0.04	0.02	0.22	0.06
Cr	0.05	0.02	0.02	0.02	0.04	0.06
P	0.27	0.16	0.20	0.22	0.13	0.22
S	0.11	0.04	0.06	0.07	0.68	0.16
C	0.31	0.32	0.03	0.06	0.05	0.11
Total	100.52	99.48	99.81	100.18	100.83	100.58
G.	7.734	7.798	7.718	7.709	7.715	7.693

1. Average hexahedrite. 2. Average very coarse-grained octahedrite. 3. Average very fine-grained octahedrite. 4. Average low-nickel ataxite. 5. Average high-nickel ataxite. 6. Average of 360 iron meteorites.

In addition to the foregoing elements the following have been found in iron meteorites: chlorine in lawrencite and traces of manganese, platinum, iridium, palladium, and ruthenium alloyed with the nickel-iron. Gold has been reported in minute grains. The occluded gases are hydrogen, nitrogen, carbon monoxide, carbon dioxide, and methane. Almost all the known elements have been detected spectroscopically in meteorites.[7]

Iron-Stone and Stony Meteorites. These bodies are mostly of irregular form with rounded surfaces and a thin, black, glassy skin. The metallic portion, which pervades the mass as a continuous cellular mesh, or is segregated in clots, grains, or scales, usually shows the octahedral structure and otherwise resembles the metal of the siderites. In the *pallasites* the cellular iron mesh is charged with more or less rounded crystals of olivine which are commonly half a centimeter in diameter. In other types of iron-stone meteorites the metallic and silicate portions separate into irregular nodules and the spongelike structure is absent.

Most of the stony meteorites are made up of *chondri* or *chondrules* (χόνδρος, *grain*) of silicate minerals and are therefore classed as *chondrites*. The chondri are rarely as large as a walnut, mostly the size of millet seeds. They may consist of a single mineral, usually chrysolite, or of several minerals, namely bronzite, augite, plagioclase, glass, and nickel-iron, in order of decreasing abundance.

The stony meteorites without chondri, named *achondrites*, show porphyritic, ophitic, and granular textures resembling those found in some terrestrial rocks.

The chemical elements found in the stony meteorites include those already given under iron meteorites, together with the normal constituents of feldspars, pyroxenes, and olivines, also chromium and traces of vanadium in chromite, and titanium in small amount in the pyroxenes.

Tektites.[8] These bottle-green to blackish vitreous bodies, named *tektites* (τηκτός, *melted*), include the moldavites of Bohemia and Moravia, the australites or blackfellows' buttons of southern Australia, Darwin glass or queenstownite of northestern Tasmania, the billitonites of the East Indies, the rizalites of the Philippines, the indochinites of Cambodia, Annam, and Siam, and perhaps the silica glass of the Libyan Desert. The largest tektites weigh up to 4 kg.; most of them are much smaller. The common forms are rude spheroids, ovoids, pear-shapes, buttons, lenses, dumbbells, spindles, and less regular shapes. The surfaces are pitted, grooved, and molded in a manner suggesting flight through the atmosphere. They consist wholly of siliceous glass whose composition is unlike that of obsidian. For the australites, whose cosmic origin can hardly be disputed, the percentage composition is about SiO_2 70, Al_2O_3 13, FeO and Fe_2O_3 6, CaO 3, MgO 2, Na_2O and K_2O 4, with traces of Mn, Ti, Ni, Co. G. 2.3–2.5. The silica glass of the Libyan Desert carries $97\frac{1}{2}$ per cent of SiO_2.

Ref.

1. General works: Cohen (**1**, 1894; **2**, 1903; **3**, 1905); Farrington (1915); Merrill, *U. S. Nat. Mus.*, *Bull. 149*, 1930; Heide (1934). Reviews and summaries: Berwerth; *Fortschr. Min.*, **1**, 257 (1911); **2**, 227, 1912; **3**, 245, 1913; **5**, 265, 1916); Michel *ibid.*, **7**, 245 (1922). Collections: Vienna, Berwerth, *Ak. Wien, Ber.*, **127** [1], 715 (1918);

London, Prior (1923; 1927); Chicago, Farrington, *Field Mus. Chicago, Pub. 188*, 1916; Washington, D. C., Merrill, *U. S. Nat. Mus., Bull. 94*, 1916; Cambridge, Massachusetts, Palache, *Proc. Am. Ac. Arts Sc.*, **61** (1926).

2. Farrington (117, 1915).
3. Heide (86, 1934).
4. On the structure of meteoric iron: Vogel, in Doelter (3 [2], 562, 1926); Young, *Roy. Soc. London, Proc.*, **112**, 630 (1926); Vogel, *Ges. Wiss. Göttingen, Abh. math.-phys. Kl.*, **12** (1927); **3** (1932); Mehl and Barrett, *Trans. Am. Inst. Min. Met. Engr., Inst. Met. Div.*, 78, 1931; Mehl and Marzke, *ibid.*, 123, 1931; Derge and Kommel, *Am. J. Sc.*, **34**, 203 (1937). The last-named authors have shown that kamacite and taenite are mutually oriented with (110) and [1$\bar{1}$1] of kamacite parallel to (111) and [1$\bar{1}$0] of taenite. In this relation the spacings of the parallel atomic planes in the two types of nickel-iron, and the interatomic distances in the parallel atomic rows are nearly alike. They have also reproduced the Widmanstetter structure by slowly cooling artificial Fe-Ni alloys from high temperatures.
5. Berwerth and Michel, in Doelter (1926), list 415 analyses.
6. Averages calculated by Tschirvinsky, from analyses compiled by Farrington, in Doelter (1926).
7. On rare elements in meteorites: Noddack and Noddack, *Naturwiss.*, **18**, 757 (1930); Breckpot and Lecompte, *Mus. Belgique Mem.*, **69** (1935); Goldschmidt, *Fortschr. Min.*, **19**, 183 (1935).
8. Lacroix, *Arch. Mus. Paris*, **8**, 139 (1932); Spencer, *Min. Mag.*, **24**, 503 (1937); Fenner, *ibid.*, **25**, 82 (1938). Barnes (*North Am. Tektites*, Texas Univ., Econ. Geol. Bur., 477–573, 1940).

1173   COHENITE [(Fe, Ni)$_3$C].   Cohenit *Weinschenk* (*Ann. Mus. Wien*, 4, 94, 1889).   Lamprit, Glanzeisen, pt. *Reichenbach* (*Ann. Phys.*, 114, 485, 1861).   Kohlenstoffeisen *Germ.*

Cryst.[1] Orthorhombic;   dipyramidal — $2/m\ 2/m\ 2/m$.

$$a : b : c = 0.891 : 1 : 1.329; \qquad p_0 : q_0 : r_0 = 1.491 : 1 : 1.329$$

Structure cell. Space group *Pbnm*; a_0 4.518, b_0 5.069, c_0 6.736; $a_0 : b_0 : c_0 = 0.891 : 1 : 1.329$;   contains Fe$_{12}C_4$. In elongated platy crystals, rarely with measurable faces.

Phys. Cleavages, {100}, {010}, {001}. Very brittle. H. 5$\frac{1}{2}$–6. G. 7.20–7.65; 7.68 (calc., Fe$_3$C). Strongly magnetic. Tin-white, changing to light bronze to gold-yellow on exposure. Opaque.

Chem. A carbide of iron and nickel (Fe,Ni)$_3$C, usually with some cobalt.

Anal.[2]

	1	2	3	4	5
Fe	93.3	89.81	82.70	91.69	92.73
Ni	....	3.08	9.99	2.21	0.95
Co	....	0.69	2.21	.....	0.39
C	6.7	6.42	5.10	6.10	5.93
Total	100.0	100.00	100.00	100.00	100.00

1. Fe$_3$C. 2. Magura-Arva meteorite.[3] 3. Wichita Co., Tex., meteorite.[4] 4. Cañon Diablo, Ariz., meteorite.[5] 5. Ovifak, Greenland, terrestrial iron.[6]

Tests. B.B. infusible. Insoluble in dilute HCl; slowly soluble in concentrated acid, giving a petroleum-like odor. Soluble in copper ammonium chloride.

Occur. In elongated tabular crystals, resembling schreibersite, in iron meteorites, particularly coarse octahedrites; also in some terrestrial iron. Cohenite is known from the following iron meteorites: Magura, Hungary; Bendego, Brazil; Beaconsfield, Victoria; Wichita County, Texas; Cañon Diablo, Arizona, and others. It has also been found in the terrestrial irons at Ovifak and Niakornak, Greenland.

A r t i f. Formed as cementite, Fe_3C, in steel and in the artificial iron-carbon system.[7]

N a m e. After E. Cohen (1842–1905), Professor of Mineralogy at Greifswald.

Ref.

1. Hendricks, *Zs. Kr.*, **74**, 534 (1930), from measurements by Westgren and Phragmen, *J. Iron Steel Inst.*, **109**, 159 (1924), on cohenite from the Magura meteorite and cementite. The pyramidal class, *2mm*, and space group, *Pbn*, are not excluded. The reported distorted isometric form of cohenite in crystals from the Bendego iron, Hussak, in Derby, *Arch. Mus. Rio de Janeiro*, 160, 1896, has not been confirmed.
2. Computed to 100 per cent after deducting schreibersite, $(Fe,Ni)_3P$.
3. Weinschenk, *Ann. Mus. Wien*, **4**, 95 (1889).
4. Cohen and Weinschenk, *Ann. Mus. Wien*, **6**, 153 (1891).
5. Florence anal. in Derby, *Am. J. Sc.*, **49**, 106 (1895).
6. Sjöström anal. in Cohen, *Ann. Mus. Wien*, **12**, 60 (1897).
7. *Strukturber.*, **1**, 576 (1913–28).

1174 **M O I S S A N I T E** [Si C]. *Kunz* (*Am. J. Sc.*, **19**, 396, 1905).

C r y s t. Hexagonal — *P*; dihexagonal pyramidal — 6 *mm*.

$$a : c = 1 : 4.9060;^1 \qquad p_0 : r_0 = 5.6650 : 1$$

Forms:[2]

$c\{0001\}$	$m\{10\bar{1}0\}$	$l\{10\bar{1}5\}$	$n\{10\bar{1}4\}$	$o\{10\bar{1}3\}$	$p\{10\bar{1}2\}$	$r\{10\bar{1}1\}$
$\bar{c}\{000\bar{1}\}$		$\bar{l}\{10\bar{1}5\}$	$\bar{n}\{101\bar{4}\}$	$\bar{o}\{10\bar{1}3\}$	$\bar{p}\{10\bar{1}2\}$	$\bar{r}\{10\bar{1}\bar{1}\}$

Structure cell.[3] Space group *C6mc*; a_0 3.076 ± 0.003, c_0 15.07 ± 0.015; $a_0 : c_0 = 1 : 4.899$; contains Si_6C_6.

Habit. Tabular $\{0001\}$.

P h y s. Fracture conchoidal. H. $9\frac{1}{2}$. G. 3.1 ± 0.1; 3.21 (calc.). Luster metallic. Color green to emerald-green; also black, bluish.

O p t.[4]

λ	755	Li	589	Tl	416	
O (light blue)	2.616	2.633	2.654	2.675	2.757	Uniaxial pos. (+).
E (deep indigo blue)	2.654	2.673	2.697	2.721	2.812	Pleochroism weak.

C h e m. Silicon carbide, SiC.

Tests. F.7. Not decomposed by acids or aqua regia; not attacked by fused $KClO_3$ or KNO_3; does not burn in oxygen at 1000°. Slowly decomposed by fused KOH, forming potassium silicate; attacked by fused $PbCrO_4$, giving CO_2.

O c c u r. As small hexagonal plates in the meteoric iron of Cañon Diablo, Arizona; associated with minute diamonds.

A r t i f.[5] Produced as silicon carbide, SiC (*carborundum*), in the electric furnace.

N a m e. After H. Moissan (1852–1907) who discovered the natural occurrence.

Ref.

1. Negri, *Riv. min.*, **29**, 33 (1903), on silicon carbide, transformed by quadrupling the c-axis, Peacock and Schroeder, *Cbl. Min.*, 113, 1934, to conform to the structural lattice (Ott, *Zs. Kr.*, **61**, 515 [1925]) of Type II silicon carbide (Baumhauer, *Zs. Kr.*, **50**, 33 [1912]; **55**, 249 [1915]).
2. Moissan, *C. R.*, **139**, 778 (1904); **140**, 405 (1905); Baumhauer (1912, 1915).
3. Ott, *Zs. Kr.*, **61**, 515 (1925); **62**, 201 (1925); **63**, 1 (1926); cell edges, Borrmann and Seyfarth, *Zs. Kr.*, **86**, 472 (1933).
4. Larsen and Berman (77, 1934); Merwin, *Washington Ac. Sc., J.*, **7**, 445 (1917); on artificial crystals of unknown type.
5. The habit and color of the natural crystals suggest that moissanite is the same as the Type II silicon carbide of Baumhauer (1915).

1175   Osbornite. *Story-Maskelyne (Roy. Soc. London, Phil. Trans.*, 198, 1870).
Isometric. Occurs as small golden yellow octahedra in oldhamite and pyroxene of the Busti, India, meteorite. Titanium nitride, TiN, with a_0 4.235 and a rock-salt structure.[1]

Ref.

1. Bannister, *Min. Mag.*, **26**, 36 (1941).

1176   S C H R E I B E R S I T E [(Fe, Ni)$_3$P]. Schreibersit *Haidinger (Ber. Mitt. Freund. Wiss. Wien*, **3**, 69, 1847). Partschite *Shepard (Am. J. Sc.*, **15**, 364, 1853). Lamprit, Glanzeisen *Reichenbach (Ann. Phys.*, **114**, 477, 1861). Rhabdite *Rose (Ann. Phys.*, **124**, 196, 1865). Ferrorhabdite *Lacroix* (3, 618, 1909).

C r y s t.   Tetragonal; disphenoidal — $\overline{4}$.

$$a : c = 1 : 0.4909;^1 \qquad p_0 : r_0 = 0.4909 : 1$$

Forms:[2]

	ϕ	$\rho = C$	A	$\overline{M}$
a 010	0°00′	90°00′	90°00′	45°00′
m 110	45 00	90 00′	45 00	90 00
d 011	0 00	26 09	90 00	71 50½

Structure cell.[3] Space group $I\overline{4}$; a_0 9.013 ± 0.005, c_0 4.424 ± 0.004; $a_0 : c_0 = 1 : 0.4909$; contains (Fe,Ni)$_{24}$P$_8$.

Habit. Crystals rare; often rounded, sometimes with cavities in the terminal faces. In tables or plates (schreibersite); in rods or needles (rhabdite).

P h y s. Cleavage {001}, perfect; prismatic, {010} or {110}, imperfect.[4] Very brittle. H. 6½–7. G. 7.0–7.3; 7.44 (calc. for 28.68 per cent Ni). Highly metallic luster. Silver-white to tin-white, tarnishing to brass-yellow or brown. Opaque. Strongly magnetic.

C h e m. A phosphide of iron and nickel, (Fe,Ni)$_3$P, with small amounts of cobalt and traces of copper.

Anal.[5]

	1	2	3	4	5	6	7	8
Fe	68.37	66.92	58.54	57.46	54.34	51.60	51.10	41.54
Ni	10.07	18.16	26.08	25.78	31.48	30.89	34.13	42.61
Co	0.52	0.62	0.05	1.32	0.67	0.70	0.30	0.80
Cu	.....	.....	trace	.....	0.20	.....	.....	.....
P	15.12	14.88	15.37	15.31	12.82	14.63	14.00	15.05
Rem.	5.31	.....	.....	.....	.....	1.74	.....	.....
Total	99.39	100.58	100.04	99.87	99.51	99.56	99.53	100.00
G.		7.169–	7.20					
		7.175						

1. Zacatecas meteorite (tablets and grains); incl. Cr 0.32, S 0.39, chromite 4.60.[6]
2. Beaconsfield meteorite (large crystals).[7] 3. Cañon Diablo meteorite.[8] 4. Hraschina meteorite.[9] 5. Cañon Diablo meteorite.[10] 6. Coahuila meteorite (rhabdite); incl. Cr 0.78, residue 0.96.[11] 7. Perryville meteorite.[12] 8. Beaconsfield meteorite (rhabdite).[7]

Var. The name *schreibersite* is usually applied to material with platy habit.

Rhabdite Rose (Ann. Phys., **124**, 196, 1865), from ῥάβδος, *rod,* is generally applied to the rodlike or acicular material.

Tests. B.B. melts readily to a strongly magnetic globule. Soluble with difficulty in cold HCl or HNO_3.

O c c u r. Found in all iron meteorites, as oriented inclusions in kamacite,[13] and in troilite (pyrrhotite) and graphite. Also reported as a product of combustion in the coal mines of Commentry and Cranzac, France.

A r t i f. Formed in the artificial system Fe-Ni-P,[14] and as crystals (Fe_3P) in the cavities of iron slags.[15]

N a m e. After Director Karl Fr. A. von Schreibers (1775–1852) of Vienna.

Ref.

1. Heide, Herschkowitsch and Preuss, *Chem. Erde,* **7**, 483 (1932), from x-ray measurements on schreibersite (rhabdite) with 28.68 per cent nickel, from the Buey Huerto (i.e. Buey Muerto) meteorite. Wherry, *Am. Min.*, **2**, 80 (1917) adopted the alternative setting. Smith and White, *Australian Mus., Rec.*, **15**, 66 (1926) took another position. Transformations: Wherry to Heide, Herschkowitsch, and Preuss: $\frac{1}{2}\bar{1}0/\frac{1}{2}\frac{1}{2}0/001$; Smith and White to H. H. P.: $0\bar{1}0/100/001$.
2. Wherry (1917); Smith and White (1926). Uncertain: {130}, {147}, {134}, {1·11·4}, {717}, {232}.
3. Space group, not certain, Hägg, *Zs. Kr.*, **68**, 470 (1928) on artificial Fe_2P. Cell edge, Heide, Herschkowitsch and Preuss (1932).
4. Cohen (**1**, 124, 1894).
5. Doelter (**3** [2], 810, 1926); Cohen (**1**, 132, 1894; **2**, 233, 1903).
6. Scheerer anal. in Cohen (**1**, 132, 1894).
7. Sjoström anal. in Cohen, *Ak. Berlin, Ber.*, **46**, 1035 (1897).
8. Tassin anal. in Merrill and Tassin, *Smithsonian Misc. Coll.*, **50**, 203 (1907).
9. Cohen (**1**, 132, 1894).
10. Florence anal. in Derby, *Am. J. Sc.*, **149**, 101 (1895).
11. Cohen, *Ann. Mus. Wien*, **9**, 98 (1894).
12. Whitfield anal. in Merrill, *U. S. Nat. Mus., Proc.*, **43**, 595 (1912).
13. In a piece of the Cape York, Greenland, meteorite Bøggild, *Med. om Grønland,* **74**, 11 (1927) noted (001) and (110) [probably (100) in our notation] of schreibersite parallel to (100) and (012), respectively, of the surrounding kamacite.

14. Vogel, *Ges. Wiss. Göttingen, Abh.*, **6** (1932).
15. Spencer, *Min. Mag.*, **17**, 340 (1916).

1177   Siderazot [Fe_5N_2]. *Silvestri* (*Ann. Phys.*, **157**, 165, 1876). Silvestrite *D'Achiardi* (*I Metalli*, **2**, 84, 1883). A product of volcanic eruption, observed on Mount Etna after the eruption of August, 1874, as a very thin coating on lava; also from Vesuvius.[1] Luster metallic. Color silvery white, resembling steel. G. 3.147. Slowly attacked by acids. Analysis gave: Fe 90.86, N 9.14 = 100.00, corresponding to the iron nitride Fe_5N_2 = Fe 90.9, N 9.1 = 100.0, which is known as an artificial compound.[2]

Ref.

1. See Zambonini (**34**, 1935).
2. Mellor (**8**, 131, 133, 1928).

118   TANTALUM [Ta]. *Walther* (*Nature*, **81**, 335, 1909; *von John, ibid.*, **83**, 398, 1910).

C r y s t. Isometric; hexoctahedral — $4/m \bar{3} \, 2/m$. Minute cubic crystals; fine grains.

Structure cell.[1] Space group $Im3m$; a_0 3.2959 ± 0.0003 (20°); contains 2Ta.

P h y s. H. 6–7. G. 11.2 ; 16.72 (calc.). Luster bright. Color grayish yellow.

C h e m. Tantalum, Ta, with some columbium and traces of gold and manganese.

Anal.

Ta 98.5, Cb 1.5, Mn 0.001, total 100.

O c c u r. Reported sparingly in the gold washings of the Ural and Altai Mountains.[2]

N a m e. From the element, tantalum, which was named, in allusion to its nonabsorbent quality, after Tantalus (Greek mythology), who was condemned to die of thirst.

Ref.

1. Hull, *Phys. Rev.*, **17**, 571 (1921). Cell edge, Neuburger, *Zs. Kr.*, **93**, 312 (1936), on very pure tantalum.
2. The reported occurrence in the Altai is doubted by Pilipenko, *Tomsk Univ., Bull.*, **63** (1915) — *Min. Abs.*, **2**, 109 (1923).

119   TIN [Sn] Plumbum candidum *Pliny* (**34**, 47, A.D. 77). Jupiter *Alchem.* Gediegen Zinn *Germ.* Gediget Tenn *Swed.* Étain natif *Fr.* Stagno nativo *Ital.* Estano nativo *Span.*

C r y s t. Tetragonal; ditetragonal dipyramidal — $4/m \, 2/m \, 2/m$.

$$a : c = 1 : 0.5455;^1 \qquad p_0 : r_0 = 0.5455 : 1$$

Structure cell.[2] Space group $I4/amd$; a_0 5.8194 ± 0.0003; c_0 3.1753 ± 0.0009; $a_0 : c_0$ = 1 : 0.5456; contains 4Sn.

P h y s. No distinct cleavage. Fracture hackly. Ductile, malleable. H. 2. G. 7.31; 7.278 (calc.). M.P. 231.8°. Luster metallic. Color tin-white. Opaque.

C h e m. Tin, Sn.

Tests. Easily soluble in concentrated HCl to SnCl₂, with evolution of hydrogen.

O c c u r.[3] Natural crystals unknown. In irregular rounded grains, or aggregates of grains, from 0.1 to 1 mm. in size, with platinum, iridosmine, gold, copper, cassiterite, corundum, in sands of the Aberfoil and Sam rivers (headwaters of the Clarence River) near Oban, New South Wales. Reported in volcanic gases on the islands of Volcano and Stromboli. Other described occurrences are doubtful.

A l t e r. Oxidizes only upon heating. Solid white tin (β-tin), by contact with gray tin (α-tin), alters to a gray powder ("tin plague").

A r t i f.[4] Crystals of white tin are obtained by electrolysis; also from melts.

N a m e. From the Latin *stannum*, which however was not applied to *tin* until the fourth century.

Ref.

1. Miller, *Phil. Mag.*, **22**, 263 (1843) on artificial crystals, transformed to the structural lattice of Mark and Polanyi, *Zs. Phys.*, **18**, 75 (1923); **22**, 200 (1924). Dana (24, 1892) adopted the setting of Miller. Transformation: Miller to Mark and Polanyi: $\frac{11}{22}0/\frac{11}{22}0/001$. Artificial crystals, Groth (**1**, 14, 1906), Mügge, *Zs. Kr.*, **65**, 604 (1927), show the forms: {010}, {110}, {011}, {031}, {112}, {332}; uncertain: {001}. Twinning on {011}, common, and {031}. Habit, dipyramidal {011}. Gliding: $K_1(031)$, $K_2(01\bar{1})$; $T\{110\}$, $t\{001\}$; $T\{010\}$, $t\{001\}$; $T\{010\}$, $t\{\bar{1}01\}$; $T\{110\}$, $t\{1\bar{1}1\}$, Mügge (1927).
2. Mark and Polanyi (1923). Cell edges, Stenzel and Weerts, *Zs. Kr.*, **84**, 20 (1932) on 99.99 per cent pure Sn at 20°.
3. New South Wales: Howell in Genth, *Am. Phil. Soc, Proc.*, **23**, 30 (1885); Stromboli: Bergeat, *Zs. pr. Geol.*, **43**, 1899.
4. A reported orthorhombic modification, Trechmann, *Min. Mag.*, **3**, 186 (1879), has been shown to be stannous sulfide, SnS (Spencer, *Min. Mag.*, **18**, 113 (1921).

11·10 Z I N C [Zn] Zink *Germ.* Zinco *Ital.*

C r y s t. Hexagonal — P; dihexagonal dipyramidal — $6/m\ 2/m\ 2/m$

$$a : c = 1 : 1.8560;^1 \qquad p_0 : r_0 = 2.1431 : 1$$

Structure cell.[2] Space group $C6/mmc$; a_0 2.6591 ± 0.0005; c_0 4.9353; $a_0 : c_0 = 1 : 1.8560 ± 0.0005$ (18°); contains 2Zn.

P h y s. Cleavage {0001} perfect. Rather brittle. H. 2. G. 6.9–7.2; 7.135 (calc.). M.P. 420°. Luster metallic. Color and streak white, slightly grayish. Opaque.

C h e.m. Zinc, Zn.

O c c u r. Has been reported from several places (Australia, New South Wales, New Zealand, Alabama, Colorado, California) but its existence in nature remains doubtful.

A r t i f. Crystals have been obtained from melts, and by condensing the vapor in various ways.

Ref.

1. Owen, Pickup, and Roberts, *Zs. Kr.*, **91**, 70 (1935), by x-ray measurements on artificial zinc, 99.9 per cent pure. Artificial crystals, Straumanis, *Zs. phys. Chem.* **13**, 316 (1931); **19**, 63 (1932); **26**, 246 (1934), Gough and Cox, *Roy. Soc. London, Proc.*, **123**, 143 (1929); **127**, 453 (1930) are prismatic [0001], barrel-shaped, to tabular {0001}; strongly striated horizontally; forms: {0001}, {10$\bar{1}$0}, {11$\bar{2}$0}, {10$\bar{1}$1}, also {20$\bar{2}$5}, {10$\bar{1}$2}, {20$\bar{2}$3} on stepped crystals; twinning on the plane {10$\bar{1}$2}; gliding, T{0001}, t{2$\bar{1}$$\bar{1}$0}; hexagonal percussion figure on {0001}, with rays parallel to the axes [2$\bar{1}$$\bar{1}$0].

2. Neuburger, *Zs. Kr.*, **86**, 395 (1933). Cell edges, Owen, Pickup, and Roberts (1935).

121 ARSENIC GROUP

1211	Arsenic	As
1212	Arsenolamprite	As
1213	Allemontite	AsSb
1214	Antimony	Sb
1215	Bismuth	Bi

These native elements are hexagonal — R, scalenohedral — $\bar{3}\,2/m$. They all have the same structure (arsenic type) which has the symmetry of the space group $R\bar{3}m$. The simple cell is an acute rhombohedron containing two atoms, one at each lattice point, the other at the center of the cell. The two atoms are structurally dissimilar; they may be chemically alike (arsenic, antimony, bismuth), or chemically different (allemontite). The form and structure of the minerals of this group have also been referred to a face-centered (pseudocubic) rhombohedral lattice.[1]

Some of the properties of these minerals show systematic variation.

	Arsenic	Allemontite	Antimony	Bismuth
a_{rh}	4.142	4.336	4.501	4.736
α	54°07′	55°36′	57°05′	57°16′
H.	3½	3–4	3–3½	2–2½
G.	5.704	6.277	6.680	9.753

The increase in metallic character is accompanied by some decrease in hardness and an increase in specific gravity.

Ref.

1. Bragg (50, 1937).

1211 A R S E N I C [As].   Gediegen Arsenik, Arsen, Scherbenkobalt *Germ.*   Arsenic natif *Fr.*   Arsenico nativo *Ital., Span.*

C r y s t.   Hexagonal — R; scalenohedral — $3\,2/m$.

$a : c = 1 : 2.8059;$ $\alpha = 54°07′$.[1] $p_0 : r_0 = 3.2400 : 1;$ $\lambda = 111°41′$

Forms:[2]

		ϕ	$\rho = C$	A_1	A_2
c 0001	111	. . . . .	0°00′	90°00′	90°00′
e 10$\bar{1}$4	211	30°00′	39 00½	56 58	90 00
h 30$\bar{3}$4	10·1·1	30 00	67 38	36 47	90 00
z 01$\bar{1}$8	332	−30 00	22 03	90 00	71 02
p 01$\bar{1}$2	110	−30 00	58 19	90 00	42 32
f 02$\bar{2}$1	11$\bar{1}$	−30 00	81 13½	90 00	31 08½

Structure cell.[3] Space group $R\bar{3}m$. a_{rh} 4.142, α 54°07′; contains 2As. For hexagonal axes: a_0 3.768, c_0 10.574; $a_0 : c_0 = 1 : 2.806$; contains 6As.

Habit. Pseudocubic {01$\bar{1}$2}. Common forms on artificial crystals: Pce. Natural crystals rare, usually acicular. Generally granular massive; often in concentric layers; sometimes reticulated, reniform, stalactitic; rarely columnar.

Twinning. Twin plane {10$\bar{1}$4}, rare.

Phys. Cleavage {0001} perfect, very easy; {10$\bar{1}$4} fair. Fracture uneven and fine granular.

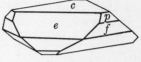

Sterling Hill, N. J.

Brittle. H. $3\frac{1}{2}$. G. 5.63–5.78; 5.704 (calc.). Luster nearly metallic in fresh fracture. Color and streak tin-white, tarnishing soon to dark gray. Opaque. In polished section[4] white with strong reflectivity, feebly pleochroic and distinctly anisotropic. Percentage reflection: green, 61.5; orange, 50; red, 50.

Chem. Arsenic, As, usually with antimony, iron, nickel, silver, sulfur, rarely bismuth, vanadium.[5]

Anal. Mount Royal, near Montreal, Canada:[6] As 98.14, Sb 1.65, S 0.16, insoluble 0.15, total 100.10; G. 5.74.

Tests. B.B. volatile without fusion, garlic odor (AsH₃); on charcoal, white As_2O_3 coating which volatizes in R. F., tingeing the flame blue. In the open tube, crystalline As_2O_3 on the upper side; in the closed tube, As mirror. On plaster with iodide flux, orange-yellow AsI₃.

Occur. Found in hydrothermal veins, most commonly with silver, cobalt, or nickel ores; also associated with barite, arsenolite, cinnabar, realgar, orpiment, stibnite, galena, sphalerite, pyrite; in dolomitic limestone.

Found in many places in Saxony, especially at Freiberg, Schneeberg, Marienberg, and Annaberg. At Andreasberg, Harz Mountains, in fine reniform masses. In Bohemia, at Joachimstal, Přibram, and Líšnice. In Roumania, at Nagyág, Hunyad, and at Kapnik. In Italy, at Valle Malenco, Lombardy. In Alsace, at Ste. Marie aux Mines, in fine specimens. From Province of Sarawak, Borneo. In Chile, at Copiapó. In Western Australia at Kalgoorlie. In Japan, at Akadani, Echizen province, as globular masses composed of small rhombohedral crystals.

Occurs infrequently in the United States. It has been found at Washington Camp, Santa Cruz County, Arizona, in reniform masses, sometimes several pounds in weight. Also in Louisiana, as spheroids $\frac{1}{4}$ in. in diameter, in the anhydrite cap rock of the Winnfield salt dome. In Canada it occurs near Montreal, Quebec, with calcite in a vein cutting nepheline syenite; in the Lake Superior region, Ontario; on Alder Island, Queen Charlotte Islands, British Columbia.

Alter. Oxidizes on exposure, producing a black crust, which is a mixture of arsenic and arsenolite (As₂O₃), also producing pure arsenolite.

A r t i f.[7] Good crystals can be very easily obtained by sublimation, on heating arsenopyrite; by passing arsenic vapors in a stream of CO_2 over red hot AgCl; by treating realgar or orpiment with KOH, then heating with Na_2CO_3 to 300°.

Various allotropic modifications are known; the rhombohedral is the stable form and, with the possible exception of arsenolamprite, the only one that occurs in nature.

N a m e. From ἀρρενικόν or ἀρσενικόν, *masculine*, a term applied to orpiment or sulfide of arsenic, on account of its potent properties.

Ref.

1. From x-ray measurements by Bradley, *Phil. Mag.*, **47**, 657 (1924), on artificial crystals, leading to $(01\bar{1}2) \wedge (1\bar{1}02) - 94°56'$, in agreement with Rose, *Ak. Berlin, Abh.*, 82, 1849, who gives the same value, also for artificial crystals. The adopted lattice cell is the simple structural cell, first recognized by Friedel (230, 1904). Rose (1849) proposed the pseudocubic unit rhombohedron, adopted by Dana (11, 1892) and Goldschmidt (54, 1897; **1**, 106, 1913). Transformation: Rose to Friedel: 0100/1000/0010/0002.
2. Goldschmidt (1913); Palache, *Am. Min.*, **26**, 716 (1941), described crystals from Sterling Hill, N. J., with the forms c, e, p, and f as shown in the figure.
3. Bradley (1924). Hägg and Hybinette, *Phil. Mag.*, **20**, 913, 1935 — Strukturber., **3**, 211 (1935), for purest As, give a_{rh} 4.123, α 54°06'.
4. Schneiderhöhn and Ramdohr (**2**, 25, 1931).
5. Simpson, *Roy. Soc. Western Australia, J.*, **20**, 47 (1934).
6. Evans, *Am. J. Sc.*, **15**, 92 (1903).
7. Doelter (3 [1], 596, 1914).

1212   Arsenolamprite [As]. Arsenolamprit *Hintze* (*Zs. Kr.*, **11**, 606, 1886). Arsenikwismuth *Werner*. Arsenikglanz *Breithaupt* (129, 250, 1823). Wismuthischer Arsenglanz *Breithaupt* (273, 1832). Hypotyphite *Breithaupt*. Kryptischer Arsenolamprit *Breithaupt* (3, 1847 — *Hintze* (1 [1], 111, 1904)).

Originally described as an allotropic form of arsenic. Massive, with fibrous foliated structure. Cleavage, perfect in one direction. H. 2. G. 5.3–5.5. Luster metallic, brilliant. Color lead-gray. Streak black. Composition nearly pure arsenic; the original mineral from Marienberg, Saxony, contained 3 per cent bismuth. Reported from Ste. Marie aux Mines, Alsace; found in Copiapó region, Chile. Two specimens, one from Marienberg, the other from Copiapó, gave identical x-ray powder patterns, similar to that of rhombohedral arsenic but not enough to be conclusive: arsenolamprite may be either impure arsenic or a distinct modification.[1] Name, from λαμπρὸς, *brilliant*.

Ref.

1. See Jung, *Cbl. Min.*, 111, 1926.

1213   A L L E M O N T I T E [AsSb]. Antimoine natif arsenifère *Hauy* (4, 281, 1822). Arsenikspiessglanz *Zippe* (*Ges. Mus. Böhmen, Vh.*, 102, 1824). Arsenik-Antimon *Hausmann*. Arséniure d'antimoine *Beudant* (469, 1824). Antimon-Arsen, Arsenantimon *Germ.* Arsenical antimony. Allemontit *Haidinger* (557, 1845A). Antimoniferous arsenic.

C r y s t.[1] Hexagonal — R; scalenohedral — $\bar{3}\,2/m$.

Structure cell. Space group $R\bar{3}m$. a_{rh} 4.336, α 55°36'; contains AsSb.

Habit. Indistinct branching crystals, fibrous.[2] More often in reniform masses, coarse to fine mammillary; curved lamellar; fine granular.

P h y s. Cleavage, perfect in one direction. H. 3–4. G. 5.8–6.2; 6.277 (calc). Luster metallic, occasionally splendent; sometimes dull. Color tin-white or reddish gray; tarnishes gray or brownish black. Streak gray. Polished sections of most specimens show a fine graphic intergrowth of two constituents[3] in varying proportions: one is allemontite, the other either nearly pure arsenic[4] (vein occurrences) or nearly pure antimony with some arsenic in solid solution[5] (pegmatite occurrence); homogeneous allemontite, however, has also been observed in polished surfaces.[6] Electrical resistance, close to that of arsenic and antimony, decreases with increasing temperature.[7]

C h e m. Probably an intermetallic compound of arsenic and antimony, AsSb.

Anal.

	1	2	3	4	5
Sb	61.9	61.5	73.9	28.68	37.85
As	38.1	35.0	25.4	70.08	62.15
Bi	....	0.02	0.24	.....	.....
Fe	....	0.85	0.07	.....	.....
Au	....	.....	0.00	0.05	.....
S	....	0.20	0.12	0.25	.....
Insol.	....	2.20	0.00	.....	.....
Total	100.0	99.77	99.73	99.06	100.00

1. AsSb. 2. Varuträsk (homogeneous).[8] 3. Varuträsk (intergrown with antimony).[9] 4. Atlin (intergrown with arsenic).[10] 5. Allemont (intergrown with arsenic).[11]

Tests. F.1. B.B. on charcoal emits fumes of As and Sb, and fuses to a metallic globule, which takes fire and burns away, leaving a white coating of As_2O_3. In C.T. gives a sublimate of As and a globule of Sb.

O c c u r. Mostly in veins, associated with arsenic, arsenolite, antimony, kermesite, stibnite, sphalerite, siderite, quartz, calcite. Described from the mine des Chalanches, near Allemont, Isère, France. Occurs sparingly at Přibram, Bohemia; Andreasberg, in the Harz Mountains; Sztanizsa, Transylvania; Marienberg, Saxony; Valtellina, Italy. In America, at the Ophir mine, Comstock Lode, Nevada; at Atlin and Alder Island, British Columbia.

Also found in a lithium pegmatite, with cleavelandite, tourmaline, lepidolite, and quartz, at Varuträsk, Sweden; formed at a late stage of the mineralization, at a temperature thought to be less than 470°.

A l t e r. To valentinite, Sb_2O_3,[12] or arsenostibite, a supposed hydrous oxide of antimony and arsenic.[13]

A r t i f.[14] By fusion and recrystallization of the constituents. No break down of solid solutions into two-phase systems could be obtained on cooling.

N a m e. From Allemont, France, the type locality.

Ref.

1. Ahlborg and Westgren, *Geol. För. Förh.*, **59**, 140 (1937) proved that arsenic and antimony form an unbroken series of solid solutions at high temperature. They analyzed a series of (As,Sb) alloys by the powder method and found each alloy to be a single phase having the same rhombohedral structure as arsenic and antimony, with intermediate lattice dimensions. Unit cell volumes (in $Å^3$) of various allemontite specimens are as follows: (*a*) homogeneous specimens: Varuträsk, 50.0; Allemont, 51.2; (*b*) allemontite phase of heterogeneous specimens: Varuträsk, 51.0–51.7; Příbram, 51.2. The artificial materials gave: As, 42.8; As : Sb = 1 : 1, 51.7; Sb, 60.0; hence the identification of allemontite with the 1 : 1 alloy. The parameters given are those of the artificial alloy. The inference is that, in nature, the arsenic-antimony solid solutions become unstable on cooling, breaking down into a two-phase system, composed of AsSb and the released excess of As (Příbram) or Sb (Varuträsk). Allemontite was originally thought to be $SbAs_3$; the name is now restricted to the AsSb phase, which is stable under natural conditions and probably is an intermetallic compound, although the available x-ray evidence is not conclusive.
2. Quensel, *Geol. För. Förh.*, **59**, 135 (1937).
3. Van der Veen (70, 1925).
4. Holmes, *Am. Min.*, **21**, 202 (1936).
5. Quensel, Ahlborg and Westgren (1937).
6. Odman and Gavelin, in Quensel (1937).
7. Beijerinck, *Jb. Min., Beil.-Bd.*, **11**, 421 (1896).
8. Svedberg anal. in Quensel (1937).
9. Berggren anal. in Quensel (1937).
10. Walker, *Am. Min.*, **6**, 98 (1921).
11. Rammelsberg, *Ann. Phys.*, **62**, 137 (1844).
12. Laspeyres, *Zs. Kr.*, **9**, 192 (1884).
13. At Varuträsk, Quensel (1937); *Geol. För. Förh.*, **59**, 145 (1937).
14. Ahlborg and Westgren (1937).

1214   **A N T I M O N Y** [Sb].   Gediget Spitsglas *Swab* (*Ak. Stockholm, Handl.*, **10**, 100, 1748), Cronstedt (201, 1758).   Spiesglas, Gediegen Antimon *Germ.*   Antimoine natif *Fr.*   Antimonio nativo *Ital., Span.*

C r y s t.   Hexagonal — *R*; scalenohedral — $\bar{3}\ 2/m$.

$a : c = 1 : 2.6183$; $\alpha = 57°05'$.[1] $p_0 : r_0 = 3.0234 : 1$; $\lambda = 110°37'$

Forms:[2]

		ϕ	$\rho = C$	A_1	A_2
c 001	111	.....	0°00′	90°00′	90°00′
a 11$\bar{2}$0	10$\bar{1}$	0°00′	90 00	60 00	60 00
e 10$\bar{1}$4	211	30 00	37 05	58 31	90 00
r 10$\bar{1}$1	100	30 00	71 42	34 41$\frac{1}{2}$	90 00
Z 01$\bar{1}$8	332	−30 00	20 42	90 00	72 10
P 01$\bar{1}$2	110	−30 00	56 31	90 00	43 45$\frac{1}{2}$
x 3·2·$\bar{5}$·16	853	6 35	39 28$\frac{1}{2}$	67 44	75 22

Structure cell.[3]   Space group $R\bar{3}m$. a_{rh} 4.501 ± 0.003, α 57°05′; contains 2Sb.   For hexagonal axes: a_0 4.301, c_0 11.26; $a_0 : c_0 = 1 : 2.618$; contains 6Sb.

Habit.   Pseudocubic {01$\bar{1}$2}; thick tabular {0001}.   Common forms: *P c e r*.   Generally massive, lamellar and distinctly cleavable; also radiated; sometimes botryoidal or reniform with a granular texture.

Twinning.   On {10$\bar{1}$4}, common; in complex groups, fourlings and sixlings; also polysynthetic.

P h y s.   Cleavage {0001} perfect and easy; {10Ī1} sometimes distinct; {10Ī4} imperfect; {11Ī0} indistinct.   Fracture uneven.   Very brittle. H. 3–3½.   G. 6.61–6.72; 6.680 (calc.).   Luster metallic.   Color tin-white.   Streak gray. Opaque.   In polished section[4] brilliant white, with very strong reflectivity; very feebly pleochroic; weakly anisotropic.   Percentage reflection: green, 67.5; orange, 58; red, 55.

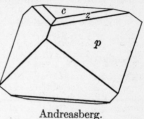

Andreasberg.

C h e m.   Antimony, Sb, sometimes containing arsenic, iron, or silver.

Tests.   F.1.   B.B. on charcoal gives, near the assay, a coating of oxide which tinges the R.F. bluish green (Sb); if the blowing be intermitted, the globule continues to glow, giving off fumes, until it is crusted over with needles of valentinite (Sb_2O_3).   Crystallizes from fusion.   In O.T., only the volatile, crystalline Sb_2O_3; in C.T., cannot be volatilized. On plaster with iodide flux, orange sublimate stippled with peach-red (SbI_3).   In concentrated HNO_3, oxidizes to $HSbO_3$.

O c c u r.   In veins, with silver, antimony, and arsenic ores, often with stibnite and allemontite; also with sphalerite, pyrite, galena, quartz. Occurs at Přibram, Bohemia; at Andreasberg in the Harz Mountains, Germany; Allemont, Isère, France; near Sarrabus, Sardinia; near Sala, Sweden.   Found in fine specimens in the Province of Sarawak, Borneo; also in Australia in Queensland and at Broken Hill and Lucknow, New South Wales.   At Huasco, Atacama, Chile.   Occurs in the United States in Kern County, and at South Riverside, Riverside County, California.   In Canada at South Ham, Wolfe County, Quebec; near Lake George, Prince William parish, York County, New Brunswick.

A l t e r.   To valentinite.

A r t i f.[5]   Artificial crystals are easily obtained in various ways, such as the reduction of $SbCl_3$ by hydrogen.   Various allotropic modifications are known; the rhombohedral is the stable form, the only one found in nature.

N a m e.   Antimonium *Constantinus Africanus* (ca. 1060), applied, however, to stibnite.

Ref.

1. From x-ray measurements by Persson and Westgren, *Zs. phys. Chem.*, **136**, 208 (1928), leading to (01Ī2) ∧ (1Ī02) = 92°29′, in good agreement with Rose, *Ak. Berlin, Abh.*, 73, 1849, who gives 92°25′ for the same angle.   The adopted lattice cell is the simple structural cell, first recognized by Friedel (230, 1904).   Mohs-Haidinger (**2**, 426, 1825) proposed the pseudocubic rhombohedron, adopted by Rose (1849), Dana (12, 1892) and Goldschmidt (46, 1897; **1**, 60, 1913).   Transformation: Mohs to Friedel: 0100/1000/0010/0002.
2. Goldschmidt (1913); *a r x* on artificial crystals only.
3. Persson and Westgren (1928).   Jette and Foote, *J. Chem. Phys.*, **3**, 605 (1935), for material tempered 18 hours at 475°, give a_{rh} 4.49762 ± 0.00018, α 57°06′27″ ± 19″.
4. Schneiderhöhn and Ramdohr (**2**, 29, 1931).
5. Doelter (3 [1], 752, 1914).

1215　BISMUTH [Bi]. Bisemutum, Plumbum cinereum *Agricola* (439, 1546), Antimonium femininum, Tectum argenti *Alchem.* Gediegen Wismuth *Germ.* Bismuth natif *Fr.* Bismuto nativo *Ital., Span.*

C r y s t.　Hexagonal — R; scalenohedral — $\bar{3}\,2/m$.

$a : c = 1 : 2.6073$;　$\alpha = 57°16'$.[1]　$p_0 : r_0 = 3.0107 : 1$;　$\lambda = 110°33'$

Forms:[2]

		ϕ	$\rho = C$	A_1	A_2
c	0001	111	....	0°00′	90°00′	90°00′
m	10$\bar{1}$0	2$\bar{1}\bar{1}$	30°00′	90 00	30 00	90 00
e	10$\bar{1}$4	211	30 00	36 58	58 37	90 00
g	20$\bar{2}$5	311	30 00	50 17½	48 13	90 00
p	10$\bar{1}$2	411	30 00	56 24	43 50	90 00
r	10$\bar{1}$1	100	30 00	71 37½	34 43½	90 00
P	01$\bar{1}$2	110	−30 00	56 24	90 00	43 50

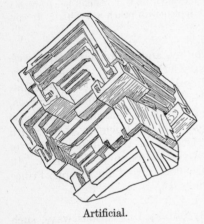

Artificial.

Structure cell.[3]　Space group $R\bar{3}m$. a_{rh} 4.736, α 57°16′; contains 2Bi. For hexagonal axes: a_0 4.55, c_0 11.85; $a_0 : c_0 = 1 : 2.6073$; contains 6Bi.

Habit.　Natural crystals, indistinct. Artificial crystals, pseudocubic {01$\bar{1}$2}. Common forms: *P c r e*. Crystals in parallel groups; often mazelike or hopper-shaped. Usually in reticulated and arborescent shapes; foliated; granular.

Twinning.　On {10$\bar{1}$4}, frequent, polysynthetic; can be produced by pressure.[4]

P h y s.　Cleavage {0001}, perfect and easy; {10$\bar{1}$1} good; {10$\bar{1}$4} very imperfect. Sectile. Somewhat malleable when heated, otherwise brittle. H. 2–2½. G. 9.70–9.83; 9.753 (calc.). Luster metallic. Color and streak silver-white, with reddish hue; subject to iridescent tarnish. Opaque. In polished section[5] brilliant creamy white, soon tarnishing yellow; very feebly pleochroic, distinctly anisotropic. Percentage reflection: green, 67.5; orange, 62; red, 65.

C h e m.　Bismuth, Bi, with small amounts or traces of tellurium, sulfur, arsenic, antimony.

Tests. F.1. M.P. ca 270°. B.B. on charcoal fuses and volatilizes, giving a coating of oxide, orange-yellow while hot and lemon-yellow on cooling. Crystallizes from fusion. On plaster with iodide flux, purplish chocolate sublimate with underlying scarlet (BiI₃). Soluble in HNO₃, subsequent dilution causes a white precipitate.

O c c u r.　In hydrothermal veins accompanying various ores of cobalt, nickel, silver, and tin. Also in pegmatites. Reported in topaz-bearing quartz veins.

Abundant in Saxony, especially at Schneeberg, Annaberg, Johann-georgenstadt, also in tin veins at Altenberg. In Bohemia, at Joachimstal (Jáchymov), mostly in the uraninite veins. In France, at Meymac (Corrèze), with various bismuth minerals. In Norway, at Modum; in Sweden, at Broddbo near Fahlun, and other localities. In Cornwall, at St. Just, St. Ives, Camborne, and elsewhere; in Devonshire, at Tavistock. In the Cape Province, South Africa, as an accessory mineral in pegmatite veins; in Madagascar, as cleavable masses from a lithic pegmatite. The most productive deposits occur in Bolivia, at San Baldomero, near Sorata, in La Paz; at Huaina, in Potosí; at Oruro and Tazna; also at Uncia-Llallagua, associated with cassiterite in veins. There are important deposits in pegmatites in Australia, at Chillagoo, Queensland, and at Kingsgate, New England Range, New South Wales, where it has been found in masses weighing up to 30 lb.

Occurs sparingly in the United States: in Monroe, Connecticut; in the Chesterfield district, South Carolina; in the placers of French Creek, Summit County, and at Las Animas mine, Boulder County, Colorado. In Canada, in fine specimens associated with the silver ores of the Cobalt district, Ontario; also filling cracks in pitchblende veins, Great Bear Lake, Mackenzie.

A r t i f.[6] The best artificial crystals have been obtained from melts. Poor crystals can be made in the wet way. Bismuth can also be obtained electrolytically.

N a m e.[7] The etymology is in dispute; possibly from $\psi\iota\mu\nu\theta\sigma$, *lead white.*

Ref.

1. Computed from the axial angle $\alpha = 87°34'$ of the face-centered pseudocubic lattice determined by Ogg, *Phil. Mag.*, **42**, 163 (1921). The adopted lattice cell is the simple structural cell; it agrees with the primary rhombohedron chosen by Haidinger, *Ak. Wien, Ber.*, **1**, 624 (1848). Rose, *Ak. Berlin, Abh.*, 90, 1849, proposed the pseudocubic unit rhombohedron, adopted by Dana (13, 1892) and Goldschmidt (364, 1897; **9**, 78, 1923). Transformation: Rose to Haidinger: 0100/1000/0010/0002.
2. Goldschmidt (1923).
3. Hassel and Mark, *Zs. Phys.*, **23**, 269 (1924), confirming the axial angle of Ogg (1921). Jette and Foote, *J. Chem. Phys.*, **3**, 605 (1935), for three samples differently tempered give a_{rh} 4.7364 ± 0.0003, α 57°14'13'' ± 23''; anal. Bi 99.95, Fe 0.008, Sn 0.003, Pb 0.010, S 0.01, Cu 0.005, Ag 0.010 = 99.996.
4. Mügge, *Jb. Min.*, **1**, 183, 1886.
5. Schneiderhöhn and Ramdohr (**2**, 32, 1931).
6. Doelter (3 [1], 811, 1918).
7. Hintze (**1** [1], 122, 1904).

122 TELLURIUM GROUP

1221	Selenium	Se
1222	Selen-tellurium	Te, Se
1223	Tellurium	Te

These semi-metals are hexagonal — P, trigonal trapezohedral — 3 2. Their structures are alike, having the symmetry of the space groups

$C3_12$ or $C3_22$, with three atoms in the simple hexagonal cell. The lattice dimensions compare as follows:

	SELENIUM	TELLURIUM
a_0	4.34	4.445
c_0	4.95	5.91

Although the two species are isostructural, they show striking morphological differences: the hexagonal lattice of tellurium is clearly indicated by the importance of $\{10\bar{1}0\}$ and $\{0001\}$ as forms and cleavages, and by the simultaneous occurrence of complementary rhombohedrons; in selenium, however, the cleavage is rhombohedral $\{01\bar{1}2\}$ and the positive unit rhombohedron is not accompanied by the complementary negative form.

Since selenium and tellurium are miscible in all proportions, natural *selen-tellurium* is probably a mix crystal in the series.

Structurally this group is intermediate between the sulfur group, with which artificial monoclinic selenium shows analogies, and the arsenic group, to which tellurium is related.

1221   S E L E N I U M [Se]. Selen *Germ.* Selenio *Ital.* γ-Selenium.

C r y s t.   Hexagonal — P; trigonal trapezohedral[1] — 3 2.

$$a : c = 1 : 1.1341;^2 \qquad p_0 : r_0 = 1.3095 : 1$$

Forms:[3]

	ϕ	$\rho = C$	M	A_2
m $10\bar{1}0$	30°00′	90°00′	60°00′	90°00′
a' $11\bar{2}0$	0 00	90 00	90 00	60 00
h' $21\bar{3}0$	10 53½	90 00	79 06½	70 53½
$'h$ $3\bar{1}\bar{2}0$	49 06½	90 00	40 53½	109 06½
$-e$ $01\bar{1}2$	−30 00	33 13	90 00	61 41
r $10\bar{1}1$	30 00	52 38	66 35	90 00
$'f$ $2\bar{1}\bar{1}3$	60 00	37 05½	58 31	107 33

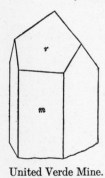

United Verde Mine.

Structure cell.[4] Space group $C3_12$ or $C3_22$. a_0 4.34, c_0 4.95; $a_0 : c_0 = 1 : 1.14$; contains 3Se.

Habit.[5] Acicular [0001]; crystals often hollow and tubelike; sometimes clustered in sheets. Common forms: m r. Also in glassy droplets.

P h y s. Cleavage $\{01\bar{1}2\}$ good. Crystals very flexible. H. 2. G. 4.80; 4.84 (calc.). M. P. 220°. Luster metallic. Color gray. Streak red. Conductor of electricity, with resistance dependent on the action of light.[6] Transparent (red) in thinnest fragments only. Indices (Na): O 3.0, E 4.04.[7] Polished sections have fairly high reflectivity; distinctly pleochroic (O light creamy white, E darker); very strongly anisotropic.

C h e m.[8] Selenium, Se, with a trace of sulfur.

Tests. F.1. B.B. on charcoal volatilizes as brownish smoke with decayed radish odor, giving a silvery coating (SeO_2) which tinges the R.F. azure-blue. In O.T. crystals of volatile SeO_2 are obtained.

Occur.[9] At Jerome, Yavapai County, Arizona, where needles up to 2 cm. long have been found, encrusting quartzite and fritted sandstone in the fire zone of the United Verde mine; formed under the artifically induced fumarolic conditions. At Kladno, Bohemia, on burning heaps of Carboniferous sediments rich in pyrite.

Artif.[10] Has been produced from solutions of alkali selenides; also by heating the other modifications; crystals (not measurable) obtained by sublimation.[11] There are two red monoclinic modifications. X-ray measurements[12] suggest a structure similar to that of orthorhombic sulfur.

Name. From σελήνη, *the moon*, in allusion to the similarity of its properties to those of tellurium, named after *tellus, the earth*.

Ref.

1. According to x-ray results of Bradley, *Phil. Mag.*, **48**, 477 (1924), confirmed by Slattery, *Phys. Rev.*, **25**, 333 (1925).
2. Palache, *Am. Min.*, **19**, 194 (1934), on crystals from Jerome, Arizona.
3. Palache (1934), whose published forms have been revised and given merohedral symbols (Palache) in agreement with the symmetry of the crystal class, as determined by x-rays (Bradley [1934]; Slattery [1925]). Uncertain: {01̄11}.
4. Bradley (1924); Slattery (1925).
5. Palache (1934). Artificial crystals are acicular [0001], thin tabular {101̄0}, or form crystal aggregates with fibrous structure, the fiber elongation being [0001] (Tanaka, *Kyoto Univ.*, **17**, 59 (1934)).
6. Rankine, *Phil. Mag.*, **3**, 1482 (1920).
7. Skinner, *Phys. Rev.*, **9**, 148 (1917); Winchell (153, 1931).
8. Gonyer anal. in Palache (1934).
9. The first described occurrence from Culebras, Mex., is discredited. Minute deep red transparent prisms, with parallel extinction, found associated with meta-hewettite in the vanadium ores of Paradox Valley, Montrose Co., Colo., the Henry Mountains and Thompson's, Grand Co., Utah, have been reported as native selenium on the basis of sublimation tests.
10. Groth (**1**, 32, 1906).
11. Tanaka (1934).
12. Klug, *Zs. Kr.*, **88**, 128 (1934).

1222 **Selen-tellurium** [Se, Te]. *Dana* and *Wells* (*Am. J. Sc.*, **40**, 78, 1890).

Massive, indistinct columnar. Cleavage, hexagonal prismatic perfect. Brittle. H. 2–2½. Luster metallic. Color blackish gray. Streak black. Opaque. Composition: Tellurium, Te, and selenium, Se, with Te : Se nearly 3 : 2. Analysis gave: Te 70.69, Se 29.31 = 100.00 (El Plomo mine). F. 1. Occurs embedded in a gangue, consisting largely of quartz with some barite, at El Plomo silver mine, Ojojona district, Tegucigalpa, Honduras.

Selenium and tellurium are miscible in all proportions at moderate temperatures (200–450°).[1] Selen-tellurium is probably a mixed crystal, and the Te : Se ratio, which approaches 3 : 2 in the only occurrence known, may not be significant.

Ref.

1. Pellini and Vio, *Acc. Linc., Att.*, **15**, 46 (1906); Kimata (*Kyoto Univ., Mem. Coll. Sc.* **1**, 119, 1915).

1223   **T E L L U R I U M** [Te]. Metallum problematicum, Aurum paradoxum *Müller von Reichenstein* (*Phys. Arb., Wien*, **1**, 1782). Sylvanite *Kirwan* (**2**, 324, 1796). Gediegen-Tellur *Klaproth* (**3**, 2, 1802). Gediegen-Silvan *Werner* (*Haüy* [**4**, 378, 1822]). Tellure natif *Haüy* (**4**, 379–381, 1822). Tellur *Germ.* Tellure *Fr.* Tellurio *Ital.* Lionite *Berdell* (*Dana* [11, 1892]).

C r y s t.   Hexagonal — P; trigonal trapezohedral — 3 2.

$$a : c = 1 : 1.3298;^1 \qquad p_0 : r_0 = 1.5355 : 1$$

Forms:[2]

	ϕ	$\rho = C$	M	A_2
c 0001	....	0°00′	90°00′	90°00′
m 10$\bar{1}$0	30°00′	90 00	60 00	90 00
r 10$\bar{1}$1	30 00	56 55½	65 14	90 00
$-r$ 01$\bar{1}$1	−30 00	56 55½	114 46	43 28½

Less common:

    a' 11$\bar{2}$0 $'a$ 2$\bar{1}\bar{1}$0 $-e$ 01$\bar{1}$2 ξ' 11$\bar{2}$2 $'\xi$ 2$\bar{1}\bar{1}$2 s' 11$\bar{2}$1 $'s$ 2$\bar{1}\bar{1}$1

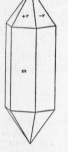

Simoda, Japan.   Zalatna, Roumania.

Structure cell.[3]   Space group $C3_12$ or $C3_22$; a_0 4.445, c_0 5.91; $a_0 : c_0 = 1 : 1.33$; contains 3Te.

Habit. Prismatic to acicular [0001], with {10$\bar{1}$1} and {01$\bar{1}$1} generally together and equally developed; sometimes flattened {10$\bar{1}$0}. Crystals usually minute, singly or doubly terminated, isolated or in parallel grouping; with rounded edges. Commonly massive, columnar to fine granular.

P h y s. Cleavage {10$\bar{1}$0} perfect, {0001} imperfect. Somewhat brittle. H. 2–2½. G. 6.1–6.3; 6.225 (calc.). Luster metallic. Color tin-white. Streak gray. Opaque. In polished section[4] white, with very strong reflectivity; feebly pleochroic; fairly strongly anisotropic. Percentage reflection: green, 63.5; orange, 63; red, 55.

C h e m. Tellurium, Te, sometimes with a little Se in solid solution, also admixed gold, silver, iron.

Anal.

	1	2	3	4	5
Te	97.92	92.29	97.94	99.45	96.94
Se	trace	....	....	0.40	....
Au	0.15	3.40	1.04	....	2.40
Ag	....	1.69	0.20	....	....
Fe	0.53	0.12	0.89	0.11	....
Rem.	1.62	2.44	0.32	....	....
Total	100.22	99.94	100.39	99.96	99.34
G.	6.084				6.2

1. Zalatna (Zlatna).[5] 2. Ballarat district, Colo.[6] 3. John Jay mine, Boulder Co., Colo.[6] 4. Gunnison Co., Colo.[7] 5. Hannans district, Western Australia.[8]

Tests. F.1. Completely soluble in hot concentrated H_2SO_4, with carmine-red coloration ($TeSO_3$); black powdery Te precipitated on dilution. In O.T. white sublimate (TeO_2) which melts to transparent yellow droplets turning opaque white on cooling. B.B. on charcoal volatilizes almost entirely, tingeing the flame green (Te), and giving a white coating.

Occur. Tellurium is a hypogene mineral, found in hydrothermal veins; associated with various gold and silver tellurides, pyrite, gold, galena, alabandite; the gangue is usually quartz, sometimes a carbonate.

It occurs at several places in Transylvania, at Faczebaja, the original locality, Zalatna (Zlatna), and Offenbánya. Found at Kalgoorlie, Hannans district, Western Australia; in the mines of Balia, Asia Minor, where the largest tellurium crystal on record (3 by 2 cm.) came from; fairly abundant in the Teine mine, northwest of Sapporo, Hokkaidô, Japan; also in the Kawazu mine, near Simoda, Izu Peninsula, Japan, which provided some excellent crystals and where tellurium is used as an indicator of gold.

In the United States, mostly in Colorado: Cripple Creek, Teller County; Magnolia, Goldhill, Ballarat, and Central districts, Boulder County; Vulcan, Garfield County; Gunnison County. Also in Nevada, at Delamar, Lincoln County.

Artif.[9] Good crystals of various habits are obtained by fusion from bismuth, potassium, or ammonium tellurides; by evaporation of a potassium telluride solution; by sublimation; also by fusion and slow cooling in vacuum.[10]

Name. From the element, named after *tellus, the earth.*

Ref.

1. Rose, *Ak. Berlin, Abh.,* **84,** 14 (1849), on crystals from Faczebaja and on artificial crystals; confirmed by Watanabe, *Hokkaidô Univ., J. Fac. Sc.,* **3,** 101 (1936), on Japanese material.
2. Goldschmidt (**8,** 117, 1923); Watanabe (1936); Tokody, *Cbl. Min.,* 114, 1929; a' $'a$ e ξ' $'\xi$ on artificial crystals only. Uncertain: {0·3·$\bar{3}$·11}, {50$\bar{5}$4}, {07$\bar{7}$5}, {20$\bar{2}$1}.
3. Bradley, *Phil. Mag.* **48,** 477 (1924), Slattery, *Phys. Rev.* **25,** 333 (1925). The evidence, morphological as well as structural, is against the rhombohedral interpretation of Olshausen, *Zs. Kr.,* **61,** 463 (1925).
4. Schneiderhöhn and Ramdohr (**2,** 24, 1931).
5. Loczka, *Zs. Kr.,* **20,** 319 (1892).
6. Genth, *Zs. Kr.,* **2,** 1 (1877).
7. Headden, *Colorado Sc. Soc. Proc.,* **7,** 139 (1903).
8. MacIvor, *Chem. News,* **82,** 272 (1900).
9. Hintze (**1** [1], 104, 1904); Groth (**1,** 35, 1906).
10. Schmidt and Wassermann, *Zs. Phys.* **46,** 653 (1928).

123 SULFUR GROUP

1231	α-Sulfur	S
1232	β-Sulfur	S
1233	γ-Sulfur	S

Common sulfur (α-sulfur) is orthorhombic; the β- and γ-modifications are monoclinic with no apparent geometrical relation to the orthorhombic form. The complex atomic structure of α-sulfur has been determined,[1] but the structures of the monoclinic modifications have not been studied.

Selenium may enter the structure of α-sulfur, progressively raising the specific gravity and increasing the lattice dimensions. Se 3.05 atomic per cent (7.2 weight per cent) raises the specific gravity from 2.037 in pure α-sulfur to 2.130 with increase of $d_{[111]}$ from 7.744 to 7.84.[2] *Selensulfur*, whose composition lies within this range, is therefore not a mineral species but a variety of sulfur.

Ref.

1. Warren and Burwell, *J. Chem. Phys.*, **3**, 6 (1935).
2. Halla and Bosch, *Zs. phys. Chem.*, **10**, 149 (1930).

1231   **SULFUR** [S]. α-sulfur. Schwefel *Germ.* Svafvel *Swed.* Soufre *Fr.* Solfo *Ital.* Azufre *Span.* Tellursulphur *Lewis (Dana* [9, 1892]). Daiton-sulphur *Suzuki (Beitr. Min., Japan,* 1915). Sulphurite *Wherry (Chem. News,* **116**, 251, 1917) (not the sulfurite of *Rinne*).

Schwefelselen *Stromeyer (Schweigger's J.,* **43**, 452, 1825). Selenschwefel. Volcanite *Adam* (54, 1869). Eolide *Bombicci* (2, 186, 1875). Selensulphur *Dana* (10, 1892). Sulphoselenium *Quercigh (Acc. Napoli, Rend.,* **31**, 65, 1925). Seleniferous sulfur.

C r y s t. Orthorhombic; dipyramidal $- 2/m\ 2/m\ 2/m$.[1]

$$a:b:c\ = 0.8131:1:1.9034;^2\quad p_0:q_0:r_0 = 2.3409:1.9034:1$$

$$q_1:r_1:p_1 = 0.8131:0.4272:1;\quad r_2:p_2:q_2 = 0.5254:1.2298:1$$

Forms:[3]

		ϕ	$\rho = C$	ϕ_1	$\rho_1 = A$	ϕ_2	$\rho_2 = B$
c	001	....	0°00′	0°00′	90°00′	90°00′	90°00′
b	010	0°00′	90 00	90 00	90 00	....	0 00
a	100	90 00	90 00	....	0 00	0 00	90 00
m	110	50 53	90 00	90 00	39 07	0 00	50 53
v	013	0 00	32 23½	32 23½	90 00	90 00	57 36½
n	011	0 00	62 17	62 17	90 00	90 00	27 43
u	103	90 00	37 58	0 00	52 02	52 02	90 00
e	101	90 00	66 52	0 00	23 08	23 08	90 00
ψ	119	50 53	18 32	11 56½	75 43½	75 25	78 26
ω	117	50 53	23 19	15 12½	72 07	71 03½	75 32½
t	115	50 53	31 06½	20 50½	66 22	64 54½	70 58½
o	114	50 53	37 01½	25 27	62 08½	59 40	67 40½
s	113	50 53	45 10	32 23½	56 37	52 02	63 25½
y	112	50 53	56 27½	43 35	49 42½	40 30½	58 16½
p	111	50 53	71 39½	62 17	42 34	23 08	53 13
δ	221	50 53	80 35½	75 17	40 03	12 03½	51 30½
γ	331	50 53	83 41½	80 04	39 32½	8 06	51 10
z	135	22 17½	50 59	48 47½	72 51½	64 54½	44 02
x	133	22 17½	64 04½	62 17	70 03	52 02	33 41
β	315	74 50	55 30	20 50½	37 18	35 27	77 33
α	313	74 50	67 35½	32 23½	26 50	23 08	76 00½
q	131	22 17½	80 48	80 04	68 00½	23 08	24 01½
r	311	74 50	82 10½	62 17	17 01½	8 06	74 59

Less common:

h	130	w	023	j	021	i	201	v	227	η	553	Λ	155	l	344
k	120	d	045	θ	031	B	1·1·25	L	5·5·13	ϵ	551	μ	319	Q	4·11·4
λ	210	ξ	043	π	102	C	1·1·10	g	337	S	3·1·21	R	215	F	151
ρ	310	W	053	K	305	τ	116	f	335	D	177	κ	122	ζ	211
														M	511

Structure cell.[4] Space group *Fddd*; a_0 10.48, b_0 12.92, c_0 24.55; $a_0 : b_0 : c_0 = 0.811 : 1 : 1.900$; contains 128 S.

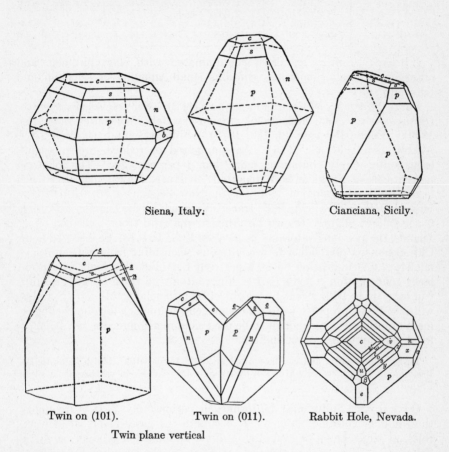

Siena, Italy.　　　　　　　　Cianciana, Sicily.

Twin on (101).　　　Twin on (011).　　　Rabbit Hole, Nevada.

Twin plane vertical

Habit. Dipyramidal {111}; thick tabular {001}; disphenoidal {111}. Common forms: *c n e s p*. Also massive, in spherical, reniform shapes; incrusting, stalactitic, stalagmitic; in powder.

Twinning. On {101}, {011}, {110}, rare.

P h y s. Cleavages {001}, {110}, {111}, imperfect. Parting {111}. Gliding,[5] $T = (111)$. Rather brittle to imperfectly sectile. Fracture conchoidal to uneven. Luster resinous to greasy. Streak white. H. $1\frac{1}{2}$–$2\frac{1}{2}$. G. 2.07. M.P. 112.8°. B.P. 444.6°. Nonconductor of electricity; negatively electrified by friction.

O p t.[6] Crystals sulfur-yellow, straw- to honey-yellow, yellowish brown, greenish, reddish, or yellowish gray. Transparent to translucent. Pleochroic.

Orientation	n(Li)	n(Na)	n(Tl)	
$X = a$	1.9398	1.9579	1.9764	Bx. pos. (+).
$Y = b$	2.0171	2.0377	2.0586	$r < v$.
$Z = c$	2.2158	2.2452	2.2754	
$2V$	.....	68°58′	68°46′	

Chem. Sulfur, S; often contaminated with clay, bitumen, and other impurities. Sometimes contains small amounts of selenium and tellurium.

Var. *Selenian.* Selensulphur *Dana* (1892). Schwefelselen *Stromeyer* (*Schweigger's J.*, **43**, 452, 1825). Selenschwefel. Volcanite *Adam* (54, 1869). Eolide *Bombicci* (**2**, 186, 1875). Sulphoselenium *Quercigh* (*Acc. Napoli, Rend.*, **31**, 65, 1925). An orange-red or reddish brown seleniferous sulfur rarely containing more than 1 per cent Se. The following percentages of Se have been reported: Kilauea, Hawaii (specimen collected by J. D. Dana in 1840), 5.18; New Zealand, 0.30, 0.19; Lipari Islands, 0.28, 0.27; Sicily, 0.07, trace;[7] Vulcano, Lipari Islands, 1.03, 0.83. On a yellow, slightly orange birefringent material from Vulcano, Lipari Islands, the portion soluble in CS_2 gave Se 1.03, Te 0.18; Se 0.83, Te none. Old specimens of reddish brown vitreous selensulfur from Vulcano gave n 2.544–2.675 indicating 83–90.5 per cent Se;[8] but this high Se content lacks confirmation. Some dark sulfur contains no trace of Se.[9] α-sulfur will take up to 20 per cent by weight of Se into solid solution.[10] S and Se will mix in all proportions to give homogeneous melts which on cooling remain amorphous long enough to be used as immersion media (n 2.05–2.72) for determining refractive indices.[11]

Tests. Melts easily and can be ignited at 270°; burns with a bluish flame to SO_2. Insoluble in water; scarcely attacked by strong acids; soluble in various oils, easily in CS_2.

Occur.[12] Sulfur may be formed in various ways. It is frequently the result of volcanic activity. It occurs in the gases given off at fumaroles, at times being deposited as a direct sublimation product, as at the Solfatara at Pozzuoli near Naples, at Etna, on the island of Vulcano and in the Yellowstone Park, Wyoming. It is also said to be formed by the incomplete oxidation, by the oxygen of the air, of hydrogen sulfide gas derived from volcanic sources. In some cases it may result from the interaction of hydrogen sulfide and sulfur dioxide. This latter mode of origin is doubtful as these two gases seldom occur together in the same fumarole. It is produced abundantly in mine fires by the "roasting" of pyrite ore. Further it is formed by the decomposition of the hydrogen sulfide that frequently occurs in thermal spring waters. This may come from volcanic sources by the action of acid water on metallic sulfides, or by the reduction of sulfates, especially gypsum. This last reaction is aided by certain microorganisms. The living processes of the so-called sulfur bacteria result in the separation of sulfur from sulfates. Sulfur is rarely formed by the reduction of metallic sulfates. It is also formed, apparently under conditions of low accessibility of air, by the oxidation of pyrite.

Sulfur is most commonly found in the Tertiary sedimentary rocks and most frequently associated with gypsum and limestone; in salt domes; frequently associated with bituminous deposits.

The sulfur deposits on the island of Sicily are especially noteworthy because of their size and the fine crystals that occur in them. The chief associated minerals are celestite, calcite, aragonite, gypsum. The important localities are at Agrigento (Girgenti) and the neighboring Cianciana, Racalmuto, and Cattolica. Sulfur occurs elsewhere in Italy as at the solfatara at Pozzuoli near Naples; in fine crystals with asphalt at Perticara south of Cesena, Romagna; near Bologna; at Carrara, Tuscany, Siena. On the island of Milos, Cyclades. In Spain at Conil, near Cadiz. Common in the volcanic regions of Iceland, Japan, Dutch East Indies, Hawaii, Mexico and in the Andes; in many localities in Russia.

In the United States the most productive deposits are in Louisiana and Texas; these are "mined" by superheated steam, and they furnish most of the world's supply. Near Lake Charles in Calcasieu Parish, Louisiana, a bed of sulfur 100 ft. thick is found at a depth of between 300 and 400 ft. It is underlain by beds of gypsum and salt. A similar deposit occurs near Freeport in Brazoria County, Texas. In numerous other western localities; Utah, at Sulphurdale, Beaver County, in a rhyolitic tuff; Wyoming, in limestones near Cody and Thermopolis and about the fumaroles in Yellowstone Park; Nevada, in Esmeralda County, near Luning and Cuprite in Humbolt County; near Rosebud at times in crystals and at Eureka, Eureka County, California, at the Sulphur Bank mercury mine on Clear Lake, Lake County; at the geysers in Sonoma County, on Lassen Peak, Tehama County, in Colusa, San Bernadino and other counties; Colorado, at Vulcan, Gunnison County, and in Mineral County.

A r t i f.[13] α-sulfur is easily obtained in simple crystals from solutions; more complex crystals are generally obtained by sublimation.

Ref.

1. The symmetry of α-sulfur has been much studied and discussed. The disphenoidal class, 222, is indicated by the forms and natural etch figures of some crystals (Rosický, *Zs. Kr.*, **58**, 113 [1923]) and by some artificial etch figures (Novák, *Zs. Kr.*, **76**, 169 [1930]). On the other hand the forms and etch figures of other crystals, and the structure as completely determined by Warren and Burwell, *J. Chem. Phys.*, **3**, 6 (1935), point to the dipyramidal class — 2/m 2/m 2/m. Since growth and solution in an "active" medium may produce forms and figures of lower symmetry than that of the crystal (Friedel and Weil, *C.R.*, **190**, 243 [1930], Royer, *C.R.*, **190**, 503 [1930]), α-sulfur may now be accepted as dipyramidal.

2. Koksharov (**6**, 1874), on crystals from Germany, Spain, and Lower Egypt, in exact agreement with the values obtained by Zepharovich, *Geol. Reichsanst. Jb.*, **19**, 225 (1869), on crystals from Swoszowice, Poland.

3. Goldschmidt (**8**, 20, 1922); Bichowsky, *Washington Ac. Sc., J.*, **9**, 126 (1919); Comucci, *Acc. Linc., Mem.*, **12**, 804 (1919); Ohashi, *Geol. Soc. Tokyo, J.*, **31**, 166 (1924); Billows, *Acc. Linc., Rend.*, **2**, 563 (1925); Ranfaldi, *Acc. Linc., Mem.*, **2**, 266 (1927). Doubtful forms: {107}, {203}, {3·3·13}, {337}, {449}, {155}, {11·7·45}, {213}, {433}, {13·1·1}.

4. Warren and Burwell (1935) on crystals grown from CS_2 solution.

5. Mügge, *Jb. Min.*, 4, 1920.
6. Refractive indices and 2V abbreviated after Schrauf, *Zs. Kr.*, **18**, 157 (1890), on natural prisms from Galicia, at 20°.
7. Brown, *Am. Min.*, **2**, 116 (1917).
8. Quercigh, *Acc. Napoli, Rend.*, **31**, 65 (1925).
9. Palache and Gonyer, priv. comm., 1938.
10. Hansen, *Zweistoffleg.*, 1034, 1936.
11. Merwin and Larsen, *Am. J. Sc.*, **34**, 42 (1912).
12. On the important occurrence of sulfur in salt domes: Wolf, in DeGolyer (*Geology of Salt Dome Oil Fields*, 1926 — Am. Ass. Petrol. Geol.)　On the distribution and origin of sulfur in Russia: Murzaiev, *Econ. Geol.*, **32**, 69 (1937).
13. Doelter (4 [1], 1925).

SULFURITE.　Sulfurit *Rinne* (*Cbl. Min.*, 500, 1902) (not the sulfurite = β-sulphur of *Fröbel*).　Arsensulfurit *Rinne* (*Cbl. Min.*, 499, 1902) (not the arsenschwefel = orpiment (?) of *Monaco*).　Rubber-sulphur *Wada* (21, 1916).　Jeromite *Lausen* (*Am. Min.*, **13**, 227, 1928).

Amorphous sulfur; the material, however, crystallizes with age (to α-sulfur).　In plastic masses at the Kobui sulfur mine, Oshima Province, Japan.　An arsenian variety (*arsensulfurite*) is found in the crater of Papandagan volcano, Java, as red-brown isotropic crusts, H. $2\frac{1}{2}$, with the composition S 70.81 and As 29.22; also from the solfatara near Naples, with S 87.6, As 11.2 and Se 0.3, total 99.1.

An arsenian and selenian variety (*jeromite*) occurs as an amorphous black globular coating on rock fragments lying underneath iron hoods placed over vents in the burning ore body of the United Verde mine, Jerome, Arizona.　In thin splinters transparent and cherry-red in color.　Analysis: S 40.8, Se 7.5, As 46.8, insoluble 4.9, total 100.00. This is approximately $As(S, Se)_2$, but there is no evidence that this substance is of definite composition.　A vitreous selenian variety also occurs, as at Vulcano, Lipari Islands, but this material usually has crystallized (see selensulfur).

1232　β-**Sulfur** [S].　Sulfurit *Fröbel* (in *Haidinger*, 573, 1845).　β-Sulphur *Dana* (10, 1892).

Cryst.　Monoclinic; prismatic — $2/m$.

$a : b : c = 0.9958 : 1 : 0.9998;$　$\beta = 95°46';$[1]　$p_0 : q_0 : r_0 = 1.0040 : 0.9947 : 1$

$r_2 : p_2 : q_2 = 1.0053 : 1.0093 : 1;$　$\mu = 84°14';$　$p_0' = 1.0091;$　$q_0' = 0.9998;$

$$x_0' = 1.1010$$

Forms:[2]

		ϕ	ρ	ϕ_2	$\rho_2 = B$	C	A
c	001	90°00′	5°46′	84°14′	90°00′	0°00′	84°14′
b	010	0 00	90 00	. . . .	90 00	90 00	90 00
a	100	90 00	90 00	0 00	90 00	84 14	0 00
m	110	45 16	90 00	0 00	45 16	85 $54\frac{1}{2}$	44 14
n	210	63 39	90 00	0 00	63 39	84 50	26 21
w	012	11 $25\frac{1}{2}$	27 $01\frac{1}{2}$	84 14	63 $33\frac{1}{2}$	26 $26\frac{1}{2}$	84 $50\frac{1}{2}$
q	011	5 46	45 $08\frac{1}{2}$	84 14	45 09	44 51	85 55
x	021	2 $53\frac{1}{2}$	63 $27\frac{1}{2}$	84 14	26 41	63 19	87 25
e	101	90 00	47 59	42 01	90 00	42 13	42 01
p	111	47 $59\frac{1}{2}$	56 12	42 01	56 $12\frac{1}{2}$	52 01	51 52
ω	$\bar{1}11$	-42 15	53 29	132 $14\frac{1}{2}$	53 $29\frac{1}{2}$	57 28	112 $42\frac{1}{2}$

Less common:

k 130	d 102	G $\bar{1}03$	E $\bar{1}01$	s 221	S $\bar{2}21$	u 311	O $\bar{1}21$
l 120	f 201	D $\bar{1}02$	r 112	R $\bar{1}12$	t 211	Q $\bar{2}12$	U $\bar{3}11$

Habit. Thick tabular {001}; elongated [001], [100], [010]; pseudo-isometric. Common forms: $c\, b\, a\, m\, q\, e\, p$. Also in skeletal forms.

Twinning. On {011}, {012}, {100}.

Phys. Cleavage {001}, {110}. G. 1.982, 1.958. H. slightly greater than in α-sulfur. M.P. 119°.

Opt.[3] Light yellow, almost colorless; often brownish due to organic matter. $Y = b$; on (110), $X' \wedge c = 44°$. Birefringence weak; Biax. neg.$(-)$; $2V = 58°$.

Chem. Sulfur, S.

Occur. Found in fumaroles at Vesuvius and at Vulcano, Lipari Islands.

Artif.[4] Obtained in crystals from fused sulfur, and from an alcoholic solution of ammonium polysulfide.

Ref.

1. Muthmann, *Zs. Kr.* **17**, 345 (1899), from the measurements of Mitscherlich, *Ann. chim.*, **24**, 264 (1823); *Ak. Berlin, Abh.*, June 26, 1823, on artificial crystals.
2. Goldschmidt (**8**, 29, 1922); Panichi, *Acc. Catania, Att.*, **5**, 6 (1912). Rare or uncertain:

310	031	302	$\bar{3}$02	$\bar{3}$01	212	312	321	421	$\bar{3}$12	$\bar{2}$11	$\bar{4}$11
013	103	301	$\bar{2}$01	122	121	412	411	$\bar{1}$22	$\bar{4}$12	$\bar{3}$21	

3. Gaubert, *Bull. soc. min.*, **28**, 163 (1905).
4. Mitscherlich (1823); Muthmann (1899); Mellor (**10**, 26, 1930).

1233 γ-**Sulfur** [S]. Soufre nacré *Gernez* (*C.R.*, **97**, 1477, 1883). Nacreous sulfur. Dritte Modification des Schwefels *Muthmann* (*Zs. Kr.*, **17**, 337, 1890). Sulfur III. γ-Sulphur *Dana* (10, 1892). Rosický it *Sekanina* (*Zs. Kr.*, **80**, 174, 1931).

Cryst. Monoclinic; prismatic — $2/m$.

$a : b : c = 1.0609 : 1 : 0.7094;$ $\beta = 91°47';$[1] $p_0 : q_0 : r_0 = 0.6687 : 0.7191 : 1$
$r_2 : p_2 : q_2 = 0.9431 : 1.4103 : 1;$ $\mu = 88°13';$ $p_0' = 0.6690;$ $q_0' = 0.7094;$
$$x_0' = 0.0311$$

Forms:[2]

		ϕ	ρ	ϕ_2	$\rho_2 = B$	C	A
b	010	0°00'	90°00'	....	0°00'	90°00'	90°00'
a	100	90 00	90 00		90 00	88 13	0 00
m	110	43 19$\frac{1}{2}$	90 00	0°00'	43 19$\frac{1}{2}$	88 46$\frac{1}{2}$	46 40$\frac{1}{2}$
q	012	5 01	19 36	88 13	70 28$\frac{1}{2}$	19 31$\frac{1}{2}$	88 19
s	011	2 31	35 22$\frac{1}{2}$	88 13	54 39$\frac{1}{2}$	35 20$\frac{1}{2}$	88 32$\frac{1}{2}$
o	111	44 37$\frac{1}{2}$	44 54$\frac{1}{2}$	55 00	59 50$\frac{1}{2}$	43 40	60 16$\frac{1}{2}$
ω	$\bar{1}$11	-41 57$\frac{1}{2}$	43 39	122 32	59 07	44 51$\frac{1}{2}$	117 29

Less common:

c 001   1 230 n 210 p 101 π $\bar{1}$01 y 121

Habit. Crystals minute; equidimensional; thick tabular {010}; short prismatic {110}; rarely acicular [001]; also dipyramidal {111}, {$\bar{1}$11}; skeletal. Artificial crystals thin tabular {010}.

Twinning. On {101}.

P h y s. Cleavage not observed. Gliding on {001}, {101}, {$\bar{1}$01}. Luster adamantine. H. low. G. less than that of α-sulfur.

O p t.[3] Light yellow, almost colorless; transparent. $Y = b$; $X \wedge c = \pm 1\frac{1}{4}°$. Refringence and birefringence strong.

C h e m. Sulfur, S.

O c c u r. Reported with α- and β-sulfur from a fumarole at Vulcano, Lipari Islands. In well-developed crystals (rosickýite) from Havírna, near Letovice, Bohemia.

A l t e r. Inverts slowly to α-sulfur at room temperature.

A r t i f.[4] Obtained from melts, also from aqueous solutions of sodium thiosulfate and potassium hydrosulfide; from an alcoholic solution of sodium sulfide, and in other ways.

Ref.

1. Muthmann, *Zs. Kr.* **17**, 337 (1890) on artificial crystals; Sekanina (1931) obtained closely similar elements on natural crystals (rosickýite).
2. Goldschmidt (**8**, 31, 1922); Sekanina (1931). Uncertain: {321}.
3. Sekanina (1931).
4. Mellor (**10**, 26, 1930).

In addition to the three modifications (α, β, γ) of sulfur known in nature, three further crystalline modifications (δ, ϵ, ζ) have been prepared in the laboratory.[1] An amorphous modification is also known (sulfurite). δ-sulfur is probably monoclinic; ϵ-sulfur is hexagonal — R; ζ-sulfur (black sulfur) has been thought to be hexagonal — R.

Ref.

1. Hintze (**1** [1], 94, 1904); Mellor (**10**, 23, 1930).

PHOSPHORUS. *Farrington* (*Am. J. Sc.*, **15**, 71, 1903).
Native phosphorus has been reported in the Saline Township, Kansas, meteorite.

124   CARBON GROUP

1241	Diamond	C
1242	Graphite	C

These two modifications of carbon present the greatest contrast in structure and properties. *Diamond* is isometric; each carbon atom in the structure is linked tetrahedrally to four neighbors (diamond type). This firmly bonded type of structure is expressed in the great hardness of diamond and is connected with its high dispersion and brilliant luster. *Graphite* is hexagonal with a layer structure (graphite type) in which the carbon atoms are hexagonally arranged in widely spaced horizontal sheets. This arrangement offers an explanation of the low hardness of graphite, the scaly crystal habit and the perfect and very easy basal cleavage.

1241   D I A M O N D [C]. Adamas, pt. *Pliny* (**37**, 15, A.D. 77). Diamant *Germ., Fr.* Diamante *Ital., Span.*

C r y s t. Isometric; hextetrahedral — $\bar{4}3m$, perhaps hexoctahedral — $4/m \bar{3} 2/m$.[1]

Forms:[2]

$$a\{001\}, \ d\{011\}, \ o\{111\}, \ n\{112\}, \ \beta\{223\}, \ q\{133\}, \ p\{122\}, \ r\{233\}$$

Structure cell.[3] Space group $Fd3m$; a_0 3.5595 ± 0.0010; contains 8C.

Habit.[4] Predominantly octahedral; less commonly dodecahedral; rarely cubic; occasionally tetrahedral. Faces commonly much curved by

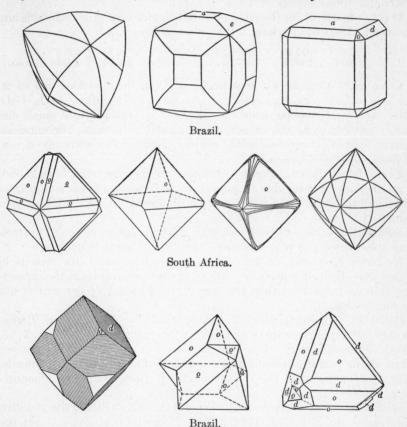

Brazil.

South Africa.

Brazil.

growth and solution facets and often striated, usually [110]. Often flattened {111}; built of successive flattened octahedral plates; variously distorted; in groups; in spherical forms with radiated structure; rarely massive. Variously etched on {111}.

Twinning. (a) On {111} very common, giving simple and multiple twins usually flattened parallel to the twin plane; penetration twins; cyclic groups.[5] (b) On {001} or about the axis [001], giving grooved octahedrons resulting from the interpenetration of twinned tetrahedrons.

P h y s. Cleavage {111} perfect. Fracture conchoidal. Brittle. H. 10.[16] G. 3.50–3.53; purest blue-white, 3.511;[6] 3.511 (calc.).[7] Luster adamantine to greasy. Pale yellow to deep yellow; pale brown to deep brown; white to blue-white; occasionally orange, pink, mauve, green, blue, red, black. Transparent to translucent; sometimes nontranslucent owing to inclusions and cavities. Sometimes strongly fluorescent in ultraviolet light and phosphorescent after exposure. Triboelectric. Not sensibly pyroelectric or piezoelectric.

O p t. Isotropic for the most part, but birefringent near inclusions and cavities.[8] Dispersion strong. Refractive indices.[9]

λ	687.6	656.3	589.3 (Na)	527.0	486.1	430.8
n	2.4076	2.4103	2.4175	2.4269	2.4354	2.4513 ($\pm$0.0001)

C h e m.[10] Carbon, C. Specimens of bort have yielded up to 20 per cent of ash consisting principally of SiO_2, Fe_2O_3, MgO, Al_2O_3, CaO, TiO_2; also spectroscopic traces of Ba, Sr, Cr. Inclusions of small diamonds are common, also of graphite, magnetite, ilmenite, carbonaceous matter, garnet, chrome-diopside, chlorite, biotite; less certainly zircon, olivine, phlogopite, quartz.[11]

Var. Bort. Boŏrt. Boart. Granular to cryptocrystalline diamond, gray to black in color due to impurities and inclusions, without distinct cleavage; also applied to badly colored or flawed diamond without gem value.

Shot Bort, a variety of bort with little impurity, in milky white to steel-gray spherical stones with radiated structure and great toughness.

Hailstone Bort, gray or gray-black, rounded in form, like cement in appearance, built of concentric shells of clouded diamond and the cement-like material; less hard than common bort; yielded 1–3½ per cent of ash on combustion.

Framesite. Black diamond McDonald (*Geol. Soc. South Africa, Trans.*, **16**, 156, 1913); Framesite Sutton (*Roy. Soc. South Africa, Trans.*, **7**, 75, 1918). Framesite bort. Like common bort, but still more difficult to cut; often shows minute brilliant points possibly due to included diamonds; gave 4½–6½ per cent of ash. Named after P. Ross Frames of Johannesburg.

Stewartite. Sutton (*Nature*, **87**, 550, 1911). (Not Stewartite Schaller, *Washington Ac. Sc., J.*, **2**, 143 [1912].) Magnetic bort giving 3–19½ per cent of ash due in part to iron oxides. Named after James Stewart of Kimberley.

Carbonado. Carbon. Black or gray-black bort, massive, sometimes granular to compact, as hard as, or harder than crystals and less brittle; specific gravity less than that of diamond due in part to slight porosity.

Tests. Burns in oxygen at 1000° to produce CO_2; unattacked by acids and alkalis.

O c c u r.[12] Diamond is frequently a product of the deep-seated crystallization of certain ultrabasic igneous rocks. Diamonds occur in the groundmass and nodules of olivine- and phlogopite-rich porphyry (kimberlite) in pipes or volcanic necks; in alluvial deposits (stream beds, potholes, river terraces), associated with concentrations of other heavy resistant minerals; in wave-concentrated deposits along shore lines and old sea levels; in conglomerates and other consolidated sediments; in a phyllite (a narrow metamorphosed dike); doubtfully in a pegmatite; in meteorites.

India was the source of diamonds from very early times down to the discovery of the Brazilian mines shortly after 1700. The yield from India is now small. The three principal localities were the Golgonda region of southern India, including the districts of Cuddapah, Bellary, Kurnool, Kistna, Godavari; a more northerly region including Sambalpur and Wairagarh, 80 miles southeast of Nágpur; Bundelkhand, especially near the town of Panna in central India.

In Borneo the valley of the Kapaus River near Pontianak was the most important field.

Diamonds were discovered in Brazil in 1729 at the time of colonization, and the deposits were actively exploited until the deposits in South Africa were found. The diamonds were found chiefly in the district extending from the state of Minas Geraes to that of Bahia, and also in the states of Parana, Goyas, and Matto Grosso. The most important region was that near Diamantina, Minas Geraes; it is situated along the crest and on the flanks of the Serrado Espinhaço, the mountain ridge separating the São Francisco River and its branches, especially the Rio das Velhas on the west from the Jequitinhonha and the Doce on the east. The diamonds were found partly in river gravels and partly on the high lands where they occur in a sort of breccia. The river deposits consist of rolled quartz pebbles mixed with or cemented by ferruginous clay resting on a bed of clay. The most commonly associated minerals, so-called "favas," are rutile, anatase, brookite, hematite, martite, ilmenite, magnetite; quartz, kyanite, tourmaline, lazulite, gold, garnet, zircon, euclase, and topaz are also present in the concentrates. Other Brazilian localities are those of Bagagem and Abaete, southwest of Diamantina; the Lençoes and other mines in Bahia (carbonado); places on the branches of the Rio Pardo, inland from the port of Canavieiras. More recent discoveries are in the sands of the river Tibagy in Parana and the Rio das Garças on the boundary between Goyas and Matto Grosso.

Diamonds were discovered in South Africa in 1867. They were first found in the gravels of the Vaal River from Potchefstroom down to the junction with the Orange River and along the latter as far as Hope Town; then in the so-called dry diggings in Griqualand West, south of the Vaal River on the border of the Orange Free State. In this region, near Kimberley, the principal mines, Kimberley, De Beers, Dutoitspan, Wesselton, Bulfontein, occupy roughly circular areas lying in a district $3\frac{1}{2}$ miles in diameter. In all the mines the geological relations are much the same: a wall of nearly horizontal black shale with upturned edges encloses the diamantiferous rock of the pipe. The upper portion of the deposit consists of a pale yellow friable mass called the "yellow ground"; below, beyond the direct reach of the atmosphere, is the firmer bluish green or greenish "blue ground" which represents the altered basic eruptives (kimberlite) filling the pipes. There are two main types of kimberlite, an olivine-rich porphyry and an olivine-phlogopite-rich porphyry, both considerably serpentinized. The diamonds are sparsely distributed through the rock; some claims give 4 to 6 carats per cubic yard but the average yield is about 0.2 carat per cubic yard or one part in fourteen million. Other important mines similar to those near Kimberley are the Jagersfontein in the Orange Free State, and the Premier near Pretoria in the Transvaal.

Some pipes of diamond-bearing kimberlite have recently been found in Rhodesia. More recently many new gravel and beach deposits have been found in widely scattered parts of Africa, some of these surpassing the older localities in the quality and quantity of the stones. Lüderitz Bay on the desert West Coast is a deposit of beach sand rich in stones of good quality. To the south, in Little Namaqualand in the northwestern part of the Cape Province, rich beach terrace deposits of high-quality stones were found in 1927 but are not yet developed. Near Lichtenburg, Transvaal, pothole concentrates were discovered in 1926 and have yielded rich returns. From 1919 industrial diamonds of inferior quality but in large quantity have been recovered from the gravels of the Bushimaie River in the Belgian Congo; these fields extend into Angola. Recently opened gravel workings in the Gold Coast are productive, and some diamonds were found in Tanganyika and French Equatorial Africa.

In Australia diamonds have been found in a number of localities, especially in New South Wales near Mudgee and at Bingara in the valley of the Horton River; also from gold washings in Victoria, Queensland, and South Australia.

In the United States a few stones have been found in gravels in North Carolina, Georgia, Virginia, Colorado, California, and Wisconsin. Diamonds, associated with platinum, have also been reported from Idaho and Oregon. In 1906 diamonds were found near Murfreesboro in Pike County, Arkansas, both loose in the soil and in a rock very similar to that found in the pipes of the South African diamond deposits, and associated with tuffs and breccias in Carboniferous and Lower Cretaceous strata. The Arkansas kimberlite consists of porphyritic olivine and phlogopite in a groundmass of phlogopite, with augite, perovskite, chromite, and magnetite as important accessories. As in South Africa the rock is highly serpentinized. Considerable exploration has been done in this locality and several thousand stones of good color have been found; these are mostly small, but one weighing 21 carats was found in 1921.

Some famous diamonds with their weights are:[13] the Florentine or Grand Duke of Tuscany, 133 carats; the Regent or Pitt, 137 carats; the Kohinoor, which weighed 186 carats when brought to England, 106 carats after recutting; the Orloff, 194 carats; the Star of the South, from Bagagem, Brazil, which weighed 254 carats before cutting, 125 after cutting. Famous stones of rare color are the green Dresden diamond, 40 carats; the deep blue Hope diamond from India, 44 carats; and the orange-yellow Tiffany,

125$\frac{3}{8}$ carats. South Africa has yielded the largest stones among which are (weights in English carats, before cutting): the Imperial, 457; the Jubilee, 634; the Jonker, 726, found in 1934; the Excelsior, 969$\frac{1}{2}$; and the unrivalled Cullinan, or Star of Africa, from the Premier mine, presented by the Transvaal Assembly to King Edward VII, weighing 3025 carats when found and cut into 105 stones including two of 309 and 516$\frac{1}{2}$ carats, the largest cut stones in existence.

A r t i f.[14] Obtained by reaction of alkali metals, kerosene and bone oil in sealed iron tubes at high temperature and pressure.[15] The numerous other reported syntheses are questionable.

N a m e. By corruption from 'αδάμας, *the invincible.*

Ref.

1. The long-disputed question of the symmetry of diamond is not yet finally decided. The repeatedly noted tetrahedral development of the faces and the natural and artificial solution forms on some crystals (Fersmann and Goldschmidt, *Der Diamant*, 1911, Heidelberg) and the twinning on {001} or about [001], led to the classical view that diamond is hextetrahedral (Beckenkamp), *Jb. Min., Beil.-Bd.*, **54**, 63 [1926]). The hexoctahedral class is indicated by the holohedral development of most diamonds, the arrangement of the centers of the carbon atoms in the well-established structure (Bragg and Bragg, *Roy. Soc. London, Proc.*, **33**, 277 [1913]), and the absence of a sensible piezoelectric effect (Elings and Terpstra, *Zs. Kr.*, **67**, 279 [1928], Wooster, *Min. Mag.*, **22**, 65 [1929]). The x-ray photographs show, however, weak reflections from (222), in keeping with the tetrahedral symmetry sometimes expressed by the morphology.

2. Fersmann and Goldschmidt (1911); Ramsdell, *Am. Min.*, **7**, 158 (1922). The forms given are those accepted as certain and typical by Fersmann and Goldschmidt (1911) in an extended morphological study; the remaining reported forms are regarded by these authors as untypical or uncertain.

013	023	045	113	179	135	123
025	034	0·10·11	277	137	145	234
012	079	115	255	156	134	579

3. The structure of diamond was first determined by Bragg and Bragg (1913); cell edge, Ehrenberg, *Zs. Kr.*, **63**, 320 (1926).

4. The habits of diamond are copiously illustrated in Fersmann and Goldschmidt (1911) who also made a special study of the curved growth and solution surfaces.

5. Palache, *Am. Min.*, **17**, 360 (1932).

6. Williams (*The Genesis of the Diamond*, **2**, 467, 1932, London).

7. Ehrenberg (1926), from x-ray measurements.

8. Due to strain caused by the inversion (Friedel, *Zs. Kr.*, **83**, 42 [1932]) of an isotropic high-temperature modification at 1885°.

9. After Wülfing, *Min. Mitt.*, **15**, 49 (1896).

10. Williams (**2**, 470, 1932), and Chesley, *Am. Min.* **27**, 20 (1942).

11. Colony, *Am. J. Sc.*, **5**, 400 (1923).

12. General references: *Stutzer* (**6**, 1–204, 1935); for South Africa: Wagner (*The Diamond Fields of Southern Africa*, Johannesburg, 1914); Williams (1932); for Brazil: Betim, *Bull. soc. min.*, **52**, 51 (1929); Moraes and Guimaraes, *Econ. Geol.*, **26**, 502 (1931); for Arkansas, U.S.A.: Miser and Ross, *U.S. Geol. Sur. Bull. 735* [I], 1923; in meteorites: Farrington (*Meteorites*, 1915, Chicago); Ksanda and Henderson, *Am. Min.*, **24**, 677 (1939).

13. Spencer, *Min. Mag.*, **16**, 140 (1911). The weight of the carat was approximately 205 mg., but different in different countries until 1913 when the metric carat of 200 mg. was universally adopted.

14. Stöber, *Chem. Erde*, **6**, 440 (1931). On the crystallization of carbon from molten iron see Moissan, *C.R.*, **116**, 218 (1893); **118**, 320 (1894); **123**, 206 (1896).

15. See Bannister and Lonsdale, *Min. Mag.*, **26**, 315 (1943) on the experiments of Hannay, *Roy. Soc. London, Proc.*, **30**, 188, 450 (1880).

16. On the relation of hardness to structure see Bergheimer, *Jb. Min., Beil.-Bd.*, **74**, 318 (1938), and Kraus and Slawson, *Am. Min.*, **24**, 661 (1939); **26**, 153 (1941).

1242   **G R A P H I T E** [C].   Plumbago, Molybdaena, Bly-Ertz, *Bromell* (58, 1739).
Blyertz pt., Mica pictoria nigra, Molybdaena pt. *Wallerius* (131, 1747).   Mica
des Peintres, Crayon *Wallerius* (1753).   Black Lead.   Reissblei *Germ.*   Molybdaenum
Linnaeus (1768).   Plombagine *de Lisle* (1783).   Graphit *Werner (Bergm. J.*, 380, 1789).
Melangraphit *Haidinger* (513, 1845).   Fer carburé *Fr.*   Grafite, Pombaggine *Ital.*
Grafita *Span.*   Graphitoid *Sauer (Zs. geol. Ges.*, 37, 441, 1885).   Cliftonite *Fletcher*
(*Min. Mag.*, 7, 121, 1887; 12, 171, 1899).   Graphitite *Luzi (Zs. Nat. Halle*, 64, 257,
1891).   Tremenheerite *Piddington* (in *Dana* [8, 1892]).

C r y s t.   Hexagonal — P; dihexagonal-dipyramidal — $6/m\,2/m\,2/m$.[1]

$$a : c = 1 : 2.7522;^2 \quad p_0 : r_0 = 3.1780 : 1$$

Forms:[3]

	ϕ	$\rho = C$	M	A_2
c 0001	.....	0°00′	90°00′	90°00′
r 10$\bar{1}$3	30°00′	46 39	68 41	90 00
o 10$\bar{1}$2	30 00	57 49	64 58	90 00
p 10$\bar{1}$1	30 00	72 32	61 31	90 00
ρ 11$\bar{2}$3	0 00	61 24½	90 00	63 37½
ϕ 11$\bar{2}$2	0 00	70 02	90 00	61 58

Structure cell.[4]   Space group $C6/mmc$ (?); a_0 2.47, c_0 6.79; $a_0 : c_0 =$
1 : 2.75; contains 4C.

Habit.   Six-sided tablets {0001}, with 60° triangular striations on
{0001}.   Commonly in embedded foliated masses.   Also scaly, columnar,

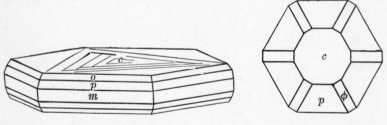

Ticonderoga, N. Y.   Sterling Hill, N. J.

radiated, granular, earthy, compact, in globular aggregates with a radial
structure.

Twinning.   (a) Twin plane a steep second-order pyramid, probably
{11$\bar{2}$1}.[5]   The twinning is due to gliding under pressure, and produces
trigonal or hexagonal striae on the base.   (b) Twinning by 30° (90°) rotation about the axis [0001].[6]

P h y s.   Cleavage {0001} perfect and easy.   Flexible, but not elastic.
Greasy feel.   Sectile.   H. 1–2.   G. 2.09–2.23; 2.23 (calc.).   Luster metallic,
sometimes dull, earthy.   Color iron-black to steel-gray.   Streak black to
dark steel-gray, shining.   Transparent only in extremely thin flakes.   A
conductor of electricity.   Thermoelectrically negative.[7]

O p t.   In transmitted light thinnest flakes are deep blue.   Strongly
pleochroic.   Uniaxial negative (—). O 1.93–2.07,[8] for red.   In polished

section[9] pleochroism and birefringence extreme. Reflection percentages: green, O 22.5, E 5; orange, O 23.5, E 5; red, O 23, E 5.5.

Chem. Carbon, C. Often impure due to admixed clay, iron oxides, and various minerals. The iron reported in some graphite may be in interstitial solid solution in the graphite structure.[10] Many coals give x-ray powder patterns showing graphite lines.[11]

Tests. At a high temperature some graphites burn more easily than diamond, others less so. B.B. infusible. Fused with niter, in a platinum spoon, deflagrates forming potassium carbonate which effervesces with acids. Unaltered with acids.

Occur.[12] Results from the metamorphism of carbonaceous material entrapped in sediments, the assimilation and reduction of carbon compounds by hydrothermal solutions or magmatic fluids, and possibly the crystallization of original magmatic carbon. However, there is no general agreement as to the physical-chemical conditions leading to the formation of large bodies of graphite.

Found in eastern Siberia at the Alibert mine, west of Irkutsk, in a large productive deposit resulting from an assimilation process, associated with augite, amphiboles, and biotite in nepheline syenite and to a less extent in the adjacent rocks. In Ceylon, an important source, in sharply defined veins in the gneisses interbedded with limestones. In Madagascar disseminated in the schists. Common in Central Europe, as at Passau, Bavaria, in the schistose rocks. At Pargas, Finland, disseminated in a metamorphosed limestone. In England, at Barrowdale, near Keswick, compact masses associated with basic igneous rocks. At Ovifak, Greenland, with native iron in basalt associated with coal beds. In Mexico at Santa Maria, Sonora, as a fine-grained bedded deposit due to the metamorphism of coal beds. Important Canadian occurrences at Buckingham and Grenville, Quebec, and adjacent parts of eastern Ontario.

In the United States the most productive region is in New York in the eastern and southeastern Adirondacks, particularly in the vicinity of Ticonderoga, where the graphite occurs in quartzites, in veinlets through the gneiss and in pegmatites; at Rossie, St. Lawrence County. In New Jersey at Franklin disseminated in limestone, and in notable crystals at Sterling Hill. Near Providence and Tiverton, Rhode Island, in metamorphosed carbonaceous bedded deposits. In Maine at Yarmouth, Lewiston, and Madrid, in pegmatites. In Clay County, Alabama, in the granites and schists; in Chester County, Pennsylvania, at various localities in North Carolina. Near Dillon, Montana. In Colfax County, New Mexico, amorphous material formed through the metamorphism of coal beds. In meteorites, associated with the iron.

Artif.[13] Graphite is formed from coal, principally anthracite, by subjecting it to high temperatures in an electric furnace; the process converting the amorphous carbon to a comparatively coarsely crystalline graphite of great purity. Graphite formed in an iron melt usually contains iron.

N a m e. From γράφειν, *to write*, in allusion to its use as a crayon.

CLIFTONITE.   *Fletcher (Min. Mag.,* **7**, 121, 1887; **12**, 171, 1899).

A name given to small isometric crystals of graphitic carbon found in the Youndegin, Australia, and other[14] meteoric irons.   Crystals cubic, sometimes with {011}, {111}, or {0kl}.   Shown to be pseudomorphs of graphite,[15] perhaps after diamond.[16]   Named after R. B. Clifton, Professor of Physics at Oxford.

Ref.

1. Palache, *Am. Min.,* **26**, 709 (1941), on crystals from Sterling Hill, New Jersey, with a new orientation.   The trigonal or rhombohedral symmetry proposed by Kenngott, *Ak. Wien, Ber.,* **13**, 469 (1854), and Dana (7, 1892) is rejected.   The monoclinic symmetry proposed by Nordenskiöld, *Ann. Phys.,* **96**, 110 (1855), was rejected by Sjögren, *Ak. Stockholm, Öfv.,* **41**, no. 4, 29 (1884), who found it hexagonal.   The trigonal aspect of striae on the base is due to twin gliding on a second-order pyramid.
2. Palache (1941).
3. Palache (1941).   Less common forms: {10$\bar{1}$0}, {10$\bar{1}$8}, {10$\bar{1}$5}, {10$\bar{1}$4}, {20$\bar{2}$3}, {40$\bar{4}$5}, {20$\bar{2}$1}, {11$\bar{2}$6}, {22$\bar{4}$3}, {11$\bar{2}$1}.
4. The structure of natural and artificial graphite found by Hull, *Phys. Rev.,* **10**, 661 (1917) has been essentially confirmed by Bernal, *Roy. Soc. London, Proc.,* **106A**, 749 (1924) and Hassel and Mark, *Zs. Phys.,* **25**, 317 (1924).   The holohedral space group C6/mmc is accepted by Bragg (54, 1937); space groups of lower symmetry are excluded by the morphological data of Palache (1941).   Cell sides after Hassel and Mark (1924) on almost ash-free graphite from Ceylon.
5. Palache (1941).
6. Wesselowski and Wassiliew, *Zs. Kr.,* **89**, 494 (1934) on natural and artificial material by x-ray methods.
7. Jannetaz, *Bull. soc. min.,* **15**, 136 (1892).
8. Pilipenko and Oreshkin, *Ac. sc. U.S.S.R., Vernadsky Festschrift,* **2**, 723 (1936). Gaubert, *C.R.,* **177**, 1123 (1923), gives V 1.93–2.07.
9. Schneiderhöhn and Ramdohr (**2**, 18, 1931).
10. Konobejewski, *Zs. Kr.,* **72**, 381 (1929).
11. Ruff, Olbrich, and Schmidt, *Zs. anorg. Chem.,* **148**, 313 (1925).
12. On the geological relations see Stutzer, **5**, 99 (1933); origin, Clark, *Econ. Geol.,* **16**, 167 (1921); Adirondack region, Alling, *New York State Mus., Bull. 199,* 1917; occurrence and properties, Ryschkewitsch (*Graphite,* Leipzig, 1926); in meteorites, Farrington (*Meteorites,* Chicago, 123, 1915).
13. Ryschkewitsch (1926).
14. See Farrington (1915).
15. Hey, *Min. Mag.,* **25**, 81 (1940).
16. Brezina, *Ann. Mus. Wien,* **4**, 102 (1889); Rose, *Ak. Wiss. Berlin, Abh.,* 40, 1863; 532, 1872.

SCHUNGITE.   *Inostrantzev (Jb., Min.,* I, 97, 1880; I, 92, 1886).

A black vitreous material, in composition essentially carbon with small amounts of nonessential water.   Fracture conchoidal.   H. 3$\frac{1}{2}$–4.   G. 1.84–1.98.   Incombustible in air at ordinary temperatures.   Soluble without residue in $HNO_3 + KClO_4$ or $HNO_3 + H_2SO_4$ solution.   Found as thin pure layers or admixed with clay and pyrite as thick beds in a phyllite near Schunga, Government of Olenetz, Russia.   Apparently a highly metamorphosed coal.

SULFIDES AND SULFOSALTS

As in previous editions the sulfides and sulfosalts are placed in separate classes, with the general formulas $A_m X_n$ and $A_m B_n X_p$ respectively. (These are analogous to the simple oxides and multiple oxides.) In the sulfides A consists of the metallic elements principally, and less frequently As, Sb, and Bi, as the table below shows.

ELEMENTS IN THE SULFIDES

A					X	
Ag	Fe	Pb	As	Ru*	S	As
Cu	Co	Hg	Sb*	Sn*	Se	Sb*
Tl*	Ni	Mn*	Bi*	Mo*	Te	Bi*
Au*	Zn	Ca*	Pt*	W*		
	Cd					

* Rare or uncommon.

The sulfosalts have very few elements as major constituents: A = Cu, Ag, Pb, and Sn; B = As, Sb, Bi, Sn; X = S. When the number of species and the complexities of composition are considered, this class of minerals shows almost as much diversity in combinations of the same chemical elements as do the silicates.

There are close structural similarities between sulfides with $A : X = m : n$ and $A + B : X = m : n$; that is, the B part of the sulfosalt minerals often plays much the same role in a structure as the A elements in the sulfides. Thus enargite, Cu_3AsS_4, has a slightly distorted wurtzite (ZnS) structure where the three Cu atoms occupy positions equivalent to three of the Zn atoms of the wurtzite, and one As atom occupies a position equivalent to one of the Zn atoms in wurtzite. Further, in the chemistry of enargite some evidence is found that the ratio Cu : As is not strictly 3 : 1, and a reasonable explanation of the deviation could be that some of the Cu in the structure is actually replaced by As. In other words, the formula might, from the strictly chemical point of view, appropriately be written $(Cu,As)_4S_4$ or $(Cu,As)S$ with only a small deviation from a ratio of 3 : 1 for Cu : As. Tetrahedrite has a structure similar in some respects to that of sphalerite, and the same explanation holds true as that given above for the enargite-wurtzite relation.

As in the other classes, the arrangement in the sulfides is according to the decreasing $A : X$ ratio, and in the sulfosalts according to the decrease in the $A + B : X$ ratio. It is believed that valence control plays little part in isomorphous substitution, and it is for this reason that argentite, Ag_2S, (A_2X type) is not retained in the galena group (AX). Ag_2 very likely never replaces Pb in a sulfide or sulfosalt mineral.

155

Little is as yet known of the controlling principles in the structures of the sulfosalts so that a more elaborate classification than that used here is of doubtful value. The investigation of the crystal structure of these complex minerals offers a fruitful field of study.

Most sulfides (and sulfosalts) are opaque and, in addition, they are nearly always intimately intermixed. These two characteristics, not nearly so common in other classes of minerals, serve to increase the difficulties of investigation, and consequently the descriptive mineralogy of the sulfides and sulfosalts is less well known than that of most other minerals. A considerable number of the sulfides and sulfosalts still have no universally accepted chemical formula. In others the amount of substitution of certain minor elements is not known (the problem of nickelian pyrite is an example). Adequate crystallographic discussions of such minerals as *sartorite* are not yet available, chiefly because we do not know whether the crystals examined are individuals or twins, and how they are twinned or aggregated. The reflecting microscope has helped to solve the difficulty of opacity, but the quantitative data obtained from a reflecting surface is not, at this time, nearly so useful as that which can be obtained by the standard methods applied to nonopaque minerals. In order to obtain pure samples for chemical analysis of many sulfides, it is necessary to extract material under the reflecting microscope. This is an arduous and well nigh impossible task when analytical quantities for macroanalysis are required. Further clarification of the chemistry of certain sulfides and sulfosalts must therefore be accomplished by micromethods.

2 SULFIDES

21 $A_m X_n$ TYPE WITH $m : n > 3 : 1$

211	TETRADYMITE GROUP	
2111	Tellurobismuthite	Bi_2Te_3
2112	Tetradymite	Bi_2Te_2S
2113	Gruenlingite	Bi_4TeS_3
2114	Joseite	Bi_3TeS
2115	Wehrlite	Bi_3Te_2 ?
212	Nagyagite	$Pb_5Au(TeSb)_4S_{5-8}$?

213	COPPER ARSENIDE GROUP	
2131	Algodonite	Cu_6As
2132	Domeykite ·	Cu_3As
2133	Horsfordite	Cu_5Sb
2134	Cocinerite	Cu_4AgS

22 A_3X TYPE

221	Dyscrasite	Ag_3Sb
222	Stibiopalladinite	Pd_3Sb

23 A_2X TYPE

231	ARGENTITE GROUP	
2311	Argentite	Ag_2S
2312	Aguilarite	$Ag_2(Se, S)$
2313	Naumannite	Ag_2Se
2314	Digenite	$Cu_{2-x}S$
2315	Berzelianite	Cu_2Se
2316	Crookesite	$(Cu, Tl, Ag)_2Se$
2317	Eucairite	$CuAgSe$
2318	Hessite	Ag_2Te
2319	Petzite	Ag_3AuTe_2

232	CHALCOCITE GROUP	
2321	Chalcocite	Cu_2S
2322	Stromeyerite	$AgCuS$
2323	Acanthite	Ag_2S

24 A_3X_2 TYPE

241	Maucherite	$Ni_{11}As_8$
242	Umangite	Cu_3Se_2
243	Bornite	Cu_5FeS_4

25 A_4X_3 TYPE

251	Dimorphite	As_4S_3
252	Rickardite	Cu_4Te_3
253	Weissite	Cu_5Te_3

26 AX TYPE

261	GALENA GROUP	
2611	Galena	PbS
2612	Clausthalite	$PbSe$
2613	Altaite	$PbTe$
2614	Alabandite	MnS
2615	Oldhamite	CaS

262	SPHALERITE GROUP	
2621	Sphalerite	ZnS
2622	Metacinnabar	$(Hg,Fe,Zn)S$
2623	Tiemannite	$HgSe$
2624	Coloradoite	$HgTe$

263	CHALCOPYRITE GROUP	
2631	Chalcopyrite	$Cu_2Fe_2S_4$
2632	Stannite	Cu_2FeSnS_4

264	WURTZITE GROUP	
2641	Wurtzite	ZnS
2642	Greenockite	CdS
2643	Voltzite	Zn_5S_4O

265	NICCOLITE GROUP	
2651	Pyrrhotite	$Fe_{1-x}S$
2652	Valleriite	
2653	Niccolite	NiAs
2654	Breithauptite	NiSb
2655	Millerite	NiS
2656	Pentlandite	$(Fe,Ni)_9S_8$
266	Cubanite	$CuFe_2S_3$
267	Sternbergite	$AgFe_2S_3$

268	COVELLITE GROUP	
2681	Covellite	CuS
2682	Klockmannite	CuSe
269	Cinnabar	HgS
26·10	Realgar	AsS
26·11	Cooperite	PtS
26·12	Braggite	$(Pt,Pd,Ni)S$
26·13	Herzenbergite	SnS
26·14·1	Empressite	AgTe
26·14·2	Muthmannite	$(Ag,Au)Te$

27 A_3X_4 TYPE

271	LINNAEITE SERIES	
2711	Linnaeite	Co_3S_4
2712	Siegenite	$(Co,Ni)_3S_4$
2713	Carrollite	Co_2CuS_4
2714	Violarite	Ni_2FeS_4
2715	Polydymite	Ni_3S_4
272	Daubreelite	Cr_2FeS_4
273	Badenite	$(Co,Ni,Fe)_3(As,Bi)_4$?

28 A_2X_3 TYPE

281	Orpiment	As_2S_3

282	STIBNITE GROUP	
2821	Stibnite	Sb_2S_3
2822	Bismuthinite	Bi_2S_3
2823	Guanajuatite	Bi_2Se_3
283	Kermesite	Sb_2S_2O

29 AX_2 TYPE

291	PYRITE GROUP	
2911	Pyrite	FeS_2
2912	Bravoite	$(Ni,Fe)S_2$
2913	Laurite	RuS_2
2914	Sperrylite	$PtAs_2$
2915	Hauerite	MnS_2
2916	Penroseite	$(Ni,Cu,Pb)Se_2$

292	COBALTITE GROUP	
2921	Cobaltite	CoAsS
2922	Gersdorffite	NiAsS
2923	Ullmannite	NiSbS

293	LOELLINGITE GROUP	
2931	Loellingite	$FeAs_2$
2932	Safflorite	$(Co,Fe)As_2$
2933	Rammelsbergite	$NiAs_2$
2934	Pararammelsbergite	$NiAs_2$
294	Marcasite	FeS_2

295	ARSENOPYRITE GROUP	
2951	Arsenopyrite	FeAsS
2952	Glaucodot	$(Co,Fe)AsS$
2953	Gudmundite	FeSbS
2954	Wolfachite	$Ni(As,Sb)S$?
2955	Lautite	CuAsS

296	MOLYBDENITE GROUP	
2961	Molybdenite	MoS_2
2962	Tungstenite	WS_2

297	KRENNERITE GROUP	
2971	Krennerite	$AuTe_2$
2972	Calaverite	$AuTe_2$
2973	Sylvanite	$(Ag,Au)Te_2$
298	Melonite	$NiTe_2$
299	Parkerite	NiS_2 ?

2·10 AX_3 TYPE

2·10·1	SKUTTERUDITE SERIES	
2·10·11	Skutterudite	$(Co,Ni)As_3$
2·10·12	Smaltite	$(Co,Ni)As_{3-x}$
2·10·13	Nickel-Skutterudite	$(Ni,Co)As_3$
2·10·14	Chloanthite	$(Ni,Co)As_{3-x}$
2·10·2	Niggliite	$PtTe_3$?

211   TETRADYMITE GROUP

RHOMBOHEDRAL

			G.	a_0	c_0	$\frac{c_0}{a_0}$
2111	Tellurobismuthite	Bi_2Te_3	7.65	4.24	11.10	2.618
2112	Tetradymite	Bi_2Te_2S	7.3	4.32	30.01	6.946
2113	Gruenlingite	Bi_4TeS_3	8.08	....	.....	.....
2114	Joseite	Bi_3TeS	8.18	....	.....	.....
2115	Wehrlite	Bi_3Te_2 ?		....	.....	.....

The members of the tetradymite group possess a perfect basal cleavage, a lamellar habit and many of the properties of metals. The structure of tetradymite[1] is of the layered type, with successive planes composed entirely of Bi, Te, or S atoms stacked along [0001], and apparently this general structural scheme runs through the entire group.

The several minerals of the group resemble each other very closely in physical properties and in polished surface tests, and their distinction is best accomplished by x-ray methods. Bi_2Te_3 is the only member of the group that has been recognized in the artificial systems Bi–Te or Bi–Te–S, although the compound $Bi_4Te_3S_3$, not found in nature, has been observed.

Ref.

1. Harker, *Zs. Kr.*, **89**, 175 (1934).

2111 **TELLUROBISMUTHITE** [Bi_2Te_3]. Tellurbismuth *Balch* (*Am. J. Sc.*, **35**, 99, 1863). Tellurwismuth *Germ.* Tetradymite pt. Tellurobismuthite *Wherry* (*Washington Ac. Sc. J.*, **10**, 490, 1920); *Frondel* (*Am. J. Sc.*, **238**, 880, 1940).
Vandiestite pt. *Cumenge* (*Bull. soc. min.*, **22**, 25, 1899).

C r y s t. Hexagonal — R.[1]

Structure cell.[2] Rhombohedral; a_0 4.375 ± 0.01, c_0 30.39 ± 0.010; $a_0 : c_0 = 1 : 6.946$; a_{rh} 10.44 ± 0.03, α 24°11$\frac{1}{2}$′; contains Bi_2Te_3 in the rhombohedral unit. Space group $R\bar{3}m$.

Habit. Found only as irregular plates or foliated masses.

P h y s. Cleavage {0001} perfect. May exhibit a parting inclined about 62° to {0001}.[3] Laminae flexible, but not elastic. Somewhat sectile. H. 1$\frac{1}{2}$–2; soils paper. G. 7.815 ± 0.15;[4] 7.86 (calc.). M.P. 573° (artif.[5]). Luster metallic, splendent on fresh cleavages. Color and streak pale lead-gray. Opaque. Thermoelectrically negative. In polished section[3] white in color and weakly anisotropic. May exhibit a triangular set of striations at 60° on cleavage surfaces, due to deformation. Translation gliding with T{0001}.[3]

C h e m. An intermetallic compound, Bi_2Te_3. Se is often present in traces.

Anal.[6]

	1	2	3	4	5	6	7	8
Bi	52.09	53.15	53.07	52.90	52.77	52.14	51.99	51.46
Te	47.91	46.12	48.19	45.33	46.87	46.62	47.89	48.26
S	.....	.....	.....	0.71	0.29	0.14	0.12	.....
Rem.	.....	0.73	.....	0.52	0.52	0.57	.....	.....
Total	100.00	100.00	101.26	99.46	100.45	99.47	100.00	99.72
G.	7.86		7.83			7.82		7.64

1. Bi_2Te_3. 2. Mt. Sierra Blanca, Col. (*vandiestite*). Rem. is Pb 0.73. Recalculated after deduction of 5.08 per cent Ag as hessite.[7] 3. Tellurium mine, Fluvanna Co., Va. With Se trace.[8] 4. Little Mildred mine, Hachita, N. M. Rem. is Fe 0.52, Mg trace.[9] 5. Whitehorn, Fremont Co., Col. Rem. is Fe 0.52, with trace of Se and Mg.[10] 6. Whitehorn, Fremont Co., Col. Mean of three analyses. Rem. is Se 0.20, Fe_2O_3 0.22, insol. 0.15.[11] 7. Oya, Miyagi prefecture, Japan.[12] 8. Field's Vein, Dahlonega, Ga. With Se trace.[13]

Tests. In O.T. a white sublimate of TeO_2. On charcoal fuses, gives white fumes and entirely volatilizes; sometimes gives disagreeable selenium odors.

O c c u r. Found in Japan at Oya, Miyagi prefecture. From Boliden, Sweden. In the United States in gold-quartz veins at Tellurium mine,

Fluvanna County, Virginia, and at Field's vein, Dahlonega, Georgia. In Montana in flakes in a gold placer at Highland, and with native gold in calcite at Garnet. From the Little Mildred mine, Hachita, New Mexico, in a quartz vein with tourmaline. In Colorado from near Whitehorn, Fremont County; at the Little Gerald and Hamilton mines, Mount Sierra Blanca, San Luis County (vandiestite), with hessite and gold in quartz; at the Treasure Vault mine, Clear Creek County, with beegerite (?); at Mount Chipeta, near Salida, Chaffee County. In Canada found with native gold and sulfides at the Hunter mine, Khutze Inlet, near Swanson Bay, British Columbia, and at the Ashloo mine near Squamish, Howe Sound, British Columbia.

Alter. To montanite and ill-defined bismuth oxides.

Artif. Observed in the system Bi–Te.[14]

Name. In allusion to the composition. Tellurobismuthite was formerly classed by most authors as a sulfur-free variety of tetradymite, but the mineral was later shown[3] to be a distinct species.

VANDIESTITE. *Pearce (Colorado Sc. Soc., Bull. 6, 4, 1898; Colorado Sc. Soc., Proc., 6, 163, 1902).* Von Diestite *Cumenge (Bull. soc. min., 22, 25, 1899).* Diestit.
A supposed telluride of silver and bismuth from the Little Gerald and Hamilton mines, Mount Sierra Blanca, Colorado. Shown[3] to be a mixture of tellurobismuthite and hessite.

Ref.

1. The rhombohedral character of artificial Bi_2Te_3 was established by Lange, *Naturwiss*, 27, 133 (1939). The rhombohedral character and identity with artificial Bi_2Te_3 of tellurobismuthite was shown by Frondel, *Am. J. Sc.*, 238, 880 (1940), and Peacock, *Univ. Toronto Stud., Geol. Ser.*, 44, 67 (1940), by x-ray powder study.
2. Cell dimensions of Peacock (1940) on artificial material. Frondel (1940) obtained a_0 4.38, c_0 30.6 on natural material from Whitehorn, Colorado (anal. 6).
3. Frondel (1940).
4. Range of the determinations of Frondel (1940), Peacock (1940), and Hillebrand (1905).
5. Mönkmeyer, *Zs. anorg. Chem.*, 46, 415 (1905).
6. For additional analyses see Dana (39, 1892) and Warren and Davis, *Univ. Toronto Stud., Geol. Ser.*, 44, 107 (1940).
7. Gonyer anal. in Frondel, *Am. J. Sc.*, 238, 880 (1940).
8. Genth, *Am. J. Sc.*, 19, 16 (1855).
9. Short and Henderson, *Am. Min.*, 11, 316 (1926).
10. Henderson anal. in Wells, *U. S. Geol. Sur., Bull. 878*, 87 (1938).
11. Hillebrand, *U. S. Geol. Sur., Bull. 262*, 57 (1905).
12. Yagi anal. in Harada (235, 1936).
13. Balch, *Am. J. Sc.*, 35, 99 (1863).
14. See Mellor (11, 61, 1931).

2112 TETRADYMITE [Bi_2Te_2S]. Ore of Tellurium (from Tellemark) *Esmark (Geol. Soc. London, Trans.*, 3, 413, 1815). Tellurwismuth (from Riddarhyttan) *Berzelius (Ak. Stockholm, Handl.*, 1823; *Ann. Phys.*, 1, 271, 1824). Telluric Bismuth. Tetradymite, Rhomboëdrische Wismuthglanz (from Schubkau) *Haidinger (Zs. Phys. Math.*, 9, 129, 1831). Bismuth telluré, Tellure selenié bismuthifère *Fr.* Bornine *Beudant* (2, 538, 1832). Bismuthotellurites pt. *Glocker* (19, 1847). Schwefel-Tellurwismuth *Rammelsberg* (1860).

Cryst. Hexagonal — R.

$$a : c = 1 : 6.952;^1 \qquad p_0 : r_0 = 8.027 : 1$$

Forms:[2]

			ϕ	ρ	A_1	A_2
c	0001	111	0°00′	0°00′	0°00′	0°00′
P	10$\bar{1}$4	211	30 00	63 30½	39 11	90 00
f	01$\bar{1}$2	110	0 00	76 00½	32 49½	90 00
r	10$\bar{1}$1	100	30 00	82 54	30 45	90 00

Structure cell.[3] Space group $R\bar{3}$, $R32$, or $R\bar{3}m$; a_0 4.32, c_0 30.01, $a_0 : c_0 = 1 : 6.946$; a_{rh} 10.31, α 24°10′; contains Bi_2Te_2S in the rhombohedral unit.

Habit. Crystals rarely distinct; acutely pyramidal with {10$\bar{1}$1} and {01$\bar{1}$2}, resembling hexagonal prisms, with the pyramidal faces horizontally striated. Commonly foliated to granular massive, and in bladed forms.

Twinning.[4] Fourlings, twin plane (a) {01$\bar{1}$8}; (b) {01$\bar{1}$5}.

Schubkau   Schubkau, Fourling

P h y s. Cleavage {0001} perfect. Laminae flexible, but not elastic. Not very sectile. H. 1½–2; soils paper. G. 7.3 ± 0.2; 7.21 (calc.). M.P. 600°.[5] Luster metallic, splendent on fresh cleavages. Color and streak pale steel-gray; tarnishes dull or iridescent. Opaque. Thermoelectrically positive.[8] Sometimes exhibits a triangular set of striations on {0001} due to deformation. In polished section[6] white in color and weakly anisotropic; sometimes exhibits a graphic-like intergrowth.[7] Reflection percentages: green 48.5, orange 48, red 47.5.

C h e m. An intermetallic compound, Bi_2Te_2S. Se has been reported up to 2 per cent, but is usually present only in traces.

Anal.[9]

	1	2	3	4	5	6	7	8
Bi	59.27	62.23	60.53	60.36	59.66	59.56	59.12	56.35
Te	36.19	33.25	33.34	35.25	33.16	35.46	35.94	35.62
S	4.54	4.50	4.23	4.20	4.54	4.98	4.75	4.38
Se	.....	.....	1.46	trace	.....	trace	.....	2.17
Rem.	.....	.....	0.68	.....	0.82	.....	.....	1.48

	1	2	3	4	5	6	7	8
Total	100.00	99.98	100.24	99.81	98.18	100.00	99.81	100.00
G.		7.184			7.09	7.39		

1. Bi_2Te_2S. 2. Bradshaw City, Ariz.[10] 3. Csiklova, Hungary. Average of four closely agreeing analyses. Rem. is Fe trace, Pb 0.68.[11] 4. Schubkau, Hungary.[12] 5. Norongo, New South Wales. Rem. is Fe 0.42, SiO$_2$ 0.40.[13] 6. West Gwanda district, Rhodesia. Recalculated after deduction of 5.90 per cent gangue.[14] 7. Csiklova, Hungary.[15] 8. Trail Creek, Idaho. Rem. is Pb 1.48. Recalculated after deduction of 6.57 per cent gangue.[16]

Tests. In O.T. a white sublimate of TeO_2. On charcoal fuses, gives white fumes, and entirely volatilizes; coats the coal at first white (TeO_2), and finally orange-yellow (Bi_2O_3).

Occur.[17] Not uncommon in gold-quartz veins formed at moderate to high temperatures; also in contact metamorphic deposits. Usually associated with hessite, petzite, altaite, and other tellurides, pyrite, galena, and other sulfides in small amounts, native bismuth, hematite, and, in particular, native gold. Noted as oriented flattened inclusions (possibly tellurobismuthite) in galena, with {0001} parallel {111}.[18]

Found in Roumania at Rezbánya, Csiklova, Moravicza, and Oravicza. In fine twinned crystals at Schubkau, near Schemnitz, Bohemia. At Boholiby, near Jílové, Bohemia. In Norway at Narverud, Tellemark, and at Gjelleboek, near Drammen. In Sweden at Boliden, Västerbotten. In Africa, in the New Mystery mine, West Gwanda district, Rhodesia; reported from elsewhere in Rhodesia. At Norongo, near Captain's Flat, New South Wales. In Japan at the Rendaizi mine, Idu, in quartz veins with nagyagite. At the Dunallen mine, Western Australia, and at Mount Shamrock, near Gayndah, Queensland. Near Sorata, Bolivia.

In the United States, in California in the Cerro Gordo district, Inyo County, with bismutite in quartz veins, and at the Melones and Morgan mines on Carson Hill, Calaveras County. In Colorado at the Red Cloud mine, Boulder County, with hessite, altaite, and tellurium, and at Camp Albion, Boulder County, as platy inclusions in galena. In Arizona from the Montgomery mine, Hassayampa district, and in bladed crystals in quartz from near Bradshaw City, Yavapai County. In Montana at the Uncle Sam Lode, Highland, and at the Keating mine, Radersburg. In Idaho at Trail Creek, Hailey quadrangle. In New Mexico in the Sylvanite district, Hidalgo County, in the Organ district, Dona Ana County, and from Sierra, Colfax and Grant counties. Widespread in small amounts in gold-quartz veins in the Appalachian states. In Virginia at the Whitehall mines, Spotsylvania County, at Monroe, Stafford County, and at the Tellurium mine, Fluvanna County. In North Carolina at the Phoenix mine, Cabarrus County, at the Asbury mine, Montgomery County, and about 5 miles west of the Washington mine, Davidson County. In South Carolina in the York district. In Georgia, 4 miles east of Dahlonega, Lumpkin County, and also in Cherokee, Polk, and Spaulding counties.

In Canada near Liddell Creek, West Kootenai, British Columbia, with hessite and altaite; in Ontario at Painkiller Lake, near Matheson, Cochrane District, at the Gold Shore mine, Red Lake, at Bigstone Bay, Lake of the Woods, and at Straw Lake, Kenora district; in Quebec at the McWatters mine, Rouyn Township, at the Eureka mine, Abitibi County, and in Montbray Township.

Alter. To montanite usually, also to bismutite; observed coated by native gold.

A r t i f. No evidence of the compound Bi_2Te_2S has been found[19] in the system Bi–Te–S.

N a m e. From τετράδυμος, *fourfold*, in allusion to the twin crystals.

Ref.

1. Orientation and unit of Harker, *Zs. Kr.*, **89**, 175 (1934), on crystals from Schubkau, by x-ray methods. The unit for the new elements is the {04$\overline{4}$1} of Haidinger, *Zs. Phys. Math.*, **9**, 129 (1831). Transformation: Haidinger to Harker 0$\overline{1}$00/00$\overline{1}$0/ $\overline{1}$000/0004.
2. Haidinger (1831).
3. Harker (1934).
4. The twin plane {04$\overline{4}$1} observed by Haidinger (1831) becomes {10$\overline{1}$8} in the new elements, which could not occur as a first-order plane in the rhombohedral system. A check on the twinning by Wolfe and Berman (priv. comm., 1939) disclosed that the twin plane is actually {01$\overline{1}$8}. A new well-defined twin law with twin plane {01$\overline{1}$5} was also observed.
5. Borgström, *Finska Vet.-Soc., Öfv.*, **57**, 9 (1915).
6. Schneiderhöhn and Ramdohr (**2**, 91, 1931); Larsen in Frondel, *Am. J. Sc.*, **238**, 880 (1940).
7. The intergrowth is presumably with related telluride minerals — see Frondel (1940).
8. Schrauf and Dana, *Am. J. Sc.*, **8**, 262 (1874).
9. For additional analyses see Doelter (4 [1], 855, 1926).
10. Genth, *Am. J. Sc.*, **14**, 114 (1890).
11. Clauder (Inaug. Diss., Budapest, 1931 — *Jb. Min.*, I, 152, 1935.
12. Muthmann and Schröder, *Zs. Kr.*, **29**, 143 (1897).
13. Mingaye, *New South Wales Geol. Sur., Rec.*, **1**, 25 (1908).
14. Golding anal. in Lightfoot, *Geol. Soc. South Africa, Trans.*, **30**, 1 (1928).
15. Antal (Gyógysz. Diss., Budapest, 1928 — *Min. Abs.*, 4, 480 [1931]).
16. Shannon, *Am. Min.*, **10**, 198 (1925).
17. The distinction between tetradymite and tellurobismuthite has not been established for some of the localities here cited.
18. Neuhaus, *Chem. Erde*, **12**, 35 (1938) and Wahlstrom, *Am. Min.*, **22**, 906 (1937).
19. Amadori, *Acc. Linc., Att.*, **24**, 200 (1915); **27**, 131 (1918).

TAPALPITE.   *Monroy (Naturaleza*, **1**, 76 (1869); *Landero (Zs. Kr.*, **13**, 320, 1887); *Genth (Am. Phil. Soc., Proc.*,[**24**, 41, 1887). Tellurwismuthsilber *Rammelsberg (Zs. deutsche geol. Ges.*, **21**, 81, 1869). Tapalpaite.

Described as a massive granular sulfo-telluride of bismuth and silver, $Ag_3Bi(S,Te)_3$, from the San Antonio mine, San Rafael district, Sierra Tapalpa, Jalisco, Mexico.

Shown to be a mixture,[1] probably of argentite and tetradymite.

Ref.

1. Murdoch (107, 125, 1916) found a specimen from the locality to be a mixture of two minerals, one of which was considered tapalpite. Schneiderhöhn and Ramdohr (**2**, 423, 1931) also found the material to be a mixture, composed of the " tapalpite " and the other mineral noted by Murdoch, and a third mineral. Short (105, 1931) found that the material was an intergrowth of tetradymite and argentite. The etch reactions of the two minerals described by Murdoch are similar to tetradymite and argentite.

2113   **G R U E N L I N G I T E** [Bi_4TeS_3]. Grünlingite *Muthmann and Schröder (Zs. Kr.*, **29**, 144, 1897).

Oruetite pt. *de Rubies (An. soc. español. fis. quim.*, **17**, 83, 1919).

Occurs as lamellar masses with a steel-gray color, tarnishing darker or iridescent. Luster metallic. Cleavage perfect in one direction. Flexible. H. 2. G. 8.08.[1] Sometimes exhibits a triangular set of striations on cleavage surfaces, due to mechanical deformation. In polished section white in color and weakly anisotropic.[2]

C h e m. Bismuth sulfide-telluride, Bi_4TeS_3, or near $Bi_2(Te,Bi)S_2$ with Te : Bi = 3 : 2.

Anal.

	1	2
Bi	78.89	79.07
Te	12.03	12.74
S	9.08	9.37
Total	100.00	101.18

1. Bi_4TeS_3. 2. Carrock Fell, Cumberland. Average of two analyses.[3]

O c c u r. Found in quartz, associated with native bismuth and bismuthinite, at Carrock Fell, Cumberland, England. From the Serrania de Ronda, Spain (*oruetite*), in dolomite with native bismuth, bismuthinite, arsenopyrite, and scheelite.

N a m e. After Dr. F. Grünling, formerly curator of the mineral collection, University of Munich.

The relation of gruenlingite to joseite is uncertain.[4]

ORUETITE. *de Rubies (Anal. soc. español. fís. quím.,* 17, 83, 1919).
Occurs as lamellar masses with brilliant metallic luster and steel-gray color, tarnishing dull. Cleavage perfect. Flexible. G. 7.6. H. 1½–2. Melts at about 500°, with loss of S. Analysis (average of seven) : Bi 86.78, Te 6.35, S 6.84, total 100.97. Found in dolomite in the Serrania de Ronda, Spain. Named after the discoverer, Domingo de Orueta. Shown[5] to be a mixture of gruenlingite and native bismuth.

Ref.
1. Measured on 29-mg. sample from Cumberland (Frondel, priv. comm., 1939).
2. Larsen in Frondel, *Am. J. Sc.,* 238, 880 (1940).
3. Muthmann and Schröder (1897).
4. X-ray powder studies by Frondel (priv. comm., 1939) and Garrido and Feo, *Bull. soc. min.,* 40, 202 (1938) indicate that tetradymite, tellurobismuthite, gruenlingite, and joseite are distinct species, but Peacock, *Univ. Toronto Stud., Geol. Ser.,* 44, 47 (1940) found the pattern of joseite and gruenlingite to be identical. See also Peacock, *Univ. Toronto Stud., Geol. Ser.,* 46, 83 (1941).
5. Garrido, *An. Soc. español. fís. quím.,* 31, 99 (1933), Garrido and Feo (1938).

Ill-defined bismuth tellurides not certainly identical with any known species have been reported from several localities. A mineral found associated with bismuthinite at Glacier Gulch, near Smithers, British Columbia,[1] approximates to the formula Bi_4TeS_2 (anal. 1). Somewhat similar substances have been found with garnet and native bismuth at the Whipstick mine, New South Wales[2] (anal. 2), and with gruenlingite and native bismuth at Carrock Fell, Cumberland[3] (anal. 3). *Rubiesite Doelter* (4 [1], 838, 1926; de Rubies; *An. soc. español. fís. quím.,* 18, 335 (1920), from the Serrania de Ronda, Spain, is probably a mixture composed chiefly of gruenlingite.

	1	2	3
Bi	81.3	82.92	84.33
Te	12.5	9.16	6.73
S	6.2	6.19	6.43
Rem.		1.56	.....
Total	100.0	99.83	97.49
G.	8.6 ± 0.3	7.74	

1. Glacier Gulch, B. C.   Recalculated to 100 per cent from original sum of 97.5.[4]
2. Whipstick mine, New South Wales.   Rem. is Mn 0.77, Fe 0.47, insol. 0.32, Se trace.[2]
3. Carrock Fell, Cumberland.[3]

Ref.

1. Warren and Davis, *Univ. Toronto Stud., Geol. Ser.*, **44**, 107 (1940).
2. Mingaye, *New South Wales Geol. Sur., Rec.*, **9**, 127 (1916).
3. Rammelsberg (5, 1875).
4. Forward anal. in Warren and Davis (1940).

2114   **Joseite** [Bi₃TeS ?].   Tellure de Bismuth *Damour* (*Ann. chim. phys.*, **13**, 372, 1845).   Bornit *Hausmann* (*Jb. Min.*, 701, 1852).   Tellure bismuthifère du Brésil *Dufrénoy* (not Bornine [= tetradymite] *Beudant* [**2**, 538, 1832]).   Josëite *Kenngott* (121, 1853).   Schwefelselen-tellurwismuth *Rammelsberg* (5, 1875).

C r y s t.   In irregular laminated masses.

P h y s.   Cleavage perfect in one direction.   Flexible.   H. 2.   G. 8.18.[1]
Luster metallic.   Color grayish black to steel-gray, tarnishing darker or iridescent.   In polished section[2] white in color and weakly anisotropic.

C h e m.   An intermetallic compound of Bi, Te, Se, and S of uncertain formula, perhaps Bi₃Te(Se,S).[3]

Anal.

	1	2	3	4
Bi	79.71	79.15	78.40	81.23
Te	16.21	15.93	15.68	14.67
Se	.....	1.48	} 4.58	2.84
S	4.08	3.15		1.46
Total	100.00	99.71	98.66	100.20
G.		7.93		

1. Bi₃TeS.   2. San José, Brazil.[4]   3. San José, Brazil.[4]   4. San José, Brazil.[5]

Tests.   In O.T. gives off some S, then white fumes of TeO₂, and then affords a decided odor of Se; in the upper part of the tube a white coating of TeO₂ with some brick-red over it, due to the Se, and a yellowish residue of Bi₂O₃ below.

O c c u r.   Found in granular limestone at San José, near Marianna, Minas Geraes, Brazil.

A l t e r.   To montanite (?)

N a m e.   From the locality at San José, Brazil.

Ref.

1. Frondel (priv. comm., 1939) by microbalance on type material.
2. Larsen in Frondel, *Am. J. Sc.*, **238**, 880 (1940).
3. Peacock, *Univ. Toronto Stud., Geol. Ser.*, **44**, 60 (1940) states that the x-ray powder patterns of joseite and gruenlingite are identical, but the x-ray powder studies of

Frondel (priv. comm., 1939) and Garrido and Feo, *Bull. soc. min.*, **41**, 196 (1938) indicate that joseite is distinct from the other known bismuth tellurides.
4. Damour (1845).
5. Genth, *Am. Phil Soc., Proc.*, **23**, 31 (1885).

2115 Wehrlite [Bi_3Te_2 ?]. Argent molybdique *de Born* (**2**, 419, 1790). Wasserblei-silber, Molybdän-silber *Werner* (18, 48, 1817). Molybdic silver. Wismuthglanz *Klaproth* (**1**, 254, 1795). Tellurwismuth *Berzelius* (*Ak. Stockholm, Handl.*, 1823). Wismuthspiegel *Weiss*. Spiegelglanz *Breithaupt*. Tetradymite pt., Wehrlite *Huot* (**1**, 188, 1841). Pilsenit *Kenngott* (121, 1853). Börzsönyite *Papp* (*Földt. Közl.*, **62**, 61, 1933).

In foliated masses with perfect cleavage resembling tetradymite. Flexible; thin foliae slightly elastic. H. $1\frac{1}{2}$–$2\frac{1}{2}$. G. 8.41 ± 0.03. Luster bright metallic, tarnishing dull. Color tin-white to light steel-gray. Thermoelectrically positive.[1]

Chem. Composition uncertain. Analysis 2 corresponds to Bi_8Te_5S, or to Bi_3Te_2 after excluding S as Ag_2S and Bi_2S_3; analysis 3 corresponds to $AgBi_7Te_7$.

Anal.

	1	2	3
Ag	2.07	0.48	4.37
Bi	61.15	70.02	59.47
Te	29.74	28.52	35.47
S	2.33	1.33	.....
Total	95.29	100.35	99.31
G.	8.44		8.368

1. Deutsch-Pilsen.[2] 2, 3. Deutsch-Pilsen.[3]

Found at Deutsch-Pilsen (Börzsöny), near Gran, Hungary. Named after former Mining Commissioner A. Wehrle (1791–1835) of Schemnitz. Needs further study.

Ref.

1. Schrauf and Dana, *Am. J. Sc.*, **8**, 262 (1874).
2. Wehrle, *Zs. Phys. Math.*, **9**, 144 (1831).
3. Sipöcz, *Zs. Kr.*, **11**, 212 (1885).

STUETZITE. Tellursilberblende *Schrauf* (*Zs. Kr.*, **2**, 245, 1878). An uncertain silver telluride with the possible composition Ag_4Te, the Ag determined approximately with the blowpipe. The highly modified crystals found on the only specimen are either hexagonal with $c = 1.2530$, or pseudohexagonal. Fracture uneven to subconchoidal. Luster metallic. Color lead-gray with reddish tinge. Streak blackish lead-gray. Easily fusible to a dark bead from which a silver globule is obtained by reduction with soda; yields tellurium dioxide in the open tube.

Found on a single specimen in the collection of Vienna University; locality probably Nagyág, Transylvania. Associated with gold and hessite on quartz. Named after the Viennese mineralogist A. Stütz (1747–1806), who in 1803 described a tellurium mineral from Nagyág which is regarded by Schrauf as probably identical with this.

CHILENITE. Aleación de plata con bismuto *Domeyko* (187, 1845). Plata bismutal *Domeyko* (185, 1860). Chilenite *Dana* (36, 1868). Described as a compound of silver and bismuth (Ag_6Bi ?). The original analysis[1] is very unsatisfactory. A specimen from the original locality (San Antonio mine, Potrero Grande, Copiapó, Chile) is a mixture of silver and cuprite.[2]

Ref.

1. Dana (45, 1892).
2. Short (104, 1931).

212   **N A G Y A G I T E** [Pb$_5$Au(Te,Sb)$_4$S$_{5-8}$]. Aurum Galena, Ferro et particulis volatilibus mineralisatum, *Scopoli* (*Ann. Hist. Nat.*, **3**, 107; *von Born*, **1**, 68, 1772). Nagiakererz *Werner* (*Bergm. J.*, 1879). Or gris lamelleux *von Born* (1790). Blättererz *Karsten* (56, 1800). Foliated Tellurium; Black Tellurium. Elasmose *Beudant* (**2**, 539, 1832). Elasmosine *Huot* (**1**, 185, 1841). Nagyagite *Haidinger* (566, 1845).

C r y s t. Monoclinic?[1]

$a : b : c = 0.2807 : 1 : 0.2761;$ $\beta\ 90°00';$[2] $p_0 : q_0 : r_0 = 0.9836 : 0.2761 : 1$

$q_1 : r_1 : p_1 = 0.2807 : 1.0167 : 1;$ $\mu\ 90°00';$ $r_2 : p_2 : q_2 = 3.6219 : 3.5625 : 1$

Forms:[3]

	ϕ	$\rho = C$	ϕ_1	$\rho_1 = A$	ϕ_2	$\rho_2 = B$
b 010	0°00′	90°00′	90°00′	90°00′	. . . . .	0°00′
o 160	30 42	90 00	90 00	59 18	0°00′	30 42
e 120	60 41½	90 00	90 00	29 18½	0 00	60 41½
d 011	0 00	15 26	15 26	90 00	90 00	74 36
t 111	74 19	45 37	15 26	46 31½	45 28½	78 52
r 121	60 41½	48 26½	28 54½	49 16	45 28½	68 30½

Less common:

$i\{130\}$ $m\{110\}$ $f\{031\}$ $g\{051\}$ $\epsilon\{101\}$ $s\{343\}$ $p\{252\}$ $x\{131\}$ $y\{141\}$

Structure cell.[4] Tetragonal or pseudotetragonal (?). a_0 12.5, c_0 30.25; $a_0 : c_0 = 1 : 2.420;$ contains Pb$_{50}$Au$_{10}$(Te,Sb)$_{40}$S$_{50-80}$.

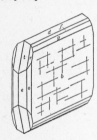

Nagyág.

Habit. Crystals thin tabular ‖ {010}. Faces {010} striated ‖ [100] and [001]. Also granular massive, in particles of various sizes; generally foliated, the crystals often bent.

Twinning. Possibly with [201] as twin axis, and composition plane {010}.[5] Shows complex twinning in polished section.[6]

P h y s. Cleavage {010} perfect. Laminae flexible; slightly malleable. H. 1–1½. G. 7.41 ± 0.05.[7] Luster metallic, splendent on fresh cleavages. Color and streak blackish lead-gray. Opaque. In polished section[6] gray-white in color, with distinct anisotropism and weak pleochroism; shows mosaic twinning in sections ‖ {010}.[6] Reflection percentages: green 43, orange 35, red 34.[8]

C h e m. Perhaps an intermetallic compound. Formula uncertain, probably Pb$_5$Au(Te,Sb)$_4$S$_{5-8}$.[9] Early analyses[10] show less or no Sb; see also anal. 7. Ag and Se are present only in amounts less than 2 per cent.

Anal.

	1	2	3	4	5	6	7
Pb	57.16	56.81	55.44	54.50	53.55	52.55	51.18
Au	7.41	7.51	8.43	7.61	9.47	10.16	8.11
Sb	6.99	7.39	6.61	8.62	6.05	7.00	. . . . .
Te	17.87	17.72	18.92	17.80	18.99	18.80	29.88
S	10.01	10.76	9.69	9.10	11.90	8.62	10.83
Rem.	0.60	0.41	0.90	3.05	0.56	1.12	. . . . .
Total	100.04	100.60	99.99	100.68	100.52	98.25	100.00
G.	7.347	7.4613					

1. Nagyág. Average of two analyses. Rem. is Fe 0.32, SiO_2 0.28.[11] 2. Nagyág. Rem. is Fe 0.41.[12] 3. Nagyág. Average of three closely agreeing analyses. Rem. is Fe 0.59, gangue 0.31.[13] 4. Nagyág. Rem. is Fe 0.93, insol. 2.12.[14] 5. Nagyág. Rem. is insol. 0.56.[15] 6. Oroya, Kalgoorlie district, Western Australia. Rem. is Ag 1.12.[16] 7. Nagyág. Recalc. after deducting quartz 1.56.[17]

Tests. In O.T. gives, near the assay, a grayish sublimate of antimonate and tellurate, with perhaps some sulfate of lead, farther up the tube the sublimate consists of antimony trioxide and tellurium dioxide. B.B. on charcoal easily fusible and forms two coatings; one white and volatile, consisting of a mixture of antimonate, tellurate, and sulfate of lead, and the other, less volatile, of yellow lead oxide quite near the assay. When treated for some time in O.F. a globule of gold remains. Soluble in HNO_3 with a residue of gold, and in aqua regia with the separation of sulfur and sometimes of silver chloride.

Occur. An uncommon mineral, found associated with altaite and other tellurides, gold, sulfides in minor amounts, and carbonates. Found in Transylvania at Nagyág, in foliated masses and crystals accompanying rhodochrosite, tetrahedrite, sphalerite, proustite, altaite, arsenic, and gold, and at Offenbánya with sylvanite and antimonial ores. From Kalgoorlie, Western Australia, associated with krennerite, petzite and tetrahedrite, and from the Sylvia mine, Tararu Creek, New Zealand. In the Tavua gold field, Vitu Levu, Fiji Islands. Reported from the Rendaizi mine, Idu, Japan, with tetradymite in quartz veins. In the United States said to occur at various localities: Gold Hill, Boulder County, Colorado, with hessite at the Dorleska mine, Coffee Creek district, Trinity County, California, and with altaite at the Kings Mountain mine, Gaston County, North Carolina. Reported from the Huronian mine, Ontario, Canada.

Alter. Pseudomorphs after nagyagite of chalcopyrite, bournonite, and of galena mixed with gold have been described.

SILBERPHYLLINGLANZ. *Breithaupt (J. Chemie u. Phys.*, **1**, 178, 1828), NOBILITE *Adam* (35, 1869) from Deutsch-Pilsen, Hungary, and BLATTERINE *Huot* (**1**, 189, 1841) (*Blätterin, Blättererz* Germ.) from Nagyág are probably identical with nagyagite.[18]

Ref.

1. Schrauf, *Zs. Kr.*, **2**, 239 (1878) regarded the crystals as monoclinic, but the measurements were inadequate to prove the symmetry. The tetragonal symmetry earlier reported was based on approximate measurements. Gossner, *Zbl. Min.*, 321, 1935, however, gives the x-ray elements in terms of a tetragonal cell, and finds no evidence of lower symmetry. Schneiderhöhn and Ramdohr (**2**, 330, 1931) show that the crystals are twinned, in support of Schrauf's interpretation.
2. Schrauf (1878). The orientation of Goldschmidt (**6**, 68, 1920) is not adopted here. Transformations; Goldschmidt to Schrauf: 010/002/100; Gossner to Schrauf: 0$\frac{4}{5}$0/002/$\frac{4}{5}$00.
3. Schrauf (1878); Fletcher, *Phil. Mag.*, **9**, 188 (1880).
4. Gossner (1935) failed to recognize lower than tetragonal symmetry. No statement of the effect of twinning on the x-ray results is given.
5. Schrauf (1878), on the basis of rather uncertain data.
6. Schneiderhöhn and Ramdohr (**2**, 330, 1931).
7. Average of three values, from anals. 1, 2, and one determination, 7.40, by Frondel (priv. comm., 1939) on Nagyág material.
8. Other reflectivity measurements by Martin, *C. R.*, **204**, 598 (1937), and Fastré, *C. R.*, **196**, 630 (1933).
9. Berman (priv. comm., 1939). See also Boldirew, *Cbl. Min.*, 193, 1924, and Giusca, *Zs. Roumanian geol. Ges.*, **3**, 118 (1937) — *Jb. Min.*, I, 422, 1938, for other formulas.

10. In Dana (106, 1892). For spectroscopic examination see de Gramont, *Bull. soc. min.*, **18**, 355 (1895).
11. Hanko, *Zs. Kr.*, **17**, 514 (1890).
12. Sipöcz, *Zs. Kr.*, **11**, 211 (1885).
13. Clauder (Inaug. Diss., Budapest, 1931 — *Jb. Min.*, I, 152, 1935).
14. Endredy anal. in Tokody, *Cbl. Min.*, 117, 1930.
15. Muthmann and Schröder, *Zs. anorg. Chem.*, **14**, 432 (1897).
16. Shipman anal. in Simpson, *Western Australia Geol. Sur., Bull.*, **42**, 108, 1912.
17. Priwoznik, Österreich *Zs. Berg.-Hüttenwes.*, 265, 1895 — *Zs. Kr.*, **32**, 185 (1899).
18. Dana (106, 1892).

213 COPPER ARSENIDE GROUP

2131	Algodonite	Cu_6As
2132	Domeykite	Cu_3As

The minerals domeykite and algodonite are distinct species with definite properties[1] and characteristic x-ray powder patterns.[2] They occur as masses of essentially homogeneous material of composition as given. Domeykite is apparently isometric with a large unit cell ($a_0 = 19.19 \pm 0.01$).[3] Algodonite gives a powder pattern consistent with a hexagonal close-packed structure,[4] and it is weakly anisotropic under the microscope.[5] The composition is not definitely established, but it has been shown[6] that essentially homogeneous material with 83.2 per cent Cu gives the algodonite x-ray pattern, and this composition corresponds closely to Cu_6As. Whitneyite, as originally described, consists of at least two substances, and four variants of whitneyite have been proposed.[7] However, examination of polished sections and x-ray analysis show that the principal constituent is arsenian copper, and the next most abundant is algodonite,[8] these two occurring in all so-called whitneyite specimens. The name whitneyite may perhaps be retained for the variety of copper rich in arsenic (which see).

Ledouxite Richards (*Am. J. Sc.*, **11**, 457, 1901), *keweenawite Koenig* (*Am. J. Sc.*, **14**, 410, 1902), and *mohawkite Koenig* (*Am. J. Sc.*, **10**, 440, 1900), are mixtures of the three previously mentioned distinct copper arsenic minerals.[9] *Mohawk-algodonite, mohawk-whitneyite, semi-whitneyite Koenig* (*Am. J. Sc.*, **14**, 404, 1902) are likewise mixtures.

The natural compounds are not reproduced in the artificial system Cu–As,[10] except that arsenical-copper with a saturation at about 5 per cent As is a component of the artificial system and is the principal constituent of the whitneyite mixture.

Ref.

1. Butler, Burbank, and others, *U. S. Geol. Sur., Prof. Pap. 144*, 56, 1929.
2. Ramsdell, *Am. Min.*, **14**, 188 (1929). Machatschki, *Jb. Min., Beil.-Bd.*, **59**, 137 (1929).
3. Machatschki, *Cbl. Min.*, 19, 1930.
4. Machatschki (1929).
5. Schneiderhöhn and Ramdohr (**2**, 233, 1931).
6. Ramsdell (1929).
7. Butler, Burbank, and others (1929).
8. Ramsdell (1929). Machatschki (1929).
9. Murdoch (38, 1916); Thomson, *Univ. Toronto Stud., Geol. Ser.*, **20**, 35 (1925).

10. Ramsdell (1929). Machatschki, *Cbl. Min.*, 371, 1929; 1930. The artificial domeykite of Koenig, *Am. Phil. Soc., Proc.*, **42**, 219 (1903), crystals of which were measured by Wright, is not the same as the natural material. Fusion experiments on algodonite and whitneyite by Borgström, *Geöl. För. Förh.*, **38**, 95 (1916), showed that these minerals had a melting interval and were unstable at the melting point.

2131   A L G O D O N I T E [Cu_6As].   *Field (J. Chem. Soc. London*, **10**, 289, 1857).

C r y s t.[1]   Hexagonal. $a : c = 1 : 1.622$.
Structure cell.

$$a_0 \, 2.599, \quad c_0 \, 4.214, \quad a_0 : c_0 = 1 : 1.622$$

Contains 2 (Cu,As) atoms in unit cell, with $Cu : As = 4 : 1$ to $5 : 1$ (or $6 : 1$).[2]

Habit. Minutely crystalline incrustations. Commonly massive and distinctly granular.

P h y s. Cleavage none. Subconchoidal fracture. H. 4, G. 8.38[3] (meas.), 8.72 (calc.). Bright metallic luster when freshly broken, tarnishing and becoming dull on exposure. Color steel-gray to silver-white. Opaque. Weakly anisotropic.

C h e m. A copper arsenide, Cu_6As, intimately intermixed with other copper arsenides, especially whitneyite.
Anal.

	1	2	3
Cu	83.58	83.11	83.53
As	16.42	16.44	16.55
Ag	.....	trace	.....
Total	100.00	99.55	100.08

1. Cu_6As.   2. Rancagua.[4]   3. Champion mine, Mich.[5]

Tests. As for domeykite, but more difficultly fusible.

O c c u r. In Chile at the silver mine of Algodones in Coquimbo, and in the Cerro de los Seguas, Rancagua. In the United States in Michigan at the Mohawk mine and others in Keweenaw County and also from Baraga County.

A r t i f. The compound Cu_6As does not represent a phase of the artificial system Cu–As. When fused, algodonite breaks up to Cu_3As and arsenian copper. An argentian compound $(Cu,Ag)_6As$ (*argentoalgodonite*) has been reported.[6]

N a m e. After the mine in which it was first found.

Ref.

1. Machatschki, *Jb. Min., Beil.-Bd.*, **59**, 137 (1929), from powder patterns.
2. The range of composition proposed by Machatschki (1929) is not in agreement with Ramsdell's findings, *Am. Min.*, **14**, 188 (1929). The latter gives $Cu : As = 6 : 1$.
3. The value of the specific gravity (7.62) given by Genth, *Am. J. Sc.*, **33**, 192 (1862), for Chilean algodonite is too low according to Koenig, *Am. J. Sc.*, **14**, 410 (1902).
4. Genth (1862).
5. Koenig (1902).
6. Koenig, *Am. Phil. Soc., Proc.*, **42**, 229 (1903).

2132 **DOMEYKITE** [Cu₃As]. Arsenikkupfer *Zinken* (*Ann. Phys.*, **41**, 659, 1837). Arseniure de cuivre *Domeyko* (*Ann. mines*, **3**, 3, 1843). Cobre Blanco *Domeyko* (138, 1845). Weisskupfer *Hausmann* (**1**, 82, 1847). Cuivre arsenical *Fr.* Arsenical copper. Domeykite *Haidinger* (562, 1845). Condurrite *Phillips* (*Phil. Mag.*, **2**, 286, 1827). Stibiodomeykite pt. *Koenig* (*Am. J. Sc.*, **10**, 445, 1900).

C r y s t. Isometric. a_0 19.19 ± 0.01. Contains about 500 atoms of (Cu,As) with ratio of Cu : As = 3 : 1.[1]

Habit. Reniform and botryoidal. Massive.

P h y s. Fracture uneven. H. 3–3½. G. 7.2–7.9. Luster metallic, but dull on exposure. Color tin-white to steel-gray. Tarnishes yellowish to pinchbeck-brown and subsequently to iridescence. Isotropic.

C h e m. A copper arsenide, Cu_3As, with some Ni and Co reported in early analyses. Intimately intergrown with algodonite.

Anal.

	1	2	3	4
Cu	71.79	70.56	70.68	71.45
As	28.21	29.50	29.25	27.98
Insol.	.....	.....	.....	0.28
Total	100.00	100.06	99.93	99.71

1. Cu_3As. 2. Mohawk mine, Mich.[2] 3. Michigan. G. = 7.56.[3] 4. Långban.[4]

Tests. F. 2. Insoluble in HCl, but soluble in HNO_3.

O c c u r. Domeykite is found in several localities in Chile, at San Antonio near Copiapó in Atacama and at Chañarcillo, in Coquimbo, and at Rancagua. Also from Zwickau, Saxony, in porphyry. At Långban, Sweden; in Cornwall at Condurrow mine, near Helstone (*condurrite*). In the Cerro de Paracatas, between Cutzalama and Tlachapa, Guerrero, Mexico. Occurs in Michigan in the Sheldon-Columbia mine on Portage Lake, Houghton County, and from the Mohawk and other mines in Keweenaw County. On Michipicoten Island in Lake Superior, Ontario.

A l t e r. Alters readily on an exposed surface to a brownish coating.

A r t i f. The compound Cu_3As of the artificial system Cu–As does not correspond with the natural substance. Argentodomeykite is an artificial compound, $(Cu,Ag)_3As$, not reported in nature.[5]

N a m e. After the Chilean mineralogist, Ignacio Domeyko (1802–1889).

Ref.

1. Machatschki, *Cbl. Min.*, 19, 1930. Since the density is not accurately known, the number of atoms per unit cell is uncertain. For a density of 7.3 the cell contents are 117 Cu_3As; for 7.6, 123; for 7.9, 127.
2. Koenig, *Am. J. Sc.*, **14**, 404 (1902).
3. Genth, *Am. J. Sc.*, **33**, 193 (1892).
4. Aminoff, *Ak. Stockholm Handl.*, **9**, no. 5, 49 (1931) — *Jb. Min.*, 525, 1931.
5. Koenig, *Am. Phil. Soc., Proc.*, **42**, 229 (1903).

ORILEYITE. *Waldie* (*Asiatic Soc. Bengal, Proc.*, 279, September, 1870). Massive. H. 5½. G. 7.39 ± 0.05. Color steel-gray. Luster metallic. Streak dark gray. Analysis yields approximately $(Fe,Cu)_2As$ with Fe : Cu = 4 : 1. From Burma, but exact locality unknown. Needs confirmation.

2133   Horsfordite [Cu₅Sb]. *Laist* and *Norton* (*Am. Chem. J.*, **10**, 60, 1888).
Only known massive. Brittle. Fracture uneven. H. 4–5. G. 8.812. Luster
metallic, brilliant. Tarnishes easily. Color silver-white. Opaque. Composition near
Cu₅Sb.[1] F. 1½. Occurs as a large deposit in the eastern part of Asia Minor, not far
from Mytilene. Named after the Rumford Professor of Chemistry, E. N. Horsford
(1818–1893), of Harvard University.

Ref.
1. The artificial system Cu-Sb as given in Hansen (616, 1936) and also by Mura-
kami and Shibata, *Tôhoku Imp. Univ., Sc. Rep.*, ser. 1, **25**, 527 (1936), indicates that
a compound of the composition Cu₁₁Sb₂ may be formed, but according to the latter it is
an unstable high-temperature phase.

2134   Cocinerite [Cu₄AgS]. *Hough* (*Am. J. Sc.*, **48**, 206, 1919).
Massive. H. 2½. G. 6.14. Color silver-gray, slowly tarnishing to black. Streak
lead-gray. Homogeneous in polished section. A copper and silver sulfide, close to
Cu₄AgS.

Anal.

	Cu	Fe	Ag	S	Total
1	64.50	....	27.37	8.13	100.00
2	60.58	1.55	27.54	9.65	99.32

1. Cu₄AgS.   2. Cocinera mine.

O c c u r. In small amount in a pocket of oxidized ores consisting largely of oxides
of copper, some carbonates, metallic silver, and copper, on the 1100-ft. level of the
Cocinera mine at Ramos, San Luis Potosí, Mexico.
Needs confirmation.

221   D Y S C R A S I T E [Ag₃Sb]. Argentum nativum antimonio adunatum
Bergmann (159, 1782). Spiesglanz-Silber *Selb* (*Lempe's Mag.*, **3**, 5, 1786). Silber-
spiessglanz, Spiessglas-Silber, Antimonsilber pt. *Germ.* Discrase *Beudant* (**2**, 613,
1832). Discrasites *Fröbel* in *Glocker* (44, 1847). Dyscrasite *Dana* (35, 1868). Stibio-
triargentite *Peterson* (*Ann. Phys.*, **137**, 377, 1869). α-dyscrasite *Short* (26, 1934).

C r y s t. Orthorhombic; pyramidal — *m2m*.[1]

$$a : b : c = 0.5722 : 1 : 0.9225;^2 \quad p_0 : q_0 : r_0 = 1.6122 : 0.9225 : 1$$

$$q_1 : r_1 : p_1 = 0.5722 : 0.6205 : 1; \quad r_2 : p_2 : q_2 = 1.0840 : 1.7476 : 1$$

Forms:[3]

	ϕ	$\rho = C$	ϕ_1	$\rho_1 = A$	ϕ_2	$\rho_2 = B$
e 021	0°00′	61°32½′	61°32½′	90°00′	90°00′	28°27½′
p 111	60 13½	61 42	42 41½	40 09½	31 48½	64 04

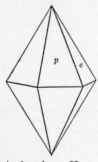

Andreasberg, Harz.

Structure cell.[4] Space group *Pmm*; a_0 2.990,
b_0 5.225, c_0 4.820 (all ± 0.005); $a_0 : b_0 : c_0 = 0.5722 : 1$
: 0.9225; contains Ag₃Sb.

Habit. Pyramidal. Usually massive, foliated or
granular.[5]

Twinning.[6] On {110} to form hexagonal aggregates by repeated twinning.

P h y s. Cleavage {001}, {011} distinct; {110}
imperfect. Fracture uneven. Sectile. H. 3½–4. G.
9.74 ± 0.07;[4] 9.75 (calc.). Luster metallic. Color
and streak silver-white; usually tarnished to a lead-

gray, to yellowish or blackish color. Opaque. In polished section[7] weakly anisotropic. Percentage reflection: green 66, orange 62.5, red 61.

Chem. Silver antimonide, Ag_3Sb, with some silver in excess, due to substitution for Sb or perhaps to inhomogeneities.[8] Small amounts of As are sometimes reported.

Anal.[9]

	Ag	Sb	Total	G.
1	72.66	27.34	100.00	9.85
2	75.41	24.37	99.78	9.76 ± 0.13

1. Ag_3Sb. 2. St. Andreasberg. Average of seven analyses of crystals with thin sheets of native silver on the faces.[10]

Tests. F. $1\frac{1}{2}$. Decomposed by HNO_3, leaving Sb_2O_3.

Occur. Found as a vein mineral in silver deposits, with antimonian silver and other silver minerals, galena, and other sulfides generally in a calcite gangue. At St. Andreasberg in the Harz Mountains with other silver minerals, as crystals and foliated masses in calcite; at Wolfach on the Kinzig, Baden, as the chief silver mineral, with galena, ruby silver, argentite, silver, and barite. In Alsace at Ste. Marie aux Mines. Occurred as large masses with stromeyerite, tetrahedrite, galena, and other silver minerals at the Consols mine, Broken Hill, Australia. Reported from the Reese River district, Nevada. Found in the silver ores of Cobalt, Ontario.

Alter. To pyrargyrite or antimony oxides, admixed with native silver.

Artif. Produced from the melt in the system Ag–Sb,[11] or by melting the constituents in the proportions required.[12]

Name. From δυσκρᾶσις, *a bad alloy.*

Ref.

1. Crystal class from x-ray study of Peacock, *Univ. Toronto Stud., Geol. Ser.*, **44**, 31 (1940). Machatschki, *Zs. Kr.*, **67**, 169 (1928), assigned the mineral to the hexagonal system on the basis of x-ray powder pictures, but he admitted the possible pseudo-hexagonal symmetry. Liebisch, *Ak. Berlin, Ber.*, **20**, 365 (1910), demonstrated the pseudosymmetry of the mineral, and Goldschmidt (3, 62, 1916) described the crystals as orthorhombic.
2. From x-ray Weissenberg measurements of Peacock (1940). The morphological elements earlier reported in the literature (cf., Hausmann [57, 1847]) probably refer to stephanite.
3. Peacock (1940). It is not certain whether the forms {021} and {111} are distinct or are twinned equivalents.
4. Peacock (1940).
5. The granular material is most often antimonian silver (with high silver content) according to Liebisch (1910).
6. See Liebisch (1910) and Peacock (1940).
7. Schneiderhöhn and Ramdohr (2, 236, 1931). See also Short (26, 1934) and Peacock (1940).
8. Machatschki (1928) gives the formula as (Ag,Sb) with Ag : Sb = 3 : 1. However, the analyses of Liebisch (1910) and others indicate that there is little variation in the composition; antimonian silver often occurs intimately associated with the dyscrasite. See Walker, *Univ. Toronto Stud., Geol. Ser.*, 20, 1921, Schwartz, *Am. Min.*, **13**, 495 (1928), and Peacock (1940). The dyscrasite from Cobalt, Ontario, of high silver content may be a eutectic mixture.

9. Older analyses in Doelter (4 [1], 234, 1925).
10. Liebisch, *Ak. Berlin, Ber.*, **20**, 365 (1910).
11. Petrenko, *Zs. anorg. Chem.*, **50**, 133 (1906).
12. V. M. Goldschmidt, in Machatschki (1928). The material was shown to have the same x-ray powder picture as that of the natural mineral.

222   S T I B I O P A L L A D I N I T E [Pd₃Sb]. *Adam* (*Chem. Met. Mining Soc., South Africa, J.*, **27**, 249, 1927 — *Min. Abs.*, **3**, 369, 1927). Stibiopalladinite *Schneiderhöhn* in *Wagner* (1929).

C r y s t. Isometric?

P h y s. Cleavage none. Fracture uneven. H. 4–5. G. 9.5±. Metallic luster. Silver-white to steel-gray, under microscope white with yellowish pink or bronze-pink tint. Isotropic or faintly anisotropic. Reflection percentages: for green, orange, and red, 56 to 57.

C h e m. A palladium antimonide, Pd₃Sb.

Anal.

	1	2	3
Pd	72.44	70.35	70.4
Sb	27.56	27.95	26.0
Fe₂O₃	.....	.....	0.9
Insol.	.....	.....	1.4
Total	100.00	98.20	98.7

1. Pd₃Sb.   2. Transvaal.   3. Transvaal.

Tests. Soluble in hot aqua regia. In C.T. gives off Sb.

O c c u r. Found with sperrylite in the concentrates from the Potgietersrust, Transvaal, platinum deposits. Found also in the ore at Tweefontain farm and in the contact metamorphic lime silicate rocks at Zwartfontein, north of Potgietersrust.

A r t i f.[1] In the system Pd–Sb a phase corresponds in composition to stibiopalladinite.

Ref.

1. Grigorjew, *Zs. anorg. Chem.*, **209**, 308 (1932).

DIENERITE. *Hackl* (*Geol. Bundesanst., Wien, Vh.*, 107, 1921). *Doelter* (4 [1], 718, 1926).
Isometric. Bright metallic luster. Grayish white. Composition Ni₃As (Ni 70.13, As 29.87). Analysis yields Ni 67.11, As 30.64, Cu 0.99, Fe 0.61, Co 1.29, Ag 0.02. Total 100.66. Found as a single cubic crystal of ½ cm. along its edge at Radstadt, Salzburg, Austria. Named after Professor C. Diener (1862–1928) of Vienna, who discovered the mineral.
The synthesis of Ni₃As has been reported.[1]

Ref.

1. Descamps, *C.R.*, **86**, 1065 (1878).

23 SULFIDES A_2X TYPE

ISOMETRIC DIVISION

231 ARGENTITE GROUP

2311	Argentite	Ag_2S	Isom. at 179°
2312	Aguilarite	Ag_4SSe	
2313	Naumannite	Ag_2Se	Isom. at 133°
2314	Digenite	$Cu_{2-x}S$	
2315	Berzelianite	Cu_2Se	
2316	Crookesite	$(Cu,Tl,Ag)_2Se$	
2317	Eucairite	$CuAgSe$	
2318	Hessite	Ag_2Te	Isom. at 149.5°
2319	Petzite	Ag_3AuTe_2	

NONISOMETRIC DIVISION

2321	Chalcocite	Cu_2S	Orth. 0.5822 : 1 : 0.9701 hex. at 91°
2322	Stromeyerite	$AgCuS$	Orth. 0.5822 : 1 : 0.9668 isom. at 93°
2323	Acanthite	Ag_2S	Orth. ? 0.690 : 1 : 0.996

A_2X TYPE

The minerals of this type are sulfides, selenides, or tellurides of silver and copper. In general, there is little solid solution between the silver and copper species so that eucairite, $CuAgSe$, and the more common stromeyerite, $CuAgS$, have definite Cu–Ag ratios. Another significant characteristic of most of the minerals of this type is that at elevated temperatures they are isometric and invert readily on cooling to a nonisometric form, usually orthorhombic. It is for this reason that argentite, while retaining the outward form of an isometric mineral, gives an x-ray powder picture identical with that of the orthorhombic acanthite.

The members of the argentite group are body-centered cubic at elevated temperatures. Digenite and hessite are face-centered.

The inversion of these minerals has led to descriptions of some of the species wherein the physical properties and crystallography of the two modifications have been jumbled together. All the measurements of argentite have been made on pseudomorphs which, despite the excellence of the faces, are more or less distorted. The anisotropism of most of the minerals of this type is indicative of the inverted form.

The minerals in the nonisometric division have been formed presumably below the inversion temperature, and consequently their crystal form is consistent with their inner structure. Of these, chalcocite and stromeyerite have closely similar axial ratios and may form an isomorphous series. The high-temperature modification of chalcocite is hexagonal.

2311 **ARGENTITE** [Ag_2S]. Argentum rude plumbei coloris et Galenae simile, cultro diffinditur, dentibus compressum dilatatur, *Agricola* (438, 1529). Glaserz *Agricola* (463, 1546B); *Henckel* (1734) (proving it a sulfur compound). Silfverglas, Minera argenti vitrea, Argentum sulphure Mineralisatum *Wallerius* (308, 1746);

Sage (Ann. chim., **2**, 250, 1789) (with earliest analysis). Glanzerz, Silberglas, Silberglanz, Schwefelsilber, Weichgewächs, *Germ.* Vitreous Silver, Sulphuret of Silver, Silver Glance, Argent sulfuré *Fr.* Argyrose *Beudant* (**2**, 392, 1832). Argentit *Haidinger* (565, 1845). Argyrit *Glocker* (23, 1847). Argirose *Ital.* Plata sulfurea *Span.* Petlanque nero *Span.* S.A. Jalpaite *Breithaupt (B. H. Ztg.,* **17**, 85, 1858). α-Argentite *Schneiderhöhn (Am. Min.,* **12**, 210, 1927).

C r y s t. Isometric; hexoctahedral — $4/m\,\bar{3}\,2/m$ at 179°.[1]

Forms:[2]

$a\{001\}$ $d\{011\}$ $o\{111\}$ $f\{013\}$ $m\{113\}$ $n\{112\}$ $p\{122\}$ $Y\{125\}$ $s\{123\}$

Structure cell.[3] Space group $Im3m$. a_0 4.88 ± 0.02;   contains Ag_4S_2.

Twinning. Twin plane $\{111\}$, penetration twins.

Habit. Cubic, octahedral, rarely dodecahedral; often in groups of parallel individuals. Reticulated. Arborescent, filiform, massive, embedded, as a coating.

P h y s. Cleavage $\{001\}$, $\{011\}$, both poor. Fracture subconchoidal. Very sectile. H. 2–2½. G. 7.2–7.4; 7.04 (calc.). Metallic luster. Color blackish leadgray. Streak shining. Opaque. Faintly anisotropic (inverted). Reflection percentages, green 37, orange 33, red 30.[4]

Kongsberg.

C h e m. Silver sulfide, Ag_2S; often with some copper (*jalpaite*). *Anal.*

	1	2	3
Ag	87.06	86.71	71.65
Cu	.....	.....	13.97
S	12.94	13.13	16.17
Total	100.00	99.84	101.79
G.	7.04		6.765 ± 0.003

1. Ag_2S. 2. Montezuma, Colo.[5] 3. Jalpaite. Zmyeinogorsky mine, Altai, Tomsk, Siberia. Average of two incomplete and one complete analysis. High percentage of S attributed to use of commercial bromine in analysis.[6]

Var. **Ordinary.** The pseudomorph after high-temperature isometric silver sulfide with little or no copper.

Cuprian. Jalpaite *Breithaupt (B. H. Ztg.,* **17**, 85, 1858). A variety with about 14 per cent copper.[7]

Tests. B.B. on charcoal fuses with intumescence in O.F. emitting sulfurous fumes and yielding a globule of silver.

O c c u r.[8] Argentite, probably the most important primary mineral of silver, occurs in the epithermal type of sulfide deposits, together with other silver minerals, such as the ruby silvers, stephanite, polybasite with which it sometimes forms parallel growths, native silver, and cerargyrite. It is sometimes found in large masses, and also as microscopic inclusions in the so-called argentiferous galena.

Notable occurrences are as follows: in Czechoslovakia at Kremnitz
(Körmöczbánya) and Schemnitz (Selmeczbánya) where the veins are in
eruptive rocks; at Přibram and Joachimstal; in Saxony in the Freiberg
district in exceptionally fine crystals, associated with the cobalt and nickel
minerals of Schneeberg, Annaberg, Marienberg, and Johanngeorgenstadt;
in the Harz Mountains, especially at Andreasberg. In Sardinia at Monte
Narba, near Sarrabus. With native silver at Kongsberg, Norway. In
Cornwall at Liskeard especially. Found in Bolivia at Colquechaca; in
Peru; in Chile at Chañarcillo and Atacama. Common in the silver mines
of Mexico, especially at Pachuca, Guanajuato, Zacatecas, and at Arizpe,
Sonora.

In the United States, argentite is found in Montana, at Butte, in the
silver veins; in Colorado at Aspen and Leadville, and in the mines of the
San Juan district; in Nevada at the Comstock Lode in large amounts,
and in Tonopah associated with gold in the quartz veins.

Alter. Alters to native silver, silver sulfosalts and other silver
minerals. A polished surface is darkened on exposure to a strong light.

Artif.[9] Very easily prepared in numerous ways. Sulfur, sulfur
dioxide or hydrogen sulfide will act upon metallic silver or any of its common compounds, as solids or in solution, to produce silver sulfide.

Ref.

1. Ramsdell, *Am. Min.*, **10**, 286 (1925), has shown that argentite at room temperature
gives a powder pattern identical with that of acanthite. Emmons, Stockwell, and
Jones, *Am. Min.*, **11**, 326 (1926), Barth, *Cbl. Min.*, 284 (1926), and later Rahlfs, *Zs.
Phys. Chem.*, **31B**, 157 (1936), have measured the high-temperature modification of
Ag$_2$S and have shown that it is isometric.
2. Goldschmidt (**8**, 42, 1922). Ellsworth, *Ontario Bur. Mines Rep.*, **25** [1], 200 (1916).
Shannon, *U. S. Nat. Mus., Bull. 131*, 84, 1926. Rare or uncertain: 016, 015, 012, 023,
335, 223, 334, 556, 169, 158, 136, 237, 235, 347. Palache (priv. comm., 1941) found on
crystals from Butte the following forms. Common: 123, 125; rare: 223, 334, 144, 233,
169, 158, 136, 237, 347, 2·5·11.
3. Emmons, Stockwell, and Jones (1926). Barth (1926). Rahlfs (1936). All
measurements made above 179°. See also Ramsdell, *Am. Min.*, **12**, 25 (1927), for a
discussion of the structure.
4. Schneiderhöhn-Ramdohr (**2**, 265, 1931).
5. Sharp anal. in Van Horn, *Geol. Soc. Am. Bull.*, **19**, 93 (1908).
6. Kalb and Bendig, *Cbl. Min.*, 516 (1924).
7. Schwartz, *Econ. Geol.*, **30**, 128 (1935). Also Kalb and Bendig (1924).
8. Lindgren (486, 1933).
9. Doelter (4 [1], 231, 1925).

2312   **A G U I L A R I T E** [Ag$_4$SeS].   *Genth* (*Am. J. Sc.*, **41**, 401, 1891).

Cryst. Isometric at elevated temperature.[1] In skeleton dodecahe-
drons, often elongated in the direction of a cubic or octahedral edge. Also
massive.

Phys. No cleavage. Fracture hackly. Sectile. H. 2$\frac{1}{2}$. G. 7.586.
Luster metallic, brilliant. Color iron black. Opaque. Isotropic or
faintly anisotropic in polished section.

Chem. A silver sulfide and selenide with a composition near Ag$_4$SeS.

Anal.

	1	2	3	4	5
Ag	79.50	79.07	79.41	80.27	84.40
Cu	.....	.....	0.50	0.07	0.49
Fe				0.26	
S	5.91	5.86	5.93	6.75	11.36
Se	14.59	14.82	13.96	12.73	[3.75]
Sb	.....	.....	.....	0.41	.....
Total	100.00	99.75	99.80	100.49	100.00

1. Ag_4SeS. 2–5. Guanajuato.[2]

Tests. In the open tube heated slowly yields metallic silver, a slight sublimate of selenium, silky needles of selenium dioxide, and sulfur dioxide, the latter forming a small quantity of silver sulfate.

Occur.[3] Associated with argentite and silver at the San Carlos mine, Guanajuato, Mexico. Also reported from the Comstock Lode, Virginia City, Nevada.

Alter. Altered on the surface, the crystals losing their sharp edges and sometimes becoming penetrated by holes containing metallic silver and microscopic black crystals of cuprian stephanite.

Name. After Señor Aguilar, superintendent of the mine where the original material was found.

Ref.

1. An x-ray powder pattern of aguilarite could not be indexed with the isometric formula. The mineral is therefore inverted to a lower symmetry, but its pattern is different from that of acanthite (Berman, priv. comm., 1938).
2. Analysis 2, Genth (1891). Analyses 3–5, Genth, *Am. J. Sc.*, **44**, 381 (1892).
3. The Nevada occurrence described by Coats, *Am. Min.*, **21**, 532 (1936).

2313   **NAUMANNITE** [Ag_2Se]. Selensilber *Rose* (*Ann. Phys.*, **14**, 471, 1828). Selensilberglanz *Germ.* Séléniure d'Argent *Fr.* Naumannit *Haidinger* (565, 1845). Cacheutaite *Adam* (52, 1869).

Cryst. Isometric above 133°.[1]

Structure cell. (On artificial Ag_2Se above 133°) a_0 4.983 ± 0.016 of the body-centered cubic cell containing Ag_4Se_2.[2]

Habit. In cubes. Also massive granular and in thin plates.

Phys. Cleavage {001} perfect.[3] Sectile and malleable. H. $2\frac{1}{2}$. G. 7.0± (Idaho), 8.00 (Harz); 7.866 (calc.). Luster metallic, splendent. Color and streak iron-black. Opaque. In polished section[4] sensibly anisotropic. Reflection percentages: green 36, orange 34.5, red 30.

Chem. Silver selenide, Ag_2Se, with minor amounts of S. The Pb given in earlier analyses[5] is apparently due to intimately associated clausthalite.[6]

Anal.

	1	2	3
Ag	73.15	65.56	75.98
Pb	.....	4.91	.....
Se	26.85	[29.53]	22.92
S	.....	.....	1.10
Total	100.00	100.00	100.00

1. Ag_2Se. 2. Tilkerode.[7] 3. Idaho. Recalc. after deducting clay and marcasite.[8]

Tests. B.B. on charcoal melts easily in the outer flame, in the inner with some intumescence.

O c c u r. Associated with clausthalite and other selenides in the carbonate-quartz veins of Tilkerode, Harz, Germany. Also reported from Cerro de Cacheuta (*cacheutaite*), Mendoza, Argentina. In the United States formerly found in quantity at the De Lamar mine, Silver City district, Owyhee County, Idaho.

A r t i f.[9] Produced by the reaction of selenium vapor on silver. The artificial crystals are dodecahedral in habit.

N a m e. After the German crystallographer and mineralogist, C. F. Naumann (1797–1873).

Ref.

1. Schneiderhöhn-Ramdohr (**2**, 272, 1931) state that naumannite at normal temperatures shows distinct anisotropic effects with mimetic twinning visible under the microscope. Rahlfs, *Zs. phys. Chem.*, **31**, 157 (1936), obtained an isometric x-ray powder pattern above 133°. Other physical measurements, such as electrical resistance, indicate a change in form at 133°. See Doelter (4 [1], 825, 1926).
2. Rahlfs (1936).
3. Shannon, *Am. J. Sc.*, **50**, 390 (1920), does not find the supposed cleavage on the Idaho material.
4. Schneiderhöhn and Ramdohr (1931).
5. Dana (52, 1892).
6. Schneiderhöhn and Ramdohr (1931).
7. Rose, *Ann. Phys.*, **14**, 471 (1828).
8. Shannon (1920).
9. Doelter (1926).

2314 D I G E N I T E. [$Cu_{2-x}S$]. Digenite *Breithaupt* (*Ann. Phys.*, **61**, 673, 1844). Blauer kupferglanz *Schneiderhöhn* and *Ramdohr* (**2**, 278, 1931). Blue chalcocite. α-chalcocite. Isometric chalcocite.

Carmenite (?) pt. *Hahn* (*B. H. Ztg.*, **24**, 86, 1865). Digenite *Buerger* (*Econ. Geol.*, **36**, 19, 1941).

C r y s t. Isometric.[1]

Forms:[2]

$$d\{011\} \qquad o\{111\}$$

Structure cell. Isometric (with a probable anti-fluorite structure);[3] a_0 5.56 ± 0.01;[4] contains $Cu_{8-4x}S_4$ ($x = 0.12$ to 0.45).[5]

Habit. Octahedral. Usually massive.

Oriented intergrowths. Chalcocite, covellite, and bornite intergrowths have been observed.[6]

P h y s. Cleavage {111} (artif.). Brittle. Conchoidal fracture. H. 2½–3. G. 5.546 ($x = 0.24$), 5.706 ($x = 0.16$).[7] Color blue to black (the most copper-deficient members are the deepest blue). In polished section[8] distinctly blue. Opaque. Isotropic (for the most part). Reflection percentages: green 24.5, orange 18, red 15.5.

C h e m. Sulfide of copper with a variable amount of copper according to the formula $Cu_{2-x}S$,[9] where $x = 0.12$ to $0.45(?)$. Small amounts of Fe are present in most of the natural occurrences, owing perhaps to admixed bornite.

Anal.

	1	2	3	4	5	6	7
Cu	78.85	78.96	78.11	77.99	76.59	76.19	75.30
Fe	.....	.....	none	0.26	0.20	0.37	0.16
S	21.15	20.62	21.85	21.48	23.21	23.44	24.54
Rem.	.....	0.42	.....	0.13	.....	.....	.....
Total	100.00	100.00	99.96	99.86	100.00	100.00	100.00
G.		5.710		5.610			

1. $Cu_{2-x}S(x = 0.12)$. 2. Tularosa district, N. M. Impurities = 0.42 per cent with part of Cu as malachite.[10] 3. Jerome, Ariz. crystals.[11] 4. Bonanza mine, Kennecott. Contains SiO_2 0.13, and has admixed covellite of about 1 to 2 per cent.[10] 5. Khan, South-West Africa. Average of two analyses.[12] 6. Kennecott. Average of two analyses.[12] 7. Tsumeb. Average of two analyses.[12]

Tests. B.B. on charcoal melts to a globule which boils with spurting. Soluble in HNO_3.

Occur.[13] Digenite has been found associated with chalcocite and as a replacement of bornite, with chalcopyrite and other copper ores. Most of the reported occurrences are the result of microscopic examinations, and pure masses or crystals are rare. In South-West Africa reported from Tsumeb, Khan, and Ehlers. In Sweden from Kiruna. In Sonora, Mexico, at Cananea. In the United States at Butte, Montana; at the United Verde mine, Jerome, Arizona, in the fire zone as distinct crystals. Plentiful in Kennecott, Alaska.

Alter. Alters to native copper, chalcopyrite, bornite, covellite, malachite, and azurite. Pseudomorphous after chalcopyrite, bornite, pyrite, galena, and millerite.

Artif.[10] Prepared by heating fused copper sulfide in a vacuum furnace up to the melting point.

Name. Digenite from διγενής, *of two sexes or kinds*, because supposedly containing both cupric and cuprous atoms (or chalcocite and covellite, according to the usual interpretation). Dana (56, 1892) discarded the species name because he thought it was a mixture of chalcocite and covellite. It is not certain that the digenite of Breithaupt from Sangerhausen was actually homogeneous, but the name may well be used for this isometric species, as recently proposed by Buerger (1941).

Ref.

1. Established by Posnjak, Allen, and Merwin, *Econ. Geol.*, **10**, 491 (1915), on artificial material. Kurz, *Zs. Kr.*, **92**, 408 (1935), examined a number of occurrences of the natural material. Buerger, *Econ. Geol.*, **36**, 19 (1941), reexamined artificial preparations and indicated the stability ranges and probable composition.
2. On crystals from the fire zone of the United Verde mine, Jerome, Ariz. (Berman, priv. comm., 1938).
3. Barth, *Cbl. Min.*, 285, 1926, obtained 5.59 Å. cell edge at 200°, and proposed the anti-fluorite structure. Rahlfs, *Zs. phys. Chem.*, **31B**, 157 (1936), proposed a modification of the Barth structure, i.e., essentially a disordered anti-fluorite structure, but with the composition $Cu_{1.8}S$. The Cu_2S composition did not give the isometric pattern at an elevated temperature. See also Buerger (1941).
4. Kurz (1935) determined the spacings for a number of natural occurrences, and showed that they had little variation.

5. Berman (priv. comm., 1938) using the data of Kurz (1935) and Posnjak, Allen, and Merwin (1915). Buerger (1941) considers the formula to be near Cu_9S_5.

6. Kurz (1935).

7. Posnjak, Allen, and Merwin (1915) on artificial material. Other values by them are: 5.596, x 0.22; 5.649, x 0.19.

8. Schneiderhöhn and Ramdohr (2, 278, 1931).

9. The variation in composition here indicated is often expressed as covellite in solid solution, i.e., $Cu_2S + xCuS$. Using the densities of Posnjak, Allen, and Merwin (1915) and the evidence presented by Kurz (1935) that the cell edge shows little variation with composition change, it can be shown that the S atoms in the composition are essentially constant in number, and the Cu atoms decrease with the density decrease. The data at hand suggest that the formula here used better expresses the composition than that recently proposed for digenite by Buerger (1941). Berman (priv. comm., 1941).

10. Posnjak, Allen, and Merwin (1915).

11. Gonyer (priv. comm., 1934).

12. Kurz (1935).

13. For general discussion of "isometric chalcocite": Posnjak, Allen, and Merwin (1915); Schneiderhöhn and Ramdohr (1931); Bateman and Lasky, *Econ. Geol.*, **27**, 52 (1932); Kurz (1935); Buerger (1941); Bateman and McLaughlin, *Econ. Geol.*, **15**, 1 (1920), p. 62 on isometric chalcocite. Also Graton and Murdoch, *Am. Inst. Min. Engr., Trans.*, **45**, 26 (1914), for a discussion of inherited cleavage in chalcocite after bornite.

2315　**BERZELIANITE** [Cu_2Se]. Selenkupfer *Berzelius* (*Afhandl. Fys. Kem. Min.*, **6**, 42, 1818). Cuivre sélénié *Fr.* Berzeline *Beudant* (**2**, 534, 1832). Berzelianite *Dana* (509, 1850).

C r y s t. Isometric.

Structure cell.[1] Isometric, a_0 5.731 $\pm$ 0.008, contains Cu_8Se_4.

Habit. As thin dendritic crusts and disseminated.

P h y s. Cleavage none. Somewhat malleable. H. 2. G. 6.71; 7.23 (calc.). Luster metallic. Color silver white, soon tarnishing. Streak shining. Opaque. In polished section[2] isotropic. Reflection percentages: green 29, orange 25, red 18.5.

C h e m. Copper selenide, Cu_2Se, with some silver, which may be due to admixed eucairite.[3]

Anal.

	1	2
Cu	61.62	57.21
Ag	.....	3.51
Se	38.38	39.22
Total	100.00	99.94

1. Cu_2Se.　2. Skrikerum.　Also reports 0.0073 Au.[4]

Tests. F. $1\frac{1}{2}$. Yields fumes of selenium. Soluble in concentrated HNO_3.

O c c u r. Found associated with other selenides in Germany in the Harz Mountains, at Lehrbach in the iron ores, and at Zorge. In Sweden at Skrikerum near Tryserum, Kalmar, in calcite veins in serpentine. Reported from Cerro de Cacheuta, Mendoza, Argentina.

A r t i f.[5] Crystals and massive berzelianite have been prepared by melting the constituents together or by passing selenium vapor over heated copper.

N a m e. After the Swedish chemist, J. J. Berzelius (1779–1848).

Ref.

1. Hartwig, *Zs. Kr.*, **64**, 503 (1926), measured natural berzelianite. Rahlfs, *Zs. phys. Chem.*, **31**, 157 (1936), however, obtained the cell dimension a_0 5.840 ± 0.006 on artificial material. This latter value is more nearly in agreement with the observed density of berzelianite. There is no general agreement on the structure.
2. Schneiderhöhn and Ramdohr (**2**, 301, 1931).
3. Schneiderhöhn and Ramdohr (1931).
4. Svedmark, *Zs. Kr.*, 34, 693 (1901) — abstract.
5. Doelter (4 [1], 818, 1926).

2316   Crookesite [(Cu,Tl,Ag)$_2$Se]. *Nordenskiöld* (*Ak. Stockholm, Öfv.*, **23**, 365, 1866).

Massive, compact. Brittle. H. $2\frac{1}{2}$–3. G. 6.90. Luster metallic. Color lead-gray.

A selenide of copper, thallium, and a small amount of silver. The analyses yield approximately (Cu,Tl,Ag)$_2$Se.

Anal.

	1	2
Cu	46.55	44.21
Ag	5.04	5.09
Fe	0.36	1.28
Tl	16.27	16.89
Se	30.86	32.10
Total	99.08	99.57

Tests. B.B. fuses easily to a greenish black enamel, coloring the flame strongly green. Insoluble in HCl; completely soluble in HNO$_3$.

Occur. From the mine at Skrikerum, Sweden, where it occurs with other selenides. Formerly regarded as berzelianite.

Name. After Sir William Crookes (1832–1919), the discoverer of the element thallium.

2317   EUCAIRITE [CuAgSe]. Eukairite *Berzelius* (*Afhandl. Fys. Kem. Min.*, **6**, 42, 1818). Cuivre sélénié argental *Haüy.* Selenkupfersilber *Germ.*

Cryst. The mineral is not isometric at normal temperatures,[1] since polished surfaces in reflected light show strong anisotropic effects.

Massive and granular, also in black metallic films staining the calcite in which it is contained.

Phys. Cleavage none. Somewhat sectile. H. $2\frac{1}{2}$. G. 7.6–7.8. Luster metallic. Color between silver-white and lead-gray. Streak shining. Opaque. Strongly anisotropic. Reflection percentages:[2] green 33, orange 27, red 28.

Chem. A selenide of copper and silver, CuAgSe, with the Cu and Ag apparently in definite 1 : 1 ratio.

Anal.

	1	2	3
Ag	43.04	42.20	42.71
Cu	25.36	25.41	25.47
Se	31.60	32.43	31.53
Total	100.00	100.04	99.71

1. CuAgSe. 2. Argentina. Se average of 2 determinations, 32.32, 32.54.[3] 3. Argentina.[4]

Tests. B.B. fuses readily emitting fumes of Se. Dissolved in boiling HNO_3.

Occur. Usually associated with other selenides. At the copper mine of Skrikerum near Tryserum, Kalmar, Sweden, in serpentine with calcite. Also reported from the Harz, Germany. In Atacama, Chile, at Aguas Blancas, near Copiapó, and at the mines of Flamenco, north of Tres Puntas. In Argentina, in the Sierra de Umango in La Rioja, with tiemannite in calcite.

Name. From εὐκαίρως, *opportunely*, because found soon after the discovery of the element *selenium*.

Ref.

1. Schneiderhöhn and Ramdohr (**2**, 307, 1931).
2. *Ibid.*
3. Klockmann, *Zs. Kr.*, **19**, 266 (1891).
4. Fromme, *J. pr. Chem.*, **42**, 57 (1890).

2318 **HESSITE** [Ag_2Te]. Tellursilber *Rose* (*Ann. Phys.*, **18**, 64, 1830). Savodinskite *Huot* (**1**, 187, 1841). Telluric Silver. Hessit *Fröbel* (49, 1843). Botesite *Vrba* (in *Doelter* 4 [1], 868, 1926).

Cryst. Isometric above 149.5°.[1] Monoclinic at normal temperature[2] with relic crystals preserving isometric forms.

Forms:[3] (isometric)

a 001	f 013	m 113	ρ 144	p 122
d 011	e 012	n 112	q 133	r 233
o 111	g 023	β 223	Γ 255	s 123

Structure cell.[4] The isometric high-temperature form has a_0 6.572 ± .010 with a face-centered lattice and contains Ag_8Te_4. The inverted room-temperature form is probably monoclinic,[5] with a_0 6.57, b_0 6.14, c_0 6.10, β 61°15'; $a_0 : b_0 : c_0 =$ 1.070 : 1 : 0.993, contains Ag_6Te_3.

Habit. Highly modified, often much distorted. Also massive, compact, or fine grained.

Twinning.[6] Under the microscope twinning lamellae are visible in the low-temperature form. These disappear on heating to 149.5°.

Boulder City, Colo.

Phys. Cleavage {001} indistinct.[7] Fracture even. Somewhat sectile. H. 2–3. G. 8.24–8.45; 7.98 (calc. for isometric); 7.875 (calc. for monoclinic). M.P. 955°–959°. Luster metallic. Color between lead-gray and steel-gray. Opaque. Anisotropic at low temperature; becomes isotropic on heating to 149.5°. Percentage reflection:[3] green 43, orange 40, red 42.

Chem. Silver telluride, Ag_2Te, with some Au and thus possibly grading into petzite. The Pb and Fe reported in some analyses are probably due to impurities.

Anal.

	1	2	3	4	5
Ag	62.86	62.80	61.52	61.16	59.41
Au	.....	.....	1.01	.....	4.73
Pb	.....	.....	.....	1.90	.....
Te	37.14	35.80	37.77	36.11	35.97
Rem.	.....	1.24	.....	[0.83]	.....
Total	100.00	99.84	100.30	100.00	100.11
G.	7.875	8.0	8.390	8.24	8.35

1. Ag_2Te. 2. Transbaikalia. Rem. is Fe_2O_3 0.80, CaO 0.34, MgO 0.10, S, Se nil.[9]
3. Botés.[10] 4. San Sebastian. S, Fe, Zn 0.83 by difference.[11] 5. Botés.[12]

Tests. F. 1. In O.F. on charcoal gives a globule of silver which may contain some gold.

O c c u r. In hydrothermal veins together with other tellurides, gold, and native tellurium. In Siberia at the Zavodinsk mine, near Ziryanovsk, Semipalatinsk, Altai Mountains, in a talcose rock with pyrite, chalcopyrite, sphalerite, and altaite. Specimens from this locality have reached a cubic foot in size. At Karahissar, Asia Minor. In Roumania at Nagyág, Rézbánya, and in highly modified crystals at Botés near Zalatna. Occurs at Kalgoorlie, Western Australia; at the Condorriaco mine east of Arqueros, Coquimbo, Chile; in Mexico at San Sebastian, Jalisco. In the United States it is found in Colorado in the mines of Goldhill, Boulder County, and in Eagle and San Juan counties; in California at the Stanislaus mine on Carson Hill, Calaveras County, at Nevada City in Nevada County.

A r t i f.[13] Prepared by passing tellurium vapor over heated silver; by melting together the constituents.

N a m e. After G. H. Hess (1802–50) of St. Petersburg.

Ref.

1. Inversion temperature given by Borchert, *Jb. Min., Beil.-Bd.*, **69**, 466 (1935). Ramsdell, *Am. Min.*, **10**, 287 (1925) showed the nonisometric character of x-ray powder patterns. Tokody, *Zs. Kr.*, **82**, 154 (1932); **89**, 416 (1934), gives x-ray data on high- and low-temperature modifications.
2. Tokody (1934). Becke, *Min. Mitt.*, 3, 301 (1881), made the distorted crystals triclinic. Kenngott, *Ak. Wien, Ber.*, **9**, 20 (1853), referred them to the orthorhombic system; Hess, *Ann. Phys.*, **28**, 407 (1833), made them rhombohedral. Most recently Soriano Garces, *Treballs del Mus. de Cienc. Nat. de Barcelona*, 9, no. 3, 26 (1932), has referred crystals from Tarragona to the monoclinic system, twinned on {011}, and with the elements $a : b : c = 0.6883 : 1 : 0.9966$, β 91°16′. These elements are close to those of acanthite. It is not clear from the data whether the crystals are distorted relic crystals of the higher-temperature isometric form, or are truly of lower symmetry and therefore represent the low-temperature modification morphologically. Tokody (1934) found the inverted form retained, in part, an orientation with respect to the original crystal.
3. Goldschmidt (4, 134, 1918). The form E {445} and the less certain β {277} and T {570} on crystals from Botés by Tokody, *Cbl. Min.*, 129, 1925.
4. Rahlfs, *Zs. phys. Chem.*, **31**, 157 (1936), on artificial material, G. **8.318**. The structure is similar to that of Cu_2Se, and not the same as isometric Ag_2S.
5. Tokody (1932; 1934) on powder data principally, and one rotation picture about [100] of the relic isometric form.
6. Schneiderhöhn and Ramdohr (2, 274, 1931); also Borchert, *Jb. Min. Beil.-Bd.*, **61**, 101 (1930).

7. On heating to the inversion point the cleavage becomes more prominent (Borchert [1935]).
8. Schneiderhöhn and Ramdohr (1931).
9. Nenadkevich, *C. r. ac. sc. U.R.S.S.*, **A**, 139, 1926 — *Min. Abs.*, 3, 264 (1927).
10. Loczka, *Zs. Kr.*, **20**, 317, (1892).
11. Hillebrand, *Am. J. Sc.*, **8**, 298 (1899).
12. Tokody (1932).
13. Doelter (4 [1], 870, 1926).

2319 **PETZITE** [Ag₃AuTe₂]. Tellursilber *Petz* (*Ann. Phys.*, 57, 470, 1842). Tellurgoldsilber *Hausmann* (**2**, 51, 1847). Petzit *Haidinger* (556, 1845).

Cryst. Perhaps isometric at elevated temperatures.
Habit. Massive; fine granular to compact.
Phys. Cleavage {001}.[1] Fracture subconchoidal. Slightly sectile to brittle. H. $2\frac{1}{2}$–3. G. 8.7–9.02.[2] Luster metallic. Color steel-gray or iron-gray to iron-black, often tarnishing. Opaque. In polished section, anisotropic in part.[3]
Chem. A silver-gold telluride, with most analyses yielding a composition close to Ag₃AuTe₂. It is not certain that petzite is simply a gold-bearing hessite, since few intermediate compositions are known and no complete gradation has been established. Some of the Au reported in petzite analyses may be admixed native gold.
Anal.[4]

	1	2	3	4
Ag	41.71	41.37	41.87	45.32
Au	25.42	23.42	25.16	19.00
Te	32.87	33.00	33.21	34.90
Rem.	......	2.42	0.08	0.63
Total	100.00	100.21	100.32	99.85
G.			8.925	8.735

1. Ag₃AuTe₂. 2. Kalgoorlie. Contains also Hg 2.26, Cu 0.16.[5] 3. Mother Lode district, Calif. Contains also Mo 0.08, Se trace.[6] 4. Khorogoch River, Transbaikalia.[7] Rem. Fe₂O₃ 0.63.

Tests. F. $1\frac{1}{2}$. On charcoal in O.F. yields a globule containing Au and Ag. Decomposed by HNO₃ with a residue of Au.[8]

Occur.[9] With other tellurides, especially hessite, in vein deposits. In Roumania at Nagyág; in Western Australia at Kalgoorlie. In the United States in Colorado in the mines of Goldhill and Sunshine, Boulder County, at Lake City, Hinsdale County, and reported from Leadville. In California at the Stanislaus and Melones mines, Carson Hill, Calaveras County, and at the Golden Rule and other mines near Tuttletown, Tuolumne County. In Canada from the Hollinger mine, Timmins, Ontario.
Name. After W. Petz.

Ref.

1. Short (86, 1931).
2. The specific gravity value of 7.53 given by Walker and Parsons, *Univ. Toronto Stud., Geol. Ser.*, **20**, 39 (1925), is apparently too low.
3. Schneiderhöhn and Ramdohr (**2**, 275, 1931).

4. Early analyses in Dana (48, 1892) and Doelter (4 [1], 871, 1926). The material analyzed by Rickaby (Walker and Parsons, 1925) contains 11.10 Au.

5. Carnot, *Bull. soc. min.*, 24, 357 (1901).

6. Hillebrand, *Am. J. Sc.*, 8, 298 (1899).

7. Nenadkevich, *C. r. ac. sc. U.R.S.S.*, A, 139, 1926 — *Min. Abs.*, 3, 264 (1927).

8. Carnot (1901).

9. Occurrence at Kalgoorlie, Stillwell, *Australasian Inst. Mining Met., Proc.*, 84, 116 (1931). Also Simpson and Gibson, *Western Australia Geol. Sur. Bull. 42*, 90 (1912).

ANTAMOKITE. *Alvir (Philippine J. Sc.*, 41, 137, 1930; *Eng. Mining J.*, 125, 616, 1928). A doubtful telluride of gold with some silver found in polished sections of ore from Antamok, Mountain Province, Philippine Islands. Color in polished section grayish white with tinge of blue; powder dark gray. H. probably 2–3. Said to contain Te, Au, and a little Ag; no Pb, Cu, or Sb. Associated with calaverite, chalcopyrite, tetrahedrite, and quartz. The etch reactions described correspond to petzite, and this mineral has since[1] been identified, together with altaite, in telluride ore from this locality.

Ref.

1. Stillwell, *Australasian Inst. Mining Met., Proc.*, no. 84, 118, 1931.

2321 **CHALCOCITE** [Cu_2S]. Aes rude plumbei coloris pt. *Germ.* Kupferglaserz *Agricola* (461, 1546B). Koppar-Glas pt. Cuprum vitreum *Wallerius* (282, 1746). Cuivre vitreux *Wallerius* (1, 509, 1753). Kopparmalm, Cuprum sulphure mineralisatum pt. *Cronstedt* (174, 1758). Vitreous Copper, Sulphuret of Copper. Cuivre sulfuré *Fr.* Cuivre sulfuré spiciforme, argent en épis *Haüy* (3, 458, 1822). Kupferglanz *Germ.* Copper Glance. Chalcosine *Beudant* (2, 408, 1832). Digenite *Breithaupt (Ann. Phys.*, 61, 673, 1844). Cyprite *Glocker* (1847). Redruthite *Nicol* (1849). Harrisite *Shepard* (1855). Kuprein *Breithaupt (B. H. Ztg.*, 22, 35, 1863). Cobre sulfureo *Span.* Calcosina, Rame vetroso *Ital.* Carmenite *Hahn (B. H. Ztg.*, 24, 86, 1865). β-chalcocite. Lamellarer Kupferglanz *Schneiderhöhn* and *Ramdohr* (2, 277, 1931).

Cryst. Orthorhombic; dipyramidal — $2/m \, 2/m \, 2/m$.

$a : b : c = 0.5822 : 1 : 0.9701;$[1] $p_0 : q_0 : r_0 = 1.6663 : 0.9701 : 1$

$q_1 : r_1 : p_1 = 0.5822 : 0.6001 : 1;$ $r_2 : p_2 : q_2 = 1.0308 : 1.7176 : 1$

Forms:[2]

		ϕ	$\rho = C$	ϕ_1	$\rho_1 = A$	ϕ_2	$\rho_2 = B$
c	001	0°00′	0°00′	0°00′	90°00′	90°00′	90°00′
b	010	0 00	90 00	90 00	90 00	0 00	0 00
a	100	90 00	90 00	0 00	0 00	0 00	90 00
l	130	29 47½	90 00	90 00	60 12½	0 00	29 47½
n	230	48 52	90 00	90 00	41 08	0 00	48 52
m	110	59 47½	90 00	90 00	30 12½	0 00	59 47½
f	012	0 00	25 52½	25 52½	90 00	90 00	64 07½
e	023	0 00	32 53½	32 53½	90 00	90 00	57 06½
g	011	0 00	44 08	44 08	90 00	90 00	45 52
k	053	0 00	58 16	58 16	90 00	90 00	31 44
d	021	0 00	62 44	62 44	90 00	90 00	27 16
h	052	0 00	67 35½	67 35½	90 00	90 00	22 24½
z	113	59 47½	32 43½	17 55	62 08½	60 57	74 13
v	112	59 47½	43 57	25 52½	53 08½	50 12	69 33½
p	111	59 47½	62 35	44 08	39 54	30 58	63 28½
x	441	59 47½	82 36½	75 33	31 01	8 32	60 04

Structure cell.[3] Orthorhombic; a_0 11.8, b_0 27.2, c_0 22.7; $b_0/4 : a_0 :$ $c_0/2 = 0.576 : 1 : 0.963$; contains $Cu_{320}S_{160}$.

Habit. Short prismatic [001], thick tabular {001}, also prismatic [100]. {001} striated [100]. Also compact massive, impalpable. Common forms: *c b m e d z v p*.

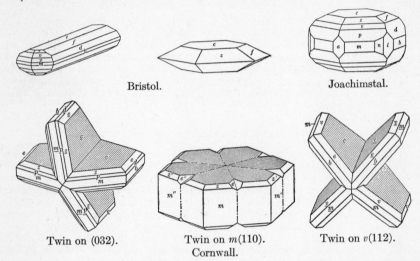

Bristol.   Joachimstal.

Twin on (032).   Twin on *m*(110).   Twin on *v*(112).
                       Cornwall.

Twinning. (*a*) On {110} common, giving pseudohexagonal stellate forms; (*b*) On {032} in cruciform intergrowths; (*c*) On {112}. Under microscope, lamellar twinning. Pressure twinning with X_1{201}, σ [100], and X_1'{131}, σ_2'[110].[4]

P h y s. Cleavage {110} indistinct. Fracture conchoidal. Rather brittle. Imperfectly sectile. H. $2\frac{1}{2}$–3. G. 5.5–5.8,[5] 5.77 (calc.). Luster metallic. Color and streak blackish lead-gray. Opaque. In polished section[6] weakly anisotropic. Reflection percentages: green 22.5, orange 16, red 15.

C h e m. Cuprous sulfide, Cu_2S. The more recent analyses show little Ag or Fe.

Anal.

	1	2	3	4	5
Cu	79.86	79.67	79.30	79.65	79.50
Fe	.....	0.14	0.18	....	0.17
S	20.14	20.16	[20.04]	20.02	20.05
SiO₂	.....	0.09	......	0.06	0.17
Gangue	.....	.....	0.30	....	.....
Rem.	.....	.....	0.18	0.20	.....
Total	100.00	100.06	100.00	99.93	99.89
G.	5.77	5.791		5.797	5.800

1. Cu_2S. 2. Butte. Contains Fe as pyrite.[7] 3. Tsumeb, "lamellar chalcocite." Includes 0.178 Ag.[8] 4. Bristol.[7] Contains PbO 0.20. 5. New London, Md.[7] Contains Fe as bornite.

Tests. F. 2–2½. After roasting on charcoal gives globule of Cu in R.F. Soluble in HNO₃.

O c c u r.[9] Chalcocite, one of the most important sources of copper, occurs principally as a supergene mineral in the enriched zone of sulfide deposits, as the so-called " chalcocite blanket " (Rio Tinto; Ely; Morenci). Another type of occurrence is with bornite and other minerals in sulfide veins, and here the chalcocite often replaces the bornite (Butte; Kennecott; Tsumeb). Covellite is often intimately associated with the chalcocite. In the oxidation zone of the ore deposits cuprite, malachite, and azurite are found with chalcocite.

Splendid crystals have been found at Cornwall, especially in the districts of St. Just, St. Ives, Camborne, and Redruth (*redruthite*). Also in crystals from Russia, near Bogolovsk in the Urals; in Roumania at Dognácska. In Germany at various localities; at Joachimstal, Bohemia, as crystals. Found in the copper ores of Mte. Catini, Tuscany. In South-West Africa, in large amounts at Tsumeb. From the French Congo, at Mindouli. In various mines in Chile, Peru, and Mexico.

In the United States exceptional crystals came from Bristol, Connecticut. Found in large amounts as a copper ore in many western mining districts such as Butte, Montana; Miami, Morenci, Bisbee, and Ray in Arizona; at Bingham, Utah; at Ely, Nevada; at Santa Rita, New Mexico. Also found at Ducktown, Tennessee. At Kennecott in the Copper River district, Alaska.

A l t e r. Alters to native copper, bornite(?), chalcopyrite(?), covellite, malachite, and azurite. Pseudomorphous after bornite, chalcopyrite, galena, millerite, pyrite, and enargite.

A r t i f.[10] Prepared by heating fused cuprous sulfide in vacuum to the melting point. The high-temperature form of Cu_2S above 105°± is hexagonal with a_0 3.89, c_0 6.68, containing Cu_4S_2 in hexagonal unit. Space group $C6/mmc$.[11]

Ref.

1. Miller in Brooke and Miller (159, 1852).
2. Goldschmidt (5, 63, 1918). Hawkins, *Am. Min.*, **14**, 309 (1929). Uncertain {530}, {10·3·0}, {067}, {103}, {102}, {203}, {101}, {201}, {114}, {337}, {136}, {134}, {133}, {132}, {131}.
3. Alsen, *Geol. För. Förh.*, **53**, 111 (1931) on crystals which may have been twinned, because most natural crystals are twinned. The simplest relation between Alsen's ratio and the morphological ratio is: Alsen to morphology 040/100/002. However, if the x-ray cell expresses the periodicities in a twinned lattice, the transformation is: Alsen to morphology 1⅖0/1¾0/001. The axial directions of the x-ray unit would then not conform with the crystallographic axes, but because of the pseudohexagonal aspect of the crystals (and the twinning) these x-ray axes would be at very nearly right angles.
4. Mügge, *Jb. Min.*, 24, 1920 — chalcocite, p. 39. Twinning produced by moderate pressures on planes not heretofore noted as twin planes in chalcocite.
5. The value 5.783 given by Posnjak, Allen, and Merwin, *Econ. Geol.*, **10**, 491 (1915), for pure Cu_2S is on the orthorhombic form, and is thus close to the calculated value from the x-ray data (priv. comm., H. E. Merwin).
6. Schneiderhöhn and Ramdohr (2, 278, 1931).
7. Posnjak, Allen, and Merwin (1915).

8. Schneiderhöhn, *Senck. Ges. Frankfurt, Abh.*, **2**, 1 (1920).
9. General account of occurrence of chalcocite in Lindgren (831, 1933). For Butte: Locke, Hall, and Short, *Am. Inst. Min. Met. Engr., Trans.*, **70**, 933 (1924). See also on Engels, Calif., Graton and McLaughlin, *Econ. Geol.*, **12**, 1 (1917); **13**, 81 (1918). On the relation of high and low chalcocite and also digenite see Buerger, *Econ. Geol.*, **36**, 19 (1941).
10. Posnjak, Allen, and Merwin (1915).
11. Buerger (priv. comm., May 17, 1941).

2322 **S T R O M E Y E R I T E** [CuAgS]. Silberkupferglanz *Hausmann* and *Stromeyer* (*Göttingen Gel. Anz.*, **2**, 1249, 1816; *Schweigger's J.*, **19**, 325, 1817). Argent et cuivre sulfuré *Bournon* (212, 1817). Sulphuret of Silver and Copper. Argentiferous Sulphuret of Copper. Kupfersilberglanz *Germ.* Cuivre sulfuré argentifère *Fr.* Stromeyerine *Beudant* (**2**, 410, 1832). Stromeyerite *Shepard* (**2**, 211, 1835). Cyprargyrite *Glocker* (24, 1847).

C r y s t.[1] Orthorhombic; dipyramidal — $2/m\ 2/m\ 2/m$.

$$a : b : c = 0.5822 : 1 : 0.9668; \qquad p_0 : q_0 : r_0 = 1.6606 : 0.9668 : 1$$

$$q_1 : r_1 : p_1 = 0.5822 : 0.6022 : 1; \qquad r_2 : p_2 : q_2 = 1.0343 : 1.7176 : 1$$

Forms:

	ϕ	$\rho = C$	ϕ_1	$\rho_1 = A$	ϕ_2	$\rho_2 = B$
c 001	....	0°00′	0°00′	90°00′	90°00′	90°00′
b 010	0°00′	90 00	90 00	90 00	....	0 00
m 110	59 47½	90 00	90 00	30 12½	0 00	59 47½
u 012	0 00	25 48	25 48	90 00	90 00	64 12
e 021	0 00	62 39	62 39	90 00	90 00	27 21
w 114	59 47½	25 39½	13 35½	68 01½	67 27½	77 25
p 111	59 47½	62 30½	44 02	39 57	31 03½	63 29½

Habit. Prismatic, pseudohexagonal [001]. Also massive, compact. Common forms: *c b m w*.

Twinning. Twin plane $m\{110\}$ common.

Gliding. Glide plane $\{201\}$ developed under pressure.[2]

P h y s. Cleavage none. Fracture subconchoidal to conchoidal. Brittle. H. $2\frac{1}{2}$-3. G. 6.2–6.3. Luster metallic. Color and streak dark steel-gray, blue on exposed surface.[3] Opaque. In polished section[4] strongly anisotropic. Reflection percentages: green $27\frac{1}{2}$, orange 26, red 26.

C h e m. A sulfide of silver and copper, AgCuS, with definite Ag : Cu = 1 : 1.

Anal.[5]

	1	2	3	4	5
Ag	53.01	53.31	52.10	51.80	48.64
Cu	31.24	31.00	32.14	31.46	30.64
Fe	.....	trace	.....	0.30	0.20
Zn	.....	.....	.....	.....	3.28
Pb	.....	.....	.....	.....	1.53
S	15.75	16.02	15.26	16.08	16.23
Insol.	.....	.....	.....	0.32	.....
Total	100.00	100.33	99.50	99.96	100.52
G.		6.260		6.26	6.122

1. AgCuS. 2. Foster mine, Cobalt.[6] 3. Guarisamey, Mexico, average of three analyses.[7] 4. Morrison mine, Gowganda, Ont.[6] 5. Yellow Pine mine, Boulder Co., Colo. Massive and apparently homogeneous.[8]

Tests. F. 1½. B.B. on charcoal fuses to a semimalleable globule. Soluble in HNO_3.

O c c u r.[9] Stromeyerite is usually intimately associated with argentian tetrahedrite (freibergite) and bornite. Found with chalcopyrite at Zmeyewskaja-Goro (Schlangenberg) near Zmyeinogorsk, Altai, Siberia; at Rudelstadt and Kupferberg, Silesia. Disseminated in a quartz matrix, with bornite and chalcopyrite at Mount Lyell, Tasmania. In Chile in Santiago, at San Lorenzo in Aconcagua, at Copiapó in Atacama and in Tarapacá; also in Peru. With chalcopyrite and galena in Zacatecas, Mexico. In Arizona at the Heintzelman and Silver King mines, Pinal County. At Butte, Montana; Colorado in Gilpin and Ouray counties. In British Columbia at the Silver King mine, Toad Mountain, in the Nelson mining district; from Cobalt and Gowganda in the Timiskaming District, Ontario.

A r t i f.[10] By compressing powdered Ag_2S and Cu_2S in the required proportions, stromeyerite is slowly formed at room temperature and rapidly at 75°.

N a m e. After Fr. Stromeyer (1776–1835), Professor of Chemistry at Göttingen, who first analyzed and established the species.

Ref.

1. Rose, *Ann. Phys.*, **28**, 427 (1833). Above 93° stromeyerite inverts to an apparently isometric modification according to work of Schwartz, *Econ. Geol.*, **30**, 128 (1935), and Ramdohr (in Schneiderhöhn and Ramdohr [2, 303, 1931]).
2. Mügge, *Jb. Min.*, 24, 1920.
3. Walker and Parsons, *Univ. of Toronto Stud.*, *Geol. Ser.*, **24**, 15 (1927).
4. Schneiderhöhn and Ramdohr (**2**, 303, 1931).
5. Early analyses in Dana (56, 1892).
6. Walker and Parsons (1927).
7. Kalb and Bendig, *Cbl. Min.*, 516, 1924.
8. Headden, *Am. Min.*, **10**, 41 (1925).
9. The occurrence of stromeyerite is discussed by Guild, *Econ. Geol.*, **12**, 297 (1917) and Schwartz (1935).
10. Schwartz (1935).

2323   **A C A N T H I T E** [Ag_2S]. Akanthit *Kenngott* (*Ak. Wien, Ber.*, **15**, 238, 1855; *Ann. Phys.*, **95**, 462, 1855). β-argentite *Schneiderhöhn* (*Am. Min.*, **12**, 210, 1927). Daleminzite *Breithaupt* (*B. H. Ztg.*, **21**, 98, 1862; **22**, 44, 1863).

C r y s t. Orthorhombic?.[1]

$$a : b : c = 0.6886 : 1 : 0.9944^2$$

Forms:[3]

c 001	τ 210	o 101	e 301	p 111	n 211	r 123	δ 241	ω 141	φ 163
b 010	m 110	ν 504	d 001	z 554	l 534	u 122	s 131	β 152	ε 183
a 100	α 120	u 201	x 113	χ 214	h 125	k 121	λ 143	π 161	

Structure cell.[4] Orthorhombic; a_0 4.77, b_0 6.92, c_0 6.88; $a_0 : b_0 : c_0 = 0.690 : 1 : 0.996$. Contains Ag_8S_4.

Habit. Prismatic to long prismatic [001].

Twinning. Twin plane {101}?.

P h y s. Cleavage indistinct. Fracture uneven. Sectile. H. 2–2½. G. 7.2–7.3 (meas.),[2] 7.18 (calc.). Luster metallic. Color iron-black. Opaque.

C h e m.[5] Silver sulfide, Ag_2S, like argentite; Ag 87.06, S 12.94, total 100.00 per cent.

Tests. As for argentite.

O c c u r. All the argentite occurrences are valid for acanthite, and no clear evidence of occurrence of crystals proper to acanthite has as yet been presented. However, the following supposed occurrences of crystals are given. Found at Joachimstal, Bohemia, with pyrite, argentite, and calcite, usually on quartz; in Saxony at the Himmelfürst and other mines near Freiberg, with argentite and stephanite. A specimen found at Freiberg in 1860 shows brilliant crystals 22 mm. long. Also at Annaberg, Saxony; in Baden at Wolfach on the Kinzig. From Mexico in Chihuahua and at the Sombrerete mine, Zacatecas. In Colorado, reported from Georgetown, Clear Creek County, and from Rice, Dolores County.

N a m e. From ἄκανθα, *thorn*, in allusion to the shape of the crystals.

Ref.

1. By Dauber, *Ak. Wien, Ber.*, **39**, 685 (1857), on crystals from the Himmelsfürst mine, Freiberg. Krenner, *Zs. Kr.*, **14**, 388 (1888), however, showed the close correspondence of the orthorhombic angles of Dauber with those required by the isometric system. Palache (priv. comm., 1941) states that not only do the angles correspond to the isometric system, but also the forms on Himmelsfürst acanthite are relatively simple isometric forms, practically all of which have been found on argentite. The transformation acanthite (Dauber) to argentite is: 200/011/0$\bar{1}$1. Further evidence that the crystals examined by Dauber (and others) might be distorted isometric crystals, is to be found in the fact that all argentite crystals are distorted due to the inversion to the nonisometric form on cooling. X-ray investigations (Berman, priv. comm., 1941) are inconclusive. The Himmelsfürst crystals give a rather distorted single crystal pattern as does the Butte argentite. The work of Palacios and Salvia, *An. soc. españ. fis. quím.*, **29**, 269 (1931) — *Min. Abs.*, **6**, 328 (1936), is inconclusive because the acanthite measurements, if considered as taken on an isometric crystal, (using the transformation above) yield a unit cell close to the isometric cell found by Barth, *Cbl. Min.*, 284, 1926, and others. There is no doubt, however, that a nonisometric silver sulfide exists in nature, but its crystallographic properties are not certainly known. See also, Ramsdell, *Am. Min.*, **28,** 401 (1943).
2. Dauber (1857).
3. In the orthorhombic interpretation of Dauber (1857).
4. Palacios and Salvia (1931). See also ref. 1. The b_0 and c_0 values become|4.88|Å± if they are considered as [011] axes of an isometric crystal.
5. The analyses of all argentites are actually on material inverted to acanthite.

TYPE A_3X_2

241   **M A U C H E R I T E** [$Ni_{11}As_8$]. Plakodin (artif.) *Breithaupt* (*Ann. Phys.*, **53**, 631, 1841). Maucherite *Grünling* (*Cbl. Min.*, 225, 1913). Nickelspeise *Germ.* Temiskamite *Walker* (*Am. J. Sc.*, 37, 170, 1914).

C r y s t. Tetragonal; trapezohedral — 4 2 2.[6]

$$a : c = 1 : 3.190;^7 \qquad p_0 : r_0 = 3.190 : 1$$

Forms:[8]

		ϕ	$\rho = C$	A	$\overline{M}$
c	001	....	0°00′	90°00′	90°00′
v	023	0°00′	64 49	90 00	50 13
g	054	0 00	75 55½	90 00	46 42
h	032	0 00	78 12	90 00	46 12
b	021	0 00	81 05½	90 00	45 41
q	031	0 00	84 02	90 00	45 18½

Structure cell.[7] Space group $P4_12_1$ or $P4_32_1$; a_0 6.844 ± 0.01, c_0 21.83 ± 0.05; $a_0 : c_0 = 1 : 3.190$. The observed cell contents are $Ni_{44}As_{32}$.

Habit. Commonly tabular {001}; also pyramidal. The pyramidal planes are striated ‖ their intersection with {001}. Massive, radiated fibrous, or granular.

Twinning. Reported on {203};[9] also {106}?.[1]

P h y s. No cleavage. Fracture uneven. Brittle. H. 5. G. 8.00 (Sudbury[10]), 8.03 (artif.[11]); 8.04 (calc. for $Ni_{11}As_8$). Luster metallic. Color on fresh fracture platinum-gray with a reddish hue, tarnishing coppery red. Streak blackish gray. Opaque. In polished section[12] pinkish gray in color and weakly anisotropic. Shows twinning. Reflection percentages: green 60, orange 55½, red 51.

C h e m. An arsenide of nickel. The formula is uncertain, perhaps $Ni_{11}As_8$ or, more probably, $Ni_{12-x}As_8$, where $x \sim 1$, with the ideal formula Ni_3As_2.[1] Small amounts of Co, Cu, and Fe substitute for Ni, and S substitutes for As in small amounts.

Anal.

	1	2	3	4	5
Ni	54.02	51.85	49.96	49.07	50.03
Co	......	......	0.20	1.73	0.84
Fe	......	......	0.84	....	trace
Cu	......	......	0.69	.....	0.13
As	45.98	48.15	45.88	46.34	45.90
S	......	......	0.97	1.03	0.18
Rem.	......	......	0.68	0.55	1.66
Total	100.00	100.00	99.22	98.72	98.74
G.		8.04	8.00	7.95	7.83

1. Ni_3As_2. 2. $Ni_{11}As_8$. 3. Sudbury, Ont. Rem. is H_2O 0.36, gangue 0.32.[3] 4. Moose Horn mine. Elk Lake, Ont. (*temiskamite*). Rem. is Bi.[4] 5. Eisleben, Thuringia. Rem. is gangue 1.66.[3]

Tests. F. 2. Soluble in strong HNO_3; slowly decomposed by H_2SO_4 or HCl. Deposits metallic silver from solutions of Ag_2SO_4.[5]

O c c u r. In Germany at Eisleben, Saxony, associated with niccolite, chloanthite, bismuth, calcite, barite, anhydrite, and manganite; reported with safflorite, niccolite, smaltite-chloanthite, chalcopyrite in hydrothermal veins cutting the sedimentary copper deposit at Mansfeld, Thuringia; in cobalt-silver veins at Niederramstadt near Darmstadt, Hesse; with cobalt-nickel ores near Schladming, Styria. Reported also with niccolite at Los Jarales, Malaga, Spain. Found in Canada as rounded radial-fibrous masses with niccolite, native bismuth, native silver and calcite at the Moose Horn mine, Elk Lake, Timiskaming District, Ontario (*temiskam-ite*); reported from Cobalt, Ontario. With pyrrhotite, chalcopyrite, and cobalt-nickel minerals in the Sudbury district, Ontario, and with millerite, calcite, pyroxene, and uvarovite at Orford, Quebec.

A l t e r. To niccolite.

A r t i f.[13] The compound Ni_3As_2 has been observed in the system Ni–As. Also found as a furnace product (placodine).

N a m e. After Wilhelm Maucher (1879–1930), a mineral dealer of Munich. Placodine from πλακώδης, *flat*, in allusion to the tabular habit of the crystals.

Ref.
1. See Peacock, *Min. Mag.*, **25**, 557 (1940).
2. For additional analyses see Grünling, *Cbl. Min.*, 225, 1913.
3. International Nickel Co. laboratory anal. in Peacock (1940).
4. Walker, *Am. J. Sc.*, 37, 170 (1914).
5. Palmer, *Econ. Geol.*, **9**, 664 (1914).
6. Crystal class from x-ray Weissenberg study of Peacock (1940).
7. Peacock (1940) by Weissenberg x-ray study; a well-marked pseudo-cell has a_0 halved and its space group apparently is $I4/amd$.
8. Rosati, *Zs. Kr.*, **53**, 389 (1914); uncertain forms: {103}, {101}. Transformation: Rosati to Peacock $\frac{1}{4}\frac{1}{4}0/\frac{1}{4}\frac{1}{4}0/001$. Additional forms observed on artificial material (placodine) are {205}, {102}, {508}, {506} (Rosati). Peacock (1940) has indicated that the so-called rammelsbergite of Palache and Wood, *Am. J. Sc.*, **18**, 343 (1904), from Orford, Quebec, is actually maucherite, with the transformation Palache and Wood to Peacock; $00\frac{1}{4}/\frac{1}{2}00/010$. Four of the forms of Palache and Wood (1904) are new for maucherite; they are {110}, {108}, {104}, {304}.
9. Rosati (1914) on crystals from Eisleben.
10. Berman in Peacock (1940).
11. Breithaupt, *Ann. Phys.*, **53**, 631 (1841).
12. Orcel, *Bull. soc. min.*, **51**, 197 (1928), Peacock (1940), Schneiderhöhn and Ramdohr (**2**, 227, 1931).
13. See Mellor (**9**, 79, 1929).

242   **U M A N G I T E** [Cu_3Se_2].   *Klockmann* (*Zs. Kr.*, **19**, 269, 1891).

Found only massive, in small grains or fine granular aggregates.

P h y s. Fracture uneven to small conchoidal.[1] Not very brittle. H. 3. G. 5.620. Luster metallic. Color on fresh fracture dark cherry-red with violet tint; tarnishes easily to violet-blue. Streak black. Opaque. In polished section[2] dark red-violet in color. Apparently uniaxial.[3] Strongly anisotropic; markedly pleochroic with O dark violet-red, E blue-gray. Reflection percentages: (O) green 17, orange 14, red 16; (E) green 19, orange 14, red 14. Sometimes exhibits lamellar twinning.

C h e m. A selenide of copper, Cu_3Se_2.

Anal.

	1	2	3
Cu	54.70	56.03	54.35
Ag	.....	0.49	0.55
Se	45.30	41.44	45.10
Rem.	......	[2.04]	......
Total	100.00	100.00	100.00
G.		5.620	

1. Cu_3Se_2. 2. Sierra de Umango. Rem. is CO_2, H_2O, etc. 3. Sierra de Umango. Recalculated after deduction of portion soluble in acetic acid (alteration products) and the correction of the Se value from a duplicate Se determination.

Tests. Easily fusible. Soluble in HNO₃.

O c c u r. In Argentina in the Sierra de Umango, La Rioja Province, associated with eucairite, tiemannite, bornite, and calcite; also reported from the Sierra de Sañagasta, La Rioja, and from the Sierra Cacheuta, Mendoza Province. In Germany in the Harz Mountains associated with clausthalite, tiemannite, berzelianite, guanajuatite, chalcopyrite, cobaltite, and pyrite in calcite veins at Andreasberg, with clausthalite, tiemannite, and calcite at Zorge, with dolomite and selenides at Lehrbach, and at Clausthal. At Skrikerum, Sweden, with berzelianite and chalcopyrite. Reported from Rio Tinto, Spain.

A l t e r. To malachite and chalcomenite.

N a m e. From the locality, Sierra de Umango, Argentina.

Ref.

1. Ramdohr, *Cbl. Min.*, 225, 1928, states that two cleavages at right angles, with optical extinction parallel thereto, are sometimes seen.
2. Schneiderhöhn and Ramdohr (2, 309, 1931).
3. Ramdohr (1928).

243   **B O R N I T E** [Cu₅FeS₄]. Kupferkies pt. Kupfer-Lazul *Henckel* (1725). Lefverslag, Brun Kopparmalm, Minera Cupri Hepatica, Cuprum sulfure et ferro mineralisatum *Wallerius* (283, 1747). Cuivre vitreuse violette *Wallerius* (1753). Koppar-Lazur, Minera Cupri Lazurea *Cronstedt* (175, 1758). Buntkupfererz *Werner*. Purple Copper Ore *Kirwan* (2, 338, 1796). Variegated Copper Ore. Cuivre pyriteux hepatique *Haüy* (3, 536, 1801). Cuivre panaché *Fr.* Phillipsite *Beudant* (2, 411, 1832). Pyrites erubescens *Dana* (408, 1837). Poikilopyrites *Glocker* (328, 1839). Bornit *Haidinger* (562, 1845A). Poikilit *Breithaupt*. Erubescite *Dana* (510, 1850). Cobre abigarrado, Cobre panaceo, Pecho de paloma *Span. S. A.* Peacock ore pt., Horse-flesh ore, *English miners.* Brokig Kopparmalm *Swed.* Chalcomiklit *Blomstrand* (*Ak. Stockholm Öfv.*, 27, 24, 1870).

C r y s t. Isometric; hexoctahedral — $4/m\ \overline{3}\ 2/m$.

Forms:[1]

$a\{001\}$ $d\{011\}$ $o\{111\}$ $n\{112\}$ $\beta\{223\}$ $\sigma\{335\}$

Structure cell.[2] Space group $Fd3m$. a_0 10.93; contains $Cu_{40}Fe_8S_{32}$ or $8Cu_5FeS_4$.

Habit. Cubic, dodecahedral, more rarely octahedral. Faces often rough or curved. Massive, granular, or compact.

Twinning. Twin plane $\{111\}$; often shows penetration twins.

P h y s. Cleavage $\{111\}$ in traces.[3] Fracture small conchoidal, uneven. Brittle. H. 3. G. 5.06–5.08; 5.074 (calc.). Luster metallic. Color between copper-red and pinchbeck-brown on fresh fracture, quickly becomes purplish iridescent from tarnish upon exposure to moist atmosphere. Streak pale grayish black. Opaque. Isotropic in part.[4] Color under microscope pinkish brown when fresh. Reflection percentages: for green 18.5, orange 19, red 21.

C h e m.[5] A sulfide of copper and iron, Cu_5FeS_4.

Anal.

	1	2	3	4	5	6	7
Cu	63.33	63.90	63.24	63.08	62.99	63.20	63.24
Fe	11.12	10.79	11.12	11.22	11.23	11.34	11.20
Pb	.....	none	.....	none	0.10	.....	.....
Ag	.....	none	.....	none	none	.....	.....
S	25.55	25.17	25.54	25.54	25.58	25.65	25.54
Total	100.00	99.86	99.90	99.84	99.90	100.19	99.98
G.	5.074		5.079	5.037	5.061		5.072

1. Cu_5FeS_4. 2. Guilford Co., N. C. Contains about 3 per cent chalcocite.[6] 3. Messina, Transvaal.[6] 4. Costa Rica.[6] 5. Superior, Ariz.[6] 6. Fanambana, Madagascar.[7] 7. Bristol, Conn. Crystals.[8]

Tests. F. 2. In the closed tube gives a faint sublimate of sulfur. In the open tube yields sulfurous fumes but no sublimate. B.B. on charcoal fuses in R.F. to a brittle magnetic globule. Soluble in HNO_3 with separation of sulfur.

Occur.[9] Bornite is a common and widespread mineral occurring in many of the important copper deposits in considerable amounts. It is nearly always of hypogene origin. Occurs in dikes (Evergreen mine), in basic intrusives (Ookiep), and disseminated in basic rocks (Engels). In contact metamorphic deposits (Marble Bay), and in pegmatites. Also found in quartz veins (Virgilina) and in veinlets in copper shales (Mansfeld). Crystals of bornite are rare and have been found only in druses in veins (Bristol; Butte). Replacement by chalcocite and chalcopyrite is common and many intergrowth textures of these minerals have been described.

In the Austrian Tirol near Prägratten and Windisch-Matrei in crystals. From Freiberg and elsewhere in Saxony; in the cupriferous shales (Kupferschiefer) of the Mansfeld district in the Harz Mountains. At Montecatini, Tuscany. In crystals from Redruth, Cornwall. From Androta, southwest of Vohémar, Madagascar, of fine color. An important ore at Mount Lyell, Tasmania. At Ookiep in Namaqualand Cape Province, South Africa, occurs in the basic intrusive rocks; at the Messina mine, in Transvaal, South Africa. In Chile at the Braden or Teniente mine; at Morococha, Peru.

In the United States at Bristol, Connecticut, as fine crystals in the drusy portions of the veins. Occurs in quartz veins in the Virgilina district, Virginia and North Carolina. Found in many of the copper mines of the West, especially at Butte, Montana; at the Evergreen mine, near Apex, Gilpin County, Colorado, bornite occurs in a monzonite dike, associated with garnet, calcite and wollastonite. Also at the Magma mine, Superior, Pinal County, Arizona, and as a primary ore at Bisbee, Globe and Ajo. At the Engels mine, Plumas County, California, bornite, with chalcocite, are disseminated in norite and quartz diorite. At Kennecott, Alaska.

In Canada frequently found in eastern Quebec, at the Acton mine, Bagot County. Also at the Marble Bay mine, Texada Island, British Columbia, in a contact metamorphic zone.

A l t e r.[10] Bornite alters readily to chalcocite, also to chalcopyrite, covellite, cuprite, chrysocolla, malachite, and azurite.

A r t i f.[11] Produced by melting the elements in the required proportion, under vacuum.

N a m e. After Ignatius von Born, a distinguished Austrian mineralogist of the eighteenth century (1742–1791).

Ref.

1. Goldschmidt (**1**, 248, 1913).
2. Lundqvist and Westgren, *Ark. Kemi*, **12B** [23], 1936.
3. Unusual cleavage shown in specimens from Usk, B. C. See Walker, *Am. Min.,* **6**, 3 (1921).
4. Short (76, 1931), and Schneiderhöhn and Ramdohr (**2**, 335, 1931).
5. The composition first properly established by Harrington, *Am. J. Sc.*, **16**, 151 (1903) and confirmed by Allen, *Am. J. Sc.*, **41**, 409 (1916), using material whose purity was established by microscopic examination. Earlier analyses given in Hintze (**1** [1], 915, 1901) and in Doelter (**4** [1], 152, 1925) are not reliable because precautions against using inhomogeneous samples for analysis were not generally observed.
6. Allen (1916).
7. Lacroix (**3**, 300, 1923). Material examined under microscope by Orcel, *Bull. soc. min.*, **48**, 272 (1926).
8. Harrington (1903). Other analyses of high quality given by Harrington.
9. General discussion of occurrence, Lindgren (612, 809, 839, 1933), also Graton and Murdoch, *Am. Inst. Min. Engr. Trans.*, 741, 1913. For general account of properties and paragenesis, D. H. McLaughlin (The occurrence and significance of bornite, Doctorate thesis, Harvard University, 1917). For discussion of intergrowths of bornite with chalcocite and chalcopyrite: Graton and Murdoch (1913); Schneiderhöhn and Ramdohr (**2**, 289, 337, 1931); McLaughlin (1917); Locke, Hall, and Short, *Am. Inst. Min. Met. Eng., Trans.*, 1308, 1924; Graton and McLaughlin, *Econ. Geol.*, **12**, 1 (1917).
10. Zies, Allen, and Merwin, *Econ. Geol.*, **11**, 407 (1916), give reactions for various temperatures and reagents in producing artificial alterations.
11. Lundqvist and Westgren (1936) who tested their product by x-ray powder pictures. Earlier experiments in Doelter (**4** [1], 161, 1925) not adequately tested. See also Merwin and Lombard, *Econ. Geol.*, **32**, 203 (1937).

CASTILLITE. *Rammelsberg* (*Zs. deutsche geol. Ges.*, **18**, 23, 1866) resembles bornite in appearance but has been shown by study of a polished section[1] to be a mixture of sphalerite, tetrahedrite, galena, bornite, and stromeyerite.

Ref.

1. Kalb, *Cbl. Min.*, 545, 1923.

251 Dimorphite [As_4S_3]. Dimorfina *Scacchi* (116, 1849). Dimorphite *Dana* (28, 1868).

C r y s t.[1] Orthorhombic; dipyramidal — $2/m\ 2/m\ 2/m$.

$a : b : c = 0.6032 : 1 : 0.9068;$[2] $\quad p_0 : q_0 : r_0 = 1.5033 : 0.9068 : 1$

$q_1 : r_1 : p_1 = 0.6032 : 0.6652 : 1; \quad r_2 : p_2 : q_2 = 1.1028 : 1.6578 : 1$

Forms:

		ϕ	$\rho = C$	ϕ_1	$\rho_1 = A$	ϕ_2	$\rho_2 = B$
c	001	.....	0°00′	0°00′	90°00′	90°00′	90°00′
b	010	0°00′	90 00	90 00	90 00	.....	0 00
m	110	58 54	90 00	90 00	31 06	0 00	58 54
t	021	0 00	61 07½	61 07½	90 00	90 00	28 52½
d	101	90 00	56 22	0 00	33 38	33 38	90 00
p	111	58 54	60 20	42 12	41 55½	33 38	63 20

Habit. Dipyramidal {111}, with {110}, {101} also large. Artificial crystals tabular {001}, or prismatic [001] with large {110} and {001}. Mostly in groups of minute parallel individuals.

P h y s. Cleavage none. Brittle. H. $1\frac{1}{2}$. G. 2.58; 2.60 (artif.). M.P. 200°±. Luster almost adamantine. Color orange-yellow. Transparent.

O p t.[3]

$X = c$	$2H_a = 108°46'$
$Y = b$	Bx. pos. (+). Pleochroic. $r > v$.
$Z = a$	Moderate birefringence.

C h e m. A sulfide of arsenic, As_4S_3.
Anal.

	As	S	Total	G.
1	75.70	24.30	100.00	
2	75.45	24.55	100.00	2.58

1. As_4S_3. 2. Italy.[4]

Tests. Melts on heating, turns red, then brown, gives off abundant yellow fumes, ignites and burns without residue. Completely soluble in warm HNO_3 and in CS_2.

O c c u r. Found with realgar, sal ammoniac, sulfur, and various sulfates at a fumarole (70–80°) of the Solfatara, Phlegraean fields, Italy.

A r t i f.[5] By melting a mixture of AsS and As and purifying the product either by crystallization from CS_2 or by sublimation.

N a m e. From δίς, *double*, and μορφή, *form*, in allusion to the two forms in which the mineral was believed to exist.

Ref.

1. Since the first type of dimorphite (Type A of Dana [35, 1892]) is near orpiment in habit and angles and probably identical with it, and Scacchi (1849) considered his own analysis as indecisive, dimorphite has been regarded as a doubtful species. Krenner, *Zs. Kr.*, **43**, 476 (1907), has shown, however, that the forms and angles of the second type (Type B of Dana) agree closely with those of artificial As_4S_3 prepared by Schuller, *Mat. termés. Ért.*, **12**, 255 (1894) — *Zs. Kr.*, **27**, 97 (1897), and that dimorphite (signifying Scacchi's second type) is a valid species.
2. Recomputed by Peacock (priv. comm., 1937) from Scacchi's fundamental angles in Krenner's orientation.
3. Krenner (1907).
4. Scacchi (1849).
5. Schuller (1894).

252   **R I C K A R D I T E** [Cu_4Te_3]. *Ford* (*Am. J. Sci.*, **15**, 69, 1903). Sanfordite (*Ores and Metals*, April, 1903).

Massive. Fracture irregular. Brittle. H. $3\frac{1}{2}$. G. 7.54. Luster metallic. Color on fresh fracture purple-red, resembling the color of a tarnished surface of bornite. In polished section[1] strongly anisotropic and strongly pleochroic; probably uniaxial, with O carmine, E violet-gray.

C h e m. A telluride of copper, Cu_4Te_3.
Anal.

Cu 40.74, Te 59.21, total 99.95. For Cu_4Te_3: Cu 39.93, Te 60.07, total 100.00

Tests. F. 1 to a brittle globule. Soluble in HNO_3.

O c c u r. Originally found at the Good Hope mine, Vulcan, Colorado, in lens-shaped masses intimately associated with native tellurium, petzite, and berthierite in pyrite veins. Some native sulfur is also present. Reported from the Empress Josephine mine, Bonanza, Colorado; at Warren, Arizona; in the San Sebastian mine, San Salvador. Said to occur at Kalgoorlie, Western Australia.

N a m e. After T. A. Rickard, mining engineer.

Ref.

1. Ramdohr, *Zbl. Min.*, 193, 1937.

253 **Weissite** [Cu_5Te_3]. *Crawford* (*Am. J. Sci.*, **13**, 345, 1927). (Not Weissite *Trolle-Wachtmeister* [*Ann. Phys.*, **14**, 190, 1828] = altered cordierite.)

Massive. H. 3. G. 6. Color dark bluish black on fresh surfaces, tarnishing to deep black. Streak black. Luster shiny metallic. Aniso-tropic.[1] Composition Cu_5Te_3; Te 54.62, Cu 45.38, total 100.00. Anal. Te 53.97, Cu 45.84, total 99.81.

Occurs associated with pyrite, tellurium, sylvanite, petzite, and rickardite in the Good Hope and Mammoth Chimney mines at Vulcan, Gunnison County, Colorado. Named after the late Dr. Louis Weiss, owner of the Good Hope mine.

Ref.

1. Short (72, 1931).

AX TYPE

Galena group	Cinnabar
Sphalerite group	Realgar
Chalcopyrite group	Cooperite
Wurtzite group	Braggite
Niccolite group	Herzenbergite
Cubanite	Empressite
Sternbergite	Muthmannite
Covellite group	

The minerals of this type possess high symmetry generally, the two most important groups being isometric and most of the others hexagonal. The chief structural features in AX compounds[1] are shown by the minerals of this type. Galena is of the NaCl class; sphalerite is of the cubic polar class with coordination four, and wurtzite is of the close-packed hexagonal class, with the latter two closely related structurally; niccolite is the type representative of the so-called nickel-arsenide structure. Most of the other members of the type are modifications of the principal structural classes, as, for example, cinnabar which is a distorted rock-salt structure; and chalcopyrite which is very similar to the sphalerite structure. Another feature of the type is dimorphism. Sphalerite and wurtzite, cinnabar and metacinnabar are examples in nature. Alabandite also has an artificial modification of the sphalerite class, and millerite has an artificial modification in the niccolite group.

The metallic elements entering into the type composition are nearly all divalent, and the structural class to which a given compound belongs is largely governed by the ratio of the metallic atoms to sulfur, and by their polarizability.[2]

Some of the minerals here listed are not strictly of the AX type since the metallic atoms are of two kinds, as in chalcopyrite, sternbergite, and cubanite. However, the sum of these atoms is equal to the number of sulfur atoms and the structures are similar to AX structures. In some few instances the ratio $A : X \neq 1$, as in pyrrhotite, where an iron deficiency occurs.

Ref.

1. A résumé of the structures of minerals of the type is given in Bragg (1937).
2. The relation of radius ratio and polarizability to structure is discussed by Goldschmidt, *Trans. Faraday Soc.*, **25**, 253 (1929), and Hassel (1935).

261   **GALENA GROUP**

ISOMETRIC HEXOCTAHEDRAL

			a_0	G.
2611	Galena	PbS	5.93 Å	7.57
2612	Clausthalite	PbSe	6.162	8.079
2613	Altaite	PbTe	6.439	8.274
2614	Alabandite	MnS	5.214	4.050
2615	Oldhamite	CaS	5.686	2.589

The members of this group are face-centered cubic with the rock-salt structure, containing eight atoms per unit cell, and with the coordination number 6. The Pb members are metallic of high luster, whereas alabandite and the rare oldhamite are distinctly nonmetallic. The crystal habit, where known, is cubic, or cubo-octahedral.

There are no natural series between the minerals of the group and the composition of the species is fairly constant.

2611   **G A L E N A** [PbS]. Galenite. Galena *Pliny* (**33**, 31, A.D. 77). (Not Galena or Molybdaena [= litharge-like product from the ore], *Pliny* [**34**, 47, 53, A.D. 77]). Molybdaena pt., Plumbago pt. Galena, Pleiertz, Plei Glanz *Agricola* (1546). Plumbago pt., Blyglants, Galena, Plumbum sulfure et argento mineralisatum, *Wallerius* (292, 1747), *Cronstedt* (167, 168, 1758). Galenit *von Kobell* (201, 1838). Lead glance, Lead sulphide. Bleiglanz *Germ.* Blyglans *Swed.* Galène, Plomb sulfuré *Fr.* Plumbago, Pleischweis ? *Agricola* (467, 1546B). Bleischweif, Plumbago, Plumbum sulfure et arsenico mineralisatum *Wallerius* (294, 1746). Steinmannite *Zippe* (*Ges. Mus. Böhmen, Verk.*, 39, 1833. Targionite *Bechi* (*Am. J. Sc.*, **14**, 60, 1852). Supersulphuretted Lead *Johnston* (*Brit. Assoc. Adv. Sc., Rep.*, 572, 1833); *Thomson* (**1**, 552, 1836). Johnstonite *Greg and Lettsom* (448, 1858), *Haidinger* (566, 1845A). U-galena *Kerr* (*Am. Min.*, **20**, 443, 1935).

Cuproplumbite pt. *Breithaupt* (*Ann. Phys.*, **61**, 672, 1844). Plumbocuprite. Alisonite pt. *Field* (*Am. J. Sc.*, **27**, 387, 1859). Fournetite *Mène* (*C.R.*, **51**, 463, 1860). Galena blendosa *Domeyko* (168, 1860). Sulphide of Lead and Zinc *Forbes* (*Phil.*

Mag., **25**, 110, 1863).   Huascolite *Dana* (42, 1868).   Kilmacooite *Tichborne* (*Proc. Dublin Soc.*, 4, 300, 1885).

C r y s t.   Isometric;   hexoctahedral — $4/m\,\overline{3}\,2/m$.

Forms:[1]

a	001	o	111	φ	116	m	113	β	223	ρ	144	p	122
d	011	f	013	μ	114	n	112	χ	334	q	133	s	123

Structure cell.[2]   Space group $Fm3m$; a_0 5.93 ± 0.02; contains Pb_4S_4.
Habit.[3]   Commonly cubic or cubo-octahedral, less often octahedral. Tabular (001).   Also in skeletal crystals, reticulated.   Massive, cleavable, coarse, or fine granular to impalpable, occasionally fibrous, or plumose.

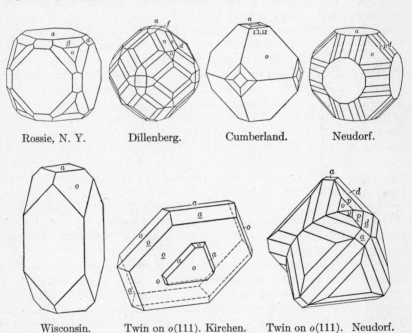

Rossie, N. Y.   Dillenberg.   Cumberland.   Neudorf.

Wisconsin.   Twin on *o*(111). Kirchen.   Twin on *o*(111). Neudorf.

Frequently shows etching on the octahedral faces, also overgrowths of oriented small crystals, usually octahedral on cubic crystals.   Large crystals commonly made up of subparallel segments.

Twinning.   (*a*) Twin plane {111} common in penetration and contact twins.   (*b*) Twin plane {114}, lamellar, (*c*) Twin plane {144}, caused by deformation.[4]

Gliding. T{001}, t[001],[5] and t[1$\overline{1}$0].[6]

P h y s.   Cleavage {001} easy and highly perfect.   Parting or cleavage on {111}.[7]   Fracture flat subconchoidal.   H. $2\frac{1}{2}$–$2\frac{3}{4}$.   G. 7.58 ± 0.01; 7.57 (calc.).   M.P. 1115°.   Luster metallic.   Color and streak pure lead-gray. Opaque. In polished section[8] isotropic. Reflection percentages: green 33.5, orange 37.5, red 35.

Chem.[9] Sulfide of lead, PbS. Pb 86.60, S 13.40, total 100.00. The silver given in most galena analyses is presumably due to admixed silver minerals such as argentite, tetrahedrite. As and Sb are due to impurities. The elements Se, Fe, Zn, Cd, Cu, and sometimes Au, Pt have been reported in analyses, but without proof that the analyzed material was homogeneous.

Tests. F.2. Decomposed by HNO_3 with separation of some S and the formation of $PbSO_4$.

Occur.[10] Galena is the most important lead mineral and one of the most widely distributed sulfide minerals. It occurs in many different types of deposit ranging from the remarkable Mississippi Valley deposits in the sedimentary rocks to the unique cryolite pegmatite of Greenland. Of equal commercial importance with the sedimentary types are the hydrothermal vein deposits. Galena occurs in notable amounts with sphalerite, chalcopyrite, pyrite, tetrahedrite, and silver minerals, in siderite and quartz veins (Coeur d'Alene) or in barite and siderite (Clausthal), or sometimes with fluorite and barite (Bleiberg). Very often these contain notable amounts of silver (Freiberg). Vein deposits formed at a higher temperature are represented by the Broken Hill deposit of galena in green feldspar, garnet, rhodonite gangue, the Alta vein (Montana) with quartz and tourmaline, or the deposits containing garnet, diopside, actinolite, and biotite (Kimberley, British Columbia). Large galena deposits are found as replacements of limestones or dolomites (Santa Eulalia, Mexico) with rich silver values. In deposits of contact metamorphic origin (Darwin, California) the galena is associated with lime silicates and fluorite.

Only those occurrences of galena which are or have been commercially important or of special mineralogical interest can be mentioned here. In Upper Silesia at Tarnowitz; in Czechoslovakia at Schemnitz, in the silver mines of Příbram and Mies; in Roumania at Kapnik and Rodna; from Bleiberg and Raibl in Carinthia, Austria. In Germany at Freiberg, Saxony, as fine crystals in the silver lead veins; from near Ems, Hesse-Nassau, and at Dillenburg; in Westphalia in unusual crystals from the Gonderbach mine near Laaspe; also from Müsen; common and often in fine specimens from the Harz Mountains, especially at Andreasberg, Neudorf, Clausthal, and Zellerfeld. In Belgium at Moresnet; in Italy at Bottino near Saravezza, Tuscany, and also in the Vesuvius lavas; at Monteponi, Sardinia, in limestone. Notable localities in France are at the mines of Pontgibaud, Puy-de-Dôme, at Pont-Péan near Bruz, Ille-et-Vilaine, and at Poullaouen, Finistère. Occurs in the granite at Linares, Province Jaen, Spain. Fine specimens come from Truro and Liskeard in Cornwall, at Alston Moor in Cumberland, and at Weardale,

Durham; in Scotland at Wanlockhead, Dumfries. In Mexico at Santa Eulalia, with pyrrhotite, sphalerite, and other sulfides together with iron and manganese silicates. In New South Wales at Broken Hill.

The extensive galena deposits of the Mississippi Valley produce about 35 per cent of the total lead mined in the United States. The productive region consists of (a) the Tri-State district embracing Joplin in Missouri, Galena in Kansas, and Picher in Oklahoma; (b) Upper Mississippi Valley district of southwestern Wisconsin at Mineral Point, northwestern Illinois at Galena, and eastern Iowa; (c) southeastern Missouri chiefly in St. Francis, Washington, and Madison counties. Galena occurs in solution cavities and zones of brecciation in limestones and cherts associated with sphalerite, pyrite, chalcopyrite, marcasite, sometimes enargite, on dolomite and calcite. In Colorado at Leadville, Aspen, Georgetown, and the San Juan district; from Breckenridge in Summit County as fine specimens, also from Lake City, Hinsdale County. In the lead-silver mines of the Coeur d'Alene region in Idaho generally in a siderite-quartz gangue, and near Hailey at Wood River, Idaho, in a siderite gangue; at the Park City and the Tintic districts in Utah; at the Alta mine, Wickes, Montana, in a quartz vein containing tourmaline. In California at Darwin, Inyo County, associated with lime silicates and fluorite in a contact metamorphic deposit.

In Canada at the Sullivan mine, Kimberley, Kootenay district, British Columbia, fine-grained galena and sphalerite together with other sulfides in a gangue of garnet, diopside, actinolite and biotite; also at Slocan. At Buchans mine, Newfoundland, in fine-grained barite.

Alter. Easily altered to produce secondary lead minerals such as cerussite (often with formation of sulfur crystals), anglesite, pyromorphite, mimetite, phosgenite, cotunnite. Chalcocite and covellite have been found as pseudomorphs after galena. Galena has been noted as pseudomorphs after cerussite, anglesite, and pyromorphite; also after wood. Banded nodules of anglesite and cerussite with galena cores are often found (Santa Eulalia).

Artif.[11] Formed in the laboratory in numerous ways: (a) A mixture of $PbCl_2$ and $NaHCO_3$ with H_2S in a sealed tube produces galena after standing for several months; (b) pyrite or marcasite heated with a solution of $PbCl_2$ will react to produce galena; (c) lead nitrate when heated with ammonium sulfohydrate will yield galena. Galena is frequently observed in furnace slags.

Name. The name galena is from the Latin *galena* (γαλήνη), a name given to lead ore or the dross from melted lead. In Spanish South America, galena is called *carne de vaca*, when showing broad crystalline surfaces; when presenting small surfaces, *soroche*; when granular, *acerilla*; of a fibrous structure, *frangilla*. Galena, coarse-grained and in lumps large enough to be used to glaze potters' ware, is sometimes called *potters' ore*; also called Glasurerz *Germ.*, alquifoux *Fr.*, archifoglio *Ital.*

Ref.

1. Goldschmidt (**1**, 199, 1913), Mélon, *Soc. géol. Belgique Ann.*, **45**, 151 (1913). Rare, vicinal, and uncertain forms:

0·1·15	1·1·36	1·1·11	2·2·13	1·40·40	277	128
0·1·10	1·1·16	1·1·10	115	1·14·14	477	2·3·10
014	1·1·15	119	227	199	455	125
012	1·1·13	118	447	166	9·10·10	3·5·10
1·1·40	1·1·12	2·2·15	335	155	2·3·20	234

2. *Strukturber.*, I, 131, 1913–28.
3. On the genetic significance of habit see Kalb and Koch, *Cbl. Min.*, 309 (1929), and Obenauer, *Jb. Min., Beil.-Bd.*, **65**, 87 (1932). On etching, Becke, *Min. Mitt.*, **6**, 237 (1884); **9**, 16 (1887), and Ichikawa, *Am. J. Sc.*, **42**, 111 (1916). On " lineage " and composite structure, Buerger, *Am. Min.*, **17**, 177 (1932), and Sadebeck, *Zs. deutsche geol. Ges.*, **26**, 617 (1874).
4. Seifert, *Jb. Min., Beil.-Bd.*, **57**, 690 (1928), regards lamellar twinning also on {233} as nearly certain, and on several other planes. Twinning on {133} not confirmed. Rosický, *Zs. Kr.*, **71**, 326 (1929), describes a penetration twin on {025} or {037} from Ratibořice, Bohemia.
5. Taricco, *Acc. Linc., Att.*, **19**, 508 (1910).
6. Mügge, *Jb. Min.*, I, 123, 1898. For other deformation experiments see Buerger, *Am. Min.*, **13**, 1 (1928) and Osborne and Adams *Econ. Geol.*, **26**, 884 (1931).
7. When galena contains Bi it cleaves on {111} according to Goldschmidt, *Strukturber*, I, 131, 1913–28. Seifert (1928) concludes, however, that the octahedral separation is not cleavage but parting on {111} glide planes and is independent of composition. This plane of separation disappears on heating. Tertsch, *Zs. Kr.*, **85**, 17 (1933), considers that planes other than {001} are not cleavage planes. See also Neuhaus, *Chem. Erde*, **12**, 23 (1938), and Wahlstrom, *Am. Min.*, **22**, 906 (1937), on oriented platy intergrowths of tetradymite (?) along {111} as a cause of the octahedral parting.
8. Schneiderhöhn and Ramdohr (**2**, 242, 1931).
9. For silver minerals in galena see Nissen and Hoyt, *Econ. Geol.*, **10**, 172 (1915). For solubility of other elements in PbS see Friedrich, *Metall.*, 4, 479, 671 (1907); 5, 116 (1908); and Doelter (4 [1], 406, 1925). For old analyses see Doelter (1925). Varieties based on supposed chemical differences (Dana [51, 1892]) are not well established. U-galena of Kerr, *Am. Min.*, **20**, 443 (1935), from Bedford, New York, contains uranium-derived lead of isotope Pb[206].
10. General work on occurrence, Lindgren (423, 566, 589, 598, 691, 724, 1933).
11. Doelter (1925).

QUIROGITE. Quiroguite *Navarro* (*An. soc. españ. hist. nat., Actas*, 24, 96, 1895). A supposedly tetragonal lead-antimony sulfide from the San Andrés and other mines in the Sierra Almagrera, Spain. Named after the Spanish mineralogist, F. Quiroga. Probably an impure galena in distorted crystals.[1]

Ref.

1. Schrauf (cited in Spencer, *Min. Mag.*, **11**, 241 [1897]).

2612 **C L A U S T H A L I T E** [PbSe]. Selenblei *Zinken* (1823; *Ann. Phys.*, **2**, 415, 1824; 3, 271, 1825); *Rose* (*Ann. Phys.*, **2**, 415, 1824; 3, 281, 1825). Plomb sélénié *Fr.* Clausthalie *Beudant* (2, 531, 1832).

Kobalt-Bleiglanz *Hausmann* (*Nordd. Beitr. Berg.- u. Hüttenk.*, 3, 120). Kobaltbleierz *Hausmann* (183, 1813), *Stromeyer* and *Hausmann* (*Göttingen gel. Anz.*, 329, 1825). Selenkobaltblei, Selenkupferblei, Selenbleikupfer *Rose* (*Ann. Phys.*, 3, 288, 290, 1825). Selenkupferbleiglanz *Glocker* (429, 1831; 292, 1839). Tilkerodite *Haidinger* (566, 1845A). Zorgite *Brooke* and *Miller* (153, 1852). Lehrbachite *Brooke* and *Miller* (153, 1852). Rhaphanosmit *von Kobell* (6, 1853).

C r y s t. Isometric; hexoctahedral. — $4/m\,\bar{3}\,2/m$.
Structure cell.[1] Space group $Fm3m$; a_0 6.162; contains Pb$_4$Se$_4$.
Habit. Massive, commonly fine granular, sometimes foliated.

P h y s. Cleavage {001} good. Fracture granular. H. $2\frac{1}{2}$–3. G. 7.8; 8.079 (calc.). Luster metallic. Color lead-gray, somewhat bluish. Streak darker. M.P. 1065° to 1088°. Opaque. In polished section[2] isotropic. Reflection percentages: green 50, orange 43, red 40.

C h e m. Selenide of lead, PbSe. Hg, Ag, Cu, Co, Fe may be present in small amounts, probably owing to admixed impurities.

Tests. F.2. Decrepitates in closed tube. B.B. on charcoal, partially fusible, largely volatile. Soluble in HNO_3.

O c c u r. In Germany at Clausthal, Lehrbach, Tilkerode, and Zorge in the Harz Mountains, with other selenides, in Saxony at Reinsberg, north of Freiberg. In Spain at the Rio Tinto mines, Huelva Province. In Sweden at Fahlun. In Argentina at Cerro de Cacheuta, on the Mendoza River. Reported from Kweichow, China.

N a m e. From the locality, at Clausthal, Germany.

The following have been shown to be mixtures containing clausthalite as one of the principal constituents.[3]

TILKERODITE. *Haidinger* (566, 1845A) is a mixture of clausthalite, cobaltite, and hematite.

ZORGITE. Selenblei mit Selenkupfer *Rose* (*Ann. Phys.*, **2**, 415, 1824). Selenkupferblei, Selenbleikupfer *Rose* (*Ann. Phys.*, **3**, 293, 294, 296, 1825). Selenkupferbleiglanz *Glocker* (429, 1831; 292, 1839). Zorgite *Brooke* and *Miller* (153, 1852). Rhaphanosmit *Kobell* (6, 1853). Glasbachite *Adam* (52, 1869).

A supposed selenide of lead and copper, reported from Tilkerod and Zorge in the Harz, from Glasbach, Thuringia, and from Cacheuta, Mendoza, Argentina. The analyses[4] varied widely. Shown[5] to be a mixture of clausthalite and umangite, in part with tiemannite and an unidentified green birefringent mineral.

Ref.

1. Oldhausen, *Zs. Kr.*, **61**, 463 (1925), no locality given. Ramsdell, *Am. Min.*, **10**, 281 (1925), obtained $a_0 = 6.14$ Å on synthetic material.
2. Schneiderhöhn and Ramdohr (**2**, 262, 1931).
3. Frebold, *Cbl. Min.*, 16, 1927; also for zorgite, Murdoch (39, 1916).
4. Dana (54, 1892); Geilmann and Wrigge, *Zs. anorg. Chem.*, **197**, 362 (1931).
5. Frebold, *Cbl. Min.*, 22, 1927; Olsacher, *Cbl. Min.*, 170, 1927; Geilmann and Wrigge (1931).

2613   **A L T A I T E** [PbTe]. Tellurblei *Rose* (*Ann. Phys.*, **18**, 68, 1830). Elasmose *Huot* (**1**, 1841); *d'Halloy* (1833). [Not the elasmose (= nagyagite) of *Beudant* (**2**, 539, 1832).] Altait *Haidinger* (556, 1845A). Plomo telural *Domeyko*.

C r y s t. Isometric; hexoctahedral — $4/m\ \bar{3}\ 2/m$.

Forms:[1]

$$a\{001\} \qquad o\{111\} \qquad \beta\{223\}$$

Structure cell.[2] Space group $Fm3m$. a_0 6.439 ± 0.006; contains Pb_4Te_4.

Habit. Usually massive. Rarely in cubes and cubo-octahedrons.

Gliding. $T\{001\}$, $t[1\bar{1}0]$,[3] as for galena.

P h y s. Cleavage {001} perfect.[4] Fracture subconchoidal. Sectile.

H. 3.   G. 8.15; 8.274 (calc.).   Luster metallic.   Color tin-white with a yellowish tinge tarnishing to bronze-yellow.   Opaque.   In polished section[5] isotropic.   Reflection percentages: green 61, orange 55, red 52.

C h e m.   Telluride of lead, PbTe.   Small amounts of Ag, Au, Cu, and Fe reported in analyses are probably present as impurities.

Anal.

	1	2	3	4	5
Pb	61.91	62.60	61.52	61.33	60.71
Ag	.....	.....	.....	0.43	1.17
Au	.....	.....	.....	0.02	0.26
Cu	.....	.....	.....	0.01	.....
Fe	.....	.....	.....	0.13	.....
Te	38.09	37.40	38.48	38.43	37.31
Se				0.08	
Total	100.00	100.00	100.00	100.43	99.45
G.	8.274		8.060	8.223	

1. PbTe.   2. Choukpazat, Upper Burma.   Recalc. after deducting 5.90 per cent quartz.[6] 3. Red Cloud mine, Boulder Co., Colo.   Recalc. after deducting small amounts of impurities.[7] 4. Kalgoorlie.[8] 5. Stanislaus mine.   Some petzite present.[9]

Tests.   F.1.5.   Gives fumes of TeO_2 in open tube, forming a white sublimate.   Usual reactions for Pb and Te.

O c c u r.   Altaite occurs with native gold, other tellurides and sulfides in veins.   It has been found near Ziryanovsk in the Altai Mountains. Province of Semipalatinsk, Siberia, associated with hessite.   At Kalgoorlie, Western Australia with other tellurides.   In Chile, at the Condorriaco mine, Coquimbo, east of Arqueros.   In North Carolina at the King's Mountain mine, Gaston County, in quartz with gold, galena, pyrite, tetrahedrite, and rarely nagyagite; in Colorado at a number of the mines of Goldhill, Boulder County, with native tellurium, sylvanite, pyrite, siderite, and quartz; in New Mexico, near Las Cruces, in the Organ Mountains, Dona Ana County; in California at the Stanislaus mine, Carson Hill, Calaveras County, with hessite and petzite; at the Golden Rule mine, near Tuttletown, and at Sawmill Flat, Tuolumne County; at Nevada City, Nevada County.   Has been reported from several localities in British Columbia.

A r t i f.[10]   Prepared by melting the components together in an atmosphere of nitrogen.

N a m e.   After the locality in the Altai Mountains.

HENRYITE.   *Endlich (Eng. Mining J.,* Aug. 29, 1874), is a mixture of altaite and pyrite.

Ref.

1. Eakle, *Univ. California Dept. Geol. Bull. 2,* 315 (1901).
2. Goldschmidt, *Vidensk. Skr. Oslo, Mat.-Nat. Kl.* pt. 8, 43, 1927, on artificial material.
3. Buerger, *Am. Min.,* **15**, 169 (1930).
4. Octahedral cleavage noted for the Kalgoorlie altaite.

5. Schneiderhöhn and Ramdohr (2, 264, 1931); Fastré *C. R.*, **196**, 630 (1933), gets higher values with the photo-electric cells, 465 mμ 74, 527 mμ 70, 589 mμ 64 ± 0.01 per cent.
6. Louis, *Min. Mag.*, **11**, 215 (1897).
7. Genth, *Am. Phil. Soc., Proc.*, **14**, 225 (1874).
8. Simpson, *Western Australian Geol. Sur. Bull. 42*, 94 (1912).
9. Genth, *Am. J. Sc.*, **45**, 312 (1868).
10. Goldschmidt (1927).

2614   **ALABANDITE** [MnS].   Schwarze Blende *v. Reichenstein* (*Phys. Arb. Wien*, 1, 2nd quart. 86, 1784); *Bindheim* (*Ges. Nat. Freunde Berlin, Schr.*, 5, 452, 1784). Schwarzerz *Klaproth* (3, 35, 1802). Braunsteinkies *Leonhard* (70, 1806). Braunsteinblende, Manganblende *Blumenbach* (1, 707, 1807). Manganglanz *Karsten* (72, 1808). Manganese sulfuré *Haüy* (3, 1809). Schwefel Mangan *Germ.* Alabandine *Beudant* (2, 399, 1832). Blumenbachit *Breithaupt* (*B. H. Ztg.*, **22**, 193, 1866).

C r y s t. Isometric; hexoctahedral[1] — $4/m$ $\bar{3}$ $2/m$.

Forms:[2]

$$a\{001\} \quad d\{011\} \quad o\{111\} \quad n\{112\}$$

Structure cell. Space group $Fm3m$; a_0 5.214,[3] contains Mn$_4$S$_4$.
Twinning. Twin plane $\{111\}$, simple twins, sometimes repeated. Lamellar twinning visible in polished section.
Habit. Cubic, octahedral. Granular massive.
P h y s. Cleavage $\{001\}$ perfect. Fracture uneven. Brittle. H. $3\frac{1}{2}$–4. G. 4.0±; 4.050 (calc.). Luster submetallic, color iron-black, tarnishing brown on exposure. Streak green.
O p t. Under microscope green transmission in very thin splinters. n_{Li} 2.70 ± 0.02. Isotropic.[4] Reflection percentages: green 24, orange 21, red 20.[5]
C h e m. Manganese sulfide, MnS.
Anal.

	1	2
Mn	63.14	63.03
S	36.86	36.91
Total	100.00	99.94
G.	4.050	4.031−4.040

1. MnS. 2. Arizona.[6]

Tests. Unchanged in the closed tube. Soluble in dilute HCl with evolution of H$_2$S.

O c c u r.[7] Alabandite occurs in vein deposits presumably of the epithermal type. The sulfides most commonly associated are sphalerite, galena, and pyrite, and gangue minerals are chiefly quartz, calcite, rhodochrosite, and rhodonite, with some of the rare manganese silicates occasionally associated (Eureka Gulch). Occurs in Roumania in the gold-bearing veins of Kapnik, and Offenbánya, and Nagyág, associated with tellurium, rhodochrosite, and quartz. In Saxony at Gersdorf west of

Berggieshübel. In Asia Minor at Alabanda in Aïdin. In France at Adervielle, Hautes-Pyrénées. In Peru at Morococha, Province of Junin. In Mexico at Puebla in the Preciosa mine on Cerro Tlachiaque. In Japan at Saimyoji, Ugo. In the United States at a number of western localities; fairly abundant at the Lucky Cuss mine, Tombstone, Arizona; in Bisbee at the Higgins mine. In Colorado at the Queen of the West mine on Snake River, Summit County, in crystals and as massive material with rhodochrosite, galena, argentite and pyrite; at Eureka Gulch with oxidized manganese minerals including some of the rare manganese silicates. In Nevada at Schellbourne in White Pine County; in Montana at Wickes.

A r t i f.[8] Produced by passing H_2S over a manganese salt at dull red heat.

N a m e. From the locality, Alabanda, Aïdin, Asia Minor.

Ref.

1. Generally classed with sphalerite. The supposed tetrahedral symmetry due to Peters, *Jb. Min.*, 665, 1861, and Moses, *Zs. Kr.*, **22**, 18 (1894). The drawings of Haidinger-Mohs (1825) and Schrauf, *Ann. Phys.*, **127**, 348 (1866), are holohedral. Wyckoff, *Am. J. Sc.*, **2**, 239 (1921) gives a structure consistent with holohedral symmetry, or with lower classes. Ott, without published evidence, *Zs. Kr.*, **63**, 222 (1926), considers alabandite to be holohedral. Goldschmidt (**8**, 44, 1927) assigns the holohedral rock-salt structure to artificial MnS. The evidence for tetrahedral symmetry is inadequate; the structural work and physical characteristics indicate that alabandite is more closely related to galena than to sphalerite.
2. Peters (1861), Schrauf (1866), Moses (1894).
3. Wyckoff (1921).
4. Larsen (36, 1921).
5. Schneiderhöhn and Ramdohr (**2**, 100, 1931). A calculation of the refractive index from the reflectivities using Fresnel's relationship gives n_{Li} 2.62.
6. Moses (1894).
7. Hewett and Rove, *Econ. Geol.*, **25**, 36 (1930), for a comprehensive discussion of the occurrence.
8. Further details in Doelter (4 [1], 483, 1925).

KANEITE. *Kane* (*Q. J. Sc.*, **28**, 381, 1829); *Haidinger* (559, 1845A) is a dubious species with the supposed composition MnAs. Has not yet been confirmed.

PLUMBOMANGANITE. *Hannay* (*Min. Mag.*, **1**, 151, 1877), a manganese lead sulfide of unknown source and not shown to be a valid species.

YOUNGITE. *Hannay* (*Min. Mag.*, **1**, 152, 1877; **2**, 88, 1878), is of doubtful homogeneity, containing S, Pb, Zn, Fe, and Mn.

2615　　OLDHAMITE [CaS]. *Maskelyne* (1862; *Phil. Trans.*, **160**, 195, 1870).

C r y s t. Isometric; hexoctahedral,[1] — $4/m\ \bar{3}\ 2/m$.

Structure cell.[2] Space group $Fm3m$; a_0 5.686 $\pm$ 0.006; contains Ca_4S_4.

Habit. Small spherules.

P h y s. Cleavage {001}. H. 4. G. 2.58;[3] 2.589 (calc.). Color pale chestnut-brown, transparent. Isotropic. n_{Na} 2.137 (artif.).[3]

C h e m. Calcium sulfide, CaS; with some Mg reported as substituting for the Ca. Theoretical composition Ca 55.55, S 44.45, total 100.00.

Anal.

	1	2
Ca	44.86	44.03
Mg	1.26	1.23
S	37.56	36.86
Osbornite	0.28	0.30
Enstatite	1.53	1.15
Gypsum	3.57	3.68
Calcite	3.10	....
Troilite	.....	2.02
Insoluble	7.64	8.46
Fe	0.51	0.26
Total	100.31	97.99

1, 2. Impure oldhamite. Busti meteorite.

Tests. B.B. Infusible. Readily dissolved in HCl with evolution of H_2S and deposition of sulfur. Decomposed by boiling water.

O c c u r. Found embedded in enstatite or augite in the Busti meteorite, India, and apparently also that of Bishopville, South Carolina. Probably in other meteorites.[4]

A l t e r. Coated by calcium sulfate as an alteration.

N a m e. After T. Oldham (1816–78), director of the Indian Geological Survey (1850–76).

Ref.

1. Artificial CaS, Davy, *Phys. Rev.*, **21**, 213 (1923), has the galena structure, and it is inferred that oldhamite is identical with the artificial material. In a private communication of November, 1938, F. A. Bannister of the British Museum reports as follows: "Occurs as reddish nodules up to 3 mm. across in the Busti meteorite. These are single crystals without external faces but they possess good cubic cleavage directions. An x-ray photograph confirms that each nodule is a single crystal and gives a pattern to be expected for a compound with the rock-salt structure. The cubic cell edge is 5.675."
2. Davy (1923) artificial.
3. For artificial material, Spangenberg, *Naturwiss.*, **15**, 266 (1927) gives 2.71 as density.
4. Farrington (138, 1915).

262   SPHALERITE GROUP

ISOMETRIC — HEXTETRAHEDRAL

			a_0	G.
2621	Sphalerite	(Zn,Fe)S	5.400	4.083
2622	Metacinnabar	(Hg,Fe,Zn)S	5.854	7.65
2623	Tiemannite	HgSe	6.069	8.26
2624	Coloradoite	HgTe	6.444	8.092

The members of the sphalerite group have the tetrahedral coordination structure possessed by many other compounds of the AX type. The space group is $F\bar{4}3m$; the unit cell contains 8 atoms. The structure is reflected in the crystal habit, which is tetrahedral, where known. All except sphalerite have a metallic luster. Isomorphism in this group is common. Sphalerite commonly contains Fe substituting for Zn in part, but not more than 26·per cent, and no straight Fe member of the sphalerite group is known.

The structure is closely related to diamond and also to chalcopyrite, tetrahedrite, colusite, and to the sulfosalt famatinite. In these, such a relation is suggested by the crystal habit, and also by frequent intergrowths of the sulfides with sphalerite.

2621 **S P H A L E R I T E** [ZnS]. Galena inanis *Germ.* Blende *Agricola* (465, 1546). Blände, Pseudo-galena, Zincum S, As, et Fe mineralisatum *Wallerius* (248, 1747). Zincum cum Fe, S mineralisatum *Bergmann* (1782). Sulphuret of zinc. Zinc sulfuré *Fr.* Zinc Blende. Sphalerit *Glocker* (17, 1847). Black-Jack, Mock-Lead, False Galena, Ruby blende, Ruby zinc, *Engl.* and *Amer. miners.* Blende or Zinkblende, Schalenblende pt., Leberblende, *Germ.* Blenda, *Ital., Span.* Chumbe *Span. S. A.*

Cleiophane *Nuttal* (in *Henry, Phil. Mag.*, **1**, 23, 1851). Cramerite *Henry* (*Phil. Mag.*, **1**, 23, 1851). Marmatite *Boussingault* (*Ann. Phys.*, **17**, 399, 1829). Przibramite *Huot* (298, 1841). Newboldite *Piddington* (*J. Asiatic Soc. Bengal*, **26**, 1129, 1847). Merasmolite *Shepard* (*Am. J. Sc.*, **12**, 210, 1851). Christophit *Breithaupt* (*B. H. Ztg.*, **22**, 27, 1863). Rahtite *Shepard* (*Am. J. Sc.*, **41**, 209, 1866). Gumucionit *Herzenberg* (*Cbl. Min.*, 77, 1933). Brunckite *Herzenberg* (*Zbl. Min.*, 373, 1938).

C r y s t. Isometric; hextetrahedral — $\bar{4}\ 3\ m$.

Forms:[1]

a 001	h 014	$-\omega\ \bar{1}15$	$-\tau\ \bar{2}27$	$\gamma\ \bar{2}25$	q 133	Z $\bar{3}57$
d 011	e 012	$\mu\ 114$	m 113	n 112	p 122	
o 111	g 023	$-\mu\ \bar{1}14$	$-m\ \bar{1}13$	$-n\ \bar{1}12$	$-p\ \bar{1}22$	
$-o\ \bar{1}11$	$-\phi\ \bar{1}16$	$\tau\ 227$	$\gamma\ 225$	$-\beta\ 223$	$-s\ \bar{1}23$	

Commonest forms: *a d o —o m —m n —n —p —s.*

Since the majority of the secondary forms and all the well-established hextetrahedrons lie in the negative octants, the form development may be used as a guide to orientation. Vicinals and face markings are also useful, but unequivocal orientation is best obtained by etch tests. Relative size and luster do not distinguish {111} from {$\bar{1}$11}.[2] Etching experiments[3] give sharply defined triangular or hexagonal pits on {111} and no figures on {$\bar{1}$11}.

Structure cell.[4] Space group $F\bar{4}3m$; a_0 5.400 ± 0.008; containing Zn$_4$S$_4$.

Habit.[5] Tetrahedral; dodecahedral; often distorted and resembling rhombohedral forms. Frequently highly complex. Curved faces common, the {113} and {011} faces often rounded together into a low conical form. Cleavable masses; coarse to fine granular; fibrous; concretionary (schalenblende); botryoidal; cryptocrystalline.

Twinning.[6] Twin axis [111]; composition surface may be parallel or perpendicular to {111}, and is not always planar. Frequently in simple or multiple contact twins or in complicated lamellar intergrowths. Sometimes in penetration fivelings. Heavy directed pressure causes pressure twinning on {111}.[7]

P h y s. Cleavage {011} perfect.[8] Fracture conchoidal. Brittle. H. $3\frac{1}{2}$–4. G. 3.9–4.1[9] (the specific gravity decreases with the increase in Fe content); 4.083 (calc.). Color commonly brown, black, yellow, also red, green, to white to nearly colorless (*cleiophane*) when pure. The high Fe content members (*marmatite*) approach black in color. Luster resinous to adamantine. Streak brownish to light yellow and white. Transparent to translucent. Pyroelectric; polar in the direction [111];[10] sometimes triboluminescent, also fluorescent[11] under ultraviolet light and x rays. Inverts to wurtzite at 1020° ± 5°, the inversion temperature decreasing with the increase in Fe content.

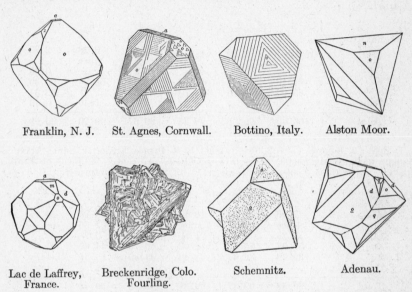

| Franklin, N. J. | St. Agnes, Cornwall. | Bottino, Italy. | Alston Moor. |

| Lac de Laffrey, France. | Breckenridge, Colo. Fourling. | Schemnitz. | Adenau. |

O p t. Isotropic. Sometimes shows birefringence probably induced by strain, which can be produced artificially. The following refractive indices are on nearly pure sphalerite (0.15 per cent Fe, from Sonora).[12]

λ	n	λ	n
420	2.517	589 (Na)	2.369
434	2.493	630	2.353
486	2.436	671 (Li)	2.340
535 (Tl)	2.399	760	2.320

With an increase in the Fe content the refractive indices increase as follows.[13]

PERCENTAGE FE	n(NA)	LOCALITY
0.15	2.3688	Sonora
5.47	2.40	Spain
10.8	2.43	Australia
17.06	2.47	Saxony

In polished section[14] isotropic; shows internal reflections in white to yellow to dark brown. Low reflectivity: green 18.5, orange 14.5, red 18 (Santander).[14]

C h e m.[15] Zinc sulfide, nearly always containing iron, (Zn,Fe)S. The maximum iron content is about 26 per cent (*christophite*). Mn, with a maximum of 5.81 per cent (Sardinia), and Cd, with a maximum of 1.66 per cent (Sardinia), are usually present in small amounts. Hg has been reported in minor amounts in some of the older analyses. Traces of In, Ga, Tl have been noted. Au and Ag have been reported in traces, but these are possibly due to impurities.

Anal.[16]

	1	2	3	4	5	6
Sn	.....	.....	.....	0.45	.....	.....
Fe	.....	0.15	.....	0.40	0.28	2.33
Mn	.....	.....	.....	.....	trace	.....
Cd	.....	.....	.....	.....	trace	0.95
Zn	67.10	66.98	65.68	65.44	65.25	63.36
S	32.90	32.78	33.33	33.38	32.21	32.94
Gangue	.....	.....	0.27	.....	1.46	0.40
Total	100.00	99.91	99.28	99.67	99.20	99.98
G.	4.084				3.96	4.05

1. ZnS. 2. Sonora. $n = 2.37$, G. 4.090.[17] 3. Prince Frederick mine, Arkansas. Gangue includes MgO 0.03, Fe_2O_3 0.15, SiO_2 0.09 per cent.[18] 4. Picos de Europa, Spain.[19] 5. Sardinia (Cantieri di Murdegu).[20] 6. Sardinia (Montevecchio).[21]

	7	8	9	10	11	12
Sn	.....	.....	.....	.....	.....	1.4
Fe	7.99	11.05	12.17	10.12	18.25	26.2
Mn	trace	.....	trace	5.81	2.66	.....
Cd	1.23	0.30	1.66	.....	0.28	.....
Zn	57.38	55.89	52.02	50.75	44.67	37.6
S	32.99	32.63	33.46	33.30	33.57	34.7
Gangue	.....	.....	.....	.....	.....	.....
Total	99.59	99.87	99.31	99.98	99.43	99.9
G.	4.13		3.89	3.99	3.911–3.923	

7. Sardinia (Gadoni, Istrizzu-Talesi).[22] 8. Bodenmais. Brownish black (marmatite).[23] 9. Sardinia (Correboi).[22] 10. Sardinia (" Su Porru " between Correboi and Fonni).[22] 11. St. Christoph mine, Isère, France (christophite).[24] 12. St. Agnes, Cornwall (christophite). Dark brown. Recalculated after deducting 14 per cent impurities.[25]

Var. *Ordinary.* Contains less than 10 per cent Fe, with the ratio of Zn : Fe > 5 : 1. Color white to light brown. *Ruby zinc* and *ruby blende* are usually within the iron content here specified. The Cd bearing so-called *pŕibramite* is likewise here included because its low Cd content is insufficient to establish a separate variety.

Ferroan. Marmatite *Boussingault* (*Ann. Phys.*, **17**, 399, 1829). Christophite *Breithaupt* (*B. H. Ztg.*, **22**, 27, 1863). Dark-colored varieties with more than 10 per cent Fe. The range in this variety is 6 : 5 > Zn : Fe > 5 : 1 with a maximum of 26 per cent Fe in christophite.

Tests. F.5. Soluble in HCl with evolution of H_2S.

Occur.[26] Sphalerite, the most common zinc mineral, and galena, the most abundant lead mineral, are intimately associated in most of the important deposits of these metals. Sphalerite has been reported in small amounts as a primary constituent of granite, and in pegmatites; often found in contact metamorphic deposits; in vein deposits in important amounts throughout the temperature range of such deposits; abundant in sedimentary (?) deposits of the Mississippi Valley type. Replacement deposits are common. Sphalerite has been reported in small amounts in lignite and coal deposits. Sphalerite sometimes contains oriented inclusions of chalcopyrite and, less commonly, tetrahedrite or stannite. A banded intergrowth of sphalerite and the hexagonal zinc sulfide wurtzite (*schalenblende*) together with galena and marcasite in concentric layers occurs in some of the sedimentary deposits.

Only those localities can be mentioned here which are of importance either because of their valuable deposits of zinc ore, or because of the beautiful mineral specimens that they furnish. Some of the chief localities are: in Czechoslovakia at Přibram, green or yellow crystals, and at Schlaggenwald as black crystals, also at Schemnitz. In Roumania at Kapnik and at Felsöbánya; in Transylvania, Roumania at Orodna, black crystals. In Saxony at Freiberg, Breitenbrunn; at Neudorf in the Harz Mountains; in Hesse-Nassau at Friedrickssegen near Ems; at Aachen (Aix-la-Chapelle) in Rhenish Prussia. In fine specimens at Bottino, near Seravezza, Tuscany; in the Binnental, Switzerland, in isolated crystals of great beauty, yellow to brown in color, in dolomite cavities. Fine specimens from France at Laffrey, Isère and Pont-Péan near Bruz, Ille-et-Vilaine. A beautiful golden transparent variety yielding large cleavage masses occurs at Picos de Europa, Santander, Spain. From Alston Moor, Cumberland, England, in black crystals; from St. Agnes and elsewhere in Cornwall; from Derbyshire, at Laxey, Isle of Man, from Weardale in Durham; in Scotland at Wanlockhead, Dumfries. Large deposits occur at Åmmeberg on Lake Vetter, Örebro, Sweden. In Japan large crystals are found at the Ani mine, Kayakusa, Ugo, and at Shiraita, Echigo. Transparent material of fine color (much like the Santander specimens) comes from the Chivera mine, Cananea, in Sonora, Mexico. From Santa Eulalia, Chihuahua, Mexico.

In the United States found at many localities, the important ore districts being in the Tri-State area and other parts of the Mississippi Valley, as described under galena; also in Wisconsin, Colorado, Montana, and Idaho, where it is mined together with galena. Localities where specimens of note have been found are: at Roxbury, Connecticut, as brownish crystals; in New Jersey at Franklin, occasional crystals of a fine white to light green color (*cleiophane*) have been found in vugs in the limestone; in New York at Balmat and Edwards, with pyrite and lime silicates; in Pennsylvania at Phoenixville in the Wheatley mine and others, near Friedensville, Lehigh County, a grayish waxlike sphalerite; at Tiffin, Ohio; in Illinois at Marsden's diggings near Galena, as stalactites some 6 in. or more in diameter and covered with crystallized marcasite and galena; in Wisconsin at Mineral Point in fine crystals often altered to smithsonite; in the Joplin district of Missouri, and the adjacent Kansas and Oklahoma area, fine crystals are being found, associated with galena, marcasite, and calcite. At Butte, Montana, exceptional specimens have been found; at

Bingham, Utah, sphalerite of octahedral habit. Twinned crystals from Breckenridge, Summit County, Colorado, are reported.

A l t e r. Changes by oxidation to the zinc sulfate goslarite. Hemimorphite, smithsonite, and limonite occur as pseudomorphs. Pseudomorphs after galena, tetrahedrite, barite, and calcite have been found.

A r t i f.[27] Produced by passing H_2S through a zinc solution in a sealed tube; by passing H_2S over heated zinc chloride.

N a m e. Sphalerite from ($\sigma\phi\alpha\lambda\epsilon\rho\delta s$), treacherous. Blende because, while often resembling galena, it yielded no lead, the word in *German* meaning *blind* or *deceiving*.

BRUNCKITE. *Herzenberg* (*Zbl. Min.*, 373, 1938).
A name given to a pulverulent massive zinc sulfide presumably of colloidal origin. White. Luster dull. Clings to the tongue. Found in the Cercapuquio mine, west of Cerro de Pasco, Peru. Named after Otto Brunck, of Freiberg, Saxony.

Ref.

1. Compiled from the more important morphological studies: Sadebeck, *Zs. deutsche geol. Ges.*, **21**, 620 (1869); Becke, *Min. Mitt.*, **5**, 457 (1883); Hochschild, *Jb. Min., Beil.-Bd.*, **26**, 151 (1908); Gebhardt, *Jb. Min., Beil.-Bd.*, **67**, 1 (1933). The established forms are largely according to Gebhardt.

Uncommon, vicinal, and uncertain forms:

018	2·2·17	449	$\bar{1}$·10·10	$\bar{3}55$	$5\cdot9\cdot21$
025	116	$\bar{4}49$	$\bar{1}88$	$\bar{5}88$	$\bar{1}34$
0·5·12	4·4·21	$\bar{4}47$	$\bar{2}\cdot15\cdot15$	$\bar{5}77$	$\bar{2}36$
079	115	$\bar{7}\cdot7\cdot11$	$\bar{1}66$	$\bar{4}55$	$5\cdot8\cdot11$
045	$\bar{6}\cdot6\cdot17$	$\bar{13}\cdot13\cdot19$	$\bar{1}44$	$9\cdot10\cdot10$	$\bar{7}\cdot11\cdot15$
1·1·12	4·4·11	$\bar{5}57$	$\bar{1}33$	$\bar{1}\cdot10\cdot11$	$\bar{2}34$
1·1·10	$\bar{3}38$	$\bar{13}\cdot13\cdot18$	$\bar{3}88$	159	345
$\bar{1}18$	$\bar{5}\cdot5\cdot12$	$\bar{4}45$	$\bar{2}55$	168	$\bar{5}79$
$\bar{2}29$	$\bar{3}37$	$\bar{10}\cdot10\cdot13$	$\bar{10}\cdot19\cdot19$	$\bar{1}36$	

2. The distinction between positive and negative octants is discussed by Sadebeck (1869); Becke (1883); Hochschild (1908); Kalb, *Zs. Kr.*, **76**, 386 (1931); Gebhardt (1933).

3. Gebhardt (1933) whose etching results largely agree with those of Hochschild (1908) and Becke (1883). A hot 10 per cent HCl sol. acting 10–20 minutes on polished surfaces, used in the etching experiments. The {$\bar{1}11$} surface produces no regular etch pits but is strongly attacked and becomes matte and velvety.

4. Bragg, *Roy. Soc. London, Proc.*, **89A**, 468 (1913). The cell edge value here used by Harting (on Santander material) *Ak. Wiss. Berlin, Ber.*, **79**, (1926); de Jong on sphalerite from the same locality obtained $a_0 = 5.395 \pm 0.005$, *Zs. Kr.*, **66**, 515 (1928). For the relation of form to structure see Niggli, *Zs. Kr.*, **63**, 49 (1926) — p. 95 for sphalerite. The structure of wurtzite, the hexagonal modification of ZnS, is related to that of sphalerite so that {111} of sphalerite corresponds to {0001} of wurtzite (see Aminoff, *Zs. Kr.*, **58**, 203 [1923]).

5. For relation between habit and occurrence see Kalb and Koch, *Cbl. Min.*, 353, 1929.

6. Hochschild (1908) distinguished the sphalerite law (hextetrahedral) from the spinel law (hexoctahedral).

7. Buerger, *Am. Min.*, **13**, 35 (1928), has shown that applied pressure produces twinning and not translation gliding as reported by .Veit, *Jb. Min., Beil.-Bd.*, **45**, 121 (1921).

8. For the relation of cleavage to structure see Tertsch, *Min. Mitt.*, **35**, 13 (1921).

9. Allen, Crenshaw, and Merwin, *Am. J. Sc.* **34**, 341 (1912), relate the specific gravity to the iron content as follows: 0.2 per cent FeS, G. 4.090; 8.6 per cent, G. 4.030; 17.0 per cent, G. 3.98; 28.2 per cent, G. 3.935.

10. Friedel, *Bull. soc. min.*, **2**, 31 (1879).

11. Sphalerite from Tsumeb strongly triboluminescent and fluorescent, Spencer, *Min. Mag.*, **21**, 388 (1927). The sphalerite of the ore body at Franklin is fluorescent.

Early fluorescent screens for x-ray work were made of ZnS. Further details on fluorescence of sphalerite (*Handb. der Experimental Phys.*, **23** [1], 1928 [Leipzig]).

12. By Merwin, in Allen, Crenshaw, and Merwin (p. 385, 1912). The older values of Ramsay, *Zs. Kr.*, **12**, 218 (1886), are not more accurate, and the composition was not given. For the effect of temperature on the refractive indices, Friedel, *Bull. soc. min.*, **2**, 32 (1879); **6**, 191 (1883) and Calderon, *Zs. Kr.*, **4**, 504 (1879); **5**, 113 (1880).

13. Merwin, in Allen, Crenshaw, and Merwin (1912).

14. Schneiderhöhn and Ramdohr (**2**, 103, 1931).

15. The ratio of total metals to sulfur in sphalerite has been shown to be 1 : 1 by Matzke (Inaug. Diss., Breslau, 1914) and the work of Weber, *Zs. Kr.*, **44**, 212 (1908), showing an excess of sulfur is presumably in error.

16. About 90 modern analyses are listed in Doelter (4 [1], 307, 1925). Spectroscopic examination for traces are tabulated by Rimatori, *Acc. Linc., Rend.*, **14** [1], 688 (1905). For more recent spectrographic work see Stoiber, *Econ. Geol.*, **35**, 501 (1940), Borovik and Prokopenko, *Bull. ac. sc. U.S.S.R., Ser. Geol.*, 341, 1938, de Rubies and de Azcona, *An. soc. españ. fis. quim.*, **35**, 180 (1937). Older chemical analyses are listed in Dana (61, 1892).

17. Allen, Crenshaw, and Merwin (1912).

18. Branner, *Am. Inst. Min. Engr., Trans.*, **31**, 572 (1902); Doelter (4 [1], 312, 1925).

19. Matzke (1914).

20. Rimatori, *Acc. Linc., Rend.*, **13** [1], 277 (1904).

21. Rimatori, *Acc. Linc., Rend.*, **12** [1], 263 (1903).

22. Rimatori (1905).

23. Thiel, Inaug. Diss., Erlangen, 1891; *Zs. Kr.*, **23**, 295 (1894).

24. Breithaupt, *B. H. Ztg.*, **22**, 27 (1863).

25. Collins, *Min. Mag.*, **3**, 91 (1879).

26. General discussion of various types of occurrence, Teas, *Am. Inst. Min. Engr., Trans.*, **59**, 68 (1918), also Lindgren (1933). An extensive list of old occurrences in Hintze (**1** [1], 550, 1900).

27. Allen, Crenshaw, and Merwin (1912). Also Doelter (1925).

ZINCSELENIDE. *Geilmann* and *Rose* (*Jb. Min., Beil.-Bd.*, **57**, 785, 1928). Supposedly found in minute grains associated with clausthalite, tiemannite, guanajuatite, cobaltite, hematite, native gold and calcite at Andreasberg, Harz Mountains, Germany. In polished section dark brown with a greenish tint; no cleavage, H. low. Thought to be ZnSe.[1] Artificial ZnSe[2] is isometric,[3] yellow in color, with G. 5.28. Probably not valid as a species.

Ref.

1. Based on the presence of ca. 0.2–0.5 per cent Zn in analyses of specimens containing mixed clausthalite, tiemannite, etc., and otherwise free from recognizable zinc minerals.

2. In Mellor (**10**, 776, 1930).

3. Zachariasen, *Zs. phys. Chem.*, **124**, 436 (1926) found a_0 5.66 and a sphalerite-type structure for artificial material.

2622 **METACINNABAR** [HgS]. *Moore* (*J. pr. Chem.*, **2**, 319, 1870; *Am. J. Sc.*, **3**, 36, 1872). Aethiops mineral. Quecksilber-Mohr, Metazinnober *Germ.* Metacinnabarite.

Schwefelselenquecksilber *Castillo* and *Burkhart* (*Jb. Min.*, 414, 1866). Guadalcazite *Adam* (59, 1869). Guadalcazarite *Petersen* (*Min. Mitt.*, 69, 1872); *Burkhart* (*Min. Mitt.*, 243, 1872). Leviglianite *D'Achiardi* (*Att. soc. tosc., Mem.*, **2**, 112, 1876). Selenschwefelquecksilber *Rose* (*Ann. Phys.*, **46**, 315, 1839). Merkur-Glanz *Breithaupt* (316, 1832). Onofrite *Haidinger* (565, 1845A).

C r y s t. Isometric; hextetrahedral — $\bar{4}\,3\,m$.

Forms:[1]

a 001	−o Ī11	e 012	ν 056	m 113	β 223
d 011	η 015	l 035	L 118	n 112	
o 111	f 013	g 023	φ 116	−n Ī12	

Structure cell.[2] Space group $F\bar{4}3m$; a_0 5.854; contains Hg_4S_4.

Habit. Tetrahedral, with rough faces; also massive.

Felsöbánya.

Twinning. Twin plane {111}, common.

Phys. Fracture subconchoidal to uneven. Brittle. H. 3. G. 7.65;[3] 7.65 (calc.). Luster metallic. Color grayish black. Streak black. Opaque. In polished section,[4] grayish white in color and isotropic; in part very weakly anisotropic and pleochroic. Exhibits lamellar twinning.

Chem. Mercuric sulfide, HgS, polymorphous with cinnabar. Small amounts of Zn and Se substitute for Hg and S, respectively.

Anal.[5]

	1	2	3	4	5	6
Hg	86.22	77.68	79.73	79.69	83.38	81.33
Fe	.....	5.36	trace	1.04	.....	.....
Zn	.....	.....	4.23	3.32	2.17	.....
Se	.....	.....	1.08	.....	.....	6.49
S	13.78	14.97	14.58	14.97	14.24	10.30
Rem.	.....	1.41	.....	.....	0.52	.....
Total	100.00	99.42	99.62	99.02	100.31	98.12
G.		7.54	7.150			

1. HgS. 2. Felsöbánya, Transylvania. Rem. is insol.[6] 3. Guadalcazar, Mexico (guadalcazarite).[7] 4. Pola de Lena, Spain.[8] 5. Levigliani, Italy (leviglianite). Rem. is FeO.[9] 6. San Onofre, Mexico (onofrite).[10]

Var. *Zincian.* Guadalcazarite. Schwefelselenquecksilber *Castillo* and *Burkhart* (*Jb. Min.*, 414, 1866). Guadalcazite *Adam* (59, 1869). Guadalcazarite *Petersen* (*Min. Mitt.*, 69, 1872); *Burkhart* (*Min. Mitt.*, 243, 1872). Leviglianite *D'Achiardi* (*Att. soc. tosc., Mem.*, 2, 112, 1876). Contains Zn in substitution for Hg to at least Zn : Hg = 1 : 6.14 (anal. 3).

Selenian. Onofrite. Selenschwefelquecksilber *Rose* (*Ann. Phys.*, 46, 315, 1839). Merkur-Glanz *Breithaupt* (316, 1832). Onofrite *Haidinger* (565, 1845A). Contains Se in substitution for S to at least Se : S = 1 : 3.9 (anal. 6).

Occur. Found associated with cinnabar, wurtzite, stibnite, marcasite, native mercury, realgar, barite, calcite, chalcedony, hydrocarbons. Found in Italy at Idria, Gorizia, in hemispherical aggregates, and at Levigliani, Tuscany (*zincian*). In definite crystals at Felsöbánya, Transsylvania. At Mernik in eastern Slovakia. In Spain near Pola de Lena, Asturias (*zincian*). Reported from Wen-Shan-Chang, Kweichow, China (*selenian*). In Mexico from San Onofre, near Plateros, northwest of Zacatecas (*selenian*). In the United States, in numerous places in California: in the Redington and other mines near Knoxville, Napa County, sometimes in crystals; in the Baker mine and elsewhere in Lake County; in considerable amounts at New Almaden, Santa Clara County; at Skaggs Springs, Sonoma County ,with curtisite and opal; at New Idria, San Benito

County. A selenian variety was reported from near Marysvale, Utah.[11] In Canada reported from Read Island, British Columbia.

A l t e r. To cinnabar. Metacinnabar inverts to the stable form of HgS (cinnabar) on heating to 400–550°. The inversion takes place at 200° in 30 per cent sulfuric acid; at 100° in ammonium sulfide.[12]

A r t i f.[13] Metacinnabar is the same as the black modification of HgS obtained in the laboratory by precipitation from solution. Obtained in relatively coarsely crystalline form by adding an excess of sodium thiosulphate to a dilute solution of sodium mercurichloride.

N a m e. From μετά, *with*, and cinnabar, because found associated with cinnabar; guadalcazarite, and onofrite from the localities.

Ref.

1. Goldschmidt (**6**, 33, 1920), Manasse, *Att. soc. tosc., Mem.*, **33**, 156, 1921, Krenner, *Cbl. Min.*, 362, 1927. Uncertain {579}.
2. Lehmann, *Zs. Kr.*, **60**, 379 (1924), showed that metacinnabar and artificial black HgS have the same structure (sphalerite type); see also Hartwig, *Ak. Berlin, Sitzber.*, 79, 1926. Cell edge of Buckley and Vernon, *Min. Mag.*, **20**, 382 (1925), on artificial material.
3. Frondel (priv. comm., 1941) by microbalance on single crystal from the Redington mine. Schrauf, *Geol. Bundesanst., Wien, Jb.*, **41**, 354 (1891), gives 7.643–7.678 on crystals from Idria.
4. Ramdohr, *Zbl. Min.*, 131, 1938.
5. For additional analyses see Doelter (**4** [1], 364, 370, 830, 1925) and Krenner (1927).
6. Vavrinecz, *Magyar Chem. Foly.*, **38**, 140 (1932) — *Min. Abs.*, **5**, 379 (1933).
7. Petersen, *Min. Mitt.*, 69, 1872.
8. Cesaro in Dory, *Zs. pr. Geol.*, 203, 1896.
9. Manasse (1921).
10. Rose, *Ann. Phys.*, **46**, 315 (1839).
11. Short (105, 1931) found supposed selenian material from Marysvale to be a mixture of sphalerite and tiemannite.
12. Allen, Crenshaw, and Merwin, *Am. J. Sc.*, **34**, 341 (1912). On the formation of metacinnabar in nature see also Dreyer, *Econ. Geol.*, **35**, 17 (1940), and Fahey, Fleischer, and Ross, *Econ. Geol.*, **35**, 465 (1940).
13. See Doelter (1925), Schwartz, *Am. Min.*, **17**, 478 (1932).

2623   **T I E M A N N I T E** [HgSe]. Selenquecksilber *Marx* (*Schweigger's J.*, **54**, 223, 1828). Selenmercur, Tiemannit *Naumann* (425, 1855).

C r y s t. Isometric; hextetrahedral — $\bar{4}\,3\,m$.

Forms:[1]

$$a\{001\} \quad o\{111\} \quad -o\{\bar{1}11\} \quad \omega\{115\} \quad m\{113\} \quad -m\{\bar{1}13\} \quad \lambda\{337\}$$

Structure cell.[2] Space group $F\bar{4}3m$; a_0 6.069 ± 0.006;   contains Hg_4Se_4.

Twinning. Twin axis [111], common.

Habit. Tetrahedral. {111} is usually dull, {$\bar{1}11$} bright. Commonly massive, compact granular. Frequently striated [1$\bar{1}$0].

P h y s. Cleavage none. Fracture uneven to conchoidal. Brittle. H. $2\frac{1}{2}$. G. 8.19 (crystals from Utah), 8.30–8.47; 8.26 (calc.). Luster metallic. Color steel-gray to blackish lead-gray. Streak nearly black. Opaque. In polished section[5] isotropic. Reflection percentages: green 30, orange 27, red 25.

C h e m. Mercuric selenide, HgSe, with small amounts of Cd and S. Other elements reported in early analyses are due to impurities.

Anal.

	1	2	3
Pb	.....	0.12	.....
Hg	71.70	75.15	69.84
Cd	.....	.....	0.34
Se	28.30	24.88	29.19
S	.....	0.20	0.37
Insol.	.....	.....	0.06
Total	100.00	100.35	99.80
G.	8.26		

1. HgSe. 2. Clausthal.[3] 3. Utah.[4]

Tests. Decrepitates in the closed tube, and, when pure, entirely sublimes, giving a black sublimate, with the upper edge reddish brown; in the open tube emits odor of selenium, and forms a sublimate with a border of mercury selenate.

O c c u r. In the Harz Mountains, Germany, occurs near Zorge, at Tilkerode and at Clausthal. In Utah, Piute County, near Marysvale in crystals with barite, manganese oxide and calcite in a vein in limestone, the ore in places being 4 ft. in thickness.

N a m e. After Tiemann, who discovered the mineral.

Ref.

1. Penfield, *Am. J. Sc.*, **29**, 450 (1885), *Zs. Kr.*, **11**, 301 (1886).
2. Hartwig, *Ak. Berlin, Ber.*, **79**, 1926. Material from the Charlotte mine, Clausthal.
3. Peterson, *Jahresber. Chem. Min.*, 919 (1866).
4. Penfield (1885).
5. Schneiderhöhn and Ramdohr (**2**, 319, 1931).

LEHRBACHITE. Selenblei mit Selenquecksilber *Rose* (*Ann. Phys.*, **2**, 418, 1824; **3**, 297, 1825). Selenquecksilberblei *Leonhard* (592, 1826), *Zincken* (*Ann. Phys.*, **3**, 277, 1825). Selenquecksilberbleiglanz *Glocker* (430, 1831; 292, 1839). Lehrbachite *Brooke* and *Miller* (153, 1852).

A supposed selenide of lead and mercury,[1] from Tilkerode and Lehrbach, in the Harz. Shown[2] to be a mixture of tiemannite and clausthalite.

Ref.

1. Analyses in Dana (53, 1892).
2. Frebold, *Cbl. Min.*, **16**, 1927. The material described by Murdoch (131, 1916) is similar in most reactions to tiemannite.

2624 **C O L O R A D O I T E** [HgTe]. *Genth* (*Am. Phil. Soc., Proc.*, **17**, 115, 1877). Kalgoorlite *Pittman* (*New South Wales Geol. Sur. Rec.*, **5**, 203, 1898). Tellurquecksilber *Germ.*

C r y s t. Isometric; hextetrahedral[1] — $\bar{4}$ 3 *m*.

Structure cell.[2] Space group $F\bar{4}3m$; a_0 6.444 ± 0.006; contains Hg_4Te_4.

Habit. Massive, granular.

P h y s. Cleavage none.[6] Brittle and friable. Fracture uneven to subconchoidal. H. $2\frac{1}{2}$. G. 8.04 (average); 8.092 (calc.). Luster metallic.

Color iron-black, inclining to gray. Opaque. In polished section[7] isotropic.

Chem. Telluride of mercury, HgTe.

Anal.[3]

	1	2	3
Hg	61.14	60.95	61.62
Te	38.86	39.38	38.43
Total	100.00	100.33	100.05
G.	8.092	8.07	8.025

1. HgTe. 2. Kalgoorlie.[4] 3. Kalgoorlie.[5]

Tests. In the open tube decrepitates slightly, fuses and yields metallic mercury as a sublimate, also TeO_2 in drops, and next to the assay, metallic Te. Soluble in HNO_3.

Occur. At Kalgoorlie (*kalgoorlite*), Western Australia, with gold and silver tellurides. Also sparingly in the Kingston, Mountain Lion, Smuggler and Ellen mines, Boulder County, Colorado.

Ref.

1. Inferred to be of tetrahedral symmetry from the similarity with sphalerite.
2. de Jong, *Zs. Kr.*, **63**, 466 (1926), who showed that coloradoite had the sphalerite struct., with a_0 6.43; also Hartwig, *Ak. Berlin, Ber.*, 79, 1926, whose value for the cell edge is here used. Material from Kalgoorlie used.
3. Older analyses made on impure material from Colorado.
4. Spencer, *Min. Mag.*, **13**, 268 (1903).
5. Simpson, *Western Australia Geol. Sur. Bull. 42*, 97 (1912).
6. Genth (1877) reported a poor cleavage {111}.
7. Schneiderhöhn and Ramdohr (**2**, 320, 1931).

263 CHALCOPYRITE GROUP

TETRAGONAL — SCALENOHEDRAL

			a_0	c_0	c_0/a_0	G.
2631	Chalcopyrite	$Cu_2Fe_2S_4$	5.24	10.30	1.9705	4.283
2632	Stannite	Cu_2FeSnS_4	5.46	10.725	1.9666	4.437

The two members of the chalcopyrite group are not identical in structure, but are closely similar and related to the sphalerite structure. The pseudo-isometric character of chalcopyrite is better seen if the axial ratio is halved (1.9705/2 = 0.9853).

2631 CHALCOPYRITE [CuFeS₂]. ? Χαλκῖτις (from Cyprus) *Aristotle.* ? Χαλκῖτις, Πυρίτης pt. *Dioscorides* (A.D. 50). ? Chalcites pt., Pyrites pt. *Pliny* (A.D. 77). Pyrites aerosus pt., Pyrites aureo colore, Geelkis, Kupferkis *Agricola* (212, 1546A). Pyrites, pt. *Germ.* Kupferkies *Gesner* (1565). Pyrites flavus, Chalcopyrites *Henckel* (1725). Gul Kopparmalm, Cuprum sulphure et ferro mineralisatum. Chalcopyrites *Wallerius* (284, 1747). Cuivre jaune, Pyrite cuivreuse *Wallerius* (**2**, 514, 1753). Copper Pyrites. Pyritous Copper. Chalcopyrite *Beudant* (**2**, 412, 1832). Towanite *Brooke* and *Miller* (182, 1852). Barnhardtite pt. *Genth* (*Am. J. Sc.*, **19**, 17, 1855). Homichlin pt. *Breithaupt* (*B. H. Ztg.*, **17**, 385, 1858). Ducktownite *Shepard* (1859). Cupropyrite *Wherry* (*Washington Ac. Sc., J.*, **10**, 494, 1920).

Kupferkies *Germ.* Cuivre pyriteux *Fr.* Kopparkis *Swed.* Kobberkis *Danish.* Calcopirite, Rame giallo, Pirite di rame *Ital.* Cobre amarillo, Bronze amarillo, Bronze de cuivre *Span.* Peacock ore pt. (when tarnished).

C r y s t. Tetragonal; scalenohedral — $\bar{4}\,2\,m$.

$$a : c = 1 : 1.9705;^1 \qquad p_0 : r_0 = 1.9705 : 1$$

Forms:[2]

		ϕ	ρ	A	$\bar{M}$
c	001	.....	0°00′	90°00′	90°00′
a	010	0°00′	90 00	90 00	45 00
m	110	45 00	90 00	45 00	90 00
g	013	0 00	33 18	90 00	67 09½
e	012	0 00	44 34½	90 00	60 15
z	011	0 00	63 05½	90 00	50 54½
p	112	45 00	54 20	54 56½	90 00
−p	1̄12	−45 00	54 20	125 03½	35 40
t	111	45 00	70 15½	48 16½	90 00
y	136	18 26	46 05	76 50	71 12½
χ	124	26 34	47 46	70 40	76 27½

Less common forms:

W	130	Q	058	h	034	d	118	r	334
i	0·7·12	π	023	X	078	x	116	δ	156
T	035	ε	0·7·10	λ	119	n	114	τ	134

Structure cell.[15] Space group, $I\bar{4}2d$; a_0 5.24, c_0 10.30; $a_0 : c_0 = 1 : 1.966$; contains $Cu_4Fe_4S_8$.

Habit. Commonly tetrahedral in aspect, the sphenoidal faces {112} large, dull in luster or oxidized and striated $\parallel$ [11̄0]; the faces of {1̄12} are small, brilliant, not striated, and not oxidized. Often modified by scalenohedral faces with striae $\parallel$ intersection with {112}. Less commonly striated in other directions. Often massive, compact; sometimes botryoidal or reniform. Crystals sometimes show pseudoisometric habits due to the nearly isometric angular relations ($\frac{1}{2}c = 0.9853$). Common forms: $c\,a\,m\,g\,z\,p\,-p\,t\,y\,x$.

Twinning. (*a*) Twin plane {112}, composition face usually {112} penetration twins, also $\perp$ {112}. Sometimes repeated as a fiveling. (*b*) Twin plane {012}, with composition face {012}. (*c*) Twin axis [001] with composition plane {110}[3](?), producing complementary penetration twins. Gliding, T\{111\}.[4]

P h y s. Cleavage {011} sometimes distinct. Fracture uneven. Brittle. H. $3\frac{1}{2}$–4. G. 4.1–4.3; 4.283 (calc.). Luster metallic. Color brass-yellow, often tarnished and iridescent. Streak greenish black. Opaque. In polished section[5] weakly anisotropic. Reflection percentages: green 41.5, orange 40.5, red 40. Lamellar and polysynthetic twinning often observed in polished section.

Chem. Sulfide of copper and iron, $CuFeS_2$. Some Ag and Au reported in analyses, also traces of Se and Tl. Indium (0.1 per cent) reported in chalcopyrite from Cornwall.

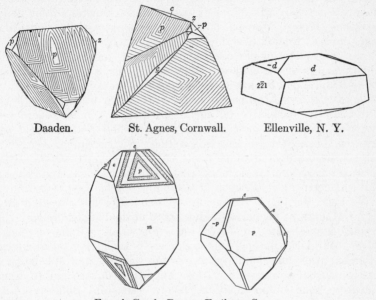

Daaden.   St. Agnes, Cornwall.   Ellenville, N. Y.

French Creek, Pa.   Freiberg, Saxony.

Anal.

	1	2	3	4	5	6
Cu	34.64	33.60	33.10	31.5	33.54	34.36
Fe	30.42	30.92	30.60	32.4	31.78	30.61
S	34.94	34.90	35.12	36.5	33.97	35.01
SiO_2	....	......	1.43	.....	0.90	.....
Total	100.00	99.42	100.25	100.4	100.19	99.98
G.	4.283	4.170	4.120			

1. $CuFeS_2$. 2. Wheal Towan, St. Agnes, Cornwall.[6] 3. Syrianowski mine, western Altai.[7] 4. Insizwa, South Africa.[8] 5. Arakawa mine, Japan. Average of two analyses.[9] 6. Erora, Portugal.[10]

Tests. In C.T. decrepitates and gives a sublimate of S. On charcoal fuses to a magnetic globule. Soluble in HNO_3, with separation of S.

Occur.[11] Chalcopyrite is the most widely occurring copper mineral, and one of the most important sources of that metal. Many sulfide ore deposits have more or less chalcopyrite in them, but the mesothermal and hypothermal vein deposits carry notable amounts of the mineral and some of the important sources of copper are in such ore bodies. In the hypothermal deposits pyrite is the important associated mineral, with tourmaline (Braden) and quartz (Prince William Sound) as important gangue minerals; cassiterite is sometimes associated (Cornwall) in the high temperature type. Mesothermal deposits of chalcopyrite contain large amounts of pyrite (Mount Lyell, Rio Tinto). Small amounts of chalcopyrite, associated with pyrite and other sulfides, are frequently found in sediments (southeastern United States). Contact metamorphic deposits in limestone (Bisbee, Morenci, Silver Bell, Arizona; Seven Devils, Idaho) contain garnet, tremolite and other lime silicates associated with the mineral. Some deposits of close magmatic affiliations (Sulitjelma) contain notable amounts of chalcopyrite. The mineral is an invariable associate of pyrrhotite and pentlandite in the sulfide ores of nickel.

Chalcopyrite forms intimate intergrowths, often oriented, with other minerals, notably sphalerite, tetrahedrite, cubanite. It has been noted as an oriented growth on galena and sphalerite, and tetrahedrite crystals coated with chalcopyrite in oriented position have been found.

Only those localities in which fine specimens or important ore deposits of the metal are found can be listed here. In Czechoslovakia at Schemnitz and at Schlaggenwald, Bohemia; at Kitzbubel, Tyrol, Austria, with pyrite, ankerite, and siderite; in Saxony in well-defined crystals at Freiberg; in the Harz Mountains region at Rammelsberg in the banded ore with sphalerite, galena, and barite; in Westphalia at Siegen, often in fine crystals; in the Mansfeld district in the " kupferschiefer." In Tuscany at Montecatini and Massa Marittima with pyrite, bornite, galena, and sphalerite. In France as unusual crystals at Ste. Marie aux Mines, Alsace, and at the mine of Gardette near Bourg d'Oisans, Isère; also from Baigorry, Basses-Pyrénées. In Spain at Rio Tinto, Huelva, where the chalcopyrite is disseminated in a pyrite ore body which has been worked since Phoenician times. At Fahlun, Sweden, occurs with pyrite and pyrrhotite with andalusite, spinel, and garnet. At Sulitjelma, Norway, with pyrite, sphalerite, and pyrrhotite. In Cornwall in crystals and botryoidal masses associated with cassiterite and quartz in the tin veins at Camborne, Carn Brea, Liskeard, Redruth, and other localities. From Laxey on the Isle of Man, and Tavistock, Devonshire.

In Chile at the Braden mine with pyrite, bornite, carbonates, tourmaline, and anhydrite. In Peru at Morococha. In Mexico at the Los Pilares mine, Nacozari district, occurs with pyrite in a rhyolite breccia.

In Japan fine crystal groups are found at Ani and Arakawa, Province of Ugo. At Mount Lyell, Tasmania, with pyrite; at Cobar, New South Wales.

In the United States it is found in New York, St. Lawrence County, at the Rossie lead mines in crystals; in very large crystals and massive at Ellenville, Ulster County. In Pennsylvania in exceptional crystals at the French Creek mines, Chester County. In Missouri at Joplin in crystals on sphalerite and galena. At Ducktown, Tennessee, with pyrite, pyrrhotite, sphalerite, magnetite, and various silicate gangue minerals. At Jerome, Arizona; at Silver Bell, with garnet. In New Mexico in San Miguel County and other southwestern localities in the sandstone " red-bed " deposits, with other copper sulfides and pyrite. In Utah at the Cactus mine, San Francisco district, with pyrite, tourmaline, and quartz, and in the Beaver Lake district with molybdenite in a quartz pegmatite. In Alaska occurs at Prince William Sound with pyrite, pyrrhotite, and cubanite in a quartz gangue.

In Canada chalcopyrite occurs in the gold-quartz veins at the Noranda mine, Rouyn district, Quebec, with pyrite, pyrrhotite, sphalerite, and as gangue minerals amphibole, cordierite, chlorite, and sericite. In Ontario, at Sudbury, with the nickel ores; at the Britannia mine, near Vancouver, British Columbia; in Manitoba at the Flin Flon mine, with other sulfides and gold.

Alter.[12] Changes to a sulfate on exposure, with moisture, especially if heated. Alters to chalcocite, covellite, chrysocolla, malachite, melaconite, and iron oxides. The following pseudomorphs after chalcopyrite have been observed: copper, chalcocite, bornite, pyrite, tetrahedrite, calcite, and iron oxide. Chalcopyrite has been found as pseudomorphs after tetrahedrite, pyrrhotite, chalcocite, and other species.

Artif. May be prepared by (a) fusing pyrite and copper sulfide together; (b) gently heating cupric and ferric oxides in an atmosphere of H_2S. Chalcopyrite-bornite intergrowths may be made to form a homogeneous phase at 550° having a structure similar to that of chalcopyrite.[13]

Name. Named from χαλκός, brass, and pyrites by Henckel, who observes in his *Pyritology* (1725) that chalcopyrite is a good distinctive name for the ore. Aristotle calls the copper ore of Cyprus *chalcitis*; and Dioscorides uses the same word; but what ore was intended is doubtful. There is no question that copper-pyrites was included by Greek and Latin authors under the name *pyrites*.

BARNHARDTITE. *Genth* (*Am. J. Sci.*, **19**, 17, 1855) has been shown[14] to be chalcopyrite partly altered to chalcocite and covellite.

HOMICHLIN. *Breithaupt* (*B. H. Ztg.*, **17**, 385, 1858), is chalcopyrite partly altered to limonite and chalcocite.

DUCKTOWNITE. *Shepard* (1859) is a mixture of pyrite and chalcocite.

Ref.

1. Measurements of Haidinger, *Mem. Wern. Soc.*, 4, 1 (1822). Ratio from structure cell by Pauling and Brockway, *Zs. Kr.*, **82**, 188 (1932). Friedel (286, 1904) also suggested this ratio. Transformation Haidinger to Pauling 100|010|002.
2. Forms in Goldschmidt (5, 71, 1918). Tschermak (449, 1921); DeAngelis, *Ist. Lombardo, Rend.*, **57**, 265 (1924); Oebike, *Zs. Kr.*, **60**, 502 (1924); Mauritz, *Zs. Kr.*, **60**, 504 (1924); Andreatta, *Acc. Padova, Att.*, **20**, 1929; Ungemach (unpublished notes); Tokody, *Jb. Min.*, I, 532, 1936; Ito (136, 1937). Rare or uncertain forms:

0·3·16	045	1·1·14	$\bar{3}$34	1·12·24	4·7·12
015	056	1·1·12	556	$\bar{1}$·9·24	$\bar{4}$·7·12
105	0·9·10	1·1·10	13·13·14	$\bar{1}$·8·20	123
014	0·10·11	$\bar{1}$·1·10	$\bar{1}$11	1·7·14	$\bar{1}$23
0·5·18	0·13·14	$\bar{1}$·1·8	887	$\bar{1}$·3·12	$\bar{4}$·5·11
0·3·10	0·15·16	$\bar{1}$16	554	3·6·32	358
038	0·17·18	$\bar{1}$14	11·11·8	1·5·10	2·11·5
025	0·23·24	3·3·10	332	$\bar{2}$·5·13	5·7·12
0·31·64	0·16·15	5·5·16	774	156	132

0·9·16	076	3·3·8	221	3·5·16	$\bar{1}42$
0·5·9	054	7·7·18	$\bar{2}21$	2·5·10	152
0·11·18	032	225	773	145	$\bar{2}·5·3$
0·7·11	0·11·6	5·5·12	552	3·7·14	5·13·6
0·9·14	021	13·13·30	772	$\bar{1}24$	121
0·17·26	031	5·5·11	11·11·2	237	231
057	072	7·7·12	1·20·80	257	4·14·1
0·31·40	1·1·16	223	1·15·30	236	

3. Buerger and Buerger, *Am. Min.*, **19**, 289 (1934), also observed lamellar twinning on {110} under the microscope.
4. Mügge, *Jb. Min.*, 30, 1920. Buerger, *Am. Min.*, **13**, 41 (1928).
5. Schneiderhöhn and Ramdohr (**2**, 346, 1931).
6. Prior, *Min. Mag.*, **13**, 186 (1902).
7. Pilipenko, *Tomsk.*, *Univ.*, *Bull.*, **62**, 387 (1915) — Doelter (4 [1], 143, 1925).
8. Scholtz, *Geol. Soc. South Africa, Trans.*, **39**, 81 (1936).
9. Harada (239, 1936).
10. Zies, Allen, and Merwin, *Econ. Geol.*, **11**, 407 (1916).
11. The occurrences of economic importance have been taken mainly from Lindgren (1933).
12. Zies, Allen, and Merwin, *Econ. Geol.*, **11**, 407 (1916), have studied the alteration of chalcopyrite with various reagents and at varying temperatures.
13. Schwartz, *Econ. Geol.*, **22**, 44 (1927).
14. Murdoch (37, 1916).
15. Pauling and Brockway (1932).

2632   **S T A N N I T E** [Cu_2FeSnS_4].   Geschwefeltes Zinn (from Cornwall) *Klaproth*, (*Ges. nat. Freunde Berlin, Schr.*, 7, 169, 1787; *N. Schr.*, 2, 257, 1797; *Mag.*, 5, 228, 1810). Zinnkies *Werner* (*Bergm. J.*, 385, 397, 1789). Tin Pyrites *Kirwan* (2, 300, 1796). Bell metal Ore. Etain sulfuré *Fr.* Stannine *Beudant* (2, 416, 1832). Stannite *Dana* (68, 1868). (Not the Stannit of *Breithaupt* [a mixture] [3, 772, 1847].)

C r y s t.   Tetragonal; scalenohedral — $\bar{4}\,2\,m$.[1]

$$a : c = 1 : 1.9666^{[2]} \qquad p_0 : r_0 = 1.9666 : 1$$

Forms:[3]

		ϕ	ρ	A	$\bar{M}$
c	001	....	0°00′	90°00′	90°00′
a	010	0°00′	90 00	90 00	45 00
m	110	45 00	90 00	45 00	90 00
w	130	18 26	90 00	71 34	63 26
v	120	26 34	90 00	63 26	71 34
e	012	0 00	44 30½	90 00	60 17
z	011	0 00	63 02½	90 00	50 56
x	032	0 00	71 16	90 00	47 57½
d	118	45 00	19 10	76 34½	90 00
n	114	45 00	34 48	66 12	90 00
−n	$\bar{1}14$	−45 00	34 48	113 48	55 12
p	112	45 00	54 16½	54 58	90 00
−p	$\bar{1}12$	−45 00	54 16½	125 02	35 43½
t	111	45 00	70 13	48 17½	90 00
u	123	26 34	55 37½	68 20½	74 52

Structure cell.[4]   Space group $I\bar{4}2m$; a_0 5.46, c_0 10.725; contains $Cu_4Fe_2Sn_2S_8$.

Habit.   Crystals rare. Pseudododecahedral habit common due to twinning. Pseudotetrahedral. Most crystals striated. The positive pyramids bright and smooth, the negative often dull and rough. Common forms: $c\,m\,e\,z\,n\,p\,-n\,-p$. Also massive granular, and disseminated.

Twinning. (a) On $\{102\}$ producing penetration twins. (b) With [112] as twin axis and $\{112\}$ as composition plane, producing penetration and juxtaposition twin groups. Under the microscope often shows lamellar and polysynthetic twinning.

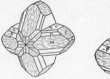

P h y s. Cleavage $\{110\}$ and $\{001\}^5$ indistinct. Fracture uneven. H. 4. G. 4.3–4.5; 4.437 (calc.). Luster metallic. Streak blackish. Color steel-gray to iron-black, sometimes a

San José, near Oruro, Bolivia.

bluish tarnish; often yellowish from chalcopyrite inclusions. Opaque. In polished section[6] anisotropic. Reflection percentages: green 23, orange 21, red 19.

C h e m. Sulfide of copper iron and tin, Cu_2FeSnS_4, with apparently little variation in composition. Deviations from the formula may well be due to inclusions of chalcopyrite and sphalerite, commonly seen in polished sections.[7]

Anal.

	1	2	3	4	5
Cu	29.58	31.52	29.00	29.38	29.24
Fe	12.99	12.06	13.75	13.89	13.95
Sn	27.61	27.83	27.50	27.20	27.14
Zn	.....	.....	0.75	0.02	0.08
S	29.82	28.59	29.00	28.77	28.88
Insol.	.....	.....	.....	0.62	0.51
Total	100.00	100.00	100.00	99.88	99.80
G.	4.437	4.45	4.495		

1. Cu_2FeSnS_4. 2. Oruro, Bolivia. Recalculated after deducting 8.53 per cent andorite.[8] 3. Veta del Estano, Potosí, Bolivia. Recalculated after deducting 6.96 per cent gangue.[9] 4. Oruro.[10] 5. Chocaya, Bolivia.[10]

Tests. F. 1.5. In the C.T. decrepitates and gives a faint sublimate. B.B. on charcoal fuses to a globule. Decomposed by HNO_3 with separation of sulfur and SnO_2.

O c c u r. Stannite occurs in tin-bearing veins, associated principally with chalcopyrite, sphalerite, tetrahedrite, pyrite, cassiterite, wolframite, and quartz. Oriented inclusions of chalcopyrite and sphalerite have been noted, and an oriented deposition of stannite twinned crystals on tetrahedrite has been reported. The $\{111\}$ of tetrahedrite is $\parallel$ to $\{112\}$ of stannite, and the [110] directions in both are parallel.[11]

From Zinnwald, Bohemia, with sphalerite and galena. Frequently occurs in the tin veins at Cornwall, associated with arsenopyrite, chalcopyrite, sphalerite, wolframite, various sulfides, and cassiterite; as at Wheal Rock, near St. Agnes, and at Carn Brea where it constituted a considerable vein, and more recently in considerable quantity at St. Michael's Mount, also at Redruth, at Stenna Gwynne near St. Austell, and at Camborne. In the mines of Zeehán, Tasmania. Most recent finds have been in Bolivia, especially at Oruro, Potosí, Chocaya, and Uncia, where the stannite occurs with cassiterite, tetrahedrite, arsenopyrite, pyrite and rare sulfosalts. A group of many twinned crystals, each up to an inch in diameter, and clustered together in a ball-like aggregate, has recently been described from Uncia.[12] Sparingly found in the Black Hills, South Dakota. Noted from one locality on the Seward Peninsula, Alaska.

N a m e. From the Latin name for tin.

Ref.

1. Symmetry established by Kenngott (**1**, 41, 1849).
2. Measurements of Ahlfeld, Himmel, and Schroeder, *Zbl. Min.*, 161, 1935; unit of Brockway, *Zs. Kr.*, **89**, 434 (1934), by x-ray methods on crystal from Oruro. Spencer, *Min. Mag.*, **13**, 54 (1901), obtained $a : c = 1 : 0.9827$. Transformation, Spencer and Ahlfeld, Himmel, and Schroeder to Brockway: 100/010/002.
3. Goldschmidt (**9**, 135, 1923). Forms from Spencer (1901), except {130}, {120}, {032}, from Ahlfeld, Himmel, and Schroeder (1935).
4. Brockway (1934).
5. Spencer (1901) notes a fair cleavage in these directions on the Cornish material. No cleavage, however, is noted on the Bolivian crystals. Early observers also noted cleavages in the Cornwall specimens. These separations may be due to parting of twinned aggregates, well shown on Oruro specimens (Palache priv. comm., 1939).
6. Schneiderhöhn and Ramdohr (**2**, 472, 1931).
7. See Schwartz, *Am. Min.*, **8**, 162 (1923), Lindgren and Creveling, *Econ. Geol.*, **23**, 233 (1928) and Reinheimer, *Jb. Min. Beil.-Bd.*, **49**, 159 (1924), for a discussion of inclusions in stannite.
8. Spencer (1901).
9. Stelzner, *Zs. deutsche geol. Ges.*, **49**, 131 (1897).
10. Ahlfeld, *Jb. Min. Beil.-Bd.*, **68A**, 268 (1934).
11. Spencer, *Min. Mag.*, **14**, 308 (1907).
12. Ahlfeld (1934) describes the Bolivian occurrence.

BOLIVIANITE. *Pauly* (*Cbl., Min.*, 43, 1926). (Not the bolivian of *Breithaupt, B. H. Ztg.*, **25**, 188 [1866].)
From the Bolivian tin mines; an inadequately described mineral which may be either stannite[1] or a mixture of sphalerite and covellite.[2]

Ref.

1. Ahlfeld, *Cbl. Min.*, 320, 1927.
2. Foshag, *Am. Min.*, **11**, 194 (1926).

264 WURTZITE GROUP

HEXAGONAL — DIHEXAGONAL PYRAMIDAL

			a_0	c_0	c_0/a_0	G.
2641	Wurtzite	ZnS	3.811	6.234	1.6358	4.10
2642	Greenockite	CdS	4.142	6.724	1.6223	4.772
2643	Voltzite	Zn_5S_4O		massive		3.7–3.8

The wurtzite group is related to the sphalerite group as cubic close packing is to hexagonal close packing, with the [111] of sphalerite corresponding to the [0001] polar axis of wurtzite. The hemimorphic character of the structure is well displayed by the crystal habit.

Voltzite, from its physical and chemical properties, about which little is known, might well be a member of this group.

Optically the minerals of the group are similar in that they are uniaxial positive, with high refractive index.

2641 W U R T Z I T E [ZnS]. *Friedel* (*C.R.*, **52**, 983, 1861). Spiauterite *Breithaupt* (*B. H. Ztg.*, **21**, 98, 1862; **25**, 193, 1866). Faserige Blende, Schalenblende, pt. *Germ.*

C r y s t. Hexagonal — *P*; dihexagonal pyramidal — 6 *m m.*

$$a : c = 1 : 1.6349;^1 \qquad p_0 : r_0 = 1.8878 : 1$$

Forms:[2]

Lower	Upper		ϕ	$\rho = C$	M	A_2
$\bar{c}$	c	0001	....	0°00′	90°00′	90°00′
	m	$10\bar{1}0$	30°00′	90 00	60 00	90 00
	a	$11\bar{2}0$	0 00	90 00	90 00	60 00
	x	$20\bar{2}5$	30 00	37 03½	72 28	90 00
$\bar{p}$		$10\bar{1}2$	30 00	43 21	69 55½	90 00
t		$50\bar{5}6$	30 00	57 33½	65 02½	90 00
	g	$70\bar{7}8$	30 00	58 48½	64 40½	99 00
$\bar{r}$	r	$10\bar{1}1$	30 00	62 05½	63 46½	90 00
	l	$50\bar{5}2$	30 00	78 02	60 43	90 00
	u	$40\bar{4}1$	30 00	82 27½	60 17	0 00

Structure cell.[3] Space group *C6mc*; a_0 3.811 ± 0.004, c_0 6.234 ± 0.006; $a_0 : c_0 = 1 : 1.6358$; contains Zn_2S_2.

Habit. Hemimorphic pyramidal $\{50\bar{5}2\}$ and $\{10\bar{1}1\}$. Short prismatic to tabular $\{0001\}$. Usually striated horizontally on $\{10\bar{1}0\}$ and $\{10\bar{1}1\}$. The small base $\{0001\}$ is taken as the positive form, and is often absent;

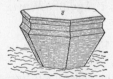

Nordmark, Sweden.   Beaver County, Utah.

the large base $\bar{c}\{000\bar{1}\}$ is dominant. Often fibrous or columnar; as concentrically banded crusts.

P h y s. Cleavage $\{11\bar{2}0\}$ easy, $\{0001\}$ difficult. H. 3½–4, G. 3.98; 4.1 (artif.); 4.10 (calc.). Luster resinous. Color brownish black. Streak brown.

O p t.[4] Uniaxial positive (+). Indices (for Na): *O* 2.356, *E* 2.378; (for Li) *O* 2.330, *E* 2.350.

C h e m.[5] Zinc sulfide, ZnS, like sphalerite. Contains, in addition, some Fe (8 per cent maximum) and Cd (3.66 per cent maximum).

Anal.

	1	2	3
Fe	....	2.43	6.02
Zn	67.10	62.64	59.70
Cd	....	1.84	1.07
Pb	....	0.41	0.15
S	32.90	32.10	32.90
Gangue	....	0.30	0.13
Total	100.00	99.72	99.97
G.	4.10		

1. ZnS.   2. Přibram.[6]   3. Portugal.[6]

Tests. Same as for sphalerite.

O c c u r.[7] Wurtzite is the rarer and unstable form of zinc sulfide and can crystallize from acid solutions. Often occurs intimately intergrown with sphalerite (schalenblende), marcasite, and other sulfides.

From Mies, Bohemia, and from Přibram (schalenblende); at Felsö-bánya, Roumania. In Bolivia as crystals in Oruro and Chocaya, Potosí; from Quispisiza near Castro Virreyna, Peru, as tabular crystals, some of which are one-third of an inch across. In Cornwall at Liskeard.

In the United States in fine pyramidal crystals from Butte, Montana; at Goldfield, Nevada, as radially fibrous crusts, with sphalerite. Occurs frequently in the ores of the Mackay Region, Idaho; at Frisco, Beaver County, Utah. Found infrequently as crystals in the Joplin district, Missouri.

A l t e r. Wurtzite inverts to sphalerite.

A r t i f.[3] May be formed by heating sphalerite above $1020° \pm 5°$, the inversion point, and cooling with moderate rapidity. As the iron content of the sphalerite increases, the inversion point is lowered (for 17.06 per cent iron, inversion at $880°$). Wurtzite is formed in acid solutions above $250°$.

N a m e. After the French chemist, Adolphe Wurtz.

Ref.

1. Friedel's calculated value, *C. R.*, **62**, 1002 (1866), with the x-ray unit of Bragg, *Phil. Mag.*, **30**, 647 (1920).
2. Goldschmidt (9, 99, 1923).
3. Cell dimensions for artificial material by Fuller, *Phil. Mag.*, **8**, 658 (1929). Aminoff, *Zs. Kr.*, **58**, 203 (1923), obtained a_0 3.80, c_0 6.23 on Přibram wurtzite.
4. On artificial crystals, measured under microscope, by Merwin, in Allen, Crenshaw, and Merwin, *Am. J. Sc.*, **34**, 341 (1912).
5. Analyses in Doelter (4 [1], 329, 1925).
6. Beutell and Matzke, *Cbl. Min.*, 263, 1915.
7. Umpleby, J. B., *U. S. Geol. Sur.*, *Prof. Pap. 97*, 87, 1917; also Ransome, *Washington Ac. Sc.*, *J.*, **4**, 482 (1914). Allen, Crenshaw, and Merwin, *Am. J. Sc.*, **38**, 393 (1914).
8. Allen, Crenshaw, and Merwin (1912).

2642   **G R E E N O C K I T E** [CdS]. *Jameson* (*Edinburgh N. Phil. J.*, **28**, 390, 1840). Sulphuret of Cadmium *Connel* (*Edinburgh N. Phil. J.*, **28**, 390, 1840). Xanthochroite *Rogers* (*J. Geol.*, **25**, 515, 1917). Cadmium-blende. Cadmium sulfuré *Fr.* α-CdS (artif.).

C r y s t.[1] Hexagonal — P; dihexagonal pyramidal — $6\,m\,m$.

$$a : c = 1 : 1.6218; \qquad p_0 : r_0 = 1.8727 : 1$$

Forms:[2]

Lower	Upper		ϕ	$\rho = C$	M	A_2
$\bar{c}$	c	0001	....	$0°00'$	$90°00'$	$90°00'$
	m	$10\bar{1}0$	$30°00'$	$90\ 00$	$60\ 00$	$90\ 00$
$\bar{x}$	x	$10\bar{1}2$	$30\ 00$	$43\ 07$	$70\ 01$	$90\ 00$
	p	$20\bar{2}3$	$30\ 00$	$51\ 18\frac{1}{2}$	$67\ 02$	$90\ 00$
	o	$50\bar{5}6$	$30\ 00$	$57\ 21$	$65\ 06$	$90\ 00$
	y	7078	$30\ 00$	$58\ 36\frac{1}{2}$	$64\ 44$	$90\ 00$
	r	$10\bar{1}1$	$30\ 00$	$61\ 54$	$63\ 49\frac{1}{2}$	$90\ 00$
	w	$50\bar{5}3$	$30\ 00$	$72\ 14$	$61\ 34$	$90\ 00$
	v	$20\bar{2}1$	$30\ 00$	$75\ 03$	$61\ 07$	$90\ 00$
	z	$50\bar{5}2$	$30\ 00$	$77\ 56\frac{1}{2}$	$60\ 43\frac{1}{2}$	$90\ 00$
	s	$11\bar{2}2$	$0\ 00$	$58\ 20\frac{1}{2}$	$90\ 00$	$64\ 48\frac{1}{2}$

Less common:

a	$11\bar{2}0$	n	$1{\cdot}0{\cdot}\bar{1}{\cdot}14$	π	$1{\cdot}0{\cdot}\bar{1}{\cdot}\bar{1}0$	ρ	$10\bar{1}3$	l	$30\bar{3}8$	u	$30\bar{3}2$
k	$21\bar{3}0$	$\bar{\gamma}$	$3{\cdot}0{\cdot}\bar{3}{\cdot}\bar{4}0$	i	$10\bar{1}4$	ρ	$10\bar{1}3$	q	$40\bar{4}5$	t	$30\bar{3}1$

Structure cell. Space group $C6mc$; $a_0\ 4.142$, $c_0\ 6.724$;
$a_0 : c_0 = 1 : 1.623$; contains Cd_2S_2.

Habit. Hemimorphic pyramidal, the positive end more complex in development. Often striated horizontally and in oscillatory combination. Usually as an earthy coating.

Twinning. Twin plane $\{11\bar{2}2\}$, rare.

P h y s. Cleavage $\{11\bar{2}2\}$ distinct, $\{0001\}$ imperfect. Fracture conchoidal. Brittle. H. $3-3\frac{1}{2}$. G. 4.9 (average), 4.820 (artif.); 4.772 (calc.). M.P. 780° (artif.). Luster adamantine to resinous. Color various shades of yellow and orange.[5] Streak between orange-yellow and brick-red.

Renfrewshire, Scotland.

O p t.[6] Uniaxial positive (+) for red to blue-green, negative from blue-green to blue, and isotropic for 523 mμ. From 500 mμ to violet absorption is very strong. Pleochroism weak. Indices:

	Na (589)	Li (670)
E	2.529	2.456
O	2.506	2.431

C h e m. Cadmium sulfide, CdS. Cd 77.81, S 22.19, total 100.00. The few analyses available vary only slightly from the theoretical composition.

Tests. Infusible. In the C.T. assumes a carmine red color while hot, fading to the original yellow on cooling. B.B. on charcoal gives reddish brown coating of CdO. Soluble in concentrated HCl with evolution of H_2S.

O c c u r. Occurs usually as an earthy coating on zinc minerals, especially sphalerite. Rarely crystals are found in amygdaloidal cavities in basic

230   SULFIDES

igneous rocks. In Scotland at Bishopton, Renfrew, in the cavities in a labradorite porphyry, on prehnite with natrolite and calcite; at Wanlockhead, Dumfries, as a coating on sphalerite and quartz. At Přibram, Bohemia, coating smithsonite and sphalerite; at Bleiberg, Carinthia, in dolomite; at Pierrefitte, Hautes-Pyrénées, France. Reported from Montevecchio, Sardinia; at Laurium, Greece. Found at Llallagua, Bolivia. In the United States, found sparingly as a coating at Franklin and in crystals with zeolites at Paterson, New Jersey; also as a coating at Friedensville, Pennsylvania. As a thin film at Granby and other localities in the Joplin district of Missouri; in Marion County, Arkansas, as a bright yellow coating on smithsonite. Reported from Topaz, Mono County, California, (*xanthochroite*) on magnetite and sphalerite.

A r t i f. May be prepared in a number of ways: (*a*) by fusing precipitated CdS with K_2CO_3 and S; (*b*) by fusing $CdSO_4$, CaF_2 and BaS; (*c*) by heating CdO in sulfur vapor. The isometric CdS may be formed by heating CdS in S vapor for two hours at 700–800°.

N a m e. Named after Lord Greenock (later Earl Cathcart). The first crystal was found about 1810 by a Mr. Brown of Lanfyn and was mistaken for sphalerite. It was over half an inch across.

XANTHOCHROITE. *Rogers* (*J. Geol.*, **25**, 515, 1917), has been shown to be the same as greenockite.[9]

Ref.

1. Axial ratio from measurements of Mügge, *Jb. Min.*, **2**, 18 (1882). Unit from x-ray cell of Bragg, *Phil. Mag.*, **39**, 647 (1920). First crystals described by Breithaupt, *Ann. Phys.*, **51**, 507 (1840).
2. Goldschmidt (4, 90, 1918). Jezek, *Ak. Česká, Roz.*, **29**, no. 26 (1920) — *Min. Abs.*, 1, 292 (1922), also gives forms {10$\bar{1}$5}, {11·0·$\bar{1}\bar{1}$·40}, {60$\bar{6}$1}; Whitlock, *Am. Mus. Nov. 372*, 1929, gives no new forms on New Jersey crystals.
3. Ulrich and Zachariasen, *Zs. Kr.*, **62**, 260 (1925), on artificial material.
4. Whitlock (1929) observed a twin from Paterson. Also Merwin, in Allen, Crenshaw, and Merwin, *Am. J. Sc.*, **34**, 341 (1912), on artificial material observed twinning on {10$\bar{1}$2} and {10$\bar{1}$3}.
5. For a discussion of the color of greenockite see Allen, Crenshaw, and Merwin (1912, p. 390).
6. Allen, Crenshaw, and Merwin (1912).
7. Doelter (4 [1], 344, 1925).
8. Doelter (1925) for more details on synthesis of greenockite. See also Allen, Crenshaw, and Merwin (1912); Ulrich and Zachariasen (1925) for formation of isometric CdS, with a_0 5.820 Å.
9. X-ray powder picture of the earthy material from Mono Co., Calif., gives a pattern identical with that of greenockite crystals (Berman, priv. comm., 1939).

2643 **V O L T Z I T E** [Zn_5S_4O]. Voltzine *Fournet* (*Ann. mines*, 3, 519, 1833). Leberblende *Breithaupt* (*J. pr. Chem.*, **15**, 333, 1838; *B. H. Ztg.*, **22**, 26, 1863). Voltzit *Rammelsberg* (260, 1841).

In implanted spherical globules, and as a radially fibrous or thin lamellar crust.

P h y s. Sometimes shows a pearly cleavage surface H. 4–4½. G. 3.7–3.8. Luster vitreous to greasy. Color dirty rose-red, yellowish, brownish.

O p t.[1] Uniaxial pos. (+). $E\,2.03\pm$. Rather strong birefringence. Sections under microscope show parting planes at 60° to each other.

C h e m. An oxysulfide of zinc, Zn_5S_4O. Zn 69.38, S 27.22, O 3.40, total 100.00. Modern analyses are lacking for this species of unusual composition.[2]

Tests. B.B. like sphalerite. In HCl affords odor of H_2S.

O c c u r. Presumably occurs always as a secondary incrustation. From the Elias mine, near Joachimstal, Bohemia, on galena, sphalerite and other sulfides; from Geroldseck near Lahr, Baden. First found at the Rosières mine, near Pontgibaud, Puy-de-Dôme, France. Reported from Djebel Reças, Tunis.

N a m e. After the French mining engineer, Philippe Louis Voltz (1785–1840).

Ref.

1. Optical properties most recently discussed by Larsen (155, 1921).
2. For early analyses see Dana (107, 1892).

265 NICCOLITE GROUP

DIHEXAGONAL DIPYRAMIDAL

			a_0	c_0	c_0/a_0	G.	Twinning
2651	Pyrrhotite	$Fe_{1-x}S$	3.43	5.68	1.66	4.7	$\{10\bar{1}2\}$
2653	Niccolite	NiAs	3.602	5.009	1.3905	7.834	$\{10\bar{1}1\}$
2654	Breithauptite	NiSb	3.938	5.138	1.305	8.629	$\{10\bar{1}1\}$

RHOMBOHEDRAL — SCALENOHEDRAL

			a_0	c_0	c_0/a_0	G.	Twinning
2655	Millerite	NiS	9.60	3.15	0.3274	5.36	$\{01\bar{1}2\}$

ISOMETRIC

2656	Pentlandite	$(Fe,Ni)_9S_8$

Members of the niccolite group have the so-called nickel-arsenide structure possessed by many of the metallic compounds of the AX type. Millerite, the natural nickel sulfide, is not of this structure but the artificial hexagonal NiS has the nickel-arsenide structure.

A noteworthy feature of the artificial compounds of the type is the frequent deficiency of the metallic element in the composition. Pyrrhotite is a natural example of this.

2651 P Y R R H O T I T E [$Fe_{1-x}S$]. Vattenkies, Pyrites fusca, Minerà hepatica, pt. *Wallerius* (209, 212, 1747). Pyrites en prismes hexagonales *Forster* (1772); *Bournon* in *de Lisle* (3, 243, 1783). Magnetischer-Kies *Werner* (*Bergm. J.*, 383, 1789). Magnetic Pyrites *Kirwan* (1796). Magnetic Sulphuret of Iron. Magnetkies *Germ.* Fer sulfuré magnetique *Fr.* Leberkies pt. *Germ.* Leberkies *Leonhard* (665, 1826). Leberkise *Beudant* (2, 404, 1832). Magnetopyrite *Glocker* (1839). Pyrrotin pt., Magnetischer Pyrrotin *Breithaupt* (*J. pr. Chem.*, 4, 265, 1835). Magnetkis *Swed.* Pirrotina *Ital.* Pirita magnética *Span.* Pyrrhotine. Troilite *Haidinger* (*Ak. Wien,*

Ber., 47 [2], 283, 1863). Dipyrite *Readwin* (1867). Pyrrhotite *Dana* (58, 1868). Inverarite *Forbes* (*Phil. Mag.*, 35, 174, 180, 1868); *Heddle* (*Enc. Brit.*, 16, 392, 1883). Kroeberite *Forbes* (*Phil. Mag.*, 29, 9, 1865).

C r y s t. Hexagonal — P; dihexagonal dipyramidal — $6/m\ 2/m\ 2/m$.

$$a : c = 1 : 1.6502;^1 \qquad p_0 : r_0 = 1.9055 : 1$$

Forms:[2]

		ϕ	$\rho = C$	M	A_2
c	0001	....	0°00′	90°00′	90°00′
m	10$\bar{1}$0	30°00′	90 00	60 00	90 00
a	11$\bar{2}$0	0 00	90 00	90 00	60 00
t	10$\bar{1}$4	30 00	25 28½	77 35	90 00
s	10$\bar{1}$2	30 00	43 37	69 49½	90 00
r	10$\bar{1}$1	30 00	62 18½	63 43½	90 00
u	20$\bar{2}$1	30 00	75 18	61 04½	90 00
A	50$\bar{5}$2	30 00	78 08½	60 42	90 00
v	11$\bar{2}$2	0 00	58 47	90 00	64 41

Structure cell.[3] Space group perhaps $C6/mmc$; a_0 3.43, c_0 5.68; $a_0 : c_0 = 1 : 1.66$; contains $2(Fe_{1-x}S)$.

Habit. Commonly tabular to platy {0001}; steep pyramidal with faces striated horizontally (Elizabethtown) or flat pyramidal (Switzer-

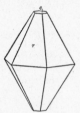

Hügel, near Osnabrück, Germany.

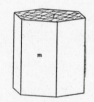

Pont-Péan, France.

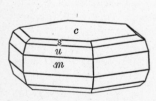

Cyclopean Isles.

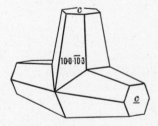

Elizabethtown, Canada.

land). Sometimes in rosettes due to subparallel aggregation on {0001}. Nodular (*troilite*). Usually massive, granular.

Twinning.[4] Twin plane {10$\bar{1}$2}.

P h y s. Cleavage none. Parting on {0001} sometimes distinct, on {11$\bar{2}$0} less so. Fracture uneven to subconchoidal. Brittle. H. 3½–4½,

G. 4.58–4.65 (troilite to 4.79); 4.69 (calc. for $Fe_{0.9}S$).[5] Luster metallic. Color bronze-yellow to pinchbeck brown, tarnishing quickly on exposure, sometimes to iridescence. Streak dark grayish black. Magnetic, but varying much in intensity, the less magnetic kinds having more Fe (*troilite*). Magnetism lost on heating to 348°. Sometimes polar magnetic. Opaque. In polished section[21] strongly anisotropic and weakly pleochroic. Reflection percentages; green 37, orange 37, red 36.

C h e m.[7] Sulfide of iron, $Fe_{1-x}S$, with x between 0 and 0.2. Troilite is close to FeS; most other pyrrhotites vary in composition between the stated limits. Ni, although reported in most analyses, has been shown to be due, for the most part, to admixed pentlandite. Small amounts of Co, Mn, Cu, generally less than 1 per cent, are often reported.

Anal. (Recent analyses of better quality.)

	1	2	3	4	5	6	7
Cu	.....	.....	.....	.....	.....	0.06	.....
Fe	63.53	57.49	62.70	63.40	60.87	61.49	61.29
Co	.....	1.50	.....	.....	.....	.....	.....
Ni	.....	4.30	.....	0.20	.....	0.39	.....
S	36.47	35.71	35.40	36.21	36.56	37.18	37.97
Insol.	.....	0.33	.....	.....	.....	0.46	.....
SiO₂	.....	.....	.....	.....	2.42	.....	0.82
Rem.	.....	.....	.....	.....	.....	.....	.....
Total	100.00	99.33	98.10	99.81	99.85	99.58	100.08
G.		4.738	4.67	4.789	4.65		4.49?

1. FeS. 2. Troilite, Beaconsfield meteorite. Contains 0.33 per cent graphite.[8] 3. Troilite. Calif.[9] 4. Troilite. Casas Grandes meteorite.[10] 5. Finkenberg. Includes MnO 0.78, SiO₂ 0.31, CaO 0.50, MgO 0.83. In basalt.[11] 6. Knittelfeld, Styria.[12] Cu due to chalcopyrite, Ni to pentlandite. 7. Sarrabus, Sardinia. In schist.[13]

	8	9	10	11	12	13
Cu	1.1	.....	.....	.....	.....	.....
Fe	60.4	59.62	59.91	60.18	56.74	58.22
Co	...	.....	0.12	.....	0.49	.....
Ni	0.3	.....	0.61	.....	1.10	.....
S	38.1	39.33	39.69	39.82	41.67	41.78
Insol.	....	0.61	.....	.....	.....	.....
SiO₂	....	.....	.....	.....	.....	.....
Total	99.9	99.56	100.33	100.00	100.00	100.00
G.		4.560				

8. Griqualand, Insizwa Range. Cu due to chalcopyrite, Ni to pentlandite.[14] 9. Monte Arco, Elba.[15] 10. Freiberg, Saxony.[16] 11. Homestake mine. Average of four analyses after deducting insol.[17] 12. Himmelfürst mine, Freiberg, Saxony.[16] 13. $Fe_{1.8}S_2$.

Var.[18] *Ordinary.* Includes the Fe-deficient members $Fe_{1-x}S$.
Troilite. The variety having a composition near FeS.

Tests. F. $2\frac{1}{2}$–$3\frac{1}{2}$ to a magnetic globule. Unchanged in the closed tube. Decomposed by HCl with evolution of H_2S.

O c c u r.[20] Pyrrhotite, intimately associated with pentlandite and other sulfides, occurs principally in basic igneous rocks, from which it may have been formed by magmatic segregation (Sudbury). Occasionally found in pegmatites; sometimes in contact metamorphic deposits. Often as massive pyrrhotite in association with other sulfides in veins and replacement bodies of the higher-temperature type, in which it is often one of the earliest sulfide minerals to form. More rarely as crystals with quartz and dolomite in cavities in vein deposits (Morro Velho). Reported in fumaroles (Vesuvius) and in basalts (Finkenberg). Frequently found as nodules (troilite) in iron meteorites.

Fine large crystals and crystal groups found at Kisbánya in Transylvania, Roumania; at Leoben near St. Leonhard, in the Lavant-Tal, Austria; in Val Passiria (Passeier Thal, Tirol), Trentino, Italy, as fine crystals. In Saxony at Freiberg and Schneeberg; in Bavaria at Bodenmais, with sphalerite; at Andreasberg in the Harz Mountains. In Switzerland in the Bristenstock tunnel, Canton Uri. In Italy in Valle della Desia, Piedmont, and at Bottino near Seravezza, Tuscany. In France, Ille-et-Vilaine, at Pont-Péan near Bruz, as crystal groups. In Norway at Kongsberg, Modum, and Snarum; in Sweden at Fahlun in Kopparberg, and in Klefva, Småland. Some of the largest crystals of this species found at the Morro Velho gold mine on Rio das Velhas, northwest of Ouro Preto, Minas Geraes, Brazil, associated with cubanite on dolomite and quartz. Also in large crystals often highly iridescent from tarnish, at the Potosí mine, Santa Eulalia, Chihuahua, Mexico.

In the United States occurs at many of the important western mines. Crystals were found at Standish, Maine, with andalusite. In Connecticut at Trumbull, with topaz, also at Monroe; in New York at Brewster, Putnam County. In New Jersey at Hurdstown, at the Gap mine, Lancaster County, Pennsylvania, with chalcopyrite and millerite. Found abundantly at Ducktown, Tennessee. Troilite has been found in serpentine in Del Norte County, California.

In Canada at Elizabethtown and Webster, Ontario, as twinned crystals in calcite veins. At Sudbury, Ontario, abundant in the nickel mines, where it is intimately intergrown with pentlandite. At Kimberley, British Columbia, with sphalerite and galena.

Alter. Pseudomorphs after pyrrhotite of marcasite, chalcopyrite, pyrite, arsenopyrite, magnetite, and quartz are known. Alters by oxidation to iron sulfates, limonite, and siderite.

Artif.[19] Has been synthesized by the direct union of iron and sulfur, and by heating pyrite, FeS_2, in an atmosphere of H_2S at 550°. Various crystalline modifications have been produced at elevated temperatures.

Name. Pyrrhotite from πυρρός, *reddish*. Troilite named after Dominico Troili, who in 1766 described a meteorite that fell that year at Albareto in Modena, containing that species.

Ref.

1. The unit chosen is that of Rose, *Ann. Phys.*, **4**, 173 (1825), on crystals from the Juvenas meteorite; axial ratio that of Seligmann, *Zs. Kr.*, **11**, 337 (1886) — p. 343, on crystals from the Cyclopean Islands. An orthorhombic form of pyrrhotite was early suggested by Streng, *Jb. Min.*, 799, 1878, and others. Later Streng, *Jb. Min.*, **1**, 183 (1882), withdrew his suggestion. Larsen, in Allen, Crenshaw, Johnston, and Larsen,

Am. J. Sc., **33**, 169 (1912), concluded that α-pyrrhotite, a synthetic product, is ortho-rhombic, and that the low-temperature form β-pyrrhotite is hexagonal. The principal forms of β-pyrrhotite and their angular relations correspond closely to natural pyrrho-tite; the chief proof of their symmetry is given in the habit and twinning of the crystals.

2. The forms *c*, *m*, *s*, *u* from Seligmann (1886); the forms *c*, *m*, *a*, *s*, *r*, *v* from Rose (1825). Rare and uncertain $\{1 \cdot 0 \cdot \bar{1} \cdot 10\}$, $\{80\bar{8}7\}$, $\{30\bar{3}1\}$, $\{70\bar{7}2\}$, or $\{10 \cdot 0 \cdot \bar{10} \cdot 3\}$, $\{11\bar{2}6\}$, $\{11\bar{2}4\}$, $\{22\bar{4}3\}$.

3. Unit cell dimensions by Alsen, *Geol. För. Förh.*, **45**, 606 (1923); **47**, 19 (1925), on Kongsberg crystals, by powder method. Slightly different values were obtained by other methods and on other material. Hägg and Sucksdorff, *Zs. phys. Chem.*, **22B**, 444 (1933), obtained a_0 3.433, c_0 5.860, $a_0 : c_0 = 1 : 1.707$ on pyrrhotite; with normal FeS (troilite) they found a superstructure with a_0 5.946 ($\sqrt{3} \times 3.433$), c_0 11.720 (2×5.860). This latter cell has six times the volume of the pyrrhotite cell. The form $\{20\bar{2}1\}$ of the small lattice becomes $\{11\bar{2}1\}$ of the larger. No dominance of one structural cell or the other over the form development of natural pyrrhotite (or troilite) has as yet been shown.

4. The synthetic α-pyrrhotite has two twin laws, $\{021\}$ and $\{023\}$ (Larsen [1912]).

5. The density varies with the composition: for S 36.72 per cent, G 4.755; S 38.64, G 4.648; S 40.30, G 4.533; all on synthetic material. See Allen, Crenshaw, Johnston, and Larsen (1912).

6. Schneiderhöhn and Ramdohr (**2**, 132, 1931).

7. Hägg and Sucksdorff (1933) have shown that lattice positions occupied in the normal FeS structure are vacant in the pyrrhotite structure, and that the composition is to be expressed in terms of an Fe deficiency rather than a S excess. Dickson, *Am. Inst. Min. Met. Engr., Trans.*, **34**, 3 (1904), showed by magnetic separation and analyses that the Ni content of Sudbury pyrrhotite is due almost entirely to pentlandite. See also Newhouse, *Econ. Geol.*, **22**, 288 (1927), and Schneiderhöhn and Ramdohr (**2**, 131, 1931) for mineralographic evidence.

8. Cohen, *Ak. Berlin, Ber.*, **46**, 1035 (1897) — troilite p. 1044.

9. Eakle, *Am. Min.* **7**, 77 (1922).

10. Tassin, *U. S. Nat. Mus., Proc.*, **25**, 69 (1902).

11. Brauns (158, 1922).

12. Zeleny, *Min. Mitt.*, **23**, 413 (1904).

13. Serra, *Acc. Linc., Rend.*, **16** [1], 347 (1907).

14. Scholtz, *Geol. Soc. South Africa, Trans.*, **39**, 81 (1936).

15. Manasse, *Att. soc. Tosc.*, **28**, 118 (1912).

16. Stelzner, *Zs. pr. Geol.*, 400 (1896).

17. Sharwood, *Econ. Geol.*, **16**, 729 (1911).

18. For structural differences between troilite and pyrrhotite see Hägg and Sucks-dorff (1933); for solubility and magnetic differences see Eakle (1922).

19. Allen, Crenshaw, Johnston, and Larsen (1912). Also Roberts, *J. Am. Chem. Soc.*, **57**, 1034 (1935), for thermal study of system FeS-S.

20. For the paragenesis of pyrrhotite see Schwartz, *Econ. Geol.*, **32**, 31 (1937).

21. Schneiderhöhn and Ramdohr (**2**, 131, 1931).

2652   **Valleriite** [$Cu_2Fe_4S_7$?]. *Blomstrand* (*Ak. Stockholm, Öfv.*, **27**, 19, 1870). Unbe-kanntes Nickelerz (?) *Schneiderhöhn* and *Ramdohr* (**2**, 127, 1931).

A massive metallic mineral resembling pyrrhotite in color and graphite in physical properties. Possibly orthorhombic.[1] Cleavage perfect. Very soft. G. 3.14 (?). Composition uncertain,[2] perhaps $Cu_2Fe_4S_7$ or $Cu_3Fe_4S_7$. In polished section[3] cream-white in color and strongly anisotropic. Strongly pleochroic, with *O* light golden white to rose, *E* dull gray. Reflec-tion: (for *O*) green 47.5, orange 46, red 45; (for *E*) green 19, orange 16, red 18.

Originally found at the Aurora mine, Nya-Kopparberg, Sweden. Later reported[4] from a number of occurrences in high-temperature copper deposits. Named for the Swedish mineralogist G. Wallerius (Vallerius) (1683–1742).

Needs further investigation.

Ref.

1. Suggested by the x-ray powder study of Hiller, *Zs. Kr.*, **101**, 425 (1939), who reported a_0 6.13, b_0 9.81, c_0 11.40 and who gives the space group as probably *Pmma*.
2. Analyses of material greatly admixed with gangue are given by Ramdohr and Ödman, *Geol. För. Förh.*, 54, 89 (1932) and Hiller (1939).
3. See Ramdohr and Ödman (1932), Schneiderhöhn and Ramdohr (2, 127, 1931).
4. See Grondijs and Schouten, *Econ. Geol.*, 32, 427 (1937), who report localities for material presumably the same as valleriite; see also Ramdohr and Ödman (1932).

HYDROTROILITE. *Siderenko* (*Me. soc. nat. nouvelle Russie, Odessa*, **21**, 121, 1907; **24**, 107 1909 — *Doelter*, 4[1], 526, 1926). Eisensulfhydratgel, Hydratisches Eisensulfur *Germ*.
A black finely divided, colloidal, material reported in many muds and clays.[1] Composition given as $FeS \cdot H_2O$, but more likely $FeS \cdot nH_2O$. Little evidence of species validity has been presented.

Ref.

1. Doss, *Jb. Min., Beil.-Bd.*, **33**, 662 (1912); see also Doelter (4 [1], 526, 1926).

2653   **N I C C O L I T E** [NiAs]. Kupfernickel *Hiärne* (76, 1694). Cuprum Nicolai *Woodward* (1728). Kupfernickel, Arsenicum sulphure et cupro mineralisatum, aeris modo rubente *Wallerius* (228, 1747). Niccolum ferro et cobalto arsenicatis et sulphuratis min. *Cronstedt* (*Ak. Stockholm, Handl.*, 1751, 1754); (208, 1758). Cuprum min. arsen. fulvum *Linnaeus* (1768). Mine de cobalt arsenicale tenant cuivre *Sage* (58, 1772), *de Lisle* (3, 135, 1783). Niccolum nativum *Bergmann* (2, 440, 1780). Rotnickelkies, Arseniknickel *Germ*. Copper Nickel, Arsenical Nickel. Nickeline *Beudant* (2, 586, 1832). Arsenischer Pyrrotin *Breithaupt* (*J. pr. Chem.*, 4, 266, 1835). Niccolite *Dana* (60, 1868). Niquel rojo *Span.*, Nickelin *Germ*.
Antimonarsennickel *Petersen* (*Ann. Phys.*, 137, 396, 1869). Aarite pt. *Adam* (40, 1869). Arite pt. *Pisani* (*C.R.*, 76, 239, 1873).

C r y s t.[1] Hexagonal — *P*; dihexagonal dipyramidal — $6/m\,2/m\,2/m$.

$$a : c = 1 : 1.3972; \qquad p_0 : r_0 = 1.6134 : 1$$

Forms:[2]

	ϕ	$\rho = C$	M	A_2
c 0001	..	0°00′	90°00′	90°00′
m 10$\bar{1}$0	30°00′	90 00	60 00	90 00
a 11$\bar{2}$0	0 00	90 00	90 00	60 00
e 10$\bar{1}$3	30 00	28 16$\frac{1}{2}$	76 18	90 00
x 10$\bar{1}$2	30 00	38 53$\frac{1}{2}$	71 42	90 00
r 10$\bar{1}$1	30 00	58 12$\frac{1}{2}$	64 51	90 00
w 30$\bar{3}$2	30 00	67 33	62 28$\frac{1}{4}$	90 00
t 20$\bar{2}$1	30 00	72 47	61 28$\frac{1}{2}$	90 00
γ 50$\bar{5}$2	30 00	76 04$\frac{1}{2}$	60 58	90 00
y 30$\bar{3}$1	30 00	78 19$\frac{1}{2}$	60 41	90 00
s 11$\bar{2}$3	0 00	42 58	90 00	70 04$\frac{1}{2}$
p 11$\bar{2}$2	0 00	54 24$\frac{1}{2}$	90 00	66 00$\frac{1}{2}$

Structure cell.[3] Space group $C6/mmc$; a_0 3.602, c_0 5.009; $a_0 : c_0 = 1 : 1.3905$; contains Ni_2As_2.

Habit. Crystals rare, pyramidal $\{10\bar{1}1\}$. Often distorted, striated

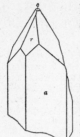

horizontally. Usually massive, reniform, with columnar structure, also reticulated and arborescent.

Twinning. Twin plane $\{10\bar{1}1\}$ producing fourlings;[2] also possibly $\{31\bar{4}1\}$.[4]

P h y s. Cleavage none. Brittle. H. 5–5½. G. 7.784 ± 0.001 (on pure material); 7.834 (calc.). Luster metallic. Color pale copper-red, with a gray to blackish tarnish. Streak pale brownish black. Opaque. In polished section[10] strongly anisotropic and

Richelsdorf, Germany.

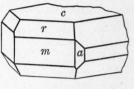

Eisleben.

pleochroic. Shows hexagonal zoning in section $\parallel \{0001\}$.[5] Reflection percentages:[6] (for O) red 59.5, orange 57.1, green 48.9; (for E) red 58.5, orange 55.2, green 42.8.

C h e m.[7] Nickel arsenide, NiAs. Sb is sometimes present, perhaps due to intergrown breithauptite. Contains also Fe, Co, S in small amounts.

Anal.

	Fe	Co	Ni	Sb	As	S	Others	Total	G.
1	..	..	43.92	..	56.08	..	..	100.00	7.834
2	0.05	0.49	43.25	0.15	55.10	0.15	0.65	99.84	7.784
3	trace	2.04	40.64	4.95	50.78	1.47	..	99.88	7.66

1. NiAs. 2. Hohendahl-Schacht, Eisleben. Includes Cu 0.02 per cent, CaCO₃ 0.35, SiO₂ 0.23, insol. 0.05.[5] 3. Hudson Bay mine, Cobalt. The Sb and S are present largely as breithauptite and cobaltite.[8]

Tests. F. 2. Soluble in aqua regia.

O c c u r. Niccolite, together with other nickel arsenides and sulfides, pyrrhotite, and chalcopyrite frequently occurs in norites or ore deposits derived from them. Also found in vein deposits with cobalt and silver minerals.

In Japan, at the Natsume nickel deposits as spheroids, some of which are a foot in diameter, consisting of alternating concentric shells of niccolite and arsenopyrite. In Austria at Schladming, Styria; in Bohemia at Joachimstal in Saxony at Freiberg, Annaberg, Schneeberg, and Sangerhausen; in the Harz Mountains at Andreasberg, Mansfeld, and Eisleben; in Hesse-Nassau at Richelsdorf in crystals; in France at Chalanches near Allemont, Isère, and at the Ar mine (*arite*) near Eaux-Bonnes, Basses-Pyrénées.

Found sparingly at Franklin, New Jersey. At Silver Cliff, Custer County, Colorado. In Canada in the Cobalt and Gowganda districts, Ontario, with silver and cobalt; at Sudbury in the nickel ores, with pyrrhotite, pentlandite, and maucherite; on Silver Islet, Thunder Bay; and at Tilt Cove, Newfoundland.

A l t e r. Quickly becomes coated with annabergite in a moist atmosphere.

N a m e.[9] The first name of this mineral, *kupfernickel*, gave the name *nickel* to the metal. The latinized *niccolum* was not adopted so that the species name *niccolite* given by Dana is unfortunate; *nickeline* or *nickelite* would be preferable.

Ref.

1. Axial ratio from Faber, *Zs. Kr.*, **84**, 408 (1933), on analyzed material corresponding to essentially pure NiAs, from Hohendahl-Schacht, Eisleben. Faber's suggestion of trigonal hemimorphic symmetry is not supported by conclusive morphological evidence. Structural studies on NiAs as well as other compounds of this type indicate hexagonal holohedral symmetry, with a possibility that the crystal class 6 *m m* may also explain the structural data. Goldschmidt and Schröder, *Beitr. Kr. Min.*, **2**, 35 (1923) obtained $p_0 = 1.590$ on unanalyzed niccolite from Richelsdorf, Mansfeld, Harz Mountains. Doubtful forms: {71$\bar{8}$0}, {10$\bar{1}$9}, {11$\bar{2}$4}.
2. Goldschmidt and Schröder (1923).
3. Aminoff, *Zs. Kr.*, **58**, 203 (1923). Cell dimensions from Faber (1933) on same material as that used for morphological and chemical work.
4. Faber (1933), who also proposed the less likely twin planes {20$\bar{2}$3} and {0001}, mainly from etch experiments in polished section.
5. Faber (1933).
6. Faber, *Zs. Kr.*, **85**, 223 (1933).
7. Older analyses in Dana (72, 1892).
8. Ellsworth, *Ontario Bur. Mines, Rep.*, **25**, 1 (1916), showed that niccolite and breithauptite form microscopic intergrowths.
9. See Mellor (15, 1, 1936) for a historical account of the name nickel.
10. Schneiderhöhn and Ramdohr (2, 147, 1931) and Faber *Zs. Kr.*, **85**, 223 (1933).

2654　BREITHAUPTITE [NiSb]. Antimonnickel *Stromeyer* and *Hausmann* (*Gel. Anz.*, 2001, 1833; *Ann. Phys.*, **31**, 134, 1834). Hartmannite *Chapman* (145, 1843). (Not the breithauptite of *Chapman* [125, 1843].) Breithauptit *Haidinger* (559, 1845).

Arite pt. *Adam* (40, 1869).

C r y s t.[1] Hexagonal — *P*; dihexagonal dipyramidal — 6/*m* 2/*m* 2/*m*.

$$a : c = 1 : 1.2924 \qquad p_0 : r_0 = 1.4924 : 1$$

Forms:[2]

		ϕ	$\rho = C$	M	A_2
c	0001	....	0°00′	90°00′	90°00′
m	10$\bar{1}$0	30°00′	90 00	60 00	90 00
i	10$\bar{1}$3	30 00	26 27	77 08	90 00
r	10$\bar{1}$1	30 00	56 10$\frac{1}{2}$	65 27$\frac{1}{2}$	90 00
V	40$\bar{4}$3	30 00	63 19	63 28	90 00
s	14·0·$\overline{14}$·3	30 00	81 49$\frac{1}{2}$	60 20	90 00

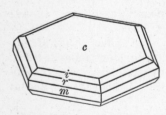

Structure cell.[3] Space group $C6/mmc$; a_0 3.938, c_0 5.138; $a_0 : c_0 = 1 : 1.305$; contains Ni_2Sb_2.

Habit. Crystals rare, thin tabular {0001}, prismatic [0001] (artif.). Arborescent and disseminated, massive.

Twinning. Twin plane {1$\bar{1}$01}.

P h y s. Cleavage none. Fracture uneven to small subconchoidal. Brittle. H. 5$\frac{1}{2}$.

G. 8.23;[4] 8.629 (calc.). Luster metallic, splendent. Color on fresh fracture light copper-red, inclining strongly to violet. Streak reddish brown. Opaque. In polished section[5] strongly anisotropic and pleochroic. Reflection percentages: (for O) green 45, orange 49, red 51; (for E) green 35, orange 42, red 42.5.

C h e m. Nickel antimonide, NiSb. As is sometimes present, but may be due to admixed niccolite.

Anal.

	Fe	Co	Ni	Sb	As	S	Total	G.
1	....	....	32.52	67.48	....	..	100.00	8.629
2	0.04	0.59	32.09	66.62	0.58	nil	99.92	8.23

1. NiSb. 2. Hudson Bay mine, Cobalt. The As in part due to niccolite.[6]

Tests. F. 1½–2. Soluble in HNO₃ and aqua regia.

O c c u r. Breithauptite occurs in calcite veins, commonly associated with silver minerals, ullmannite, sphalerite, galena, and niccolite. Found at Andreasberg in the Harz Mountains; at Mte. Narbo near Sarrabus, Sardinia; at Cobalt, Ontario, with niccolite, cobaltite, and native silver, in calcite gangue.

A r t i f.[7] Prepared by melting the constituents in the required proportion. Also formed as a furnace product.

N a m e. After the Saxon mineralogist J. F. A. Breithaupt (1791–1873).

Ref.

1. Axial ratio from measurements of Busz, *Jb. Min.*, I, 111, 1895 — 119 for breithauptite, on crystals from Andreasberg. Unit from x-ray cell. Transformations: Busz to x ray: 1000/0100/0010/000⅔; Goldschmidt to x ray: 1000/0100/0010/0003.
2. Goldschmidt (**1**, 231, 1913).
3. de Jong, *Physica*, **5**, 241 (1925).
4. The wide variation for the specific gravity as given in the literature is in part due to impurities in the tested samples. Ellsworth, *Ontario Bur. Mines, Rep.*, **25**, 1 (1916), made a careful determination on analyzed material, previously examined under the microscope.
5. Schneiderhöhn and Ramdohr (**2**, 153, 1931).
6. Ellsworth (1916).
7. Doelter (4 [1], 712, 1926).

2655 M I L L E R I T E (NiS). Haarkies *Werner* (*Bergm. J.*, 383, 1789), *Hofmann* (*Bergm. J.*, 175, 1791). Fer sulfuré capillaire (as a variety of pyrite) *Haüy* (4, 89, 1801). Capillary Pyrites. Gediegen Nickel *Klaproth* (5, 231, 1810). Schwefelnickel *Berzelius; Arfvedson* (*Ak. Stockholm, Handl.*, 427, 1822). Harkise *Beudant* (**2**, 400, 1832). Capillose *Chapman* (135, 1843). Millerite *Haidinger* (561, 1845A). Trichopyrit *Glocker* (43, 1847). Nickelkies *Germ.* Sulphuret of Nickel. Nickel sulfuré *Fr.* Sulfuro di Nickel, Archise *Ital.* Sulfuro de niquel *Span.*

C r y s t. Hexagonal — R; Scalenohedral — $\bar{3} \, 2/m$.[1]

$$a : c = 1 : 0.3274;^2 \qquad p_0 : r_0 = 0.3781 : 1$$

Forms:[3]

			ϕ	$\rho = C$	A_1	A_2
m	$10\bar{1}0$	$2\bar{1}\bar{1}$	30°00′	90°00′	30°00′	90°00′
a	$11\bar{2}0$	$10\bar{1}$	0 00	90 00	60 00	60 00
k	$21\bar{3}0$	$5\bar{1}4$	10 53½	90 00	49 06½	70 53½
d	$72\bar{9}0$	$16\cdot\bar{5}\cdot\bar{1}\bar{1}$	17 47	90 00	42 13	77 47
x	$41\bar{5}0$	$3\bar{1}\bar{2}$	19 06½	90 00	40 53½	79 06½
r	$10\bar{1}1$	100	30 00	20 42½	72 10	90 00
p	$02\bar{2}1$	$11\bar{1}$	−30 00	37 06	90 00	58 30½
$-\mu$	$14\bar{5}3$	$32\bar{2}$	−19 06½	30 00½	84 34½	67 47

Less common forms:

c	0001	R	$53\bar{8}0$	P	$31\bar{4}0$	D	$40\bar{4}3$	e	$01\bar{1}2$	G	$63\bar{9}5$
H	$32\bar{5}0$	L	$52\bar{7}0$	M	$61\bar{7}0$	ν	$50\bar{5}2$	F	$11\bar{2}2$	s	$21\bar{3}1$

Structure cell.[4] Most probable space groups $R\bar{3}m$ and $R3m$; a_0 9.60, c_0 3.15; a_{rh} 5.64, α 116°37′; contains Ni_9S_9 in hexagonal unit.

Habit. Usually very slender to capillary crystals elongated [0001], often in delicate radiating groups; sometimes interwoven like a wad of hair. Also in columnar tufted coatings, partly semiglobular and radiated. Single crystals often twisted helically about [0001].

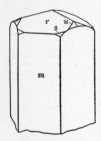

Brompton Lake, Quebec.

Twinning. On {01$\bar{1}$2}, produced by pressure.[5]

Phys. Cleavage {10$\bar{1}$1}, {01$\bar{1}$2} perfect. Fracture uneven. Brittle; capillary crystals elastic. H. 3–3½. G. 5.5 ± 0.2; 5.36 (calc.). Luster metallic. Color pale brass-yellow, inclining to bronze-yellow, with often a gray iridescent tarnish. Streak greenish black. Opaque. In polished section[6] strongly anisotropic. Reflection percentages: green 53, orange 54, red 54. Frequently shows zoning on basal sections.

Chem. Nickel sulfide, NiS. Ni 64.67, S 35.33, total 100.00. Old analyses give small amounts of Co, Fe, and Cu.

Tests. F. 1½–2. On charcoal fuses to a magnetic globule. Yields bead test for Ni.

Occur. Millerite occurs most frequently as a low-temperature mineral, often in cavities, or in carbonate veins; also as an alteration of other nickel minerals, or as crystal inclusions in other minerals. Found in rocks associated with the coal measures (Saarbrücken); in serpentines (Quebec). Reported as a sublimation product (Vesuvius); in meteorites (Santa Catharina).

In Bohemia at Joachimstal with nickel, cobalt, and silver ores. In Germany at Johanngeorgenstadt, Saxony; at Müsen, Westphalia; at Saarbrücken, Rhineland; with niccolite and other nickel and cobalt minerals at Richelsdorf, Hesse-Nassau; at Andreasberg in the Harz Mountains; at Freiberg, Saxony. In very fine hairlike crystals in cavities in siderite at Merthyr-Tydfil, Glamorgan, Wales.

In the United States in New York at the Sterling mine, Antwerp, in cavities in hematite as radiating groups of capillary crystals, with ankerite; in Pennsylvania, Lancaster County, at the Gap mine, as thin coatings of a radiated fibrous structure, often with a velvety surface, associated with pyrrhotite. At Keokuk, Iowa, St. Louis, Missouri, and Milwaukee, Wisconsin in geodes in the limestone, with calcite, dolomite, and fluorite, forming delicate tangled hairlike tufts, often penetrating the calcite crystals of the geode. With a green chrome garnet, in Orford Township, Quebec; from the Sudbury district, Ontario.

A r t i f.[7] Millerite may be prepared by passing H_2S into a $NiSO_4$ solution acidified with H_2SO_4. β-NiS, another crystalline modification, may likewise be prepared in an acetate solution. An amorphous NiS may be precipitated with $(NH_4)_2S$. β-NiS is structurally like the members of the niccolite group. Artificial millerite on standing inverts to the β-NiS form.

N a m e. In honor of the mineralogist W. H. Miller (1801–80), who first studied the crystals. The Haarkies (capillary pyrites) of Werner was true millerite,[8] but capillary pyrite and marcasite have sometimes gone by the same name.

BEYRICHITE. *Ferber, Liebe (Jb. Min.*, 840, 1871) from Oberlahr, near Altenkirchen, Rhineland, is probably the same as millerite, since it is said to differ principally in having a lower specific gravity (4.7), and perhaps a slight difference in color. It has been suggested,[9] but not confirmed, that millerite is a paramorph after beyrichite. Polished sections show no difference between the two.[6]

Ref.

1. The morphological study of Palache and Wood, *Am. J. Sc.*, **18**, 344 (1904), indicates a symmetry not lower than 3 2/m; the structure can be referred to this class, but the preferred structural class is 3 *m*, according to recent x-ray studies. See Alsen, *Geol. För. Förh.*, **45**, 606 (1923); **47**, 19 (1925), also Ott, *Zs. Kr.*, **63**, 222 (1926); Willems, *Physica*, **7**, 203 (1927).
2. Axial ratio of Palache and Wood (1904), unit of Miller, *Phil. Mag.*, **6**, 104 (1835). The ratio of Dana (70, 1892), based on the assumption that millerite belongs to the niccolite group, is not justified.
3. Goldschmidt (**6**, 44, 1920), Kaspar, *Soc. sc. Bohême, Mém.*, **12**, 1933 — *Min. Abs.*, **5**, 476 (1934), Billows (*Studi cristallografici di minerali Sardi*, ser. 2, Cagliari, 1925). Rare or uncertain forms:

6·5·$\bar{1}\bar{1}$·0	31·13·$\bar{4}\bar{4}$·0	28·3·$\bar{3}\bar{1}$·0	40$\bar{4}$1	0·18·$\bar{1}\bar{8}$·1	42$\bar{6}$5
43$\bar{7}$0	13·2·$\bar{1}\bar{5}$·0	41·2·$\bar{4}\bar{3}$·0	50$\bar{5}$1	53$\bar{8}$5	52$\bar{7}$6
11·6·$\bar{1}\bar{7}$·0	15·2·$\bar{1}\bar{7}$·0	70$\bar{7}$6	03$\bar{3}$1	7·4·$\bar{1}\bar{1}$·9	36·9·$\bar{4}\bar{5}$·4
9·4·$\bar{1}\bar{3}$·0	17·2·$\bar{1}\bar{9}$·0	30$\bar{3}$1	09$\bar{9}$1		

4. Alsen (1925) for cell dimensions. Also Ott (1926); Willems (1927).
5. Palache and Wood (1904).
6. Schneiderhöhn and Ramdohr (**2**, 144, 1931).
7. For earlier methods of synthesis, see Doelter (4 [1], 701, 1926). Also Thiel and Gessner, *Zs. anorg. Chem.*, **86**, 1 (1914), and Levi and Baroni, *Zs. Kr.*, **92**, 210 (1935), who studied the different forms of NiS by x-ray methods.
8. Hoffmann (4, 168, 1817).
9. Laspeyres, *Zs. Kr.*, **20**, 535 (1892).

The following are incompletely described, probably not valid species.

JAIPURITE. *Mallet* (*Geol. Sur. India, Rec.*, **14**, 190, 1880), and MODDERITE *Cooper* (*J. Chem. Met. Min. Soc. South Africa*, **24**, 90, 1923; **24**, 264, 1924), are said to be CoS, but no confirmation of the composition has as yet been presented.

HAUCHECORNITE. *Scheibe* (*Zs. deutsche geol. Ges.*, **40**, 611, 1888). Hauche-cornit *Scheibe* (*Jb. preuss. Landesanst.*, **12**, 91, 1893). Tetragonal crystals from the Friedrich mine, Schönstein, Prussia, said to have the formula $(Ni,Co)_7(S,Sb,Bi)_8$. Shown[1] to be a mixture of two unknown minerals, one containing Ni, Bi, and S, and the other Ni, As, Sb, and S. The original elaborate description needs revision.

Ref.

1. Short (104, 1931). A polished section of authentic crystals (checked by Palache) from the type locality showed undoubted inhomogeneity as described by Short (Berman, priv. comm., 1939). The descriptions given in Schneiderhöhn and Ramdohr (**2**, 372, 1931) and by Hüttenhain, *Min. Mitt.*, **42**, 285 (1932) — p. 298, are presumably on the same inhomogeneous material.

2656 **PENTLANDITE** $[(Fe,Ni)_9S_8]$. Eisen-Nickelkies *Scheerer* (*Ann. Phys.*, **58**, 315, 1843). Pentlandite *Dufrénoy* (**2**, 549, 1856). Nicopyrite *Shepard* (**307**, 1857). Horbachite pt. *Knop* (*Jb. Min.*, 521, 1873). Lillhammerit *Weisbach* (**57**, 1875). Gunnarite *Landström* (*Geol. För. Förh.*, **9**, 368, 1887). Folgerite *Emmens* (*J. Am. Chem. Soc.*, 14, 205, 1892). Heazlewoodite *Petterd* (47, 1896).

Cryst. Isometric; hexoctahedral — $4/m\,\bar{3}\,2/m$.

Structure cell.[1] Space group, $Fm3m$. a_0 10.09, containing $Fe_{24}Ni_{12}S_{32}$; a_0 9.91, containing $Fe_{18}Ni_{18}S_{32}$.

Habit. Massive, usually in granular aggregates, sometimes in large pieces showing continuous parting plane (?).

Phys. Cleavage none. Parting {111}.[2] Fracture conchoidal. Brittle. H. $3\frac{1}{2}$–4. G. 4.6–5.0; 4.956 (calc. for $(Fe,Ni)_9S_8$ with Fe : Ni = 1 : 1 and a_0 9.91); 5.185 (calc. for $(Fe,Ni)_9S_8$ with Fe : Ni = 2 : 1 and a_0 10.09). M.P. 878°. Luster metallic. Color light bronze-yellow. Streak light bronze-brown. Nonmagnetic. Opaque. In polished section[3] isotropic. Reflection percentage: for green, orange, and red, 51.

Chem.[4] A sulfide of iron and nickel, $(Fe,Ni)_9S_8$, usually with Fe : Ni close to 1 : 1, but varying somewhat. Older analyses show more Fe, but this may be due to admixed pyrrhotite. Small amounts of Co (maximum 1.28 per cent) are given in most analyses.

Anal.

	1	2	3	4	5
Fe	32.55	30.68	30.25	30.04	30.00
Ni	34.22	34.48	34.23	34.98	34.82
Co	.....	1.28	0.85	0.85	0.84
S	33.23	32.74	33.42	33.30	32.90
Insol.	.....	0.56	0.67	0.83	1.44
Total	100.00	99.74	99.42	100.00	100.00
G.	4.956		4.946		

1. $(Fe,Ni)_9S_8$ with Fe : Ni = 1 : 1. 2. Sudbury, Worthington mine.[5] 3. Sudbury, Copper Cliff.[2] 4. Sudbury, Frood mine.[4] 5. Sudbury, Creighton mine.[4]

Tests. F. $1\frac{1}{2}$–2. Fusible to steel-gray bead.

O c c u r.[6] Pentlandite is nearly always intimately associated with pyrrhotite, often in an oriented intergrowth, due, presumably, to an exsolution of the nickel-rich constituent. It occurs in highly basic rocks such as the norites, and is perhaps derived from them by magmatic segregation. Often found also with chalcopyrite, cubanite, and other iron and nickel sulfides and arsenides.

In South Africa, in the Bushveld, Rustenberg district, Transvaal, in the norite. In Norway with chalcopyrite in the hornblende rocks at Espedalen, northwest of Lillehammar, Opland, and at Eiterfjord, south of Bodö, Nordland, where it occurs in pyrrhotite at the contact of a norite with a garnet-mica schist. In the United States reported at the Key West mine, Clark County, Nevada. Also from Yakobi Island and elsewhere in southeastern Alaska. In Canada occurs intimately associated with pyrrhotite at Sudbury, Ontario, where it is the chief source of the nickel in the ore. Also reported from the Yale mining division, Emory Creek, British Columbia, in basic rocks.

A r t i f.[7] Prepared by melting Fe, Ni, and S in a graphite crucible, with repeated additions of the S until the desired product is obtained. Excess Fe forms pyrrhotite in addition to the pentlandite.

N a m e. After J. B. Pentland, who first noted the mineral.

The following have been shown to be probably pentlandite, or impure materials with pentlandite as the essential constituent:[8] Horbachite *Knop* (*Jb. Min.*, 521, 1873) from Horbach in Baden; folgerite *Emmens* (*J. Am. Chem. Soc.*, 14, 205, 1892), from the Worthington mine, at Sudbury; gunnarite *Landström* (*Geol. För. Förh.*, 9, 368, 1887) in Östergötland, Sweden; heazlewoodite *Petterd* (47, 1896), from Tasmania.

Ref.

1. Lindqvist, Lindqvist, and Westgren, *Svensk. Kem. Tidskr.*, 48, 156 (1936) — *Min. Abs.*, 6, 409 (1937), and Alsen, *Geol. För. Förh.*, 45, 606 (1923); 47, 19 (1925).
2. Penfield, *Am. J. Sc.*, 45, 493 (1893), considers the plane of separation as a parting plane.
3. Schneiderhöhn and Ramdohr (2, 122, 1931).
4. Dickson, *Am. Inst. Min. Met. Engr., Trans.*, 34, 3 (1903), has shown that the usual formula with the metals to sulfide as 1 : 1 is erroneous. All the modern analyses indicate an excess of metals over the simple ratio. See also Walker, *Econ. Geol.*, 10, 539 (1915).
5. Walker (1915).
6. Study of oriented intergrowths of pentlandite and pyrrhotite by Ehrenberg, *Zs. Kr.*, 82, 309 (1932), showed that {110} of pentlandite is ‖ to {10$\bar{1}$0} of pyrrhotite and [111] of pentlandite is ‖ to [0001] of pyrrhotite.
7. Newhouse, *Econ. Geol.*, 22, 288 (1927), who studied relations in the pentlandite-pyrrhotite system mainly on artificial material.
8. Penfield (1893) showed that folgerite is the same as pentlandite.

266   **C U B A N I T E** [$CuFe_2S_3$]. Weisskupfererz pt. Cuban *Breithaupt* (*Ann. Phys.*, 59, 325, 1843). Cubanite *Chapman; Dana* (65, 1868). Chalkopyrrhotit pt. *Blomstrand* (*Ak. Stockholm, Öfv.*, 27, 23, 1870). Chalmersit *Hussak* (*Cbl. Min.*, 69, 1902).

C r y s t.[1] Orthorhombic; dipyramidal — $2/m\ 2/m\ 2/m$.

$$a : b : c = 0.5822 : 1 : 0.5611; \qquad p_0 : q_0 : r_0 = 0.9638 : 0.5611 : 1$$

$$q_1 : r_1 : p_1 = 0.5822 : 1.0376 : 1; \qquad r_2 : p_2 : q_2 = 1.7822 : 1.7176 : 1$$

Forms:[2]

		ϕ	$\rho = C$	ϕ_1	$\rho_1 = A$	ϕ_2	$\rho_2 = B$
c	001	....	0°00'	0°00'	90°00'	90°00'	90°00'
b	010	0°00'	90 00	90 00	90 00	....	0 00
a	100	90 00]	90 00	....	0 00	0 00	90 00
l	130	29 47½	90 00	90 00	60 12½	0 00	29 47½
m	110	59 47½	90 00	90 00	30 12½	0 00	59 47½
y	011	0 00	29 18	29 18	90 00	90 00	60 42
g	101	90 00	43 56½	0 00	46 03½	46 03½	90 00
w	111	59 47½	48 07	29 18	49 57½	46 03½	68 00
o	122	40 39	36 29	29 18	67 13	64 16½	63 11
r	121	40 39	55 56½	48 17½	57 20	46 03½	51 23½
p	131	29 47½	62 43½	59 17	63 47½	46 03½	39 31½

Less common:

$e\{102\}$ $h\{032\}$ $f\{102\}$ $d\{201\}$ $t\{112\}$ $s\{221\}$

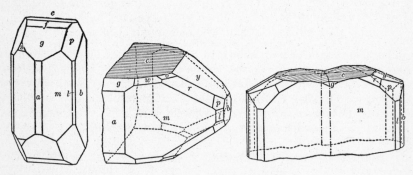

Minas Geraes, Brazil.   Sudbury, Ontario.

Structure cell.[3] Space group $Pcmn$; a_0 6.43, b_0 11.04, c_0 6.19; $a_0 : b_0 : c_0 = 0.582 : 1 : 0.561$; contains $Cu_4Fe_8S_{12}$.

Habit. Elongated [001]; thick tabular $\{001\}$; thick tabular $\{110\}$. Common forms: $c\ b\ l\ m\ y\ o\ r\ p$; $\{001\}$ striated [010]. Also massive.

Twinning.[4] Twin plane $\{110\}$ common; simple pairs, also fourlings and sixlings. Composition surface in most twins $\{110\}$, occasionally a surface near $\{1\bar{3}0\}$.

Phys. Cleavage none. Parting on $\{110\}$ and $\{1\bar{3}0\}$.[5] Fracture conchoidal. H. 3½ (crystals). G. 4.03–4.18 (massive), 4.101 (Sudbury crystals); (4.076) calc. Strongly magnetic with [010] as the magnetic axis. Color brass to bronze-yellow. Opaque. In polished section[18] anisotropic. Reflection percentages: green 41, orange 41, red 39.

Chem. Copper iron sulfide, $CuFe_2S_3$.

Anal.

	1	2	3	4	5	6	7
Cu	23.42	24.32	23.57	23.52	22.96	22.88	22.27
Fe	41.15	41.15	41.24	41.14	42.51	41.41	43.13
S	35.43	34.37	36.00	35.30	34.78	35.35	35.11
Total	100.00	99.84	100.81	99.96	100.25	99.64	100.51

1. $CuFe_2S_3$. 2. Barracanao, Cuba.[6] 3. Tunaberg, Sweden.[7] 4. Landlocked Bay, Prince William Sound, Alaska.[8] 5. Cuba. Original material. Includes Pb trace.[9] 6. Frood Mine, Sudbury.[10] 7. Morro Velho, Brazil (on 0.0896-gm. crystals).[11]

Tests. F. 2. Reactions as with chalcopyrite.

O c c u r.[12] Cubanite generally occurs in deposits formed at relatively high temperatures such as the pyrrhotite-pentlandite deposits (Sudbury), the contact metamorphic deposits (Fierro), or gold-quartz veins of higher-temperature type (Morro Velho). Most often associated with chalcopyrite as an oriented intergrowth[13] such that the {001} of cubanite lies || {111} of the chalcopyrite. Also with sphalerite, pyrite and pyrrhotite.

Occurs at Barracanao, Cuba, with chalcopyrite and pyrrhotite. In Sweden at Tunaberg, Södermanland, and at Kaveltorp near Ljusnarsberg, Örebro; in Norway at Sulitjelma, in chalcopyrite; at Traversella, Piedmont, Italy. The original *chalmersite*[14] came from the Morro Velho gold mine on Rio das Velhas, 70 km. northwest of Ouro Preto, Minas Geraes, Brazil, associated with pyrrhotite and dolomite. Occurs as a prominent constituent of the ore deposits of Prince William Sound, Alaska. Noted at Fierro, New Mexico, with chalcopyrite and magnetite. In Canada at Sudbury, Ontario, rarely in crystals; also at Parry Sound.

A l t e r. Pseudomorphs of pyrite after cubanite have been observed under the microscope. An alteration product of cubanite, perhaps similar in composition, but differing in properties under the microscope, has been described.[15]

A r t i f.[16] Oriented intergrowths of cubanite and chalcopyrite can be made to form a homogeneous phase at 450°, this latter having a structure similar to that of chalcopyrite. Upon slow cooling the cubanite will reprecipitate in an oriented intergrowth.

N a m e. After the locality, Cuba. Chalmersite was named after G. Chalmers, Superintendent of the Morro Velho mine.

BARRACANITE, CUPROPYRITE *Schneider* (*J. pr. Chem.*, **160**, 556, 1895), is probably the same as cubanite but is said to have the composition $CuFe_2S_4$.

CHALCOPYRRHOTITE. Chalkopyrrhotit *Blomstrand* (*Ak. Stockholm, Öfv.*, **27**, 23, 1870) has been shown to be essentially cubanite.[17]

Ref.

1. Axial ratio and setting of Hlawatsch, *Zs. Kr.*, **48**, 205 (1910), on "chalmersite" from Morro Velho. Also Peacock and Yatsevitch, *Am. Min.*, **21**, 55 (1936). Hussak, *Cbl. Min.*, **69**, 1902, and Palache, *Am. J. Sc.*, **24**, 249 (1907), adopted a different setting. Transformation: Palache and Hussak to Hlawatsch 010/300/001. Holohedral symmetry is shown on crystals from Sudbury (Peacock and Yatsevitch [1936]).

2. Forms of Palache (1907). {012} new form from Sudbury by Peacock and Yatsevitch (1936). Rare form: u{314} (Palache [1907]).

3. Buerger, *Am. Min.*, **22**, 1117 (1937). The space group *Pna* is possible if the crystals are not holohedral. Hexagonal pseudosymmetry is marked in the equatorial *c*-axis rotation Weissenberg picture.

4. Peacock and Yatsevitch (1936) show that the supposed twin plane {130} implied by Hussak (1902) and Hlawatsch (1910) is not valid. They also failed to verify {132} mentioned by Hussak.

5. Peacock and Yatsevitch (1936) observed no cleavage on crystals. They offer a suggestion that the supposed cleavage observed by previous workers is due to parting along twin boundaries. The cleavage {001} reported by Merwin, Lombard, and Allen, *Am. Min.*, **8**, 135 (1923), is unexplained.

6. Schneider, *J. pr. Chem.*, **52**, 555 (1895).

7. Kalb and Bendig, *Cbl. Min.*, 643, 1923.

8. Johnson, *Econ. Geol.*, **12**, 519 (1917).

9. Scheidhauer, *Ann. Phys.*, **64**, 280 (1845).

10. International Nickel Co. Lab. anal. in Peacock and Yatsevitch (1936).

11. Hussak (1902).

12. For a detailed account of the paragenesis and occurrence of cubanite see Ramdohr, *Zs. pr. Geol.*, **36**, 169 (1928).

13. Buerger and Buerger, *Am. Min.*, **19**, 289 (1934), verify the orientation previously suggested by Kalb and Bendig (1923) and Schwartz, *Econ. Geol.*, **22**, 44 (1927), and further (priv. comm.) state that the pseudohexagonal [001] axis of cubanite is parallel to the [111] of chalcopyrite.

14. The investigations on *Cuban* (Breithaupt, 1843) and *Chalmersit* (Hussak, 1902) are examined by Zenzen, *Geol. För. Förh.*, **47**, 385 (1925), who reaches the well-founded decision that the minerals described as cubanite or chalmersite are identical, and that cubanite has priority. The deciding observation is that of Kalb and Bendig (1923), who identified a polished section of Breithaupt's original material from Cuba with material from Tunaberg, Sweden, which has all the properties of the typical chalmersite from Brazil.

15. Ramdohr (1928).

16. Schwartz, *Econ. Geol.*, **22**, 44 (1927).

17. Geijer, *Geol. För. Förh.*, **46**, 354 (1924).

18. Schneiderhöhn and Ramdohr (**2**, 360, 1931).

---

267   **S T E R N B E R G I T E** [AgFe$_2$S$_3$].   *Haidinger (Roy. Soc. Edinburgh, Trans.*, **11**, 1, 1828; *Edinburgh J. Sc.*, **7**, 242, 1827). Silberkies pt. *Breithaupt (J. Chem. Phys.*, **68**, 289, 1833). Argyropyrrhotin *Blomstrand (Ak. Stockholm, Öfv.*, **27**, 26, 1870).

C r y s t.   Orthorhombic; dipyramidal — $2/m\,2/m\,2/m.$[1]

$a : b : c = 0.5679 : 1 : 1.0885;$[2] $p_0 : q_0 : r_0 = 1.9167 : 1.0885 : 1$

$q_1 : r_1 : p_1 = 0.5679 : 0.5217 : 1;$ $r_2 : p_2 : q_2 = 0.9187 : 1.7609 : 1$

Forms:[3]

		ϕ	$\rho = C$	ϕ_1	$\rho_1 = A$	ϕ_2	$\rho_2 = B$
c	001	...	0°00′	0°00′	90°00′	90°00′	90°00′
b	010	0°00′	90 00	90 00	90 00	0 00	0 00
a	100	90 00	90 00	0 00	0 00	0 00	90 00
e	011	0 00	47 25½	47 25½	90 00	90 00	42 34½
d	102	90 00	43 47	0 00	46 13	46 13	90 00
t	111	60 24½	65 36	47 25½	37 38½	27 33	63 16½
q	132	30 24½	62 09½	58 31	63 24½	46 13	40 18½
r	263	30 24½	68 23½	65 19½	61 55½	38 03	36 42
s	131	30 24½	75 12½	72 58½	60 42	27 33	33 30½

Structure cell.[4] Space group *Ccmm*; a_0 6.61, b_0 11.64, c_0 12.67; $a_0 : b_0 : c_0 = 0.5679 : 1 : 1.0885$; contains Ag$_8Fe_{16}S_{24}$.

Habit. Thin plates {001} pseudohexagonal in basal section. Lightly striated on {001} ∥ [100], more rarely ∥ [010]. Forms rosettes or fanlike aggregates. Common forms: *c e d t r s*.

Twinning. On {130}, sometimes without reentrants, often with clear separation of the individuals. On twins the striations of the basal planes produce a feathered symmetrical arrangement about the trace of the twin plane.

Joachimstal.

P h y s. Cleavage {001} perfect and easy. Thin laminae flexible (foil-like). H. 1–1½. G. 4.101–4.215; 4.275 (calc.). Luster metallic, brilliant on {001}. Color pinchbeck-brown, occasionally a violet-blue tarnish on some faces. Streak black. Opaque. Anisotropic.

C h e m.[5] A sulfide of silver and iron, $AgFe_2S_3$.

Anal.

	1	2	3	4	5
Ag	34.17	35.27	33.2	30.69	29.1
Fe	35.37	35.97	36.0	35.44	37.4
S	30.46	29.10	30.0	33.87	33.0
Total	100.00	100.34	99.2	100.00	99.5

1. $AgFe_2S_3$. 2. Joachimstal.[6] 3. Joachimstal.[7] 4. Joachimstal. After deducting 1.32 per cent SiO_2.[8] 5. Frieseite. Joachimstal.[8]

Tests. F. 1.5 B.B. on charcoal gives off S and fuses to a magnetic globule, the surface of which shows separated metallic silver. Soluble in aqua regia with separation of S and AgCl.

O c c u r. Found with the silver ores, particularly ruby silvers, stephanite, argentite, and with cobaltite, pyrite, and calcite at Joachimstal and at Pribram in Bohemia. Reported from Saxony at Johanngeorgenstadt and Schneeberg.

N a m e. After Count Caspar Sternberg (1761–1838) of Prague.

FRIESEITE. Frieseit *Vrba* (*Zs. Kr.*, **2**, 153, 1878; **3**, 186, 1879), is crystallographically similar to sternbergite with $a : b : c = 0.5969 : 1 : 0.7352$[9] and the forms $c\{001\}$, $b\{010\}$, $w\{301\}$, $r\{102\}$, $\{101\}$, $\{043\}$, $\{131\}$. Twinned like sternbergite. G. 4.217. The habit is, however, thick tabular, and the composition yields a formula $Ag_2Fe_5S_8$. In these two respects frieseite differs from sternbergite.

Ref.

1. Symmetry class by Peacock, *Am. Min.*, **21**, 103 (1936).
2. Axial ratio and unit by Buerger, *Am. Min.*, **22**, 847 (1937) with Weissenberg x-ray goniometer on same crystals as used by Peacock. Another orientation and unit used by Haidinger, *Edinburgh J. Sc.*, **7**, 243 (1827). Transformations: Haidinger to Buerger 010/300/002; Peacock to Buerger 910/300/003.
3. Goldschmidt (8, 83, 1922) from Haidinger (1827). Peacock (1936). Uncertain forms: {014}, {092}, {101}, {501}, {232}.

4. Buerger (1937).

5. The constitution of sternbergite and its relation to the other " silberkies " minerals has been discussed at great length, most recently by Zambonini, *Riv. min.*, **47**, 1 (1916), and Cesáro, *Riv. min.*, **49**, 3 (1917), but without new evidence. The analyses available, on the whole, are very poor.

6. Rammelsberg (66, 1875).

7. Zippe, *Ann. Phys.*, **27**, 690 (1833).

8. Vrba, *Zs. Kr.*, **3**, 187 (1878).

9. The frieseite axial ratio as given can be compared directly with the Haidinger ratio for sternbergite. (See ref. 2.)

The following are related minerals, all incompletely described. They may all represent one species, dimorphous with sternbergite, since the analyses point to a close similarity in composition. Further work must be done to establish any of these species.

ARGENTOPYRITE. Silberkies *Waltershausen* (*Ges. Wiss. Göttingen, Nachr.*, **9**, 66, 1866). Originally described as monoclinic. In prismatic six-sided twinned crystals. No cleavage. Fracture uneven, brittle. H. $3\frac{1}{2}$–4. G. 6.47. Luster metallic. Color steel-gray to tin white, tarnishing. An incomplete analysis on 22 mg. yielded a composition consistent with the formula $AgFe_3S_4$. From Joachimstal, Bohemia.

Material later described[1] as pseudomorphs consisting of argentite, marcasite, pyrrhotite, and pyrargyrite were regarded as identical with argentopyrite. Still later work[2] attempted to sustain the species, and showed that it was probably orthorhombic, and pseudohexagonal by twinning.

ARGYROPYRITE. *Weisbach* (*Jb. Min.*, 906, 1877). Described as prismatic crystals hexagonal in outline and often grouped in hemispherical aggregates. A cleavage $\parallel$ {001}, not so marked as in sternbergite. Not brittle as contrasted with argentopyrite. H. $1\frac{1}{2}$–2. G. 4.206. Color on fresh fracture bronze-yellow. The material from Marienberg on analysis gave the formula $Ag_3Fe_7S_{11}$. A similar substance was also reported from Freiberg.

"SILBERKIES." *Streng* (*Jb. Min.*, 785, 1878) is likewise a prismatic, hexagonal, or pseudohexagonal mineral, probably in twinned crystals. No cleavage observed. Fracture uneven. Brittle. H. $3\frac{1}{2}$–4. G. 4.18. Weakly magnetic. Color pale bronze-yellow; on the surface liver-brown with a steel-blue to iridescent tarnish. Streak dark blackish green to dark gray-green. Analysis gave: Ag 32.89, Cu 0.19, Fe 35.89, S 30.71, yielding $AgFe_2S_3$. From Andreasberg.

Ref.

1. Tschermak, *Ak. Wien, Ber.*, **54** [1], 342 (1866).

2. Schrauf, *Ak. Wien, Ber.*, **64** [1], 192 (1871).

2681   COVELLITE [CuS]. Blaues Kupferglas *Freiesleben* (3, 129, 1815). Kupferindig *Breithaupt* (in *Hoffmann* [**4b**, 178, 1817]). Bi-solfuro di Rame che formasi attualmente nel Vesuvio *Covelli* (1826; *Acc. Napoli, Att.*, 4, 9, 1839). Indigo-Copper; Blue Copper. Covelline, Sulfuré de cuivre du Vesuve *Beudant* (**2**, 409, 1832). Breithauptite *Chapman* (125, 1843). Cantonite *Pratt* (*Am. J. Sc.*, **22**, 449, 1856; **23**, 409, 1857). Cobre anilada *Span. S.A.*

C r y s t. Hexagonal — P; dihexagonal dipyramidal — $6/m\ 2/m\ 2/m$.

$$a : c = 1 : 4.3026^1 \qquad p_0 : r_0 = 4.9682 : 1$$

Forms:[2]

		ϕ	$\rho = C$	M	A_2
c	0001	....	$0°00'$	$90°00'$	$90°00'$
x	$10\bar{1}4$	$30°00'$	$51\ 09\frac{1}{2}$	$67\ 04\frac{1}{2}$	$90\ 00$
l	$10\bar{1}3$	$30\ 00$	$58\ 52\frac{1}{2}$	$64\ 39\frac{1}{2}$	$90\ 00$
d	$30\bar{3}8$	$30\ 00$	$61\ 46\frac{1}{2}$	$63\ 51\frac{1}{2}$	$90\ 00$
n	$10\bar{1}2$	$30\ 00$	$68\ 04\frac{1}{2}$	$62\ 22$	$90\ 00$
h	$9.0.\bar{9}.16$	$30\ 00$	$70\ 18\frac{1}{2}$	$61\ 55$	$90\ 00$
i	$50\bar{5}8$	$30\ 00$	$72\ 09$	$61\ 35$	$90\ 00$
r	$10\bar{1}1$	$30\ 00$	$78\ 37$	$60\ 39$	$90\ 00$
w	$20\bar{2}1$	$30\ 00$	$84\ 15$	$60\ 10$	$90\ 00$

Less common forms:

k	$1.0.\bar{1}.16$	z	$3.0.\bar{3}.32$	t	$10\bar{1}6$	α	$10\bar{1}5$	δ	$20\bar{2}3$	y	$15.0.\bar{15}.16$
q	$1.0.\bar{1}.12$	s	$10\bar{1}8$	g	$3.0.3.16$	γ	$20\bar{2}5$	ϵ	$30\bar{3}4$	v	$90\bar{9}8$

Structure cell.[3] Space group $C6/mmc$; a_0 3.802, c_0 16.43; $a_0 : c_0 =$ 1 : 4.321; contains Cu_6S_6.

Habit. Rarely in hexagonal plates {0001}, with the pyramidal faces horizontally striated, and hexagonal striation pattern on the base. Commonly massive or spheroidal; surface sometimes crystalline.

Bor, Serbia.

P h y s. Cleavage {0001} highly perfect. Flexible in thin leaves. H. $1\frac{1}{2}$–2. G. 4.6–4.76, 4.671 (artif.); 4.602 (calc.). Luster of crystals submetallic inclining to resinous, a little pearly on cleavage; subresinous or dull when massive. Color indigo-blue or darker. Often highly iridescent in brass-yellow and deep red. Streak lead-gray to black, shining. Opaque except in very thin plates, and then green.

O p t.[4] Transmits green light only, in plates of 0.0005-mm. thickness or less. Uniaxial positive. Dispersion extreme; pleochroism marked, $O > E$. Refractive indices (± 0.03):

λ	635	610	589(Na)	570	520	505
O	1.00	1.33	1.45	1.60	1.83	1.97

Under the reflecting microscope[5] shows strong anisotropism in sections containing [0001]; strong pleochroism, O deep blue with violet undertone, E blue-white. Reflection percentages: green 18.5, orange 15, red 10.

C h e m. Copper sulfide, CuS; with small amounts of Fe often reported in the best analyses.

Anal.

	1	2	3	4
Cu	66.48	66.06	66.43	65.49
Fe	.....	0.14	0.05	0.25
S	33.52	33.87	33.28	33.45
Insol.	.....	0.11	0.07	.....
Total	100.00	100.18	99.83	99.19
G.	4.602	4.760	4.683	4.668

1. CuS.   2. Butte.[6]   3. Butte.   Insol. is silica.[7]   4. Bor, Serbia.[8]

Tests. F. 2½. B.B. on charcoal burns with a blue flame and fuses to a globule. Yields S in C. T.

O c c u r. Covellite is associated with other copper minerals, principally chalcopyrite, chalcocite, enargite, and bornite, in the zone of secondary enrichment, and it is, in most instances, derived from these by alteration. Primary covellite has, however, been noted (Butte).[9] Also rarely observed as a sublimation product (Vesuvius). Intergrowths with chalcopyrite, chalcocite are common.[10] Oriented pyrite crystals with the [111] axis || to [0001] of covellite have been reported.[11] Also an oriented covellite coating on sphalerite noted had the relation, [0001] covellite parallel [111] sphalerite, $\{10\bar{1}0\}$ covellite parallel to $\{110\}$ sphalerite.[12]

Found at Bor, northwest of Zaječar, Serbia, Yugoslavia; at Leogang, Salzburg, Austria; at Dillenburg in Hesse-Nassau; at Sangerhausen, Saxony; at Badenweiler, Baden. In large crystals and crystal groups with iridescent colors on the surface, from the Calabona mine, Alghero, Sardinia. On Kawau Island, New Zealand. With enargite and luzonite on Luzon Island, Philippines. With enargite in the Sierra de Famatina, Argentina.

In the United States fine crystals and crystal groups, much like the Sardinian material, occur at Butte, Montana, in the primary ore; in Colorado at Summitville, Rio Grande County, and at Wagon Wheel Gap, Mineral County; near Laramie, Wyoming; in the La Sal district, San Juan County, Utah. Also found at Kennecott, Alaska.

A l t e r.[13] Covellite is derived from the alteration of a number of copper sulfide minerals, notably chalcopyrite, chalcocite, bornite, and stromeyerite.

A r t i f.[7] Formed in a dry way by heating Cu in a sealed evacuated tube over sulfur; in a wet way by precipitating a cupric salt with H_2S. Many other methods for synthesis have been used.

N a m e. In honor of N. Covelli (1790–1829), the discoverer of the Vesuvian covellite.

Ref.

1. Axial ratio from measurements of Adam on crystals from Sardinia, *Beitr. Kr. Min.*, **3**, 1 (1926); unit of Kenngott, *Ak. Wien, Ber.*, **12**, 22 (1854). The unit of Dana (68, 1892) following Groth (24, 1889) is not retained, since structural evidence does not support the assumption that covellite and cinnabar are crystallographically closely related. Transformations: Dana to Kenngott (and structure) $\frac{1}{3}0\frac{1}{3}0/\frac{1}{3}\frac{1}{3}00/0\frac{1}{3}\frac{1}{3}0/0002$. Adam to Kenngott, 1000/0100/0010/0002.
Uncertain forms:

$10\bar{1}0$	$1\cdot0\cdot\bar{1}\cdot24$	$3\cdot0\cdot\bar{3}\cdot40$	$5\cdot0\cdot\bar{5}\cdot32$	$5\cdot0\cdot\bar{5}\cdot24$	$9\cdot0\cdot\bar{9}\cdot40$
$1\cdot0\cdot\bar{1}\cdot48$	$1\cdot0\cdot\bar{1}\cdot20$	$1\cdot0\cdot\bar{1}\cdot10$	$3\cdot0\cdot\bar{3}\cdot16$	$7\cdot0\cdot\bar{7}\cdot32$	$13\cdot0\cdot\bar{13}\cdot32$
$1\cdot0\cdot\bar{1}\cdot32$					

Stevanović, *Zs. Kr.*, **44**, 349 (1908), proposed that crystals from Bor, Serbia, were pseudo-hexagonal by twinning, and actually monoclinic, or less probably, triclinic, with $a : b : c = 0.5746 : 1 : 0.6168$, β 90°46′. This interpretation has not been upheld by subsequent crystallographic and structural studies.
2. Goldschmidt (5, 70, 1918).

3. Cell dimensions of Roberts and Ksanda, *Am. J. Sc.*, **17**, 489 (1929). See also Oftedal, *Zs. Kr.*, **83**, 9 (1932), who gives structural details, leading to a formula Cu_3SS_2; Bragg (77, 1937).

4. Merwin, *Washington Ac. Sc., J.*, **5**, 341 (1915), who also gives a description and explanation of the striking color changes in covellite when immersed in colorless inert liquids of different refractions; in alcohol, brilliant purple; in benzene, reddish purple; in methylene iodide, red.

5. Schneiderhöhn and Ramdohr (2, 312, 1931).

6. Hillebrand, *Am. J. Sc.*, **7**, 56 (1899).

7. Posnjak, Allen, and Merwin, *Econ. Geol.*, **10**, 491 (1915) — p. 529 for analysis.

8. Stevanović, *Zs. Kr.*, **44**, 349 (1908).

9. Locke, Hall, and Short, *Am. Inst. Min. Met. Engr., Trans.*, **70**, 933 (1924).

10. Bateman and Lasky, *Econ. Geol.*, **27**, 52 (1932), discuss chalcocite-covellite intergrowths in the light of artificial exsolution experiments.

11. Adam (1926) on crystals from Sardinia.

12. Gliszczynski and Stoicovici, *Zs. Kr.*, **96**, 389 (1937), on crystals from Transylvania.

13. Zies, Allen, and Merwin, *Econ. Geol.*, **11**, 407 (1916), give reactions of covellite with $CuSO_4$ and Cu_2SO_4 at various temperatures, and discuss alteration.

2682   **K L O C K M A N N I T E** [CuSe].   Klockmannit *Ramdohr* (*Cbl. Min.*, 225, 1928); *Schneiderhöhn and Ramdohr* (**2**, 317, 1931).

C r y s t.   Hexagonal? $a : c = 1 : 4.382$ (artif.).

Habit.   Granular aggregates.   Crystal plates (artif.).

P h y s.   Cleavage {0001} (?) perfect. H. 3. G. > 5, probably. Color slate-gray tarnishing to blue-black.   Metallic luster soon becoming dulled.   In polished section strongly anisotropic.   Pleochroism: brownish gray (O) to gray-white (E).   Reflection percentages: (for O) green 18.5, orange 15., red 10.; (for E) green 30.5, orange 25., red 24.

C h e m.   An analysis of material of about 50 per cent purity leads to the formula CuSe, after deducting chalcomenite, clausthalite, quartz, and a silver selenide.   Said to be isomorphous with covellite.

O c c u r.   Found originally at Sierra de Umango, Argentina, with umangite, clausthalite, eucairite, and chalcomenite, the latter as an alteration product of the klockmannite.   Also reported in small amounts from Lehrbach in the Harz Mountains, and Skrikerum, Sweden.

N a m e.   In honor of Professor Klockmann (1858–) of Aachen.

269   **C I N N A B A R** [HgS]. κινναβαρις, *Theophrastus* (ca. 315 B.C.). 'Αμμιον, *Dioscorides* (ca. A.D. 50).   Minium *Pliny* (A.D. 77).   Minium nativum *Germ.*   Bergzinober *Agricola* (466, 1546).   Cinnabarite.   Zinnober, Schwefelquecksilber, Merkur-Blende *Germ.*   Cinnober *Swed.*   Cinabre *Fr.*   Cinabro *Ital.*   Cinabrio *Span.*

C r y s t.   Hexagonal — *P*;   trigonal-trapezohedral — 3 2

$a : c = 1 : 2.2905;^1$ $p_0 : r_0 = 2.6449 : 1;$ $\alpha\ 62°58\frac{1}{2}';$ $\lambda\ 108°12'$

Forms:[2]

		ϕ	$\rho = C$	M	A_2
c	0001	....	0°00′	90°00′	90°00
m	10ī0	30°00′	90 00	60 00	90 00
f	10ī5	30 00	27 52½	76 29	90 00
−f	01ī5	−30 00	27 52½	103 31	66 06½
g	10ī4	30 00	33 28½	73 59½	90 00
−g	01ī4	−30 00	33 28½	106 00½	61 28
h	10ī3	30 00	41 24	70 41½	90 00
−h	01ī3	−30 00	41 24	109 18½	55 03½
i	2025	30 00	46 37	68 41½	90 00
Δ	1012	30 00	52 54½	66 30	90 00
−Δ	01ī2	−30 00	52 54½	113 30	46 18½
r	10ī1	30 00	69 17½	62 07	90 00
−r	01ī1	−30 00	69 17½	117 53	35 54
o	30̄32	30 00	75 51	61 00	90 00
−q	02̄21	−30 00	79 17½	119 25½	31 41
u:′	1124	0 00	48 52½	90 00	67 52½
′y	2īī3	60 00	56 47½	43 34½	114 43½
−′D	1·2·3̄·14	−10 53½	26 33½	94 51	72 59
−D′	ī·3·2̄·14	−49 06½	26 33½	109 45	63 57½
R′	31̄44	16 06	67 14½	75 11	77 12
′R	41̄34	43 54	67 14½	50 15	102 48

Less common:

a′	11̄20	k:	5·0·5̄·28	ν	13·0·ī3̄·18	ρ	70̄72	−L′	2̄·5·3̄·23
′a	2ī10	α	20̄29	χ	50̄56	t	40̄41	T′	3·2̄·5·12
b:	1·0·ī·24	i:	5·0·5̄·19	Ξ	80̄89	σ:	50̄51	′T	5·2̄·3·12
ψ	0·1·ī·18	M	5·0·5̄·18	ν	40̄43	Σ	70̄71	−′F	3·5̄·8·10
b	1·0·ī·16	β	3·0·3̄·10	Y	11·0·ī1̄·8	v:	80̄81	−F′	3̄·8·5̄·10
−b	0·1·ī·16	γ	7·0·7̄·18	−o	03̄32	Γ′	11̄29	Q′	21̄35
e	1·0·ī·10	σ	50̄59	δ	50̄53	N′	11̄28	W′	21̄34
K	10ī8	η	30̄35	n:	70̄74	′P	2ī16	−W′	1̄32̄4
−K	01ī8	k	50̄58	q	20̄21	′x	2ī15	′H	4·ī·3̄·20
y:	3·0·3̄·20	l	20̄23	λ	50̄52	u′	11̄22	I′	4·1̄·5·11
d	10ī6	−l	02̄23	π	30̄31	′ξ	2ī11	−′E	1·5̄·6̄·26

Structure cell.[3] Space group $C3_12$ or $C3_22$; a_0 4.160, c_0 9.540; $a_0 : c_0 = 1 : 2.293$; contains Hg_3S_3.

Habit. Rhombohedral, with dominant development of the positive rhombohedrons; thick tabular {0001}; stout to slender prismatic [10ī0]; rarely with prominent trapezohedrons. Also in crystalline incrustations; granular, massive; as an earthy coating.

Twinning. Twin plane {0001}, twin axis [0001], common; simple twins in contact on {0001}; six-pointed star forms; penetration twins; also concealed, giving intergrowths of hexagonal appearance.

P h y s. Cleavage {10ī0} perfect. Fracture subconchoidal, uneven. Somewhat sectile. H. 2–2½. G. 8.090 (meas.); 8.05 (calc.).[4] Luster adamantine, inclining to metallic when dark colored, to dull in friable varieties. Cochineal-red, often inclining to brownish red and lead-gray. Streak scarlet. Transparent in thin pieces.

O p t. Positive; refraction, birefringence and dispersion strong.
Refractive indices:[5]

λ	598.5	607.5	612.7	623.9	672.0	690.7	718.8	762.0 mμ
nO	2.905	2.884	2.876	2.862	2.814	2.799	2.780	2.756
nE	3.256	3.233	3.224	3.205	3.143	3.121	3.095	3.065

Optically active; rotary power, 315° for red. Some crystals show either
right-handed or left-handed rotation; others are intergrowths of right- and
left-handed parts arranged in six sectors or irregularly distributed.

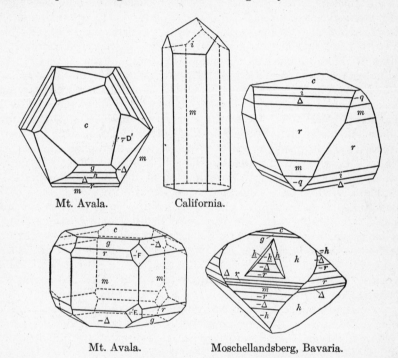

Mt. Avala. California.

Mt. Avala. Moschellandsberg, Bavaria.

C h e m. Mercuric sulfide, HgS, like metacinnabar. Hg 86.2, S 13.8 =
100.0. The ore is usually impure from admixture of clay, iron-oxide,
bitumen.

Var. Hepatic cinnabar. Quecksilberlebererz, Quecksilberbranderz,
Lebererz, Korallenerz, Idrilin *Germ.* Inflammable liver-brown cinnabar
with bituminous impurities.

Tests. Volatile. In closed tube gives a black sublimate of mercuric sulfide; with
sodium carbonate a sublimate of mercury. In the open tube gives sulfur dioxide and
mercury vapor which condenses on the cold walls of the tube.

O c c u r.[6] Commonly in veins and impregnations near recent volcanic
rocks and hot-spring deposits, and evidently deposited near the surface

from solutions which are probably alkaline. Cinnabar is frequently associated with pyrite, marcasite and stibnite in a gangue of opal, chalcedony, quartz, calcite and dolomite, less commonly with fluorite and barite; also with carbonaceous material in shales and slates.

In Asia, in the Altai and Ferghana, Russian Turkestan, there are deposits in limestone and schists which have been worked for quicksilver for a thousand years. In China, in the provinces of Kweichow and Hunan, at times in large twinned crystals on drusy quartz. In the Bakhmut district in Ekaterinoslav, Russia, as an impregnation of sandstone; occasionally in small twinned crystals from Nikitovka. In fine crystals from the mines of Mount Avala, near Belgrade, Yugoslavia; at Szlana, near Rosenau (Rožňava), Gömör, and Horowitz (Hořovice). In Germany, in the coal formation at Moschellandsberg, Bavaria. In Idria, Gorizia, Italy (formerly Carniola, Austria), there are important deposits in the form of veins and impregnations in Triassic sediments. In Tuscany, at Ripa near Seravezza, and elsewhere. The most important cinnabar deposit of the world is at Almaden, Ciudad Real, Spain, where it occurs as an impregnation and replacement of the quartzites interbedded with bituminous shale, associated with sericite, pyrite, and a zeolite. Huancavelica, Peru, has an important deposit. In water-worn pebbles in the gold placers of Dutch Guiana; in various places in Mexico, in an extension of the Terlingua deposit.

In the United States the most important deposits are in California, in the Coast Range, from Del Norte County to San Diego County. New Almaden, Santa Clara County, and New Idria, San Benito County, have produced the largest quantities; these were deposited by solfataric waters along the junction between serpentine and metamorphic sandstones and shales. Occurs with gold and stibnite near National, Nevada; also in Utah and in Oregon. In Texas, at Terlingua, Brewster County, in calcite veins and breccia, associated with chalcedony, gypsum, aragonite, pyrite and a group of rare mercury minerals produced by the alteration of cinnabar. In Pike County, Arkansas, at times in good crystals in quartz-lined vugs.

Alter. Pseudomorphs after pyrite, marcasite, tetrahedrite, dolomite, stibnite, and metacinnabarite have been described.

Artif.[7] Produced by subliming mercury and sulfur; by treating the black sulfide of mercury with solutions of alkaline sulfides; by adding sodium thiosulfate to concentrated neutral solutions.

Name. Supposed to have come from India. *Minium* now signifies red lead, early used to adulterate cinnabar. *Mine, mineral* have been said to come from Latin miniaria, *quicksilver mine*.

Ref.

1. Haüy (**3**, 313, 1822), whose fundamental angle $(10\bar{1}1) : (\bar{1}101) = 108°12'$ agrees precisely with $(2\bar{2}01) : (02\bar{2}1) = 108°12'$ calculated from the exact elements of Schabus, *Ak. Wien, Ber.*, **6**, 63 (1851), obtained from crystals from Almaden. The primary rhombohedron of Schabus was adopted by Dana (66, 1892) and Goldschmidt (377, 1897; **9**, 136, 1923); that of Haüy corresponds to the structure cell. In the adopted orientation the most numerous series of rhombohedrons is taken as positive. Transformation: Schabus to Haüy: 0100/1000/0010/0002.

2. Goldschmidt (9, 136, 1923): Steinmetz and Gossner, *Zs. Kr.*, **55**, 156 (1915); Svetolik, *Bull. soc. min.*, **45**, 134 (1922). The distinction between positive and negative forms is partly uncertain, owing to the lack of an entirely reliable means of distinguishing the nonequivalent sextants and the possibility of concealed twinning.

Uncertain forms:

$0\cdot1\cdot\bar{1}\cdot30$	$0\bar{3}38$	$11\cdot0\cdot\overline{11}\cdot10$	$11\cdot0\cdot\overline{11}\cdot4$	$8\cdot\bar{3}\cdot\bar{5}\cdot26$	$\bar{2}\cdot8\cdot\bar{6}\cdot17$
$1\cdot0\cdot1\cdot14$	$0\bar{2}25$	$5\bar{0}54$	$0\bar{3}31$	$2\cdot1\cdot\bar{3}\cdot15$	$1\cdot4\cdot\bar{5}\cdot24$
$10\bar{1}9$	$7\cdot0\cdot\bar{7}\cdot16$	$0\bar{5}54$	$11\cdot0\cdot\overline{11}\cdot2$	$5\cdot10\cdot\overline{15}\cdot24$	$\bar{1}\cdot5\cdot\bar{4}\cdot24$
$10\bar{1}7$	$4\bar{0}49$	$7\bar{0}75$	$0\cdot11\cdot\overline{11}\cdot2$	$3\bar{1}25$	$5\cdot\bar{1}\cdot4\cdot11$
$0\cdot3\cdot\bar{3}\cdot20$	$9\cdot0\cdot\bar{9}\cdot16$	$16\cdot0\cdot\overline{16}\cdot9$	$2\cdot\bar{1}\cdot\bar{1}\cdot40$	$5\cdot10\cdot\overline{15}\cdot16$	$41\bar{5}5$
$5\cdot0\cdot\bar{5}\cdot28$	$0\bar{5}58$	$0\cdot16\cdot\overline{16}\cdot9$	$2\cdot\bar{1}\cdot\bar{1}\cdot12$	$21\bar{3}3$	$\bar{1}\cdot6\cdot\bar{5}\cdot26$
$3\cdot0\cdot\bar{3}\cdot15$	$11\cdot0\cdot\overline{11}\cdot16$	$9\bar{0}94$	$2\cdot\bar{1}\cdot\bar{1}\cdot10$	$13\bar{2}1$	$6\cdot\bar{1}\cdot5\cdot14$
$0\cdot3\cdot\bar{3}\cdot16$	$3\bar{0}34$	$0\bar{9}94$	$7\cdot7\cdot\overline{14}\cdot36$	$31\bar{2}3$	
$5\cdot0\cdot\bar{5}\cdot16$	$4\bar{0}45$	$0\bar{5}52$	$14\cdot\bar{7}\cdot\bar{7}\cdot36$	$3\cdot1\cdot\bar{4}\cdot20$	
$30\bar{3}8$	$9\cdot0\cdot\bar{9}\cdot10$	$0\bar{8}83$	$2\cdot3\cdot\bar{5}\cdot23$	$3\cdot1\cdot\bar{4}\cdot12$	

3. Buckley and Vernon, *Min. Mag.*, **20**, 382 (1925), on powdered cinnabar.
4. From the dimensions and content of the structure cell.
5. Abbreviated values after Rose, *Cbl. Min.*, 528, 1912.
6. Lindgren (463, 1933).
7. Doelter (4 [1], 359, 1925).

26·10 R E A L G A R [AsS]. Σανδαράκη *Theophrastus* (315 B.C.) Σανδαραχη *Dioscorides* (A.D. 50). Sandaracha *Pliny* (35, 6, A.D. 77) Sandaracha *Germ.* Reuschgeel, Rosgeel *Agricola* (444, 1529). Rauschgelb pt., Arsenicum sulphure mixtum, Risigallum pt., Realgar, Arsenicum rubrum *Wallerius* (224, 1747). Arsenic rouge *Wallerius* (406, 1753). Réalgar natif, Rubine d'Arsenic *de Lisle* (3, 333, 1783). Red Sulphuret of Arsenic. Rothes Rauschgelb, Rauschrot, Rote Arsenblende *Germ.* Arsenic sulfuré rouge *Haüy* (4, 244, 1822). Risigallo *Ital.* Rejalgar *Span.*

C r y s t. Monoclinic; prismatic — 2/m.

$a : b : c = 0.6879 : 1 : 0.4858;$ $\beta\ 106°32'$,[1] $p_0 : q_0 : r_0 = 0.7062 : 0.4657 : 1$
$r_2 : p_2 : q_2 = 2.1472 : 1.5164 : 1;$ $\mu\ 73°28';$ $p_0'\ 0.7367,\ q_0'\ 0.4858,\ x'\ 0.2968$

Forms:[2]

		φ	ρ	φ2	ρ2 = B	C	A
b	010	0°00′	90°00′	....	0°00′	90°00′	90°00′
a	100	90 00	90 00	0°00′	90 00	73 28	0 00
μ	140	20 46	90 00	0 00	20 46	84 12½	69 14
v	130	26 49	90 00	0 00	26 49	82 37½	63 11
l	120	37 10	90 00	0 00	37 10	80 06	52 50
u	350	42 18	90 00	0 00	42 18	78 57½	47 42
w	230	45 19	90 00	0 00	45 19	78 19½	44 41
m	110	56 36	90 00	0 00	56 36	76 15½	33 24
i	210	71 45	90 00	0 00	71 45	74 19	18 15
n	011	31 25½	29 39	73 28	65 01½	24 58½	75 03
E	032	22 09½	38 12	73 28	55 04	34 56	76 30½
e	021	16 59½	45 27	73 28	47 02	42 58	77 59
k	031	11 30½	56 05	73 28	35 35½	54 24½	80 28
z	101	90 00	45 56½	44 03½	90 00	29 24½	44 03½
x	$\bar{1}$01	−90 00	23 44½	113 44½	90 00	40 16½	113 44½
d	111	69 49½	48 47½	44 03½	71 20	34 23	47 05½
r	$\bar{1}$11	−42 09½	33 14½	113 44½	66 01½	45 48	111 35
H	121	46 46	54 49	44 03½	55 57½	43 47½	53 27
o	131	35 20½	60 46	44 03½	44 37	52 16½	59 41
q	$\bar{1}$21	−24 21½	46 50½	113 44½	48 29	55 14½	106 23
y	$\bar{1}$31	−16 47½	56 42	113 44½	36 51½	62 46	103 58½
f	$\bar{2}$11	−67 34	51 51	139 38	72 32	67 20	136 37½

Less common:

c 001	D 560	Π 0·18·1	Ψ 2·13·5	d: 512	ν $\bar{1}$83	K $\bar{5}$23	
W 160	g 540	N 501	Z 122	e: 532	φ $\bar{1}$22	χ $\bar{5}$93	
δ 150	γ 320	ξ $\bar{2}$01	Ω 2·11·4	M 341	S $\bar{3}$24	ρ $\bar{7}$54	
A 270	H: 310	T 112	ψ: 3·10·5	f: 411	p $\bar{2}$12	Δ $\bar{1}$2·1·6	
j 380	λ 0·2·15	V: 332	R 213	g: 10·1·2	I $\bar{5}$65	ι $\bar{1}$4·4·7	
ζ 250	s 013	Λ: 221	l: 293	h: 511	t $\bar{2}$32	Ξ $\bar{2}$31	
h 370	σ 012	τ $\bar{1}$12	a: 212	i: 15·4·3	J $\bar{3}$73	Σ $\bar{5}$·11·2	
Γ 490	α 023	O $\bar{5}$54	b: 272	Q 521	X $\bar{1}$51	π: $\bar{3}$61	
Θ 6·13·0	P 034	V $\bar{3}$32	π 141	c: 7·10·5	k: 721	G $\bar{3}$12	σ: $\bar{2}$7·7·7
B 580	F 041	Λ $\bar{2}$21	Υ 123	η 211	S: 921	U $\bar{3}$22	j: $\bar{1}$3·4·2
β 340	ψ 051	Υ 123	η: 251	ω $\bar{1}$24	ε $\bar{3}$42	θ $\bar{3}$62	
C 450	Φ 081	L 235					

Structure cell.[3] Space group, $P2_1/n$. a_0 9.27 b_0 13.50 c_0 6.56; β 106°33′; $a_0 : b_0 : c_0 = 0.6878 : 1 : 0.4858$; contains $As_{16}S_{16}$.

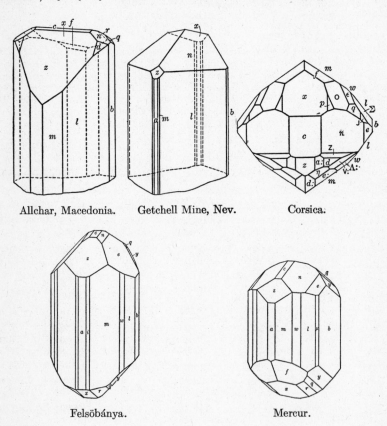

Allchar, Macedonia.　　　Getchell Mine, Nev.　　　Corsica.

Felsöbánya.　　　Mercur.

Habit. Short prismatic and striated [001]. Also granular, coarse to fine; compact; as an incrustation. Common forms: $c\ b\ a\ v\ l\ m\ n\ e\ x\ N\ q$.

Twinning. Contact twins on {100}, with irregular composition surfaces containing [001].[4]

P h y s. Cleavage {010} good; {$\bar{1}$01}, {100}, {120}, less good; {110}. Fracture small conchoidal. Sectile. H. $1\frac{1}{2}$–2. G. 3.56; 3.477;[5] 3.59 (calc.). Luster resinous to greasy. Color, aurora-red to orange-yellow. Streak orange-red to aurora-red. Transparent when fresh. Disintegrates on long exposure to light to a reddish yellow powder which is a mixture of As_2S_3 and As_2O_3. M.P. 307–314°.[9]

Opt.

ORIENTATION		n_{590}	n_{670}	PLEOCHROISM	
X	$c = -11°$	2.538	2.486	Nearly colorless	Bx. neg. (−)
Y	b	2.684	2.602	Pale golden yellow	$2V$ 40°34' (648)
Z	....	2.704	2.620	Pale golden yellow	$r > v$ very strong, inclined

C h e m. Arsenic monosulfide, AsS.

Anal.

	1	2	3	4
As	70.0	69.57	69.54	69.74
S	30.0	30.55	30.29	29.82
Rem.	....	.....	0.11	0.15
Total	100.0	100.12	99.94	99.71

1. AsS. 2. Allchar.[7] 3. Binnental. Rem. is SiO_2.[7] 4. Neu-Moldova. Rem. is SiO_2.[8]

Tests. Decomposed by HNO_3, easily by aqua regia.

O c c u r. Realgar occurs commonly as a minor constituent of certain ore veins associated with orpiment and other arsenic minerals, with stibnite and with lead, silver, and gold ores. It is also found in certain limestones or dolomites, in clay rocks, and as a volcanic sublimation product or a deposit from hot springs. Realgar occurs with ores of silver and lead at Felsöbánya, Kapnikbánya, and Nagyág in Roumania; at Joachimstal in Bohemia; at Tajowa near Neusohl, Czechoslovakia in beds of clay; on quartz in phyllite at Kreševo, Bosnia; at Allchar near Rozdan, northwest of Salonika, Macedonia; at Schneeberg in Saxony and at Andreasburg in the Harz Mountains. It is found in fine crystals in the dolomite of the Binnental, Valais, Switzerland; in coatings and minute crystals in Vesuvian lavas and at the solfataras at Pozzuoli, near Naples, Italy; in complex crystals in Corsica; in Japan in the provinces of Ribuzen and Shimotsuke. In the United States it is found in the Norris Geyser Basin, Yellowstone National Park, Wyoming, where it occurs with orpiment as a deposition from the hot waters; at Mercur, Tooele County, Utah, as fine crystals in cavities with calcite; and at Manhattan, Nye County, Nevada; also, as elongated crystals at the Getchell mine, 27 miles north of Golconda, Nevada; in the Monte Cristo Mining district, Snohomish County, Washington.

A l t e r. On exposure to light changes to orpiment and arsenolite.

A r t i f.[10] Obtained in crystals by fusion or sublimation of the constituents. Frequently formed as a furnace product.

N a m e. From *Arab., Rahj al ghar, powder of the mine.*

Ref.

1. Goldschmidt, *Zs. Kr.*, **39**, 113 (1904), transformed to the structural cell of Buerger, *Am. Min.*, **20**, 36 (1935), which differs from that of Dana (33, 1892). Transformations; Dana to Buerger, $\overline{1}0\overline{1}/0\overline{2}0/001$; Goldschmidt to Buerger $\overline{1}0\overline{1}/0\overline{1}0/001$.

2. Goldschmidt (7, 115, 1922), Liffa and Emszt, *Földt. Kölz.*, **50**, 21, 106 (1921) — *Min. Abs.*, **2**, 173 (1923); Tokody, *Zs. Kr.*, **61**, 553 (1925); Ungemach, *Bull. soc. min.*, **53**, 394 (1930); Buttgenbach, *Ac. Belgique, Bull.*, 1019 (1933); Barić, *Rad. Jugoslav Ak.*, **249**, 95 (1934) — *Min. Abs.*, **6**, 185 (1935). Uncertain forms: {311}, {$\overline{1}$41}, {$\overline{5}$·10·2}, {$\overline{6}$72}, {$\overline{4}$61}, {$\overline{6}$51}, {$\overline{1}$4·3·2}.

3. Buerger (1935), on a crystal from Allchar.

4. Ungemach (1930).

5. Weigel, *Min. Mitt.*, **38**, 288 (1925), on a crystal from Felsöbánya.

6. Weigel (1925); Larsen and Berman (212, 1934).

7. Jannasch anal. in Goldschmidt (1904).

8. Emszt anal. in Liffa and Emszt (1921).

9. Borgström, *Jb. Min.*, I, 10, 1916.

10. Doelter (4 [1], 42, 1925).

26·11   C O O P E R I T E [PtS].   *Wartenweiler* in discussion of paper by *Cooper* (*J. Chem. Met. Mining Soc. South Africa*, **28**, 281, 1928). (Not the cooperite [= serpentine] of *Adam* [7, 1869].) *Bannister* and *Hey* (*Min. Mag.*, **23**, 188, 1932).

C r y s t.[1]   Tetragonal; Ditetragonal dipyramidal — $4/m\ 2/m\ 2/m$.

$$a_0 : c_0 = 1 : 1.758; \qquad p_0 : r_0 = 1.758 : 1$$

Forms:

$$c\{001\}, \quad a\{010\}, \quad d\{011\}$$

Structure cell.   Space group $P4/mmc$; $a_0\ 3.47$, $c_0\ 6.10$; $a_0 : c_0 = 1 : 1.758$; contains Pt_2S_2.

Habit.   Irregular grains, and infrequently as distorted crystal fragments elongated parallel to [101].

P h y s.[2]   Cleavage {011}. Fracture conchoidal. H. 4–5. G. 9.5; 10.20 (calc.). Metallic luster. Color steel-gray.

C h e m.   Essentially platinum sulfide, PtS, with perhaps a small amount of Pd and a trace of Ni.

Anal.

	1	2	3	4	5
Pt	85.89	[85.6]	82.5	80.26	82.2
Pd	.....	trace	....	4.31	2.6
Ru,Ir,etc.	.....	....	....	0.62	....
Ni	.....	0.1	....	trace	....
S	14.11	14.3	17.5	14.36	14.4
Total	100.00	100.0	100.0	99.55	99.2
G.	10.20	9.5			

1. PtS. 2. Potgietersrust. (Analysis on 8.28 mg.).[4] 3. Rustenberg. (Analysis on 2.18 mg.).[4] 4, 5. Potgietersrust.[3]

O c c u r.   In the concentrates from the platiniferous norites of the Bushveld complex, in the Rustenberg and Potgietersrust districts, Transvaal, South Africa. Associated minerals are sperrylite, native platinum, braggite, and laurite, as well as some still unidentified precious-metal minerals.

A r t i f.[4]   Prepared by fusion of Pt, K_2CO_3, and S in a porcelain crucible for 15 minutes.

N a m e.   After R. A. Cooper, who first described the mineral.

Ref.

1. Bannister and Hey (1932).   The supposed orthorhombic material measured by White, in Adam, *Geol. Soc. South Africa, Trans.*, **33**, 103 (1930), has been shown to be isometric (Bannister) and not the same as cooperite (probably laurite).
2. Schneiderhöhn, *Cbl. Min.*, 193 (1929), examined material of uncertain authenticity and his physical data for cooperite are therefore not used.
3. Adam anal. in Bannister and Hey (1932).
4. Hey anal. in Bannister and Hey (1932).

26·12   **B R A G G I T E** [PtS].   *Bannister* and *Hey* (*Min. Mag.*, **23**, 188, 1932).

C r y s t.   Tetragonal;   Tetragonal pyramidal — 4   or   tetragonal dipyramidal — $4/m$.

Structure cell.   Space group, $P4_2/m$ or $P4_2$; a_0 6.37, c_0 6.58; $a_0 : c_0 =$ 1 : 1.031; contains $(Pt,Pd,Ni)_8S_8$.[1]

P h y s.   In rounded grains and prisms.   G. 10; 8.9 (calc.).   Steelgray.   Metallic luster.

C h e m.   A sulfide of platinum, palladium, and nickel, $(Pt,Pd,Ni)S$, with Pt : Pd : Ni = 4.5 : 2.5 : 1.0.

Anal.

	1	2	3
Pt	60.15	[58.2]	59.1
Pd	18.27	18.1	20.87
Ni	4.02	4.7	2.8
S	17.56	19.0	16.8
Total	100.00	100.0	99.99
G.	8.9	10±	

1. $(Pt,Pd,Ni)S$ with Pt : Pd : Ni = 4.5 : 2.5 : 1.   2. Potgietersrust.   Analysis on 10.28 mg.[2]   3. Potgietersrust (?)   Includes Rh, Ir, etc. 0.42 per cent.[3]

O c c u r.   In the concentrates from the platiniferous norites of the Bushveld complex, in the Rustenberg and Potgietersrust districts, Transvaal, South Africa, with sperrylite, cooperite, and laurite.

N a m e.   After Sir William H. Bragg and his son, Professor W. L. Bragg, this being the first new mineral isolated and determined by x-ray methods.

Ref.

1. The structure and cell dimensions of braggite are identical with those of artificial PdS, and have no simple relation to cooperite, PtS.
2. Hey anal. in Bannister and Hey (1932).
3. Adam anal. in Bannister and Hey (1932).

26·13   **Herzenbergite** [SnS].   Kolbeckine *Herzenberg* (*Cbl. Min.*, 354, 1932).   Herzenbergit *Ramdohr* (*Jb. Min., Beil.-Bd.*, **68A**, 292, 1934; *Zs. Kr.*, **92**, 186, 1935).

An incompletely described species, presumably the same as artificial SnS.[1]   Fine-grained material;   color and streak black;   metallic luster. Imperfect analysis yields approximately Sn_2S_3.   Easily soluble in HCl and H_2SO_4 with evolution of H_2S.   Found in the Maria-Teresa mine near

Huari, between Oruro and Uyuni, Bolivia, intimately associated with cassiterite, pyrite, and quartz.

Named for the German chemist, R. Herzenberg.

Ref.

1. Hofmann, *Fortschr. Min.*, **19**, 30 (1935); *Zs. Kr.*, **92**, 161 (1935), gives the following for artificial SnS: space group *Pnma*; a_0 3.98, b_0 4.33, c_0 11.18; $a_0 : b_0 : c_0 = 0.919 : 1 : 2.58$; contains Sn_4S_4. This is related to the ratio $a : b : c = 0.3883 : 1 : 0.3566$ of Stevanović, *Zs. Kr.*, **40**, 321 (1905), as follows: Hofmann to Stevanović 001/100/010.

26·14·1 **E M P R E S S I T E** [AgTe]. *Bradley (Am. J. Sc.*, **38**, 163, 1914; **39**, 223, 1915).

P h y s. Massive. In fine granular and compact masses. Fracture finely conchoidal to uneven. Brittle to friable. H. 3–3½. G. 7.510. Color pale bronze. Streak grayish black to black.

C h e m.[1] A silver telluride, AgTe.

Anal.

	1	2	3
Ag	45.81	45.17	43.70
Fe	.....	0.22	2.16
Te	54.19	54.75	53.84
Insol.	.....	0.39	0.33
Total	100.00	100.53	100.03

1. AgTe. 2. Average of two analyses. 3. Average of two analyses.[2]

Tests. F. 1. Readily soluble in HNO_3.

O c c u r. With galena and native tellurium at the Empress Josephine mine, Kerber Creek district, Colorado.

A r t i f.[3] AgTe is a probable phase in the system Ag-Te, but not certainly identified, and not shown to be the same as empressite.

Ref.

1. Schaller, *Washington Ac. Sc., J.*, **4**, 497 (1914), considers empressite to be an end member of the muthmannite series (Ag,Au)Te. The evidence is not, however, complete, and empressite is in any event a valid species name, with muthmannite reserved for the gold-bearing variety, should it so prove to be.
2. Dittus anal. in Bradley (1915).
3. A discussion of the artificial system in Hansen (65, 1936).

26·14·2 **M U T H M A N N I T E** [(Ag,Au)Te]. Krennerite pt. *Schrauf (Zs. Kr.*, **2**, 209, 1878). *Scharizer (Geol. Reichsanst., Jb.*, **30**, 604, 1880). Muthmannit *Zambonini (Zs. Kr.*, **49**, 246, 1911).

In tabular crystals usually elongated in one direction, with a perfect cleavage in the zone of elongation. H. 2½. G. 5.598.[1] Color bright brass-yellow, on fresh fracture gray-white. Powder iron-gray.

C h e m.[2] Silver-gold telluride, (Ag,Au)Te, with Ag : Au = 1 : 1 to 2 : 1. A small amount of Pb has been reported.

Anal.

	1	2	3	4	5
Au	24.78	22.90	31.	30.03	35.20
Ag	27.11	26.36	21.	16.69	19.25
Pb	.....	2.58	...	.....	.....
Te	48.11	46.44	[48.]	39.14	45.55
Sb	.....	.....	...	[9.75]	.....
S	.....	.....	...	4.39	.....
Total	100.00	98.28	100.	100.00	100.00
G.				5.598	

1. (Ag,Au)Te with Ag : Au = 2 : 1.   2. Nagyág?   Contains small amounts of Cu and Fe not determined.[3]   3. Nagyág.   0.0021 gm. used and metal button of assay weighed.[4]   4. Nagyág.   The Sb and S as stibnite impurity.[5]   5. (Ag,Au)Te with Ag : Au = 1 : 1.

Tests. B.B. as with sylvanite. Mostly soluble in HNO_3, leaving residue of Au. With HCl gives ppt. of AgCl.

O c c u r. Intimately associated with other tellurides, especially krennerite, with which it was at first confused, at Nagyág, Transylvania.

N a m e. After Professor W. Muthmann (1861–1913) of Munich, chemist and crystallographer.

Ref.

1. Density from Scharizer (1880).
2. Early analyses listed by Dana (105, 1892) under krennerite.
3. Zambonini (1911).
4. Schrauf (1878).
5. Scharizer (1880).

27 A_3X_4 TYPE

Members of this type, the linnaeite series, and daubreelite, are of the spinel structure type, and might therefore be written as A_2BX_4. In linnaeite A = Co, Ni; in daubreelite A = Cr. The B atoms are Co, Ni, Fe, Cu in linnaeite, and Fe in daubreelite. Consistent with the spinel type, the crystals of the linnaeite series are isometric, dominantly octahedral in habit, and have spinel law twins.

Badenite, $(Co,Ni,Fe)_3(As,Bi)_4$, is not certainly a member of this type and needs further study.

Linnaeite Series

$$(Co,Ni)_2(Co,Ni,Fe,Cu)S_4$$

		a_0
Linnaeite	Co_3S_4	9.398
Siegenite	$(Co,Ni)_3S_4$	9.41
Carrollite	Co_2CuS_4	9.458
Violarite	Ni_2FeS_4	9.40
Polydymite	Ni_3S_4	9.405

A more or less complete chemical variation exists in this series within the limits of the series formula, which shows the relation to the spinel formula. The structures of these species are likewise of the spinel type. Physical properties of the series are very similar. Most of the analyses fall between linnaeite and polydymite, and these are here called siegenite.

2711   **L I N N A E I T E** [Co_3S_4]. Kobolt med Jern och Svafelsyra *Brandt* (*Ak. Stockholm, Handl.*, 119, 1746). Kobalt med förvswafladt Järn, Cobaltum Ferro Sulphurato mineralisatum, *Cronstedt* (213, 1758). Cobaltum pyriticosum *Linnaes* (1768); *de Born* (1, 144, 1772). Mine de Cobalt sulfureuse *de Lisle* (3, 134, 1783). Kobalt-Glanz pt. *Werner, Kirwan*. Svafelbunden Kobolt *Hisinger* (*Afhandl.*, 3, 316, 1810). Kobaltkies *Hausmann* (158, 1813). Schwefelkobalt. Sulphuret of Cobalt; Colbalt Pyrites. Cobalt sulfuré *Fr.* Koboldine *Beudant* (2, 417, 1832). Linneit *Haidinger* (560, 1845A). Koboltkis *Swed.* Selenolinnaeite *Cuvelier* (*Natuurw. Tijdschr.*, 11, 176, 1929).

2712   **S I E G E N I T E** [$(Co,Ni)_3S_4$]. Kobaltnickelkies (not Kobaltkies) *Rammelsberg*. Siegenite, Nickel linnaeite *Dana* (687, 1850).

2713   **C A R R O L L I T E** [Co_2CuS_4]. *Faber* (*Am. J. Sc.*, 13, 418, 1852). Sychnodymite *Laspeyres* (*Zs. Kr.*, 19, 17, 1891).

2714   **V I O L A R I T E** [Ni_2FeS_4]. Ferriferous Polydymite *Clarke* and *Catlett* (*Am. J. Sc.*, 37, 372, 1889). Violarite *Lindgren* and *Davy* (*Econ. Geol.*, 19, 309, 1924).

2715   **P O L Y D Y M I T E** [Ni_3S_4]. Grünauite pt. *Nicol* (458, 1849). Saynit pt. *Kobell* (13, 1853A). Nickellinnaeite *Zambonini* (*Riv. min.*, 47, 1916).

C r y s t.   Isometric; hexoctahedral — $4/m\ \bar{3}\ 2/m$.

Forms:[1]

		LINNAEITE	SIEGENITE	CARROLLITE	POLYDYMITE
a	001	x	x	x	x
d	011	x	x	x	...
o	111	x	x	x	x
m	113	x	x	x	x
n	112	...	x	x	...
q	133	...	...	...	x
z	234	x	x	...	...

Structure cell.[2]   Space group $Fd3m$; a_0 9.398 (linnaeite), 9.41 (siegenite), 9.458 (carrollite), 9.40 (violarite), 9.405 (polydymite). Contains $(Co,Ni)_{16}(Co,Ni,Cu,Fe)_8S_{32}$.

Habit.   The species of this series are all dominantly octahedral. Also massive, granular to compact. Larger crystals usually with rough faces. Violarite has not been reported as crystals. Etching effects are similar to those on magnetite.[3]

Twinning. On {111}. Some members of the series, especially polydymite, show polysynthetic twin lamellae.

Phys. Cleavage {001} imperfect. Fracture uneven to subconchoidal. H. $4\frac{1}{2}$–$5\frac{1}{2}$. G. 4.5–4.8; calculated: 4.85 (linnaeite), 4.83 (siegenite, polydymite, carrollite), 4.79 (violarite).

Luster metallic, brilliant on fresh surface, easily tarnished to copper-red or violet-gray. Color light gray to steel-gray to violet-gray (violarite). Opaque. Isotropic. Percentages of reflection:[4]

	LINNAEITE	CARROLLITE	POLYDYMITE
Green	46.5	45	45
Orange	44	44	44.5
Red	46	43	49

Chem.[5] Essentially cobalt and nickel sulfides, with iron and copper present in nearly all analyses, but not exceeding one-third of the metal atoms. Formula $(Co,Ni)_2(Co,Ni,Fe,Cu)S_4$.

Anal.[6]

	1	2	3	4	5	6	7	8
Cu	.....	2.40	8.79	.....	....	3.16	20.53	20.42
Fe	.....	2.36	1.30	.....	0.62	3.22	.....	2.33
Co	57.96	48.70	40.71	29.02	26.08	20.36	38.06	35.30
Ni	.....	4.75	7.35	28.89	31.18	31.24	.....	1.76
S	42.04	41.70	41.43	42.09	42.63	42.43	41.41	39.47
Insol.	.....	0.40	0.14	.....	0.16	.....	.....	.....
Total	100.00	100.31	99.72	100.00	100.67	100.41	100.00	99.28
G.		4.851			4.826			4.831

1. Co_3S_4. 2. Linnaeite; Carroll Co., Md.[7] 3. Linnaeite; Gladhammar.[8] 4. $(Co,Ni)_3S_4$ with Co : Ni = 1 : 1. 5. Siegenite; Littfeld.[9] 6. Siegenite; Mine la Motte, Mo.[10] 7. Co_2CuS_4. 8. Carrollite; Gladhammar.[8]

	9	10	11	12	13	14	15	16	17
Cu	18.98	13.90	9.98	.....	1.05	1.12	.....	.....	.....
Fe	0.93	2.18	2.25	18.52	19.33	17.01	15.47	3.98	.....
Co	35.79	35.15	36.08	.....	2.50	1.05	.....	0.63	.....
Ni	3.66	7.01	7.65	38.94	33.94	38.68	43.18	54.30	57.86
S	40.64	40.74	41.89	42.54	42.17	41.68	41.35	41.09	42.14
Insol.	.....	0.27	0.50	.....	1.31	0.40	.....	.....	.....
Total	100.00	99.25	98.35	100.00	100.30	99.94	100.00	100.00	100.00
G.	4.758			4.79				4.81	4.828

9. Carrollite (sychnodymite); Siegen. After deducting 1.95 per cent quartz.[11] 10. Carrollite; Gladhammar.[8] 11. Carrollite; Mineral Hill mine, near Sykesville, Md.[7] 12. Ni_2FeS_4. Violarite. 13. Violarite; Julian, Calif. Analysis made on 0.12 gm.[12] 14. Violarite; Vermilion mine, Sudbury.[12] 15. Violarite; Sudbury. Calculated to 100 per cent after deducting SiO_2 and eliminating Cu as chalcopyrite.[13] 16. Polydymite; Grunau mine, Siegen. Recalculated after deducting 5 per cent impurities of gersdorffite and ullmannite.[14] 17. Ni_3S_4.

Tests. F. $1\frac{1}{2}$–2, B.B. to a magnetic globule. The roasted mineral gives with the fluxes reactions of the various elements present. Yields sulfur in C.T. Decomposed by HNO_3 with separation of sulfur. Insoluble in HCl.

Occur. The minerals of the series are comparatively rare, with siegenite the most common, linnaeite less so, carrollite, polydymite, and violarite rare. They usually are associated with other copper, nickel, and iron sulfides, such as chalcopyrite, pyrrhotite, pyrite, millerite, gersdorffite, ullmannite, in hydrothermal vein deposits. Siderite and quartz are associated gangue minerals; galena, sphalerite, and bismuthinite are other associated minerals.

Oriented inclusions of millerite in linnaeite have been observed[15] in polished section. The millerite crystals lie on {001} of the linnaeite.

In the Siegen district of Westphalia all the members of the series, except violarite, are found, principally at Müsen (*linnaeite* and *siegenite*), Littfeld (*siegenite*), at the Kohlenbach mine, southeast of Eisenfeld (*sychnodymite-carrollite*) in a quartz-siderite gangue with tetrahedrite. At Kladno, Bohemia (*siegenite*); in Sweden, at the Bastnäs mine, near Riddarhyttan, Våstmanland, a cuprian linnaeite, and at Gladhammar, Kalmar (*linnaeite* and *carrollite*). Found as large octahedrons of linnaeite at Katanga (selenian?) in the Belgian Congo and also at N'Kana, Northern Rhodesia.

In the United States found in Carroll County, Maryland, principally at the Patapsco mine, Finksburg (*carrollite*), at the Springfield mine, Sykesville (*linnaeite*) and at the Mineral Hill mine (*cuprian linnaeite*). At Mine La Motte in Missouri (*siegenite*); at Julian, California (*violarite*) associated with chalcopyrite and pyrrhotite.

At Sudbury, Ontario, violarite occurs rarely in the nickel ores (the species was originally described from the Vermilion mine) associated with pyrrhotite, millerite, and chalcopyrite.

A l t e r. Alters to the so-called yellow earthy cobalt (gelb Erdkobalt), a mixture of erythrite and pitticite.

N a m e. Linnaeite, after Linnaeus. First applied to the Bastnäs material. Siegenite and carrollite are after the localities in which these species were found. Polydymite is from πολυς, *many*, and διδυμος, *twin*, because observed in twinned forms. Violarite is from the Latin *violaris*, *of violet*, in allusion to its color, especially under the reflecting microscope.

Ref.

1. Goldschmidt (5, 163, 1918, for linnaeite; 6, 166, 1920, for polydymite; 8, 101, 1922, for carrollite [sychnodymite]). Also Witteborg, *Zs. Kr.*, 83, 374 (1932), for siegenite; Schoep, *Soc. géol. Belgique, Bull.*, B215, 1927, for linnaeite from Katanga.

2. Menzer, *Zs. Kr.*, 64, 506 (1926), showed the practical identity of x-ray effects in linnaeite, polydymite, and carrollite (sychnodymite). de Jong and Hoog, *Zs. Kr.*, 66, 168 (1927), showed the identity of powder pictures of carrollite and sychnodymite with $a_0 = 9.458$. de Jong and Willems, *Zs. anorg. Chem.*, 161, 311 (1927), give values as follows: linnaeite (or siegenite) 9.36, polydymite 9.65Å. Value for siegenite here used by Natta and Passerini, *Acc. Linc., Rend.*, [6] 14, 38 (1931), on material from Littfeld (anal. 5 of text). Value for violarite by Berman (priv. comm.) on Sudbury material.

3. Becke, *Min. Mitt.*, 7, 225 (1885).

4. Schneiderhöhn and Ramdohr (2, 367, 1931).

5. The formulas here given for the series were first proposed by Zambonini, *Riv. min.*, 47, 48 (1916), who also showed that sychnodymite was essentially the same as carrollite. See also Tarr, *Am. Min.*, 20, 69 (1935), who compiled a list of analyses. For a discussion of other formulas previously proposed see Doelter (4 [1], 654, 1926).

6. Older analyses in Dana (75, 78, 79, 1892).

7. Shannon, *Am. J. Sci.*, 11, 489 (1926).

8. Johansson, *Ark. Kemi*, **9**, no. 8 (1924).
9. Eichler, Henglein, and Meigen, *Cbl. Min.*, 225, 1922.
10. Tarr, *Am. Min.*, **20**, 69 (1935).
11. Laspeyres, *Zs. Kr.*, **19**, 19 (1891).
12. Short and Shannon, *Am. Min.*, **15**, 1 (1930).
13. Clarke and Catlet, *Am. J. Sci.*, **37**, 372 (1889); *Jb. Min.*, **737, 1876.**
14. Laspeyres, *J. pr. Chem.*, **14**, 397 (1876) — Dana (75, 1892).
15. Schneiderhöhn and Ramdohr (2, 368, 1931).

272   **D A U B R E E L I T E** [Cr_2FeS_4].   *Smith (Am. J. Sc.*, **12**, 109, 1876; **16**, 270, 1878).

C r y s t.[1]   Isometric; hexoctahedral — $4/m\, \bar{3}\, 2/m$.

Structure cell.   Space group $Fd3m$; a_0 9.966 ± 0.002 (from Cerros del Buei Muerto hexahedrite).

Habit.   Massive, somewhat scaly to platy.   No crystals found.

P h y s.   Cleavage distinct.[2]   Brittle.   Fracture uneven.   G.   5.01,[3] 3.81 ± 0.01;[4] 3.842 (calc.).   Luster metallic, brilliant.   Color black. Streak black.   Nonmagnetic.

C h e m.   Chromium iron sulfide, Cr_2FeS_4, with no recorded variation from this composition.

Anal.

	Cr	Fe	S	Total
1	36.10	19.38	44.52	100.00
2	35.91	20.10	42.69	98.70

1. Cr_2FeS_4.   2. From the Coahuila, Mexico, meteorite.   Average of three analyses.

Tests.   B.B. infusible; in R.F. loses luster and becomes magnetic.   Not attacked by HCl, but completely dissolved in HNO_3 without liberation of free sulfur.

O c c u r.   First found in the iron meteorite from Bolson de Mapimi, Mexico, intergrown with troilite or on the borders of troilite nodules. Reported in small amounts in many meteorites, more especially from Toluca, Mexico; Sevier, Tennessee; Cranbourne, Australia; the Coahuila meteorite.   Also found in the stony meteorite from Hvittis, Finland.

A r t i f.[5]   Prepared by passing H_2S gas over chromium and iron salts at red heat.

N a m e.   In honor of Professor Gabriel Auguste Daubrée (1814–96) of Paris, who worked extensively with meteorites.

Ref.

1. Since crystals have not been found, the crystallography is based on x-ray powder pictures, which are similar to those of linnaeite and establish the relationship of daubreelite to the linnaeite series.   See Heide, Herschkowitsch, and Preuss, *Chem. Erde*, **7**, 483 (1932).
2. Smith (1878) says, " The fracture is uneven, except in one direction where there appears to be a cleavage."
3. The old density determination by Smith (1878) needs confirmation, since it is not consistent with the x-ray data.
4. Heide, Herschkowitsch, and Preuss (1932).
5. See Doelter (4 [1], 6517, 1926).

273   **Badenite** [(Co,Ni,Fe)$_3$ (As,Bi)$_4$?].   *Poni (Min. Roumanie,* 17, 1900; *Ann. Sci. Univ. Jassy,* 1, 29, 1900).

Massive, granular to fibrous. G. 7.104. Luster metallic. Color steel-gray, becoming dull on exposure to air. Analysis[1] yields approximately the composition (Co,Ni,Fe)$_3$(As,Bi)$_4$. Fuses to a magnetic bead; yields arsenical fumes. Easily soluble in HNO$_3$. Occurs near Badeni-Ungureni, Muscel, Roumania, associated with erythrite, annabergite, malachite and siderite. Needs confirmation.

Ref.

1. For analysis see Dana-Ford (12, 1908).

28 A_2X_3 TYPE

281   Orpiment
282   Stibnite group
283   Kermesite

The members of the type are sulfides (and, in one instance, guanajuatite, a selenide) of the semi-metals, As, Sb, Bi. Kermesite has, in addition, some oxygen in its composition.

The structures of stibnite and bismuthinite have been determined,[1] and an explanation of the perfect cleavage and the flexibility of these minerals consistent with the structural data has been presented. The other members of the type have equally fine cleavages and the same properties of flexibility. No structural data are as yet available for these other minerals and crystallographic considerations indicate that no simple relation holds between the various members. All the minerals are soft (between 1 and 2, for the most part), and have a low fusibility (F. 1). They are, in general, minerals that occur in low-temperature deposits.

Ref.

1. Hofmann, *Zs. Kr.,* 86, 225 (1933).

281   **O R P I M E N T** [As$_2$S$_3$].   'Αρρενικόν *Theophrastus* (315 B.C.). 'Αρσενικόν *Dioscorides* (A.D. 50) Auripigmentum *Germ.* Operment *Agricola* (463, 1546). Orpiment, Rauschgelb pt., Risigallum pt., Arsenicum flavum *Wallerius* (224, 1747). Arsenic jaune *Wallerius* (1, 406, 1753). Auripigment, Gelbe Arsenblende, Gelbes Rauschgelb *Germ.* Arsenic sulfuré jaune *Haüy* (4, 244, 1822). Orpiment *Ital.* Oropiment *Span.* Yellow Sulphuret of Arsenic.

C r y s t. Monoclinic;[1] prismatic — 2/m.

$a : b : c = 1.1924 : 1 : 0.4433,$ β 90° 41';[2] $p_0 : q_0 : r_0 = 0.3718 : 0.4433 : 1$

$r_2 : p_2 : q_2 = 2.2558 : 0.8387 : 1,$ μ 89°19'; p_0' 0.3718, q_0' 0.4433, x_0' 0.0119

Forms:[3]

		ϕ	ρ	ϕ_2	$\rho_2 = B$	C	A
b	010	0°00′	90°00′	....	0°00′	90°00′	90°00′
a	100	90 00	90 00	0°00′	90 00	89 19	0 00
g	230	29 12½	90 00	0 00	29 12½	89 40	60 47½
m	110	39 59	90 00	0 00	39 59	89 33½	50 01
U	210	59 12	90 00	0 00	59 12	89 25	30 48
s	310	68 19½	90 00	0 00	68 19½	89 22	21 40½
e	101	90 00	20 59½	69 00½	90 00	20 18½	69 00½
o	301	90 00	48 25½	41 34½	90 00	47 44½	41 34½
v	$\overline{3}31$	−39 41	59 56½	137 49	48 14	60 23	123 33
x	$\overline{3}11$	−68 07	49 56½	137 49	73 25½	50 34½	135 15
ν	$\overline{3}21$	−51 13	54 45½	137 49	59 14	55 17½	129 33

Less common:

w	450	p	$\overline{3}01$	C	616	π	612	q	$\overline{4}23$
l	011	i	221	B	232	μ	12·3·4	β	$\overline{12}·9·4$
d	$\overline{1}01$	k	$\overline{1}11$	γ	121	z	511	χ	$\overline{4}11$

Structure cell.[4] Space group $P2_1/n$; a_0 11.46, b_0 9.59, c_0 4.24; $a_0 : b_0 : c_0 = 1.195 : 1 : 0.4421$, β 90°27′; contains As_8S_{12}.

Habit. Short prismatic [001] and pseudoorthorhombic; also monoclinic in aspect with prominent zones [001] and [103]. Crystals small,

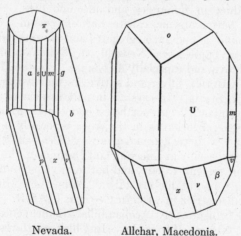

Nevada.   Allchar, Macedonia.

rarely distinct. Usually in foliated, columnar, or fibrous masses; as reniform or botryoidal aggregates; granular, sometimes pulverulent.

Twinning.[5] Twin plane {100}.

Oriented growths.[6] Observed upon realgar with orpiment {010} [100] ‖ realgar {100} [001].

Phys. Cleavage {010} perfect, {100} in traces. Cleavage lamellae flexible, inelastic. Sectile. H. 1½–2. G. 3.49;[5] 3.48 (calc.). M.P. 320°; B.P. 690°.[7] Luster pearly on cleavage surfaces, elsewhere resinous.

Color lemon-yellow of several shades; golden yellow; brownish yellow. Streak pale lemon-yellow. Transparent. Translation gliding[8] with $T\{010\}$, t [001].

O p t.[9] In transmitted light, shades of lemon-yellow in color.

ORIENTATION		n_{Li}	ABSORPTION	
X	b	2.4	...	Bx. neg. $(-)$.
Y	...	2.81	Yellow	$2V = 76°$.
Z	$:c + 1\frac{1}{2}°$ to $-3°$	3.02	Greenish yellow	$r > v$, strong.

C h e m. Arsenic trisulfide, As_2S_3. As 60.91, S 39.09, total 100.00. The few available analyses[10] are close to the stated formula.

Tests. F. 1. In C.T. fuses, volatilizes, and gives a dark yellow sublimate. Soluble in alkalies and aqua regia. Reacts with solutions of silver salts to give a coating of silver sulfide.

O c c u r. Found typically as a very low-temperature product in hydrothermal veins and as a hot-spring deposit. A common alteration product of other arsenic minerals, especially realgar. Also found as a sublimation product in fumaroles and in mine fires. Associated with stibnite, realgar, native arsenic, calcite, barite, gypsum.

In Hungary found as nodular aggregates and as rounded single crystals in druses in clay at Tajowa near Neusohl; in Roumania in veins at Felső-bánya, Neu-Moldova and especially at Kapnik. In the Harz, Saxony, at St. Andreasberg with ruby silver and native arsenic; with realgar in brown coal at Fohnsdorf, Styria. In crystals in part associated with fluorite at Kreševo, Bosnia, and at Allchar, northwest of Salonika, Macedonia. Found with realgar at several localities in the Alps, especially in the Binnental, Valais, Switzerland, with realgar and a variety of lead sulfosalts in the dolomite. In France especially at Luceram and Duranus in the Maritime Alps, with native sulfur, realgar, calcite, and barite in veins in marl. In fumaroles on Vesuvius. In notable crystals at Balin, Asia Minor, and in the Lukhumis-Tokhali district in western Georgia, U.S.S.R. A large deposit near Julamerk, Kurdistan. At Acobambilla, Huancavelica, Peru, as large cleavage masses; also at Morococha. In China southwest of Hsia-kuan, Yunnan Province, with realgar and pyrite in joints and fractures in quartzite. Found as a hot-spring deposit in the Kuriyama geyser district, Shimotsuke, Japan.

In the United States, orpiment occurs as fine large crystals at Mercur, Tooele County, Utah. In Nevada especially at Manhattan, Nye County, and among the deposits of Steamboat Springs, Washoe County. As a hot-spring deposit in the Yellowstone National Park, Wyoming. With realgar and stibnite in the kernite deposit, Kern County, California.

A l t e r. Often observed as an alteration product of realgar. Also as an alteration of native arsenic (Kapnik) and, less commonly, arsenopyrite and other arsenic minerals.

Artif.[11] Readily formed by artificial means; obtained in crystals by heating arsenious acid with H_2S under pressure.

Name. Orpiment is a corruption of the Latin name *auripigmentum*, *golden paint*, given in allusion to the color and also because the substance was supposed to contain gold. The artificial product has been called *King's yellow* (Konigsgelb).

Ref.

1. Not accepted as monoclinic by Dana (35, 1892); the early suspected monoclinic symmetry was proved by Stevanović, *Zs. Kr.*, **39**, 14 (1904).
2. Orientation and angles of Stevanović (1904); unit of Buerger (priv. comm., 1941) from x-ray Weissenberg study. Transformation: Mohs (2, 613, 1824), Dana (1892) and Stevanović (1904) to new unit: 200/010/00⅔.
3. Stevanović (1904), Farrington, and Tillotson *Field Mus. Chicago, Geol. Ser.*, **3**, 154 (1908), Cesaro, *Ac. Belgique, Bull., Cl. sc.*, **7**, 202 (1921), Palache and Modell, *Am. Min.*, **15**, 371 (1930). Uncertain forms:

001	14·1·0	16·3·8	$\overline{17}$·5·7	$\overline{6}$32	$\overline{12}$·15·4	$\overline{21}$·10·1
130	434	$\overline{2}$32	$\overline{12}$·3·4	$\overline{3}0$·24·10	$\overline{6}$92

4. Buerger (priv. comm., 1941) by Weissenberg x-ray method on crystals from Mercur (from the Harvard collection).
5. Stevanović (1904).
6. Buttgenbach, *Ac. Belgique, Bull., Cl. sc.*, 1019, 1933.
7. Borgström, *Finska Vet.-Soc., Öfv.*, **57**, no. 24, 1915.
8. Mügge, *Jb. Min.*, I, 154, 1898.
9. Larsen and Berman (213, 1934).
10. See Doelter (4 [1], 43, 1926).
11. See Mellor (**9**, 272, 1929).

ARSENSCHWEFEL. *Monaco* (*Ann. Scuola Super. Agric. Portici*, 1902 — *Zs. Kr.*, **40**, 297, 1904).

A blue-gray, granular crystalline (tetragonal?) material found mixed with realgar in the solfatara of Pozzuoli, near Naples, Italy. Analysis gave: As 56.90, S 35.92, H_2O 7.00, total 99.82.

ARSENOTELLURITE. *Hannay* (*J. Chem. Soc.*, **26**, 989, 1873).

Found as brownish scales associated with native tellurium and arsenopyrite. Analysis gave the formula $Te_2As_2S_7$:

	Te	As	S	Total
1	39.59	24.18	36.23	100.00
2	40.71	23.61	35.81	100.13

1. $Te_2As_2S_7$.   2. Arsenotellurite.

Locality unknown. Efforts to prepare the material artificially were unsuccessful.

282 STIBNITE GROUP

2821	Stibnite	Sb_2S_3
2822	Bismuthinite	Bi_2S_3
2823	Guanajuatite	Bi_2Se_3

Stibnite and bismuthinite are orthorhombic, dipyramidal — $2/m\ 2/m\ 2/m$, with space group *Pbnm*. The two minerals are nearly alike in their crystallographic and physical properties. The lattice dimensions compare as follows.

	STIBNITE	BISMUTHINITE
a_0	11.20	11.13
b_0	11.28	11.27
c_0	3.83	3.97

An important feature of the atomic structure is the close association of Sb_4S_6 in continuous bands extended with [001], flattened with {010}, and relatively loosely connected perpendicular to {010}. This type of structure, together with the relatively short vertical parameter, offers an explanation of the habitual vertical elongation of the crystals and the weak cohesion transversely to {010}, resulting in the perfect cleavage {010} and the flexibility about [100], with slipping on {010} along [001].

The relation of guanajuatite to the stibnite group is suggested by the appearance of the imperfect crystals but requires röntgenographic verification.

2821   **STIBNITE** [Sb_2S_3]. Στιμμι, Στιβι, Πλατυόφθαλμον, *Dioscorides* (ca. A.D. 50). Stimmi, Stibi, Stibium *Pliny* (33, 33, 34, A.D. 77). Al-kohl, Alcohol *Arabic.* Spiessglas *Valentine* (1430) Lupus metallorum *Alchem.* Spiess-Glass-Erz *Bruckmann* (Bergwerke, 1727). Spitzglasmalm, Minera Antimonii, Antimonium Sulphure mineralisatum *Wallerius* (237, 1747). Grauspiessglaserz, Grauspiessglanzerz, Spiessglanz, Antimonglanz *Germ.* Antimoiné sulfuré *Haüy* (4, 291, 1822). Sulphuret of Antimony, Gray Antimony, Antimony Glance, Stibina, Antimonio grigio *Ital.* Antimonio gris , Estibnita *Span.* Stibine *Beudant* (2, 421, 1832). Antimonit *Haidinger* (568, 1845). Stibnite *Dana* (33, 1854).

C r y s t.   Orthorhombic;   dipyramidal $- 2/m\,2/m\,2/m$.

$$a : b : c = 0.9926 : 1 : 0.3393;^1 \qquad p_0 : q_0 : r_0 = 0.3418 : 0.3393 : 1$$

$$q_1 : r_1 : p_1 = 0.9926 : 2.9257 : 1; \qquad r_2 : p_2 : q_2 = 2.9472 : 1.0074 : 1$$

Forms:[2]

		ϕ	$\rho = C$	ϕ_1	$\rho_1 = A$	ϕ_2	$\rho_2 = B$
b	010	0°00′	90°00′	90°00′	90°00′	....	0°00′
o	120	26 44	90 00	90 00	63 16	0°00′	26 44
d	230	33 53	90 00	90 00	56 07	0 00	33 53
m	110	45 12½	90 00	90 00	44 47½	0 00	45 12½
n	210	63 36	90 00	90 00	26 24	0 00	63 36
h	310	71 41½	90 00	90 00	18 18½	0 00	71 41½
N	021	0 00	34 09½	34 09½	90 00	90 00	55 50½
s	111	45 12½	25 43	18 44½	72 04	71 08	72 12
ζ	221	45 12½	43 55½	34 09½	60 30	55 38½	60 44½
p	331	45 12½	55 18½	45 30½	54 18	44 17	54 36
ψ	142	14 08	34 59	34 09½	81 57	80 18	56 13½
e	121	26 44	37 13½	34 09½	74 12½	71 08	57 17½
σ	211	63 36	37 21	18 44½	57 05	55 38½	74 21
σ:	261	18 33½	65 02	63 50½	73 13½	55 38½	30 45
τ	341	37 04½	59 33	53 37	58 41½	44 17	46 32½

Less common:

a	100	I:	510	μ	334	ρ	151	i:	2·12·1	v:	72·63·16
B	1·12·0	J:	910	v	667	q:	685	B:	11·3·5	ω:	511
C	180	M:	12·1·0	L:	665	H	6·15·5	l:	12·6·5	ω	521
D	170	O:	034	N:	443	d:	423	ζ:	532	G:	561
F	160	P:	011	K:	15·15·11	U:	433	ρ:	572	Ω	581
t	150	Q:	065	π	332	O	10·16·7	Ψ	823	m:	5·10·1
I	290	ν	032	ξ	991	f	634	λ	311	Σ:	5·11·1
i	140	u	031	T:	6·15·14	U	322	Δ	321	η:	5·12·1
g	270	Q	041	V:	3·12·7	Γ	342	α	12·9·4	u:	631
q	130	J	051	W:	214	g:	694	Z	652	γ:	671
x	250	Π	061	X:	3·27·5	h:	352	ε	24·21·8	ε:	6·14·1
γ	5·11·0	j	091	S	2·10·3	β:	362	f:	9·10·3	W	20·30·3
l	350	Y	0·12·1	Y:	12·9·16	δ:	523	β	672	y:	871
r	340	H	0·14·1	G	3·12·4	k:	15·20·8	χ:	9·11·3	a:	9·10·1
κ	450	R	102	s:	414	Ξ:	412	α:	692	A	9·18·1
χ	560	L	101	Z:	313	o:	623	η	351	E	10·15·1
θ	650	y	302	δ	454	j:	673	v:	361	X	12·9·1
Υ	540	Σ	201	ψ:	343	K	231	w	391	T	15·6·1
ι	320	z	301	Γ:	232	n:	241	V	10·30·3	R:	30·15·2
Λ	530	S:	501	Δ:	353	π:	492	M	411	μ:	18·9·1
Θ	940	Φ	27·0·1	t:	131	b:	251	λ:	461	k	430
A:	520	P	6·6·11	E:	4·15·4	c:	271	φ:	4·10·1		
C:	410	r:	335	φ	141	e:	281	z:	4·12·1		
D:	920	p:	223	F:	292	x:	291	w:	13·9·3		

Structure cell.[3] Space group *Pbnm*; a_0 11.20 ± 0.02, b_0 11.28 ± 0.02, c_0 3.83 ± 0.01; $a_0 : b_0 : c_0$ 0.9926 : 1 : 0.3395; contains Sb_8S_{12}.

Habit. Stout to slender prismatic [001], striated or channeled [001]. Commonest forms: *b o m n s p e σ τ*. Often bent or twisted.[4] Commonly in confused aggregates of acicular crystals; also in radiated groups, columnar masses, granular to impalpable.

Twinning.[5] Rare. (*a*) Twin plane {130}; (*b*) twin plane {310}, doubtful; (*c*) twin plane {120}.

P h y s. Cleavage {010}, perfect and easy; {100}, {110}, imperfect.[6] Highly flexible; not elastic. Slightly sectile. Fracture subconchoidal. H. 2. G. 4.63 ± 0.02; 4.63 (calc.). M.P. 546–551°; B.P. 990°.[7] Luster metallic, splendent on cleavage surfaces and untarnished faces. Color and streak lead-gray inclining to steel-gray. Subject to blackish tarnish; sometimes iridescent. Opaque, except in strong red light. The crystals are very easily bent about [100] or twisted around [001]. Translation gliding[8] with *T*{010}, *t*[001].

O p t. Transparent in the infrared region.

n_{760}[9]

$X = c = 3.194 ± 0.01$
$Y = a = 4.046 ± 0.01$
$Z = b = 4.303 ± 0.01$

Bx. neg. (−).

$2V = 25°45'$ (calc.).
Dispersion very strong.

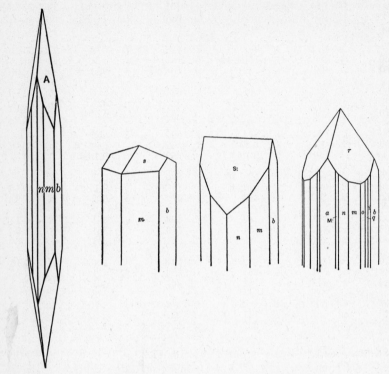

Wolfsberg, Harz.   California.   Manhattan, Nev.

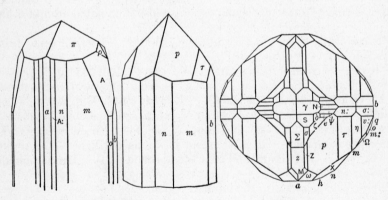

Felsöbánya.   Japan.

In polished section[10] white in color. Strongly anisotropic and pleochroic. Zonal growth banding and lamellar twinning is common. Frequently exhibits undulose extinction due to mechanical deformation. Reflection percentages:

	GREEN	ORANGE	RED
b = dull gray with olive tint = 30.5		26.4	24.9
a = dull gray-white = 38.6		34.2	32.0
c = pure white, very bright = 43.9		37.8	35.4

Chem. Antimony trisulfide, Sb_2S_3. Small amounts of Fe, Pb, Cu, and traces of Zn, Co, Ag, and Au are sometimes present. *Anal.*

	1	2	3	4	5
Pb	.....	.....	.....	.....	0.23
Cu	.....	.....	.....	.....	0.09
Fe	.....	.....	.....	0.11	0.12
Sb	71.69	71.45	71.51	71.84	71.83
S	28.31	28.42	28.66	28.25	26.90
Total	100.00	99.87	100.17	100.20	99.17
G.	4.63	4.656			4.515

1. Sb_2S_3. 2. Wolfsberg.[11] 3. Ichinokawa.[12] 4. Felsöbánya.[13] 5. Calston.[14]

Tests. F. 1. Colors the flame greenish blue. Soluble in HCl; decomposes in HNO_3 with separation of Sb_2O_5. Instantly tarnished by KOH, which deposits a highly characteristic yellow coating.

Occur.[15] Stibnite is the most important ore of antimony, but while it is widely distributed its occurrence as large deposits is rare. The mineral is typically formed at low temperatures in hydrothermal vein or replacement deposits and in hot springs. Associated with realgar, orpiment, galena, lead sulfantimonides, marcasite, pyrite, cinnabar, calcite, ankerite, barite, chalcedonic quartz.

Stibnite occurs at Wolfsberg, in the Harz Mountains; at Bräunsdorf near Freiberg, Saxony; near Arnsberg, Westphalia; at Přibram in Bohemia; in Roumania at Felsöbánya and Kapnik in radiating aggregates with crystals of barite; at Kremnitz and Schemnitz, Czechoslovakia. Stibnite occurs in fine crystals associated with realgar and cinnabar in the limestone rocks at Pereta, Tuscany, Italy; also at Cetine di Cotormiano, near Siena. At Calston, England. Fine crystals are found in the veins of Central France, at Lubilhac, Haute-Loire, and the neighboring locality of Massiac, Cantal; also from La Lucette in the Genest, Mayenne. The important deposits of Djebel Haminate, Constantine, Algeria, consist mostly of the oxides of antimony derived by the alteration of stibnite. Occurs in large prisms at Bau, Province of Sarawak, Borneo. From the Province of Puno, Peru. Magnificent groups of splendent crystals up to 20 in. in length have been brought from the extensive antimony mines at Ichinokawa in the Province of Iyo, island of Shikoku, Japan. Important deposits are located in China, particularly in the provinces of Hunan and Kwantung. Also found at several Mexican mines.

There is no deposit of great importance in the United States. A vein of considerable extent occurred in Sevier County, Arkansas. Found in the Coeur d'Alene district, Shoshone County, Idaho; Nevada has several deposits, mostly in the northwest section (Manhattan district). In California stibnite occurs in a number of places in Kern County, in finely crystallized material near Hollister, San Benito County, and elsewhere in the state. From Alaska in gold-quartz veins. Found in New Brunswick near Lake George, southwest of Fredericton, Prince William Parish, York County; at South Ham, Wolfe County, Quebec.

A l t e r. To kermesite and, on complete oxidation, to cervantite, stibiconite, senarmontite, valentinite. Also observed altered to cinnabar, realgar, and sulfur, and as an alteration product of senarmontite.

A r t i f.[16] Obtained in good crystals by passing H_2S and HCl over Sb_2O_3 at 450°.[17] Easily formed by fusion of the constituents, by heating the amorphous red precipitate Sb_2S_3 above ca. 250°, by direct reaction of the Sb and S under high pressure.

N a m e. From στίμμι, στίβι. This mineral was employed by the ancients as a cosmetic to increase the apparent size of the eye; whence they called it πλατυόφθαλμον, from πλατύς, broad, and ỏφθαλμός, eye.

Ref.

1. Dana, *Am. J. Sc.*, **26**, 214 (1883), on crystals from Japan, transformed to the lattice proposed by Ungemach, *Bull. soc. min.*, **57**, 202 (1934), which agrees with the structural lattice. Dana (36, 1892) and Goldschmidt (47, 1897; 1, 64, 1913) retained the pseudo-cubic lattice of Haüy (4, 291, 1822). Transformation, Haüy to Ungemach: 300/030/001.
2. Goldschmidt (1913); Neff, *Beitr. Kr. Min.*, **1**, 107 (1916); **2**, 47 (1923); Aminoff, *Ark. Kemi*, **7**, no. 7 (1919); Ježek, *Ak. Česká, Roz.*, **30** (1921) — *Min. Abs.*, **2**, 140 (1923); Gravino, *Acc. Linc. Rend.*, **3**, 210 (1926); Mélon, *Soc. géol. Belgique, Ann.*, **53**, 18 (1929); Palache and Modell, *Am. Min.*, **15**, 365 (1930); Cesaro, *Bull. soc. min.*, **54**, 103 (1931).

Rare or uncertain:

001	580	15·1·0	54·54·25	131	15·20·4
1·32·0	450	32·1·0	9·9·17	10·18·9	7·12·1
1·25·0	780	037	9·9·16	4·10·3	45·27·5
1·17·0	50·51·0	094	9·9·13	15·9·10	45·81·5
5·28·0	20·19·0	0·33·1	15·15·19	352	9·27·1
5·19·0	11·9·0	0·27·2	124	3·12·2	12·19·1
5·18·0	25·13·0	661	163	10·9·5	15·20·1
5·16·0	7·3·0	39·39·5	4·17·9	5·10·2	33·15·2
5·14·0	11·4·0	33·33·5	112	45·60·16	45·36·1
7·15·0	25·9·0	39·39·10	152	39·36·13	15·25·2
3·8·0	8·3·0	27·27·10	1·28·2	57·60·19	
470	25·6·0	12·12·5	416	39·45·13	

Tokody, *Ann. Mus. Hungarici, Pars. Min.*, **31**, 165 (1937–38), adds, for Nagyág: {790}, {9·11·0}, {9·10·0}, {980}, {740}.
3. Hofmann, *Zs. Kr.*, **86**, 225 (1933).
4. See Spencer, *Min. Mag.*, **19**, 263 (1919).
5. Neff (1916; 1923).
6. Mügge, *Jb. Min.*, I, 97 (1890) also reports cleavages on {001} and {301}.
7. Borgström, *Finska Vet.-Soc. Forh., Öfv.*, **57**, 1 (1914–15).
8. Mügge, *Jb. Min.*, I, 77 (1898).

9. Hutchinson, *Min. Mag.*, **14**, 199 (1907) on a prism cut from a crystal from Japan. Bailly, *Ac. roy. Belgique Bull.*, Cl. sc., **24**, 791 (1938), gives for λ 8521 : $z = c = 4.137$, $Y = 3.875$.

10. Schneiderhöhn and Ramdohr (**2**, 77, 1931); Cissarz, *Zs. Kr.*, **78**, 445 (1931).

11. Schmidt and Koort anal. in Koort (Inaug. Diss., Freiburg, 1884) — Doelter (**4** [1], 49, 1925).

12. Friedrich, *Metall.*, **6**, 177 (1909).

13. Loczka, *Zs. Kr.*, **20**, 317 (1892).

14. Weyl anal. in Rammelsberg (81, 1875).

15. A lengthy list of localities is given in Hintze (**1** [1], 373, 1899).

16. Doelter (**4** [1], 59, 1925).

17. Ligabo, *Per. Min.*, **8**, 291 (1937).

METASTIBNITE. *Becker* (*Proc. Am. Phil. Soc.*, **25**, 168, 1888; *U. S. Geol. Sur., Monog. 13*, 343, 389, 1888).

A name originally given to a red precipitate, supposedly Sb_2S_3, found as a pigment in siliceous sinter at Steamboat Springs, Washoe County, Nevada. A mineral from the Socavon mine, Oruro, Bolivia, referred[1] to metastibnite occurs as a purplish gray mammillary coating. Luster submetallic, streak red, H. 2–3, transparent in thin splinters. In polished section anisotropic but not pleochroic. Analyses of impure material gave: Sb 62–63, S 25–26, Pb 8.8. A similar mineral occurs at Pulacayo and elsewhere in Bolivia in the tin veins.[2]

Artificial precipitated Sb_2S_3 is red and does not give an x-ray diffraction pattern, but on heating increases in particle size, turns black and gives the x-ray pattern of stibnite.[3]

Ref.

1. Lindgren and Abbott, *Econ. Geol.*, **26**, 453 (1931), and Ramdohr, *Cbl. Min.*, 193, 1937.

2. See Ahlfeld and Reyes (7, 1938).

3. Klug and Heisig, *J. Am. Chem. Soc.*, **61**, 1920 (1939), and Schwartz, *Am. Min.*, **17**, 478 (1932).

2822   **B I S M U T H I N I T E** [Bi_2S_3]. Visimutum Sulphure mineralisatum *Cronstedt* (193, 1758). Wismuthglanz *Germ.* Bismuth sulfuré *Haüy* (**4**, 210, 1822). Sulphuret of Bismuth. Bismuth Glance. Bismuthine *Beudant* (**2**, 418, 1832). Bismutholamprite *Glocker* (27, 1847). Bismutinite, Bismutina *Ital.* Bismuthinite *Dana* (30, 1884).

Karelinite pt. *Hermann, J. pr. Chem.*, **75**, 448 (1858).

C r y s t.   Orthorhombic; dipyramidal — $2/m\ 2/m\ 2/m$.

$a : b : c = 0.9862 : 1 : 0.3498;$[1] $p_0 : q_0 : r_0 = 0.3547 : 0.3498 : 1$

$q_1 : r_1 : p_1 = 0.9862 : 2.8193 : 1;$ $r_2 : p_2 : q_2 = 2.8588 : 1.0141 : 1$

Forms:[2]

		ϕ	$\rho = C$	ϕ_1	$\rho_1 = A$	ϕ_2	$\rho_2 = B$
b	010	0°00′	90°00′	90°00′	90°00′		0°00′
a	100	90 00	90 00	...	0 00	0°00′	90 00
m	110	45 24	90 00	90 00	44 36	0 00	45 24
N	021	0 00	34 58½	34 58½	90 00	90 00	55 01½
L	101	90 00	19 31½	0 00	70 28½	70 28½	90 00
z	301	90 00	46 46½	0 00	43 13½	43 13½	90 00
σ	211	63 45	38 20½	19 16½	56 12	54 39	74 04½
λ	311	71 48	48 14½	19 16½	44 52½	43 13½	76 31½

Less common:

c 001	q 130	d 230	k 430	h 310	u 031	α 221	β 351
t 150	χ 250	r 340	ι 320	f: 410	Σ 201	p 331	
i 140	o 120	g: 450	n 210	e: 510	s 111	t: 131	

Structure cell.[3] Space group $Pbnm$; a_0 11.13 $\pm$ 0.02, b_0 11.27 $\pm$ 0.02, c_0 3.97 $\pm$ 0.01; $a_0 : b_0 : c_0 = 0.9874 : 1 : 0.3523$; contains Bi_8S_{12}.

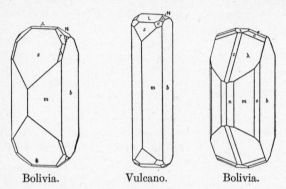

Bolivia.   Vulcano.   Bolivia.

Habit. Stout prismatic to acicular, elongated and striated [001], with {110}, {301} usually dominant; also dipyramidal {311}. Usually massive with foliated or fibrous texture.

P h y s. Cleavage {010} perfect and easy; {100}, {110}, imperfect.[4] Gliding: $T = (010)$, $t = [001]$. Flexible. Somewhat sectile. H. 2. G. 6.78 $\pm$ 0.03; 6.81 (calc.). Luster metallic. Color lead-gray inclining to tin-white, with a yellowish or iridescent tarnish. Streak lead-gray. Opaque. In polished section[5] weakly pleochroic and strongly anisotropic. Percentage reflection: green 49, orange 43, red 40.

C h e m. Bismuth trisulfide, Bi_2S_3. Small amounts of Pb, Cu, Fe, and, rarely, Te have been reported; also Se, in substitution for S, to about Se : S = 1 : 4 (anal. 7).

Anal.

	1	2	3	4	5	6	7
Pb	....	0.69	1.68	....	1.51	....	....
Cu	....	0.57	0.48	0.57	0.57	....	....
Fe	....	0.40	0.74	0.17	0.66	....	....
Bi	81.3	80.04	79.28	79.47	79.04	76.51	76.94
Sb	....	....	....	....	....	3.58	....
Te	....	....	....	0.94	....	....	....
Se	....	....	....	....	....	....	8.80
S	18.7	18.46	18.46	18.42	18.40	20.07	14.15
Insol.	....	....	....	0.50	0.35	....	....
Total	100.0	100.16	100.64	100.07	100.53	100.16	99.89

1. Bi_2S_3. 2. Vaskö.[6] 3. Jonquière.[7] 4. Riddarhyttan.[8] 5. Crodo.[9] 6. Tazna (antimonian).[10] 7. Guanajuato (selenian).[11]

Tests. F. 1. Dissolves readily in HNO_3; forms a white precipitate on diluting with water.

O c c u r. Bismuthinite is comparatively rare. Found typically in hydrothermal veins formed at relatively high temperatures, associated with native bismuth, arsenopyrite, quartz, sulfides; also in low- to moderate-temperature sulfide veins (Bolivia); in tourmaline-bearing copper deposits, and with or without wolframite in tin deposits; in granite pegmatites.

Found in Saxony at Schneeberg and Altenberg; in Roumania at Rézbánya, Moravicza, and Vaskö; in Italy at Brosso, Piedmont, at Crodo, Val d'Ossola, and at Vulcano, Lipari Islands; in France at Meymac, Corrèze; in Sweden at the Bastnaes mine at Riddarhyttan, Västmanland, and at Persberg, Vermland. In England it is found in Cornwall at Redruth and at the Fowey Consols mine near St. Blazey, in Devonshire at Tavistock, and in Cumberland at Carrock Fell. In New South Wales at Kingsgate; in Queensland on Mount Shamrock, Chowey Creek, near Gayndah, and at Kilkivan; in South Australia at Balhannon, Adelaide County. The most important deposits of bismuthinite are in Bolivia, at San Baldamero, near Sorata; at Llallagua; and in the Huanina, Tazna, and Chorolque districts, Potosí. Also found at Guanajuato, Mexico.

In the United States it has been found at Haddam, Connecticut, with chrysoberyl; in Delaware County, Pennsylvania; at Wickes, Jefferson County, Montana; in various localities in Colorado; abundantly with almandine garnet and barite in the Granite mining district, Beaver County, Utah. In Quebec at Jonquière, Chicoutimi County, and in several places in Timiskaming County.

A l t e r. Alters readily to various ill-defined bismuth carbonates and to bismite (?). Found as an alteration of native bismuth and as pseudomorphs after molybdenite. Chalcopyrite, cassiterite, and siderite have been found as pseudomorphs after bismuthinite.

A r t i f.[12] Obtained in crystals by passing H_2S with HCl over heated Bi_2O_3, and in other ways.

N a m e. See bismuth.

Ref.

1. Peacock, *Zs. Kr.*, **86**. 203 (1933), on crystals from Tazna (anal. 6), transformed to correspond to the structural lattice determined by Hofmann, *Zs. Kr.*, **86**, 225 (1933). Peacock retained the lattice of Groth, *Zs. Kr.*, **5**, 252 (1880), adopted by Dana (38, 1892) and Goldschmidt (364, 1897; Atlas, **9**, 79, 1923). Transformation: Groth to Hofmann: 300/030/001.

2. Goldschmidt (1923); Peacock (1933); Wolfe, *Am. Min.*, **23**, 790 (1938), adds for Vulcano $w\{121\}$, and rare or uncertain:

180	370	10·7·0	20·7·0	10·1·0	023	904	601	955	12·1·2
3·10·0	470	730	610	12·1·0	504	502	377	16·3·6	631

3. Hofmann (1933) on crystals from Kilkivan.
4. The reported imperfect cleavages require confirmation.
5. Schneiderhöhn and Ramdohr (**2**, 86, 1931).
6. Koch, *Cbl. Min.*, 50, 1930.
7. Johnston, in Hoffmann, *Geol. Sur. Canada, Ann. Rep.*, **6**, 19R (1892–93) — *Zs. Kr.*, **28**, 324 (1897).
8. Lindström, *Geol. För. Förh.*, **28**, 198 (1906).
9. Bianchi, *Acc. Linc., Rend.*, **33**, 254 (1924).

10. Gonyer, in Peacock (1933).
11. Genth, *Am. J. Sc.*, **41**, 402 (1891).
12. Doelter 4 [1], 76 (1925); Carpanese, *Per. Min.*, **7**, 1 (1936).

The following ill-defined substances are probably identical with bismuthinite or are mixtures containing bismuthinite.

AUROBISMUTHINITE. *Koenig* (*Ac. Sc. Philadelphia, J.*, **15**, 423, 1912). A leadgray massive cleavable mineral from an unknown locality. Anal.: Bi 69.50, Au 12.27, Ag 2.32, S 15.35 = 99.44; giving $(Bi,Au,Ag)_5S_6$. This may represent a mixture of $(Bi,Au,Ag)S$ and Bi_2S_3, or a solid solution of Au,Ag in Bi_2S_3.

STIBIOBISMUTHINITE. *Koenig* (*Ac. Sc. Philadelphia, J.*, **15**, 424, 1912). Large cleavable prisms resembling stibnite rather than bismuthinite, from Nacozari, Sonora, Mexico. Anal.: Bi 69.90, Sb 8.12, S [21.92] = 100.00 (sic), giving $(Bi,Sb)_4S_7$. Perhaps an antimonian bismuthinite.

BOLIVITE. *Domeyko* (App. **6**, 19, 1878 — Dana [38, 1892]). An alteration product of bismuthinite; described as an oxysulfide of bismuth, but is probably a mixture of Bi_2O_3 with Bi_2S_3. From Tazna and Chorolque, Bolivia.

KARELINITE. *Hermann* (*J. pr. Chem.*, **75**, 448, 1858), has been shown[1] to be a mixture of bismuthinite, bismuth, and bismite, with a trace of carbonate.

Ref.

1. Parascandola, *Riv. fis. Napoli*, **7**, 7 (1932) — *Min. Abs.*, **6**, 534 (1937).

2823 **G U A N A J U A T I T E** [Bi_2Se_3]. Una nueva especie mineral de bismuto *Castillo* (*Naturaleza*, **2**, 274, 1873; *Jb. Min.*, 225, 1874). Guanajuatite *Fernandez* (*La Republica* of Guanajuato, July 13, 1873). Selenwismuthglanz *Frenzel* (*Jb. Min.*, 679, 1874). Frenzelite *Dana* (App. II, 22, 1875). Castillite *Domeyko* (310, 1879). Selenwismut. Selenobismutite *Vernadsky* (**2**, 34, 1918 — *Min. Mag.*, **19**, 349 [1922]). Silaonite pt. *Fernandez* and *Salvia* (*La Republica*, Guanajuato, Mexico, Dec. 25, 1873 — Dana [39, 1892]).

C r y s t. Orthorhombic,[1] with (110) $\wedge$ ($1\bar{1}0$) near 90°, as in stibnite. Crystals acicular, striated lengthwise, often forming semicompact masses. Also massive, with granular, foliated or fibrous texture.

P h y s. Cleavage {010} distinct; {001} indistinct. Somewhat sectile. H. $2\frac{1}{2}$–$3\frac{1}{2}$. G. 6.25–6.98. M.P. 690°.[2] Luster metallic. Color bluish gray. Streak shiny gray. Opaque. In polished section[3] white in color with strong anisotropism and distinct pleochroism.

C h e m. Bismuth selenide, Bi_2Se_3, with considerable sulfur reported in some analyses.

Anal.

	1	2	3	4
Bi	63.8	65.01	68.86	67.38
Se	36.2	34.33	25.50	24.13
S	....	0.66	4.68	6.60
Total	100.00	100.00	99.04	98.11

1. Bi_2Se_3. 2. Guanajuato.[4] 3. Guanajuato.[5] 4. Guanajuato.[6]

Tests. B.B. on charcoal fuses with a blue flame, giving a strong selenium odor. Dissolved by aqua regia on slow heating.

O c c u r. From the Santa Catarina and La Industrial mines, Sierra de Santa Rosa, near Guanajuato, Mexico, where it is associated with bismutosphaerite, bismuthinite, native bismuth, pyrite. Reported from Andreasberg, Harz Mountains, Germany, with clausthalite and other selenides in a calcite vein. Reported from Fahlun, Sweden, with cosalite and bismuthinite. From near Salmon, Lemhi County, Idaho.

Artif. A rhombohedral modification of Bi_2Se_3 has been obtained in crystals by passing H_2Se and HCl over Bi_2O_3.[7]

Name. From the locality, Guanajuato, Mexico.

Needs confirmation.

Ref.

1. The crystallography of natural Bi_2Se_3 requires investigation. Artificial Bi_2Se_3 has been found to be rhombohedral by Parravano and Caglioti, *Gazz. chim. ital.*, **60**, 923 (1930), and Carpenese, *Per. Min.*, **8**, 289 (1937), with $\{0001\} \wedge \{10\bar{1}1\} = 63\frac{1}{4}°$, and presumably is isostructural with tellurobismuthite.
2. Borgström, *Finska Vet.-Soc., Öfv.*, **57**, 1 (1914–15).
3. Schneiderhöhn and Ramdohr (**2**, 89, 1931).
4. Mallet, *Am. J. Sc.*, **15**, 294 (1878), after deducting halloysite 6.72 and quartz 0.56.
5. Genth, *Am. J. Sc.*, **41**, 403 (1891), with Se : S = 2 : 1.
6. Frenzel, *Jb. Min.*, 680, 1874, with Se : S = 3 : 2.
7. Carpenese (1937).

283 · **KERMESITE** [Sb_2S_2O]. Röd Spitsglasmalm, Antimonium Sul. et Ars. mineralisatum, Minera Ant. colorata *Wallerius* (239, 1747), *Cronstedt* (203, 1758). Antimonium plumosum *von Born* (**1**, 137, 1772). Mine d'Antimoine en plumes, ib. granuleuse, = Kermes mineral natif, *Sage* (**2**, 251, 1779), *de Lisle* (**3**, 56, 60, 1783). Roth-Spiesglaserz *Werner* (1789). Rothspiessglanzerz *Emmerling* (1793), *Klaproth* (**3**, 132, 1802). Antimoine oxyde sulfuré *Haüy* (1809). Red Antimony. Spiessglanzblende pt. *Hausmann* (225, 1813). Antimony Blende *Jameson* (**3**, 421, 1820). Antimonblende *Leonhard* (157, 1821). Kermes *Beudant* (**2**, 617, 1832). Kermesite *Chapman* (61, 1843). Pyrostibite *Glocker* (16, 1847). Pyrantimonite *Breithaupt*. Antimonio rosso *Ital.* Antimonio rojo *Span.*

Cryst. Monoclinic; prismatic — $2/m$.[1]

$a : b : c = 1.339 : 1 : 1.265^2$; $\beta\ 101°45'$; $p_0 : q_0 : r_0 = 0.9447 : 1.238 : 1$
$r_2 : p_2 : q_2 = 0.8074 : 0.7628 : 1$; $\mu\ 78°15'$; $p_0'\ 0.9650$, $q_0'\ 1.265\ x_0'\ 0.2080$

Forms:[3]

		ϕ	ρ	ϕ_2	ρ_2	C	A
c	001	90°00'	11°45'	78°15'	90°00'	0°00'	78°15'
a	100	90 00	90 00	0 00	90 00	78 15	0 00
o	101	90 00	49 33	40 27	90 00	37 48	40 27
p	121	24 52½	70 16½	40 27	31 21	65 43½	66 40½

Structure cell.[4] Space group probably $C2/m$; $a_0\ 10.97$, $b_0\ 8.19$, $c_0\ 10.36$; $\beta\ 101°45$; $a_0 : b_0 : c_0 = 1.339 : 1 : 1.265$; contains $Sb_{16}S_{16}O_8$.

Habit. Crystals lath-shaped on $\{001\}$ and markedly elongated $\|$ [010]. Tufted radiating aggregates; sometimes hairlike.

Phys. Cleavage $\{001\}$ perfect, $\{100\}$ less perfect. Sectile; thin splinters flexible. H. 1–1½. G. 4.68;[4] 4.69 (calc.). M.P. 516–518°.[5] Luster adamantine to semimetallic. Color cherry-red. Streak brownish red. In thin splinters translucent and red in color. Optically pos. (+). $Z = b =$ elongation. $nX > 2.72$. Birefringence very strong to extreme.[6]

Chem. Antimony oxysulfide, Sb_2S_2O.
Anal.

	Sb	S	O	Total
1	75.24	19.82	4.94	100.00
2	75.13	20.04	4.83	100.00

1. Sb_2S_2O. 2. Locality unknown.[7]

Tests. F. 1. In C.T. blackens and gives, at first, a white sublimate (Sb_2O_3), turns black or dark red on stronger heating.

Occur. Found as an alteration product of stibnite, associated with senarmontite, valentinite, cervantite, and stibiconite. In Czechoslovakia at Pernek, near Bösing, northwest of Bratislava (Pressburg), it occurs in quartz veins with stibnite and valentinite; at Přibram, Bohemia; Braunsdorf, near Freiberg, Saxony. Also found at Sarrabus, Sardinia. In France at Chalanches, near Allemont, Isère. In Algeria at Djebel Haminate, southeast of Constantine associated with stibnite and senarmontite.

In California, at the Mojave antimony mine, about 15 miles north of Mojave, Kern County, associated with stibnite. Reported from the Stanley antimony mine, Burke, Shoshone County, Idaho, as a brownish red powder on stibnite. In crystalline tufts, with antimony, stibnite, valentinite, and senarmontite at South Ham, Wolfe County, Quebec; in cavities in antimony and stibnite near Lake George, southwest of Fredericton, Prince William parish, York County, New Brunswick; with stibnite at the West Gore mines, Rawdon, Hants County, Nova Scotia.

Artif. Variously reported,[8] but without certain identification of the product.

Name. From *kermes* (from the Persian *qurmizq, crimson*) as given in the older chemistry to red amorphous antimony trisulfide, often mixed with antimony trioxide.

Ref.

1. Symmetry given by Mohs (**2**, 598, 1824), verified by x-ray study (Wolfe, priv. comm., 1939). The orthorhombic interpretation of Kenngott (**1**, 1, 1849) was followed by Pjatnitzky, *Zs. Kr.*, **20**, 417 (1892), who measured a number of poor crystals.
2. Ratio from the x-ray study (Wolfe, 1939) on single crystal from Pernek.
3. Forms from Pjatnitsky (1892) and verified by Wolfe (priv. comm., 1939). Uncertain forms:

507	504	401	20·0·3	$\overline{2}5$·0·3	$\overline{1}5$·0·1	$\overline{3}23$
506	10·0·3	501	10·0·1	$\overline{1}0$·0·1	$\overline{2}0$·0·1	$\overline{1}21$

The transformation from Wolfe (x-ray) to Pjatnitsky is uncertain; it is approximately $001/0\frac{2}{3}0/\frac{1}{5}0\frac{1}{3}$.
4. Wolfe (priv. comm., 1939).
5. Borgström, *Finska Vet.-Soc. Förh., Öfv.*, **57** [24], (1914–15).
6. Larsen (96, 1921) on material from Braunsdorf.
7. Baubigny, *C. R.*, **119**, 737 (1894). Original analyses given in Dana (187, 1868).
8. Literature in Hintze (**1** [1], 1206, 1900).

29 AX_2 TYPE

291 Pyrite group
292 Cobaltite group
293 Loellingite group
294 Marcasite group

295 Arsenopyrite group
296 Molybdenite group
297 Krennerite group
      Melonite

In the sulfide minerals of the type AX_2, A = Fe, Co, Ni for the most part, and X_2 = S_2, As_2 or As–S (and in some instances Sb–S). In general, the pyrite group consists of sulfides, the loellingite group of arsenides, the cobaltite and arsenopyrite groups of arsenide-sulfides. The.diploidal symmetry of the pyrite group is reduced to tetartoidal of the cobaltite group by the nonequivalence of the X_2 atomic pair in the latter; the orthorhombic symmetry of marcasite is reduced to monoclinic symmetry in the arsenopyrite group in the same way. With the exception of the dimorphism of pyrite and marcasite, there is no overlap in the groups. For this reason the supposed member of the pyrite group, arsenoferrite ($FeAs_2$), is a dubious species. Further, marcasite (FeS_2) is not a member of the loellingite group. The members of the arsenopyrite group are essentially iron minerals (glaucodot always has some Fe) and the cobaltite group consists of cobalt and nickel minerals with Fe subordinate.

The exceptions to these general tendencies, such as sperrylite ($PtAs_2$) in the pyrite group, have been explained by crystallochemical considerations.[1] Only two minerals, molybdenite and tungstenite, of the layered structure AX_2 type are found in the sulfides.

The tellurides are apparently unrelated to the other structures of the type.

Ref.

1. For a general crystallochemical treatment of the AX_2 minerals and the relation to artificial compounds of the same type, see Stillwell (1938).

PYRITE GROUP — AX_2
ISOMETRIC; DIPLOIDAL $2/m\,\bar{3}$

	COMPOSITION	a_0	G.
Pyrite	FeS_2	5.405	5.018
Bravoite	$(Ni,Fe)S_2$	5.56 (Fe : Ni = 1 : 1)	4.66
Laurite	RuS_2	5.59	6.23
Sperrylite	$PtAs_2$	6.00	10.58
Hauerite	MnS_2	6.11	3.463
Penroseite	ASe_2	6.01	7.56
? Arsenoferrite	$FeAs_2$		

The unit cell contents of members of the pyrite group can be expressed as $A_4(X_2)_4$, with X = S,As,Se. The X-atoms lie along the trigonal axes of the space lattice, in pairs, and account for the diploidal symmetry of the members in the group.[1]

The minerals of the group are metallic in luster (with the exception of hauerite), and some are among the hardest of sulfide minerals (laurite,

$7\frac{1}{2}$; pyrite 6–$6\frac{1}{2}$). The cleavages are not the same in direction or perfection in the various members.

Crystallochemical relations[2] indicate that arsenoferrite, $FeAs_2$, is probably not a member of the group, and recent work[3] substantiates this conclusion. The mineral penroseite is essentially the same as the artificial $NiSe_2$,[4] which has been shown to be of this group. Bravoite, $(Ni,Fe)S_2$, is apparently a member of this group and may form a complete series with pyrite.[7] In cobaltite and related minerals the structural similarity with pyrite is marked. The lower symmetry of the former[5] is due to the polarity of the trigonal axes along which the X_2 pairs lie, since these pairs are no longer of equivalent atoms. The {001} plane of pyrite corresponds to the {101} of marcasite in the structure,[6] and intergrowths of the two with these as the contact planes have been observed.

Ref.

1. Bragg (71, 1937).
2. Stillwell (193, 1938).
3. Buerger, *Am. Min.*, **21**, 70 (1936).
4. Bannister and Hey, *Am. Min.*, **22**, 319 (1937).
5. Bragg (71, 1937).
6. Buerger (priv. comm., 1939).
7. Bannister, *Min. Mag.*, **25**, 609 (1940).

2911   **PYRITE** [FeS₂]. Σπῖνος *Theophrastus*. Πυρίτης pt. *Dioscorides*. Pyrites pt. *Pliny* (36, 30). Pyrites pt., Marchasita *Arabian*. Kis *Germ.; Agricola* (1529, 1546). Pyrites pt., Marchasita (crystallized pyrite) *Wallerius* (208, 211, 1747). Marcasite (crystallized pyrite), Mundic (massive) *Hill* (324–332, 1771).   Xanthopyrites *Glocker* (314, 1839).

Schwefelkies, Eisenkies *Germ.* Svafvelkis *Swed.* Svovl Kis *Danish.* Iron Pyrites. Bisulphuret of Iron.   Fer sulfuré *Fr.* Pirite *Ital.* Pirita, Pirita amarilla, Bronce *Span.* and *Span. S. A.*

Tombazite pt. *Breithaupt* (*J. pr. Chem.*, **15**, 330, 1839). Ballesterosite pt. *Schulz* and *Paillette* (*Bull. géol. fr.*, **7**, 16, 1849). Telaspyrine *Shepard* (Dana [App. III, 119, 1884]).

Blueite *Emmens* (*J. Am. Chem. Soc.*, **14**, 207, 1892). Whartonite *Emmens* (*J. Am. Chem. Soc.*, **14**, 207, 1892). Bravoite pt. ? *Hillebrand* (*Am. J. Sc.*, **24**, 149, 1907). Kobaltnickelpyrit, Kobaltpyrit pt. *Vernadsky* (240, 1910; *Cbl. Min.*, 494, 1914). Cobaltpyrite pt. *Johansson* (*Ark. Kemi*, **9**, 2, 1924). Melnikovite *Doss* (*Ann. géol. min. Russie*, **13**, 130 [1911] — *Min. Mag.*, **16**, 352 [1913]); Melnikowit *Germ.*; Melnikowit-Pyrit. Pyritogelite *Tučan* (*Cbl. Min.*, 768, 1913). Pyrogelite.

Cryst. Isometric; diploidal — $2/m\ \bar{3}$.

Forms:[1]

a	001	$'h$	104	$'e$	102	$'\nu$	506	p	122	$'s$	213
d	011	$'f$	103	$'g$	203	m	113	$'\nu$	315	$'U$	325
o	111	e'	012	$'\theta$	304	n	112	$'t$	214		

Structure cell. Space group $Pa3$; a_0 5.405; contains Fe_4S_8.

Habit.[2] Most commonly cubic, often pyritohedral {012}, not rarely octahedral; also frequently modified by the diploid {213}. Commonest forms a, $'e$, o, s, and somewhat less common, n, t, p. The pyritohedral and cubic faces often striated parallel to the edge between them, [100]; the striae due to oscillatory combination of these forms, and tending to produce rounded faces. Crystals sometimes acicular [001]; also abnormally developed with pseudotetragonal, pseudorhombohedral, or pseudo-ortho-

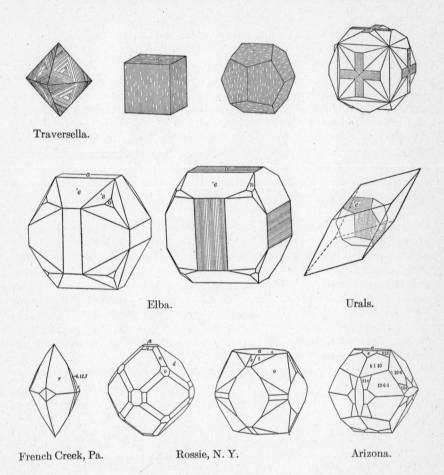

Traversella.

Elba.   Urals.

French Creek, Pa.   Rossie, N. Y.   Arizona.

rhombic symmetry. Rarely, highly distorted or twisted.[3] Frequently massive, fine granular, sometimes subfibrous, radiated, reniform, globular, and stalactitic.

Natural crystals frequently show etch and growth accessories consistent with the symmetry.[4]

Twinning. Twin axis [001] and twin plane {011}, producing penetration twins, rarely contact twins. Many other twin laws have been described but are uncommon.[5]

Oriented growths. Pyrite has been found in oriented growths with sphalerite[6] and with[7] marcasite, arsenopyrite, galena, tetrahedrite, and pyrrhotite.

Pyrite	{001}	[110]	‖	sphalerite	{001}	[110]
Pyrite	{001}	[110]	‖	pyrrhotite	{10$\bar{1}$0}	[0001]
Pyrite	{001}	[001]	‖	galena	{111}	[110]
Pyrite	{001}	[110]	‖	arsenopyrite	{001}	[010]
Pyrite	{111}	[001]	‖	tetrahedrite	{111}	[001]
Pyrite	{001}	[001]	‖	marcasite	{010}	[101]
Pyrite	{001}	[110]	‖	marcasite	{010}	[100]

P h y s. Cleavage {001} indistinct; {011} and {111} indistinct separation due to either cleavage or parting. Fracture conchoidal to uneven. Brittle. H. 6–6$\frac{1}{2}$,[8] decreasing with increasing substitution of Ni for Fe. G. 5.018,[9] 5.013 (calc.); 4.82 (4.80, calc.) for material with Ni : Fe = 1 : 1.84 (anal. 6). M.P. 642°C ±.[10] Luster metallic, splendent to glistening. Color pale brass-yellow. Iridescent when tarnished. Streak greenish black or brownish black. Shows both positive and negative thermoelectricity.[11] Paramagnetic. Translation or twin gliding not observed.[12] Emits sparks when struck with steel. Conducts electricity.[13]

In polished section,[14] creamy white in color and isotropic, sometimes anisotropic. May exhibit zonal growth-banding. Reflection percentages: green 54, orange 53.5, red 52.5. Nickelian pyrite has a violet-gray tint of color and often exhibits zonal growth-banding with the inner zones relatively high in Fe.

C h e m.[15] Disulfide of iron, FeS_2. Ni (with Ni : Fe = 1 : 1.84 in anal. 6) and Co (with Co : Fe = 1 : 2.5 in anal. 8) rarely substitute for Fe, and a possibly complete series extends to bravoite. As sometimes present in small amounts. V, Mo, Cr, W, Tl reported as spectroscopic traces. Au and Cu often reported but presumably as microscopic impurities.

Anal.[16] Many modern and old analyses confirm the formula given.

	1	2	3	4	5	6	7	8
Fe	46.55	46.49	46.49	.....	.....	29.30	45.20	33.32
Ni	.....	.....	.....	.....	.....	16.69	.....	0.19
Co	.....	.....	.....	.....	.....	trace	1.25	13.90
S	53.45	53.49	.....	53.53	53.46	53.40	53.30	52.45
SiO₂	.....	0.04	.....	.....	.....	.....	0.03	.....
Total	100.00	100.02	.....	.....	.....	99.39	99.78	99.86
G.	5.013					4.82		4.965

1. FeS_2. 2–5. Elba.[17] 6. Mill Close · mine, Derbyshire (nickelian). Semimicroanalysis.[18] 7. Franklin, N. J. (cobaltian). Average of two. With Ca trace.[19] 8. Gladhammar, Sweden (cobaltian).[20]

Var. *Nickelian.* Blueite *Emmens* (*J. Am. Chem. Soc.*, **14**, 207, 1892). Whartonite *Emmens* (*J. Am. Chem. Soc.*, **14**, 207, 1892). Bravoite *Hillebrand* (*A. J. Sc.*, **24**, 149, 1907). Kobaltnickelpyrit *Vernadsky* (240, 1910; *Cbl. Min.*, 494, 1914).

Contains Ni, often with subordinate amounts of Co, in substitution for Fe, with Ni : Fe = 1 : 1.84 in anal 6. A possibly complete series exists

to bravoite (which see).[21]   The substitution of Ni for Fe is accompanied by
a regular increase in the cell dimensions and by a decrease in hardness.
Color inclining from brass-yellow to silvery white, violet-gray and gray
with increasing content of Ni.

  Cobaltian. Kobaltpyrit *Vernadsky* (240, 1910; *Cbl. Min.*, 494, 1914).
Cobaltpyrite *Johansson* (*Ark. Kemi*, **9**, 2, 1924).
  Contains Co in substitution for Fe, with Co : Fe = 1 : 2.5 in anal. 8.

  Tests. F. $2\frac{1}{2}$–3. Gives abundant sublimate of S in C.T. Insoluble in HCl. Fine
powder completely soluble in strong HNO_3.

  O c c u r.[22] Pyrite is the most widespread and most abundant of
sulfide minerals. It occurs under almost all conditions of mineral deposition, being a leading example of the so-called *persistent* minerals. Found
especially in large bodies in the moderate to high-temperature hydrothermal deposits (Rio Tinto). May be deposited as a direct magmatic
segregation (Sulitjelma), and as an accessory mineral in igneous rocks;
infrequently reported from pegmatites. Large bodies of pyrite are found
in contact metamorphic ore deposits (Clifton, Arizona) where the chief
metal mined is copper from the associated copper sulfides such as chalcopyrite and chalcocite. Most sulfide veins contain pyrite in large amounts.
Has been noted as a sublimation product (Vesuvius). In sedimentary
beds pyrite is a common constituent, rarely as oolitic deposits (Meggen,
Germany), more often as disseminated crystals or in concretionary forms;
frequently in fossiliferous deposits (central New York in the shales) and
in coal beds, where the quantity is sometimes large enough to be mined
profitably. Many metamorphosed sediments contain pyrite; sometimes
in exceptional crystals in the chlorite schists (Chester, Vermont). Since
all the occurrences of pyrite cannot be listed here, only those in which
notable quantities occur or those in which fine specimens or unusual types
are found can be given.

  Naturally etched crystals have been described from the Udo mine,
Hikawa-gun, Igumo, Japan. Found abundantly in Tasmania at Mount
Lyell, as large fine-grained masses with quartz, barite, and chalcopyrite.
In Czechoslovakia at Schemnitz, at Schmöllnitz in a large deposit; at
Příbram, Bohemia, and at Kladno as concretions with radiating structure
in the coal formation. In Roumania at Facebay near Zalatna and at
Kisbánya. In Austria at Waldenstein as fine crystals. In Germany at
Freiberg, Saxony, in the veins with galena and other sulfides, rarely as
pseudomorphs after arsenopyrite; in Westphalia at Siegen, fine crystals;
in remarkable complex crystals from clay at Vlotho, southwest of Minden,
and at Meggen on the Lenne as an oolitic deposit; in concretions from
Grossalmerode in Hesse-Nassau; replacing fossils in the shale at Wissen-
bach and Bundenbach. In fine specimens from St. Gotthard, Switzerland.
In Italy reported as a sublimation product at Vesuvius; on the isle of Elba
exceptional crystals of great variety and large size, associated with hematite, have been described in detail; from Traversella and Brosso in the

Piedmont, many fine pyritohedral crystals with complex modifications have been described. In France occurs in fine crystals at Saint-Pierre-de-Mésage near Vizille, Isère, and in large crystals altered to limonite from Estrèmes de Salles in Agos (vallée d'Argelès); at Arnave as octahedral crystals in the limestone, and at Angers, Department Maine et Loire in striated cubes. In Spain pyrite occurs in large deposits, as at Rio Tinto, Huelva, where lenses of granular pyrite with associated chalcopyrite have been mined to the extent of four million metric tons of ore in a year. In Portugal at Aljustrel, in schist. In Sweden at Fahlun, Kopparberg, Glad-hammar (*cobaltian*) and at Klefra, Småland; in Norway at Sulitjelma, Nordland, as corroded phenocrysts in chalcopyrite of supposed magmatic origin, and at Roros, Sör-Tröndelag.

In England at Lyme Regis as pyritized fossils (ammonites); in the Cornwall region especially at Liskeard, St. Ives and St. Just, in fine crystals; in Cumberland with quartz and barite; at Tavistock in Devonshire; a nickelian variety at the Mill Close mine, Derbyshire. In Chile the large pyritic ore body at Chuquicamata is notable as a copper mine and as the source of many iron sulfate minerals resulting from the oxidation of the pyrite. Large octahedrons are records from the Orlandini tin mine, Ubina, Bolivia. At Minasragra, Peru (*bravoite*) with vanadium minerals.

In the United States, in New Hampshire at Grafton in the pegmatites; in Vermont a notable new occurrence of fine cubic crystals with magnetite crystals in chlorite schist at the talc mine of Chester; in Connecticut acicular crystals reported from Middletown. In New York, at Rossie, St. Lawrence County, fine dodecahedral crystals; at Schoharie abundant as iron-cross twins; in various parts of central New York as pyritized fossils, especially at Holland Patent, northwest of Utica, after trilobite fossils in the Frankfort shale. In the limestone at Franklin, New Jersey (*cobaltian*, pt.). In Pennsylvania at the French Creek mines (*cobaltian* pt.) as highly distorted or twisted, skeletonized, crystals and as octahedra; at Cornwall (*cobaltian* and *nickelian*, pt.) lustrous crystals of steel-like luster with magnetite. Lenses in sericite schist have been mined in Louisa and Prince William counties in Virginia. In a large deposit at Ducktown, Tennessee. In the coal beds of Ohio, as concretions. In Illinois at Sparta, Randolph County, as disklike radiating concretions (pyrite suns) in shale; at Galena as stalactitic growths, and Elizabeth, Jo Daviess County, as concentric masses. In Colorado many localities produce fine crystals, especially at Leadville, in the Ibex mine (pyritohedrons), and in Gilpin County at Central City and Russell Gulch. In Arizona as good crystals from near Tucson, at Clifton associated with lime silicates of the contact metamorphic deposit, and at the United Verde mine in Jerome, where the underground fire in the pyritic ore body has produced some unusual alteration products of the pyrite and other sulfides. In Utah fine crystal groups are often found at Bingham Canyon, also at American Fork, Utah County, and in the Park City district. In California reported as acicular crystals in albite from Calaveras County; also found at New Almaden.

In Canada at Elizabethtown, Ontario, as octahedral crystals. On the west coast of Newfoundland as concretions. In the Sudbury district, Ontario (*nickelian*).

Alter. Pyrite changes readily by oxidation to various iron sulfates, or as an end product of the process, to limonite. The so-called *gossan*, or iron capping (*eisener Hut, Germ.*) of pyritic mineral deposits is formed in this way. The sulfuric acid generated in the oxidation of pyrite plays an important role in the formation of zones of enrichment in ore deposits, especially of copper, and as such has received careful study in the field and laboratory.[23]

Pseudomorphs after pyrite are common. Most often they are of limonite; other pseudomorphs reported are hematite, chalcocite, jarosite, graphite. Molds of pyrite crystals in quartz or clay are common, and sometimes are partially filled with iron sulfate or oxide or may contain particles of metallic gold which itself had been present as inclusions in the pyrite. Pyrite has been observed as pseudomorphs after pyrrhotite, hematite, chalcopyrite, arsenopyrite, marcasite, fluorite, calcite, and barite; also as the petrifying material of wood, shells, bone.

Artif. Pyrite may be formed in various ways, including the action of sulfur on ferrous sulfide in weakly acid, nearly neutral or alkaline solutions.[24] Solutions of high acidity and low temperature tend to form marcasite.

Name. The name pyrite is derived from πῦρ, *fire*, and alludes to the sparks from friction. Pliny mentions several things as included under the name (**36**, 30) : (*a*) a stone used for grindstones; (*b*) a kind which so readily fires punk or sulfur that he distinguishes it as *pyrites vivus*, and which may have been flint or a related variety of quartz, as has been supposed, but more probably was *emery* since he describes it as the heaviest of all; (*c*) a kind resembling brass or copper; (*d*) a porous stone, perhaps a sandstone or buhrstone. The brassy kind was in all probability our pyrite, but with it were confounded copper pyrite (chalcopyrite), besides marcasite and pyrrhotite, although these last three kinds of pyrites fail of scintillations. In fact, Dioscorides calls pyrite an ore of copper, yet in the next sentence admits that some kinds contain no copper; and, moreover, he states that the mineral gives sparks. This confounding of iron and copper pyrites is apparent also in the descriptions of the vitriols (sulfates of iron and copper) by Pliny and other ancient writers, and equally so in the mineralogy of the world for more than fifteen centuries after Pliny, as is even now apparent in the principal languages of Europe; *Kupferwasser* (copper-water) of the Germans being the copperas (iron sulfate) of the English and couperose of the French. It is quite probable that *copperas* and *couperose* are in fact corruptions of the German word, instead of derivatives from *cuprosa* or *cupirosa*, as usually stated, for the Latin *u* would not have become *ou* in French.

Under the name *marcasite* or *marchasite*, of Spanish or Arabic origin, the older mineralogists Henckel, Wallerius, Linnaeus, etc., included distinctively crystallized pyrite, the cubic preeminently; the nodular and other varieties being called *pyrites*, and the less yellow or brownish and softer kinds, *wasserkies*, this last including our *marcasite* and *pyrrhotite*, and some *true pyrite*. Werner first made *pyrrhotite* a distinct species. The " marcasite " used for personal adornment in the eighteenth century was pyrite.

MELNIKOVITE. *Doss (Ann. géol. min. 'Russie*, 13, 130 [1911] — *Min. Mag.*, 16, 352 [1913]). Melnikowit *Germ.* Melnikowit-Pyrit.

Black finely divided pyrite regarded as having been derived from iron sulfide gel.[25] Sometimes weakly magnetic, apparently due to admixed magnetite.[26] Found in sedimentary muds and clays, as a hot-spring deposit, and in ore deposits. Concentrically banded microcrystalline mixtures of pyrite and marcasite, also stated to be of metacolloidal origin, have been termed melnikovite-pyrite.[27] Named from the occurrence in Miocene clay on the Melnikov estates, Government of Samara, Russia.

Ref.

1. Tokody, *Zs. Kr.*, 80, 255 (1931); also Wacker, *Jb. Min.*, *Beil.-Bd.*, 67, 273 (1933). Uncertain forms listed in Tokody. Rare forms:

1·0·29	0·7·11	5·5·11	2·1·12	7·3·13	11·7·15
1·0·21	023	8·8·15	6·1·12	8·3·13	548
1·0·17	90·13	6·6·11	9·1·12	15·6·25	10·13·20
1·0·15	7·0·10	559	11·4·46	4·3·12	346
1·0·14	057	447	13·2·23	328	436
1·0·12	507	7·7·12	2·4·20	7·4·16	234
1·0·10	0·11·15	335	5·1·10	124	324
1·0·9	11·0·15	558	6·1·10	528	5·8·10
018	14·0·19	223	7·1·10	134	3·5·6
108	034	7·7·10	9·2·18	314	748
107	10·0·13	557	519	12·5·19	5·9·10
106	790	334	218	10·5·18	7·6·11
2·0·11	045	445	318	427	759
3·0·16	405	556	418	9·4·14	547
105	9·0·11	667	518	6·3·10	11·8·14
209	14·0·17	14·14·15	3·2·15	9·3·10	345
014	056	166	217	8·4·13	435
3·0·11	067	155	137	7·11·22	658
207	607	144	417	14·7·22	9·7·11
2·0·10	078	133	3·2·13	6·5·15	456
5·0·16	708	4·11·11	6·2·13	326	546
4·0·11	089	255	3·2·12	123	11·9·13
3·0·8	809	377	216	4·6·11	8·7·10
5·0·13	9·0·10	599	136	3·4·8	11·10·14
025	0·10·11	477	316	538	768
205	10·9·11	355	416	638	879
5·0·12	13·0·14	588	5·2·11	5·4·10	11·10·12
307	1·1·36	233	6·3·16	235	
409	119	577	5·4·20	10·6·15	
5·0·11	117	344	125	7·4·10	

7·0·13	116	455	215	425
509	115	566	5·2·10	15·10·24
047	114	4·1·20	415	437

407	3·3·11	9·1·17	12·5·24	537
7·0·12	227	8·1·16	9·3·14	649
305	338	9·1·16	329	7·5·11

0·8·13	225	1·6·14	429	8·5·11
8·0·13	337	8·1·14	529	10·5·11
508	449	7·1·13	629	9·6·13

2. Cell dimensions from Parker and Whitehouse, *Phil. Mag.*, **14**, 939 (1932). The cell dimensions increase with substitution of Ni or Co for Fe; nickelian pyrite with Ni : Fe = 1 : 1.84 (anal. 6) from Derbyshire has a_0 5.49 (Bannister, *Min. Mag.*, **25**, 609 [1940]).

3. Shannon, *U. S. Nat. Mus., Proc.*, **62**, 9, 2 (1922). On twisting in pyrite see Frondel, *Am. Mus. Nov. 829*, 1936.

4. Early etching experiments by Becke, *Min. Mitt.*, **8**, 239 (1887), and Tokody, *Földt. Közl.*, 1921–22 — *Min. Abs.*, **2**, 317 (1924). More recent studies of natural etch patterns by Ichikawa, *Am. J. Sc.*, **17**, 245 (1929), and by Wacker, *Jb. Min., Beil.-Bd.*, **67A**, 273 (1933).

5. Smolar, *Zs. Kr.*, **52**, 461 (1913), lists 48 doubtful twin laws. Schaake, *Zs. Kr.*, **98**, 281 (1937), discusses the relation between twinning and structure in pyrite.

6. Neuhaus, *Chem. Erde*, **12**, 23 (1938).

7. See Mügge, *Jb. Min., Beil.-Bd.*, **16**, 338, 339, 343, 363, 365 (1903).

8. Pöschl, *Zs. Kr.*, **48**, 576 (1911), has measured the hardness (tear hardness) with a sclerometer, obtaining 199.1 (50 gm. wgt.) and 182.2 (20 gm. wgt.) against 1000 for topaz.

9. Average value from pycnometer measurements by Kenngott on 10 selected crystals, *Ak. Wien, Ber.*, **11**, 392 (1853), with a range 5.000–5.028 and with an average weight of 6 gm. for the crystals. Zepharovich, *Ak. Wien, Ber.*, **12**, 286 (1854), and more recently Pöschl (1911) obtained a somewhat wider range.

10. Cusack, *Proc. Roy. Irish Acad.*, **4**, 399 (1897).

11. Thermoelectric properties observed by Friedel, *Ann. chim.*, **17**, 79 (1868); Rose, *Ann. Phys.*, **142**, 1 (1875); Curie, *Bull. soc. min.*, **8**, 127 (1885); Schrauf and Dana, *Ak. Wien, Ber.*, **69** [1], 145, 157 (1875).

12. cf. Buerger, *Am. Min.*, **13**, 1 (1928), Mügge, *Jb. Min.*, I, 24, 1920.

13. See Smith, *Univ. Toronto Stud., Geol. Ser.*, **49**, 83 (1940), on the electrical conductivity.

14. Schneiderhöhn and Ramdohr (2, 158, 1931). For reflectivity data see Orcel and Fastré, *C. R.*, **200**, 1485 (1935).

15. Spectroscopic traces reported by Claussen, *Am. Min.*, **19**, 221 (1934) and by Newhouse, *Am. Min.*, **19**, 209 (1934). On the presence of As in pyrite see Schneiderhöhn, *Chem. Erde*, **5**, 385 (1930). Juza and Biltz, *Zs. anorg. Chem.*, **205**, 273 (1932), believe that artificially prepared pyrite may have a slight deficiency or excess of S.

16. Additional analyses are cited in Doelter (4 [1], 527, 1925).

17. Allen and Johnston, *J. Ind. Eng. Chem.*, **2** [5], 1 (1910) who determined the constituents with special precision, and give an elaborate discussion of their procedure.

18. Hey anal. in Bannister, *Min. Mag.*, **25**, 609 (1940).

19. Kraus and Scott, *Zs. Kr.*, **44**, 144 (1907).

20. Johansson, *Ark. Kemi*, **9**, no. 8, 2 (1924).

21. For additional analyses of nickelian and cobaltian material see Doelter (1926), Bannister (1940), Henglein, *Cbl. Min.*, 129, 1914, Thomson and Allen, *Univ. Toronto Stud., Geol. Ser.*, no. 42, 135, 1939. The validity of the variety was first firmly established by Bannister (1940).

22. See Lindgren (1933) for a more detailed description of important deposits of pyrite.

23. For a study of the system Fe_2O_3-SO_3-H_2O see Posnjak and Merwin, *J. Am. Chem. Soc.*, **44** [2], 1965 (1922); Zies, Allen, and Merwin, *Econ. Geol.*, **11**, 407 (1916); Merwin and Posnjak, *Am. Min.*, **22**, 567 (1937); Bandy, *Am. Min.*, **23**, 669 (1938) for a field study.

24. Allen, Crenshaw, Johnston, and Larsen, *Am. J. Sc.*, **33**, 169 (1912).

25. For a summary of the literature on melnikovite see Hintze (351, 355, 1936).
26. Berz, *Cbl. Min.*, 569, 1922.
27. See Schneiderhöhn and Ramdohr (2, 170, 1931).

CAYEUXITE. *Sujkowski* (*Arch. Min. Soc. Warsaw*, **12**, 118, 138, 1936). Cayeuxyt.
A name given to pyritic nodules rich in As, Sb, Ge, Mo, Ni from Lower Cretaceous
shales along the Czeremosz River, Carpathians. Named after Professor Lucien Cayeux
(1864–   ), of Paris.

2912 **BRAVOITE** [(Ni,Fe)S₂]. Bravoite pt. *Hillebrand* (*Am. J. Sc.*, **24**, 149,
1907). Villamaninite (?) *Schoeller* and *Powell* (*Min. Mag.*, **19**, 14, 1920). Kobaltnickelpyrit *Henglein* (*Cbl. Min.*, 129, 1914). Hengleinite *Doelter* (4 [1], 643, 1926).

C r y s t. Isometric; diploidal — $2/m\,\overline{3}$.[1]
Structure cell.[2] Space group $Pa3$; a_0 5.74 (artif. NiS_2), a_0 5.57 (Mechernich, anal. 2). The cell dimensions apparently decrease regularly
with increasing substitution of Fe to pyrite (a_0 5.405). Cell contents
$(Ni,Fe)_4S_8$.
Habit. Usually as crusts or nodular masses with a radially fibrous or
columnar structure. The surfaces of the crusts sometimes show indistinct
crystals with pyritohedral, octahedral, or cubic faces.
P h y s. Cleavage {001}. Fracture conchoidal to uneven. Brittle.
H. $5\frac{1}{2}$–6, decreasing as the Ni content increases. G. 4.62 (anal. 2, with
Fe : (Ni,Co) = 1 : 1.53); 4.66 (calc. for Fe : Ni = 1 : 1), 4.28 (calc. for
NiS_2). Luster metallic. Color steel-gray. Opaque. In polished section
isotropic.[3] Often exhibits zonal growth banding; the successive zones
vary in hardness and color (rose, brown, dark brown) depending on the
Ni content.
C h e m. A disulfide of nickel and iron, $(Ni,Fe)S_2$, with Ni > Fe.
Co substitutes for Ni and Fe to a small extent. Natural material with
Fe : (Ni,Co) > 1 : 1.56 (anal. 2) has not been described. A probably
complete series with increasing substitution of Fe extends from bravoite
through nickelian pyrite to pyrite. Material with Ni < Fe is placed
with pyrite.
Anal.

	1	2	3	4
Fe	23.00	17.08	21.15	20.68
Ni	24.17	24.73	17.50	24.81
Co	.....	3.28	[6.61]	.....
Cu	.....	0.47	......	
S	52.83	51.15	53.70	54.51
Rem.	.....	0.40	1.04	.....
Total	100.00	97.11	100.00	100.00
G.	4.66	4.62	4.716 ± 0.028	

1. $(Ni,Fe)S_2$ with Ni : Fe = 1 : 1. 2. Mechernich, Germany. Rem. is 0.40 insol.[4]
3. Müsen, Siegen, Germany.[5] 4. Lower Copper River Valley, Alaska. Analysis recalc.
after elimination of ca. 20 per cent impurities.[6]

O c c u r. At Mechernich, Rhenish Prussia, Germany, with galena,
sphalerite, chalcopyrite, nickelian pyrite. In the Victoria mine, Müsen,
Siegen district, (*kobaltnickelpyrite*) with siderite, pyrite, chalcopyrite, and

barite. Probably occurs in mines in the Cármenes district, near Villa-manín, Leon Province, Spain (*villamaninite*). At the Mill Close mine, Derbyshire, England, with nickelian pyrite. In Alaska with chalcopyrite and pyrrhotite in altered peridotite on Spirit Mountain, Canyon Creek Valley, Lower Copper River Valley.

Artif.[7] NiS_2 and CoS_2 have been prepared by adding the mono-sulfides to fused sulfur.

Name. After José J. Bravo (1874–1928) of Lima, Peru. The name bravoite was originally applied[8] to a mineral now classed as a nickelian variety of pyrite, and is here given to material in the series FeS_2-NiS_2 with Ni > Fe.

Ref.

1. Crystal class and space group from isostructural relation to pyrite shown by the x-ray studies of de Jong and Willems, *Zs. anorg. Chem.*, **160**, 189 (1927), on artificial NiS_2 and bravoite from Mechernich and of Bannister, *Min. Mag.*, **25**, 609 (1940), on natural material from Darbyshire. CoS_2 also is isostructural with NiS_2.
2. de Jong and Willems (1927) and Bannister (1940).
3. See Schneiderhöhn and Ramdohr (**2**, 173, 1931) and Ramdohr, *Zbl. Min.*, 289, 1937.
4. Kalb and Meyer, *Cbl. Min.*, 26, 1926.
5. Varga anal. in Henglein, *Cbl. Min.*, 129, 1914.
6. Buddington, *Econ. Geol.*, **19**, 521 (1924).
7. de Jong and Willems (1927).
8. Hillebrand, *Am. J. Sc.*, **24**, 149 (1907).

2913 **LAURITE** [RuS₂]. *Wöhler* (*Ges. Wiss. Göttingen, Nachr.*, 155, 1866; 327, 1869).

Cryst. Isometric; diploidal — $2/m \ \overline{3}$.[1]

Forms:

$a\{001\}$ $o\{111\}$ $'e\{102\}$ $m\{113\}$ $n\{112\}$ $'s\{213\}$

Structure cell.[2] Space group $Pa3$; a_0 5.59 ± 0.01. Contains Ru_4S_8.

Habit. Minute octahedrons (Borneo), cubic and pyritohedral (Potgietersrust); in rounded or spherical forms and grains.

Phys. Cleavage {111} perfect. Fracture subconchoidal. Very brittle. H. 7½. G. 6–6.99; 6.23 (calc.). Luster metallic, bright. Color dark iron-black; powder dark gray. Percentage of reflection: green 41, orange 37, red 32.5.[3]

Chem. Ruthenium disulfide, RuS_2, presumably with some osmium.

Anal.

	1	2	3
Ru	61.1	65.18	[67]
Os	....	[3.03]	....
S	38.9	31.79	33
Total	100.00	100.00	100
G.	6.23	6.99	6.

1. RuS_2. 2. Borneo. Analysis on 0.3 gm. The Ru value contains some Os.[4] 3. Potgietersrust. Analysis on 0.00178 gm.[5]

Tests. Infusible. Decrepitates on heating. B.B. gives off fumes of S and Os. Insoluble in aqua regia, and unattacked by potassium disulfate.

Occur. Found in the platinum sands of Borneo; reported from Colombia and Oregon. Recently found in the platinum concentrates from Potgietersrust, Waterberg district, Transvaal, South Africa, together with cooperite, braggite, and sperrylite.

Artif.[6] Ruthenium melted together with borax and iron sulfide produces octahedral crystals having the composition of laurite.

Name. Named by Wöhler as a compliment to the wife of a personal friend.

Ref.

1. The symmetry class established on the Transvaal material by x-ray comparison with pyrite. See Bannister, *Min. Mag.*, **23**, 188 (1932) — p. 195, laurite.
2. Bannister (1932). On artificial crystals a_0 5.57, found by Oftedal, *Zs. phys. Chem.*, **135**, 291 (1928).
3. Schneiderhöhn and Ramdohr (**2**, 181, 1931).
4. Wöhler (1866).
5. Hey anal., in Bannister (1932).
6. In Doelter (4 [1], 789, 1926).

2914   **SPERRYLITE** [PtAs$_2$]. *Wells* (*Am. J. Sc.*, **37**, 67, 1889). *Penfield* (*Am. J. Sc.*, **37**, 71, 1889).

Cryst. Isometric; diploidal — $2/m\,\bar{3}$.

Forms:[1]

a 001	o 111	$'f$ 103	g' 023	p 122	$'t$ 214
d 011	f' 013	$'e$ 102	n 112	X 5·2·10	

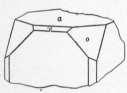

Structure cell.[2] Space group $Pa3$; a_0 6.00; contains Pt$_4$As$_8$.

Habit. Cubic, cubo-octahedral; sometimes highly modified, producing rounded corners and edges.[3]

Phys. Cleavage {001} indistinct. Fracture

Vermilion mine, Sudbury.   conchoidal. Brittle. H. 6–7. G. 10.58;[3] 10.59 (calc.). Color tin-white. Streak black. Opaque. Isotropic. Percentage of reflection: green 56.5, orange 55, red 52.5.[4]

Chem. Platinum diarsenide, PtAs$_2$, with small amounts of Sb, Rh, Fe, Cu reported in analyses.

Anal.

	1	2	3	4
Pt	56.58	52.57	56.2	54.83
Pd	.....	trace	....	nil
Rh	.....	0.72	....	1.66
Cu	.....	....	0.7	.....
Fe	.....	0.07	0.4	.....
Sb	.....	0.50	....	.....
As	43.42	40.98	40.6	39.89
Rem.	.....	4.62	1.3	2.90
Total	100.00	99.46	99.2	99.28
G.	10.59	10.602		10.6

1. PtAs$_2$. 2. Vermilion mine, Sudbury. Average of 2 analyses. Rem. is cassiterite.[5] 3. Amur, Siberia. Rem. is SiO$_2$.[6] 4. Tweefontain, Potgietersrust.[7]

Tests. B.B. decrepitates slightly. In C.T. remains unchanged at fusing point of glass. In O.T. gives sublimate of As_2O_3, without fusing if slowly roasted, but if rapidly heated it melts very easily after losing a part of the As. When dropped on a red-hot platinum foil, instantly melts, gives off fumes of As_2O_3, and porous excrescences of Pt are formed on the foil.

Occur. Found originally at the Vermilion mine, Algoma district, 22 miles west of Sudbury, Ontario. Subsequently reported from the Victoria mine of the same district, and, more recently, from the Frood mine, associated with the norite, where crystals have been found sparingly in the mill concentrates. A crystal measuring 2 cm. along the cube edges has been reported from the Tweefontain farm about 10 miles north-northwest of Potgietersrust, Waterberg district, Transvaal, South Africa, in the Bushveld Igneous Complex. Also found in the Nikolaevsky gold washings on the Timpton River, in Amur, eastern Siberia. Reported from the ruby-bearing gravels in Caler Fork and Mason Branch, tributaries of the Little Tennessee River, near Franklin, Macon County, North Carolina. In covellite, from the Rambler mine, Medicine Bow Mountains, Wyoming.

Artif.[8] Formed by heating Pt to redness and passing As vapor over it in a current of hydrogen.

Name. After Francis L. Sperry, chemist of Sudbury, Ontario, who first found the mineral.

Ref.
1. Goldschmidt (**8**, 69, 1922), Spencer, *Min. Mag.*, **21**, 94 (1926); Padurova, *Mem. soc. russe min.*, ser. 2, **59**, 181 (1930); *Min. Abs.*, **4**, 519 (1931). Rare forms: 017, 012, 025, 035, 144, 113, 335, 223, 133, 677, 123, 213.
2. Aminoff and Parsons, *Univ. Toronto, Geol. Ser.*, **26**, 1 (1928), on crystals from the Vermilion mine, Sudbury, the type locality.
3. Crystals from Potgietersrust measured by Spencer, *Min. Mag.*, **21**, 95 (1926).
4. Schneiderhöhn and Ramdohr (**2**, 178, 1931).
5. Wells, *Am. J. Sc.*, **37**, 67 (1889).
6. Pilipenko, *Ac. sc. Leningrad, Bull.*, ser. 6, **9**, 1229 (1915) — *Min. Abs.*, **2**, 138 (1923).
7. Cooper anal. in Wagner (**17**, 1929).
8. Wells (1889), and recently Wöhler, *Zs. anorg. Chem.*, **186**, 324 (1930), prepared artificial sperrylite.

2915 HAUERITE [MnS_2]. Hauerit *Haidinger* (*Ber. Mitt. Freund. Wiss. Wien*, **2**, 2, 1846 — *Naturwiss. Abh. Wien*, **1**, 101, 107, 1846).

Cryst. Isometric; diploidal — $2/m \, \bar{3}$.[1]

Forms:[2]

| a 001, | d 011, | $'f$ 103, | $'e$ 102, | o 111, | ζ 122, | Δ 477, | $'s$ 213, | $'t$ 214 |

Structure cell.[3] Space group $Pa3$; a_0 6.11; contains Mn_4S_8.

Habit. Commonly octahedral; sometimes cubo-octahedral; also in globular clusters.

Phys. Cleavage {001} perfect.[4] Fracture uneven to subconchoidal. Brittle. H. 4. G. 3.463; 3.444 (calc.). Luster metallic-adamantine due to alteration. Color reddish brown to brownish black, with red internal reflections in the cleavage. Streak brownish red.

O p t.[5] Isotropic and deep red in section; n_{Li} 2.69 ± 0.01 (Raddusa).
C h e m. Manganese disulfide, MnS_2, with less than 1.3 per cent of Fe reported in analyses.
Anal.[6]

	1	2	3
Mn	46.14	46.47	46.28
Fe	.....	0.03	.....
S	53.86	53.27	53.51
SiO_2	.....	0.16	.....
Total	100.00	99.93	99.79

1. MnS_2. 2. Raddusa.[7] 3. Raddusa.[8]

Tests. Yields a sublimate of S in C.T. In the O.T. gives off SO_2 and turns green. Soluble in warm concentrated HCl with evolution of H_2S and separation of S.

O c c u r. A rare mineral occurring with gypsum and sulfur, and apparently derived from solutions with an excess of sulfur. In Czechoslovakia at Kalinka, near Neusohl, with gypsum, sulfur and realgar in trachyte and other rocks decomposed by solfataric waters; the crystals are sometimes coated with pyrite. Also from Schemnitz. In Sicily at Raddusa, west of Catania where octahedral crystals in the clay are associated with sulfur, gypsum, and calcite. A crystal measuring 2 in. along the octahedral edge has been found at Raddusa. In the crystalline schists of the Lake Wakatipu district, and Collingwood, New Zealand. Reported from the capping of salt domes in Texas,[9] at Big Hill, Matagorda County, and at High Island salt dome, Galveston County.

A l t e r. The surface of the mineral is usually dull black owing to an alteration coating of uncertain composition.

N a m e. After Joseph von Hauer and Franz von Hauer (1822–99), Austrian geologists.

Ref.

1. The similarity of structure of hauerite and pyrite, as shown by Ewald and Friedrick, *Ann. Phys.*, **44**, 1183 (1914), and by Onorato, *Per. Min.*, **1**, 109 (1930), verifies the crystal class. Scacchi, *Acc. Napoli, Rend.*, **5**, 166 (1899), considered hauerite tetartoidal.
2. Goldschmidt (4, 119, 1918). The form $K\{124\}$ by Onorato, *Acc. Linc., Mem.*, ser. 6, **1**, 470 (1925).
3. Cell dimension by Onorato (1925) on a Raddusa crystal.
4. Beutell and Matzke, *Cbl. Min.*, 263, 1915, give cleavage as *very perfect*, and therefore not like that of pyrite. The perfect cleavage has been verified (Berman, priv. comm., 1940).
5. Larsen (83, 1921).
6. Older analyses in Doelter (4 [1], 485, 1925).
7. Beutell and Matzke (1915).
8. Onorato (1925).
9. Wolf, *Am. Assoc. Pet. Geol., Bull.* **10**, 531 (1926).

2916   P E N R O S E I T E [(Ni,Cu,Pb)Se₂]. *Gordon* (*Ac. Sc. Philadelphia, Proc.*, **77**, 317, 1926). Blockite *Herzenberg* and *Ahlfeld* (*Zbl. Min.*, 277, 1935).

C r y s t. Isometric — probably diploidal — $2/m\,\overline{3}$.[1]

Structure cell.[2] Space group, $Pa3$; a_0 6.01 ± 0.01; contains (Ni,Cu, Pb,Co,Hg,Ag)₄Se₈.

Habit. In reniform masses with one of the cube faces lying in the curved surface, the other two (cleavages) producing a radiating columnar structure in the mass.

P h y s. Cleavage {001} perfect; {011} distinct.[3] Brittle. H. $2\frac{1}{2}$–3. G. 6.9 ± 0.2;[4] 7.56 (calc.). Luster metallic; tarnishes. Color lead-gray. Streak black. Opaque. Isotropic.[5] Shows zoning in polished section.

C h e m. Reported as a selenide of nickel, copper, lead, cobalt, mercury, and silver. The extent to which the metallic elements are present as impurities is not known.[6]

Anal.

	1	2	3	4	5
Pb	17.25	0.36	13.72	8.27	10.88
Hg	.....	1.98	1.45	1.41	4.12
Ag	2.05	1.76	2.13	7.78	5.00
Cu	7.90	6.81	4.50	3.55	3.72
Fe	.....	1.31	trace	0.72	0.72
Co	1.35	2.49	1.10	0.52	0.71
Ni	11.22	14.34	8.89	10.30	9.88
Se	60.23	70.93	67.01	67.31	66.59
S	.....	.....	0.39	trace	0.52
Total	100.00	100.00	99.19	99.86	102.14
G.	6.93	6.03–6.06	6.87	7.0	6.71

1. Penroseite. Recalc. after deducting 1.08 Fe_2O_3.[7] 2. "Blockite." Includes 0.022 per cent Pt metals. 1.28 per cent insol. deducted.[8] 3. Penroseite. Microanalysis on 20 mg.[9] 4. "Blockite." Microanalysis on 20 mg.[9] 5. "Blockite." Microanalysis on 20 mg.[9]

Tests. F. easy. In C.T. decomposed forming Se on walls of tube. Easily soluble in HNO_3 with effervescence.

O c c u r. Found originally in a specimen presumably collected at Colquechaca, Bolivia. Later described from the Hiaca silver mine, approximately 30 km. east-northeast from Colquechaca (*blockite*), associated with pyrite, chalcopyrite, and naumannite in a siderite vein in quartzite.

A l t e r. To selenates such as chalcomenite and cobaltomenite, by oxidation.

A r t i f. The artificial $NiSe_2$ has a pyrite structure, with a_0 6.022, and G. 6.69; this corresponds to a pure nickel penroseite.[10]

N a m e. In honor of Dr. Richard A. F. Penrose, Jr. (1863–1931), geologist. The name *blockite* was later given to the same mineral, on the basis of an inadequate investigation. It was shown recently that the two minerals are identical.

Ref.

1. Crystal symmetry inferred from the structural similarity with pyrite, according to Bannister and Hey *Am. Min.*, **22**, 319 (1937). Gordon's (1926) statement of the orthorhombic symmetry of penroseite is not supported by the x-ray evidence.

2. Cell edge is average of 3 determinations (6.001, 6.001, 6.017) by Bannister and Hey (1937).

3. Gordon (1926) gives {110} as cleavage. Ramdohr, *Zbl. Min.*, 193, 1937 — p. 201 for " blockite " gives, however, {110} or {111}.

4. An average of seven determinations, including three new values (Berman) on small fragments yielding 7.05 ± 0.05. Herzenberg and Ahlfeld's value is not included. The calculated value is from Bannister and Hey (1937) analyses, including all of the elements reported.

5. Ramdohr, *Zbl. Min.*, 193, 1937.

6. Ramdohr (1937) reports inhomogeneities in the polished section (of blockite) consisting of clausthalite and other selenium minerals. Bannister and Hey (1937) find x-ray and polished section evidence of the presence of naumannite, and Gordon (1926) found 2 to 3 per cent of a " white selenide."

7. Whitfield anal. in Gordon (1926).

8. Herzenberg anal. in Herzenberg and Ahlfeld (1935).

9. Hey anal. in Bannister and Hey (1937).

10. de Jong and Willems, *Zs. anorg. Chem.*, 170, 241 (1928) — from Bannister and Hey (1937).

ARSENOFERRITE. *Groth* (*Zs. Kr.*, 5, 253, 1881). Arsenoferrit *Baumhauer* (*Zs. Kr.*, 51, 143, 1912).

A supposed diarsenide of iron, $FeAs_2$, belonging to the pyrite group. No satisfactory description of this material from the original locality, Binnental, Switzerland, has been presented. The supposed occurrence at Joachimstal, Bohemia,[1] has been shown to be loellingite.[2]

Ref.

1. Foshag and Short, *Am. Min.*, 15, 428 (1930).
2. Buerger, *Am. Min.*, 21, 70 (1936).

292 COBALTITE GROUP — AXY

ISOMETRIC; TETARTOIDAL — 23

	COMPOSITION		a_0	G.
2921	Cobaltite	(Co,Fe)AsS	5.58	6.33
2922	Gersdorffite	(Ni,Fe,Co)AsS	5.719	5.819
2923	Ullmannite	(Ni,Co,Fe) (Sb,As,Bi)S	5.91	6.65

The minerals of the group are closely related to pyrite; they differ structurally, and chemically, only in that the S pairs in pyrite are replaced by As-S or Sb-S pairs. This substitution in the structure makes each trigonal axis of the space lattice a polar axis with a consequent lowering of the symmetry. The space group is $P2_13$.

The cell contents can be expressed by the formula $A_4(XY)_4$; with A = Co, Ni, and, to a considerable amount, Fe, with no pure compound of the latter occurring in the group; X = As, Sb, and Bi, the latter only partially replacing the Sb in ullmannite; Y = S.

Physically the members of the group are distinguishable from the pyrite group minerals in the perfection of the cleavage {001} and the generally inferior hardness ($5\frac{1}{2}$).

2921 **C O B A L T I T E** [CoAsS]. Cobaltum cum ferro sulfurato et arsenicato mineralisatum, Glants Kobolt pt. *Cronstedt* (213, 1758). Mine de Cobalt blanche *de Lisle* (334, 1772). Mine de Cobalt arsenico-sulfureuse *de Lisle* (3, 129, 1783). Glanz-Kobold *Werner*. Kobalt Glanz *Germ*. Cobalt gris pt. *Haüy*. Glance Cobalt; Bright White Cobalt. Glanzkobaltkies *Glocker* (1831). Cobaltine *Beudant* (2, 450, 1832). Kobolt glans *Swed*. Sehta *Indian jewelers*. Cobaltite *Dana* (71, 1884).

C r y s t. Isometric; tetartoidal — 2 3.[1]

Forms:[2]

   a 001   *d* 011   *o* 111   *'h* 104   *'e* 102   *p* 122   *'s* 213   *'z* 324

Structure cell.[3] Space group $P2_13$, a_0 5.58; contains $Co_4As_4S_4$.

Habit. Commonly in cubes {001}, or pyritohedrons {102}, or combinations of these, with faces striated as in pyrite. Also octahedral. Sometimes granular massive to compact.

Twinning. Rarely on {011} and {111}.[4] In polished section shows anisotropic twin lamellae.[5]

P h y s. Cleavage {001} perfect. Fracture uneven. Brittle. H. $5\frac{1}{2}$.

Hakansbö, Sweden.   Tunaberg, Sweden.

G. 6.33 (Tunaberg);[6] 6.302 (calc.). Luster metallic. Color silver-white, inclined to red; also steel-gray, with a violet tinge, or grayish black when containing much iron. Streak grayish black. Shows both positive and negative thermoelectricity.[7]

C h e m.[8] Sulfarsenide of cobalt with considerable amounts of iron, (Co,Fe)AsS; authentic analyses give maximum of about 10 per cent Fe. Also small amounts of Ni (3.20 per cent maximum) reported. Cu, Pb, Sb probably represent impurities.

Anal.[9]

	1	2	3	4
Fe	.....	4.11	2.92	4.55
Co	35.53	28.64	32.36	29.10
Ni	.....	3.06	0.32	0.97
As	45.15	44.77	42.88	44.55
S	19.32	19.34	21.48	20.37
Total	100.00	99.92	99.96	99.54
G.	6.302			

1. CoAsS. 2. Columbus Claim, Cobalt, Ont. Microscopic examination of the material shows it to be somewhat inhomogeneous, and the Fe present is said to be due to impurities.[10] The analysis, however, yields a composition in good agreement with the formula for the mineral. 3. Columbus Claim, Cobalt, Ont.[11] 4. Hakansbö, Sweden. The Fe is deducted as pyrite, that is, the analyzed sample presumably contains 6.27 per cent of pyrite.[12]

Var. Ferrian: Stahlkobalt *Rammelsberg* (116, 1849). Ferrocobaltine *Dana* (58, 1854). No modern analyses verify the presence of large amounts of iron in cobaltite. Earlier analyses are not conclusive, and this variety is not yet established.

Tests. F. 2–3. Unaltered in C.T. Fuses to a weakly magnetic globule B.B. Decomposed by HNO_3 with separation of sulfur and arsenic oxide.

O.c c u r. Most commonly found in high-temperature deposits, as disseminations in metamorphosed rocks (Skutterud), or, more rarely, in vein deposits (Cobalt) with other cobalt and nickel sulfides and arsenides.

Occurs in considerable amount at Dashkesan near Elisaretpol, Azerbaijan, Trans-Caucasia. From Querbach, east of Flinsberg, Silesia, and from Siegen, Westphalia (*stahlcobalt*), with other cobalt minerals. Notable crystals have been found in Sweden at Tunaberg (pyritohedral), Söderman-land; at Riddarhyttan and Hakansbö in Vastmanland; at Vena in Nericke, Örebro. In Norway at Skutterud near Modum, Buskerud. In England from Botallack mine, near St. Just, Cornwall. From the Ketri mines, Rajputana, India. Reported from Ravensthorpe, Western Australia. In the Cobalt region, Coleman Township, Ontario, especially at the Columbus Claim, in fine octahedral crystals.

Ref.

1. The structure, which is presumably similar to that of ullmannite, according to Ramsdell, *Am. Min.*, **10**, 281 (1925), is the basis of the crystal class here given. The morphology (see Goldschmidt [4, 37, 1918]) indicates diploidal symmetry. The fixed ratio between the arsenic and sulfur furnishes a structural basis for the lower sym-metry. Flörke, *Cbl. Min.*, **A**, 337, 1926, has shown that cobaltite is anisotropic below 850° in polished section, which suggests further complexities of structure.
2. Goldschmidt (1918). Rare or uncertain {203}, {225}, {112}, {334}.
3. Cell value by Ramsdell (1925). Space group from the structure which is similar to that of pyrite, but without the symmetry centers between the S–S pairs. See also Bragg (73, 1937).
4. In Hintze (1 [1], 771, 1900). See also Flink, *Ark. Kemi*, **3** [11], 1908, p. 61 for cobaltite.
5. Flörke (1926).
6. Berman (priv. comm., 1939), on crystal fragment of 16 mg.
7. Schrauf and Dana, *Ak. Wien, Ber.*, **69**, 156 (1874).
8. Beutell, *Cbl. Min.*, 663, 1911, has examined the available analyses of cobaltite, and his tabulation shows that most of the Fe reported may be considered as part of the cobaltite. Some few analyses presumably have admixed pyrite. Ellsworth, *Ontario Bur. Mines, Rep. 25* [1], 1916, shows that crystals from Cobalt, Ont., have the Fe and Ni as impurities due to inclusions of other minerals.
9. Other analyses given in Beutell's compilation (1911).
10. Ellsworth (1916).
11. de Lury, *Am. J. Sc.*, **21**, 275 (1906).
12. Beutell (1911).

2922   GERSDORFFITE [NiAsS]. Niccolum Ferro et Cobalto Arsenicatis et Sulphuratis mineralisatum. Kupfernickel pt. *Cronstedt* (218, 1758; *Ak. Stock-holm, Handl.*, 1751, 1754). (The species later taken for Kupfernickel and Cobalt ore, until 1818.) Nickelglanz, Weisses Nickelerz *Pfaff* (*J. Chem. Phys.*, **22**, 260, 1818); *Berzelius* (*Ak. Stockholm, Handl.*, 251, 1820). Sulfo-arséniure de nickel *Beudant* (1824). Nickelarsenikglanz, Nickelarsenikkies, Arseniknickelglanz, *Germ.* Nickel Glance. Disomose *Beudant* (**2**, 448, 1832). Tombazite pt. *Breithaupt* (*J. pr. Chem.*, **15**, 330, 1838). Gersdorffit (from Schladming) pt. *Löwe* (*Ann. Phys.*, **55**, 503, 1843). Amoibit pt. *Kobell* (*J. pr. Chem.*, **33**, 402, 1844). Dobschauite *Dana* (73, 1868). Sommarugite pt. (*Bull. soc. min.*, **1**, 143, 1878).

Cryst.   Isometric; tetartoidal — 2 3.[1]

Forms:[2]

    c{001}   d{011}   o{111}   'e{102}   m{113}

Structure cell.[3]   Space group, $P2_13$; a_0 5.719; contains $(Ni,Fe)_4As_4S_4$, with Ni : Fe = 3 : 1.

Habit. Octahedral, cubo-octahedral, pyritohedral; sometimes striated as in pyrite; lamellar and granular massive. Variety *corynite* in octahedra or globular groups.

P h y s. Cleavage {001} perfect. Fracture uneven. Brittle. H. 5½. G. 5.9 (average);[4] 5.819 (calc. for Ni : Fe = 3 : 1). Luster metallic. Color silver-white to steel-gray, often tarnished gray or grayish black. Streak grayish black. Opaque. Isotropic.[5] Reflection percentages: green 49.5, orange 42.5, red 42.

C h e m. Essentially a sulfide-arsenide of nickel, with iron and cobalt substituting for the nickel in part, $(Ni,Fe,Co)AsS$. Antimony is often reported in amounts less than 2 per cent. The formula given is in agreement with most analyses, although important deviations have been noted.[6]

Anal. Some older analyses[7] contain as much as 16.64 per cent Fe, and the maximum Co content noted is 14.12 per cent (Schladming). Sb is nearly always present in amounts less than 2 per cent. The Cu often reported is apparently due to admixed material, usually chalcopyrite.

	1	2	3	4	5	6
Cu	.....	.....	.....	.....	4.20	1.10
Fe	.....	.....	.....	8.22	5.71	8.89
Co	.....	.....	.....	.....	.....	1.72
Ni	35.42	34.31	33.32	26.97	23.48	28.92
Sb	.....	1.17	1.15	.....	0.54	1.63
As	45.23	45.33	45.50	45.35	44.33	43.54
S	19.35	18.50	19.37	18.98	17.76	13.84
Rem.	.....	0.69	0.66	0.61	3.98	.....
Total	100.00	100.00	100.00	100.13	100.00	99.64
G.					5.96	

1. NiAsS. 2, 3. Rhodesia. Recalc. after deducting gangue.[8] 4. Unspecified locality. Rem. is gangue.[9] 5. Crean Hill mine, Sudbury. Rem. contains 0.44 per cent gangue, 3.54 per cent calcite by difference.[10] 6–11. Dobschau.[11] 6. Coburg mine, Dobschau. Cu present as chalcopyrite.[11]

	7	8	9	10	11	12	13
Cu	.....	.....	1.26	.....	.....	.....	....
Fe	8.99	9.86	10.16	15.13	3.69	1.98	3.9
Co	0.89	0.94	0.40	8.30	8.82	.....	0.7
Ni	32.81	24.14	31.67	15.64	19.82	28.86	31.6
Sb	1.89	1.24	1.61	2.46	2.99	13.45	9.1
As	39.34	50.04	42.02	52.43	57.54	37.83	34.9
S	15.56	13.61	12.99	5.92	7.55	17.19	17.1
Rem.	.....	.....	.....	.....	.....	.....	0.4
Total	99.48	99.83	100.11	99.88	100.41	99.31	97.7
G.				5.35	6.18	5.994	

7, 8. Jacobi drift. Dobschau.[11] 9. Jacobi drift. Cu present as chalcopyrite.[11] 10. Dobschau. Zoned crystal labeled " smaltite."[11] 11. Dobschau. Outer zone of crystal of analysis 10. Insol. in HNO₃. 12. Corynite. Olsa, Carinthia. Crystals.[12] 13. Corynite. Chatham, Conn. Rem. is Bi.[13]

Var. Antimonian. Korynite *von Zepharovich* (*Ak. Wien, Ber.*, **51** [1], 117, 1865). Arsenantimonnickelglanz pt. *Germ.* Corynite *Dana* (74, 1868).

Contains as much as 13.45 per cent Sb, with the formula (Ni,Fe,Co) (As,Sb)S, forming an intermediate member of a probable gersdorffite-ullmannite series.[14]

Tests.　F. 2.　Decrepitates in C.T. and gives a yellowish brown sublimate of As_2S_3. Decomposed by warm HNO_3 with separation of S.

O c c u r.　A comparatively rare mineral occurring with other nickel minerals such as niccolite, ullmannite, and chloanthite, as well as with other sulfides, in vein deposits.　Reported from Southern Rhodesia in the Rhodesia Chrome mine at Selukwe Peak.　In Bohemia at Dobschau; at Schladming in Styria; at Lobenstein, Thuringia; at Olsa, Carinthia (*corynite*); Müsen, Westphalia, and from the Harz Mountains mining district.　In Sweden at Loos, west of Hudiksvall, Geflesborg, Helsingland. In Canada, from the Sudbury district, Ontario, and from the Silver Bar mine at Cobalt with niccolite and smaltite in a calcite gangue.　Found as an incrustation of cubes on decomposed galena and sphalerite at Phoenixville, Pennsylvania.　The antimonian variety (*corynite*) is found at Chatham, Connecticut.

N a m e.　After the von Gersdorffs, owners (1842) of the nickel mine at Schladming.

Ref.

1. Ramsdell, *Am. Min.*, **10**, 281 (1925), shows that gersdorffite is structurally similar to ullmannite and therefore of this symmetry class.　The limited morphological data in Goldschmidt (**4**, 34, 1918) indicate symmetry no lower than diploidal.　See also Bragg (73, 1937).

2. Goldschmidt (1918).

3. Olshausen, *Zs. Kr.*, **61**, 463 (1925), on material from unspecified locality (anal. 4) with Ni : Fe = 3 : 1.　Ramsdell (1925) obtained a_0 5.68 on a specimen from "Germany"; Zachariasen in Goldschmidt (V. M.) (**8**, 1927) obtained 5.70 ± 0.02 Å on Lobenstein material.

4. The density range is given from 5.6–6.2 by various observers.　In view of known zoning in the crystals, and unstated purities of the samples measured, the variations are not significant.

5. Schneiderhöhn and Ramdohr (**2**, 188, 1931) give some evidence of lamellae in polished section, indicating a possible inversion and nonisometric character of some gersdorffite.　In this connection see ref. 6, below.

6. Particularly in analysis by Goll, *Ak. Ceské Roz.*, **47** [3], 1 (1937) — *Jb. Min.*, ref. 363, 1938, who finds zoning in the material in polished section.　Deviations from the simple formula may be due to inhomogeneities of this nature.

7. In Doelter (**4** [1], 720, 1926) and in Dana (90, 1892).

8. Golding anal. in Lightfoot, *Rhodesia Sc. Ass., Proc.*, **30**, 45 (1931).

9. Olshausen (1925).　The material used in the x-ray study.

10. Todd anal. in Thomson, *Univ. Toronto Stud., Geol. Ser.*, **12**, 32 (1921).

11. Goll (1937) analyzed gersdorffites previously examined in polished section.　The examination showed zoning in most crystals, with some zones richer than others in arsenic.　The analyzed material was therefore not homogeneous.

12. Payer anal. in von Zepharovich, *Ak. Wien, Ber.*, **51** [1], 117 (1865).

13. Fairchild anal. in Short (101, 1931).

14. Thomson (1921) found that corynite is not homogeneous.　However, the work of Short (97, 101, 1931), on material from the type locality, and from Chatham, indicates that the material examined by him was homogeneous, and definitely contained Sb in considerable amounts (see anal. 13).

2923   **ULLMANNITE** [NiSbS].   Nickelspiesglaserz *Ullmann* [first found by him in 1803] (166, 379, 1814).   Nickelspiessglanzerz *Hausmann* (192, 1813).   Antimonnickelglanz, Nickelantimonglanz, Antimon-Arseniknickelglanz, Arsenantimonnickelglanz pt. *Germ.*   Nickel Stibine.   Nickeliferous Gray Antimony.   Antimoine sulfuré nickelifère *Haüy* (4, 305, 1822).   Ullmannit *Frobel* (1843).   Arsenantimonnickelglanz *Germ.*   Corynite pt.   Willyamite *Pittman* (*Roy. Soc. New South Wales, Proc.*, 27, 366, 1896).   Kallilite *Laspeyres* (*Zs. Kr.*, 19, 12, 1891).   Wismuthnickelglanz *Germ.*

C r y s t.   Isometric; tetartoidal; 2 3.[1]

Forms:[2]

$a\{001\}$ $d\{011\}$ $o\{111\}$ $'e\{102\}$ $n\{112\}$

Structure cell.[3]   Space group, $P2_13$; a_0 5.91; contains $Ni_4Sb_4S_4$.

Habit.   Cubic.   Less frequently octahedral, pyritohedral; rarely tetrahedral.   Striated on the cube faces with striae [110] showing twin boundaries of enantiomorphous individuals.

Twinning.   On [110], with composition plane approximately {001}, producing penetration twins of irregular cubic form and re-entrants on the cube edges.[4]

P h y s.   Cleavage {001} perfect.   Fracture uneven.   Brittle.   H. 5-5½.   G. 6.65 ± 0.04   (ullmannite);   6.793 (calc. for NiSbS);   6.488 (with 10.28 per cent As; anal. 5);   6.76 ± 0.03 (willyamite), 6.66 (kallilite).[5]   Luster metallic.   Color steel-gray to silver-white.   Streak grayish black.   Opaque.   Isotropic.   In polished section[6] white in color and isotropic;   also anisotropic with a fine lamellar structure.   Often exhibits zonal growth-banding.   Reflection percentages: green 49, orange 42, red 42.

With a, o, d, and $\{27 \cdot 27 \cdot 1\}$. Sardinia.

C h e m.   Essentially a sulfide-antimonide of nickel, with cobalt and small amounts of iron substituting for the nickel, also arsenic and bismuth substituting for the antimony, according to the formula $(Ni,Co,Fe)(Sb,As,Bi)S$.

Anal.[7]

	1	2	3	4	5	6
Fe	.....	0.03	0.17	trace	0.40	0.28
Ni	27.62	27.82	28.17	13.41	28.91	26.94
Co	.....	0.65	trace	13.88	1.13	0.89
Sb	57.30	57.43	55.73	56.78	42.93	44.94
As	.....	.....	0.75	.....	10.28	2.02
Bi	.....	.....	.....	.....	0.68	11.76
S	15.08	14.02	14.64	15.78	16.22	14.39
Rem.	.....	.....	0.11	.....	.....	.....
Total	100.00	99.95	99.57	99.85	100.55	101.22
G.	6.793		6.733		6.488	7.01

1. NiSbS.   2, 3. Ullmannite.   Sardinia.[8]   4. Willyamite.   Willyama.   Average of two analyses.[9]   5. "Corynite."   Gossenbach, Siegen.   Average of 2 analyses.[10]   6. Kallilite.   Friedrich mine, near Schönstein.[11]

Var. *Arsenian.* Arsenantimonnickelglanz *Germ.* Corynite pt. .Contains as much as 10.28 per cent As.

Cobaltian. Willyamite *Pittman* (*Roy. Soc. New South Wales,Proc.*,**27**,366, 1896). Most analyses contain small amounts of cobalt but material from Willyama, New South Wales, has Ni : Co = 1 : 1.

Bismuthian. Kallilite *Laspeyres* (*Zs. Kr.*, **19**, 12, 1891). Wismuthnickelglanz *Germ.* Has a ratio Sb : Bi = 6.6 : 1 (anal. 6).

Tests. F. 1.5. In C.T. gives a faint white sublimate. B.B. on charcoal fuses to a globule, boils, and emits antimonial vapor. Decomposed by HNO_3.

O c c u r. Occurs in veins, most frequently in a siderite gangue, with other nickel minerals such as gersdorffite and niccolite. At the Broken Hill mines, Willyama Township, New South Wales, a cobaltian variety (*willyamite*) is associated with dyscrasite in calcite and siderite. In Westphalia in the Siegen and Müsen district at Gossenback (arsenian) and at the Friedrich mine, near Schönstein (*kallilite*) in siderite; in various other Siegen localities (*ullmannite*). In the Harz Mountains at Harzgerode; in Lobenstein, Thuringia; at Lölling near Hüttenberg, and at Waldenstein, Carinthia. In France from the mine of Ar near Eaux-Bonnes, Basses-Pyrénées. As exceptional cubic crystals at Montenarba, Sarrabus, Sardinia. In England at Brancepeth colliery, Durham; at the Settlingstones mine, Fourstones, Northumberland, with niccolite and witherite.

A l t e r. An alteration product of Waldenstein crystals gave the composition Sb 52.44, O 16.15, CaO 13.52, NiO 3.27, FeO 3.13, MgO 0.21, H_2O 11.26 per cent, total 99.98.[12]

N a m e. After J. C. Ullmann (1771–1821). Willyamite is after the locality; kallilite, from καλός (beautiful) and λίθος (stone) because it comes from the locality Schönstein.

Ref.

1. Symmetry established by Miers, *Min. Mag.*, **9**, 211 (1891). Goldschmidt (**9**, 38, 1923), without evidence, retained the diploidal symmetry. Miers' conclusions have been later verified by Mieleitner, *Zs. Kr.*, **56**, 105 (1921), on St. Andreasberg crystals; structural studies have further verified the low symmetry.
2. Goldschmidt (**9**, 38, 1923). Rare forms: {705}, {301}, {223}, {188}, {133}, {216}, uncertain forms: {1·27·27}, {122}.
3. Ramsdell, *Am. Min.*, **10**, 281 (1925). Peacock, *Univ. Toronto Stud., Geol. Ser.*, **44**, 47 (1940), gives a_0 5.918 ± 0.005 for willyamite from Broken Hill; a_0 5.899 ± 0.005 and 5.905 ± 0.005 for ullmannite from Salchendorf, Siegen, and Montenarba, Sardinia; a_0 5.915 ± 0.005 for kallilite from Obersdorf, Siegen.
4. Miers (1891).
5. Specific gravities by microbalance on single-crystal fragments (Berman, priv. comm., 1939): ullmannite from Sardinia; willyamite, average of four determinations; kallilite, average of two determinations.
6. Schneiderhöhn and Ramdohr (**2**, 191, 1931).
7. Earlier analyses in Dana (**92**, 1892).
8. Jannasch, *Jb. Min.*, II, 169, 1887.
9. Mingaye anal. in Pittman, *Roy. Soc. New South Wales, Proc.*, **27**, 366 (1896).
10. Laspeyres and Busz, *Zs. Kr.*, **19**, 8 (1891).
11. Laspeyres, *Zs. Kr.*, **19**, 12 (1891).
12. Ullik, *Ak. Wien, Ber.*, **61**, 1, 17 (1870).

293 LOELLINGITE GROUP — AX_2

ORTHORHOMBIC

2931 Loellingite	FeAs$_2$
2932 Safflorite	(Co,Fe)As$_2$
2933 Rammelsbergite	NiAs$_2$
2934 Pararammelsbergite	NiAs$_2$

The minerals of the group have the general formula $A_2(X_2)_2$, with A = Fe, Co, Ni, and X = As, and minor amounts of S and Sb. Satisfactory crystallographic and structural studies have been completed only for loellingite.

Crystallographic and structural relations between the loellingite, marcasite, and arsenopyrite groups have been studied in some detail, and it has been shown that the groups of the AX_2 type differ principally in the nature of the coordination about the A atoms.[1]

Ref.

1. Buerger, *Am. Min.*, **22**, 48 (1937).

2931 **L O E L L I N G I T E** [FeAs$_2$]. Prismatic Arsenical Pyrites pt. *Mohs, Jameson* (3, 279, 1820). Axotomer Arsenik-Kies pt. *Mohs* (525, 1823). Arsenikalkies, Arsenikeisen, Giftkies, Arseneisen pt. *Germ.* Leucopyrite pt. *Shepard* (2, 9, 1835). Arsenosiderit pt. *Glocker* (321, 1839). Mohsine pt. *Chapman* (138, 1843). Löllingit pt. *Haidinger* (559, 1845A). Sätersbergit *Kenngott* (111, 1853). Glanzarsenikkies *Breithaupt* (*J. pr. Chem.*, 4, 260, 261, 1853). Hüttenbergite *Breithaupt*. Geierit, Pazit *Breithaupt* (*B. H. Ztg.*, 25, 167, 1866). Leucopyrite *Dana* (76, 1868). Löllingite *von Zepharovich* (*Russ. Ges. Min.*, *Vh.*, 3, 84, 1867). Pharmakopyrit *Weisbach* (57, 1875). Glaucopyrite *Sandberger* (*J. pr. Chem.*, 1, 230, 1870).

C r y s t. Orthorhombic; dipyramidal — $2/m$ $2/m$ $2/m$.

$$a : b : c = 0.8847 : 1 : 0.4813;^1 \qquad p_0 : q_0 : r_0 = 0.5441 : 0.4814 : 1$$

$$q_1 : r_1 : p_1 = 0.8847 : 1.8379 : 1; \qquad r_2 : p_2 : q_2 = 2.0774 : 1.1303 : 1$$

Forms:[2]

		ϕ	$\rho = C$	ϕ_1	$\rho_1 = A$	ϕ_2	$\rho_2 = B$
b	010	0°00′	90°00′	90°00′	90°00′	. . . . .	0°00′
a	100	90 00	90 00	. . . . .	0 00	0°00′	90 00
u	140	15 46½	90 00	90 00	74 13½	0 00	15 46½
q	130	20 38½	90 00	90 00	69 21½	0 00	20 38½
s	120	29 28½	90 00	90 00	60 31½	0 00	29 28½
m	110	48 30	90 00	90 00	41 30	0 00	48 30
l	011	0 00	25 42½	25 42½	90 00	90 00	64 17½
e	101	90 00	28 33	0 00	61 27	61 27	90 00
r	111	48 30	36 00	25 42½	63 53	61 27	67 05
α	121	29 28½	47 52½	43 54½	68 36	61 27	49 47

Structure cell.[3] Space group, *Pnnm*; a_0 5.25, b_0 5.92, c_0 2.85; $a_0 : b_0 : c_0$ = 0.8850 : 1 : 0.4812; contains Fe$_{2+x}$As$_{4-x}$.[4]

Habit. Most commonly prismatic [001] (Stokö), also elongated in other axial directions. Pyramidal and doubly terminated (Franklin). Common forms *m l e r*. Also massive.

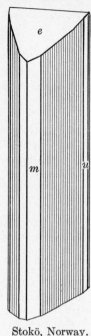

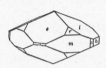

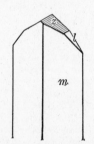

Franklin, N. J.

Stokö, Norway.　　Center Strafford, N. H.

(Old orientation; $z = s$, $l = m$, $m = e$)

Twinning. On {011}. Sometimes produces trillings.

P h y s. Cleavage {010} and {101} sometimes distinct. Fracture uneven. Brittle. H. 5–5½. G. 7.40 ± 0.01 for $x = 0.17$ (in the formula above); 7.58 (calc. for $x = 0.17$); 7.48 ± 0.02 for $x = 0.02$ (Center Strafford crystals).[5]

Luster metallic. Color between silver-white and steel-gray. Streak grayish black. In polished section[6] shows fairly strong anisotropism and weak pleochroism with absorption strongest ‖ [010]. Reflection percentages: green 57, orange 52.5, red 48. Frequently shows polysynthetic twinning on {101}.

C h e m. Essentially diarsenide of iron, $FeAs_2$, with Co and Ni substituting for Fe in part, also Sb and S substituting for As in part. Further, the Fe : As ratio departs from the ideal formula; the actual variations can be expressed in the following formula $(Fe,Co,Ni)_{2+x}(As,S,Sb)_{4-x}$ (with x probably not exceeding 0.2), indicating an excess of Fe over the ideal composition.[4]

Anal. Most recent analyses are given below.[7] Some older analyses show as much as 8.23 per cent S (geyerite); Co reaches 6.44 per cent (Chalanches); Sb is reported as high as 5.61 per cent (Chalanches).

	1	2	3	4	5	6	7
Fe	27.15	27.89	28.70	22.96	27.31	27.93	28.95
Co	.....	.....	.....	4.37	.....	.....	.....
Ni	.....	.....	.....	0.21	.....	.....	.....
Bi	.....	.....	.....	0.08	.....	.....	.....
Sb	.....						
As	72.85	70.94	71.09	71.18	71.10	70.83	68.30
S	.....	0.96	trace	0.56	1.55	0.77	1.32
Rem.	.....	.....	.....	0.39	0.02	.....	1.21
Total	100.00	99.79	99.79	99.75	99.98	99.53	99.78
G.		7.48*		7.40		7.031	

* Average of 3 determinations.

1. FeAs$_2$. 2. Center Strafford. $x = 0.02$. As : S $= 32 : 1$.[8] 3. Tamela, Finland.[9] 4. Teocalli Mt., Brush Creek, Gunnison Co., Colo. Rem. is Cu.[10] 5. Ålsbyn in Norbotten, Sweden.[11] 6. Drum's Farm, Alexander Co., N. C.[12] 7. Reichenstein, Silesia. Average of 2 anal. Rem. is insol.[13]

	8	9	10	11	12	13	14
Fe	27.83	29.40	23.75	29.45	21.22	27.83	31.20
Co	.....	.....	4.13	.....	6.44	.....	.....
Ni	.....	.....	0.20	.....	.....	.....	.....
Bi	0.05	.....	.....	.....	.....	.....	.....
Sb	.....	.....	0.29	.....	5.61	.....	.....
As	70.24	69.80	70.16	67.26	63.66	71.36	61.40
S	0.57	0.21	1.20	3.29	3.66	1.46	6.73
Rem.	.....	.....	.....	.....	.....	0.17	.....
Total	98.69	99.41	99.73	100.00	100.59	100.82	99.33
G.		7.40**			6.34		6.58

** Average of 4 determinations.

8. Vastersel, Angarmanland, Sweden.[11] 9. Franklin crystals.[14] 10. Radauthal, Harz.[15] 11. Markirch, Alsace.[16] 12. Chalanches near Allemont, Isère.[17] 13. Dolní Bory. From a pegmatite.[18] 14. Geyerite. Breitenbrunn. Aver. of 2 anal.[19]

Var.[20] *Ordinary.* Loellingite. Contains essentially only iron and arsenic.

Sulfurian. Geyerite Breithaupt (*B. H. Ztg.*, **25**, 167, 1866). Contains as much as 6.73 per cent S (anal. 14).

Cobaltian. Glaucopyrite Sandberger (*J. pr. Chem.*, **1**, 230, 1870). Contains as much as 6.44 per cent Co (anal. 12).

Antimonian. Older analyses yield Sb to 5.61 per cent (anal. 12).

Tests. F. 2. In C.T. gives a thin sublimate of metallic arsenic; sometimes a little sulfur.

Occur. Found in mesothermal vein deposits, often in a calcite gangue associated with iron and copper sulfides; more rarely with nickel-cobalt minerals such as skutterudite (Cobalt, Ontario), chloanthite and smaltite. Also found with silver and gold ores.

Occurs at Lölling near Hüttenberg in Carinthia, in siderite with bismuth and chloanthite; at Schladming, Styria, with niccolite. In Silesia at Reichenstein, with gold, in the serpentine. Found at Andreasberg in the Harz Mountains, from Breitenbrunn and from Geyer (*geyerite*) near

Ehrenfriedersdorf in Saxony. In Andalusia, Spain, from Guadalcanal in the Sierra Morena, Province Sevilla (*glaucopyrite*). In southern Norway from the augite-syenite of the Langesund district. In Chile from Chañarcillo. Reported from Potosí, Bolivia. Also reported from Japan.

In the United States, described from the pegmatites at Auburn, Maine, and at Center Strafford, New Hampshire. From Orange County, New York, at Monroe and Edenville; at Franklin, New Jersey, as fine small crystals, doubly terminated, in the limestone; from Gunnison and San Juan counties, Colorado. Reported from a number of mines in the Cobalt district, Ontario, in calcite gangue with nickel and cobalt minerals.

A l t e r. To a scorodite coating or, more rarely, to pharmacosiderite or symplesite.

A r t i f.[21] Prepared by reaction of As vapor under pressure on iron powder at 700°.

N a m e. *Mohsine* was named after Mohs[22] by whom the mineral was first described, and who mentions Lölling as the first locality at which it was found. Since the name *mohsite*[23] was previously given to a variety of ilmenite, the name *löllingite* was adopted (in the fifth edition, 1868) for the Reichenstein mineral, and the earlier name *leucopyrite*[24] (λευκός, *white*) given to the mineral conforming with the ideal composition FeAs$_2$. However, these names had earlier been used in the reverse sense,[25] and the subsequent reprints of the fifth and the sixth edition (1892) reverted to the earlier usage. In this edition *leucopyrite* is dropped as a varietal name because it refers to a probably nonexistent composition.

Ref.

1. Angles and unit of Bauer and Berman, *Am. Min.*, **12**, 39 (1927), orientation of Buerger, *Am. Min.*, **22**, 48 (1937), on crystals from Franklin (anal. 9). Transformation Bauer and Berman to Buerger 010/001/100.
2. Goldschmidt (5, 165, 1918); also Bauer and Berman (1927). Rare or uncertain forms: {203}, {023}.
3. Buerger, *Zs. Kr.*, **82**, 165 (1932), and *Am. Min.*, **22**, 48 (1937).
4. Buerger, *Am. Min.*, **19**, 37 (1934), considers the excess iron, over the ideal formula FeAs$_2$, as substituting for part of the As. The so-called *leucopyrite* molecule, now abandoned, Fe$_3$As$_4$, expresses the same deviation from the ideal formula.
5. Remeasurements on type material, using small crystals (Berman priv. comm., 1939). Old ratios in literature vary considerably. See Dana (97, 1892).
6. Schneiderhöhn and Ramdohr (2, 206, 1931).
7. Older analyses in Dana (96, 1892).
8. Gonyer anal. in Switzer, *Am. Min.*, **23**, 811 (1938).
9. Mäkinen, *Comm. géol. Finlande, Bull.*, [35] 37 (1913) — *Jb. Min.*, [2] 42 (1913).
10. Hillebrand, *U. S. Geol. Sur., Bull. 419*, 244, 1910.
11. Högbom, *Geol. För. Förh.*, **51**, 524 (1929).
12. Genth, *Am. J. Sc.*, **44**, 384 (1892).
13. Beutell and Lorenz, *Cbl. Min.*, 372, 1915.
14. Bauer and Berman (1927).
15. Klüss anal., in Scheibe, *Cbl. Min.*, 119, 1900.
16. Dürrfeldt, *Jb. Min.*, [2] 35 (1911).
17. Frenzel anal., *Jb. Min.*, 677, 1875.
18. Vysloužil anal., *Příroda, Brno*, **21**, 84 (1928) — *Min. Abs.*, **3**, 548 (1928).
19. McCay in Dana (97, 1892).
20. The varieties, with the exception of the cobalt-containing one, are based on old analyses needing confirmation.

21. In Doelter (4 [1], 605, 1925).
22. Chapman (138, 1843).
23. Lévy, *Phil. Mag.*, 1 [2], 221 (1827) — Chester (178, 1896).
24. Shepard (2, 9, 1835).
25. Zepharovich, *Russ. Ges. Min. Vh.*, 3, 84 (1867).

2932 **S A F F L O R I T E** [$(Co,Fe)As_2$]. *Breithaupt* (*J. pr. Chem.*, **4**, 265, 1835). Faserige Weisser Speiskobalt *Werner*. Grauer Speiskobalt, Arsenikkobalt *Rose* (50, 1852). Eisenkobaltkies, Spathiopyrite, Der rhombische Arsenokobalteisen, Quirlkies *Sandberger* (*Jb. Min.*, 410, 1868; 59, 1873; *Ak. München, Ber.*, 135, 1873). Schlackenkobalt *Schneeberg miners*.

C r y s t. Orthorhombic; dipyramidal — $2/m\ 2/m\ 2/m$.[1]

$$a : b : c = 0.8703 : 1 : 0.5144;^2 \quad p_0 : q_0 : r_0 = 0.5910 : 0.5144 : 1$$

$$q_1 : r_1 : p_1 = 0.8703 : 1.6920 : 1; \quad r_2 : p_2 : q_2 = 1.9441 : 1.1490 : 1$$

Forms:[3]

		ϕ	$\rho = C$	ϕ_1	$\rho_1 = A$	ϕ_2	$\rho_2 = B$
c	001	....	0°00′	0°00′	90°00′	90°00′	90°00′
b	010	0°00′	90°00	90 00	90 00	....	0 00
n	120	29 52½	90 00	90 00	60 07½	0 00	29 52½
m	110	48 58	90 00	90 00	41 02	0 00	48 58
f	011	0 00	27 13	27 13	90 00	90 00	62 47
e	101	90 00	30 35	0 00	59 25	59 25	90 00
o	111	48 58	38 04½	27 13	62 16½	59 25	66 07

Structure cell. Orthorhombic; a_0 6.35, b_0 4.86, c_0 5.80; $b_0 : c_0 : a_0/2$ = 0.8379 : 1 : 0.5474; contains Co_4As_8.[4]

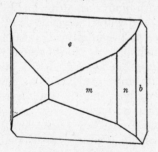
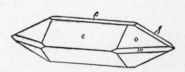

Tunaberg, Sweden.   Nordmark, Sweden.

Habit. Crystals resemble arsenopyrite, with {101} and {310} dominant; also prismatic [010].   Often massive and with a fibrous radiated structure.

Twinning. (a) Twin plane {011}, in fivelings.   (b) Twin plane {101}, as in marcasite and arsenopyrite, affording cruciform penetration twins with angles of nearly 120°, and six-rayed star forms.

P h y s. Cleavage {100} distinct.   Fracture uneven to conchoidal. Brittle. H. 4½–5. G. 7.2 ± 0.25; 7.70 (calc.).   Luster metallic.   Color tin-white, soon tarnishing to dark gray.   Streak grayish black.   Opaque. Reflection pleochroism weak; strongly anisotropic.[5] Shows zoning in polished section.   Percentage reflection: green 58, orange 52, red 51.5.

C h e m. Cobalt diarsenide with considerable Fe present (from 4 to 16 per cent), $(Co,Fe)As_2$. Ni, Bi, Cu, and S are usually present in small amounts, the Cu probably as impurity. Zoning, and consequent inhomogeneity, may account for some of the variation in composition.

Anal.[6]

	1	2	3	4
Fe	.....	9.51	13.85	15.28
Co	28.23	18.58	13.75	12.99
Ni	.....	none	.....	0.20
Cu	.....	0.62	.....	0.33
As	71.77	70.36	71.12	71.13
S	.....	0.90	0.76	0.68
Total	100.00	99.97	99.48	100.61
G.		7.167	7.08	7.41

1. $CoAs_2$. 2. Schneeberg. Massive. (Schlackenkobalt).[7] 3. Grafton, N. H. Homogeneity of the sample not investigated.[8] 4. Nordmarken.[9]

Var. *Ordinary.* With about 5 per cent Fe.

Ferroan. Spathiopyrite. Eisenkobaltkies. Contains as much as 16 per cent iron, with Co : Fe = 1 : 1.16 as the maximum reported from reliable analyses.

Tests. F. $2\frac{1}{2}$. In C.T. gives a sublimate of As.

O c c u r. Commonly found associated with smaltite, rammelsbergite, niccolite, and other Co-Ni minerals; also with silver, bismuth, and loellingite, generally in mesothermal vein deposits.

In Germany, at Schneeberg, Saxony, with quartz, smaltite, and bismuth as concentric radially fibrous masses; in twinned crystals and radial masses at Bieber near Hanau in Hesse, and similarly at Wittichen in Baden. In Sweden at Tunaberg, Sodermanland; at Nordmarken, Wermland, in prismatic crystals in dolomitic limestone associated with minerals of the humite group, tremolite, magnetite and sphalerite. At Sarrabus and Gonnosfanadiga, Sardinia, with native silver, smaltite, and pyrrhotite. At Batopilas, Mexico, with rammelsbergite and native silver.

In the United States reported from Grafton, New Hampshire (needs confirmation). In Canada at South Lorrain, Ontario, associated with loellingite, cobaltite, and rammelsbergite; at the Eldorado mine, Great Bear Lake, with uraninite, silver, rammelsbergite, and smaltite.

A l t e r.[10] Safflorite, like rammelsbergite and smaltite, is rapidly attacked by water containing oxygen or oxygen and carbon dioxide.

N a m e. From the Safflor, *safflower, bastard saffron*, in allusion to its use as a pigment. Spathiopyrite, from σπάθη, *broad blade*, is the equivalent of the German *Quirlkies*.

Ref.

1. Flink, *Ark. Kemi*, **3** [11], 73 (1908), figures doubly terminated crystals from Tunaberg.
2. Flink (1908) ratio in the loellingite orientation. See Buerger, *Am. Min.*, **22**, 48 (1937).

3. Goldschmidt (**8**, 1, 1922).
4. The wide variation in specific gravities given has not been correlated with compositional variations.
5. Schneiderhöhn and Ramdohr (**2**, 210, 1931).
6. For old analyses see Dana (100, 1892).
7. McCay, *Am. J. Sc.*, **29**, 369 (1885).
8. Palmer, *Econ. Geol.*, **12**, 207 (1917).
9. Mauzelius anal. in Sjögren, *Bull. Geol. Inst. Upsala*, **2**, 68 (1894).
10. Experiments on alteration in the laboratory reported by Walker and Parsons, *Univ. Toronto Stud., Geol. Ser.*, no. 20, 41, 1925; also on the effect of safflorite on precipitation of silver from silver sulfate solutions see Palmer, *Econ. Geol.*, **12**, 207 (1917) and Dadson, *Univ. Toronto Stud., Geol. Ser.*, no. 38, 51, 1935. For a discussion of the genesis of the Cobalt, Ontario, ores in light of these experiments see Bastin, *Econ. Geol.*, **12**, 219 (1917).

2933 **R A M M E L S B E R G I T E** [NiAs$_2$]. *Arseniknickel Hofmann* (*Ann. Phys.*, **25**, 491, 1832). *Weissnickelkies Breithaupt* (*Ann. Phys.*, **64**, 184, 1845). Rammelsbergite *Dana* (61, 1854). (Not Rammelsbergite, syn. of Chloanthite, *Haidinger* [1845A].) *Niquel blanco Domeyko*.

C r y s t. Said to be orthorhombic and related to arsenopyrite in its crystallography. No authenticated crystals have been measured.[1]

Habit. Massive; granular to prismatic or radial fibrous in structure. Rarely in crystals.

P h y s. Cleavage in zone [010]? Fracture uneven. H. 5$\frac{1}{2}$–6. G. 7.1 ± 0.1. Luster metallic. Color tin-white with a tinge of red. Streak grayish black. In polished section[2] anisotropic and pleochroic in pale yellow to violet-blue. In section[3] shows lamellae, which may be due to twinning.

C h e m.[4] Nickel diarsenide, NiAs$_2$. Co, Fe, S, and rarely Bi, are present in small amounts. No analytical evidence is found of continuous compositional variation between rammelsbergite and safflorite, CoAs$_2$.

Anal.

	1	2	3
Ni	28.15	27.84	26.47
Co	.....	1.80	2.61
Fe	.....	trace	0.66
Cu	.....	.....	.....
As	71.85	67.32	66.12
S	.....	2.03	2.45
Sb	.....	0.83	0.60
SiO$_2$	.....	.....	0.25
Total	100.00	99.82	99.16
G.		7.157	6.999

1. NiAs$_2$. 2. University mine, Cobalt, Ont.[5] 3. Silver Bar mine, Cobalt, Ont.[6] Analysis made on material containing small amounts of niccolite, cobaltite, etc.

Tests. F. 2. In C.T. gives a sublimate of metallic As.

O c c u r.[7] Commonly in mesothermal vein deposits with other nickel and cobalt minerals such as smaltite and niccolite. Also with loellingite and with bismuth and silver, or more rarely with uraninite.

In Germany, at Schneeberg, Saxony, in reniform masses with fibrous structure and a smooth or drusy surface, associated with niccolite on quartz or hornstone; at Lölling-Hüttenberg, Carinthia; Riechelsdorf, Hesse; Eisleben, Thuringia. At Cinquevald near Roncegno, Tirol, with arsenopyrite. Reported from Italy, at Bruzolo, in Torino, with smaltite and chloanthite; at Punta Corna and Sarda, Ala, Piedmont, with smaltite, cobaltite and chalcopyrite; at Sarrabus, Sardinia, with silver, safflorite, and arsenopyrite. In France at Ste. Marie aux Mines, Alsace. On the Anniviers-Thal, Valais, Switzerland, as light gray crystalline masses and crystals in dolomite. Reported from Portezuela del Carrizo, Department of Huasco, Chile.

In Canada at South Lorrain and at various mines in the Cobalt district, Ontario; at the Eldorado mine, Great Bear Lake, Northwest Territories, with safflorite, silver, and uraninite.

A l t e r.[8] Alters readily to annabergite; easily attacked by water containing dissolved air (see further under safflorite for similar experiments).

N a m e. In honor of the mineral chemist, K. F. Rammelsberg (1813–99), of Berlin.

Ref.

1. A prismatic crystal from Riechelsdorf was measured by Dürrfeld, *Zs. Kr.*, **49**, 199 (1911). The material was not, however, properly authenticated, and the ratio $a : b : c = 0.8604 : 1 : 0.5849$ (in the orientation of loellingite) is based on poor measurements. X-ray work by de Jong, *Physica*, **6**, 325 (1926), with powder (from Schlaggenwald) gave a unit with c_0 twice the value given by Buerger, *Am. Min.*, **22**, 48 (1937) for other members of the group. The values by de Jong are: a_0 6.35, b_0 4.86, c_0 5.80; $a_0 : b_0 : c_0 = 1.307 : 1 : 1.1934$, in the old orientation.
2. Orcel, *Bull. soc. min.*, **51**, 206 (1928), and Short (98, 1931).
3. Schneiderhöhn and Ramdohr (**2**, 211, 1931).
4. The high Fe, Co, and S values reported in early analyses, as given in Doelter (**4** [1], 676, 1926) have not been verified by recent work. Walker, *Univ. Toronto Stud., Geol. Ser.*, **20**, 49 (1925) reports 11.24 per cent Co, presumably on inhomogeneous material.
5. Ellsworth, *Ontario Bur. Mines, Rep.*, **25**, 1 (1916).
6. E. W. Todd in Walker and Parsons, *Univ. Toronto Stud., Geol. Ser.*, **12**, 30 (1921).
7. Palache (31, 1935) finds that the reported occurrence at Franklin, New Jersey, is doubtless chloanthite.
8. Carmichael, *Univ. Toronto Stud., Geol. Ser.*, **24**, 47 (1927).

2934   **P A R A R A M M E L S B E R G I T E** [NiAs$_2$]. Rammelsbergite *Peacock* and *Michener* (*Univ. Toronto Stud., Geol. Ser.*, **42**, 95, 1939). Pararammelsbergite *Peacock* and *Dadson* (*Am. Min.*, **25**, 561, 1940).

C r y s t. Orthorhombic or pseudo-orthorhombic.[4]

$a : b : c = 0.988 : 1 : 1.963;$[5] $p_0 : q_0 : r_0 = 1.987 : 1.963 : 1$

$q_1 : r_1 : p_1 = 0.988 : 0.503 : 1;$ $r_2 : p_2 : q_2 = 0.509 : 1.012 : 1$

Forms:[1]

		ϕ	$\rho = C$	ϕ_1	$\rho_1 = A$	ϕ_2	$\rho_2 = B$
c	001	....	0°00′	0°00′	90°00′	90°00′	90°00′
d	104	90°00′	26 25	0 00	63 35	63 35	90 00
e	304	90 00	56 08	0 00	33 52	33 52	90 00
p	113	45 21	42 57½	33 12	61 00	56 29	61 23
q	112	45 21	54 23½	44 28	54 39½	45 11	55 09

Structure cell.[5] Space group (apparently[4]), *Pbma* or *Pb2a*; a_0 5.74 ± 0.01, b_0 5.81 ± 0.01, c_0 11.405 ± 0.03; $a_0 : b_0 : c_0 = 0.988 : 1 : 1.963$; contains Ni_8As_{16}. The x-ray powder picture of this species differs markedly from that of rammelsbergite.

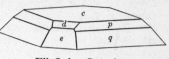

Elk Lake, Ontario.

Habit. Rectangular tablets {001}. Usually massive.

Phys. Cleavage {001}, perfect. H. about 5. G. 7.12; 7.24 (calc.). Luster metallic. Color tin-white. Opaque. In polished section white in color and strongly anisotropic. Twinning not observed.

Chem. Nickel diarsenide, $NiAs_2$, dimorphous with rammelsbergite. The high Co content of anal. 4 may be due, partly or entirely, to admixture.

Anal.

	1	2	3	4
Ni	28.15	28.1	27.08	17.46
Co	.....	0.4	1.94	11.24
Fe	.....	....	0.56	0.73
As	71.85	68.5	65.78	66.61
S	.....	2.6	3.05	3.30
Rem.	.....	....	1.07	0.84
Total	100.00	99.6	99.48	100.18
G.	7.24	7.12	7.02	7.73

1. $NiAs_2$. 2. Moose Horn mine, Elk Lake, Gowganda.[1] 3. Hudson Bay mine, Cobalt. Rem. is Cu 0.16, Sb 0.91.[2] 4. Keeley mine, South Lorrain. Rem. is SiO_2.[3]

Occur. Found in Ontario, Canada, at the Moose Horn mine, Elk Lake, Gowganda, with niccolite and smaltite; at the Hudson Bay mine, Cobalt, with smaltite-chloanthite, cobaltite, gersdorffite (?), loellingite; at the Keeley mine, South Lorrain, with smaltite and gersdorffite (?) in masses with a reniform structure.

Alter. Alters readily on exposure to erythrite.

Name. From παρά, *near*, and rammelsbergite, because near rammelsbergite.

Ref.

1. Peacock and Michener (1939).
2. Todd anal. in Walker and Parsons, *Univ. Toronto Stud., Geol. Ser.*, **12**, 27 (1921).
3. Rickaby anal. in Walker, *Univ. Toronto Stud., Geol. Ser.*, **20**, 49 (1925).
4. Less than orthorhombic symmetry is suggested by the intensity distribution on x-ray Weissenberg films (Peacock and Michener [1939]). The morphological measurements, on crystals of very poor quality, conform to orthorhombic symmetry.
5. Peacock and Michener (1939) by x-ray Weissenberg method on material from Elk Lake, Ont.

294   MARCASITE [FeS₂]. (Not the marchasite of the *Arabians* and of *Agricola* [1546].) *Henckel* (1725); *Wallerius* (1747); *Cronstedt* (1758); *Linnaeus* (1768); *de Lisle* (1783). ? Pyrites argenteo colore *Germ.* Wasserkies or Weisserkies *Agricola* (477, 1546). Ferrum jecoris colore *Germ.* Lebererz pt., *Agricola* (469, 1546). Vattenkies pt., Pyrites fuscus pt., Pyrites aquosus pt., *Wallerius* (212, 1747). Swafvelkies pt. *Cronstedt* (184, 1758). Pyrites lamellosus *Born* (**2**, 106, 1772). Pyrites aquosus ?*Born* (**2**, 107, 1772). Pyrites rhomboidales pt. *de Lisle* (1772; **3**, 242, 1783). Pyrites lamelleuse en crêtes de coq *Forster* (1772); *de Lisle* (**3**, 252, 1783). Pyrites fuscus lamellosus *Wallerius* (**2**, 134, 1778). Strahlkies, Leberkies pt. *Werner* (*Bergm. J.*, 1789). Fer sulfuré var. radié *Haüy* (180**1**); *Brongniart* (1807). Wasser-kies (Dichter o. Leberkies, Strahlkies, Haarkies pt.) *Hausmann* (149, 1813). Fer sulfuré blanc pt. *Haüy*. White Pyrites *Aikin* (1814). Fer sulphuré prismatique rhomboidale *Bournon* (301, 1817). Prismatic Iron Pyrites *Jameson* (**3**, 297, 1820). Binarkies, Binarite, Kammkies, Speerkies, Zellkies pt. *Germ.* Cockscomb, Spear, and Cellular Pyrites. Poliopyrites *Glocker* (321, 1839). Markasite *Haidinger* (467, 561, 1845A). Pirite bianca *Ital.* Marcasita, Pirita blanca *Span.*

C r y s t.   Orthorhombic; dipyramidal — $2/m \ 2/m \ 2/m$.

$$a : b : c = 0.8194 : 1 : 0.6245;^1 \qquad p_0 : q_0 : r_0 = 0.7621 : 0.6245 : 1$$

$$q_1 : r_1 : p_1 = 0.8194 : 1.3121 : 1; \qquad r_2 : p_2 : q_2 = 1.6013 : 1.2204 : 1$$

Forms:[2]

		ϕ	$\rho = C$	ϕ_1	$\rho_1 = A$	ϕ_2	$\rho_2 = B$
c	001	...	0°00'	0°00'	90°00'	90°00'	90°00'
b	010	0°00'	90 00	90 00	90 00	...	0 00
a	100	90 00	90 00	...	0 00	0 00	90 00
q	290	15 10½	90 00	90 00	74 49½	0 00	15 10½
r	140	16 53	90 00	90 00	73 07	0 00	16 53
n	270	19 13½	90 00	90 00	70 46½	0 00	19 13½
v	130	22 08	90 00	90 00	67 52	0 00	22 08
y	250	26 01	90 00	90 00	63 59	0 00	26 01
z	120	31 23½	90 00	90 00	58 36½	0 00	31 23½
w	450	44 19	90 00	90 00	45 41	0 00	44 19
m	110	50 40	90 00	90 00	39 20	0 00	50 40
l	011	0 00	31 59	31 59	90 00	90 00	58 01
e	101	90 00	52 41	0 00	52 41	52 41	90 00
s	111	50 40	44 34½	31 59	57 07	52 41	63 35
x	122	31 23½	36 11½	31 59	72 05½	69 08½	59 44

Structure cell. Space group *Pnnm*; a_0 4.436, b_0 5.414, c_0 3.381; $a_0 : b_0 : c_0 = 0.8194 : 1 : 0.6245$; contains Fe_2S_4.

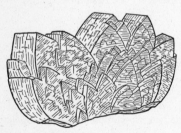

Treece, Kansas.

Habit. Commonly tabular {010}, also pyramidal; less commonly pris-matic [001]; rarely capillary (Haarkies, *Germ.*). Faces frequently curved. Com-mon forms *b r m e s*.

Stalactitic with radiating internal structure and exterior covered with pro-jecting crystals; also in concentric structures with marcasite and pyrite in alternating layers; globular, reniform and other imitative shapes.

Twinning. (*a*) On {101} common, often repeated and sometimes producing stellate fivelings and the cockscomb and spear shapes. (*b*) On {011} less common, the crystals crossing at an angle of nearly 60°.

P h y s. Cleavage {101} rather distinct, {110} in traces. Fracture uneven. Brittle. H. 6–6½. G. 4.887;[3] 4.875 (calc.). Luster metallic. Color pale bronze-yellow, deepening on exposure; tin-white on fresh

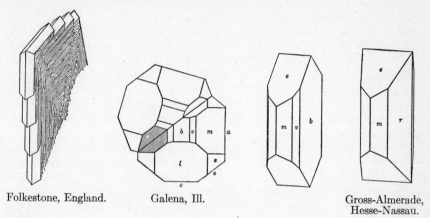

Folkestone, England.   Galena, Ill.   Gross-Almerade, Hesse-Nassau.

fracture. Streak grayish or brownish black. Opaque. Strongly aniso-tropic and pleochroic, with [100] creamy white, [010] light yellowish white, [001] white with rose-brown tint. Under polarized light the colors are more intense. Reflection percentages: green 52, orange 45.5, red 44.5.[4]

C h e m.[5] Disulfide of iron, FeS_2, with little or no variation in its composition.

Anal.

	1	2	3	4	5
Fe	46.55	46.53	46.55	47.22	46.56
S	53.45	53.30	53.05	52.61	53.40
Rem.	...	0.20	...	...	0.05
Total	100.00	100.03	99.60	99.83	100.01
G.	4.875	4.887			

1. FeS_2. 2. Joplin, Mo. Rem. is SiO_2; minute trace of Cu.[3] 3. Jasper Co., Mo. Cockscomb crystals; greenish yellow surface, silver-gray interior. Trace of As.[6] 4. Hüggel, near Osnabrück, Germany.[7] 5. Loughborough Township, Ont. Rem. is insol.[8]

Tests. F. 2½–3. Reacts like pyrite but is more easily decomposed. When boiled with a standard solution of ferric sulfate, about 12 per cent of the sulfur is oxidized.

O c c u r. Found most often in surface and near-surface deposits where it has been formed at low temperatures and from acid solutions. Under higher temperatures and conditions of low acidity or of alkalinity the more stable form (pyrite) is deposited.[10] Marcasite is, in most instances, a supergene mineral, but may perhaps be deposited from low-temperature ascending vein solutions (Freiberg) as one of the last minerals to form. Most frequently found in sedimentary deposits, such as limestone (spear-shaped twins), clays, lignite deposits; often as concretions of considerable size, also as stalactitic coatings of other sulfides (Galena, Illinois), or as replacements of fossils (reptiles of the Jurassic at Württemberg).

Oriented growths have been reported of marcasite on pseudomorphs of marcasite after pyrrhotite (Freiberg); of marcasite on pyrite (Bredelar); of pyrite on marcasite (Tavistock and Lengerich).[11]

In Bohemia at Littnitz, west of Carlsbad at Altsattel and at Teplitz, occurs abundantly as spear-shaped crystals in the plastic clay of the brown-coal formation; also at Schemnitz. Found in the Harz Mountains at Clausthal, with other sulfides; in the veins at Freiberg and at Annaberg in Saxony. In France as spear-shaped twins at Cap Blanc-Nez, Pas-de-Calais. In the Chalk at Kent, between Folkestone and Dover; as cockscomb aggregates at Tavistock, Devonshire, where pyrite oriented growths on marcasite are also found. From Guanajuato, Mexico.

In the United States, notably at Galena, Illinois, where twinned crystals of pyramidal habit occur on the exterior of stalactites consisting of concentric layers of sphalerite and galena. Near Fredericktown, Missouri, in concentric shells alternating with pyrite. In the Joplin district of Missouri, Oklahoma, and Kansas, individual curved crystals and cockscomb groups occur in abundance on the galena and sphalerite ores; also reported within calcite crystals. Marcasite and enargite are among the last-formed minerals in these deposits. In Wisconsin at Mineral Point and at Racine in the dolomite as fine crystals, and in Richland County as crystals altered to limonite. In fluorite crystals as inclusions, in central Kentucky.

Alter. Specimens of marcasite usually disintegrate with the formation of ferrous sulfate and sulfuric acid. Limonite and pyrite pseudomorphs after marcasite are found; more rarely pseudomorphous after bournonite, chalcopyrite, magnetite, and sphalerite.

Artif.[12] Prepared by the slow action of H_2S on ferric sulfate or chloride at temperatures below 300°.

Name. The word *marcasite*, of Arabic or Moorish origin (and variously used by old writers, for bismuth, antimony), was the name of common crystallized pyrite among miners and mineralogists in later centuries, until near the close of the eighteenth. The name was first given to this species by Haidinger in 1845.

The species is probably recognized by Agricola under the name *wasserkies* and *lebererz*, and also under the same by Cronstedt; and it is *Wasserkies* of Hausmann in both editions of his great work. This name, wasserkies (pyrites aquosus, as Cronstedt translates it), is little applicable; yet it may have arisen from the greater tendency of the mineral to become moist and alter to vitriol than pyrite — if it is not an early corruption, as Agricola seems to think (see above), of *Weisserkies* (white iron pyrites). It appears to have been used also for easily decomposable pyrite; and *pyrrhotite* was also included under its other name, *pyrites fuscus*. The rhombic crystallization is mentioned by de Lisle; but Haüy long afterward considered it only an irregularity of common iron pyrites. *Weisskupfererz* (also called *weisskupfer* and *weisserz*) occurs as the name of a species in all the mineralogical works of the eighteenth century, from Henckel's *Pyritology*, in 1725, where it is called a whitish copper ore, and placed near tetrahedrite; and the light color, from Henckel down, is attributed to the presence of arsenic. It has finally been run out as mostly impure marcasite; and domeykite and related species are now the only true white copper.

Marcasite is made by Breithaupt, *J. pr. Chem.*, **4**, 257 (1835), a generic name for the various species of pyrites. He used the names *lonchidite* or *kausimkies* for varieties in which Plattner found 4.4 per cent As; *kyrosite* or *weisskupfererz*, the latter an old term of varied significance; *hepatopyrite*, *leberkies* Werner; *hydropyrite* or *weicheisenkies*, *wasserkies* (see above). Cf. Frenzel, *Min. Lex. Sächsen*, pages 197–201, 1874.

Ref.

1. Orientation of Buerger, *Am. Min.*, **22**, 48 (1937); ratio of Buerger, *Zs. Kr.*, **97** 504 (1937). Transformation, Goldschmidt to Buerger 01Q/001/100. Orientation here adopted to conform with the closely related arsenopyrite and loellingite groups, according to Buerger. The morphological ratio of Goldschmidt (6, 1, 1920) is an average of a number of admittedly poor ratios and does not have the validity of Buerger's precision measurements.
2. Goldschmidt (6, 1, 1920) and Cook, *Am. Min.*, **9**, 151 (1924).
3. Allen, Crenshaw, Johnston, and Larsen, *Am. J. Sc.*, **33**, 169 (1912), on material from Joplin (anal. 2).
4. Schneiderhöhn and Ramdohr (2, 192, 1931).
5. For a discussion of analyses and composition of marcasite see Buerger, *Am. Min.*, **19**, 37 (1934). The deviation from the theoretical composition FeS_2 is probably within the limits of analytical errors (Berman, priv. comm., 1939).
6. Anal. by E. Arbeiter, "Mineralogisch-chemische Untersuchungen an Markasit, Pyrit und Magnetkies," Diss., Breslau, 1913.
7. Anal. by Dittrich in Schöndorf and Schroeder, *Niedersachs. geol. Ver.*, *Ber.*, 152, 1909 — Doelter 4 [1], 567, 1925.
8. Carmichael, *Univ. Toronto Stud.*, *Geol. Ser.*, **22**, 29 (1926).
9. Allen and Crenshaw, *Am. J. Sc.*, **38**, 371 (1914), describe the Stokes method in detail, and show that it is a useful means of distinguishing between pyrite and marcasite, and in estimating the amounts of each in a mixture of the two minerals.
10. Allen, Crenshaw, and Merwin, *Am. J. Sc.*, **38**, 393 (1914), discuss the genesis of marcasite and pyrite in light of their experiments on synthetic products.
11. In Mügge (363, 381, 1903). The following laws of intergrowth have been recorded. Pyrite on marcasite, with {001} pyrite ‖ {010} marcasite and [100] pyrite ‖ [101] marcasite; pyrite on marcasite with {001} pyrite ‖ {010} marcasite and [110] pyrite ‖ [100] marcasite; pyrite on marcasite with {001} pyrite ‖ {010} marcasite and [110] pyrite ‖ [001] marcasite (Merwin, *Am. J. Sc.*, **38**, 357 [1914]). Marcasite on pyrite, with striae of cube face of pyrite ‖ twin plane {101} of marcasite, and [001] pyrite ‖ [010] marcasite. Marcasite on pyrrhotite with {010} marcasite ‖ {10$\bar{1}$0} pyrrhotite, and [001] marcasite ‖ [1$\bar{2}$1̄0] pyrrhotite; also with [010] marcasite ‖ {0001} pyrrhotite, and [010] marcasite ‖ [10$\bar{1}$0], [01$\bar{1}$0] or [$\bar{1}$100] pyrrhotite.
12. Allen, Crenshaw, Johnston, and Larsen (1912). See also Doelter (1925).

295 ARSENOPYRITE GROUP *AXY*

2951	Arsenopyrite	FeAsS	monoclinic or triclinic
2952	Glaucodot	(Co,Fe)AsS	monoclinic or triclinic ?
2953	Gudmundite	FeSbS	monoclinic
2954	Wolfachite	Ni(As,Sb)S ?	orthorhombic ?
2955	Lautite	CuAsS	orthorhombic

It has been shown recently[1] that arsenopyrite is not orthorhombic, as was commonly accepted, but monoclinic, or perhaps triclinic, and that

gudmundite is monoclinic; at the same time it was suggested that glaucodot is monoclinic or triclinic. The pseudo-orthorhombic cell dimensions
and ratio, however, serve to describe the morphological crystallography of
the members of the group, and the diminished symmetry is only apparent
in appropriate polished sections. The monoclinic space group for the group
is $B2_1/d$.

The cell contents of the members of the group are $A_8X_8Y_8$; $A = $ Fe, Co,
Ni, and perhaps Cu (in lautite); $X = $ As, Sb, and Bi subordinate; $Y = $ S.
Considerable isomorphism is found between the two principal members of
the group (arsenopyrite, glaucodot) but a complete gradation has as yet
not been established. The range of composition as here used for the species
is as follows.

Fe : Co

Arsenopyrite	pure Fe to $2:1$
Glaucodot	$2:1$ to $1:6$

A satisfactory description of lautite is not available and its relation to the
arsenopyrite group is not established. Wolfachite is of uncertain composition and adequate data have not been presented to show its relationship to
the other group members. Danaite is, for the most part, a cobaltian
variety of arsenopyrite, although some high-cobalt varieties have here been
referred to glaucodot.

Ref.

1. Buerger, *Am. Min.*, **22**, 48 (1937).

2951   **A R S E N O P Y R I T E** [FeAsS].   ? Lapis subrutilus atque non fere aliter
ac argenti spuma splendens et friabilis *Germ.* Mistpuckel *Agricola* (465, 1546). Pyrites
candidus, Wasserkies pt. *Gesner* (1565).   Arsenikaliskkies, Mispickel *Henckel* (1725)
Arsenikaliskkies, Hvit Kies (Pyrites albus), Mispickel, Arsenik-Sten *Wallerius* (227,
228, 1747).   Mispickel, Pyrite blanche *Wallerius* (1753).   Arsenikkies *Werner*
(1789).   Rauschgelbkies.   Fer arsenical *Fr.*   Arsenical Pyrites.   Dalarnit, Giftkies,
Glanzarsenikkies *Breithaupt* (*J. pr. Chem.*, **4**, 259, 261, 1835).   Crucite pt. *Thomson*
(**1**, 435, 1836); not the crucite (= andalusite) of *Delamétherie* (**3**, 464, 1795).   Arsenopyrite *Glocker* (38, 1847).   Plinian *Breithaupt* (*Ann. Phys.*, **69**, 430, 1846; *B. H.
Ztg.*, **25**, 168, 1866).   Pacite, Pazit pt. *Breithaupt* (*B. H. Ztg.*, **25**, 167, 1866).   Bronce
blanco *Span. S. A.* Arsenomarcasite *Schaller* (*Am. Min.*, **15**, 567, 1930).

Danaite *Hayes* (*Am. J. Sci.*, **24**, 386, 1833).   Kobalt-arsenikkies *Germ.*   ? Ver-
montit, Thalheimit *Breithaupt* (*B. H. Ztg.*, **25**, 167, 1866).

C r y s t.   Monoclinic; prismatic — $2/m$.[1]

$a:b:c = 1.6833:1:1.1400;$[2] $\beta\,90°00'$ $p_0:q_0:r_0 = 0.6773:1.1400:1$
$q_1:r_1:p_1 = 1.6833:1.4765:1;$ $\mu\,90°00'$ $r_2:p_2:q_2 = 0.8771:0.5941:1$

Forms:[3]

		ϕ	$\rho = C$	ϕ_1	$\rho_1 A$	ϕ_2	$\rho_2 B$
c	001	.....	0°00′	0°00′	90°00′	90°00′	90°00′
b	010	0°00′	90 00	90 00	90 00	.....	0 00
a	100	90 00	90 00	.....	0 00	0 00	90 00
r	140	8 26	90 00	90 00	81 34	0 00	8 26
β	130	11 12	90 00	90 00	78 48	0 00	11 12
u	120	16 32½	90 00	90 00	73 27½	0 00	16 32½
m	110	30 43	90 00	90 00	59 17	0 00	30 43
q	210	49 55	90 00	90 00	40 05	0 00	49 55
e	012	0 00	29 41	29 41	90 00	90 00	60 19
n	101	90 00	34 06½	0 00	55 53½	55 53½	90 00
o	111	30 43	52 58½	48 43½	65 56	55 53½	46 39

Less common forms:

ξ 180	ι 320	s 18·1·0	v 112	d 527	w 362
ρ 250	k 410	μ 403	B 125	h 616	f 311
t 230	τ 610	ν 703	A 315	g 212	p 832
ϕ 430	l 16·1·0	x 113	i 416	z 414	

Structure cell.[4] Space group $B2_1/d$; a_0 9.51, b_0 5.65, c_0 6.42; β 90°; $a_0 : b_0 : c_0 = 1.684 : 1 : 1.136$; contains $Fe_8As_8S_8$.

Habit.[5] Prismatic [001], and less commonly [010]. Also short prismatic [010]. Prism zone striated [001]; also {101} striated in zone [$\bar{1}2\bar{1}$] or [$\bar{1}11$]. Columnar, straight or divergent; granular or compact.

Twinning. (a) on {100} and {001} to produce pseudo-orthorhombic crystals;[6] (b) on {101}, as contact or penetration twins, sometimes repeated (as in marcasite); (c) on {012} to produce cruciform twins, or star-shaped trillings (Weiler; and Franklin, New Jersey).

Phys. Cleavage on {101} distinct, {010} in traces. Fracture uneven. Brittle. H. 5½–6. G. 6.07 ± 0.15;[7] 6.18 (calc.). Luster metallic. Color silver-white inclining to steel-gray. Streak dark grayish black. Opaque. Anisotropism strong, pleochroism weak. Reflection percentages: green 57.5, orange 48.5, red 47.[8] Thermoelectrically[9] both positive and negative.

Chem. Essentially iron arsenide-sulfide, FeAsS, with Co present in nearly all analyses. The cobaltian varieties extend to Fe : Co = 2 : 1, and grade into higher cobaltian members belonging to glaucodot, arsenopyrite probably forming a series with glaucodot. Ni, Bi, and Sb are reported, but less often in more recent analyses, and may be due in part to impurities; Au, Ag, Cu, Pb are undoubtedly present only as impurities. The slight excess of S and As in some arsenopyrite analyses may substitute for some of the Fe.[10]

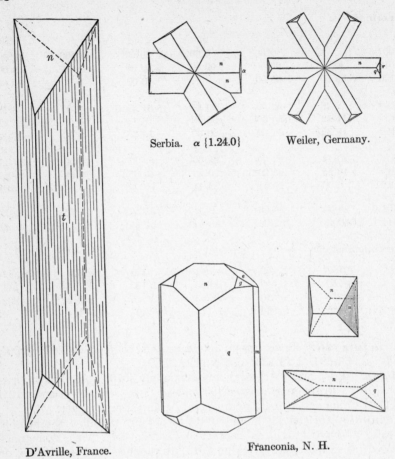

Serbia.   α {1.24.0}   Weiler, Germany.

D'Avrille, France.   Franconia, N. H.

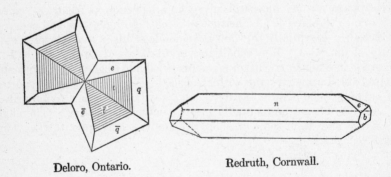

Deloro, Ontario.   Redruth, Cornwall.

Anal.[11]

	1	2	3	4	5	6	7	8
Fe	34.30	35.63	35.23	35.07	34.92	34.61	34.53	33.91
Co	.....	.....	.....	.....	0.29	.....	0.09	trace
Ni	.....	.....	.....	.....	0.73	.....	.....	.....
Bi	.....	.....	.....	.....	.....	.....	0.79	.....
Sb	.....	.....	.....	.....	.....	.....		
As	46.01	43.03	41.77	45.62	41.50	40.82	44.34	45.10
S	19.69	21.30	22.59	19.58	19.12	[22.65]	20.22	20.77
Rem.	.....	0.43	0.55	.....	2.81	1.92	.....	.....
Total	100.00	100.39	100.14	100.27	99.37	100.00	99.97	99.78
G.	6.18	5.9–6.2			6.14	6.073		5.98–6.03

1. FeAsS. 2. Nogaré, Trentino. Rem. SiO_2. Also trace Pb,Zn[12] 3. Kappusan, Kankyônandô, Korea. Rem. Cu 0.15, Zn 0.32, insol. 0.08. Trace Pb,Mn.[13] 4. Hohenstein, Saxony.[14] 5. Szadlovsky mine, Rozsnýo, Comm. Gomor, Hungary. Rem. Pb 0.32, Cu 1.13, Zn 0.84, CaO 0.22, insol. 0.3.[15] 6. Deloro, Hastings County, Ont. Rem. Pb 0.33, insol. 1.59.[16] 7. O'Brien mine, Cobalt, Ont.[17] 8. Calceranica, Trentino.[18]

	9	10	11	12	13	14	15
Fe	33.13	33.01	32.48	31.42	30.21	29.65	27.26
Co	.....	.....	1.16	3.07	0.76	3.05	8.71
Ni	.....	.....	.....	.....	.....	.....	.....
Bi	.....	.....	.....	.....	4.13	.....	.....
Sb					1.90		
As	45.83	49.91	48.72	45.77	39.96	47.60	46.93
S	20.43	16.27	18.80	[19.74]	15.92	19.70	17.10
Rem.	0.50	0.23	.....	.....	7.12	.....	.....
Total	99.89	99.42	101.16	100.00	100.00	100.00	100.00
G.						6.166	

9. Ronchi, near Caldonazzo, Trentino. Rem. is SiO_2.[19] 10. Asio, Totigi Prefect., Japan.[20] Rem. insoluble. 11. Franklin, N. J.[21] 12. Nordmark, Sweden.[22] 13. Meymac, France. Rem. is 4.90 gangue, 2.22 water.[23] 14. Evening Star mine, West Kootenai district, B. C.[24] 15. Haynes-Stellite mine, Blackbird district, Lemhi Co., Id.[25]

Var.[26] *Ordinary:* Essentially pure FeAsS with some slight substitution of the As or S for Fe, or for each other.

Cobaltian: Danaite *Hayes* (1833). Fe : Co to 2 : 1, or about 12 per cent Co by weight. Members richer in Co are here referred to glaucodot.

Bismuthian: Containing 4.13 per cent Bi (anal. 13).

Tests. F. 2. In C.T. gives an abundant sublimate of As, as bright gray crystals near the heated end, and a brilliant black amorphous deposit farther away. Decomposed by HNO_3 with separation of S.

Occur. Arsenopyrite is the most abundant and widespread arsenic mineral. It occurs in diverse types of deposits, usually as one of the earliest minerals to form. Often found sparingly in pegmatites (Buckfield). Common in high-temperature gold-quartz veins (Homestake); in high-temperature tin veins (Cornwall); in contact metamorphic sulfide deposits, associated with gold, other sulfides and calcium silicates (Nickel Plate mine, British Columbia); often with scheelite. Less common in ore veins of lower temperature of formation, as in gold-quartz veins (Mother Lode) or with nickel-cobalt minerals and native silver (Cobalt). Occurs disseminated in crystalline limestones (Franklin) and in schists (Brinton). Also rarely associated with basic rocks; sometimes in zeolitic cavities (Aschaffenberg).

Oriented growths of galena and pyrite upon arsenopyrite and of arsenopyrite upon pyrrhotite have been reported.[27]

Found in Japan at Asio, Totigi, and at Natsume in spheroids up to a foot in diameter composed of alternating shells of arsenopyrite and niccolite; in Korea analyzed from Kappusan, Kankyônandô. In the Katanga district, Belgian Congo, at the Prince Leopold mine, as crystals. In Austria large crystals in schist at Mitterberg north of Mühlbach; in Saxony at Freiberg associated with silver minerals and sulfides, and in fine crystals at Munzig near Meissen, also at Bergiesshübel with garnet, pyrite, and sphalerite, at Hohenstein and Altenberg; in Bavaria at Aschaffenberg, with zeolites in basalt. Found at Skutec, Bohemia, as crystals in quartz veins. In Hungary at the Szadlovsky mine, Rozsnýo, with siderite, tetrahedrite, and bournonite. As crystals from the Binnental, Switzerland. In France at Meymac (bismuthian); in Portugal reported from São Jão Gonzão, associated with cassiterite. In the Trentino, Italy, at Nogaré, Calceranica, and Ronchi in crystals in chlorite and sericite schists. Reported from Ransart, Belgium; from Sweden at Sala, Tunaberg, and Nordmark (cobaltian); in Norway at Skutterud near Modum, and at Buskerud, also at Sulitjelma (cobaltian) in fine crystals. At Cornwall, England, in many of the mines with cassiterite, notably at St. Agnes, St. Just, and at Redruth; in Devonshire, large crystals from Tavistock.

In Brazil at the Morro Velho gold mine, Minas Geraes; in Bolivia at Oruro, Huanini, and Chocaya in the tin and silver mines, and at the San Baldomero mine near Sorata; in Mexico at Mapimi, Durango.

In the United States found in New Hampshire at Franconia in fine crystals (danaite) in gneiss, associated with chalcopyrite; also at Jackson and at Haverhill; at Goffstown in pegmatite. In Maine, at Blue Hill with chalcopyrite and cordierite; at Corinna, Newfield (Bond's mountain), and Thomastown (Owl's Head); in pegmatite at the Westinghouse mine, Buckfield, at Auburn; in triphylite at Mount Mica. In Vermont, at Brookfield, Waterbury, and Stockbridge. In Massachusetts at Worcester in quartz veins in gneiss; at Sterling in pegmatite. In Connecticut, in fine crystals at Cobalt, with smaltite and niccolite, and at Monroe, with wolframite and pyrite; at Mine Hill, Roxbury, with siderite. In New Jersey at Franklin, in crystals in crystalline limestone. In New York, at Lewis, near Keeseville, Essex County, in masses with hornblende; in crystals and massive near Edenville, Orange County, with scorodite and gypsum; in crystals and masses in quartz, associated with pyrrhotite, pyrite, garnet, and scorodite, near Carmel, Putnam County. In Virginia at Brinton, disseminated and massive in quartz-mica schist. In North

Carolina, Alexander County, in pegmatite. Reported from Wisconsin, at Marquette, in diabase.

Found in many mines of the western states. In Montana, at the West Colusa and other mines, Butte; at Jardine, with scheelite in schist; at Emery, with sphalerite; and at Cinnabar. In Colorado at Leadville. In Idaho, at the Haynes-Stellite mine, Blackbird district, Lemhi County (*cobaltian*); at the North Star mine, Wood River district, Blaine County, with sphalerite. In New Mexico in the Tres Hermanes Mountains as cruciform and star-shaped twins. In California, in the gold-quartz veins of the Sierra Nevada; at Meadow Lake, Nevada County, (*cobaltian*) associated with gold, chalcopyrite and tourmaline.

In Canada, in the Cobalt district of Ontario, at the O'Brien mine and the Keeley mine; in the Porcupine district at the Hollinger gold mine; at Deloro, Hastings County, in the quartz veins. In British Columbia at the Nickel Plate mine, with gold, other sulfides and calcium silicates in the metamorphic limestone deposit; at the Evening Star mine, West Kootenay.

Alter. Usually alters to scorodite, less frequently to pitticite, pharmacosiderite and, rarely, to realgar. The cobaltian varieties alter to erythrite. Pseudomorphs of arsenopyrite after stephanite and pyrrhotite, and of galena, chalcocite, pyrite and hematite (*crucite*) after arsenopyrite have been noted.

Artif. Crystals have been obtained by the reaction of iron sulfate, sodium sulfarsenite and excess sodium bicarbonate at *ca.* 300°;[28] also by the prolonged action of hydrogen at high temperature and pressure on iron arsenate.[29]

Name. Arsenopyrite is a contraction of *arsenical pyrites*, from the German *arsenikaliskkies* of Henckel. Mispickel is of uncertain origin. Danaite is for J. Freeman Dana of Boston (1793–1827), who first made known the Franconia, New Hampshire, locality.

Ref.

1. Buerger, *Zs. Kr.*, **95**, 83 (1936), has shown that certain arsenopyrites (of the ideal composition) are monoclinic, but always pseudo-orthorhombic by twinning on {100} and {001}. The x-ray evidence, in the same way, points to a probably triclinic symmetry, likewise pseudo-orthorhombic, for those arsenopyrites whose composition varies from the ideal FeAsS.
2. Angles of Arzruni, *Zs. Kr.*, **2**, 430 (1878), p. 434, on Hohenstein crystals in the orientation and unit of Buerger (1936). Transformation, Arzruni to Buerger, 010/00½/100. Other ratios in Goldschmidt (**1**, 255, 1886).
3. Forms in Goldschmidt (**1**, 108, 1913); Flink, *Ark. Kemi*, **3** [11], 1 (1908); Palache, *Zs. Kr.*, **47**, 576 (1910); Andreatta, *Riv. studi, Trentino*, **9**, 90 (1928) — *Min. Abs.*, **4**, 136 (1929); Palache (33, 1935). Rare and uncertain forms: {1·12·0}, {470}, {310}, {23·0·1}, {925}, {14·5·4}, {521}, {841}.
4. Buerger (1936) on crystals from Spindlemühle, near Hohenelbe, Riesengebirge, Bohemia.
5. See Scherer, *Zs. Kr.*, **21**, 354 (1893), for a listing of habits of crystals.
6. Buerger (1936) describes such twins, as seen in polished section.
7. Average of 24 determinations, as given in the literature, of essentially FeAsS with little cobalt. The glaucodots (with Co) show no systematic variation in specific gravity from that of arsenopyrite.
8. Schneiderhöhn and Ramdohr (**2**, 199, 1931).

9. Schrauf and Dana, *Ak. Wien, Ber.*, **69** [1], 152 (1874).

10. Doelter (4 [1], 619, 1925) discusses the composition at length; also Buerger (1936), who considers that the excess As substitutes for both Fe and S. The supposed relation of composition and axial ratio proposed by Arzruni (1878) and others has been shown to be erroneous by Scherer (1893).

11. For older analyses see Dana (97, 1892) and Doelter (4 [1], 610, 1926).

12. Andreatta anal., *Riv. studi, Trentino, Sc. nat.*, **9**, 90 (1928) — *Min. Abs.*, **4**, 136 (1929). Axial ratio on this material $a : b : c = 0.6783 : 1 : 1.1910$.

13. In Harada (241, 1936).

14. Arzruni (1878).

15. Zsivny, *Hist.-Nat. Musei Nationalis Hungarici, Ann.*, **13**, 577, 1915 — *Min. Abs.*, **1**, 337 (1920). Crystals of this analysis measured by Zimanyi, *Zs. Kr.*, **54**, 578 (1915).

16. Scherer (1892). Axial ratio $a : b : c = 0.6715 : 1 : 1.19019$.

17. Ellsworth, *Ontario Bur. Mines, Rep 25* [1], 31, 1916. Crystals "are seen to be non-homogeneous " — Ellsworth.

18. Andreatta (1928–1929). Axial ratio $a : b : c = 0.6775 : 1 : 1.1840$.

19. Andreatta (1929).

20. In Harada (241, 1936).

21. Bauer anal. in Bauer and Berman, *Am. Min.*, **12**, 39 (1927). Axial ratio $a : b : c = 0.6702 : 1 : 1.189$.

22. Johansson, *Zs. Kr.*, **68**, 87 (1928). Axial ratio $a : b : c = 0.6730 : 1 : 1.1868$.

23. Carnot, *C.R.*, **79**, 479 (1874). Two other analyses of the same material differ in Bi, Sb and S by several per cent.

24. Johnston anal. in Hoffmann, *Geol. Sur. Canada, Ann. Rep. 8*, 13 1895.

25. Shannon (144, 1926).

26. The supposed nickelian variety described by Kroeber (in Dana, 99, 1892) and the antimonian variety reported by Sandberger (*Jb. Min.*, [1], 99, 1890) have not been completely verified, although smaller amounts of these elements are given in some of the early analyses.

27. Mügge (366, 1903). Galena, upon arsenopyrite: {001} [110] galena = {001} [100] arsenopyrite; pyrite upon arsenopyrite: {001} [110] arsenopyrite = {001} [100] pyrite. Frondel (priv. comm., 1939) reports arsenopyrite upon pyrrhotite (from Roumania) as follows: {010} [001] arsenopyrite = {10$\bar{1}$0} [$\bar{1}2\bar{1}$0] pyrrhotite; [010] arsenopyrite upon {0001} pyrrhotite with [010] arsenopyrite = [10$\bar{1}$0], [01$\bar{1}$0], [$\bar{1}$100] pyrrhotite.

28. De Senarmont, *Ann. Phys.*, **32**, 170 (1851), produced crystals with the forms {110}, {101}, and {014}.

29. Ipatieff and Nikolaieff, *J. Russ. Phys. Chem. Soc.*, **58**, 664 (1926).

STAHLERZ. *Münster* (*Nytt Mag.*, **32**, 269, 1892; *Zs. Kr.*, **30**, 668, 1898). Staalerts, Steel ore.

A steel-gray material from Kongsberg, Norway, with H. 6, G. 5.96–5.98, and fine granular fracture. Tarnishes lead gray or bronze. Analysis gave: Fe 29.88, Co 0.11, Ag 8.68, Cu 0.33, As 44.72, Sb 0.82, S 15.78, total 100.27.

Probably a mixture, in large part arsenopyrite or loellingite.

2952 **GLAUCODOT** [(Co,Fe)AsS]. Kobalt-haltigen Arsenikkies pt. *Scheerer* (*Ann. Phys.*, **42**, 546, 1837); Kobalt-Arsenikkies *Wöhler* (*Ann. Phys.*, **43**, 591, 1838). Glaukodot *Breithaupt* and *Plattner* (*Ann. Phys.*, **77**, 127, 1849). Glaucodot *Dana* (63, 1854).

Akontit *Breithaupt* (*J. pr. Chem.*, **4**, 258, 1835). Alloclase, Alloklas pt. *Tschermak* (*Ak. Wien, Ber.*, **53**, 220, 1866). Alloclasite *Dana* (81, 1868).

C r y s t.[1] Orthorhombic; dipyramidal — $2/m\ 2/m\ 2/m$.

$a : b : c = 1.6795 : 1 : 1.1531$;[2] $p_0 : q_0 : r_0 = 0.6855 : 1.1531 : 1$

$q_1 : r_1 : p_1 = 1.6795 : 1.4588 : 1$; $r_2 : p_2 : q_2 = 0.8686 : 0.5954 : 1$

Forms:[3]

		ϕ	$\rho = C$	ϕ_1	$\rho_1 = A$	ϕ_2	$\rho_2 = B$
c	001	0°00′	0°00′	0°00′	90°00′	90°00′	90°00′
q	230	21 39	90 00	90 00	68 21	0 00	21 39
m	110	30 46	90 00	90 00	59 14	0 00	30 46
l	210	49 58½	90 00	90 00	40 01½	0 00	49 58½
s	012	0 00	29 55½	29 55½	90 00	90 00	60 04½
J	101	90 00	34 26	0 00	55 34	55 34	90 00
V	112	30 46	33 49½	29 55½	73 27½	71 05	61 25½
g	212	49 58½	41 50	29 55½	59 17	55 34	64 36

Less common:

b	010	r	120	t	610	α	111	i	416
a	100	k	410	p	106	β	214	h	616

Structure cell.[4] Orthorhombic ?; a_0 6.67, b_0 9.62, c_0 5.73; $b_0 : c_0 : a_0 =$ 1.679 : 1 : 1.164; contains $(Co,Fe)_8As_8S_8$.

Habit. Prismatic [001], less commonly [010]. Striated in the prism zone $\|$ [001]; also striated in [010] zone $\|$ [010]. Common forms: l, J, m, q, v, g. Also massive.

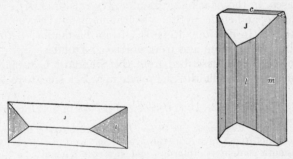

Hakansbö, Sweden.

Twinning. (a) On {101}; (b) On {012} producing cruciform twins; also trillings, as in arsenopyrite.

Phys. Cleavage perfect {010}, less perfect {101}.[5] Fracture uneven. Brittle. H. 5. G. 6.04 ± 0.12;[6] 5.90 (calc. for Fe : Co = 1 : 1). Luster metallic. Color grayish tin-white to reddish silver-white. Streak black. Opaque. Anisotropic,[7] but less strongly so than arsenopyrite. Thermo-electrically[8] both positive and negative.

Chem. A cobalt-iron arsenide-sulfide, (Co,Fe)AsS, with the ratio Co : Fe between 1 : 2 and 6 : 1.[9] Some analyses give close to $CoFeAs_2S_2$ (Hakansbö).

Anal.[10]

	1	2	3	4	5	6
Fe	22.72	21.39	19.60	13.68	5.33	16.27
Co	11.99	17.37	16.68	22.24	31.64	18.64
Ni	.....	0.46	trace	.....	.....	.....
Bi	.....	.....	.....	.....	0.10	.....
As	45.72	41.22	44.01	43.79	42.97	45.84
S	19.57	19.56	20.18	20.29	20.59	19.01
Rem.	.....	.....	0.20	.....	0.09	.....
Total	100.00	100.00	100.67	100.00	100.72	99.76
G.	5.90		6.064		6.166	

1. (Fe,Co)AsS with Fe : Co = 2 : 1. 2. Hakansbö. Recalc. after deducting 4.86 per cent chalcopyrite.[11] Also contains inclusions of magnetite. 3. Hakansbö. Rem. is insol.[12] 4. Standard Consolidated mine, Sumpter, Ore. Recalc. after deducting 9.38 per cent insol.[13] 5. " Alloclase." Oravicza, Elizabeth mine. Rem. is insol.[14] 6. Skutterud.[15]

Tests. F. 2–3. Gives S and As reactions in the O.T. In C.T. a sublimate of As is formed only on intense ignition. Decomposed by HNO_3 with separation of S, and the formation of a pink solution.

O c c u r.[16] In Sweden at Hakansbö, as large crystals, twinned and untwinned, with cobaltite and intergrown with chalcopyrite. In Norway, at Skutterud (in part cobaltian arsenopyrite). In Chile in the neighborhood of Huasco, in the Atacama region, as crystals in chlorite schist, with axinite, cobaltite, and chalcopyrite. In Roumania, at Oravicza (alloclase?) with bismuthinite in calcite. Reported from Tasmania on the southern slope of Mount Wellington, and from northeast Dundas.

In the United States described from the Standard Consolidated mine, Sumpter, Oregon, with cobaltite and pyrite in a dark silicate rock.

A l t e r. To erythrite.

N a m e. From γλαυκός, blue, because of its use in making smalt.

ALLOCLASITE. Tschermak (Ak. Wien, Ber., **53**, 220, 1866), is a supposedly bismuthian glaucodot from Oravicza.[17] However, recent work indicates[18] that the early reported bismuth content is erroneous, and that the mineral is a high cobaltian glaucodot.

Ref.

1. Buerger, Am. Min., **22**, 48 (1937) believes that glaucodot may be monoclinic or triclinic. However, the evidence has not, as yet, been presented, and, in any event, the elements here given accurately represent the angular relations.
2. Angles from Goldschmidt (**4**, 52, 1918) on crystals from Hakansbö; orientation and unit after Buerger, Am. Min., **22**, 48 (1937), to conform with arsenopyrite. Transformation Goldschmidt to Buerger 010/00½/100.
3. Goldschmidt (**4**, 52, 1918). All forms except {106} and {214} observed on arsenopyrite.
4. de Jong, Physica, **6**, 325 (1926).
5. Krenner, Cbl. Min., 39, 1929, reverses the perfection of cleavage, as found in the Oravicza material. This latter conforms to the arsenopyrite cleavage.
6. An average value for crystals containing varying amounts of Co. The Co : Fe ratio apparently has little effect on the specific gravity. Three new determinations (Frondel, priv. comm., 1940) give 6.06 ± 0.05 on Hakansbö fragments.
7. Schneiderhöhn and Ramdohr (**2**, 204, 1931).
8. Schrauf and Dana, Ak. Wien, Ber., **69** [1], 153 (1874).

9. Cobaltian arsenopyrite (which see) has a ratio of Co : Fe less than 2 : 1.
10. Older analyses in Dana (102, 1892).
11. Beutell, *Cbl. Min.*, 412, 1911.
12. Graham anal. in Thomson, *Univ. Toronto Stud.*, *Geol. Ser.*, **29**, 75 (1930), p. 79.
13. Schaller, *U. S. Geol. Sur.*, *Bull.* **262**, 132, 1905.
14. Loczka anal. in Krenner, *Cbl. Min.*, A, 40, 1929.
15. Schulz anal. in Rammelsberg (31, 1875).
16. The occurrences of less cobaltian material are given under arsenopyrite. .
17. Frenzel, *Min. Mitt.*, 5, 181 (1883), has made six analyses not varying greatly among themselves and averaging 27.28 per cent Bi. See Dana (102, 1892).
18. Krenner (1929) reexamined material from the type locality. Murdoch (37, 1916) pointed out the inhomogeneity of the material called alloclase. However, the analysis of original material does not fit the assumption that the bismuth is due to bismuthinite.

2953 **G U D M U N D I T E** [FeSbS]. Gudmundit *Johansson* (*Zs. Kr.*, **68**, 87, 1928).

C r y s t. Monoclinic; prismatic — $2/m$.[1]

$a : b : c = 1.6852 : 1 : 1.1340$; $\beta\ 90°00'$[2] $p_0 : q_0 : r_0 = 0.6729 : 1.1340 : 1$

$q_1 : r_1 : p_1 = 1.6852 : 1.4861 : 1$; $\mu\ 90°00'\ r_2 : p_2 : q_2 = 0.8819 : 0.5934 : 1$

Forms:

		ϕ	$\rho = C$	ϕ_1	$\rho_1 = A$	ϕ_2	$\rho_2 = B$
b	010	0°00'	90°00'	90°00'	90°00'	0°00'	0°00'
t	230	21 35	90 00	90 00	68 25	0 00	21 35
q	210	49 53	90 00	90 00	40 07	0 00	49 53
n	101	90 00	33 56	0 00	56 04	56 04	90 00

Structure cell.[3] Space group $B2_1/d$; $a_0\ 10.00$, $b_0\ 5.95$, $c_0\ 6.73$; $\beta\ 90°00'$; $a_0 : b_0 : c_0 = 1.6817 : 1 : 1.134$; contains $Fe_8Sb_8S_8$.

Habit. Prismatic [001], often with the prism zone tapered.

Twinning.[4] On {101}, penetration and contact, producing cruciform and butterfly twin shapes.

P h y s. No cleavage. Fracture uneven. Brittle. H. near 6. G. 6.72;[5] 6.91 (calc.). Color silver-white to steel-gray. Luster metallic. Opaque. Anisotropic.[6] Reflectivity high. Pleochroism noticeable.

C h e m. Iron antimonide-sulfide, FeSbS.

Gudmundstorp, Sweden.

Anal.

	Fe	Ni	Sb	S	Total
1	26.63	.....	58.08	15.29	100.00
2	26.79	trace	57.31	15.47	99.57

1. FeSbS. 2. Gudmundstorp. Analysis made on 0.2004 gm., 0.1429 gm. for S determination.

O c c u r.[7] A hydrothermal mineral formed at a relatively late period in sulfide deposits. Associated with pyrite, chalcopyrite, pyrrhotite, and other sulfides (usually earlier formed) and, in particular, lead sulfantimonides, native antimony, native bismuth, electrum. Originally found at Gudmundstorp, 3 km. north of Sala, Sweden, as small doubly terminated crystals in calcite veinlets in the skarn, the latter containing arsenopyrite which closely resembles the gudmundite. Reported from Boliden, Holmtjärn and other localities in the Skellefte district and from several localities in the Malanas district. From Jakobsbaken near Sulitjelma and Vigsnaes near Stavanger in Norway. Reported also from Turkal, Turkey, and Waldsassen, Upper Palatinate, Germany. Said to occur in the Yellowknife district, Northwest Territories, Canada.

N a m e. From the locality at Gudmundstorp, Sweden.

Ref.

1. The original description by Johansson (1928) gives the symmetry as orthorhombic; Buerger, *Am. Min.*, **22**, 48 (1937), in a private communication (November, 1938) shows that gudmundite, together with other members of the arsenopyrite group, is monoclinic.
2. Angles of Johansson (1928) in orientation and unit of Buerger (1937). Transformation Johansson to Buerger 010/00½/100.
3. Buerger, *Zs. Kr.*, **101**, 290 (1939).
4. Twinning to produce pseudo-orthorhombic habit in the crystals has not yet been demonstrated, as it has for arsenopyrite.
5. Specific gravity measured with micropycnometer on 100 mg. sample (Frondel priv. comm., 1940) on material of the' x-ray study.
6. Ramdohr, *Zbl. Min.*, 193, 1937.
7. See Sampson, *Econ. Geol.*, **36**, 175 (1941), for a summary of known and supposed occurrences of gudmundite.

2954 **Wolfachite** [Ni(As,Sb)S]. *Sandberger (Jb. Min.*, 313, 1869).

C r y s t. Presumably orthorhombic and resembling arsenopyrite.

Forms:[1]

{101}, sometimes {100}, and undefined prism faces.

Habit. Small crystals; also columnar radiating aggregates.

P h y s. Fracture uneven. H. 4½–5. G. 6.372. Luster metallic. Color silver-white to tin-white. Streak black.

C h e m. Only one analysis has been made.[2]

Fe	Co	Ni	Sb	As	S
3.74	trace	29.81	13.26	38.83	14.36 = 100.00

The composition yields the formula Ni(As,Sb)S, approximately.

Tests. F. 2, to a brittle magnetic globule. Decomposed by HNO_3 with separation of S and a mixture of As and Sb oxides.

O c c u r. At Wolfach in Baden, on niccolite with galena and dyscrasite, in calcite.

Ref.

1. Forms in the orientation of arsenopyrite.
2. Petersen, *Ann Phys.*, **137**, 397 (1869). 1.32 per cent Pb and 0.12 per cent Ag deducted as sulfides. The ratio Sb : As : S = 11 : 52 : 45.

2955   LAUTITE [CuAsS]. *Frenzel* (*Min. Mitt.*, **3**, 515 1881; **4**, 97, 1882).

C r y s t.   Orthorhombic; dipyramidal — $2/m\ 2/m\ 2/m$.

$a : b : c = 0.6912 : 1 : 2.0904;^{1}$ $p_0 : q_0 : r_0 = 3.0242 : 2.0904 : 1$

$q_1 : r_1 : p_1 = 0.6912 : 0.3307 : 1;$ $r_2 : p_2 : q_2 = 0.4784 : 1.4468 : 1$

Forms:[2]

		ϕ	$\rho = C$	ϕ_1	$\rho_1 = A$	ϕ_2	$\rho_2 = B$
c	001	0°00′	0°00′	0°00′	90°00′	90°00′	90°00′
f	3·0·10	90 00	42 13	0 00	47 47	47 47	90 00
e	102	90 00	56 31½	0 00	33 28½	33 28½	90 00
w	124	35 53	52 13	46 16	62 24½	52 54½	50 11
g	234	43 58	65 20½	57 28	50 53	33 28½	49 09
A	322	65 15½	78 40½	64 26	27 03½	12 26	65 46½

Less common:

O 230 θ 034 x 111 μ 359 h 123 r 313

Structure cell.[3]   Orthorhombic; a_0 3.78, b_0 5.47, c_0 11.47; $a_0 : b_0 : c_0 = 0.691 : 1 : 2.097$; contains $Cu_4As_4S_4$.

Habit.   Tabular {001}; short prismatic [100]. Striated on {001} ‖ [100]. Columnar to fine fibrous, also radiated. Sometimes fine granular, to compact.
Twinning.[4]   On {110}.

P h y s.   Cleavage {001}.[4]   Brittle. H. 3–3½. G. 4.9 ± 0.1.[5]   Luster metallic to semimetallic.[6] Color black to steel-gray with a reddish tinge (somewhat like that of enargite).   Streak black.   Opaque.   Anisotropic.[6] Reflection percentages: green 32, orange 28, red 27.

Markirch, Alsace.

C h e m.   Copper arsenide-sulfide, CuAsS, with possibly Ag substituting for Cu.
Anal.[7]

	1	2	3
Cu	37.28	36.10	37.07
As	43.92	45.66	44.53
S	18.80	17.88	18.30
Total	100.00	99.64	99.90
G.		4.91	4.53

1. CuAsS.   2. Lauta.[8]   3. Rauental.[9]

Tests.   F. 1½?   Decrepitates violently B.B.   Yields arsenical mirror in C.T.   Soluble in HNO_3.

O c c u r.   At Lauta, near Marienberg, Saxony, with native arsenic, tennantite, proustite, chalcopyrite, galena, and barite.   Also at the Gabe Gottes mine, Rauental, near Markirch (St. Marie aux Mines), Alsace-

Lorraine, associated with native arsenic, tennantite, native bismuth, loellingite, ruby silver, and quartz.

N a m e. From the locality, *Lauta*.

Ref.

1. Angles and orientation of Dürrfeld, *Geol. Landesanst., Elsass-Löthringen, Mitt.*, **7**, 121 (1909), on not completely authenticated material from Rauental, Alsace; unit of Weil and Hocart, *C. R.*, **209**, 445 (1939), by x-ray methods.
2. Dürrfeld (1909), and additional A(322) of Ungemach (unpublished notes) on the specimen of Dürr, *Geol. Landesanst., Elsass-Löthringen, Mitt.*, **6**, 249 (1907), now in the Strassburg collection. Rare and uncertain forms: {5·5·13}, {3·30·20}, {9·30·40}, {134}, {5·8·14}, {418}, {326}, {15·10·24}, {50·45·64}.
3. Weil and Hocart (1939).
4. Dürrfeld (1909).
5. Frenzel gives 4.96, Weisbach, *Jb. Min.*, II, 249, 1882, gives 4.913, 4.849 on mixtures, Dürr (1907) gives 4.53.
6. Schneiderhöhn and Ramdohr (**2**, 226, 1931).
7. Frenzel's first analyses (1881; 1882 — in Dana [67, 1884]) contained considerable amounts of silver. Weisbach (1882) showed that these analyses were similar to those made for him by Winkler on inhomogeneous material, which contained, in addition to the supposed lautite, much native arsenic. However, two analyses from the known localities support the given formula, and polished section studies by Ramdohr (in Schneiderhöhn and Ramdohr [1931]) and by Orcel, *Bull. soc. min.*, **51**, 197 (1928), p. 206, indicate probable homogeneity of the material, although Orcel is not certain on this point. Further, Ungemach examined (unpublished notes) Dürr's crystals and showed them to be of the same mineral as Dürrfeld's crystals (1909) and thus reasonably established the crystallographic character of the species.
8. Frenzel anal., *Min. Mitt.*, **14**, 121 (1894), p. 125, for lautite.
9. Dürr anal. (1907).

296   MOLYBDENITE GROUP AX_2

DIHEXAGONAL DIPYRAMIDAL — $6/m\,2/m\,2/m$

			c/a	a_0	c_0	G.	H.
2961	Molybdenite	MoS_2	3.821	3.15	12.30	5.05	$1-1\frac{1}{2}$
2962	Tungstenite	WS_2	3.93	3.18	12.5	8.1	$2\frac{1}{2}$

The chief characteristic of these minerals is the eminent basal cleavage, typical of the layered structure.[1] The chief physical difference between the two minerals is in the specific gravity.

Ref.

1. Bragg (78, 1937).

2961   M O L Y B D E N I T E [MoS_2]. Not Molybdaena of *Dioscorides*, *Pliny*, *Agricola* (a product from the partial reduction and oxidation of galena). Blyertz, Molybdena pt. (rest graphite) *Wallerius* (131, 1747), *Linnaeus* (1748, 1768). Sulphur ferro et stanno saturatum, Wasserbley pt., Molybdena pt. *Cronstedt* (139, 1758), *Scheele* (**1**, 1778). Molybdaena (with discovery of the metal) *Hjelm* (*Ak. Stockholm, Abh.*, 1782, 1788–1793). Wasserblei *Werner*. Molybdena *Kirwan* (1796) (calls the metal molybdenite). Molybdène sulfuré *Haüy* (4, 290, 1801). Molybdenite *Brongniart* (**2**, 92, 1807) (citing Kirwan as authority). Molybdenglanz *Karsten* (70, 1808). Sulphuret of Molybdena.

C r y s t. Hexagonal — P; dihexagonal dipyramidal — $6/m\,2/m\,2/m$.

$a : c = 1 : 3.815;^1$ $p_0 : r_0 = 4.406 : 1$

Forms:[2]

		ϕ	$\rho = C$	M	A_2
c	0001	0°00′	0°00′	90°00′	90°00′
m	10$\bar{1}$0	30 00	90 00	60 00	90 00
s	10$\bar{1}$5	30 00	41 23	70 42	90 00
t	10$\bar{1}$3	30 00	55 45	65 35$\frac{1}{2}$	90 00
o	10$\bar{1}$2	30 00	65 35	62 55	90 00
p	10$\bar{1}$1	30 00	77 12$\frac{1}{2}$	60 49	90 00
q	30$\bar{3}$2	30 00	81 23$\frac{1}{2}$	60 22$\frac{1}{2}$	90 00

Structure cell.[3] Space group $C6/mmc$;[4] a_0 3.15, c_0 12.30; $a_0 : c_0 =$ 1 : 3.905; contains Mo_2S_4.

Twinning.[5] Said to occur with {0001} as composition face.

Habit. Hexagonal[6] tabular; or in short, slightly tapering or barrel-shaped prisms. Prismatic and pyramidal faces horizontally striated; sometimes a triangular pattern of striae or lamellae on {0001} parallel to the trace of {10$\bar{1}$1}, and produced by deformation. Commonly foliated massive, or in scales; sometimes in rudely divergent plates.

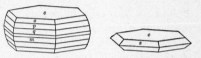

Frankford, Pa.   Enterprise, near Kingston, Canada.

Phys. Cleavage {0001}, perfect. Laminae very flexible, but not elastic. Sectile. H. 1–1$\frac{1}{2}$. G. 4.62–4.73; 4.704 (Biella[7]); 5.06 (artif.[8]); 5.05 (calc.). M.P. 1185°.[9] Luster metallic. Color pure lead-gray; the streak on porcelain greenish, on paper, bluish gray. Opaque. In extremely thin flakes translucent and very pale yellow to deep reddish brown in color, according to thickness.[10] Feel greasy. In polished section[11] white, with very strong anisotropism and pleochroism. Reflection percentages for 0: green 36, orange 31.5, red 30.5; for E: green 15.5, orange 18, red 15. Translation gliding[12] with T{0001}, and t[21$\bar{3}$0]; also secondary twin (?) striae on {0001} parallel the trace of {10$\bar{1}$1}, but the exact origin uncertain.

Chem. Molybdenum sulfide, MoS_2, with Mo 59.94 per cent, S 40.06 per cent = 100 per cent. Most analyses show no other constituents, the Mo and S being nearly in theoretical proportions. Ge has been found spectroscopically.[13]

Tests. Infusible. Decomposed by HNO_3, leaving a residue of MoO_3. Soluble in aqua regia.

Occur.[14] Molybdenite is the most common mineral containing molybdenum. Found as an accessory mineral in certain granites; in pegmatites and aplites, sometimes in large amounts. Common in many veins of the deep-seated class associated with scheelite, wolframite, topaz, and fluorite; also in contact metamorphic deposits, with lime silicates, scheelite, and chalcopyrite.

In Norway found at Telemarken, also at Raade, near Moss, at Brevik in the Langesund district, at Knabenheiem near Flekkefiord, and at Arendal. In Sweden in Ljusnarsberg, Örebrolan. From the Chibina tundra, Kola Peninsula; in the Adun-Chilon Mountains, south of Nerchinsk, Transbaikalia; at Miask in the Ilmen Mountains, Urals. Found in tin veins in Saxony at Altenberg and Ehrenfriedersdorf, and similarly in Bohemia at Schlaggenwald and Zinnwald. Occurs in England at Carrock Fells and Caldbeck Fell, Cumberland, and in tin veins in Cornwall; in Scotland at Mount Coryby on Loch Creran. In Portugal, near Mangualde, Province of Beira, in pegmatite. In Morocco at Azegour, 80 km. south of Marrakesh, disseminated in garnet hornfels. Disseminated in carbonaceous Triassic sandstone in the Hlatimbe Valley, Natal. At Windhoek, South-West Africa; in the Mutue-Fides-Stavoren tin district in the Transvaal with cassiterite in pegmatite pipes.

Found in Australia in pegmatite pipes at Deepwater and, in fine large crystals, at Kingsgate, in the New England Range, New South Wales; at Wolfram, near Chillagoe, Queensland; at Everton, Victoria. In China at Shih-ping-chuan, Tsingtien, Chekiang, in quartz veins. In Japan, found at Kawachi, Echigo Province, and at Shirakawa, Hida Province. In Mexico, near La Trinidad, Sahuaripa district, Sonora. In Peru, at Ricran, near Juaja, Junin.

In the United States, found in Maine at Blue Hill Bay and Camdage farm in large crystals, and at Tunk Pond and Cooper in pegmatite. At Westmoreland, New Hampshire, in mica schist. At Haddam, Connecticut, in pegmatite. In New Jersey in large crystals at the Ogden mine, Edison, with magnetite. In Pennsylvania, at Frankford, Philadelphia, in measurable crystals, also at Chester, near Reading, and in serpentine at Easton. In Colorado, at Climax, Lake County, in a large deposit, in quartz veinlets in silicified granite with fluorite and topaz; at Camp Urad, near Empire, Clear Creek County, and at Browns Creek, Chaffee County, in quartz with beryl. At Questa, Taos County, New Mexico. In Utah, in the Deep Creek Mountains, near Gold Hill, and at the O.K. mine, Beaver Lake district. In Arizona, from the Copper Canyon district, about 25 miles southeast of Yucca; at Helvetia. In California, near Gibson, Shasta County, in aplite; on Pine Creek, near Bishop, Inyo County, with scheelite and garnet in contact metamorphosed limestone. In Washington from near Lake Chelan, Okanogan County, and from Chelan County. In Alaska at Shakan, Prince of Wales Island.

In Canada, in pegmatite in the Temiskaming district, and at Quyon, Aldfield, Egan, Wakefield, in Quebec; near Kingston, Belleville, Ross, and Dacre, in Ontario; at Lost Creek, near Salmo, and with lime silicates in a contact deposit at Texada Island, in British Columbia; also in Manitoba and Nova Scotia.

Alter.[15] Alters to ferrimolybdite (molybdic ocher, molybdite); also to powellite and to ilsemannite. Pseudomorphs of bismuthinite and of powellite after molybdenite have been noted.

Artif.[16] Formed artificially by heating a molybdate or molybdic oxide with sulfur or hydrogen sulfide and an alkaline carbonate; also by the direct union of molybdenum and sulfur.

Ref.

1. Ratio from measurement (0001) $\wedge$ (10$\bar{1}$2) = 65°35′ of Brown, *Ac. Sc. Philadelphia, Proc.*, **210**, 1896; unit chosen to conform with structure cell by Dickinson and Pauling, *Am. Chem. Soc. J.*, **45**, 1466 (1923). The form $p\{10\bar{1}1\}$ is most prominently developed on the crystals measured by Brown (1896). Transformation: Brown to structure cell, 1000/0100/0010/0002.

2. Forms from Goldschmidt (**6**, 49, 1920). Rare and uncertain: $\{11\bar{2}0\}$, $\{10\bar{1}8\}$, $\{10\bar{1}4\}$, $\{50\bar{5}8\}$, $\{11\bar{2}4\}$.

3. Dickinson and Pauling (1923). Electron-diffraction study of extremely thin cleavage flakes by Finch and Wilman, *Trans. Faraday Soc.*, **32**, 1539 (1936).

4. Bragg (**77**, 1937). The alternative space groups $H\bar{6}c$ and $H\bar{3}c$ of Dickinson and Pauling (1923) permit accordance with the seemingly trigonal morphology of some artificial MoS_2 crystals (see ref. 6).

5. Hidden, *Am. J. Sc.*, **32**, 204 (1886), p. 210, and Brown (1896) mention twinning of this nature, but without adequate description.

6. Artificial crystals with triangular outlines have been obtained by Guichard, *Ann. chim. phys.*, **23**, 7, 552 (1901), Dickinson and Pauling (1923) and de Schulten, *Geol. För. Förh.*, **11**, 401 (1889), by fusing potassium carbonate, sulfur, and molybdic oxide or ammonium molybdate. The identity of the artificial with the natural crystals has not been shown.

7. Cossa, *Zs. Kr.*, **2**, 206 (1878), on crystals from Biella, Traversella.

8. de Schulten (1889) on artificial crystals.

9. Cusack, *Proc. Roy. Irish Acad.*, **4**, 399 (1897) — *Zs. Kr.*, **31**, 284 (1899).

10. Finch and Wilman (1936).

11. Schneiderhöhn and Ramdohr (**2**, 92, 1931).

12. Mügge, *Jb. Min.*, **1**, 110 (1898).

13. Geilmann and Brunger, *Zs. anorg. Chem.*, **196**, 312 (1931), found $5-6 \times 10^{-5}$ per cent Ge in molybdenite of unknown locality. De Gramont, *Bull. soc. min.*, **18**, 274 (1895), found no extra elements in molybdenite of unstated locality.

14. A review of world occurrences of molybdenite is given by Hess, *U. S. Geol. Sur., Bull. 761*, 1924.

15. Dittler, *Cbl. Min.*, 705, 1923, describes experiments on the alteration of molybdenite in oxygenated water.

16. Doelter (**4** [1], 70, 1926). The product obtained by van Arkel, *Rec. trav. chim. Pays-Bas*, **45**, 437 (1926), by heating Mo and S in a closed tube afforded an x-ray pattern identical with that of natural molybdenite.

JORDISITE. *Cornu (Koll.-Zs.*, **4**, 190, 1909).

A black, powdery, colloidal form of what may be molybdenum sulfide. Alters to ilsemannite. Occurs in the Himmelsfürst mine, Freiberg, Saxony.

²⁹⁶² **TUNGSTENITE** [WS$_2$]. *Wells* and *Butler (Washington Ac. Sc., J.*, **7**, 596, 1917).

Cryst. Hexagonal — *P*; dihexagonal dipyramidal — $6/m\ 2/m\ 2/m$.[1]
Structure cell.[2] Space group $C6/mmc$; a_0 3.18, c_0 12.5; $a_0 : c_0 = 1 : 3.93$; contains W_2S_4.

Habit. Found only massive, in fine scaly or feathery aggregates.

Phys. Cleavage $\{0001\}$.[3] Sectile. H. $2\frac{1}{2}$. G. 7.4;[4] 7.5 (artif.[5]); 8.1 (calc.). Color dark lead-gray; soils the fingers. Opaque. In polished section[6] as felted aggregates, pure white in color with both anisotropism and pleochroism very strong.

Chem. Probably tungsten disulfide, WS_2. The only analysis is based on impure material calculated to contain about 60 per cent WS_2.

Tests. Infusible. Insoluble in HNO_3 or HCl, but soluble in aqua regia.

Occur. Found only at the Emma mine, Little Cottonwood district, Salt Lake County, Utah, in a replacement deposit in limestone. Associated with pyrite, sphalerite, galena, tetrahedrite, wolframite, argentite, and quartz.

Artif.[7] Prepared artificially by direct union of the elements; by heating tungsten trioxide with sulfur or sulfur compounds; by decomposition of tungsten compounds containing sulfur.

Ref.

1. Crystal class from the structure data, and from the relation to molybdenite.
2. van Arkel, *Rec. trav. chim. Pays-Bas*, **45**, 437 (1926), by the powder method, on artificial material obtained by heating W and S in a closed tube. The x-ray pattern shows only slight intensity differences from that of molybdenite.
3. The unidentified cleavage noted by Wells and Butler (1917) is probably {0001}, by analogy with molybdenite.
4. Calculated by Wells and Butler (1917) from measurements on an impure sample.
5. Defacqz, *Ann. chim. phys.*, **22** [7], 239 (1901), at 10°, on artificial material from the fusion of potassium carbonate, sulfur and tungsten trioxide.
6. Ramdohr, *Zbl. Min.*, 199, 1937.
7. Mellor (**11**, 856, 1931).

297 KRENNERITE GROUP AX_2

				$a\ :b:\ c$	
2971	Krennerite	Au_8Te_{16}	Orthorhombic	$0.5323:1:0.2699$	
2972	Calaverite	Au_2Te_4	Monoclinic	$1.6298:1:1.1492$	$\beta\ 90°08'$
2973	Sylvanite	$Ag_2Au_2Te_8$	Monoclinic	$1.9778:1:1.9913$	$\beta\ 110°49\frac{1}{2}$

The members of the group are similar in chemical and physical properties. Certain crystallographic similarities are evident when the three minerals are appropriately oriented. If the b-axes of calaverite[1] and sylvanite are brought into coincidence, the a- and c-axes of one are related to those of the other as the principal diagonals are to the axial directions. Also, if the c-axis of krennerite is brought into coincidence with the b-axis of sylvanite, then the a-axes of the two are approximately the same length, but the b-axis of krennerite assumes a rather complex relationship to the principal directions in the other minerals.[2] Striking similarities in the x-ray dimensions are shown by the b-axis in sylvanite and calaverite, as compared with the c-axis of krennerite, as follows.

Krennerite — c_0	4.45 Å
Calaverite — b_0	4.40
Sylvanite — b_0	4.48

Complex twinning is found in calaverite and sylvanite, but not in krennerite; a perfect cleavage is easily developed in sylvanite and krennerite, but no cleavage is found in calaverite. These crystallographic criteria enable one to distinguish between the three minerals. In addition, the considerable differences between the specific gravities of these species serve as a good basis of identification.

Sylvanite contains Au and Ag in almost equal atomic proportions; the other two minerals are essentially gold tellurides with subordinate amounts of Ag.

Ref.

1. The complexities of the calaverite morphology are discussed briefly under that species; the crystallographic elements of the simple calaverite lattice are here considered in the comparison.

2. The relationship may be expressed more precisely by the following transformations.

Krennerite to calaverite	$\frac{2}{3}\frac{\bar{1}}{4}0/001/\frac{1}{3}\frac{\bar{1}}{4}0$
Sylvanite to calaverite	$\frac{1}{2}0\frac{1}{2}/010/\frac{1}{2}0\frac{1}{2}$
Krennerite to sylvanite	$100/001/\frac{\bar{1}}{3}\frac{1}{2}0$
Calaverite to sylvanite	$101/010/101$
Calaverite to krennerite	$101/\frac{4}{3}0\frac{\bar{8}}{3}/010$
Sylvanite to krennerite	$100/\frac{\bar{2}}{3}0\bar{2}/010$

2971 **KRENNERITE** [$AuTe_2$]. Krennerit *vom Rath* (*Ak. Berlin, Ber.*, 292, 1877; *Zs. Kr.*, **1**, 614, 1877; **2**, 252, 1878). Bunsenin *Krenner* (*Termész. Fuzetek*, **1**, 636, 1877; *Ann. Phys.*, **1**, 637, 1877). Müllerine pt. *Schrauf* (*Zs. Kr.*, **2**, 235, 1878).

Cryst. Orthorhombic; dipyramidal — $2/m\ 2/m\ 2/m$.

$a:b:c = 0.5323:1:0.2699$;[1] $p_0:q_0:r_0 = 0.5070:0.2699:1$

$q_1:r_1:p_1 = 0.5323:1.9724:1$; $r_2:p_2:q_2 = 3.7051:1.8785:1$

Forms:[2]

		ϕ	$\rho = C$	ϕ_1	$\rho_1 = A$	ϕ_2	$\rho_2 = B$
c	001	.....	0°00′	0°00′	90°00′	90°00′	90°00′
b	010	0°00′	90 00	90 00	90 00	.....	0 00
a	100	90 00	90 00	.....	0 00	0 00	90 00
n	120	43 12½	90 00	90 00	46 47½	0 00	43 12½
m	110	61 58	90 00	90 00	28 02	0 00	61 58
h	021	0 00	28 21½	28 21½	90 00	90 00	61 38½
τ	061	0 00	58 18½	58 18½	90 00	90 00	31 41½
e	101	90 00	26 53	0 00	63 07	63 07	90 00
d	201	90 00	45 24	0 00	44 36	44 36	90 00
u	111	61 58	29 52½	15 06½	63 55	63 07	76 28
t	221	61 58	48 57½	28 21½	48 15½	44 36	69 14½
o	121	43 12½	36 31½	28 21½	65 57½	63 07	64 17½
i	131	32 03	43 41½	39 00	68 29½	63 07	54 10
p	141	25 09½	50 01½	47 11½	70 59½	63 07	46 04

Less common:

f	160	*S*	320	Π	051	*δ*	403	*ψ*	232	*R*	251
L	150	*j*	210	*π*	081	*ε*	302	*ζ*	151	*F*	341
k	140	*J*	310	*ν*	0·10·1	*G*	502	*E*	161	*D*	351
l	130	*μ*	012	*P*	0·14·1	*q*	301	*ξ*	181	*β*	421
z	250	*H*	023	*λ*	0·18·1	*s*	401	*φ*	463	*γ*	451
M	5·12·0	*g*	011	*α*	103	*w*	112	*r*	211		
N	230	*ω*	0·10·3	*M*	102	*v*	331	*x*	231		
σ	340	*ρ*	041	*θ*	504	*χ*	212	*y*	241		

Structure cell.[3] Space group *Pma*; a_0 16.51, b_0 8.80, c_0 4.45, all ± 0.03; $b_0:a_0:c_0 = 0.533:1:0.270$; contains $(Au,Ag)_8Te_{16}$.

Habit. Usually short prismatic [001]; vertical zone striated [001]; terminations striated with the trace of {010}.

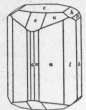

P h y s. Cleavage {001} perfect.[4] Fracture subconchoidal to uneven. Brittle. H. 2–3. G. 8.62. Luster metallic. Color silver-white to light brass-yellow (when tarnished?). Opaque. In polished section[5] creamy white in color, with strong anisotropism and weak pleochroism.

C h e m.[6] Essentially a ditelluride of gold, $AuTe_2$, with Ag reported present up to $3Ag : 8Au$ (anal. 4).

Cripple Creek, Colo.

Anal.

	1	2	3	4	5	6
Au	43.59	43.86	34.77	30.7	36.19	35.1
Ag	.....	0.46	5.87	6.3	4.87	5.4
Te	56.41	55.68	58.60	....	58.50	....
Rem.	......	......	1.58	....	0.14	....
Total	100.00	100.00	100.82	....	99.70	....
G.	9.23		8.3533		8.62	

1. $AuTe_2$. 2. Cripple Creek. Recalc. after deduction of 1.21 insol.[7] 3. Nagyág, Transylvania. Rem. is 0.65Sb, 0.34Cu, 0.59Fe.[8] 4. Kalgoorlie, Western Australia. Partial analysis.[9] 5. Moose mine, Cripple Creek. Rem. is 0.09 insol., 0.05Fe.[10] 6. Moose mine, Cripple Creek. Partial analysis.[10]

O c c u r. Rarer than sylvanite and calaverite, but having the same mode of occurrence and association. Found at Nagyág, Transylvania, associated with quartz and pyrite. At Kalgoorlie and Mulgabbie, Western Australia, associated with calaverite, coloradoite, and other tellurides. In the United States at Cripple Creek, Teller County, Colorado, with calaverite. In Canada in Montbray Township, Rouyn district, Quebec.

A l t e r. Alters to metallic gold.

N a m e. In honor of the Hungarian mineralogist, Joseph A. Krenner (1839–1920).

MÜLLERINE. *Beudant* (**2**, 541, 1832). Gelberz *Karsten* (56, 1800). Weisstellur, Weisserz *Petz* (*Ann. Phys.*, **57**, 473, 1842).

A white to brass-yellow telluride from Nagyág, Transylvania, occurring in bladed foliated forms, cleavable and massive. Analyses[11] show 2–8 per cent Sb, 2–19 per cent Pb and were unquestionably made on nonhomogeneous material. Early referred to sylvanite,[12] but later made identical with krennerite.[13]

Ref.

1. Elements of Palache and Wolfe (priv. comm., 1936), derived from numerous old and new measurements. The morphological elements are related to the x-ray elements of Tunell and Ksanda, *Washington Ac. Sc., J.*, **26**, 507 (1936), by the transformation: 010/100/001, and to the original elements of vom Rath, *Ak. Berlin, Ber.*, 292, 1877 — *Zs. Kr.*, **1**, 614 (1897), as follows: vom Rath to Palache and Wolfe 010/200/001.
2. Goldschmidt (**2**, 49, 1918). Palache and Wolfe (1936) have observed the new forms *z G H P E* on crystals from Cripple Creek.
3. Tunell and Ksanda (1936) on crystals from Cripple Creek.
4. Short, *Am. Min.*, **22**, 667 (1937) found two sets of lineations (" etch cleavage "), at right angles, developed by etching on sections ∥ {001}.

5. Short (1937) and Ramdohr, *Zbl. Min.*, 206; 1937.
6. For a discussion of composition, and relation to muthmannite, see Zambonini, *Zs. Kr.*, **49**, 246 (1911).
7. Myers anal. in Chester, *Am. J. Sc.*, **5**, 377 (1898).
8. Sipöcz, *Zs. Kr.*, **11**, 210 (1885).
9. Stillwell, *Australasian Inst. Mining Met., Proc.*, **34**, 155 (1931).
10. K. J. Murata anal., U. S. Geol. Sur. laboratories (priv. comm., 1939); material used prepared from crystals verified by G. Tunell, who also measured the specific gravity.
11. Dana (104, 1892).
12. Petz *Ann. Phys.*, **57**, 473 (1842).
13. Schrauf, *Zs. Kr.*, **2**, 235 (1878); Krenner, *Ann. Phys.*, **1**, 637 (1877).

SPECULITE. *Liveing (Eng. Mining J.*, **75**, 814, 1903).

A telluride of gold and silver from the Lake View Consols mine, Kalgoorlie, Western Australia. Color white with reddish hue, perfect cleavage, G. 8.64. Partial analyses gave Au 36.1, 36.6 and Ag 3.50, 4.45. Probably krennerite.

2972 **C A L A V E R I T E** [AuTe$_2$]. *Genth (Am. J. Sc.*, **45**, 314, 1868). Coolgardite pt. *Carnot (C.R.*, **132**, 1298, 1901; *Bull. soc. min.*, **24**, 357, 1901).

C r y s t.[1] Monoclinic; prismatic — $2/m$.

$$a : b : c = 1.6298 : 1 : 1.1492;^1 \quad p_0 : q_0 : r_0 = 0.7051 : 1.1492 : 1$$
$$r_2 : p_2 : q_2 = 0.8702 : 0.6136 : 1; \quad \beta \ 90°08', \quad \mu \ 89°52'$$

Forms:[2]

S forms:		ϕ_2	ρ_2	A	C
c	001	89°52'	90°00'	89°52'	0°00'
b	010	.....	0 00	90 00	90 00
a	100	0 00	90 00	0 00	89 52
m	110	0 00	31 32	58 28	89 56
A	304	62 01	90 00	62 01	27 51
E	801	10 03	90 00	10 03	79 49
f	112	70 28	61 34	72 54	33 57½
p	111	54 43	46 50	65 05	53 23½
w	Ī11	−54 54	46 46	55 14	126 31
C$_1$ forms:					
C		−38 42	8 02	83 44½	95 00
B		−57 20	90 00	57 20	147 12
q		32 40	15 42	76 50	81 34½
o		47 09	28 05	71 19½	69 46
y		−101 08	30 20	95 36	119 43
u		−53 02	30 58	71 58½	114 14
r		114 55	18 29	97 40½	73 18½
v		81 51	38 19	84 57½	52 07½
M		−83 35	43 58	85 33	133 36½
t		−155 52	23 20	111 11½	99 22
C$_2$ forms:					
x		−38 42	23 04	72 11½	104 08½
C$_0$ forms:					
μ		9 56	11 40	78 30½	87 58½
CC$_2$ forms:					
Λ		−7 03	90 00	7 03	96 55

Structure cell.[3] Space group $C2/m$ or $C2$; a_0 7.18, b_0 4.40, c_0 5.07, all $\pm$ 0.03; β 90° $\pm$ 30′; $a_0 : b_0 : c_0 = 1.632 : 1 : 1.152$; contains Au_2Te_4.

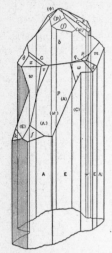

Habit. In bladed or lathlike crystals and short to slender prisms [010], strongly striated [010]. Also massive, granular to indistinctly crystalline.

Twinning.[4] (*a*) On {101} with prismatic axes parallel; (*b*) on {310} with prismatic axes making an angle of 122°58′; (*c*) on {111} with the prismatic axes at 93°40′.

P h y s. Cleavage none.[5] Fracture subconchoidal to uneven. Very brittle. H. $2\frac{1}{2}$–3. G. 9.24 $\pm$ 0.2;[6] 9.31 (calc.). M.P. 464°.[7] Luster metallic. Color brass-yellow to silver-white. Streak yellowish to greenish gray. Opaque. In polished section[8] creamy white in color; distinct anisotropism and weak pleochroism. Reflection percentages:[9] green 56.5, orange 54, red 52.5.

C h e m. A ditelluride of gold, $AuTe_2$. Ag frequently replaces the Au in small part, with Ag : Au = 1 : 4 as the largest reported ratio.

Cripple Creek, Colo.

Anal.

	1	2	3	4	5	6	7	8
Au	43.59	42.77	42.15	41.90	41.66	41.37	40.99	39.17
Ag	.....	0.40	0.60	0.79	0.77	0.58	1.74	3.23
Te	56.41	[56.75]	57.00	56.93	57.87	57.27	[57.25]	57.60
Rem.	.....	0.08	.....	.....	.....	.....	0.02	.....
Total	100.00	100.00	99.75	99.62	100.30	99.22	100.00	100.00
G.	9.31	9.388	9.314	9.163	9.148	9.311	9.328	9.0

1. $AuTe_2$. 2. Cripple Creek, Colo.[11] Rem. is insol. 3. Kalgoorlie, Western Australia.[12] 4. Cripple Creek, Colo.[13] 5. Cripple Creek, Colo.[14] 6. Kalgoorlie, Western Australia.[15] 7. Cripple Creek, Colo.[16] Rem. is insol. 8. Cripple Creek, Colo.[17] Recalc. after deducting 0.33 insol., 0.12 Fe_2O_3.

Tests. F. 1. On charcoal fuses with a bluish green flame, yielding globules of metallic gold; on cooling, the globules sometimes exhibit recalescence. Decomposed by aqua regia with the separation of a small amount of AgCl, and by hot concentrated H_2SO_4 with the separation of metallic gold and the formation of a red solution.

O c c u r. Usually in low-temperature veins; also in moderate- to high-temperature veins, but deposited toward the lower-temperature limit for the deposit in which it occurs.

From Kalgoorlie, Western Australia, in important amounts in veinlets cutting quartz veins, associated with altaite, coloradoite, krennerite, rickardite, and other tellurides, pyrite, tetrahedrite-tennantite, and other sulfides in small amounts, and gold; also at Mulgabbie. Reported from Antamok, Mountain Province, Philippine Islands. In the United States, in California from the Melones and Stanislaus mines, Carson Hill, Calaveras County; also reported from the Darling mine, near American Flats,

El Dorado County. In Colorado at Cripple Creek, Teller County, in low-temperature veins as the important ore mineral and as fine crystals, associated with chalcedonic quartz, fluorite, celestite, and small amounts of pyrite, stibnite, and other sulfides; also from the Gold Hill and Magnolia districts, Boulder County; reported from Lake City, Hinsdale County. In Canada in the Kirkland Lake and Boston Creek areas, Ontario.

A l t e r. Alters to spongy or porous, loosely coherent pseudomorphs of gold.

A r t i f.[18] The artificial compound, $AuTe_2$, has been recognized in the fusion system Au-Te, but attempts to synthesize the compound from solution have been unsuccessful.

N a m e. From the occurrence in Calaveras County, California, at the Stanislaus mine.

COOLGARDITE. *Carnot (C.R.,* **132**, 1298, 1901; *Bull. soc. min.,* **24**, 357, 1901). A supposed sesquitelluride of Au, Ag, and Hg, $(Au,Ag,Hg)_2Te_3$, from Kalgoorlie, Western Australia. The material was shown[19] to be a mixture principally of calaverite, coloradoite, and sylvanite.

Ref.

1. Orientation and unit of Penfield and Ford, *Am. J. Sc.,* **12**, 227 (1901), and angles of Goldschmidt, Palache, and Peacock, *Jb. Min., Beil.-Bd.,* **63**, 1 (1931); holohedral symmetry by Peacock from morphology (in Tunell and Ksanda, *Washington Ac. Sc., J.,* **25**, 32 [1935]); the structural study of Tunell and Ksanda reached the same conclusion. The elements are the so-called " S-elements " of Goldschmidt, Palache, and Peacock (1931). (They are not, however, directly comparable with the elements here adopted for sylvanite, but with the Schrauf, *Zs. Kr.,* **2**, 211 [1878], setting.) The large number of forms developed on calaverite which bear no simple relation to these elements have been the subject of much study and speculation. For crystallographic studies on this subject, see, in particular, Penfield and Ford (1901), Smith, *Min. Mag.,* **13**, 149 (1902), Goldschmidt, Palache, and Peacock (1931), Peacock, *Am. Min.,* **17**, 317 (1932), Donnay, *Soc. géol. Belgique, Ann.,* **58**, 222 (1935), and Tunell and Ksanda, *Washington Ac. Sc., J.,* **26**, 509 (1936). Borchert, *Jb. Min., Beil.-Bd.,* **61**, 106 (1930); **69**, 466 (1935), has studied calaverite and the other tellurides in polished section and in their thermal relations, with the conclusion that calaverite is the high-temperature modification of krennerite, and therefore a paramorph. Tunell and Ksanda (1936) reject this hypothesis on the basis of x-ray and polished section studies. The " adventive diffraction spots " of Tunell and Ksanda (1936) are not due to planes of the structural lattice, and only a few of these spots can be correlated with the " C-forms " of Goldschmidt, Palache, and Peacock (1931).
2. The most frequently observed forms of Goldschmidt, Palache, and Peacock (1931). The form symbol is omitted from the " C-forms," i.e., those forms which are not simply related to the lattice for which the elements have been calculated. Less common, rare, and uncertain forms are to be found in the paper of Goldschmidt, Palache, and Peacock (1931). The angle table departs from the usual form in order to facilitate comparison of the complex forms, with the usual method of measurement of a prismatically developed mineral on the two-circle goniometer.
3. On the basis of the morphology, the space group $C2$ is eliminated, according to Peacock (in Tunell and Ksanda [1935]).
4. Donnay (1935) discusses the twinning from the Friedel point of view.
5. Short, *Am. Min.,* **22**, 668 (1937), reports an etch cleavage.
6. An average of seven published determinations on analyzed material.
7. Pellini and Quercigh, *Acc. Linc., Rend.,* **19** [2], 445 (1910).
8. Short (1937); Schneiderhöhn and Ramdohr (**2**, 326, 1931).
9. Schneiderhöhn and Ramdohr (1931).
10. For additional analyses see Dana (105, 1892) and Doelter (**2** [1], 880, 1926).
11. Penfield and Ford (1901).

12. McIvor in Simpson, *Western Australia Geol. Sur. Bull. 42*, 107 (1912).
13. Prior, *Min. Mag.*, **13**, 149 (1902).
14. Prior (1902).
15. Simpson (1912).
16. Penfield and Ford (1901).
17. Hillebrand, *Am. J. Sc.*, **50**, 128, 426 (1895).
18. Mellor (**11**, 48, 1931).
19. Spencer, *Min. Mag.*, **13**, 282 (1903).

2973   **S Y L V A N I T E** [(Ag,Au)Te$_2$]. Weissgolderz *von Reichenstein* (*Phys. Arb. Wien*, **3**, 48, 1785). Or blanc d'Offenbanya, ou graphique, Aurum graphicum *von Born* (**2**, 467, 1790). Prismatisches weisses Golderz *von Fichtel* (**2**, 108, 1791; 124, 1794). Aurum bismuticum *Schmeisser* (**2**, 28, 1795). Schrifterz *Esmark* (*Bergm. J.*, **2**, 10, 1798); *Werner* (1800). Sylvane graphique *Brochant* (1800). Tellure ferrifère et aurifère *Haüy* (1801). Schrift-Tellur *Hausmann* (1813). Graphic Tellurium *Aikin* (1814). Goldtellur. Tellure auro-argenitifère *Haüy* (1822). Sylvane *Beudant* (1832). Sylvanite *Necker* (1835). Aurotellurite *Dana* (390, 1837). Tellursilberblende. Tellurgoldsilber. Sylvanite, Oro-graphico, Sylvanografico *Ital.* Oro gráfico, Metal escrito *Span.* Goldschmidtite *Hobbs* (*Am. J. Sc.*, **7**, 357, 1899).

C r y s t. Monoclinic; prismatic — $2/m$.

$a : b : c = 1.9778 : 1 : 1.9913; \ \beta \ 110°49\frac{1}{2}';^1 \ p_0 : q_0 : r_0 = 1.0068 : 1.8611 : 1$

$r_2 : p_2 : q_2 = 0.5373 : 0.5410 : 1; \mu \ 69°10\frac{1}{2}'; \ p_0' \ 1.0772, \ q_0' \ 1.9913; \ x_0' \ 0.3804$

Forms:^{2}

		ϕ	ρ	ϕ_2	$\rho_2 = B$	C	A
c	001	90°00′	20°49½′	69°10½′	90°00′	0°00′	69°10½′
b	010	0 00	90 00	......	0 00	90 00	90 00
a	100	90 00	90 00	0 00	90 00	69 10½	0 00
m	110	28 24½	90 00	0 00	28 24½	80 15½	61 35½
r	210	47 15	90 00	0 00	47 15	74 52	42 45
t	310	58 21½	90 00	0 00	58 21½	72 23	31 38½
ρ	012	20 54½	46 49½	69 10½	47 03½	42 56½	74 55
σ	011	10 49	63 44½	69 10½	28 15	61 45	80 18½
J	101	90 00	55 33	34 27	90 00	34 43½	34 27
N	$\bar{1}03$	−90 00	1 13½	88 46½	90 00	19 36½	88 46½
j	$\bar{1}01$	−90 00	34 52	124 52	90 00	55 41½	124 52
ν	$\bar{3}01$	−90 00	70 40½	160 40½	90 00	91 30	160 40½
Y	112	42 42½	53 34½	47 25	53 45½	41 29½	56 55½
d	111	36 12	67 56½	34 27	41 35½	56 56	56 48½
M	$\bar{1}11$	−19 17	64 38½	124 52	31 28	72 53½	107 23
y	211	51 51	72 46	21 32	53 50½	57 03	41 19
ζ	$\bar{2}11$	−41 42	69 26½	150 35½	45 38½	83 52½	128 31½
D	$\bar{3}21$	−35 36	78 27½	160 40½	37 11	90 54½	124 46½
Δ	$\bar{1}23$	0 55	44 51	58 12½	55 37	35 37½	65 00½
K	121	20 06	76 44	34 27	23 56	70 31½	70 27½
f	$\bar{2}12$	−34 59	50 33	124 52	50 45½	64 07	116 16½

Less common:

θ	320	Γ	014	l	501	λ	$\bar{1}13$	z	323	ϕ	$\bar{3}27$	χ	$\bar{5}27$	h	$\bar{4}14$	ϵ	$\bar{4}12$	v	$\bar{4}21$
γ	410	τ	013	G	$\bar{1}05$	I	$\bar{1}12$	k	311	Φ	$\bar{3}47$	g	$\bar{3}14$	e	$\bar{3}13$	F	$\bar{7}43$
δ	510	L	105	Υ	115	p	$\bar{2}21$	P	321	π	$\bar{1}22$	Z	$\bar{7}17$	A	$\bar{3}23$	u	$\bar{5}12$
β	610	X	201	ψ	113	ξ	125	w	711	i	$\bar{3}25$	U	$\bar{6}16$	R	121	χ	$\bar{3}11$
α	810	n	301	T	$\bar{1}15$	x	212	Ξ	$\bar{1}33$	μ	$\bar{2}13$	S	$\bar{5}15$	s	$\bar{3}12$	η	$\bar{4}11$

Structure cell.[3] Space group $P2/c$; a_0 8.94, b_0 4.48, c_0 14.59, all $\pm$ 0.02; β 145°26' $\pm$ 20'; $a_0 : b_0 : c_0 = 1.995 : 1 : 3.257$; contains $Au_2Ag_2Te_8$.

Habit. Short prismatic [001]; thick tabular {100}, {010}; short prismatic [010]. Often skeletal; also bladed and imperfectly columnar to granular.

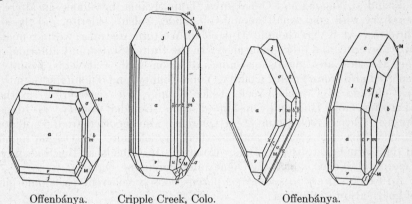

| Offenbánya. | Cripple Creek, Colo. | Offenbánya. |

Twinning.[4] Twin plane {100} common, as simple contact twins, lamellar twins, or penetration twins giving arborescent forms resembling written characters and crossing at 69°44', rarely at 55°08' or nearly at 90°.

P h y s. Cleavage {010} perfect. Fracture uneven. Brittle. H. $1\frac{1}{2}$–2. G. 8.161;[5] 8.11 (calc.[6]). Luster metallic, brilliant. Color and streak pure steel-gray to silver-white, inclining to yellow. In polished section[7] creamy white; strongly pleochroic and strongly anisotropic; shows polysynthetic twinning. Reflection percentages: green 57, orange 48, red 46.

C h e m. A ditelluride of gold and silver, $(Au,Ag)Te_2$. In most analyses Au : Ag is close to 1 : 1, but Au is sometimes present in considerable excess of this ratio (anals. 5, 6).

Anal.[8]

	1	2	3	4	5	6
Au	24.19	25.45	25.87	26.09	28.55	29.85
Ag	13.22	13.94	11.90	12.49	9.76	9.18
Te	62.59	60.61	62.45	60.82	60.83	60.45
Rem.	.....	.....	0.50	2.21	0.82	0.25
Total	100.00	100.00	100.72	101.61	99.96	99.73
G.	8.11		8.0733	8.161		

1. $AuAgTe_4$. 2. Cripple Creek, Colo.[9] Au : Ag = 1 : 1. 3. Offenbánya, Transylvania.[10] Au : Ag = 1.19 : 1. Rem. is 0.10 Cu and 0.40 Fe. 4. Cripple Creek, Colo.[11] Au : Ag = 1.14 : 1. Rem. is 1.19 Fe and 1.02 insol. 5. Coolgardie gold field, Western Australia.[12] Au : Ag = 1.60 : 1. Rem. is 0.32 Cu, 0.06 Fe, 0.10 Ni, 0.20 Se, 0.09 S and 0.05 insol. 6. Kalgoorlie, Western Australia.[13] Au : Ag = 1.78 : 1. Rem. is 0.15 Cu, 0.10 Ni.

Tests. F. 1. B.B. on charcoal fuses to a dark gray globule, and gives reactions for Te; on continued heating yields a malleable metallic bead, but less readily than calaverite. Decomposed by HNO_3 with the separation of rusty colored gold.

Occur.[14] Usually in low-temperature veins; also in moderate to high-temperature veins, but deposited toward the lower-temperature limit for the deposit in which it occurs. Associated with calaverite, krennerite, altaite, and other tellurides, pyrite and other sulfides in small amounts, gold, quartz, chalcedony, fluorite, and carbonates.

Found at Nagyág and Offenbánya, Transylvania, in veinlets in altered porphyry with gold, small amounts of sulfides, calcite, siderite, and rhodochrosite. At Kalgoorlie and Mulgabbie, Western Australia, with krennerite, calaverite, and other tellurides. In the United States, in California at the Melones and Stanislaus mines, Carson Hill, Calaveras County; reported also from Trinity County, Yuba County, and Tuolumne County. In Colorado at Cripple Creek, Teller County, with calaverite; in the Magnolia, Gold Hill, and Sunshine districts, Boulder County; at Idaho Springs, Clear Creek County; at Querida; also reported from La Plata County, Hinsdale County, and elsewhere in Colorado. In Oregon found in the Cornucopia district, Baker County. In Canada at Bigstone Bay, Lake of the Woods, and at the Dome mine, Porcupine, Ontario.

Alter. Alters to spongy or porous, loosely coherent pseudomorphs of gold; also to tellurite.

Name. From Transylvania, the country in which it was first found, and in allusion to *sylvanium*, one of the names first proposed for the metal tellurium. Called *graphic tellurium, graphic gold, schrifterz*, etc. because of a resemblance in the arrangement of the crystals to written characters.

GOLDSCHMIDTITE. *Hobbs* (*Am. J. Sc.*, **7**, 357, 1899). Shown[15] to be crystallographically the same as sylvanite, and the name was withdrawn (by Hobbs). A later analysis[16] of crystals from Cripple Creek gave Te 65.97, Au 24.25, Ag 8.68 per cent = 98.90. On the strength of this analysis it has been suggested that goldschmidtite be restored as a species with the composition $(Au,Ag)_2Te_5$. This is unjustified.

Ref.

1. Orientation and unit of Peacock (priv. comm., 1937); elements of Schrauf, *Zs. Kr.*, **2**, 211 (1878), on crystals from Offenbánya. Tunell and Ksanda, *Am. Min.*, **22**, 728 (1937), take another orientation for the x-ray cell, which is, however, less suitable than that of Peacock for morphological discussion. The Schrauf orientation (body-centered lattice), however, is the one to be compared with the accepted calaverite elements. Transformations: Schrauf to Peacock 101/010/$\bar{1}$01. Tunell and Ksanda to Peacock 101/010/100.

2. Goldschmidt (**8**, 102, 1922). Uncertain forms: 120, 230, 032, 021, 102, 123, 214, 142, 725, 523, 241, 331.

3. Tunell and Ksanda (1937).

4. Spencer, *Min. Mag.*, **13**, 271 (1903), records indications of twinning on a plane of the zone [010].

5. Palache, *Am. J. Sc.*, **10**, 419 (1900) on crystals from Cripple Creek.

6. Calculated for Au : Ag = 1 : 1.5, if Au : Ag = 1 : 1, then G. = 8.11. The former ratio is close to the values found by analysis.

7. Short (1937), and Schneiderhöhn and Ramdohr (**2**, 324, 1931). Also Martin, *C. R.*, **204**, 589 (1937), and Fastré, *C. R.*, **196**, 630 (1933).

8. For additional analyses see Doelter (**2** [1], 875, 1926).

9. Pearce, *Colorado Sc. Soc., Proc.*, **5**, 11 (1894).

10. Sipöcz, *Zs. Kr.*, **11**, 210 (1886).

11. Palache (1900).

12. Wölbling anal. in Krusch, *Cbl. Min.*, 199, 1901.
13. Carnot, *Bull. soc. min.*, **24**, 356 (1901).
14. Lindgren, *Trans. Am. Inst. Mining Eng., Tech. Pub. 713*, 13 (1936), discusses the conditions of transportation and deposition of tellurides in natural solutions. See also Lindgren (491, 677, 1933).
15. Palache (1900).
16. Gastaldi, *Acc. Napoli, Rend.*, **17**, 22 (1911).

298   **M E L O N I T E** [$NiTe_2$].   *Genth* (*Am. J. Sc.*, **45**, 313, 1868).   Tellurnickel *Rammelsberg* (17, 1875).

C r y s t. Hexagonal ?
Habit. Hexagonal plates.   Often in indistinct foliated particles.

P h y s. Cleavage {0001} eminent. Flexible. H. 1–1$\frac{1}{2}$. G. 7.35 (aver.). Luster metallic. Color reddish white, tarnishing brown. Streak dark gray. In polished section[1] light rose-white; moderate anisotropism and weak pleochroism.

C h e m. Nickel ditelluride, $NiTe_2$.[2]
Anal.

	1	2	3
Ni	18.70	18.31	16.73
Co	.....		0.75
Te	81.30	80.75	80.17
Rem.	.....	0.86	1.33
Total	100.00	99.92	98.98
G.			7.36

1. $NiTe_2$. 2. Stanislaus mine, Calaveras Co., Calif. Rem. is Ag.[3] 3. Worturpa. Rem. is Fe. Contains about 3 per cent Se (in place of Te?) and traces of Ag, Au, Bi.[4]

Tests. B.B. in open tube affords a sublimate that fuses to colorless drops. On charcoal burns with a bluish flame. Soluble in HNO_3, giving a green color.

O c c u r. Found originally at the Melones mine, Carson Hill, Calaveras County, California; also found at the Stanislaus mine of the same region, associated with petzite, hessite, pyrite, and galena in quartz veins. Reported from Colorado from the Cresson mine, Cripple Creek, Teller County, and from Magnolia, Boulder County, as tiny crystals associated with gold and forming aggregates pseudomorphous after calaverite (?); the melonite crystals are oriented relative to the calaverite (?).   Found at Illinawortina, north of Worturpa, South Australia.

N a m e. After the Melones mine, where it was first found.

Ref.
1. Short (17, 1934) and Ramdohr, *Zbl. Min.*, **A**, 193, 1937, p. 200 for melonite. Short states that the mineral is strongly anisotropic, and Ramdohr considers it only moderately so.
2. The original formula, Ni_2Te_3, assigned by Genth (1868), is retained by Short (1934). Recent analyses, however, favor the ditelluride formula.
3. Hillebrand, *Am. J. Sc.*, **8**, 295 (1899).
4. Dieseldorff, *Cbl. Min.*, 168, 1901.

299   **Parkerite.**   *Scholtz* (*Geol. Soc. South Africa, Trans.*, **39**, 81, 1937, p. 86).

C r y s t. Monoclinic (?).   Shows lamellar twinning, the composition plane of which makes an angle of 50° with a cleavage.

P h y s. Cleavage in three directions, producing rhomboidal plates, with one cleavage better than the others. H. 2+. Luster metallic. In polished section creamy white and strongly anisotropic; shows multiple lamellar twinning.

C h e m. Nickel sulfide, Ni_2S_3 or NiS_3 (on the basis of a partial analysis on a few milligrams of material).

Tests. Dissolves readily with effervescence in 1 : 1 HNO_3.

O c c u r. Found in oxidized ore on mine dumps at Waterfall Gorge, Insizwa, East Griqualand, associated with cubanite, galena, chalcopyrite, niggliite, and a gold-silver-copper alloy.

N a m e. After Professor Robert Lüling Parker (1893–   ) of Zurich. Needs confirmation.[1]

Ref.

1. See Michener and Peacock, *Am. Min.*, **28**, 343 (1943).

Skutterudite Series

2·10·11 **S K U T T E R U D I T E** [(Co,Ni)As₃].   Tesseral-Kies,   Hartkobaltkies *Breithaupt* (*Ann. Phys.*, **9**, 115, 1827).   Arsenikkobaltkies *Scheerer* (*Ann. Phys.*, **42**, 553, 1837). Hartkobalterz *Hausmann* (69, 1847). Skutterudit *Haidinger* (560, 1845). Modumite *Nicol* (457, 1849). Tesseralkies *Germ.*

2·10·12 **S M A L T I T E** [(Co,Ni)As₃₋ₓ].   ? Cobaltum cineraceum *Agricola* (459, 1529).   Kobaltmalm, Koboltglants, Minera Cobalti cinerea, Cobaltum arsenico mineralisatum, pt. *Wallerius* (231, 1747).   ? Cobaltum Ferro et Arsenico mineralisatum, Glants-Cobalt (from Schneeberg) *Cronstedt* (212, 1758). Mine de Cobalt gris *de Lisle* (333, 1772). Mine de Cobalt arsenicale *de Lisle* (3, 123, 1783). Weisser Speisskobold, Grauer Speisskobold *Werner*. Gray Cobalt ore *Kirwan* (1796). Tinwhite cobalt. Speiskobalt *Hausmann* (155, 1813). Smaltine *Beudant* (**2**, 584, 1852).

2·10·13 **N I C K E L – S K U T T E R U D I T E** [(Ni,Co)As₃].   *Waller and Moses* (*Sch. Mines Q.*, 14, 49, 1892).

2·10·14 **C H L O A N T H I T E** [(Ni,Co)As₃₋ₓ]. *Breithaupt* (*Ann. Phys.*, **64**, 184, 1845). Weissnickelkies, Weissnickelerz pt., Weisser Kupfernickel, Arseniknickel *Rammelsberg*. Rammelsbergit *Haidinger* (560, 1845). Stängelkobalt *Breithaupt* (*Ann. Phys.*, **64**, 185, 1845).

C r y s t. Isometric; diploidal — $2/m\ \bar{3}$.

Forms:[1]

a{001}   d{011}   o{111}   ʹf{103}   n{112}   ʹs{213}*

* For Skutterudite only.

Structure cell.[2] Space group probably $Im3$; a_0 8.19 (skutterudite), 8.24 (smaltite); contains (Co,Ni)₈As₂₄.

Habit. Cubic, cubo-octahedral, or octahedral, modified by {011} and, rarely, pyritohedral forms; {001} frequently convex or warped; rarely prismatic; as reticular skeletal growths; in distorted aggregates of crystals. Also massive, dense to granular.

Twinning.[3] (*a*) Sixlings with twin plane and composition plane {112} (smaltite-chloanthite); often in complex and distorted shapes. (*b*) On {011} ? (skutterudite).

P h y s. Cleavage distinct on {001} and {111}, also {011} in traces. The cleavages are variable and not characteristic, and may in part be due to parting along zonal growths in the crystals. Fracture conchoidal to uneven. Brittle. H. $5\frac{1}{2}$–6. G. 6.5 ± 0.4.[4] Luster metallic to bright metallic. Color between tin-white and silver-gray; sometimes tarnished gray, or iridescent. Opaque. In polished section[5] isotropic, gray, creamy, or golden-white in color, with strong reflectivity. The crystals characteristically are zoned,[6] with the outer portions usually richer in As.[7] Reflection percentages:[8] green 60, orange 53.5, red 51 (skutterudite); green 58.5, orange 57.5, red 50 (smaltite-chloanthite). Thermoelectrically, both negative and positive varieties.[9]

C h e m.[10] Essentially cobalt and nickel arsenides, $(Co,Ni)As_{3-x}$; with skutterudite and nickel-skutterudite respectively near $(Co,Ni)As_{3-x}$ and $(Ni,Co)As_{3-x}$ (with $x = 0$ to 0.5); smaltite and chloanthite respectively $(Co,Ni)As_{3-x}$ and $(Ni,Co)As_{3-x}$ (with $x = 0.5$ to 1). Fe often substitutes for (Ni,Co), with about 12 per cent by weight as a maximum; Bi less frequently in significant amounts. S substitutes for the As in amounts less than 2 per cent by weight. Cu, Zn, Pb, Ag (up to 4 per cent) have been reported but are probably impurities.

Anal.

	1	2	3	4	5	6
Co	20.77	19.70	20.18	17.66	10.98	20.50
Ni	.....	.....	0.11	0.66	5.14	0.20
Fe	.....	2.80	1.84	3.56	5.82	0.95
As	79.23	76.41	76.38	75.70	75.30	75.15
S	.....	1.03	1.50	0.66	.....	1.18
Bi	.....	.....	.....	0.06	.....	.....
Rem.	.....	.....	.....	1.64	1.44	1.48
Total	100.00	99.94	100.01	99.94	98.68	99.46
G.			6.79			6.519

1. $CoAs_3$. 2. Skutterudite. Skutterud, Norway. Analysis recalculated after deduction of 5.63 SiO_2. Material homogeneous in polished section.[11] 3. Skutterudite. Temiskaming mine, Sudbury, Ont. Analysis made on relatively insoluble, arsenic-rich, residue obtained by leaching zoned crystals in HNO_3.[12] 4. Skutterudite. Keeley mine, South Lorrain, Ont. Rem. is 1.64 insol.[13] 5. Skutterudite. Horace Porter mine, Gunnison Co., Colo. Rem. is 1.44 insol.[14] 6. Skutterudite. Frontier mine, northern Ontario. Rem. is 0.10 Cu, 0.16 CO_2, 1.22 insol.[15]

	7	8	9	10	11	12	13
Co	10.88	13.81	18.07	24.13	15.83	28.23	.....
Ni	9.41	11.35	1.02	1.23	15.07	.....	20.71
Fe	2.78	1.21	7.31	4.05	3.69	.....	.....
As	72.97	71.61	71.53	70.85	63.42	71.77	79.29
S	1.70	0.75	1.38	0.08	.....	.....	.....
Bi	1.31	.....	.....	.....	0.86	.....	.....
Rem.	0.58	0.96	0.01	0.41	0.32	.....	.....
Total	99.63	99.69	99.32	100.75	99.19	100.00	100.00
G.			6.11				

7. Skutterudite. Riechelsdorf, Hesse, Germany. Rem. is 0.58 insol.[16] 8. Smaltite. Foster mine, Cobalt, Ont. Rem. is 0.96 Cu. Analysis made on zoned crystal.[17] 9. Smaltite. Schneeberg, Saxony. Rem. is 0.01 Cu.[18] 10. Smaltite. Atacama. Rem. is 0.41 Cu.[19] 11. Smaltite. Schneeberg, Saxony. Rem. is 0.32 insol.[20] 12. $CoAs_2$. 13. $NiAs_3$.

	14	15	16	17	18	19
Co	5.95	3.69	7.78	2.30	4.5	6.28
Ni	12.89	12.01	12.94	19.89	15.2	14.49
Fe	3.06	5.07	1.04	0.47	3.5	5.20
As	78.10	77.94	76.78	75.78	75.4	73.55
S	.....	.....	1.67	0.61	.....	0.27
Bi	.....	.....	.....	0.16	.....	.....
Rem.	.....	.....	0.44	0.14	0.7	.....
Total	100.00	98.71	100.65	99.35	99.3	99.79
G.		6.32	6.551			

14. Nickel-skutterudite. Bullards Peak district near Silver City, Grant Co., N. Mex. Recalc. after deducting 4.56 SiO$_2$ and 8.38 Ag. S is present, but unreported.[21] 15. Nickel-skutterudite. Markirch, Alsace. Stated to be homogeneous.[22] 16. Nickel-skutterudite. Oravicza, Roumania. Rem. is 0.44 insol. Analysis made on zoned crystal.[23] 17. Nickel-skutterudite. Schneeberg, Saxony. Rem. is 0.01 Pb and 0.13 SiO$_2$.[24] 18. Nickel-skutterudite. Schneeberg, Saxony. Rem. is 0.7 Cu.[25] 19. Chloanthite. Schneeberg, Saxony.[26]

	20	21	22	23	24
Co	3.62	.....	13.70	3.82	11.72
Ni	21.18	28.15	.....	9.44	1.81
Fe	2.83	.....	3.71	11.85	5.26
As	71.47	71.85	61.59	70.11	74.52
S	0.58	.....	0.05	4.78	1.81
Bi	.....	.....	20.17	.....	3.60
Rem.	0.29	.....	0.85	.....	1.00
Total	99.97	100.00	100.07	100.00	99.72
G.	6.89		6.92		6.807

20. Chloanthite. Schneeberg, Saxony. Rem. is 0.29 Cu.[27] 21. NiAs$_2$. 22. Bismutosmaltite. Zschorlau, near Schneeberg, Saxony. Rem. is 0.69 Cu and 0.16 Sb. The Cu occurs as chalcopyrite.[28] 23. Chathamite. Chatham, Conn.[29] 24. Cheleutite. Joachimstal, Bohemia. Rem. is 1.00 Cu.[30]

Var. Ferrian. Chathamite Shepard (*Am. J. Sc.*, 47, 351, 1844). Fe is frequently present in both the cobaltian and the nickelian species, in amounts up to 12 per cent. The name chathamite has been applied to a ferrian chloanthite.

Bismuthian. Wismuthkobalterz Kersten (*J. pr. Chem.*, 47, 265, 1826). Cheleutit Breithaupt (*Ann. Phys.*, 64, 184, 1845). Wismuthkobalterz, Kobaltwismutherz Haidinger (560, 1845). Kerstenit Breithaupt (207, 1849). Bismuth-skutterudite Ramsay (*J. Chem. Soc.*, 29, 153, 1892). Bismutosmaltin Frenzel (*Min. Mitt.*, 16, 525, 1896). Bi is often present, in amounts up to 4 per cent (cheleutite); a highly bismuthian variety (bismutosmaltite, anal. 22) has been reported but needs confirmation. Bismuth-skutterudite[31] is probably a mixture.

Tests. In C.T. gives a sublimate of metallic arsenic. In O.T. a white sublimate of As$_2$O$_3$ and sometimes traces of SO$_2$. B.B. on charcoal gives an arsenical odor and fuses to a magnetic globule. Soluble in HNO$_3$ with a red (Co) or green (Ni) solution.

Occur. The minerals of the series usually occur in moderate temperature veins together with other Co and Ni minerals, especially cobaltite and niccolite. Other commonly associated minerals include arsenopyrite, native silver and silver-sulfosalts, native bismuth, calcite, siderite, barite, and quartz.

Found in Norway at Skutterud, near Modum, as crystals (*skutterudite*) associated with cobaltite and titanite in fahlbands in gneiss; at Kongsberg. In Alsace at Markirch (*nickel-skutterudite*). At Wittichen in Baden (*smaltite*). At Bieber and Riechelsdorf in Hesse (*smaltite, chloanthite*). In Bohemia, at Joachimstal (*cheleutite*), Andreasberg (*chloanthite*), and at Přibram. In Saxony, in Co-Ni-Ag veins at Johanngeorgenstadt, Annaberg (*chloanthite*), Freiberg, and, in particular, at Schneeberg (*skutterudite, smaltite, nickel-skutterudite, cheleutite*); at Zschorlau, near Schneeberg (*bismutosmaltite*). In Styria at Schladming; in Carinthia at Lölling. At Dobschau, Hungary (*chloanthite*) with siderite and copper ores. In Switzerland, in the Turtmannthal, Wallis, in crystals (*skutterudite*) with arsenopyrite and siderite; in the Anniviersthal (*chloanthite*).

In Spain in the valley of Gistain, Huesca, Aragon, with niccolite in calcite veins, and in Huelva Province, with pyrite. In France, at Rioumanou, Hautes-Pyrénées, and at Mount Chalanches, Isère. Reported from Cornwall, England, in a number of mines (unanalyzed); at Coniston, Lancashire, with niccolite in calcite. At Talnotry, Kirkcudbrightshire, Scotland. From Punta Brava, Copiapó (*smaltite*), the Atacama region, and other localities in Chile. At Balmoral, in the Transvaal, South Africa. At Broken Hill, New South Wales; in Tasmania.

In the United States, found at Chatham (Great Hill, Cobalt), Connecticut (*chathamite*) in mica slate with arsenopyrite and sometimes niccolite. At Chester, Massachusetts. At Franklin, New Jersey, in the Trotter mine (*chloanthite*) in crystals and massive, with niccolite. From the Horace Porter mine, Gunnison County, Colorado (*skutterudite*); from the Bullards Peak district (*nickel-skutterudite*) near Silver City with arsenopyrite and silver, and from the Rose mine (*chloanthite*) in Grant County, in New Mexico. Reported from Mine La Motte, Missouri.

In Canada, at Cobalt, Ontario, the members of the series are found in important amounts in the silver veins, associated with niccolite, rammelsbergite, silver, calcite, and other species; also at South Lorrain, Gowganda, and Sudbury, in Ontario. From Hazelton, British Columbia, and Great Bear Lake, Northwest Territories.

Alter. The cobaltian species usually alter to erythrite, sometimes admixed with pitticite (*gelb Erdkobalt*) and arsenolite; earthy mixtures of Co, Ni, and Fe oxides (heterogenite, asbolite, etc.) develop as the final products of oxidation. The nickelian species alter to annabergite, sometimes with arsenolite. Pseudomorphs of siderite after chloanthite and of smaltite after barite have been noted.

Artif. Smaltite has been obtained in cubes by the action at high temperatures of hydrogen on a mixture of arsenic and cobalt chlorides.[32]

Name. Chloanthite, from χλοανθής, *becoming green*, in allusion to the green color of its alteration product (annabergite), in contrast to the rose-colored product (erythrite) afforded by smaltite. Smaltite, from its use as a source of the pigment, *smalt.*ʼ Skutterudite is from the locality, Skutterud, Norway, and chathamite from the locality, Chatham, Connecticut. Cheleutite, from χηλευτός, *twisted or entwined*, in allusion to the appearance of the crystal masses.

Ref.

1. Goldschmidt (**2**, 139, 1913; **8**, 60, 1922). Also Walker, *Am. Min.*, **6**, 54 (1921). Rare and uncertain forms: (Smaltite-chloanthite) {1·0·10}, {105}, {104}, {102}, {138}, {123}; (skutterudite){102}, {122}, {233}, {643}.
2. Oftedal, *Zs. Kr.*, **66**, 517 (1928). See also Ramsdell, *Am. Min.*, 10, 281 (1925), and Holmes (in Krieger, *Am. Min.*, **20**, 715 [1936]), on nickel-skutterudite from Bullards Peak, N. M.
3. vom Rath, *Zs. Kr.*, **1**, 8 (1878). For possible twinning of skutterudite see Fletcher, *Phil. Mag.*, **13**, 1 (1882).
4. The specific gravities given show no relation to the variation in composition, since most crystals are zoned and often, in part, altered. The published values are therefore questionable.
5. Schneiderhöhn and Ramdohr (**2**, 217, 224, 1931); Short (97, 99, 1931).
6. Schneiderhöhn and Ramdohr (1931); Beutell, *Cbl. Min.*, 180, 206, 1916; Florke, *Met. Erz*, 192, 1922.
7. Vollhardt, *Zs. Kr.*, **14**, 407 (1888); Thomson, *Univ. Toronto Stud., Geol. Ser.*, 37, 1931; Ellsworth, *Ontario Bur. Mines, Rep.*, **25**, pt. 1, 23, 1916.
8. Schneiderhöhn and Ramdohr (1931).
9. Groth, *Ann. Phys.*, **152**, 249 (1874).
10. Oftedal (1928) considers smaltite and chloanthite to be arsenic-deficient minerals identical in structure with skutterudite, which is essentially the triarsenide. His x-ray study has not shown, however, how this large variation in composition can be explained, since little change in the physical properties (especially the specific gravity) or the cell dimensions, have been noted. In addition, the well-known zoning (ref. 6) in the members of the series complicates structural and chemical studies, and little is known about the variations between the zones (ref. 7). For earlier theories on the constitution of these minerals see Doelter (5 [1], 748, 1926). For a spectroscopic study of smaltite and chloanthite see de Gramont, *Bull. soc. min.*, **18**, 279 (1895).
11. Samdahl, *Norsk Geol. Tidsskr.*, **8**, 68 (1925).
12. Thomson, *Univ. Toronto Stud., Geol. Ser.*, 37, 1921; *Am. Min.*, **6**, 55 (1921).
13. Todd anal. in Walker, *Univ. Toronto Stud., Geol. Ser.*, 49, 1925.
14. Fairchild anal. in Short (99, 1931).
15. Rickaby anal. in Walker (1925).
16. Beutell and Lorenz, *Cbl. Min.*, 364, 1915.
17. Ellsworth (1916).
18. McCay, *Zs. Kr.*, **9**, 608 (1884).
19. Smith anal. in Dana (88, 1892).
20. Fahey anal. in Short (1931).
21. Moses and Waller, *Sch. Mines. Q.*, **14**, 49 (1892).
22. Vollhardt (1888).
23. Graham anal. in Thomson, *Univ. Toronto Stud., Geol. Ser.*, 81, 1930.
24. Vollhardt (1888).
25. Fairchild anal. in Short (1931).
26. Lange anal. in Rammelsberg (23, 1860).
27. Marian anal. in Hintze (**1** [1], 811, 1901).
28. Frenzel, *Min. Mitt.*, **16**, 524 (1896).
29. Genth anal. in Dana (512, 1854).
30. Marian anal. in Hintze (1901).
31. Ramsay (in Dana [93, 1892]).
32. Durocher, *C. R.*, **32**, 823 (1851). Cobalt and nickel arsenides have also been obtained by the action of As vapor on metallic Co or Ni or on lower arsenides, but the material has not been shown to be identical with the natural substances. See Beutell and Lorenz, *Cbl. Min.*, **10**, 49 (1916), Vigouroux, *C. R.*, **147**, 426 (1908), and Mellor (**9**, 75, 78, 1929).

2·10·2 **Niggliite** [PtTe₃ ?]. *Scholtz (Geol. Soc. South Africa, Trans.*, **39**, 81, 1937).

P h y s. Cleavage none. Brittle. H. 3. G. 4. Color silver-white. In polished section shows high reflectivity; intense pleochroism in pale blue to bright cream; strong anisotropism.

C h e m. Possibly a platinum telluride of the composition PtTe₃. An approximate determination of Pt gave 34.8 per cent.[1] Fuses at a low red heat to a yellowish metallic globule.

O c c u r. Found in concentrates of the oxidized ore from the mine dumps at Waterfall Gorge, Insizwa, East Griqualand.

N a m e. After Professor P. Niggli (1888–   ) of Zurich.

Ref.

1. The determination was made on " . . . a fraction of a milligram "!

PATRONITE. *Hewett (Eng. Mining J.*, **82**, 385, 1906). Rizopatronite *Bravo (Informaciones y Memorias Soc. Eng., Lima*, **8**, 171, 1906). Patronite *Hillebrand (Am. J. Sc.*, **24**, 141, 1907).

The name was originally ascribed to an admitted mixture of vanadium-bearing substances, occurring as an 8-ft. layer, together with an asphalt layer, interbedded in shales. Later[1] a chemical extract of this material, of approximately the composition VS₄, was called patronite, but this was not shown to be a homogeneous substance. The inhomogeneous nature of the originally described material was verified in polished section.[2]

Occurs at Minas Ragra, near Cerro de Pasco, Peru.

Named after Antenor Rizo-Patrona, the discoverer of the ore.

Ref.

1. Hillebrand (1907).
2. Lindgren, Hamilton, and Palache, *Am. J. Sc.*, **3**, 200 (1922).

3 SULFOSALTS

31 $A_mB_nX_p$ TYPE $m + n : p > 4 : 3$

311	POLYBASITE GROUP	
3111	Polybasite	$(Ag,Cu)_{16}Sb_2S_{11}$
3112	Pearceite	$(Ag,Cu)_{16}As_2S_{11}$
312	Polyargyrite	$Ag_{24}Sb_2S_{15}$
313	ARGYRODITE SERIES	
3131	Argyrodite	Ag_8GeS_6
3132	Canfieldite	Ag_8SnS_6
314	Stephanite	Ag_5SbS_4
315	Epigenite	$(Cu,Fe)_5AsS_6?$

32 A_3BX_3 TYPE

321	RUBY SILVER GROUP	
3211	Pyrargyrite	Ag_3SbS_3
3212	Proustite	Ag_3AsS_3
3221	Pyrostilpnite	Ag_3SbS_3
3222	Stylotypite	$(Ag,Cu,Fe)_3SbS_3$
3223	Xanthoconite	Ag_3AsS_3
323	Wittichenite	$Cu_3BiS_3?$
324	TETRAHEDRITE SERIES	
3241	Tetrahedrite	$(Cu,Fe)_{12}Sb_4S_{13}$
3242	Tennantite	$(Cu,Fe)_{12}As_4S_{13}$
325	Goldfieldite	$Cu_{12}Te_3Sb_4S_{16}?$

33 A_3BX_4 TYPE

331	SULVANITE GROUP	
3311	Sulvanite	$Cu_3VS_4?$
3312	Germanite	$Cu_3GeS_4?$
3313	Colusite	$Cu_3(Sn,Te,Fe,V,As)S_4$
332	ENARGITE GROUP	
3321	Famatinite	Cu_3SbS_4
3322	Enargite	Cu_3AsS_4
333	Beegerite	$Pb_6Bi_2S_9$
334	Samsonite	$Ag_4MnSb_2S_6$

33 A_3BX_4 TYPE (*Continued*)

335	Geocronite	$Pb_5(Sb,As)_2S_8$
336	Gratonite	$Pb_9As_4S_{15}$
337	Lengenbachite	$Pb_6(Ag,Cu)_2As_4S_{13}$
338	Jordanite	$Pb_{14}As_7S_{24}$
339	Guitermanite	$Pb_{10}As_6S_{19}$
33·10	Goongarrite	
	Warthaite	
33·11	Meneghinite	$Pb_{13}Sb_7S_{23}$
33·12	Lillianite	$Pb_3Bi_2S_6$

34 A_2BX_3 TYPE

341	BOURNONITE GROUP	
3411	Bournonite	$PbCuSbS_3$
3412	Seligmannite	$PbCuAsS_3$
3413	Aikinite	$PbCuBiS_3$
342	Berthonite	$Pb_2Cu_7Sb_5S_{13}$
343	Diaphorite	$Pb_2Ag_3Sb_3S_8$
344	Freieslebenite	$Pb_3Ag_5Sb_5S_{12}$
345	Klaprothite	$Cu_6Bi_4S_9$?

35 ABX_2 TYPE WITH $A:B \sim 1:1$

351	Boulangerite	$Pb_5Sb_4S_{11}$ to $Pb_2Sb_2S_5$
352	Owyheeite	$Pb_5Ag_2Sb_6S_{15}$
353	Schirmerite	$PbAg_4Bi_4S_9$
354	Miargyrite	$AgSbS_2$
355	Aramayoite	$Ag(Sb,Bi)S_2$
356	Matildite	$AgBiS_2$
357	Smithite	$AgAsS_2$
358	Trechmannite	
359	CHALCOSTIBITE GROUP	
3591	Chalcostibite	$CuSbS_2$
3592	Emplectite	$CuBiS_2$
35·10	Lorandite	$TlAsS_2$
35·11	Teallite	$PbSnS_2$
35·12	Benjaminite	$Pb(Cu,Ag)Bi_2S_4$
35·13	Hammarite	$Pb_2Cu_2Bi_4S_9$?

36 $A_2B_2X_5$ TYPE WITH $A : B \sim 1 : 1$

361	Dufrenoysite	$Pb_2As_2S_5$
3621	Cosalite	$Pb_2Bi_2S_5$
3622	Kobellite	$Pb_2(Bi,Sb)_2S_5$
363	Franckeite	$Pb_5Sn_3Sb_2S_{14}$
364	Fizelyite	$Pb_5Ag_2Sb_8S_{18}$
365	Ramdohrite	$Pb_3Ag_2Sb_6S_{13}$
366	Wittite	$Pb_5Bi_6(S,Se)_{14}$
367	Jamesonite	$Pb_4FeSb_6S_{14}$
368	Rathite	$Pb_{13}As_{18}S_{40}$

37 $A_2B_3X_6$ TYPE WITH $A + B : X \sim 5 : 6$

371	ANDORITE GROUP	
3711	Andorite	$PbAgSb_3S_6$
3712	Lindstromite	$PbCuBi_3S_6$
372	Baumhauerite	$Pb_4As_6S_{13}$
373	Liveingite	$Pb_5As_8S_{17}$
374	PLAGIONITE GROUP	
3741	Fuloppite	$Pb_3Sb_8S_{15}$
3742	Plagionite	$Pb_5Sb_8S_{17}$
3743	Heteromorphite	$Pb_7Sb_8S_{19}$
3744	Semseyite	$Pb_9Sb_8S_{21}$

38 AB_2X_4 TYPE WITH $A : B \sim 1 : 2$

381	Hutchinsonite	$(Pb,Tl)_2(Cu,Ag)As_5S_{10}$
382	Rezbanyite	$Pb_3Cu_2Bi_{10}S_{19}$
383	Galenobismutite	$PbBi_2S_4$
384	Weibullite	$PbBi_2(S,Se)_4$
385	Platynite	$PbBi_2(Se,S)_3$
386	Chiviatite	$Pb_3Bi_8S_{15}$
387	Alaskaite	$Pb(Ag,Cu)_2Bi_4S_8?$
388	Zinkenite	$Pb_6Sb_{14}S_{27}$
389	Sartorite	$PbAs_2S_4$
38·10	Berthierite	$FeSb_2S_4$
38·11	Cylindrite	$Pb_3Sn_4Sb_2S_{14}$
38·12	Gladite	$PbCuBi_5S_9$
38·13	Vrbaite	$TlAs_2SbS_5$

39 AB_4X_7 TYPE

391	Livingstonite	$HgSb_4S_7$

3111   **P O L Y B A S I T E** [(Ag,Cu)₁₆Sb₂S₁₁]. Sprödglaserz pt. *Werner.* Polybasit
Rose (*Ann. Phys.*, 15, 573, 1829). Euganglanz *Breithaupt* (266, 1832).

C r y s t. Monoclinic; prismatic — $2/m.$[1]

$a : b : c = 1.7309 : 1 : 1.5796$; $\beta\ 90°00'$;[2] $p_0 : q_0 : r_0 = 0.9126 : 1.5796 : 1$;
$q_1 : r_1 : p_1 = 1.7309 : 1.0958 : 1$; $\mu\ 90°00'$; $r_2 : p_2 : q_2 = 0.6266 : 0.5777 : 1$

Forms:[3]

		ϕ	$\rho = C$	ϕ_1	$\rho_1 = A$	ϕ_2	$\rho_2 = B$
c	001	....	0°00′	0°00′	90°00′	90°00′	90°00′
m	110	30°01′	90 00	90 00	59 59	0 00	30 01
l	310	59 44	90 00	90 00	30 16	0 00	59 44
Δ	$\bar{2}03$	−90 00	31 19	0 00	121 19	121 19	90 00
n	101	90 00	42 23	0 00	47 37	47 37	90 00
N	$\bar{1}01$	−90 00	42 23	0 00	132 23	132 23	90 00
π	$\bar{4}03$	−90 00	50 25	0 00	140 25	140 25	90 00
t	$\bar{2}01$	−90 00	61 17	0 00	151 17	151 17	90 00
o	114	30 01	24 31	21 33	78 01	76 48½	68 56½
r	112	30 01	42 22	38 18	70 18	65 28½	54 18
p	111	30 01	61 16	57 40	63 59	47 37	49 24
S	221	30 01	74 40½	72 26	61 09	28 43	33 22½
O	$\bar{1}14$	−30 01	24 31	21 33	101 59	103 11½	68 56½
R	$\bar{1}12$	−30 01	42 22	38 18	109 42	114 31½	54 18
P	$\bar{1}11$	−30 01	61 16	57 40	116 01	132 23	49 24

Less common:
| 010 | 100 | 109 | 103 | 115 | 229 | 225 | 335 | 223 | 443 | 331 |

Structure cell.[4] Monoclinic C; a_0 12.99, b_0 7.50, c_0 11.95, $\beta\ 90°$;
$a_0 : b_0 : c_0 = 1.731 : 1 : 1.593$; contains $(Ag,Cu)_{32}Sb_4S_{22}$.

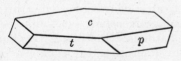

Freiberg, Saxony.

Ouray, Colo.

Habit. Short tabular {001}, pseudohexagonal or pseudorhombohedral;
striae on {001} ‖ the beveled edges producing triangular patterns. Also
massive.

Twinning. Twin plane {110}, composition plane {001},[5] repeated.

P h y s. Cleavage {001} imperfect. Fracture uneven. H. 2–3.
G. 6.1 ± 0.1; 6.36 (calc.). Luster metallic. Color iron-black; streak
black. Nearly opaque; in thin splinters translucent and dark red in color.

O p t. Biaxial negative. 2V 22° (2E 70° ±). $n_{Li} > 2.72$. Birefringence very strong. $X = c$, $Y = a$.[6] In polished section[7] gray-white in
color, sometimes with red internal reflections; moderately anisotropic with

weak pleochroism.   Reflection percentages: green 29.5,   orange 25.5, red 25.5.

C h e m.[8] Essentially a silver antimony sulfide, $(Ag,Cu)_{16}Sb_2S_{11}$.   Cu substitutes for Ag to about 30 atomic per cent.   A series toward the arsenian analogue, pearceite, $(Ag,Cu)_{16}As_2S_{11}$, extends to about 60 atomic per cent As.

Anal.

	1	2	3	4	5
Ag	74.32	68.90	67.95	64.49	57.96
Cu	.....	5.21	6.07	9.70	12.52
Sb	10.49	8.85	5.15	8.08	5.36
As	.....	1.07	3.88	1.78	4.60
S	15.19	15.33	16.37	15.10	17.45
Rem.	.....	0.09	0.76	0.75	2.11
Total	100.00	99.45	100.18	99.90	100.00
G.					5.811

1. $Ag_{16}Sb_2S_{11}$.   2. Arizpe. (?), Sonora.   Rem. is Fe 0.09.[9]   3. Quespisiza, Peru. Rem. is Pb 0.76.[10] 4. Las Chiapas, Sonora.   Rem. is Fe 0.41, Zn 0.34.[11]   5. Silver King mine, Yerranderie, New South Wales.   Rem. is Fe 0.91, gangue 0.67, rem. 0.53.[12]

Tests.   In O.T. fuses, gives sulfurous and antimonial fumes, the latter forming a white sublimate, sometimes mixed with As_2O_3.   B.B. fuses with spurting to a globule and coats the coal with Sb_2O_3; with long-continued blowing gives a metallic globule. Decomposed by HNO_3.

O c c u r. Polybasite occurs in silver veins formed at low to moderate temperatures, at times in considerable amounts.   It is associated with pyrargyrite, tetrahedrite, stephanite and other silver and lead sulfosalts, silver, argentite, gold, various sulfides, and with quartz, calcite, dolomite, and barite.   Oriented overgrowths have been noted of stephanite and of chalcopyrite upon polybasite.[13]

Found at Joachimstal and Přibram, Bohemia; at Schemnitz, Czecho-slovakia.   In Saxony, at Freiberg in the silver veins associated with argen-tite, stephanite, and silver, and at Johanngeorgenstadt; at Andreasberg in the Harz Mountains.   From Sarrabus, Sardinia.   In Chile at Tres Puntas, Atacama, and from Caldera; in Peru at Quespisiza and at Yauli.   At many localities in Mexico, especially in Zacatecas, Guanajuato, and Durango; in fine crystals from Las Chiapas and Arizpe, Sonora; from Sabinal, Chihua-hua, with pyrargyrite; from Sultepec with stephanite; from the Sierra Juarez, Oaxaca.   At Yerranderie, New South Wales.

In the United States, common in small amounts in the silver mines of Colorado, notably from the Mollie Gibson and Smuggler mines, Aspen, Pitkin County, the Georgetown and Silver Plume districts, Clear Creek County, the Ouray district, Ouray County, the Leadville district, Lake County, the Red Mountain district, San Juan County, and in the Marshall Basin near Telluride, San Miguel County.   In Montana from the Drum-lummon mine, Marysville, Lewis and Clark County, and from the Big

Seven mine, Neihart, Cascade County. From the Silver King mine, Pinal County, Arizona. In Idaho in the Silver ores of the Silver City, De Lamar, and Flint districts, Owyhee County, from near Talache, Bonner County, and with xanthoconite, proustite and argentite in the Atlanta district, Elmore County. In Nevada at Tonopah, Esmeralda County, with electrum, argentite, and pyrargyrite, in the Comstock Lode, Storey and Lyon counties, with stephanite, proustite, pyrargyrite, tetrahedrite, silver and gold, from Goldfield, Esmeralda County, the Cortez district and Austin, Lander County, and Tuscarora, Elko County. In Canada, at Cobalt and at Red Lake, Ontario.

Alter. Pseudomorphs of stephanite, silver, pyrite, and marcasite after polybasite have been noted.

Artif. Reported formed by passing H_2S over a melt of AgCl and Sb_2S_3;[14] probably formed from melts in the system Ag_2S-Sb_2S_3-CuS.[15]

Name. From πολύς, *many*, and βάσις, *base*, in allusion to the many metallic bases present.

Ref.

1. Penfield, *Am. J. Sc.*, **2**, 17 (1896), showed that polybasite (from Ouray, Colo.) is monoclinic. The earlier supposed rhombohedral symmetry by Rose (1829) and the later orthorhombic symmetry proposed by Miers, *Min. Mag.*, **8**, 204 (1889) were shown to be in error by Penfield.
2. Penfield (1896).
3. Penfield (1896).
4. Gossner and Kraus, *Cbl. Min.*, 1, 1934, did not give a definite crystal class, and their space group criteria are inadequate. Unanalyzed material from Guanajuato was used for the investigation.
5. Miers (1889).
6. Des Cloizeaux (85, 1867); Larsen and Berman (213, 1934).
7. Schneiderhöhn and Ramdohr (**2**, 455, 1931).
8. For a discussion of the formulas of polybasite and pearceite see Van Horn, *Am. J. Sc.*, **32**, 40 (1911), who shows that the analyses conform more closely to $(Ag,Cu)_{16}$-$(Sb,As)_2S_{11}$ than to $(Ag,Cu)_{16}(Sb,As)_2S_{12}$; also Gossner and Kraus (1934), who reach a similar conclusion from structural considerations.
9. Ungemach, *Bull. soc. min.*, **33**, 375 (1910).
10. Bödlander, *Jb. Min.*, I, 98, 1895.
11. Ungemach (1910).
12. White anal. in Card, *Rec. Geol. Sur. New South Wales*, **9**, 107 (1920).
13. Mügge (394, 401, 1903). With {001} [100] stephanite ∥ {001} [$\bar{1}$10] polybasite; {111} [$\bar{1}$10] chalcopyrite ∥ {001} [010] polybasite.
14. Sommerlad, *Zs. anorg. Chem.*, **18**, 424 (1898).
15. Gaudin and McGlashan, *Econ. Geol.*, **33**, 177 (1938).

3112 **PEARCEITE** [$Ag_{16}As_2S_{11}$]. Polybasit pt. *Rose* (*Ann. Phys.*, **28**, 158, 1833) (from Schemnitz). Arsenpolybasit pt. *Rammelsberg* (123, 1875). Pearceite *Penfield* (*Am. J. Sc.*, **2**, 17, 1896).

Cryst. Monoclinic; prismatic — $2/m$.

$a : b : c = 1.7309 : 1 : 1.6199$; $\beta\ 90°09'$;[1] $p_0 : q_0 : r_0 = 0.9359 : 1.6199 : 1$;

$r_2 : p_2 : q_2 = 0.6173 : 0.5778 : 1$; $\mu\ 89°51'$; $p_0'\ 0.9359$; $q_0'\ 1.6199$; $x_0'\ 0.0026$

Forms:[2]

		ϕ	ρ	ϕ_2	$\rho_2 = B$	C	A
c	001	90°00′	0°09′	89°51′	90°00′	0°00′	89°51′
b	010	0 00	90 00	....	0 00	90 00	90 00
a	100	90 00	90 00	0 00	90 00	89 51	0 00
m	110	30 01	90 00	0 00	30 01	89 55½	59 59
n	101	90 00	43 11	46 49	90 00	43 02	46 49
N	$\bar{1}01$	−90 00	43 01	133 01	90 00	43 10	133 01
t	201	90 00	61 55	28 05	90 00	61 46	28 05
T	$\bar{2}01$	−90 00	61 51	151 51	90 00	62 00	151 51
e	401	90 00	75 03	14 57	90 00	74 54	14 57
E	$\bar{4}01$	−90 00	75 02	165 02	90 00	75 11	165 02
f	601	90 00	79 54½	10 05½	90 00	79 45½	10 05½
F	$\bar{6}01$	−90 00	79 54	169 54	90 00	80 03	169 54
r	112	30 09½	43 06½	64 48	53 47	43 02½	71 03
p	111	30 05	61 53½	46 49	40 15	61 48½	63 45½
s	221	30 03	75 02½	28 05	33 15½	74 58	61 04
u	331	30 02½	79 54	19 35	31 32½	79 49½	60 28½
R	$\bar{1}12$	−29 53	43 03	114 57½	53 42½	43 07½	108 47
P	$\bar{1}11$	−29 57	61 51½	133 01½	40 10½	61 56	116 07
S	$\bar{2}21$	−29 59	75 02	151 51	33 12	75 06½	118 52
U	$\bar{3}31$	−29 59½	79 53½	160 22½	31 30	79 58	119 29

Less common forms:

h	130	k	021	Δ	$\bar{2}03$	O	$\bar{1}14$	v	332	x	311	z	3·1·12
l	310	d	102	o	114	Q	$\bar{1}13$	V	$\bar{3}32$	y	313

Structure cell. Pearceite and polybasite give nearly identical powder patterns.[3]

Habit. In short tabular six-sided prisms, with beveled edges. Triangular striations on {001}.

Twinning. (a) On {110}, composition plane perhaps {001}. (b) On {702}[4]?.

Phys. Cleavage none. Fracture conchoidal

Drumlummon Mine, Marysville, Mont.

to irregular. Brittle. H. 3. G. 6.15 ± 0.02.[5] Luster metallic. Color and streak black. Opaque; in very thin splinters translucent and brownish green or red in color.[6] In polished section[7] white, with moderate anisotropism.

Chem. A silver arsenic sulfide, $(Ag,Cu)_{16}As_2S_{11}$. Cu substitutes for Ag to about 30 atomic per cent. Sb substitutes for As to only about 4 atomic per cent, and a hiatus appears to exist between pearceite and arsenian polybasite (which see).

Anal.

	1	2	3	4	5	6	7
Ag	77.46	72.43	63.54	59.73	59.22	56.90	55.17
Cu	.....	3.04	10.70	12.91	15.65	14.85	18.11
Sb	.....	0.25	0.43	0.18	.....	0.30	.....
As	6.72	6.23	7.29	6.29	7.56	7.01	7.39
S	15.82	16.83	17.07	17.73	17.46	18.13	17.71
Rem.	.....	0.92	0.60	3.16	.....	2.81	1.47
Total	100.00	99.70	99.63	100.00	99.89	100.00	99.85
G.		6.33		6.03	6.067	6.080	

1. $Ag_{16}As_2S_{11}$. 2. Schemnitz, Czechoslovakia. Rem. is 0.33 Fe and 0.59 Zn.[8] 3. Arqueros, Chile. Rem. is 0.60 Fe.[9] 4. Mollie Gibson mine, Aspen, Colo. Rem. is 3.16 Zn. Recalc. after deduction of 28.18 per cent impurities from average of two analyses.[10] 5. Veta Rica mine, Sierra Mojada, Mexico.[11] 6. Mollie Gibson mine, Aspen, Colo. Rem. is 2.81 Zn. Recalc. after deduction of 12.81 per cent impurities.[12] 7. Drumlummon mine, Marysville, Mont. Rem. is 0.42 insol. and 1.05 Fe.[13]

Tests. F. 1. B.B. decrepitates slightly. On charcoal in O.F. a slight coating of As_2O_3 is formed. Decomposed by HNO_3.

O c c u r. An uncommon mineral, found in silver ores of low to moderate temperatures, associated with silver and lead sulfosalts, argentite, silver, sulfides, quartz, barite, and carbonates. Found at Schemnitz, Czechoslovakia. From Francoli, Tarragona, Spain, with niccolite, argentite, silver, and fluorite. In Mexico at the Veta Rica mine, Sierra Mojada, Coahuila, with argentite, silver, proustite, barite, and erythrite. In Chile at Arqueros. In the United States in the Mollie Gibson mine, Aspen, Colorado, accompanied by tennantite, silver, and pink barite; at Eureka and elsewhere in the Tintic district, Utah; at the Drumlummon mine, Marysville, Lewis and Clark County, with argentian tetrahedrite, and at Neihart, Cascade County, in Montana; in the Lakeview district, Bonner County, Idaho.

A r t i f. Probably formed from melts in the system Ag_2S-As_2S_3.[14]

N a m e. After Dr. Richard Pearce (1827–1927), chemist and metallurgist of Denver, Colorado.

Ref.

1. Penfield, *Am. J. Sc.*, **2**, 17 (1896).
2. Penfield (1896).
3. Frondel (priv. comm., 1939).
4. Van Horn and Cook, *Am. J. Sc.*, **31**, 524 (1911), are uncertain as to the twinning. Crystals from Sierra Mojada.
5. Penfield, *Am. J. Sc.*, **2**, 23 (1896). Average of 6.125, 6.160, 6.166.
6. Short (83, 1931) reported red color, and Van Horn and Cook (1911) reported brownish green.
7. Schneiderhöhn and Ramdohr (**2**, 455, 1931).
8. Rose (1833).
9. Domeyko (393, 1879).
10. Pearce anal. in Pearce and Penfield, *Am. J. Sc.*, **44**, 17 (1892).
11. Dubois anal. in Van Horn and Cook (1911).
12. Penfield anal. in Pearce and Penfield (1892).
13. Knight anal. in Penfield (1896).
14. Gaudin and McGlashan, *Econ. Geol.*, **33**, 153 (1938).

312 **Polyargyrite** [$Ag_{24}Sb_2S_{15}$?]. *Sandberger* (*Jb. Min.*, 310, 1869). *Petersen* (*Ann. Phys.*, 137, 386, 1869).

Isometric; in cubo-octahedrons, modified by {110} and {*hll*}, usually distorted and indistinct, with {110} and {*hll*}. Cleavage {001}. Fracture uneven. Malleable and sectile. H. 2.5, G. 6.974. Luster metallic. Color iron-black to blackish gray; streak black. Opaque.

Composition possibly $Ag_{24}Sb_2S_{15}$. Analysis[1] gave S 14.78, Sb 6.98, Ag 76.70, Fe 0.36, Zn 0.30, Pb trace, total 99.12. On charcoal B.B. fuses easily to a black globule, giving off antimonial fumes, and yielding a brittle globule of Ag. Soluble in concentrated HNO_3 with separation of S. Found at the Wenzel mine, Wolfach, Baden, Germany, associated with argentite and dolomite.

Needs confirmation.[2]

Ref.

1. Petersen (1869). Value for Ag is mean of 76.63 and 76.77; another sample gave 78.85 per cent.
2. Short (105, 1931) found a specimen to consist of argentite and tetrahedrite. Homogeneous according to Murdoch (114, 1916). A fine-grained, iron-gray malleable product, with G. 6.50, ascribed to polyargyrite, was obtained by Sommerlad, *Zs. anorg. Chem.*, **18**, 424 (1898), by fusion of $12Ag_2S \cdot 1Sb_2S_3$. The arsenical analogue of this material was reported by Sommerlad (429, 1898) and by Berzelius, *Ann. Phys.*, **7**, 150 (1826).

Argyrodite Series

3131   **A R G Y R O D I T E** [Ag_8GeS_6]. Plusinglanz *Breithaupt* (277, 1832). Argyrodite *Weisbach* (*Berg- u. hütten. Jb. Sachs.*, 89, 1886; *Jb. Min.*, II, 67, 1886). Canfieldite (in error) *Penfield* (*Am. J. Sc.*, 46, 107, 1893).

3132   **C A N F I E L D I T E** [Ag_8SnS_6]. *Penfield* (*Am. J. Sc.*, 47, 451, 1894). (Not canfieldite *Penfield* (*Am. J. Sc.*, 46, 107, 1893) = argyrodite.)

C r y s t.   Isometric, perhaps tetrahedral.[1]

Forms:

$$a\{001\}   \quad d\{011\}   \quad o\{111\}$$

Structure cell.[2]   Isometric (body-centered); a_0 21.11 ± 0.05 (for argyrodite with little Sn); contains $Ag_{256}(Ge,Sn)_{32}S_{192}$.

Habit.   Octahedral, dodecahedral, or combinations of these forms; canfieldite sometimes with modifying forms.[3]   Also massive, compact; in botryoidal crusts with a crystalline surface; as radiating crystal aggregates.

Twinning.   Common on the spinel law, (111); often repeated interpenetration twins of dodecahedra on $\{111\}$.[4]   The $\{011\}$ faces of canfieldite may be furrowed or striated parallel to [011], probably due to twinning.

P h y s.   Fracture uneven to small conchoidal. Brittle.   H. 2.5. G. 6.1–6.3; 6.26,[6] 6.29[7] (argyrodite); 6.276 (canfieldite); 6.32 (calc. for argyrodite).   Color black with a bluish to purple tone; on a fresh fracture steel-gray with a tint of red turning to violet.   Streak grayish black, somewhat shining.   In polished section[8] gray-white with a violet tint; isotropic (canfieldite) or with weak anomalous birefringence and very weak pleochroism (argyrodite).   Reflection percentages: green 24.5, orange 21, red 18.5.

C h e m.[9]   Argyrodite is silver germanium sulfide, Ag_8GeS_6.   Sn replaces Ge, and a series exists to the sulfostannate, canfieldite, Ag_8SnS_6.

Anal.

	1	2	3	4	5	6
Ag	76.51	76.05	75.55	75.28	74.72	75.67
Ge	6.44	6.55	6.64	6.18	6.93	6.55
Sn	.....	.....	.....	.....	.....	0.10
S	17.05	17.04	16.97	17.50	17.13	17.15
Fe	.....	} 0.13	} 0.24	.....	0.66	3.03
Zn	.....				0.22	0.11
Rem.	.....	0.29	0.34	0.69	.....	0.34
Total	100.00	100.06	99.74	99.65	99.66	99.95
G.		6.270	6.15			6.235

1. Ag_8GeS_6.   2. Argyrodite.   Bolivia.   Rem. is insol. 0.29.   Average of two analyses.[10]   3. Argyrodite.   Freiberg.   Rem. is Hg 0.34.   Ge and Ag average of two determinations.[11]   4. Argyrodite.   Freiberg.   Rem. is Sb 0.36, As and Cu trace, Fe 0.33.[12]
5. Argyrodite.   Freiberg.[13]   6. Argyrodite.   Colquechaca, Bolivia.   Rem. is Hg 0.03, Cu 0.08, As 0.05, H_2O 0.18.   Average of two analyses.[14]

	7	8	9	10	11
Ag	75.56	74.20	75.78	74.10	73.49
Ge	5.94	4.99	3.65	1.82	.....
Sn	0.82	3.36	3.60	6.94	10.14
S	17.46	16.45	16.92	16.22	16.37
Fe	.....	0.68	.....	0.21	.....
Zn	.....	.....	.....		.....
Total	99.78	99.68	99.95	99.29	100.00
G.		6.19			

7. Argyrodite.   Colquechaca, Bolivia.[15]   8. Argyrodite.   Aullagas, Bolivia.   With trace of Sb.   Ag average of two determinations.[16]   9. Argyrodite.   Chocaya, Bolivia.[17]
10. Canfieldite.   Aullagas, Bolivia.[18]   11. Ag_6SnS_6.

Tests.   F. 2.   B.B. yields a coating of the mixed oxides of Sn and Ge.   Affords a globule of Ag, which may be coated by tin oxide.   In the C.T. sulfur is given off, and at high temperature a slight deposit of GeS which fuses to yellow globules.

Occur.[19]   Argyrodite occurs at the Himmelfürst and at other mines, Freiberg, Saxony, associated with siderite, stephanite, argentite, pyrargyrite, polybasite, and marcasite and other sulfides; implanted sometimes on argentite or on marcasite or siderite.   Canfieldite has also been reported from Freiberg.   In Bolivia, argyrodite and canfieldite occur at Aullagas, near Colquechaca, Potosí, accompanying pyrargyrite, stephanite, and sphalerite.   Argyrodite also occurs in the Gallofa vein at Colquechaca in compact masses and crystals with stephanite and sulfides, at Porco in large crystals (a dodecahedron $2\frac{1}{2}$ in. on an axis) with silver sulfosalts and sphalerite, and at Chocaya with marcasite, aramayoite, and cassiterite.

Name.   Argyrodite from ἀργυρῶδης, *silver-containing*.   Canfieldite after F. A. Canfield (1849–1926), a mining engineer and private mineral collector of Dover, New Jersey.

Ref.

1. Originally described as monoclinic by Weisbach (1886), and made orthorhombic by Goldschmidt (3, 365, 1891). A Bolivian occurrence of material similar in composition to argyrodite was found to be isometric by Penfield, *Am. J. Sc.*, **46**, 107 (1893), and was established as a species, canfieldite, dimorphous with argyrodite. A later re-examination of the Freiberg argyrodite by Weisbach, *Jb. Min.*, **1**, 98 (1894), however, showed the material to be isometric. Penfield's name was then dropped, and applied to the newly discovered stannian analogue of argyrodite. Penfield, *Am. J. Sc.*, **47**, 451 (1894), and Prior and Spencer, *Min. Mag.*, **12**, 5 (1900), record no evidence of the tetrahedral symmetry found by Weisbach (1894) in the supposed presence of tetrahedra and {311}. The isometric symmetry is confirmed by the x-ray Weissenberg study of Frondel (priv. comm., 1940) on argyrodite.

2. Frondel (priv. comm., 1940) by Weissenberg method on isotropic argyrodite from Colquechaca.

3. Canfield, *Am. J. Sc.*, **23**, 21 (1907).

4. Prior and Spencer (1900). The argyrodite trilling (monoclinic orientation) figured by Weisbach (in Dana [150, Fig. 2, 1892]) consists of interpenetrating dodecahedra twinned on {111}.

5. Penfield (1894) and Canfield (1907).

6. Penfield (1893). Average of three determinations on Freiberg material (anal. 2).

7. Frondel (priv. comm., 1940) on material of the x-ray study.

8. Schneiderhöhn and Ramdohr (2, 480, 1931), and Moritz, *Jb. Min., Beil.-Bd.*, **66**, 196 (1933).

9. Spectrographic examination by Moritz (206, 1933).

10. Penfield (1893).

11. Penfield (1893).

12. Döring anal. in Kolbeck, *Cbl. Min.*, 331, 1908.

13. Winkler, *J. pr. Chem.*, **34**, 189 (1886).

14. Goldschmidt, *Zs. Kr.*, **45**, 548 (1908).

15. Krüll anal. in Moritz (1933).

16. Prior and Spencer (1900).

17. Krüll anal. in Moritz (1933).

18. Penfield (1894).

19. For an account of the occurrence and paragenesis of argyrodite-canfieldite in the Bolivian occurrences see Ahlfeld and Moritz, *Jb. Min., Beil.-Bd.*, **66**, 185 (1933), and Ahlfeld and Reyes (1938).

314   **STEPHANITE** [Ag_5SbS_4]. Argentum rude nigrum ?, *Germ.* Schvartsertz pt. *Agricola* (462, 1456). Svartgylden, Schvartsertz pt. Minera argenti nigra spongiosa (Freiberg) *Wallerius* (313, 1747). Argentum mineralisatum nigrum fragile, Röschgewächs (of Hungarian miners) *von Born* (1, 81, 1772). Sprödglaserz *Werner* (1789). Sprödglanzerz. Brittle Silver Ore, or Glance. Brittle Sulphuret of Silver. Argent noir pt. *Haüy* (1801). Argent sulfuré fragile *Fr.* Schwarzgültigerz *Leonhard* (638, 1826). Psaturose *Beudant* (2, 432, 1832). Stephanit *Haidinger* (570, 1845A). Antimonsilberglanz *Breithaupt* (1830). Schwarzsilberglanz *Glocker* (1831). Prismatischer Melanglanz *Mohs* (1824). Tigererz *Germ.* Rosicler negro, Plata agria, Estefanita *Span.* Goldschmidtine *Peacock* (*Am. Min.*, **24**, 227, 1939; **25**, 372, 1940). Melanglanz *Goldschmidt* (6, 15, 1929).

Cryst. Orthorhombic; pyramidal — $m\,m\,2$.[1]

$$a : b : c = 0.6291 : 1 : 0.6851;^2 \qquad p_0 : q_0 : r_0 = 1.0890 : 0.6851 : 1$$

$$q_1 : r_1 : p_1 = 0.6291 : 0.9183 : 1; \qquad r_2 : p_2 : q_2 = 1.4596 : 1.5896 : 1$$

Forms:[3]

		ϕ	$\rho = C$	ϕ_1	$\rho_1 = A$	ϕ_2	$\rho_2 = B$
c	001	....	0°00′	0°00′	90°00′	90°00′	90°00′
b	010	0°00′	90 00	90 00	90 00	....	0 00
a	100	90 00	90 00	....	0 00	0 00	90 00
π	130	27 55	90 00	90 00	62 05	0 00	27 55
m	110	57 49½	90 00	90 00	32 10½	0 00	57 49½
λ	310	78 09½	90 00	90 00	11 50½	0 00	78 09½
t	023	0 00	24 33	24 33	90 00	90 00	65 27
d	021	0 00	53 52½	53 52½	90 00	90 00	36 07½
e	041	0 00	69 57	69 57	90 00	90 00	20 03
β	101	90 00	47 26½	0 00	42 33½	42 33½	90 00
M	113	57 49½	23 12½	12 52	70 30½	70 03	77 53
h	112	57 49½	32 45	18 54½	62 45	61 26	73 15½
P	111	57 49½	52 08½	34 25	48 04	42 33½	65 08½
r	221	57 49½	68 45½	53 52½	37 55	24 39½	60 14½
ω	134	27 55	30 10½	27 11½	76 23½	74 46	63 37½
f	133	27 55	37 47	34 25	73 19½	70 03	57 13
v	132	27 55	49 18½	45 47	69 12½	61 26	47 56

Less common forms:

Θ	190	s	012	Φ	102	ϵ	773	B	267	N	818	S	372
J	150	o	045	g	201	z	331	C	3·9·10	A	313	Σ	211
U	120	k	011	G	301	ν	441	H	122	O	212	ρ	241
u	350	Π	065	q	114	σ	551	T	142	w	131	μ	281
Λ	230	κ	043	l	223	τ	156	D	3·13·6	Q	141	W	2·10·1
L	210	E	061	Ψ	554	ϕ	135	θ	152	γ	151	ζ	311
Ξ	510	δ	071	Ω	443	K	155	F	213	R	161	y	351
α	013	γ	081	p	332	ψ	3·9·11	I	7·11·9	ξ	312	Γ	371
										χ	352	x	461

Structure cell.[4] Space group $Cmc2$; a_0 7.70, b_0 12.32, c_0 8.48 (all $\pm$ 0.05); $a_0 : b_0 : c_0 = 0.625 : 1 : 0.688$; contains $Ag_{20}Sb_4S_{16}$.

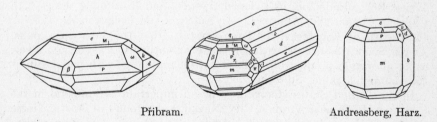

Přibram. Andreasberg, Harz.

Habit. Short prismatic to tabular [001]; less commonly elongated [100]. {110} striated [1$\bar{1}$4]. Also massive, compact or disseminated.

Twinning. (*a*) On {110}, often repeated to form pseudohexagonal groups. (*b*) Less commonly on {130}. (*c*) On {100} or {010} with composition plane {001} producing apparently holohedral symmetry.[5]

P h y s. Cleavage {010} and {021} imperfect. Fracture subconchoidal to uneven. Brittle. H. 2–2½. G. 6.25 ± 0.03; 6.47 (calc.). Luster metallic. Color and streak iron black. Opaque. In polished section[6] strongly anisotropic. Reflection percentages: green 29, orange 27.5, red 24.5.

C h e m. Silver antimony sulfide, Ag_5SbS_4.

Anal.

	1	2	3	4	5	6	7
Ag	68.33	68.65	68.36	68.33	68.30	68.25	68.21
Sb	15.42	15.22	15.30	15.26	15.00	15.20	15.86
S	16.25	16.02	16.33	16.41	16.70	16.55	15.95
Total	100.00	99.89	99.99	100.00	100.00	100.00	100.02
G.	6.47	6.26		6.240	6.233	6.284	6.24

1. Ag_5SbS_4. 2. Copiapó, Chile. As, Cu trace.[7] 3. Pedrazzini mine, Arizpe, Sonora, Mexico. Average of two analyses.[8] 4. Frontier mine, South Lorrain, Ont. Recalc. after deducting 1.35 per cent insol.[9] 5. Keeley mine, South Lorrain, Ont. Recalc. after deducting 0.72 per cent insol.[9] 6. O'Brien mine, Cobalt, Ont. Recalc. after deducting 0.49 per cent insol.[9] 7. Cornwall, England. Fe trace.[7]

Tests. F. 1. In C.T. decrepitates and then fuses. Oxidized by HNO_3 with separation of S and Sb_2O_3.

O c c u r. Found in many silver deposits, usually in small amounts, as one of the last vein minerals to form. Associated with other silver sulfosalts, argentite, silver, tetrahedrite and the commoner sulfides.

In Bohemia at Schemnitz, Kremnitz, Hodritsch, and Přibram, the latter locality furnishing exceptional crystals associated with galena, sphalerite, tetrahedrite, dolomite, and calcite. At Vihnye, comm. Hont, Hungary. Crystals from Freiberg, Saxony; also from Schneeberg, Annaberg, and in exceptional crystals from Andreasberg. Fine twins from Monte Narba, near Sarrabus, Sardinia, with argentite and pyrargyrite. At Hiendelaencina, Guadalajara, Spain. From Kongsberg, Norway. In Cornwall from Wheal Boys, Endellion, as twinned crystals, and from other mines. In Chile at Chañarcillo, Atacama. At Aullagas and Colquechaca, Bolivia. In Mexico at Zacatecas; in large crystals from the Pedrazzini mine, Arizpe, Sonora, associated with polybasite, argentite, ruby silver, and silver; as an alteration product of aguilarite at Guanajuato; with polybasite at the Campania mine, Sultepec.

In the United States stephanite was an important ore mineral in the Comstock Lode near Virginia City, Nevada; also found at Austin, Reese River, and Humboldt districts in Nevada. At Leadville, Colorado, replacing rhyolite porphyry. In California from a number of localities, especially in Mono County, and from Grass Valley, Nevada County; also from Shasta County. In Canada found in the silver mines of the Cobalt district, Ontario; at South Lorrain, Ontario, with argentite, proustite, and silver.

A l t e r. Crystals occur altered to native silver. Pseudomorphs of stephanite after polybasite, and of polybasite, pyrite, proustite, and arsenopyrite after stephanite have also been noted.

A r t i f.[10] Crystals have been prepared in a sodium carbonate solution of $AgCl + Sb_2O_3$, with the addition of H_2S, sealed in a glass tube.

N a m e. After the Archduke Stephan, formerly Mining Director of Austria.

Ref.

1. Crystal class established by Miers, *Min. Mag.*, **9**, 1 (1890) on twinned crystals from Cornwall and elsewhere.
2. Elements of Vrba, *Böhm. Ges., Ber.*, 119, 1886.
3. Goldschmidt (**6**, 15, 1920). Also Shannon, *U. S. Nat. Mus.*, **63**, art. 11, 1923; Tokody, *Cbl. Min.*, 13, 1928; Garces, *R. soc. española hist. nat.*, **31**, 49 (1931).

Rare or uncertain forms:

1·15·0	059	7·7·16	13·13·6	1·3·17	356	916
1·11·0	035	7·7·15	552	5·15·27	3·11·6	3·10·2
160	056	225	883	145	8·33·16	231
290	087	11·11·15	14·14·5	258	172	251
140	095	10·10·13	772	2·22·7	192	7·13·3
3·10·0	032	13·13·12	17·17·3	3·6·10	599	512
5·11·0	031	10·10·9	661	4·21·13	5·17·9	522
6·11·0	0·15·2	776	771	13·39·40	3·10·5	532
340	0·14·1	775	881	153	243	833
540	203	885	991	193	354	361
016	1·1·18	553	16·16·1	3·27·7	485	3·15·1
014	118	774	1·5·30	499	727	13·4·4
027	117	995	1·4·23	5·11·11	313	18·5·5
038	116	11·11·6	1·4·20	316	535	571
0·5·11	115	19·19·10	1·3·19	9·3·18	121	591
	3·3·11				3·11·3	9·11·1

4. Peacock, *Univ. Toronto Stud., Geol. Ser.*, **44**, 66 (1940), by Weissenberg method on material from Ste. Croix aux Mines, Alsace. See also Taylor, *Am. Min.*, **25**, 327 (1940), on the space group, and Salvia, *An. soc. españ. fis. quim.*, **30**, 416 (1932), for earlier x-ray work.
5. Miers, *Min. Mag.*, **9**, 1 (1890).
6. Schneiderhöhn and Ramdohr (**2**, 448, 1931). Reflectivity measurements by Phillips, *Min. Mag.*, **13**, 458 (1932).
7. Prior, *Min. Mag.*, **9**, 11 (1890).
8. Ford, *Am. J. Sc.*, **25**, 244 (1908).
9. Haller anal. in Walker, *Univ. Toronto Stud., Geol. Ser.*, **29**, 13 (1930).
10. In Doelter (**4** [1], 267, 1925).

315   Epigenite [(Cu,Fe)₅AsS₆ ?].   Arsenwismuthkupfererz *Sandberger* (*Jb. Min.*, 415, 1868).   Epigenit *Sandberger* (*Jb. Min.*, 205, 1869).

C r y s t. Said to be orthorhombic. In short prisms (69°10′) resembling arsenopyrite. Also in crustlike heaped aggregates of crystals.

P h y s. Fracture uneven. H. 3.5. G. 4.5. Luster metallic. Color steel-gray, tarnishing black and then blue. Streak black. Opaque.

C h e m. A copper and iron arsenic sulfide. Formula uncertain, perhaps (Cu,Fe)₅AsS₆, with Cu : Fe = 8 : 3.[1]

Anal.

	Cu	Fe	As	S	Total
1	40.68	14.23	12.75	32.34	100.00

1. Wittichen. Recalc. after deduction of 2.12 per cent Bi as Cu_3BiS_3 (wittichenite).[2]

Tests. In C.T. gives first sulfur, then sulfide of arsenic. B.B. on charcoal gives a magnetic slag with copper globules. Soluble in HNO_3 with separation of sulfur.

O c c u r. Found at the Neuglück mine, Wittichen, Baden, accompanying wittichenite, chalcopyrite, barite, fluorite, and calcite.

N a m e. From ἐπιγίγνομαι, *to follow after*, because always observed implanted upon the barite vein masses.

Needs further study.

Ref.

1. See also Sandberger (1868, 1869), who derives $3Cu_2S \cdot 3FeS \cdot As_2S_6$.
2. Petersen, *Ann. Phys.*, **136**, 502 (1869).

3211   **P Y R A R G Y R I T E** [Ag_3SbS_3].   Argentum rude rubrum pt. *Germ.*   Rothgolderz *Agricola* (362, 462, 1546).   Argentum rubri coloris pt., Gemein Rothguldenerz *Gesner* (62, 1565).   Rothgylden pt., Argentum arsenico pauco sulphure et ferro mineralisatum pt., Minera argenti rubra var. opaca, var. nigrescens *Wallerius* (310, 1747).   Mine d'argent rouge *Wallerius* (1753).   Ruby Silver Ore pt.   Red Silver Ore pt. *Hill* (1771).   Dunkles Rothgültigerz, Lichtes Rothgültigerz pt. *Werner* (1789).   Dark Red Silver Ore; Antimonial Red Silver.   Argent antimonie sulfuré pt. *Haüy* (1801).   Argent rouge antimoniale *Proust* (*J. Phys.*, **59**, 407, 1804).   Aerosit *Selb* (*Denks. Nat. Schwaben*, **1**, 311, 1805).   Rubinblende pt. *Mohs.*   Antimonsilberblende.   Pyrargyrit *Glocker* (388, 1831).   Argyrythrose *Beudant* (**2**, 430, 1832).   Argento rosso antimoniale *Ital.*   Rosicler oscuro *Span.*   Petlanque *Mex.*

C r y s t.   Hexagonal — *R*; ditrigonal pyramidal — 3 *m*.

$a : c = 1 : 0.7892;^1$ $\alpha\ 104°00\tfrac{1}{2}';$ $p : r_0 = 0.9113 : 1;$ $\lambda\ 71°22'$

Forms:²

Lower	Upper		ϕ	$\rho = C$	A_1	A_2
	m	$10\bar{1}0$	$2\bar{1}\bar{1}$	$30°00'$	$90°00'$	$30°00'$	$90°00'$
	$-m$	$01\bar{1}0$	$11\bar{2}$	$-30\ 00$	$90\ 00$	$90\ 00$	$30\ 00$
	a	$11\bar{2}0$	$10\bar{1}$	$0\ 00$	$90\ 00$	$60\ 00$	$60\ 00$
	β	$21\bar{3}0$	$5\bar{1}\bar{4}$	$10\ 53\tfrac{1}{2}$	$90\ 00$	$49\ 06\tfrac{1}{2}$	$70\ 53\tfrac{1}{2}$
	u	$10\bar{1}4$	211	$30\ 00$	$12\ 50$	$78\ 54\tfrac{1}{2}$	$90\ 00$
	e	$01\bar{1}2$	110	$-30\ 00$	$24\ 30$	$90\ 00$	$68\ 57\tfrac{1}{2}$
$\bar{p}$	s	$02\bar{2}1$	$11\bar{1}$	$-30\ 00$	$61\ 15$	$90\ 00$	$40\ 36$
		$11\bar{2}3$	210	$0\ 00$	$27\ 45$	$76\ 32$	$76\ 32$
	σ	$32\bar{5}4$	$41\bar{1}$	$6\ 35$	$44\ 48$	$65\ 10$	$73\ 44\tfrac{1}{2}$
	y	$32\bar{5}1$	$30\bar{2}$	$6\ 35$	$75\ 52$	$54\ 41\tfrac{1}{2}$	$67\ 20$
	Y	$7\cdot4\cdot\bar{11}\cdot6$	$81\bar{3}$	$8\ 57$	$55\ 40\tfrac{1}{2}$	$58\ 43\tfrac{1}{2}$	$72\ 44\tfrac{1}{2}$
	t	$21\bar{3}4$	310	$10\ 53\tfrac{1}{2}$	$31\ 05$	$70\ 15$	$80\ 16\tfrac{1}{2}$
	v	$21\bar{3}1$	$20\bar{1}$	$10\ 53\tfrac{1}{2}$	$67\ 28\tfrac{1}{2}$	$52\ 47\tfrac{1}{2}$	$72\ 24$
	w	$31\bar{4}5$	410	$16\ 06$	$33\ 18\tfrac{1}{2}$	$66\ 41\tfrac{1}{2}$	$82\ 25$
	ϕ	$41\bar{5}6$	510	$19\ 06\tfrac{1}{2}$	$34\ 50\tfrac{1}{2}$	$64\ 25$	$83\ 48$
	X	$11\cdot1\cdot\bar{12}\cdot1$	$8\bar{3}\bar{4}$	$25\ 41\tfrac{1}{2}$	$84\ 34$	$34\ 42$	$85\ 43$
	ω	$23\bar{5}8$	530	$-\ 6\ 35$	$26\ 24\tfrac{1}{2}$	$79\ 49$	$74\ 37\tfrac{1}{2}$
	d	$12\bar{3}2$	$21\bar{1}$	$-10\ 53\tfrac{1}{2}$	$50\ 19\tfrac{1}{2}$	$75\ 24\tfrac{1}{2}$	$59\ 44\tfrac{1}{2}$
$\bar{q}$		$16\bar{7}1$	$32\bar{4}$	$-22\ 24\tfrac{1}{2}$	$80\ 30$	$82\ 30\tfrac{1}{2}$	$38\ 36$

Less common:

Lower	Upper			Lower	Upper			Lower	Upper		
	τ	$41\bar{5}0$	$3\bar{1}\bar{2}$	.	D	$4\cdot3\cdot\bar{7}\cdot10$	730		w	$31\bar{4}5$	410
	L	$71\bar{8}0$	$5\bar{2}\bar{3}$		B	$43\bar{7}6$	$17\cdot5\cdot\bar{4}$	$\bar{\psi}$		$31\bar{4}2$	$30\bar{1}$
$\bar{u}$		$10\bar{1}4$	211		ρ	$43\bar{7}1$	$40\bar{3}$	$\bar{\phi}$		$41\bar{5}6$	510
$\bar{e}$		$01\bar{1}2$	110	$\bar{W}$	W	$7\cdot5\cdot\bar{12}\cdot2$	$70\bar{5}$	$\bar{n}$	n	$41\bar{5}3$	$40\bar{1}$
	I	$50\bar{5}8$	611		T	$32\bar{5}7$	520		l	$45\bar{9}5$	$62\bar{3}$
	b	$7\cdot0\cdot\bar{7}\cdot10$	811	$\bar{y}$	.	$32\bar{5}1$	$30\bar{2}$		v	$12\bar{3}5$	320
	A	$30\bar{3}4$	$10\cdot1\cdot1$		G	$5\cdot3\cdot\bar{8}\cdot11$	830	$\bar{d}$		$12\bar{3}2$	$21\bar{1}$
$\bar{r}$	r	$10\bar{1}1$	100		γ	$53\bar{8}2$	$50\bar{3}$	$\bar{x}$		$24\bar{6}1$	$31\bar{3}$
$\bar{\mathrm{II}}$		$30\bar{3}2$	$8\cdot\bar{1}\cdot\bar{1}$		H	$7\cdot4\cdot\bar{11}\cdot15$	$11\cdot4\cdot0$		h	$2\cdot5\cdot\bar{7}\cdot12$	750
	T	$50\bar{5}2$	$4\bar{1}\bar{1}$	$\bar{Y}$		$7\cdot4\cdot\bar{11}\cdot6$	$8\bar{1}3$	$\bar{\alpha}$	α	$25\bar{7}3$	$42\bar{3}$
$\bar{s}$	Γ	$02\bar{2}1$	$1\bar{1}\bar{1}$	$\bar{j}$	j	$9\cdot5\cdot\bar{14}\cdot10$	$11\cdot2\cdot\bar{3}$		C	$13\bar{4}7$	430
	Γ	$07\bar{7}2$	$33\bar{4}$		ζ	$9\cdot5\cdot\bar{14}\cdot4$	$90\bar{5}$	$\bar{\delta}$		$13\bar{4}4$	$32\bar{1}$
$\bar{j}$	f	$05\bar{5}1$	$22\bar{3}$	$\bar{\imath}$		$21\bar{3}4$	310	$\bar{E}$		$13\bar{4}1$	$21\bar{2}$
	o	$11\bar{2}6$	321		g	$21\bar{3}2$	$7\bar{1}2$	$\bar{U}$		$27\bar{9}2$	$13\cdot7\cdot\bar{14}$
	p	$11\bar{2}3$	210	$\bar{v}$		$21\bar{3}1$	$20\bar{1}$	$\bar{F}$		$4\cdot15\cdot\bar{19}\cdot4$	$9\cdot5\cdot\bar{10}$
	k	$11\bar{2}1$	$41\bar{2}$	$\bar{R}$	R	$7\cdot3\cdot\bar{10}\cdot4$	$70\bar{3}$	$\bar{N}$		$2\cdot9\cdot\bar{11}\cdot2$	$53\bar{6}$
	Z	$54\bar{9}1$	$50\bar{4}$		V	$12\ 5\cdot\bar{17}\cdot10$	$13\cdot1\cdot\bar{4}$	$\bar{Q}$		$4\cdot20\cdot\bar{24}\cdot11$	$13\cdot9\cdot\bar{11}$
	π	$9\cdot7\cdot\bar{16}\cdot2$	$90\bar{7}$		S	$52\bar{7}9$	720	$\bar{v}$		$15\bar{6}1$	$8\cdot5\cdot\bar{10}$

Structure cell.[4] Space group $R3c$; a_0 11.04, c_0 8.72; $a_0 : c_0 = 1 : 0.7899$; a_{rh} 7.00, α 103°59′; contains $Ag_{18}Sb_6S_{18}$ in the hexagonal unit.

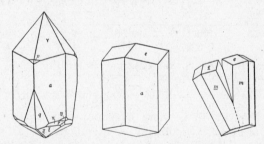

Freiberg, Saxony.   Andreasberg, Harz.

Habit. Commonly prismatic [0001] and showing hemimorphic development; striae on $\{11\bar{2}0\}$ ∥ $[1\bar{1}05]$; often with the rhombohedron e or r dominant. Also steep scalenohedral with $\{05\bar{5}1\}$ generally dominant. Also massive, compact.

Twinning. (a) On $\{10\bar{1}4\}$ by growth, as twins of complex aggregations of individuals and as lamellar twins producing striae parallel to the twin plane, and also by pressure.[6] (b) On $\{10\bar{1}1\}$, less common than in proustite. (c) About $[11\bar{2}0]$[7] to produce aggregate crystals of apparent holohedral symmetry. (d) On $\{01\bar{1}2\}$, rare.

Phys. Cleavage $\{10\bar{1}1\}$ distinct, $\{01\bar{1}2\}$ very imperfect. Fracture conchoidal to uneven. Brittle. H. 2½. G. 5.85, 5.82 (calc.). M.P.

486° (artif.).   Luster adamantine.   Color deep red.   Streak purplish red. Less translucent than proustite.

O p t.   Deep red by transmitted light.

λ	671 (Li)
O	3.084
E	2.881

Uniax. neg. (−)

In polished section[8] strongly anisotropic and pleochroic.   Reflection percentages: green 32.5, orange 27, red 24.5.

C h e m.   Silver antimony sulfide, Ag_3SbS_3, with small amounts of As. *Anal.*

	1	2	3	4	5	6
Ag	59.76	59.75	60.04	59.73	59.91	59.82
Sb	22.48	22.45	22.39	22.36	22.09	22.00
As	.....	.....	0.27	.....	0.12	0.08
S	17.76	17.81	17.74	17.65	17.79	17.82
Total	100.00	100.01	100.44	99.74	99.91	99.72
G.	5.82	5.82	5.83	5.871		5.852

1. Ag_3SbS_3.   2. Andreasberg.[10]   3. Zacatecas.[10]   4. Andreasberg.[11]   5. Andreasberg.[10] 6. Nagyág, Roumania.   Includes Cu 0.07, Fe 0.12.[12]

	7	8	9	10	11	12
Ag	59.52	60.24	60.17	60.07	60.21	60.85
Sb	21.75	21.69	21.64	21.20	20.69	18.36
As	.....	0.44	0.52	0.79	1.02	2.60
S	18.28	17.74	17.65	17.89	17.78	17.99
Total	99.55	100.11	99.98	99.95	99.70	99.80
G.		5.86	5.78	5.77	5.81	5.805

7. Colquechaca, Bolivia.[13]   8. Andreasberg.[10]   9. Freiberg, Saxony.[10]   10. Chañarcillo.[10]   11. Harz.[10]   12. Andreasberg.[10]

Tests.   F. 1.   Decomposed by HNO_3 with separation of S and Sb_2O_3.

O c c u r. Pyrargyrite is more common than proustite, and is an important ore of silver. It forms at low temperatures as one of the last silver minerals to crystallize in the sequence of primary deposition. In part, however, it may be derived from secondary enrichment processes. Commonly associated with proustite, argentite, tetrahedrite, stephanite and other silver sulfosalts, silver, calcite, dolomite, and quartz, sometimes chalcedony. Only those localities from which large amounts or exceptional specimens have been obtained can be mentioned here.

In Bohemia at Joachimstal and Příbram; at Schemnitz. At Andreasberg in the Harz in exceptional crystals with calcite, arsenic, and galena; in Saxony, notably at the Himmelfürst mine, Freiberg, with argentite, proustite, and other silver minerals. Reported from Guadalajara, Hiendelaencina, Spain. In South America at many silver mines, notably at Colquechaca in Bolivia, and at Chañarcillo, Atacama, Chile, with proustite. In Mexico it is worked as an ore at Guanajuato; reported from Durango.

In the United States found in the silver districts of the Rocky Mountains, but usually in small amounts and seldom in large crystals. In Colorado with silver and tetrahedrite in the Ruby district, Gunnison County. In Nevada abundant in the vicinity of Austin and at the Comstock Lode. In considerable amounts at the Poorman mine, in the Silver City district, Owyhee County, Idaho, with proustite and cerargyrite. From the silver district of Cobalt, Ontario, with silver.

Alter. To argentite, silver or, rarely, cerargyrite or stibnite; pyrite, argentite, and silver occur as pseudomorphs after pyrargyrite. Found as an alteration product of argentite, dyscrasite, and silver.

Artif. Formed in the system Ag-Sb-S;[14] the material has M.P. 486° and G. 5.790. Also by the reaction in a closed tube at 300°, of a solution containing a silver salt, sodium antimony sulfide, and sodium bicarbonate.[15]

Name. From $\pi\hat{\nu}\rho$, *fire*, and $\H{\alpha}\rho\gamma\nu\rho\sigma$, *silver*, in allusion to its color and composition.

Ref.

1. Miers, *Min. Mag.*, **8**, 37 (1888).
2. Common and less common forms from Goldschmidt (7, 139, 1922) and from Ungemach (unpublished notes, 1939).
Rare and uncertain forms:

0001	6·5·$\overline{11}$·16	3·7·$\overline{10}$·8	43$\overline{7}$4	4·20·$\overline{24}$·11	27$\overline{9}$1
11·8·$\overline{19}$·0	14$\overline{5}$9	27$\overline{9}$7	9·4·$\overline{13}$·8	17·11·$\overline{28}$·6	71$\overline{8}$1
11·5·$\overline{16}$·0	6·7·$\overline{13}$·20	31$\overline{4}$3	$\overline{5}$16$\overline{4}$	3·$\overline{10}$·13·$\overline{5}$	3·$\overline{8}$·11·$\overline{1}$
31$\overline{4}$0	7·6·$\overline{13}$·19	15·8·$\overline{23}$·16	7·8·$\overline{15}$·8	19·13·$\overline{32}$·6	1·9·10·$\overline{1}$
11·2·$\overline{13}$·0	7·1·$\overline{8}$·12	9·11·$\overline{20}$·13	$\overline{8}$·$\overline{23}$·31·$\overline{18}$	5·10·$\overline{15}$·4	6·5·$\overline{11}$·1
25·1·$\overline{26}$·0	$\overline{14}$56	$\overline{6}$·7·13·$\overline{8}$	15·10·$\overline{25}$·14	14·33·$\overline{47}$·11	$\overline{18}$91
01$\overline{1}$8	7·3·$\overline{10}$·13	14·4·$\overline{18}$·13	11·5·$\overline{16}$·9	7·12·$\overline{19}$·4	14·9·$\overline{23}$·2
10$\overline{1}$2	9·7·$\overline{16}$·14	7·4·$\overline{11}$·8	4·9·13·$\overline{7}$	3·7·$\overline{10}$·2	29·2·$\overline{31}$·3
50$\overline{5}$6	53$\overline{8}$8	11·6·$\overline{17}$·12	10·5·$\overline{15}$·8	3·$\overline{7}$·10·$\overline{2}$	6·8·$\overline{14}$·1
03$\overline{3}$2	11·1·$\overline{12}$·13	21$\overline{3}$2	5·10·$\overline{15}$·8	10·7·$\overline{17}$·3	9·5·$\overline{14}$·1
13·0·$\overline{13}$·6	36$\overline{9}$8	7·5·$\overline{12}$·8	8·7·$\overline{15}$·7	9·1·$\overline{10}$·2	17·15·$\overline{32}$·2
0·17·$\overline{17}$·7	12·9·$\overline{21}$·18	8·3·$\overline{11}$·8	7·2·9·$\overline{5}$	7·$\overline{17}$·24·$\overline{4}$	1·$\overline{12}$·13·$\overline{1}$
0·13·$\overline{13}$·2	7·5·$\overline{12}$·10	11·12·$\overline{23}$·14	54$\overline{9}$4	14$\overline{5}$1	5·10·$\overline{15}$·1
08$\overline{8}$1	8·$\overline{11}$·19·$\overline{15}$	19·7·$\overline{26}$·18	2·13·$\overline{15}$·7	42$\overline{6}$1	$\overline{17}$·1·18·$\overline{1}$
22$\overline{4}$3	35$\overline{8}$7	6·5·$\overline{11}$·7	9·1·$\overline{10}$·5	15·11·$\overline{26}$·4	8·$\overline{13}$·21·$\overline{1}$
3·2·$\overline{5}$·16	3·8·$\overline{11}$·10	14·11·$\overline{25}$·15	2·$\overline{13}$·15·$\overline{7}$	5·$\overline{10}$·15·$\overline{2}$	
2·1·$\overline{3}$·10	21·13·$\overline{34}$·26	19·14·$\overline{33}$·20	8·$\overline{3}$·11·$\overline{5}$	156$\overline{1}$	
3·4·$\overline{7}$·11	52$\overline{7}$6	5·3·$\overline{8}$·5	2·$\overline{15}$·17·$\overline{8}$	17·13·$\overline{30}$·4	
$\overline{2}$·3·5·$\overline{10}$	53$\overline{8}$6	$\overline{11}$·4·15·$\overline{10}$	2·9·$\overline{11}$·5	1·$\overline{19}$·20·$\overline{3}$	
$\overline{2}$·3·5·$\overline{14}$	5·9·14·$\overline{11}$	13·9·$\overline{22}$·13	2·9·11·$\overline{5}$	5·$\overline{17}$·22·$\overline{3}$	

3. The true angular relations between top and bottom forms may be derived from the given ϕ and ρ values of the bottom forms as follows: correct $\phi = 180° + \phi$ of table; correct $\rho = 180° - \rho$ of table; correct A_1 and A_2 is supplement of that given; correct index, change all signs.
4. An average of two closely agreeing unit cell determinations by Harker, *J. Chem. Phys.*, **4**, 381 (1936), and Hocart, *C. R.*, **205**, 68 (1937), the latter on Freiberg material.
5. Data on twinning principally from Miers (1888).
6. Mügge, *Jb. Min.*, 24, 1920, p. 36, found that the twin lamellae could not be produced on proustite. In this connection see Miers (1888) on striae found on growth twins.
7. Friedel (379, 1904) points out that the twin plane {11$\overline{2}$0} as given by Miers (1888), cannot be considered as such since it is a symmetry plane, and the twinning must therefore be described as an operation about an axis.

8. Schneiderhöhn and Ramdohr (**2**, 413, 1931).

9. For older analyses see Doelter (**4** [1], 242, 1926).   Spectroscopic amounts of Ge reported by Papish, *Écon. Geol.*, **23**, 660 (1928).

10. Prior anal. in Miers (1888).

11. Rethwisch, *Jb. Min., Beil.-Bd.*, **4**, 95 (1886).

12. Locza, *Ann. hist.-nat. Mus. Nat. Hungar.*, **9**, 318 (1911), in *Zs. Kr.*, **54**, 185 (1915).

13. Sommerlad, *Zs. anorg. Chem.*, **18**, 423 (1898).

14. Jaeger and van Klooster, *Zs. anorg. Chem.*, **78**, 256 (1912).   See also Hintze, **1** [1], 1067 (1901).

15. Senarmont, *C. R.*, **32**, 409 (1851).

3212   **P R O U S T I T E** [Ag₃AsS₃].   Argentum rude rubrum translucidum carbunculis simile *Germ.*   Durchsichtig Rodtguldenerz *Agricola* (362, 462, 1546).   Argentum rubri coloris pellucidum, Schön Rubin Rothguldenerz *Gesner* (62, 1565).   Minera argenti rubra pellucida *Wallerius* (311, 1747).   Ruby Silver Ore pt. *Hill.*   Argent rouge arsenicale *Proust* (*J. phys.*, **59**, 404, 1804).   Lichtes Rothgültigerz pt., Arsenical Silver Ore; Light Red Silver Ore.   Proustite *Beudant* (**2**, 445, 1832).   Argento rosso arsenicale *Ital.*   Rosicler claro *Span.*   Sanguinite *Miers* (*Min. Mag.*, **9**, 182, 1890).

C r y s t.   Hexagonal — *R*; ditrigonal pyramidal — 3 *m*.[1]

$a : c = 1 : 0.8039;$[2] $\alpha\ 103°\ 32\frac{1}{2}';$ $p : r = 0.9283 : 1;$ $\lambda\ 72°12'$

Forms:[3]

			ϕ	$\rho = C$	A_1	A_2
m	$10\bar10$	$2\bar1\bar1$	30°00′	90°00′	30°00′	90°00′
$-m$	$01\bar10$	$11\bar2$	−30 00	90 00	90 00	30 00
a	$11\bar20$	$10\bar1$	0 00	90 00	60 00	60 00
h	$31\bar40$	$7\bar2\bar5$	16 06	90 00	43 54	76 06
τ	$41\bar50$	$3\bar1\bar2$	19 06½	90 00	40 53½	79 06½
u	$10\bar14$	211	30 00	13 04	78 44	90 00
r	$10\bar11$	100	30 00	42 52	53 54	90 00
z	$10\cdot0\cdot\bar{10}\cdot1$	$7\bar3\bar3$	30 00	83 51	30 34	90 00
e	$01\bar12$	110	−30 00	24 54	90 00	68 37
s	$02\bar21$	$11\bar1$	−30 00	61 41½	90 00	40 19
p	$11\bar23$	210	0 00	28 11½	76 20½	76 20½
Ψ	$43\bar77$	$62\bar1$	4 43	38 53½	69 03	74 26½
ρ	$43\bar71$	$40\bar3$	4 43	79 57½	55 53½	65 07½
y	$32\bar51$	$30\bar2$	6 35	76 07	54 38½	67 18½
f	$53\bar88$	$72\bar1$	8 13	39 05	67 02½	76 28
γ	$53\bar82$	$50\bar3$	8 13	58 23	58 12½	71 34½
t	$21\bar34$	310	10 53½	31 33	69 58	80 08½
v	$21\bar31$	$20\bar1$	10 53½	67 51	52 40½	72 21
ω	$31\bar45$	410	16 06	33 48	66 22	82 19½
N	$41\bar53$	$40\bar1$	19 06½	54 48½	51 51	81 07
M	$35\bar87$	$63\bar2$	− 8 13	42 52	75 22½	65 06½
d	$12\bar32$	$21\bar1$	−10 53½	50 50½	75 18	59 29½
S	$3\cdot7\cdot\bar{10}\cdot4$	$17\cdot8\cdot\bar{13}$	−13 00	67 19½	74 21	51 00
α	$25\bar73$	$42\bar3$	−13 54	62 38½	75 44½	51 59½
R	$5\cdot14\cdot\bar{19}\cdot9$	$11\cdot6\cdot\bar8$	−15 17½	63 54½	76 49½	50 20
E	$13\bar41$	$21\bar2$	−16 06	73 22	76 41½	46 20
P	$15\bar62$	$32\bar3$	−21 03	52 16	82 56	52 02½

Structure cell.[4] Space group $R3c$; a_0 10.77, c_0 8.67. $a_0 : c_0 = 1 :$ 0.805; a_{rh} 6.86, α 103°30½'; contains $Ag_6As_2S_6$ in the rhombohedral unit.

Habit. Prismatic to short prismatic [0001]; often rhombohedral with $\{01\bar{1}2\}$ or $\{10\bar{1}1\}$ dominant; also scalenohedral with $\{21\bar{3}1\}$ dominant. Zone e-r frequently striated [$12\bar{3}\bar{1}$]. Also massive, compact.

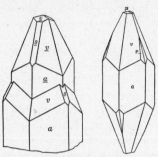 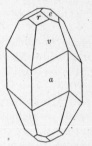

Andreasberg, Harz. Chañarcillo, Chile.

Twinning. (a) On $\{10\bar{1}4\}$ producing trillings and other aggregates. (b) On $\{10\bar{1}1\}$, common. (c) On $\{0001\}$, with composition plane $\{0001\}$. (d) On $\{01\bar{1}2\}$.

Phys. Cleavage $\{10\bar{1}1\}$ distinct. Fracture conchoidal to uneven. Brittle. H. 2–2½. G. 5.57 (pure), 5.62 (calc.). M.P. 490° (artif.[5]). Luster adamantine. Color scarlet-vermilion. Streak vermilion. Translucent.

Opt. In thin pieces transparent to red light.

λ	671 (Li)	589 (Na)	Pleochroism	
O	2.9789	3.0877	Blood-red	Uniaxial neg. $(-)$.
E	2.7113	2.7924	Cochineal-red	

In polished section[6] moderately pleochroic and strongly anisotropic. Reflection percentages: green 28, orange 21.5, red 20.5.

Chem.[7] Silver arsenic sulfide, Ag_3AsS_3, with small amounts of Sb present in most analyzed samples.

Anal.[8]

	1	2	3	4	5	6	7
Ag	65.42	64.12	64.65	65.10	65.38	65.06	64.50
Sb	.....	0.08	trace	.....	0.26	1.41	3.62
As	15.14	15.90	15.25	15.03	14.89	13.85	12.54
S	19.44	19.28	20.18	19.52	19.31	19.64	19.09
Rem.	.....	0.75	0.70	.....	.....	.....	.....
Total	100.00	100.13	100.78	99.65	99.84	99.96	99.75
G.	5.62		5.60	5.555	5.58	5.64	

1. Ag_3AsS_3. 2. Cobalt, Ont. Rem. is Fe 0.25, Co(Ni) 0.12, insol. 0.38.[9] 3. Veta Rica mine, Sierra Mojada, Coahuila, Mexico. Rem. is Cu.[10] 4. Chañarcillo, Chile.[11] 5. Chañarcillo, Chile. Crystals.[12] 6. Chañarcillo, Chile. Crystals.[13] 7. Chañarcillo, Chile. Massive. From same specimen as anal. 6, above.[13]

Tests. F. 1. Decomposed by HNO_3 with separation of S.

Occur. The ruby silvers are found in varying amounts in most silver deposits, which, as a rule, are of low-temperature formation; only the more important specimen localities can be mentioned here. Proustite (and pyrargyrite) is generally one of the late silver minerals in the sequence of primary deposition. In part, however, it may be derived from secondary enrichment processes.[14] The many finely crystallized specimens of ruby silver have generally been found in vugs in the upper portions of vein deposits.

In Bohemia at Joachimstal with sulfides, tetrahedrite, silver and uraninite in a barite-siderite gangue; at Přibram on calcite and marcasite; at Nagyág, Transylvania. In Saxony, especially at the Himmelfürst mine in Freiberg where some of the early described crystals were found; also at Annaberg and Marienberg. In France at Ste. Marie aux Mines, Alsace, as fine crystals principally with tetrahedrite, quartz, and calcite. At Sarrabus, Sardinia. Found at Chañarcillo, Atacama, Chile, in magnificent crystals, some of which were 3 in. long and twinned, associated with other silver minerals, arsenopyrite, and other sulfides in a calcite-barite gangue. In the silver mines at Batopilas, Chihuahua, Mexico, with native silver.

In the United States found in small amounts in many of the silver districts of the western states. In Colorado at Red Mountain, San Juan County, and at Georgetown, Clear Creek County. In Idaho in the Silver City district, Owyhee County, especially at the Poorman mine, where a crystalline mass of proustite weighing over 500 lb. was found (1865). In various Nevada and California mines but not as exceptional specimens. In the Cobalt, Ontario, district, especially at the Keeley mine, South Lorrain, where well-crystallized specimens have been found.

Alter. To argentite, silver or, rarely, cerargyrite or orpiment; pseudomorphs of pyrite, marcasite and pyrrhotite after proustite have been noted. Found as pseudomorphs after argentite, silver, and stephanite.

Artif. Formed in the system Ag_2S-As_2S_3.[15] The compound Ag_3AsS_3 melted congruently at 490° and had G. 5.51.

Name. After the French chemist, J. L. Proust (1755–1826).

Ref.

1. Symmetry by Miers, *Min. Mag.*, **8**, 37 (1888).
2. Ratio of Miers (1888).
3. Forms in Goldschmidt (7, 139, 1922). Also *h, z, f, R, S, E, e* from Ungemach (unpublished notes); *N* from Tokody, *Cbl. Min.*, 117, 1930A. Rare and uncertain forms, in Goldschmidt (1922); Tokody (1930); Parsons, *Min. Mag.*, **17**, 309, 1916; Ungemach (unpublished notes):

0001	13·0·$\overline{13}$·1	54$\overline{9}$1	13·7·$\overline{20}$·6	7·3·$\overline{10}$·13	31$\overline{4}$2	5·9·$\overline{14}$·1
10·1·$\overline{11}$·0	03$\overline{3}$2	19·13·$\overline{32}$·6	8·4·$\overline{12}$·1	52$\overline{7}$9	51$\overline{6}$7	16$\overline{7}$1
60$\overline{6}$1	07$\overline{7}$2	9·5·$\overline{14}$·4	11·5·$\overline{16}$·12	8·3·$\overline{11}$·2	23$\overline{5}$2	2·13·$\overline{15}$·1

No certain criterion for upper and lower forms has been found, although a study of Ungemach's extensive unpublished notes on the subject seems to indicate that the form {13$\overline{4}$1} occurs only on the lower end of crystals and might be used as a criterion, in the same manner as {16$\overline{7}$1} is definitely used in pyrargyrite.

4. Cell dimensions are an average of two closely agreeing determinations by Hocart, *C. R.*, **205**, 68 (1937), and Harker, *J. Chem. Phys.*, **4**, 381 (1936).

5. Jaeger and van Klooster, *Zs. anorg. Chem.*, **78**, 245 (1912), on artificial material.

6. Schneiderhöhn and Ramdohr (**2**, 418, 1931).

7. No evidence of a complete series between the ruby silvers has been presented.

8. Older analyses in Dana (135, 1892) and in Doelter (**4** [1], 250, 1925).

9. Ellsworth in Parsons, *Min. Mag.*, **17**, 309 (1916).

10. Dubois in van Horn, *Am. J. Sc.*, **35**, 23 (1913).

11. Rethwisch, *Jb. Min., Beil.-Bd.*, **4**, 94 (1886).

12. Prior in Miers (1888).

13. Miers and Prior, *Min. Mag.*, **7**, 196 (1887).

14. Ransome, *Econ. Geol.*, **5**, 211 (1910).

15. Jaeger and van Klooster (1912).   See also Hintze (**1** [1], 1074, 1902).

3221   **PYROSTILPNITE** [Ag₃SbS₃].   Feuerblende *Breithaupt* (285, 333, 1832).   Fireblende *Dana* (543, 1850).   Pyrostilpnite *Dana* (93, 1868).   Pyrichrolite *Adam* (60, 1869).   Pyrochrotite *Breithaupt* (in *Frenzel*, 252, 1874).

Cryst.   Monoclinic (?);[1] prismatic — $2/m$.

$a : b : c = 0.3547 : 1 : 0.1782$; $\beta\ 90°00'$; $p_0 : q_0 : r_0 = 0.5024 : 0.1782 : 1$

$r_2 : p_2 : q_2 = 5.6117 : 2.8193 : 1$; $\mu\ 90°00'$; $p_0'\ 0.5024$, $q_0'\ 0.1782$, $x_0'\ 0$

Forms:[3]

		ϕ	$\rho = C$	ϕ_2	ρ_2	A
c	001	....	0°00′	90°00′	90°00′	90°00′
b	010	0°00′	90 00	....	0 00	90 00
a	100	90 00	90 00	0 00	90 00	0 00
δ	140	35 10½	90 00	0 00	35 10½	54 49½
s	120	54 39	90 00	0 00	54 39	35 21
m	110	70 28	90 00	0 00	70 28	19 32
d	101	90 00	26 40½	63 19½	90 00	63 19½
D	1̄01	−90 00	26 40½	116 40½	90 00	116 40½
π	121	54 39	31 38	63 19½	72 20	64 40½
p	141	35 10½	41 05½	63 19½	57 30½	67 45
o	191	17 23½	59 15	63 19½	34 54½	75 07
Π	1̄21	−54 39	31 38	116 40½	72 20	115 19½
P	141	−35 10½	41 05½	116 40½	57 30½	112 15
O	1̄91	−17 23½	59 15	116 40½	34 54½	104 53

Habit. Tabular {010}, frequently forming flat rhombs; also lathlike with elongation [001].   Striated on {010} ‖ terminal edge.   Often in sub-parallel sheaf-like aggregates (like stilbite).

Twinning. On {100} with {100} sometimes as composition plane, often irregular intergrowths.

Phys. Cleavage {010} perfect.   Fracture conchoidal. Slightly flexible in thin plates.   H. 2.   G. 5.94.[4] Luster adamantine.   Color hyacinth-red.   Streak orange-yellow.

Opt. Lemon-yellow by transmitted light. $Y = b$, $X \wedge c = 8°$.   Refractive indices very high.

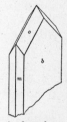

Andreasberg, Harz.

Chem. Silver antimony sulfide, Ag₃SbS₃, identical in composition with pyrargyrite.

Anal.

	Ag	Sb	S	Total
1	59.76	22.48	17.76	100.0
2	59.44	22.30	18.11	99.85

1. Ag_3SbS_3.   2. Andreasberg.[5]

Tests. F. 1.   Decomposed by HNO_3 with separation of S and Sb_2O_3.

O c c u r.   Found with the ruby silvers and other silver minerals at Andreasberg in the Harz and at Přibram, Bohemia. Reported from the Long Tunnel mine, Heazlewood, Tasmania, from Chañarcillo, Atacama, Chile, and from the Silver City district, Owyhee County, Idaho.

N a m e.   From πῦρ, *fire*, and στιλπνός, *shining*, in allusion to its color and luster.

Ref.

1. The monoclinic symmetry given by Luedecke, *Zs. Kr.*, **6**, 570 (1882), is based on optical evidence mainly. However, the symmetry may well be triclinic, with complex twinning, and the platy face ({010} of Luedecke) can then be oriented as {001}, thus bringing into coincidence the orientations of xanthoconite and pyrostilpnite.
2. The ratio here given is from Luedecke (1882). This ratio transformed into an orientation comparable with that of xanthoconite is $a : b : c = 1.9465 : 1 : 1.0973$, $\beta = 90° \pm$, according to Miers, *Min. Mag.*, **10**, 185 (1893), p. 213. As above mentioned, this latter orientation necessitates triclinic symmetry if Luedecke's optical study is valid. Transformation Luedecke to Miers 100/001/0½0.
3. Luedecke (1882).
4. Measured by Berman (priv. comm., 1940) on crystal aggregate of 6 mg. from Andreasberg. The old value of 4.3 (Luedecke, 1882) is obviously too low.
5. Hampe anal. in Luedecke (1882).

3222   Stylotypite [$(Cu,Ag,Fe)_3SbS_3$].   Stylotyp *von Kobell* (*Ak. München, Ber.* **1**, 163, 1865).

C r y s t.   Monoclinic[1]?   Prismatic [001], with square cross-section. Twinned, perhaps on {111},[2] with the individuals intersecting at nearly 90°.

P h y s.   Fracture imperfectly conchoidal to uneven.   H. 3.   G. 4.79; 5.18.   Luster metallic.   Color iron-black.   Streak black.   In polished section[3] gray-white.

C h e m.   Perhaps a copper, iron, and silver antimony sulfide $(Cu,Ag,Fe)_3SbS_3$, with (Cu,Ag): Fe near 5 : 1.

Anal.

	Cu	Fe	Ag	Sb	S	Total	G.
1	28.00	7.00	8.30	30.53	24.30	98.13	4.790
2	30.87	6.27	10.43	28.58	23.12	99.27	5.18

1. Copiapó, Chile.   Trace of Pb and Zn.[4]   2. Copiapó, Chile.   Trace of Zn.[5]

Tests. F. 1.   B.B. decrepitates, and fuses very easily. On charcoal affords a magnetic steel-gray globule and fumes of antimony oxide.

O c c u r.   From Copiapó in Chile. Reported from the Caudalosa mine, Costrovirroyna, Peru, but this material has since been shown[6] to be a mixture of tetrahedrite with enargite, pyrite and wittichenite (?).

N a m e. From στῦλος, *pillar*, and τύπος, *form*, in allusion to the columnar form, in which it differs from tetrahedrite although supposedly approaching that mineral in composition.

Ref.

1. Stevanović measured crystals from the Caudalosa mine, Peru, *Zs. Kr.*, **37**, 235 (1902), but this material was later examined and found to be inhomogeneous by Schneiderhöhn and Ramdohr (**2**, 420, 1931). The ratio of Stevanović is $a : b : c = 1.9202 : 1 : 1.0355$, and the forms found are $a\{100\}$, $m\{110\}$, $n\{210\}$, $u\{310\}$, $d\{032\}$, $r\{101\}$, $t\{302\}$, $s\{401\}$, $x\{111\}$, $y\{332\}$, $\zeta\{313\}$, $o\{311\}$. The ratio is comparable to that of xanthoconite, to which the mineral is supposedly related. See also Groth (**35**, 1898).
2. Stevanović (1902).
3. Davy-Farnham (**94**, 1920) and Murdoch (**97**, 1916) on material of unstated authenticity. The etch tests of these authors do not entirely agree.
4. von Kobell (1865).
5. Stevanović (1902).
6. Schneiderhöhn and Ramdohr (1931) showed that the material of Stevanović's investigation (1902) was a mixture.

3223 **X A N T H O C O N I T E** [Ag_3AsS_3]. Xanthokon *Breithaupt* (*J. pr. Chem.*, **20**, 67, 1840). Rittingerit *Zippe* (*Ak. Wien, Ber.*, **9**, 2, 345, 1852). Xanthoconite *Dana* (108, 1868).

C r y s t. Monoclinic;[1] prismatic — $2/m$.

$a : b : c = 1.9187 : 1 : 1.0152$; $\beta\ 91°13'$; $p_0 : q_0 : r_0 = 0.5291 : 1.0150 : 1$;
$r_2 : p_2 : q_2 = 0.9852 : 1.8900 : 1$; $\mu\ 88°47'$; $p'_0\ 0.5292$, $q'_0\ 1.0152$, $x'_0\ 0.0212$

Forms:[2]

		ϕ	ρ	ϕ_2	ρ_2	C	A
c	001	90°00′	1°13′	88°47′	90°00′	0°00′	88°47′
a	100	90 00	90 00	0 00	90 00	88 47	0 00
m	110	27 32	90 00	0 00	27 32	89 26½	62 28
d	501	90 00	69 27	20 33	90 00	68 14	20 33
D	$\bar{5}$01	−90 00	69 08½	159 08½	90 00	70 21½	159 08½
p	111	28 28	49 06½	61 10½	48 21	48 32½	68 53
q	551	27 43	80 06½	20 33	29 18	79 32½	62 43½
P	$\bar{1}$11	−26 35	48 37½	116 56	47 51	49 10½	109 37
Q	$\bar{5}$51	−27 20½	80 04½	159 08½	28 57½	80 38½	116 54

Habit. Tabular $\{001\}$ and frequently forming flat rhombs; also infrequently lath shaped with elongation [010]. Rarely pyramidal.

Twinning. On $\{001\}$ to produce pseudo-orthorhombic combinations.

P h y s. Cleavage $\{001\}$ distinct. Fracture subconchoidal. Brittle. H. 2–3. G. 5.54 ± 0.14.[3]

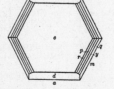

Chañarcillo, Chile.

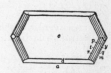

Freiberg; Markirch.

Adamantine luster. Color dark cochineal-red to dull orange to clove-brown; orange-yellow to lemon-yellow in thin splinters. Streak orange-yellow.

O p t.   In transmitted light, lemon-yellow.

$$\left.\begin{array}{l} X \text{ near } c \\ Y \\ Z = b \end{array}\right\} \quad n \text{ near } 3 \qquad \begin{array}{l} \text{Biaxial neg. } (-). \quad 2E\ 125° \pm \\ r < v, \text{ marked.} \\ \text{Biref. extreme.} \end{array}$$

C h e m.[4]   Silver arsenic sulfide, Ag_3AsS_3, identical in composition with proustite.

Anal.

	1	2	3
Ag	65.42	65.15	64.07
As	15.14	14.63	14.98
S	19.44	19.07	14.99
Total	100.00	98.85	94.04

1. Ag_3AsS_3.   2. Freiberg, Saxony.[5]   3. La Rose mine, Cobalt, Ont.   Part of the S lost in analysis.[6]

Tests.   F. 1.   In C.T. at gentle heat the color changes to dark red; the original color is regained on cooling.   At higher temperature fuses and yields a sublimate of arsenic sulfide.

O c c u r.   Found usually with the ruby silvers.   In Bohemia at the Eliaszecke mine, Joachimstal (*rittingerite*), with proustite; at Johanngeorgenstadt; crystals have been reported from Nagyág.   In the Himmelfürst mine at Freiberg, Saxony, as reniform masses with yellow tabular crystals, on calcite with proustite.   At Ste. Marie aux Mines, Alsace, as striated crystals on dolomite, with proustite, calcite and arsenic.   In Chile at the Dolores I mine, Chañarcillo, on pyragyrite with proustite.   In the United States reported from Ouray, Colorado, and from the General Petite mine, Atlanta district, Idaho.   Found at a number of mines in the Cobalt district of Ontario, especially at the La Rose and Keeley mines, as hemispherical radial aggregates of tiny crystals, associated with proustite.

N a m e.   From ξανθός, *yellow*, and κόνις, *powder*, in allusion to its color.

RITTINGERITE.   *Zippe* (*Ak. Wien, Ber.*, **9**, 2, 345, 1852), has been shown[7] to be identical with xanthoconite.

Ref.

1. Crystal system, unit and orientation of Miers, *Min. Mag.*, **10**, 186 (1893).   Crystal class not certain.
2. Miers (1893).   Tokody, *Cbl. Min.*, 122, 1930.   Less common forms: $n\{053\}$, $r\{112\}$, $t\{223\}$, $k\{334\}$, $y\{443\}$, $u\{553\}$, $z\{552\}$, $R\{\bar{1}12\}$, $T\{\bar{2}23\}$, $K\{\bar{3}34\}$, $Y\{\bar{4}43\}$, $U\{\bar{5}53\}$.
3. An average of the two best determinations by Prior (in Miers [1893]).   Other values range from 4.11 by Breithaupt (1840) to 5.41 ± 0.10 (Berman, on 4 mg., priv. comm., 1939).
4. The earlier ascribed composition, based on incomplete analyses by Plattner, *Ann. Phys.*, **44**, 275 (1845), was shown to be in error by Prior (in Miers [1893]).   The earlier report of Se in rittingerite by Schrauf, *Ak. Wien, Ber.*, **45**, 227 (1872), was shown to be in error by Prior and others.
5. Prior in Miers (1893).
6. Todd anal. in Parsons, *Univ. Toronto Stud., Geol. Ser.*, **17**, 11 (1924).
7. Miers (1893).

323   **W I T T I C H E N I T E** [Cu$_3$BiS$_3$].   Kupferwismutherz *Selb* (*Denks. Nat. Schwaben*, **1**, 419, 1805); *Klaproth* (**4**, 91, 1807). Bismuth sulfuré cuprifère *Fr.* Cupreous Bismuth; Cupriferous Sulphuret of Bismuth.   Wismuth-Kupfererz *Leonhard* (1826).   Wittichite *Kobell* (13, 1853).   Wittichenite *Kenngott* (1853, 118, 1855).

C r y s t.[1]   Orthorhombic ?.

Forms:

{001}   {010}   {100}   {011}   {101}

Habit.   Tabular {001}; also columnar or acicular.   Massive.
P h y s.   Fracture conchoidal.   H. 2–3.   G. 4.3–4.5.[2]   Color steel-gray to tin-white, tarnishing pale lead-gray.   Streak black.   In polished section[3] weakly anisotropic.   Reflection percentages: green 35, orange 29.5, red 28.
C h e m.   Perhaps copper bismuth sulfide, Cu$_3$BiS$_3$, with small amounts of As, Sb, substituting for the Bi, and Ag, Fe, Zn, substituting in small part for Cu.
Anal.[4]

	Cu	Ag	Fe	Zn	Bi	Sb	As	S	Total	G.
1	38.46	....	....	....	42.15	....	....	19.39	100.00	
2	36.22	....	....	....	44.34	....	....	19.44	100.00	
3	36.76	0.15	0.35	0.13	41.13	0.41	0.79	20.30	100.02	4.45

1. Cu$_3$BiS$_3$.   2. Neuglück mine, Wittichen.   Chalcopyrite and native bismuth deducted.[5]   3. King David mine, Wittichen.[6]

Tests.   F. 1.   B.B. fuses easily, at first throwing out sparks.   Soluble in HCl with evolution of H$_2$S; decomposed by HNO$_3$ with separation of S.

O c c u r.[7]   From the Neuglück, Daniel, King David, and other mines near Wittichen, in the Black Forest, Baden, intergrown with barite and fluorite.   Also reported from Colquijirca, Peru.
A l t e r.   Undergoes easy alteration, becoming yellowish brown, then red and blue externally, forming covellite apparently; also alters to a greenish earthy mineral, which is a mixture of malachite, bismuth oxide, and limonite; also to earthy yellow bismutite and bismuth-ocher.
A r t i f.   Reported from melts in the system Cu-Bi-S;[8] also reported by precipitation by H$_2$S from a solution of BiCl$_3$ and CuCl.[9]

Ref.

1. Breithaupt (111, 1866) in Goldschmidt (**9**, 82, 1923).   Measurements not given. Said to be similar in habit and morphology to bournonite.
2. Phillips, *Min. Mag.*, **23**, 458 (1933), p. 460, points out that the specific gravities given are obviously too low.   His calculation, from reflectivity data, yields a value 6.2.
3. Schneiderhöhn and Ramdohr (**2**, 421, 1931).
4. Older analyses in Doelter (4 [1], 138, 1925).
5. Petersen anal. in Sandberger, *Jb. Min.*, 415, 1868.
6. Petersen, *Ann. Phys.*, **136**, 501 (1869).
7. A number of indefinite occurrences have been cited in the literature, but evidence of identity with wittichenite is not given.   For the Peruvian occurrence see Lindgren, *Econ. Geol.*, **30**, 331 (1935).
8. Gaudin and Dicke, *Econ. Geol.*, **34**, 214 (1939).
9. Schneider, *Ann. Phys.*, 127, 317, 1866.

Tetrahedrite Series

3241   **T E T R A H E D R I T E** [$(Cu,Fe)_{12}Sb_4S_{13}$].   Argentum arsenico cupro et ferro mineralisatum, Falerts, Grauerts, Graue Silbererz, Minera argenti grisea *Wallerius* (313, 1747).   Falerz, Argentum cupro et antimonio sulph. mineralisatum *Cronstedt* (157, 1758).   Pyrites cupri griseus, Fahlkupfererz *Cronstedt* (175, 1758).   Argentum cinereum crystallis pyramidatis trigonis *von Born* (**1**, 82, 1772).   Cuprum cinereum cryst. trigonis, etc. *von Born* (**1**, 108, 1772).   Fahlerz, Kupferfahlerz, Kupferantimonglanz, Spiessglanzerz, Spiessglanzfahlerz, Schwarzerz pt., Antimonfahlerz *Germ.* Graugültigerz pt. *Germ.*   Mine de cuivre grise *de Lisle* (3, 315, 1783).   Cuivre gris *Fr.* Cobre gris, Pavonado *Span.*   Gray Copper Ore.   Panabase *Beudant* (**2**, 438, 1832). Tetraëdrit *Haidinger* (563, 1845).   Clinoëdrit pt., Fahlit *Breithaupt* (*B. H. Ztg.*, **25**, 181, 1866).   Nepaulite *Piddington* (*J. Asiatic Soc.*, **23**, 170, 1854).   Studerite *Fellenberg* (*Mitt. Ges. Bern*, 178, 1864).   Fieldite pt. *Kenngott* (126, 1855).

Argentum rude album pt. *Agricola* (362, 1546).   Weisgylden, Weissgülden, Minera argenti alba pt. *Wallerius* (312, 1747); *Cronstedt* (156, 1758).   Weissgültigerz pt., Graugültigerz pt., Schwarzgiltigerz pt., Dunkles Weissgiltigerz *Germ.*   Merkurfahlerz *Breithaupt* (**3**, 124, 1816).   Quecksilberfahlerz *Glocker* (33, 1847).   Silberfahlerz *Hausmann* (179, 1847).   Polytelit *Kobell* (10, 1853) (not of *Glocker* [31, 1847]).   Apthonit *Svanberg* (*Jahresber. Chem. Min.*, **27**, 236, 1848).   Freibergite *Kenngott* (117, 1853). Spaniolith *Kobell* (98, 1853).   Schwatzit *Kenngott* (117, 1853).   Schwazit.   Fournetite pt. *Mène* (*C.R.*, **51**, 463, 1860).   Kobaltfahlerz *Sandberger* (*Jb. Min.*, 584, 1865). Hermesit *Breithaupt* (105, 1866).   Coppite *Bechi* in *D'Achiardi* (**2**, 341, 1873).   Leukargyrit *Weisbach* (62, 1875).   Malinowskit *Raimondi* in *Domeyko* (App. 5, 1876); *Raimondi* (122, 1878).   Bleisilberfahlerz *Germ.*   Frigidite *D'Achiardi* (*Att. soc. tosc.*, 172, 1881).   Nickelfahlerz *Arzruni* (*Zs. Kr.*, 7, 629, 1884).

3242   **T E N N A N T I T E** [$(Cu,Fe)_{12}As_4S_{13}$].   Gray Sulphuret of Copper in dodecahedral crystals *Sowerby* (1817).   Tennantite *Wm. and R. Phillips* (*Q. J. Sc.*, 7, 95, 100, 1819).   Arsenikalfahlerz, Arsenikfahlerz, Arsenkupferfahlerz, Lichtes Arsenfahlerz *Germ.*   Binnite pt. *Des Cloizeaux* (*Ann. mines*, **8**, 389, 1855).   Cuprobinnite *Weisbach* (42, 1880).   Regnolite *D'Achiardi* (**1**, 293, 294, 1883).   Julianite *Websky* (*Zs. deutsche geol. Ges.*, **23**, 486, 1871).

Kupferblende *Breithaupt* (131, 251, 1823; *Ann. Phys.*, **9**, 613, 1827).   Annivite *Brauns* (*Mitt. Ges. Bern*, 57, 1854).   Sandbergerit *Breithaupt* (*B. H. Ztg.*, **25**, 187, 1866).   Erythroconite *Adam* (59, 1869).   Zinkfahlerz *Germ.*   Rionit *Brauns, Petersen* (*Jb. Min.*, 590, 1870).   Wismuthfahlerz *Petersen* (*Jb. Min.*, 464, 1870).   Cuprobinnit *Weisbach* (42, 1880).   Fredricite *Sjögren* (*Geol. För. Förh.*, **5**, 82, 1880).   Kobaltwismuthfahlerz *Sandberger* (392, 1885).   Miedziankite *Morozewicz* (*Spraw. Polsk. Inst. Geol.*, **2**, 1, 1923).

C r y s t.   Isometric; hextetrahedral — $\bar{4}\, 3\, m$.

Forms:[1]

a	001	f	013	ω	115	m	113	β	223	r	233
d	011	e	012	μ	114	n	112	Γ	255	−r	$\bar{2}33$
o	111	φ	116	−μ	$\bar{1}14$	−n	$\bar{1}12$	p	122	s	123
−o	$\bar{1}11$	−φ	$\bar{1}16$					Δ	477	−s	$\bar{1}23$

The form list is essentially the same for tetrahedrite and tennantite.

Structure cell.[2]   Space group $I\bar{4}3m$; a_0 10.19 (for nearly pure tennantite) to 10.33 (for nearly pure tetrahedrite); 10.40 (for silver-rich tetrahedrite from Freiberg).   Contains $(Cu,Fe,Zn,Ag)_{24}(Sb,As)_8S_{26}$.

Habit.   Tetrahedral; sometimes as groups of parallel crystals.   Also massive, coarse or fine granular to compact.   Commonest forms: $a\, d\, o\, -o\, f\, n\, -n\, -r$.

Twinning.[3] (*a*) Twin axis [111] with composition face ‖ or ⊥ to {111}. Also penetration twins. Often repeated.

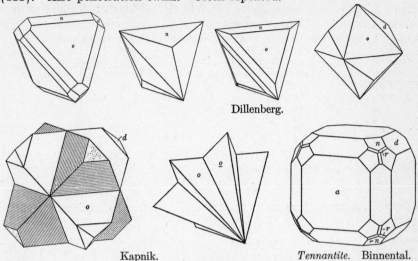

Dillenberg.

Kapnik.   *Tennantite.* Binnental.

P h y s. Cleavage none.[4] Fracture subconchoidal to uneven. Rather brittle. H. 3–4½ (with tennantite harder than tetrahedrite). G. 4.6–5.1, increasing with content of Sb.

Tennantite	4.62, anal. 42	calc. 4.61
Tetrahedrite	4.97, anal. 3	calc. 4.99
Ag-tetrahedrite	5.05, anal. 23	
Hg-tetrahedrite	5.10, anal. 26	

Luster metallic, often splendent. Color flint-gray to iron-black to dull black (Hg-tetrahedrite). Streak from black to brown to cherry-red (high As, and low Fe). Opaque except in very thin splinters, which are cherry-red by transmitted light, with $n_{Li} > 2.72$.[5] In polished section[6] gray inclining to olive-brown, isotropic. Slight variations in reflectivity with compositional changes. Reflection percentages:

	GREEN	ORANGE	RED	
Tetrahedrite	27	24	20.5	
Tennantite	29.5	24	21.5	Tsumeb

C h e m.[7] Essentially copper, iron, zinc, and silver, antimony and arsenic sulfide, $(Cu,Fe,Zn,Ag)_{12}(Sb,As)_4S_{13}$. Cu is always predominant, but considerable substitution takes place, most commonly by Fe and Zn, less commonly by Ag, Hg, and perhaps Pb. Bi sometimes substitutes for As in part (anal. 32). The Sb-As elements apparently form a complete series from tetrahedrite to tennantite, respectively, with the line between the two species here placed at Sb : As = 1 : 1.

The extent to which the various elements substitute for the Cu, to form the varieties, is not accurately known, since many of the most pronounced variations are based on early analyses of unknown worth. The following tabulation of probable maximum weight percentages of substituting elements is based on those analyses which fit the tetrahedrite formula at least moderately well. This criterion is not too safe since considerable contamination by sphalerite or galena would not affect the formula greatly.

	Tetrahedrite		Tennantite	
	Per cent	Anal. no.	Per cent	Anal. no.
Fe	13	30	11	34
Zn	8	31	9	36
Ag	18	24	14	33
Hg	17	26	..	..
Pb	16?	..	4?	..
Ni	4	28	..	..
Co	4	29	1	32
Bi	4	29	13	32

Anal.

	1	2	3	4	5	6
Cu	45.77	45.39	41.55	37.75	37.70	37.42
Fe	.....	1.32	1.02	1.10	5.13	6.60
Zn	.....	.....	2.63	6.51	3.87	1.72
Ag	.....	.....	.....	0.11	trace	.....
Hg	.....	.....	.....	.....	.....	.....
Pb	.....	0.11	0.62	0.71	.....	trace
Ni	.....	.....	.....	.....	.....	0.23
Co	.....	.....	.....	.....	.....	.....
Bi	.....	.....	0.83	0.53	.....	.....
Sb	29.22	28.85	28.32	28.66	26.81	29.28
As	.....	trace	trace	.....	trace	trace
S	25.01	24.48	24.33	24.61	26.49	25.70
Rem.	.....				.....	
Total	100.00	100.15	99.30	99.98	100.00	100.95
G.	4.99	4.921	4.969	5.079		

1. $Cu_{12}Sb_4S_{13}$. 2. Tetrahedrite. Bourg d'Oisan, France. Crystals.[9] 3. Tetrahedrite. Horhausen. Crystals.[9] 4. Zincian tetrahedrite. Horhausen. Crystals.[10] 5. Ferroan tetrahedrite. Hypotheek mine, Shoshone Co., Id. Recalc. after deducting quartz.[11] 6. Ferroan tetrahedrite. Frigido, near Mossa, Italy.[18]

	7	8	9	10	11	12
Cu	37.22	38.95	39.16	37.93	38.59	38.52
Fe	0.80	4.77	2.00	0.60	1.05	0.94
Zn	6.59	2.21	4.87	7.57	6.16	7.05
Ag	1.51	0.02	trace	0.45	0.68	0.08
Hg	.....	.....	.....	.....	.....	.....
Pb	0.33	.....	.....	.....	.....	.....
Ni	.....	.....	.....	.....	.....	.....
Co	.....	.....	0.23	.....	.....	.....
Bi	.....	.....	.....	.....	.....	.....
Sb	26.61	27.00	25.71	26.12	24.98	25.26
As	0.38	1.40	1.68	1.84	2.25	2.69
S	25.16	25.66	24.48	25.21	25.35	25.22
Rem.	0.75	.....	1.08	.....	0.14	.....
Total	99.35	100.01	99.21	99.72	99.20	99.76
G.	4.986	4.68	4.781	4.780	4.794	4.736

7. Zincian tetrahedrite. Botés, Transylvania. Rem. is Mn 0.69, insol. 0.06.[12] 8. Ferroan tetrahedrite. Hornachuelos, Spain. Massive.[10] 9. Zincian tetrahedrite. Besimjanni, Altai Mts. Rem. is Se 0.13, insol. 0.95.[21] 10. Zincian tetrahedrite. Schemnitz. Crystals.[10] 11. Zincian tetrahedrite. Kapnik. Crystals.[10] 12. Zincian tetrahedrite. Dillenburg. Crystals.[10]

	13	14	15	16	17	18
Cu	36.10	40.57	37.87	38.15	40.91	42.35
Fe	0.78	4.53	0.95	3.77	2.57	4.31
Zn	6.44	1.61	7.58	5.05	4.85	1.48
Ag	1.51	0.03	1.49	trace	0.23	0.09
Hg	.....	1.52	.....	.....	0.80	.....
Pb	2.72	.....	.....	0.53	.....	.....
Ni	.....	.....	.....	.....	.....	.....
Co	.....	.....	.....	.....	.....	.....
Bi	.....	.....	.....	1.63	.....	.....
Sb	24.00	20.60	21.30	17.47	15.77	14.51
As	2.75	5.07	5.54	6.75	9.03	10.24
S	24.99	25.21	25.66	25.58	26.34	26.38
Rem.	0.58	0.75	0.02		.....	.....
Total	99.87	99.89	100.41	98.93	100.50	99.36
G.	4.87	4.651		4.82	4.738	4.74

13. Zincian tetrahedrite. Botés. Crystals. Rem. is Mn 0.26, insol. 0.32. Sum given as 100.13 in original.[10] 14. Ferroan tetrahedrite. Kotterbach, Hungary. Rem. is barite.[10] 15. Zincian tetrahedrite. Anchor mine, Park City district, Utah. Rem. is Mn.[13] 16. Zincian tetrahedrite. Val de Villé, Alsace.[14] 17. Tetrahedrite. Brixlegg, Tirol.[10] 18. Ferroan tetrahedrite. Mouzaia, Algiers.[10]

	19	20	21	22	23	24
Cu	33.39	34.15	22.14	29.99	30.56	25.23
Fe	4.64	3.79	0.93	3.29	3.51	3.72
Zn	3.53	4.86	6.22	2.49	trace	3.10
Ag	4.86	5.94	11.20	12.74	15.26	17.71
Hg	.....	.....	.....	.....	.....	.....
Pb	.....	.....	9.38	0.25	.....	.....
Ni	trace	.....	.....	.....	0.05	.....
Co	.....	.....	.....	.....	.....	.....
Bi	0.34	.....	.....	.....	.....	.....
Sb	25.22	25.24	28.22	26.42	27.73	26.63
As	1.46	1.21	0.23	0.58	trace	.....
S	25.74	25.22	21.68	23.71	23.15	23.52
Rem.	.....	.....	.....	.....	.....	.....
Total	99.18	100.41	100.00	99.47	100.26	99.91
G.		5.10	5.082	4.769	5.047	

19. Argentian tetrahedrite. Ramshorn mine, Custer Co., Id.[22] 20. Argentian tetrahedrite. Val de Villé.[14] 21. Argentian tetrahedrite. West Kootenai district, B. C. 5.6 per cent quartz deducted.[15] 22. Argentian tetrahedrite. Huanchaca, Bolivia.[10] 23. Argentian tetrahedrite. Wolfach, Baden. Crystals.[9] 24. Argentian tetrahedrite. Wolfach, Baden.[23]

	25	26	27	28	29	30
Cu	32.76	32.19	33.30	30.04	33.83	30.10
Fe	1.46	1.41	2.66	9.83	6.40	13.08
Zn	0.38	0.10	5.32	0.59	.....	.....
Ag	1.51	.....	1.70	.....	1.37	.....
Hg	13.71	17.32	0.75	.....	.....	.....
Pb	trace	.....	0.83	0.26	.....	.....
Ni	.....	.....	2.49	3.46	trace	.....
Co	.....	0.23	.....	.....	4.21	.....
Bi	trace	1.57	.....	.....	4.55	.....
Sb	27.90	23.45	23.44	28.82	14.72	29.61
As	0.84	0.31	4.48	1.50	6.98	.....
S	20.60	21.90	23.83	24.48	26.40	27.01
Rem.	0.18	1.39	0.26	.....	.....	.....
Total	99.34	99.87	99.06	98.98	98.46	99.80
G.		5.095	4.779		4.9	4.713

25. Mercurian tetrahedrite. Iveia, Piedmont.[17] 26. Mercurian tetrahedrite. Moschellandsberg.[8] Rem. is gangue.[16] 27. Nickelian (and zincian) tetrahedrite. Müsen,

Siegerland. Rem. is insol.[10] 28. Nickelian (and ferroan) tetrahedrite (*frigidite*). Frigido, near Massa, Italy.[18] 29. Cobaltian (and bismuthian, ferroan) tetrahedrite. Freudenstadt.[24] 30. Ferroan tetrahedrite. Frigido, Massa, Italy.[19]

	31	32	33	34	35	36	37
Cu	35.64	35.72	35.72	42.22	42.05	43.40	44.50
Fe	0.80	6.51	0.42	10.90	1.48	0.10	0.62
Zn	8.19	.....	6.90	0.63	6.09	9.26	7.28
Ag	0.18	0.04	13.65	.....	0.04	0.06	0.02
Hg	2.67	.....	.....	.....	.....	.....	.....
Pb	.....	.....	0.86	.....	.....	0.15	0.35
Ni	.....	.....	.....	.....	.....	.....	.....
Co	.....	1.20	.....	.....	.....	.....	.....
Bi	.....	13.07	.....	.....	.....	.....	.....
Sb	28.07	2.19	0.13	.....	10.87	4.35	trace
As	.....	11.44	17.18	13.34	12.57	18.80	18.76
S	24.74	29.10	25.04	29.09	27.12	23.00	27.58
Rem.	.....	.....	.....	3.56	.....	0.90	0.26
Total	100.29	99.27	99.90	99.74	100.22	100.02	99.37
G.					4.597	4.61	

31. Zincian tetrahedrite. M. Avanza.[20] 32. Bismuthian tennantite (*rionite*). Cremenz.[25] 33. Argentian tennantite. Mollie Gibson mine, Aspen, Colo.[26] 34. Ferroan tennantite. Osaruzawa, Akita Prefect, Japan. Rem. is SiO_2.[27] 35. Tennantite (*sandbergerite*). San Lorenzo mine, Santiago, Chile.[10] 36. Zincian tennantite. Tsumeb, South-West Africa. Rem. is Au 0.01, insol. 0.89. Average of two analyses.[28] 37. Zincian tennantite. Tsumeb, South-West Africa. Rem. is Ge 0.14, Se 0.06, SiO_2 0.06.[29]

	38	39	40	41	42	43	44
Cu	42.03	42.15	48.50	44.12	49.83	53.24	51.57
Fe	0.62	5.44	2.77	3.68	1.11	1.58	.....
Zn	7.76	2.62	.....	.....	.....	0.23	.....
Ag	1.24	1.31	0.23	4.77	1.87	.....	.....
Hg	.....	.....	.....	.....	.....	.....	.....
Pb	.....	.....	.....	.....	0.17	.....	.....
Ni	.....	.....	.....	.....	.....	.....	.....
Co	.....	.....	.....	.....	.....	.....	.....
Bi	.....	.....	.....	.....	.....	.....	.....
Sb	.....	4.66	2.44	.....	.....	.....	.....
As	19.80	16.68	18.82	[20.49]	19.04	18.29	20.26
S	28.08	27.61	27.04	26.94	27.60	26.54	28.17
Rem.	.....	.....	0.44	.....	.....	0.23	.....
Total	99.53	100.47	100.24	100.00	99.62	100.11	100.00
G.	4.61	4.576	4.692	4.598	4.62	4.746	4.61

38. Tennantite (*binnite*). Binnental.[30] 39. Tennantite. Guanajuato, Mexico. Crystals.[10] 40. Tennantite. Kupferberg, Saxony.[10] 41. Tennantite (*binnite*). Binnental.[9] 42. Tennantite (*binnite*). Binnental.[9] 43. Tennantite. Illogen, near Redruth, Cornwall. Rem. is insol.[10] 44. $Cu_{12}As_4S_{13}$.

Var.

A. ANTIMONIAN MEMBERS — TETRAHEDRITE

1. *Ordinary.* Contains Zn, Fe, and Ag in amounts less than a few per cent. Anal. 2, 3.

2. *Zincian.* Zn is commonly present in small amounts, and apparently does not exceed about 8 or 9 per cent. Anal. 9 to 13.

3. *Ferroan.* Coppite *Bechi* in *D'Achiardi* (**2**, 341, 1873). Fe is commonly present in amounts up to 9 per cent, sometimes up to 13 per cent. Anal. 28 to 30.

4. *Argentian.* Freibergite. Argentum rude album pt. *Agricola* (362, 1546). Weisgylden, Weissgülden, Minera argenti alba pt. *Wallerius* (312, 1747); *Cronstedt* (156, 1758). Weissgültigerz pt., Graugültigerz pt., Schwarzgiltigerz pt., Dunkles Weissgiltigerz *Germ.* Silberfahlerz *Hausmann* (179, 1847). Apthonite *Svanberg* (*Jahresber. Chem. Min.*, 27, 236, 1848). Freibergit *Kenngott* (117, 1853). Polytelit *Kobell* (10, 1853), (not of *Glocker* [31, 1847]). Leukargyrit *Weisbach* (612, 1875).

Contains Ag in amounts up to 18 per cent, usually, however, in amounts less than 5 per cent. Anal. 19 to 24.

5. *Mercurian.* Schwatzite. Schwarzerz pt. *Werner.* Merkurfahlerz *Breithaupt* (3, 124, 1816). Quecksilberfahlerz *Glocker* (33, 1847). Graugiltigerz pt. *Hausmann.* Spaniolith *Kobell* (98, 1853). Schwatzit *Kenngott* (117, 1853). Hermesit *Breithaupt* (105, 1866). Schwazit.

Contains Hg, in amounts up to 17 per cent. Anal. 25 to 26.

6. *Plumbian.* Malinowskit *Raimondi* in *Domeyko* (App. 5, 1876); *Raimondi* (122, 1878). Bleisilberfahlerz pt. *Germ.* Fournetite pt. *Mène* (*C.R.*, 51, 463, 1860).

Pb has been reported up to 16 per cent. The validity of this variety is open to question, since Pb does not ordinarily substitute for the other metals found in tetrahedrite. Anal. 21.

7. *Bismuthian.* Contains Bi, usually in amounts less than 2 per cent. Anal. 29.

8. *Nickelian.* Frigidite *D'Achiardi* (*Att. soc. tosc.*, 172, 1881). Nickelfahlerz *Arzruni* (*Zs. Kr.*, 7, 629, 1884).

Contains Ni up to about 4 per cent. Anal. 27, 28.

9. *Cobaltian.* Kobaltfahlerz *Sandberger* (*Jb. Min.*, 584, 1865).

Co has been reported up to 4 per cent in some bismuthian tetrahedrites. Anal. 29.

B. ARSENIAN MEMBERS — TENNANTITE

1. *Ordinary.* Contains Zn, Fe, and Ag in small amounts. Anal. 42, 43.

2. *Zincian.* Kupferblende *Breithaupt* (131, 251, 1823; *Ann. Phys.*, 9, 613, 1827). Sandbergerit *Breithaupt* (*B.H. Ztg.*, 25, 187, 1866). Erythroconite *Adam* (59, 1869). Zinkfahlerz *Germ.* Miedziankite *Morozewicz* (*Spraw. Polsk. Inst. Geol.*, 2, 1, 1923).

Zn is commonly present in amounts up to 9 per cent. Anal. 36 to 38.

3. *Ferroan.* Fe is commonly present in amounts up to 11 per cent. Anal. 34.

4. *Argentian.* Binnite pt. *Des Cloizeaux* (*Ann. mines*, 8, 389, 1855). Cuprobinnite *Weisbach* (42, 1880). Fredricite *Sjögren* (*Geol. För. Förh.*, 5, 82, 1880).

Contains Ag, usually in amounts less than 6 per cent but as much as 14 per cent as a maximum. Anal. 41, 42.

5. *Bismuthian.* Annivit *Brauns* (*Mitt. Ges. Bern*, 57, 1854). Rionit *Brauns, Petersen* (*Jb. Min.*, 590, 1870). Wismuthfahlerz *Petersen* (*Jb. Min.*, 464, 1870). Kobaltwismuthfahlerz *Sandberger* (392, 1885).

Contains Bi, in amounts up to 13 per cent. Anal. 32.

Tests. F. 1. Decomposed by HNO_3 with the separation of S and (in the antimonian varieties) Sb_2O_3.

Occur. Tetrahedrite is one of the most common of sulfosalts, widespread in its occurrence and varied in its association. It is sometimes an ore of copper, and the argentian varieties may be an important ore of silver. Tetrahedrite and tennantite typically occur in hydrothermal veins of copper, lead, zinc, and silver minerals formed at low to moderate temperatures. Rarely in higher temperature veins (Cornwall; Broken Hill), or in contact metamorphic deposits (Fahlun). The principal associated minerals are chalcopyrite, galena, pyrite, sphalerite, bornite, and argentite, also the ruby silvers, polybasite, and bournonite. Gangue minerals associated are calcite, dolomite, siderite, barite, fluorite, and quartz.

Oriented growths have been described of galena, pyrite, stannite, chalcopyrite, and sphalerite upon tetrahedrite, and of tetrahedrite upon sphalerite and chalcopyrite.[31] Thin oriented coatings with a satin-like sheen of chalcopyrite upon tetrahedrite-tennantite are often noted.

The following occurrences are important because of the considerable quantities of tetrahedrite found, or for the fine specimens described from the locality. In Germany at Freiberg, in part argentian (*freibergite*), and at Gersdorf in Saxony; in the Harz at Clausthal, Andreasberg, and Neudorf; at Horhausen, Rhenish Prussia, in fine crystals accompanying siderite, bournonite, and galena; at Dillenburg, Hesse-Nassau; a nickelian variety at Müsen, Westphalia; from Wolfach, Baden; mercurian varieties occur at Moschellandsberg, Bavaria, with cinnabar and amalgam, at Roznava, Poracs, and Kotterbach, near Neudorf, Harz, and near Schwatz, Tirol, in dull dodecahedral crystals (*schwatzite*) associated with galena, siderite, dolomite, malachite, and azurite in veinlets in dolomite. From Gardsjön, Sweden (*apthonite*). Found in exceptional crystals at Botés, near Zalatna, and at Kapnik, Roumania. From Pribram, Bohemia, and at Schemnitz. In France at Ste. Marie aux Mines in fine crystals, and at Framont and Urbeis, in Alsace; in the mines of Pontigibaud, Puy-de-Dôme, and at Baigorry, Basses-Pyrénées; at Cabrières in Hérault. In Switzerland at Brixlegg, and at Ausserberg, near Grosstrog, Valais (*studerite*). From the mines of the Val de Frigido, near Massa in the Apuan Alps, Tuscany (*frigidite, coppite*); a mercurian variety at Pietrosanto. In Algeria near Tenès and Mouzaía. Occurs in fine specimens in the copper-tin veins of Cornwall, especially at the Herodsfoot mine at Liskeard in crystals coated with chalcopyrite, at Wheal Prosper near Falmouth, and the Levant mine, St. Just. In Bolivia at the Pulacayo mine, Huanachaca, and at Oruro and Potosí. In Peru at Huallanca, Casapalca, Cerro de Pasco, Morococha, and Huaraz (*malinowskite*). In Chile at Tres Puntas and San Antonio in Copiapó; mercurian varieties occur at Punitaqui, Audacollo, Talco, and Huasco. In New South Wales at the Broken Hill mine with dyscrasite, chalcostibite, and chalcopyrite.

In the United States tetrahedrite is widespread in the western mining districts and often is an important ore of silver. In Idaho, common in the lead-silver ores of the Wood River district, Blaine County, in large amounts in the Bayhorse district, Custer County, in the Coeur d'Alene district as the principal silver-bearing mineral. In Utah in the Little Cottonwood district and in fine crystallizations at Bingham, Salt Lake County; as an important copper ore in the Park City district. In Montana at Butte, and also in the Flint Creek district, Granite County. Found abundantly in silver ores in Colorado: in the Aspen district, Pitkin County, in the Georgetown and Silver Plume districts in Clear Creek County, in the Rico district, Dolores County, at the Ulay mine near Lake City in Hinsdale County, near Whitecross, the Bear Creek district and elsewhere in San Juan County, abundant in silver ores in Ouray and San Miguel counties. In New Mexico in Socorro County at Cooney and near Pueblo Springs, in Sierra County at Chloride, Hermosa, and Kingston. Occurs in Nevada in the Cortez district, Lander County; in the gold-silver veins of the Humboldt and Piute ranges in Humboldt County; at Columbia, Elko County. In Arizona at the Heintzelman and Silver King mines, Pinal County, and in the Bradshaw Mountain district, Yavapai County. Found in California at numerous localities, notably the Cerro Gordo and Panamint districts, Inyo County, in the Silver Mountain district, Alpine County, and at Nevada City in Nevada County. In Canada at the West Kootenai mine, Windermere district, British Columbia (mercurian).

Tennantite is less widely distributed than tetrahedrite. It has been found in the Cornish mines, particularly at Wheal Jewel in Gwennap, Wheal Unity in Gwinear, the East Relistan mine, at Carn Brea, and at Roskear and Dolcoath in Camborne. In Norway at Modum and Skutterud; at Kupferberg-Rudelstadt in Silesia (*julianite*). At Guanajuato and at the Caridad mine, Sonora, Mexico; at Huallanca and Colquijirca, Peru. The argentian variety *binnite* occurs in the Binnental, Switzerland, in cavities in dolomite as complex crystals with sartorite, dufrenoysite, realgar, and sphalerite; with geocronite and galena at Fahlun, Sweden. Zincian varieties are found at Freiberg, Saxony (*kupferblende*), Miedzianka, near Kielce, Poland (*miedziankite*), Morococha, Yauli, Peru (*sandbergerite*), with germanite at Tsumeb, South-West Africa, and at Onzin, Hokaidô, Korea. Bismuthian varieties occur in the Annivierthal (*annivite*) and at Cremenz (*rionite*) in Ober-Wallis, Switzerland; also from Neubalach, Württemberg, Germany (*wismuthfahlerz*).

In the United States tennantite is found in Colorado in Clear Creek County, at the Freeland Lode and the Crocett mine, Idaho Springs, associated with siderite, pyrite and chalcopyrite, and in the Silver Plume and Georgetown districts; in the Central City and Russell Gulch districts, Gilpin County; with polybasite at Aspen, Pitkin County; in the Red Mountain district, San Juan County; reported from Ouray and Hinsdale counties; in the Bonanza district, Saguache County. Much of the ore called tetrahedrite in Colorado is said to be tennantite. In Idaho in the Humming Bird mine, St. Charles district, Bear Lake County; in Utah at

Philipsburg; with enargite at Butte, Montana; in North Carolina at the McMakin mine, Cabarrus County; in Virginia at the Elridge mine, Buckingham County. In Canada at Capelton, Quebec; in Barrie Township, Frontenac County, Ontario; in the Lilloet district, British Columbia.

Alter. Malachite, azurite, and antimony oxides (chiefly bindheimite) are the usual oxidation products of tetrahedrite; also cuprite, limonite, chrysocolla, and, from the arsenian members, pitticite, erythrite, and other arsenates; the mercurian varieties may afford earthy cinnabar. Chalcopyrite and, rarely, covellite, pyrite, bournonite, amalgam, and sphalerite have been found as pseudomorphs after tetrahedrite.

Artif.[32] Obtained in tetrahedral crystals of varying composition by the reaction at red heat in a closed tube of $CuCl$, $FeCl_2$, $AgCl$, etc., with H_2S and $SbCl_3$ or $AsCl_3$; also in tetrahedra by heating a mixture of Cu_2S and Sb_2S_3 in H_2S; both tetrahedrite and tennantite have been reported from fusions in the system Cu-Sb-As-S. Observed incrusting Roman coins in the hot spring of Bourbonne-le-Bains.

Name. Tetrahedrite in allusion to the tetrahedral form of the crystals. Tennantite after the English chemist Smithson Tennant (1761–1815). Fahlerz, *gray ore, Germ.*

The following are discredited or doubtful species now referred to the tetrahedrite series.

REGNOLITE. *D'Achiardi* (1, 293, 294, 1883; *Nuovo Cimento*, 3, 1890). In tetrahedral crystals, essentially $Cu_5FeZnAs_2S_{12}$, associated with zincian tetrahedrite at the Jucud mines, Cajamarca, Peru. Shown to be tennantite.[33]

FIELDITE. *Field* (*J. Chem. Soc.*, 4, 332, 1851). Fieldit *Kenngott* (126, 1855). From Altar, near Coquimbo, Chile. Close to tetrahedrite in composition and probably impure.

POLYTELITE. *Glocker* (31, 1847). From Freiberg, Saxony. Said to contain Pb, Ag, Sb, S and is probably an impure tetrahedrite.[34]

CLAYITE. *Taylor* (*Ac. Sc. Philadelphia*, 306, November, 1859). In tetrahedrons, from Peru. Said to contain 68.51 per cent Pb. Probably a result of alteration.[34]

FALKENHAYNITE. *Scharizer* (*Geol. Reichsanst., Jb.*, 40, 433, 1890). A massive gray-black material from the Fiedler vein, Joachimstal, Bohemia. G. 4.83. Streak gray black. Analysis (after deducting 13.16 per cent quartz and 12.77 per cent siderite): Cu 39.51, Fe 4.20, Zn 1.89, Bi 0.32, Sb 23.10, As 4.77, S 26.21, total 100.00, from which the formula Cu_3SbS_3 was derived (after the further deduction of 3.66 per cent chalcopyrite). Named after Count J. Falkenhayn, formerly Minister of Agriculture, Austria. Probably impure tetrahedrite.[35]

Ref.

1. Goldschmidt (3, 172, 1916). For tetrahedrite from France see the discussion of the form list by Ungemach, *Bull. soc. min.*, 32, 377 (1909). Also for new forms since 1916 see Baradlai, *Mat. Termés Ért.*, 40, 128 (1923) — *Min. Abs.*, 2, 268 (1924) and Löw and Tokody, *Földt. Közl.*, 58, 212 (1929) — *Min. Abs.*, 4, 381 (1930). For a critical analysis of tennantite forms see Prior and Spencer, *Min. Mag.*, 12, 184 (1900). Rare, vicinal, and uncertain forms:

014	4·4·31	5·5·16	335	$\bar{1}$33	$\bar{2}$5·26·26
035	5·5·37	6·6·19	558	144	40·41·41
1·1·76	117	5·5·14	557	$\bar{1}$44	149
1·1·40	2·2·13	3·3·11	334	$\bar{2}$55	$\bar{1}$36
1·1·34	5·5·31	10·10·27	10·10·13	377	$\bar{1}$25
1·1·28	5·5·29	5·5·13	556	499	259
1·1·25	3·3·17	5·5·12	667	5·11·11	134
1·1·24	2·2·11	449	889	599	$\bar{2}$35
1·1·18	$\bar{1}$15	5·5·11	20·20·21	588	347
2·2·35	10·10·47	10·10·21	1·62·62	$\bar{5}$88	$\bar{5}$·7·12
1·1·16	5·5·23	12·12·25	1·35·35	577	11·12·23
1·1·14	5·5·22	10·10·19	1·30·30	344	346
1·1·12	229	9·9·17	1·22·22	10·13·13	569
5·5·51	5·5·21	8·8·15	1·14·14	$\bar{5}$66	457
1·1·10	5·5·19	7·7·13	1·12·12	677	345
119	5·5·18	559	199	$\bar{2}$5·29·29	578
2·2·17	227	447	188	17·18·18	8·9·10
118	5·5·17	10·10·17	2·11·11	$\bar{2}$5·28·28	15·17·18

2. Structure determinations principally by Machatschki, *Zs. Kr.*, **68**, 204 (1928), and by Pauling and Neuman, *Zs. Kr.*, **88**, 54 (1934). Machatschki (1928) has measured a number of tetrahedrites of varying composition.

3. Sadebeck, *Zs. deutsche geol. Ges.*, **24**, 427 (1872), on twinning. See also Hochschild, *Jb. Min., Beil.-Bd.*, **26**, 151 (1908), for a distinction between the "sphalerite law" and the "spinel law" of twinning.

4. Cleavage on {001} reported for mercurian tetrahedrite by Breithaupt (105, 107, 1866), and {111} cleavage by Durocher on artificial material, *C. R.*, **32**, 825 (1851). A {110} cleavage has been mentioned for Cornwall tennantite by Phillips, *Q. J. Sc.*, 7 (1819). All these, so rarely observed, may well be occasional planes of separation other than cleavage.

5. Larsen and Berman (67, 1934).

6. Schneiderhöhn and Ramdohr (**2**, 431, 1931). Also Orcel and Fastré, *C. R.*, **200**, 1485 (1935).

7. The formula here given was early proposed by Tschermak (364, 1894) and later by Wherry and Foshag, *Washington Ac. Sc., J.*, **11**, 1 (1921). Pauling and Neuman (1934) verified the proposed formula by their x-ray structural study. Other recent chemical studies are by Kretschmer, *Zs. Kr.*, **48**, 484 (1911); Winchell, *Am. Min.*, **11**, 181 (1926); Machatschki (1928); Nikitin *Zs. Kr.*, **69**, 482 (1929), and Vavrinecz, *Föld. Közl.*, **65**, 105 (1935).

8. A tabulation of analyses is given in Hintze (**1** [1], 1114, 1901), in Kretschmer (1911), and in Doelter (**4** [1], 173, 1926) to the date of publication, respectively. The analyses here given are either more recent, or especially chosen for their supposed excellence and to demonstrate the variation in composition.

9. Prior anal. in Prior and Spencer, *Min. Mag.*, **12**, 184 (1899).

10. Kretschmer (1911).

11. Shannon (167, 1926).

12. Loczka, *Zs. Kr.*, **34**, 84 (1900).

13. Steiger anal. in Clarke, *U. S. Geol. Sur., Bull. 419*, 323, 1910.

14. Ungemach, *Bull. soc. min.*, **29**, 219 (1906).

15. Johnston anal. in Hoffmann, *Am. J. Sc.*, **50**, 274 (1895).

16. Oellacher anal. in Sandberger, *Jb. Min.*, 596, 1865 — in Dana (139, 1892).

17. Zecchini anal. in Novarese, *Boll. com. geol. Ital.*, **23**, 319 (1902).

18. Manasse, *Att. soc. tosc.*, **22**, 81 (1906) — *Zs. Kr.*, **44**, 662 (1908).

19. Bechi anal. in D'Achiardi (**2**, 341, 1873).

20. v. Lill, *Berg.-u. Hütten. Jb.*, **13**, 24 (1854) — Kretschmer (1911) anal. 80.

21. Pilipenko, *Ac. sc. St. Pétersbourg Bull.*, **3**, 1113 (1909) — *Zs. Kr.*, **51**, 105 (1912).

22. Wells anal. in Shannon (1926).

23. Rose, *Ann. Phys.*, **15**, 579 (1829) — in Dana (139, 1892).

24. Hilger, *Jb. Min.*, 586, 1865 — in Dana (139, 1892).

25. Brauns anal. in Petersen, *Jb. Min.*, 590, 1870 — in Dana (140, 1892).

26. Penfield, *Am. J. Sc.*, 44, 18 (1892).

27. Hosina anal. in Harada (243, 1936).

28. Pufahl, *Cbl. Min.*, 289, 1920A.

29. Kriesel, *Chem.-Ztg.*, **48**, 961 (1924) — *Min. Abs.*, **3**, 59 (1928).

30. Prior, *Min. Mag.*, **15**, 385 (1916).

31. In Mügge, *Jb. Min., Beil.-Bd.*, **16**, 339, 340, 357 (1903), and Spencer, *Min. Mag.*, **14**, 327 (1907), for stannite. See also Gross and Gross, *Jb. Min., Beil.-Bd.*, **48**, 482 (1929), and Spangenberg and Neuhaus, *Chem. Erde*, **5**, 485 (1930), for a discussion of the structural control of the growths.

{111}	[?]	galena	{111}	[?]	tetrahedrite
{111}	[001]	pyrite	{111}	[001]	tetrahedrite
{111}	[$\bar{1}$10]	stannite	{111}	[$\bar{1}$10]	tetrahedrite
{111}	[001]	chalcopyrite	{111}	[001]	tetrahedrite
{001}	[001]	chalcopyrite	{001}	[001]	tetrahedrite
{111}	[001]	sphalerite	{111}	[001]	tetrahedrite
{111}	[001]	tetrahedrite	{$\bar{1}$11}	[001]	sphalerite
{111}	[001]	tetrahedrite	{101}	[001]	chalcopyrite

32. In Doelter (4 [1], 197, 1926). On the artificial system Cu-Sb-As-S see Gaudin and Dicke, *Econ. Geol.*, **34**, 49 (1939). For observations of incrustation of ancient metallic objects see Daubrée, *C. R.*, **80**, 461, 609 (1875); **81**, 182, 834 (1876).

33. Short (105, 1931). Earlier referred by Spencer, *Min. Mag.*, **11**, 77 (1895), to binnite, which was later shown to be the same as tennantite by Prior and Spencer, *Min. Mag.*, **12**, 184 (1899).

34. Dana (141, 1892).

35. Placed in the bournonite group by Scharizer (1890), with bismuthian tennantite (annivite) by Sandberger, *Jb. Min.*, I, 274, 1891, with tetrahedrite by Hintze (**1** [1], 1113, 1900), and with stylotypite by Stevanović, *Zs. Kr.*, **37**, 237 (1903), and Dana (1034, 1892).(!)

325   Goldfieldite.   *Ransome* (*U. S. Geol. Sur., Prof. Pap. 66*, 116, 1909).

Occurs with marcasite, probably famatinite, and a number of unidentified minerals at the Mohawk mine, Goldfield, Nevada. Forms crusts. Dark lead-gray in color with metallic luster. Brittle. H. 3–3½. Analysis:[1] Au 0.51, Ag 0.18, Cu 33.49, Bi 6.91, Sb 19.26, As 0.68, Te 17.00, S 21.51, gangue 2.00, total 101.57. This yields (after deducting some famatinite) the formula $Cu_{12}Sb_4Te_3S_{16}$.

No definite evidence of homogeneity has been presented,[2] and considerable doubt of the validity of the species must be maintained.

Ref.

1. Palmer anal. in Ransome (1909).

2. For a discussion of the validity of the species see Shannon, *Am. J. Sc.*, **44**, 469 (1917). Also Sharwood, *Econ. Geol.*, **6**, 31 (1911), and Tolman and Ambrose, *ibid.*, **29**, 255 (1934).

3311   S U L V A N I T E [Cu_3VS_4].   *Goyder* (*J. Chem. Soc.*, **77**, 1094, 1900).

C r y s t.   Isometric, hexoctahedral — $4/m\,\bar{3}\,2/m$.[1]

Forms:[2]

$$a\{001\} \qquad d\{011\} \qquad o\{111\}$$

Structure cell.[3]   Space group $P\bar{4}3m$; a_0 5.370 ± 0.005; contains Cu_3VS_4.

Habit.   Cubic; usually massive.

P h y s.   Cleavage {001} perfect. H. 3½. G. 4.00 (Burra-Burra), 3.86 (Mercur), 3.94 (calc.). Luster metallic, tarnishing dull. Color bronze-gold. Streak black. Opaque. In polished section[4] cream-gold in color and isotropic, sometimes weakly anisotropic. Reflection percentages: green 28, orange 25.5, red 25.5.

C h e m.   A copper vanadium sulfide, Cu_3VS_4.
Anal.

	1	2	3	4
Cu	51.47	47.97	51.20	52.27
V	13.85	12.15	14.20	13.59
S	34.68	31.66	34.60	34.14
Rem.	......	7.49	......	......
Total	100.00	99.27	100.00	100.00
G.		3.98–4.01		

1. Cu_3VS_4.   2. Burra-Burra, South Australia.   Rem. is 1.04 $(Fe,Al)_2O_3$ and 6.45 gangue.   Average of two analyses.[5]   3. Burra-Burra, South Australia.   Recalculated to 100 per cent from unstated values.[6]   4. Burra-Burra, South Australia.   Recalculated after deduction of 6.32 gangue from average of two analyses.[7]

Tests.   In C.T. a sublimate of sulfur.

O c c u r.   In the Burra-Burra district, South Australia, associated with malachite, azurite, atacamite, cuprodescloizite and gypsum, these minerals in part derived from alteration of the sulvanite.   Reported from the Sierra de Cordoba, Argentina.[8]   From near Mercur, Utah, as partly altered cubic crystals and massive, in a limestone and calcite breccia.

A l t e r.   To malachite and to green and greenish yellow earthy products, including cuprodescloizite.

A r t i f.   May be prepared by fusion of vanadium sulfide, copper and sulfur in a closed tube.[9]

N a m e.   Apparently from the composition, a *sulfovana*dite of copper (as originally termed).

Ref.

1. Schempp and Schaller, *Am. Min.*, **16**, 557 (1931), established the isometric character of the Mercur crystals; crystal class from structural study of Pauling and Hultgren, *Zs. Kr.*, **84**, 204 (1933).
2. Schempp and Schaller (1931).
3. Pauling and Hultgren (1933) on crystals from Mercur, Utah.   Verified on artificial material by Lundqvist and Westgren, *Svensk Kem. Tidskr.*, **48**, 241 (1933) — *Min. Abs.*, **7**, 83 (1938), with a_0 5.379.
4. Schneiderhöhn and Ramdohr (**2**, 458, 1931); Short (53, 1934).
5. Schultze (Inaug. Diss., München, 1908 — *Zs. Kr.*, **49**, 640 (1911).
6. de Vries anal. in de Jong, *Zs. Kr.*, **68**, 524 (1928).
7. Goyder (1900).
8. See Wiedemann, *Cbl. Min.*, 293, 1928, and Frebold, *ibid.*, 27, 1928.
9. Lundqvist and Westgren (1933).

3312   **G E R M A N I T E**   [(Cu,Ge)(S,As)].   Germanit *Pufahl* (*Met. Erz*, **19**, 324, 1922).

C r y s t.   No crystals have been found.   Isometric,[1] hextetrahedral; space group $F\bar{4}3m$; a_0 5.299 ± 0.005; contains $(Cu,Ge,Fe,Zn,Ga)_4(S,As)_4$.

P h y s.   Cleavage none.   Brittle.   H. 4.   G. 4.46–4.59; 4.30 (calc.).   Color dark reddish gray.   Metallic luster.   Dark gray to black streak.   Opaque.   In polished section[2] pinkish gray and isotropic.   Reflection percentages: green 22, orange 21.5, red 21.5.

C h e m.   Essentially a sulfide of copper and germanium, with iron, zinc, gallium, and arsenic in smaller amounts, with some of these elements undoubtedly as impurities due to admixed sulfides and arsenides. The formula is $(Cu,Ge,Fe,Zn,Ga)(S,As)$ with $Cu : (Ge + Fe + Zn + Ga) = 3 : 1$ approximately.

Anal. Most of the analyzed samples consisted of intimate mixtures of several minerals and the analyses are therefore defective in this respect.

	1	2	3	4
Pb	0.69	0.96	0.66	0.26
Cu	45.40	42.12	45.39	39.44
Ge	6.20	10.19	8.70	7.04
Ga	.....	1.85	0.76	.....
Fe	7.22	7.80	4.56	10.70
Zn	2.61	3.93	2.58	3.56
As	5.03	1.37	4.13	4.86
S	31.34	31.27	30.65	31.44
SiO$_2$	0.75	.....	0.23	1.68
Rem.	.....	.....	1.89	.....
Total	99.24	99.49	99.55	98.98

1. Tsumeb. Contains about 20 per cent tennantite.[3] 2. Tsumeb. Supposedly pure material with some galena present.[4] 3. Tsumeb. Includes WO$_3$ 0.184 per cent, TiO$_2$ 0.004, Mo 1.282, Mn 0.02, Ni 0.001, Co 0.013, Cd 0.071, CaO 0.122, MgO 0.055, C 0.136, Ag,Au 0.005.[5] 4. Tsumeb. Contains about 17 per cent pyrite, 5 per cent tennantite, 1 per cent other impurities.[6]

Tests. Difficultly fusible. Decrepitates on heating. Soluble in HNO$_3$.

Occur. At Tsumeb, South-West Africa, germanite occurs intimately associated with pyrite, tennantite, enargite, galena and sphalerite.

Name. Derived from the presence of the element germanium in the mineral.

Ref.

1. de Jong, *Zs. Kr.*, **73**, 176 (1930); the cell edge may be twice that given.
2. Schneiderhöhn and Ramdohr (**2**, 441, 1931), and Thomson, *Univ. Toronto Stud., Geol. Ser.*, **17**, 62 (1924).
3. Pufahl (1922).
4. Moritz, *Jb. Min., Beil.-Bd.*, **67**, 118 (1933).
5. Kriesel, *Chem.-Ztg.*, **48**, 961 (1924).
6. Thomson (1924).

3313   **C O L U S I T E** [Cu$_3$(As,Sn,V,Fe,Te)S$_4$].   *Sales* in *Landon* and *Mogilnor* (*Am. Min.*, **18**, 528, 1933).

C r y s t. Isometric; hextetrahedral — $\bar{4}\,3\,m$.[1]

Forms:[2] $d\{001\}$ $e\{012\}$ $o\{111\}$ $n\{112\}$

Structure cell.[2] Space group $I\bar{4}3m$?; a_0 10.60 $\pm$ 0.01;   contains Cu$_{24}$(As,Sn,V,Fe,Te)$_8$S$_{32}$.

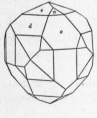

Habit. Tetrahedral, modified by {012}. Usually massive.

Phys. Cleavage none. Fracture uneven to hackly. Brittle. H. 3–4. G. 4.50; 4.434 (calc.). Luster metallic. Color bronze. Streak black. Opaque. In polished section[3] coppery cream in color and isotropic. Also exhibits growth-banding in section.

C h e m.[4] Essentially a complex sulfide of copper and arsenic $Cu_3(As,Sn,V,Fe,Te)S_4$, with V, Sn, and Te substituting for the As.

Anal.

	1	2	3
Cu	47.67	47.99	46.9
Fe	1.05	1.09	3.6
Sn	6.45	6.71	5.8
V	2.20	2.28	.....
Te	1.21	1.26	0.4
Sb	0.19	0.19	0.64
As	9.18	9.54	8.4
S	32.05	30.65	29.2
Rem.	.....	.....	0.9
Total	100.00	99.71	95.84
G.	4.434	4.50	

1. $Cu_3(As,Sn,V,Fe,Te)S_4$ with As : Sn : V : Fe : Te = 13 : 6 : 5 : 2 : 1. **2.** Butte.[5]
3. Mountain View mine, Butte.   Rem. is Zn 0.9.[6]

O c c u r. At Butte, Montana, associated with pyrite and quartz, together with the copper minerals, enargite, tetrahedrite, chalcocite, and bornite in the so-called Anaconda vein system.   Also reported from Red Mountain, San Juan County, Colorado.

A r t i f.[7] A substance having many of the properties of colusite has been prepared by pyrosynthesis.

N a m e. From the Colusa claim, at Butte, near which the mineral was first found.

Ref.

1. Berman and Gonyer, *Am. Min.*, **24**, 377 (1939).   Unconfirmed forms: {001}, {$\bar{1}$11}, {$\bar{1}$12}.
2. Berman and Gonyer (1939) found a cell edge double that of Zachariasen, *Am. Min.*, **18**, 534 (1933).
3. Nelson, *Am. Min.*, **24**, 369 (1939); Larsen in Berman and Gonyer (1939).
4. The earlier study on colusite by Landon and Mogilnor, *Am. Min.*, **18**, 528 (1933), and by Zachariasen (1933) was based on analyses shown to be probably in error.   See Berman and Gonyer (1939) and Nelson (1939).
5. Gonyer anal. in Berman and Gonyer (1939).
6. Anaconda Copper Mining Co. anal. in Landon and Mogilnor (1933).
7. Nelson (1939).

3321   **F A M A T I N I T E** [Cu_3SbS_4].   *Stelzner* (*Min. Mitt.*, 242, 1873).   Antimon-luzonit *Stevanović* (*Zs. Kr.*, **37**, 240, 1903).   Stibioluzonit *Schneiderhöhn* and *Ramdohr* (**2**, 469, 1931).   Luzonit pt. *Zerrenner* (*B. H. Ztg.*, 106, 1869).

C r y s t. Crystal measurements reported are not certainly of this species.[1]

Structure cell. Structure is of the sphalerite type, as shown by powder pictures.[2]

Habit. As crusts of minute crystals.   Usually massive, granular to dense; sometimes reniform.

Twinning. Polysynthetic twinning seen in polished section.[4]

P h y s. Fracture uneven.   Rather brittle.   H. $3\frac{1}{2}$.   G. 4.52 ± 0.05; 4.50 (Goldfield[3]).   Color gray with a tinge of copper-red.   Opaque.   In polished section[4] various shades of pink in color, with strong anisotropism and weak pleochroism. Reflection percentages: green 25–26, orange 23.5, red 25.

C h e m.[5] Essentially copper antimony sulfide, $Cu_3(Sb,As)S_4$, with As substituting for Sb to about 10 per cent by weight. Fe is found in small amounts.

Anal.[6]

	1	2	3	4	5	6
Cu	43.27	44.72	47.93	45.43	43.48	44.8
Fe	....	0.67	....	0.67	1.65	3.2
Sb	27.63	21.44	12.74	12.74	12.65	11.3
As	....	3.84	8.88	9.09	9.90	10.2
S	29.10	29.40	30.45	31.01	31.90	30.5
Rem.	....	0.59	....	0.65	0.288	....
Total	100.00	100.66	100.00	99.59	99.86	100.00
G.		4.57		4.47		

1. Cu_3SbS_4. 2. Sierra Famatina, Argentina. Average of four determinations Rem. is 0.59 Zn.[7] 3. Cerro de Pasco, Peru. Recalc. after deduction of 13.77 per cent pyrite.[8] 4. Caudalosa, Peru. Average of two analyses. Rem. is 0.65 Zn; contains 1.44 per cent pyrite.[9] 5. Laurani, Bolivia. Rem. is 0.10 Bi, 0.188 Ag, and 0.0008 Au.[10] 6. Goldfield, Nev. Recalc. after deduction of 54.94 per cent gangue. Contains a very little pyrite.[11]

Tests. C.T. decrepitates, giving off sulfur and on stronger heating also some arsenic sulfide. On charcoal fuses to a black, brittle, metallic globule.

O c c u r.[12] Occurs with enargite, with which it is frequently intimately intergrown; the two minerals sometimes apparently form oriented growths, with the trace of the twin plane in famatinite parallel to a cleavage plane in enargite. Associated also with pyrite, tetrahedrite-tennantite, chalcopyrite, barite, and quartz.

Originally from the Sierra de Famatina, La Rioja, Argentina. From Cerro de Pasco, Caudalosa, Morococha and Huaron, Peru; with enargite and tennantite at Laurani, Bolivia. From Matrabánya, near Recsz, Hungary. With germanite, enargite, and tennantite at Tsumeb, South-West Africa. From Mancayan, Luzon, Philippine Islands, with enargite. In the United States found at Goldfield, Nevada, associated with gold, bismuthinite, and pyrite, and in the Loope and Darwin districts, California. Reported from Kennecott, Alaska.

A l t e r. To enargite (?).

A r t i f. Obtained from melts in the system Cu-As-Sb-S.[13]

N a m e. From the locality, Sierra de Famatina, Argentina.

Ref.

1. Crystals measured have not been completely authenticated. See vom Rath, *Zs. Kr.*, **4**, 426 (1880), who made it orthorhombic, homeomorphous with enargite. Also Shannon, *Am. J. Sc.*, **44**, 469 (1917). The x-ray powder pictures, however, indicate that the two minerals are not isomorphous.
2. Harcourt, *Am. Min.*, **22**, 517 (1937).
3. On 11-mg. sample (Frondel, priv. comm., 1939).

4. Schneiderhöhn and Ramdohr (**2**, 466, 469, 1931); the pink material described as luzonite by these authors is here included with famatinite.

5. Neither famatinite nor enargite form complete series to their arsenian or antimonian analogues. This explains, perhaps, why the two minerals are often intimately associated.

6. For spectroscopic examination with semiquantitative estimate of composition, see Harcourt (1937).

7. Siewert, *Min. Mitt.*, 243, 1873.

8. Frenzel, *Jb. Min.*, 679, 1875.

9. Stevanović, *Zs. Kr.*, **37**, 240 (1903).

10. Herzenberg anal. in Ahlfeld and Reyes (**35**, 1938).

11. Schaller anal. in Ransome, *U. S. Geol. Sur., Prof. Pap. 66*, 118, 1909.

12. The distinction between famatinite and enargite has been established by x-ray examination by Harcourt (1937) for material from the San Pedro mine, Sierra Famatina, Argentina, the Loope district, Calif., and Cerro de Pasco, Peru, and by Frebold, *Jb. Min., Beil.-Bd.*, **56**, 316 (1927) for material from Mancayan, Philippine Islands. Also by Frondel (priv. comm., 1939) for the material from Goldfield, Nev., while a black, cleavable " famatinite " from Santiago, Chile, proved to be enargite.

13. Gaudin and Dicke, *Econ. Geol.*, **34**, 49 (1939).

3322   **E N A R G I T E** [Cu_3AsS_4]. *Breithaupt (Ann. Phys.*, **80**, 383, 1850). Guayacanite *Field (Am. J. Sc.*, **27**, 52, 1859). Garbyite *Semmons (Min. Mag.*, **5**, xxvi, 1884; **6**, 49, 124, 1884). Clarite *Sandberger (Jb. Min.*, 960, 1874; 382, 1875). Luzonite pt. *Zerrenner (B.H. Ztg.*, 106, 1869).

C r y s t.   Orthorhombic, pyramidal — $m\,m\,2$.[1]

$$a : b : c = 0.8713 : 1 : 0.8277;^2 \qquad p_0 : q_0 : r_0 = 0.9500 : 0.8277 : 1$$

$$q_1 : r_1 : p_1 = 0.8713 : 1.0526 : 1; \qquad r_2 : p_2 : q_2 = 1.2082 : 1.1478 : 1$$

Forms:[3]

		ϕ	$\rho = C$	ϕ_1	$\rho_1 = A$	ϕ_2	$\rho_2 = B$
c	001	....	0°00′	0°00′	90°00′	90°00′	90°00′
b	010	0°00′	90 00	90 00	90 00	....	0 00
a	100	90 00	90 00	....	0 00	0 00	90 00
h	120	29 51	90 00	90 00	60 09	0 00	29 51
m	110	48 56	90 00	90 00	41 04	0 00	48 56
E	012	0 00	22 29	22 29	90 00	90 00	67 31
s	011	0 00	39 37	39 37	90 00	90 00	50 23
n	102	90 00	25 24½	0 00	64 35½	64 35½	90 00
k	101	90 00	43 32	0 00	46 28	46 28	90 00
μ	201	90 00	62 14½	0 00	27 45½	27 45½	90 00
p	112	48 56	32 12½	22 29	66 18	64 35½	69 30
o	111	48 56	51 34	39 37	53 48	46 28	59 03
v	131	20 56	69 23	68 04	70 27½	46 28	29 03

Less common forms:

D	160	Π	250	F	980	f	520	C	041	B 205	P 223
Q	150	X	470	i	540	r	310	θ	051	I 304	z 134
R	140	Y	350	T	430	S	410	H	061	w 709	φ 132
L	270	Z	580	x	320	k	054	t	108	e 403	V 394
l	130	N	230	d	210	π	031	Γ	103	u 301	J 232
								q	115	W 392

Structure cell.[4]   Space group Pnm; a_0 6.46, b_0 7.43, c_0 6.18; $a_0 : b_0 : c_0 = 0.869 : 1 : 0.832$; contains $Cu_6As_2S_8$.

Habit. Tabular {001}; also prismatic [001]. Prism zone striated [001]; {001} striated ‖ [010]. Common forms: *c b a h m k p*. Also massive, granular, or prismatic.

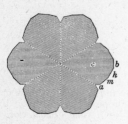

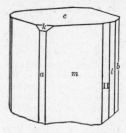

Caudaloso Costrovirroyna, Peru.   Red Mountain, Colo.   Alpine City, Calif.

Twinning. Twin plane {320},[20] common; sometimes in star-shaped trillings with adjoining parts meeting at nearly 60°.

P h y s. Cleavage {110} perfect; {100} and {010} distinct; {001} indistinct. Fracture uneven. Brittle. H. 3. G. 4.45 ± 0.05; 4.40 (calc.). Luster metallic, tarnishing dull. Color grayish black to iron-black. Streak grayish black. In polished section[5] gray to light rose-brown in color, with strong anisotropism and weak pleochroism. Reflection percentages: green 23, orange 21.5, red 21.5.

C h e m. Copper arsenic sulfide, $Cu_3(As,Sb)S_4$. Sb substitutes for As to at least 6 per cent by weight. Fe is often present up to 3 per cent by weight (older analyses report Fe up to 14 per cent and Zn up to 8 per cent). Ge has been found spectroscopically.[6]

Anal.[7]

	1	2	3	4	5	6
Cu	48.42	47.96	49.00	48.67	48.16	45.70
Fe	.....	1.22	.....	0.33	0.14	2.49
Zn	.....	0.57	.....	0.10	trace	0.17
Sb	.....	.....	1.54	1.76	1.93	5.04
As	19.02	18.16	15.88	17.91	17.53	14.02
S	32.56	32.21	33.23	31.44	32.34	32.74
Rem.	.....	.....	.....	0.11	0.08	.....
Total	100.00	100.12	99.65	100.32	100.18	100.16
G.	4.40	4.51			4.49	4.55

1. Cu_3AsS_4. 2. Cerro Blanco, Atacama, Chile.[8] 3. Bor, Serbia. May contain some covellite.[9] 4. Rarus mine, Butte, Mont. Rem. is 0.11 insol.[10] 5. Lahoczaberg, near Recsz, Hungary. Rem. is Pb and Bi 0.02, insol. 0.06, Mn and Ni trace.[11] 6. Calabona, Sardinia.[12]

Tests. In C.T. decrepitates and gives a sublimate of sulfur; at high temperatures fuses and gives a sublimate of arsenic sulfide. Soluble in aqua regia.

O c c u r.[13] Found typically in vein and replacement deposits formed at moderate temperatures, sometimes in large amounts and then an ore of copper. Also rarely found as a late mineral in low-temperature deposits (Picher, Oklahoma). Occurs associated with pyrite, sphalerite, bornite, galena, tetrahedrite, covellite, chalcocite, barite, and quartz.

Found at Matzenköpfl, Brixlegg, Tirol, Austria; at Alghere, and Cala-bona, Sardinia, with covellite; at Parád and Matrabánya, near Recsz, Hungary; in a large deposit at Bor, northwest of Zaječar, Serbia, with pyrite, covellite, and barite. Occurs at Tsumeb, South-West Africa, with tennantite, galena, sphalerite, and chalcocite. Found in Peru in important amounts at Morococha, Cerro de Pasco, and Quiruvilca. In the Sierra de Famatina, La Rioja, Argentina, with famatinite. In Chile at the Hedion-das mine in Coquimbo, the Cerro Blanco mines in Atacama, the San Pedro Nolasco mine in Santiago, at Collahuasi, and at Chuquicamata as the principal cupriferous mineral in the unoxidized ore. In Mexico at the Caridad mine, Sonora, with bornite, tennantite, barite, and alunite, and at Las Chiapas and Milpallas, Chihuahua. In the Philippine Islands at Mancayan, Luzon, with tetrahedrite and bornite. From the Kinkwaseki mine, Formosa.

In the United States enargite is an important ore mineral at Butte, Montana, where it occurs with chalcocite, covellite, bornite, and pyrite. In Utah it is found at Bingham Canyon, the Little Cottonwood Canyon district, and especially in the Tintic district associated with galena, sphal-erite, and chalcedonic quartz. In small amounts in various districts in Colorado: in the Red Mountain district, San Juan County, in the Black Hawk and Russell Gulch districts, Gilpin County, the Summit district, Rio Grande County. In California in the Mogul district, Alpine County. In Nevada in small amounts at Goldfield, Esmeralda County, and in the Tuscarora and Good Hope districts, Elko County. Rarely found with chalcopyrite, sphalerite, and galena on dolomite in the Joplin district of Missouri and near Yellville, Marion County, Arkansas; reported with arsenic, chalcopyrite, chalcocite, and realgar in the anhydrite cap rock of the Winnfield salt dome, Winn Parish, Louisiana. In Alaska at the Kennecott mine, with chalcocite and bornite.

Alter. Often to tennantite (= β-enargite = " green enargite "[14]); may afford on oxidation a wide variety of copper arsenates (Tintic); also alters to arsenic oxide.

Artif. Obtained from melts in the system Cu-Sb-As-S.[15]

Name. From ἐναργής, *distinct*, in allusion to the cleavage.

CLARITE. *Sandberger* (*Jb. Min.*, 960, 1874; 382, 1875), from the Clara mine, Schapbach, Baden, has been shown[16] to be enargite; the material is largely altered to covellite and chalcopyrite.

LUZONITE. *Zerrenner* (*B. H. Ztg.*, 106, 1869). Luzonit *Weisbach* (*Min. Mitt.*, 257, 1874). A dark, reddish, steel-gray material with the composition of enargite from Mancayan, Luzon, Philippine Islands. Fracture uneven; streak black. H. 3–4. G. 4.4. Shown to be enargite[17] or, in part, a mixture of enargite with famatinite.[18] Much of the material from other localities that has been ascribed to luzonite is famatinite.[19]

Ref.

1. Pyramidal class on the basis of the structure study of Pauling and Weinbaum, *Zs. Kr.*, **88**, 48 (1934), and the later morphological evidence of Kôzu and Watanabe, *Ac. Tokyo, Proc.*, **11**, 418 (1935) — *Min. Abs.*, **6**, 329 (1936).

2. Elements of Palache (priv. comm., 1936) in the orientation of Dauber, *Ann. Phys.*, **92**, 237 (1854). Palache's values were obtained by averaging measurements by Dauber (1854); Pirsson, *Am. J. Sc.*, **47**, 212 (1894); Spencer, *Min. Mag.*, **11**, 196 (1896); Stevanović, *Zs. Kr.*, **37**, 243 (1903); Moses, *Am. J. Sc.*, **20**, 278 (1905); Zsivny, *Zs. Kr.*, **62**, 489 (1925); and new observations. The morphological elements correspond to the structural cell of Pauling and Weinbaum (1934).

3. Goldschmidt (1916); Manasse, *Att. soc. tosc., Mem.*, **32**, 113 (1919); Thomson (priv. comm., 1939). Uncertain forms: {940}, {610}, {7·0·12}, {601}, {10·0·1}, {113}.

4. Pauling and Weinbaum (1934) on crystals from the Philippine Islands. Kôzu and Takané, *Proc. Imp. Ac. Tokyo*, **11**, 421 (1935) — *Min. Abs.*, **6**, 329 (1936), give $b_0 = 3.69$, which is half of the value given by Pauling and Weinbaum (1934). Similarity with the wurtzite structure is shown. West, *Am. Min.*, **19**, 279 (1934).

5. Schneiderhöhn and Ramdohr (**2**, 460, 1931).

6. Harcourt, *Am. Min.*, **22**, 517 (1937), has shown that there is no complete As-Sb series, and that the structure of famatinite is different from that of enargite. See also Schneiderhöhn and Ramdohr (1931) in this connection. Papish, Brewer, and Holt, *J. Am. Chem. Soc.*, **49**, 3028 (1928), report Ge spectroscopically.

7. For additional analyses see Doelter (4 [1], 122, 1926).

8. de Neufville, *Zs. Kr.*, **19**, 76 (1891).

9. Stevanović, *Zs. Kr.*, **44**, 354 (1908).

10. Hillebrand, *Am. J. Sc.*, **7**, 56 (1899).

11. Zsivny (1925).

12. Manasse (1919).

13. For a description of the principal deposits containing enargite see Lindgren (612, 1933); also Graton and Bowditch, *Econ. Geol.*, **31**, 696 (1936).

14. Originally considered by Schneiderhöhn (12, 1922) and de Jong, *Zs. Kr.*, **68**, 522 (1928), to be an isometric low temperature modification of enargite, but later found (cf. Moritz, *Jb. Min., Beil.-Bd.*, **67**, 118 [1933]) to be tennantite.

15. Gaudin and Dicke, *Econ. Geol.*, **34**, 49 (1939).

16. Spencer, *Min. Mag.*, **11**, 75 (1895).

17. Moses, *Am. J. Sc.*, **20**, 277 (1905), by crystallographic measurement.

18. Frebold, *Jb. Min., Beil.-Bd.*, **56**, 316 (1927), by x-ray and polished section study.

19. See Harcourt (1937) for an x-ray and spectroscopic study of enargite and luzonite.

20. Stevanović (1903) prefers the designation of the twin plane as {120}, an alternative to the interpretations of Spencer and Groth.

333　　**B E E G E R I T E** [Pb₆Bi₂S₉].　*Koenig (Am. Chem. J.*, **2**, 379, 1881).

C r y s t.　Isometric (?).[1]

Forms:

$$a\{100\}　　　o\{111\}　　　-o\{\bar{1}11\}$$

Habit.　Indistinctly crystallized; observed in tetrahedrons (from Minusinsk). Usually massive, fine granular to dense.

P h y s.　Cleavage perfect {001}? G. 7.27. Luster metallic. Color light to dark gray. In polished section[2] white in color and strongly anisotropic; may show lamellar twinning. Reflection percentages: green 40, orange 36, red 37.5.

C h e m.　Lead bismuth sulfide, Pb₆Bi₂S₉ with some Cu and Ag possibly substituting for Pb. The higher Ag and Cu analyses are not definitely of this mineral.[3]

Anal.

	1	2	3	4	5
Pb	63.76	64.23	63.00	45.87	50.16
Ag	.....	.....	0.02	9.98	15.40
Cu	.....	1.70	.....	1.12	.....
Bi	21.44	20.59	22.15	19.35	19.81
S	14.80	14.97	14.28	16.39	[14.63]
Rem.	.....	.....	.....	3.01	.....
Total	100.00	101.49	99.45	95.72	100.00
G.		7.273	7.271	6.565	

1. $Pb_6Bi_2S_9$. 2. Baltic Lode, Park Co., Colo. Average of four partial analyses. 2.6 per cent quartz deducted.[4] 3. Minusinsk district, Siberia. Contains trace Se and As.[5] 4. Old Lout mine, Ouray Co., Colo. Rem. is Fe 2.89, insol. 0.12. Contains chalcopyrite.[6] 5. Treasure Vault mine, Park Co., Colo. Anal. on 0.0312 gm.[7]

Tests. F. 1. Soluble in HCl with evolution of H_2S.

Occur. In Colorado from the Baltic Lode in the Montezuma Quadrangle,[8] Park County, Colorado, associated with chalcopyrite, pyrite, sphalerite, and quartz; also said to occur in the Treasure Vault mine of the same district. Reported, without good evidence, from the Old Lout mine, Poughkeepsie Gulch, Ouray County, Colorado. In the Minusinsk district, Yeniseisk, Siberia.

Name. After Hermann Beeger, metallurgist, of Denver, Colorado.

Ref.
   1. The original material of Koenig (1881) was indistinctly crystallized, apparently as distorted isometric crystals. Solodovnikova, *Ac. Sc. Leningrad*, 279, 1927 —*Jb. Min.*, ref. 50 (1929), reported tetrahedral crystals from Minusinsk, Siberia. However, material from Ouray Co., Colo. (probably from the Old Lout mine) was found to be strongly anisotropic by Schneiderhöhn and Ramdohr (2, 453, 1931). A specimen from the same locality gave a nonisometric powder pattern (Frondel, priv. comm., 1939).
   2. Schneiderhöhn and Ramdohr (1931) on material from Ouray Co., Colo., not authenticated.
   3. The formulas for the supposedly silver-bearing beegerites are not consistent with that of the original material (Berman, priv. comm., 1939); no clear evidence of homogeneity of the analyzed samples has been presented, and the analyses are obviously inferior.
   4. Koenig (1881).
   5. Solodovnikova (1927).
   6. Koenig, *Am. Phil. Soc., Proc.*, **22**, 212 (1885).
   7. Genth, *Am. Phil. Soc., Proc.*, **23**, 37 (1886).
   8. Lovering, *U. S. Geol. Sur., Prof. Pap. 178*, 53, 1935.

RICHMONDITE. *Skey (New Zealand Inst. Trans.*, **9**, 556, 1877). Massive, crystalline. Brittle. H. 4.5. G. 4.317. Luster metallic. Color black, inclining to reddish in parts. Composition approximately $6RS·Sb_2S_3$, from the analysis (after deducting 15.4 per cent gangue, SiO_2, antimony oxysulfide, etc.): Sb_2S_3 22.20, PbS 36.12, Cu_2S 19.31, Ag_2S 2.39, FeS 13.59, ZnS 5.87, MnS 0.52, Bi_2S_3 trace = 100. From Richmond Hill, New Zealand. Probably a mixture.

334   **SAMSONITE** [$Ag_4MnSb_2S_6$]. *Werner* and *Fraatz* (*Cbl. Min.*, **331**, 1910).

Cryst. Monoclinic; prismatic — $2/m$.

$a : b : c = 1.2782 : 1 : 0.8198;$[1] $\beta\ 92°41';\ p_0 : q_0 : r_0 = 0.6414 : 0.8189 : 1$

$r_2 : p_2 : q_2 = 1.2212 : 0.7832 : 1;\ \mu\ 87°19';\ p_0'\ 0.6421,\ q_0'\ 8198,\ x_0'\ 0.0469$

Forms:[2]

		ϕ	ρ	ϕ_2	ρ_2	C	A
b	010	0°00′	90°00′	......	0°00′	90°00′	90°00′
a	100	90 00	90 00	0°00′	90 00	87 19	0 00
m	110	38 04	90 00	90 00	38 04	88 21	51 56
l	210	57 27	90 00	90 00	57 27	87 44½	32 33
f	103	90 00	14 37½	75 22½	90 00	11 56½	75 22½
d	101	90 00	34 34	55 26	90 00	31 53	54 26
e	$\bar{1}$01	−90 00	30 46	120 46	90 00	33 27	120 46
g	$\bar{3}$01	−90 00	61 59	151 59	90 00	64 40	151 59
p	111	40 02½	46 57½	55 26	55 58½	45 16	61 57
π	$\bar{1}$11	−35 59	45 22½	120 46	54 50½	46 59½	114 43

Less common:

$q\{140\}$ $s\{130\}$ $n\{120\}$ $k\{012\}$ $i\{011\}$ $h\{\bar{5}01\}$ $r\{212\}$ $x\{\bar{1}21\}$ $\delta\{\bar{4}73\}$

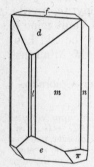

Andreasberg.

Structure cell.[3] Space group $P2_1/n$; a_0 10.29, b_0 8.05, c_0 6.61 (all ± 0.05); β 92°02′; $a_0 : b_0 : c_0 = 1.278 : 1 : 0.821$; contains $Ag_8Mn_2Sb_4S_{12}$.

Habit. Prismatic and striated [001].

Phys. Fracture conchoidal. Brittle. H. 2½. G. 5.51;[4] 5.56 (calc.). Luster metallic. Color steel-black. Streak dark red. Nearly opaque; in thin splinters translucent and deep red to brown.

Opt. In polished section[5] bluish white in color with weak anisotropism and pleochroism; deep red internal reflections. Reflection percentages: green 32.5, orange 23.5, red 23. In transmitted light deep red to brown. Extinction angle on $\{110\}$ to [001] = −28° to −30°.[6]

Chem. A silver and manganese antimony sulfide, $Ag_4MnSb_2S_6$.

Anal.

	Ag	Mn	Sb	S	Cu	Fe	CaCO₃	MgCO₃	Total
1	46.79	5.96	26.40	20.85	....	....	....	....	100.00
2	45.95	5.86	26.33	20.55	0.18	0.22	0.44	0.46	99.86

1. $Ag_4MnSb_2S_6$.   2. Andreasberg.[7]

Tests. F. 1. On charcoal in R.F. a silver button and a black crust which reacts for Mn.

Occur. Found in vugs in the Samson vein at Andreasberg in the Harz Mountains, Germany. Associated with pyrargyrite, galena, dyscrasite, tetrahedrite, pyrolusite, hackly pseudomorphous quartz, calcite, and apophyllite.

Name. From the occurrence in the Samson vein, Andreasberg.

Ref.

1. Angles by Palache, *Am. Min.*, **19**, 194 (1934), p. 200, using his average and those of previous measurements by Bruhns, *Niedersächs., geol. Ver., IV Jahresber.*, Hannover

(1911); Slavík, *Ac. Sc. Bohême, Bull.*, 16, 1911, Kolbeck and Goldschmidt, *Zs. Kr.*, 50, 455 (1912); unit of Slavík. Transformation, Bruhns to Slavík: $\overline{2}0\overline{1}/010/001$.
2. Palache (1934).
3. Frondel, *Am. Min.*, 26, 25 (1941), by Weissenberg method on material of Palache (1934).
4. Frondel (1941) by microbalance.
5. Schneiderhöhn and Ramdohr (2, 425, 1931).
6. Slavík (1911).
7. Fraatz anal. in Werner and Fraatz (1910).

335 **GEOCRONITE** [$Pb_5(Sb,As)_2S_8$]. Geokronit *Svanberg* (*Ak. Stockholm, Handl.*, 184, 1839). Kilbrickenite *Apjohn* (*Proc. Roy. Irish Ac.*, 1, 469, 1841; l'Institut, 9, 111, 1841). Kilbreckanite. Schulzit *Hausmann* (166, 1847).

Cryst. Orthorhombic; pyramidal[1] — $m\,m\,2$.

$$a : b : c = 0.5028 : 1 : 0.5805;^2 \qquad p_0 : q_0 : r_0 = 1.1545 : 0.5805 : 1$$

$$q_1 : r_1 : p_1 = 0.5028 : 0.8662 : 1; \qquad r_2 : p_2 : q_2 = 1.7227 : 1.9888 : 1$$

Forms:[3]

		ϕ	ρ	ϕ_1	$\rho_1 = A$	ϕ_2	$\rho_2 = B$
c	001	.....	0°00′	0°00′	90°00′	90°00′	90°00′
m	110	63°18½′	90 00	90 00	26 41½	0 00	90°00′
h	058	0 00	19 56½	19 56½	90 00	90 00	63 18½
							70 03½
i	067	0 00	26 27	26 27	90 00	90 00	63 33
g	011	0 00	30 08	30 08	90 00	90 00	59 52
j	032	0 00	41 03	41 03	90 00	90 00	48 57
d	021	0 00	49 15½	49 15½	90 00	90 00	40 44½
k	225	63 18½	27 20	13 04½	65 47	65 13	78 06
l	112	63 18½	32 52	16 11	61 00	60 00½	75 53½

Structure cell. Said to be monoclinic.[4]

Habit. Crystals rare (habit like stephanite); tabular {001}. Usually massive, granular, and earthy.

Twinning.[1] On {110}.

Phys. Cleavage {011} distinct, {112} less so. Fracture uneven. H. 2½. G. 6.4 ± 0.1; 6.51 (calc.). Luster me-

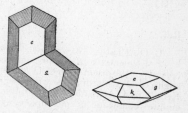

Val di Castello, Italy.

tallic. Color and streak light lead-gray to grayish blue. Opaque. In polished section[5] pure white in color; moderately anisotropic and very weakly pleochroic; exhibits lamellar twinning on {011}. Reflection percentages: green 37, orange 30.5, red 29.5.

Chem. Lead, antimony, and arsenic sulfide, $Pb_5(Sb,As)_2S_8$,[6] with Sb : As near 1 : 1 in most analyses. As is apparently lacking in the variety *schulzite*. Cu may substitute for Pb in small amounts.

Anal.[7]

	1	2	3	4	5	6	7
Pb	69.62	70.02	68.97	68.49	64.89	57.95	67.58
Cu	.....	trace	.....	.....	1.60	5.93	.....
Sb	8.07	7.78	9.20	9.13	16.00	17.33	15.67
As	5.05	4.47	4.49	4.59	.....	.....	.....
S	17.26	17.57	17.23	17.20	16.90	17.73	16.73
Rem.	.....	.....	.....	.....	.....	0.11	.....
Total	100.00	99.84	99.89	99.41	99.39	99.05	100.00
G.				6.45	6.43	6.26	

1. $Pb_5(Sb,As)_2S_8$. 2. Pietrasanta, Tuscany. Average of two analyses.[8] 3. Sala, Sweden.[9] 4. Kilbricken, Ireland.[10] 5. *Schulzite*. Meredo, Asturias, Spain.[11] 6. *Schulzite*. Björkskogsnäs, Örebro, Sweden. Rem. is Fe 0.11.[12] 7. $Pb_5Sb_2S_8$.

Var. *Schulzite.* Schulzit *Hausmann* (166, 1847). An arsenic-free variety (anal. 5,6), the validity of which is not yet established.

Tests. F. 1. In the C.T. gives a faint sublimate of S and Sb_2S_3. Soluble in hot HCl with evolution of H_2S and separation of $PbCl_2$ on cooling.

Occur. In Sweden at Sala, at Fahlun and at Björkskogsnäs, Örebro (*schulzite*). In Ireland in the Kilbricken mine, county Clare (*kilbricken-ite*). At Meredo, Asturias, Spain, as nodules in galena (*schulzite*). In Italy at Pietrasanta, Val di Castello, as crystals with barite, fluorite, quartz, pyrite, and tetrahedrite in a vein in limestone. In the United States in the Tintic district, Utah, as veinlets in galena. Said to occur at Tinder's mine, Louisa County, Virginia, and in California at Owen's Valley, Inyo County, and the Prescott district, Mono County.

Artif. Reported by fusion of PbS and Sb_2S_3 in H_2S.[13]

Name. From γῆ, *earth*, and κρόνος, *Saturn*, the alchemistic name for lead.

KILBRICKENITE. *Apjohn* (*Proc. Roy. Irish Ac.*, **1**, 469, 1841; *l'Institut*, **9**, 111, 1841), from the Kilbricken mine, county Clare, Ireland, has been shown[14] to be geocronite.

Ref.

1. D'Achiardi, *Att. soc. tosc.*, *Mem.*, **18**, 1 (1901) — *Zs. Kr.*, **35**, 516 (1902).
2. Elements from Kerndt's angles, *Ann. Phys.*, **65**, 302 (1845), on Val di Castello crystals in the orientation of D'Achiardi (1901) with the unit of Dana (143, 1892). The angles of D'Achiardi are not in close agreement with those of Kerndt. Transformation Kerndt to D'Achiardi: 001/010/100. Hiller, *Zs. Kr.*, **100**, 142 (1938), has made geocronite monoclinic by incomplete x-ray evidence. His ratio is not related to the old orientation by the transformation stated in his paper, and the work must be considered generally unconvincing.
3. Forms from Goldschmidt (4, 32, 1918) based on the approximate measurements of D'Achiardi (1901). Uncertain forms: {334}, {111}, {776}, {554}, {443}, {332}, {221}, {331}.
4. Hiller (1938) obtained a_0 14.92, b_0 8.25, c_0 14.35, β 58°26′; $a_0 : b_0 : c_0 = 1.8085 : 1 : 1.7394$, by the powder method!
5. Schneiderhöhn and Ramdohr (2, 451, 1931).
6. D'Achiardi (1901) considers geocronite to be related to jordanite both crystallographically and chemically. A table of similarities in crystal angles is given by him.
7. For additional analyses see Hintze (**1** [1], 1163, 1901).
8. D'Achiardi (1901).

9. Guillemain (Inaug. Diss., Breslau, 35, 1898 — *Zs. Kr.*, **33**, 75 [1900]).
10. Prior, *Min. Mag.*, **13**, 187 (1902).
11. Sauvage, *Ann. Phys.*, **52**, 78 (1841).
12. Nauckhoff, *Geoi. För. Förh.*, **1**, 88 (1872).
13. Sommerlad, *Zs. anorg. Chem.*, **18**, 440 (1898).
14. Prior (1902).

336   **G R A T O N I T E** [$Pb_9As_4S_{15}$].   *Palache* and *Fisher* (*Am. Min.*, **24**, 136, 1939; **25**, 255, 1940).

C r y s t.   Hexagonal — R; ditrigonal pyramidal — 3 m.

$a : c = 1 : 0.4428$; $\alpha\ 114°03\frac{1}{2}'$; $p_0 : q_0 = 0.5113 : 1$; $\lambda\ 46°26\frac{1}{2}'$

Forms:

			ϕ	ρ	A_1	A_2
c	0001	111	......	0°00′	90°00′	90°00′
m	$10\bar{1}0$	$2\bar{1}\bar{1}$	30°00′	90 00	30 00	90 00
a	$11\bar{2}0$	$10\bar{1}$	0 00	90 00	60 00	60 00
r	$10\bar{1}1$	100	30 00	27 05	66 47	90 00
M	$40\bar{4}1$	$3\bar{1}\bar{1}$	30 00	63 56½	38 55½	90 00
e	$01\bar{1}2$	110	−30 00	14 20½	90 00	77 37
s	$02\bar{2}1$	$11\bar{1}$	−30 00	45 38½	90 00	51 44½

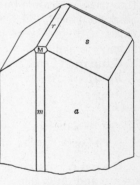

Cerro de Pasco.

Structure cell.   Space group $R3m$; a_0 17.69, c_0 7.83; $a_0 : c_0 = 1 : 0.4426$; a_{rh} 10.54, α 114°05′; contains $Pb_9As_4S_{15}$ in the rhombohedral unit.

Habit.   Prismatic [0001] with $\{11\bar{2}0\}$ dominant; $\{02\bar{2}1\}$ large and often the only terminal form present.   Also massive.

P h y s.   Cleavage none.[1]   Brittle.   H. $2\frac{1}{2}$.   G. 6.22 ± 0.02, 6.17 (calc.).   Color dark leadgray.   Streak black.   Luster metallic.   Opaque. In polished section weakly anisotropic.

C h e m.   Lead arsenic sulfide, $Pb_9As_4S_{15}$.

Anal.

	1	2	3
Pb	70.49	71.12	70.79
As	11.33	10.82	10.60
Sb	.....	0.21	0.08
S	18.18	17.38	18.01
Rem.	.....	0.39	.....
Total	100.00	99.92	99.48
G.	6.17	6.22	6.1

1. $Pb_9As_4S_{15}$.   2. Cerro de Pasco, Peru.   Rem. is Fe 0.39.[2]   3. Cerro de Pasco, Peru.[3]

Tests.   F. 1.   Decrepitates violently B.B.   In C.T. gives a slight sublimate of arsenic trisulfide.

O c c u r. Found sparingly in vugs in pyritic ore, in association with realgar, enargite, and tetrahedrite, in the Excelsior mine at Cerro de Pasco, Peru.

N a m e. After L. C. Graton (1880–   ), Professor of Mining Geology at Harvard University.

Ref.

1. In polished section shows a weak separation plane in the rhombohedral direction.
2. Gonyer anal. in Palache and Fisher (1940).
3. Analysis from the Laboratories of the Cerro de Pasco Copper Corporation, in Palache and Fisher (1940).

337   **L E N G E N B A C H I T E**   [$Pb_6(Ag,Cu)_2As_4S_{13}$]. *Solly (Nature,* **71**, 118, 1904; *Min. Mag.,* **14**, 78, 1905). Jentschite *Koechlin (Min. Mitt.,* **23**, 551, 1904). (Not Jenzschite *Dana* [201, 1877].)

C r y s t. Possibly triclinic. Very thin, blade-shaped crystals, sometimes curled. The large face is striated in the direction of elongation, and sometimes also at 58° to this direction.

P h y s. Cleavage ∥ large flat face, perfect. Also[1] two other fair cleavages across the flat face, one across the elongation, and the other ∥ to the striae. Flexible but not elastic. Somewhat malleable. Soft (leaving mark on paper). G. 5.80–5.85. Luster metallic. Color steel-gray, sometimes with iridescent tarnish. Streak black. Opaque. Weakly anisotropic[2] in polished section.

C h e m. Lead, silver, and copper arsenic sulfide, $Pb_6(Ag,Cu)_2As_4S_{13}$. *Anal.*

	Pb	Ag	Cu	Fe	Sb	As	S	Total	G.
1	58.13	5.93	2.44	....	....	14.01	19.49	100.00	
2	57.89	5.64	2.36	0.17	0.77	13.46	19.33	99.62	5.85

1. $Pb_6(Ag,Cu)_2As_4S_{13}$, with Ag : Cu = 10 : 7.   2. Binnental.[3]

O c c u r. At Lengenbach, in the Binnental, Valais, Switzerland, with pyrite and often deposited upon jordanite.

N a m e. From the locality at the Lengenbach quarry.

Ref.

1. Berman (priv. comm., 1939).
2. Guisca, *Schweiz. min. Mitt.,* **10**, 154 (1930).
3. Hutchinson, *Min. Mag.,* **14**, 204 (1906).

338   **J O R D A N I T E**   [$Pb_{14}As_7S_{24}$?]. *vom Rath (Ann. Phys.,* **122**, 387, 1864). Reniforite *Kawai (Geol. Soc. Tokyo, J.,* **32**, 106, 1925). Reniformite.

C r y s t. Monoclinic; prismatic — $2/m$.[1]

$a : b : c = 0.2794 : 1 : 0.2655;$ $\beta\ 117°47';$[2] $p_0 : q_0 : r_0 = 0.9503 : 0.2349 : 1$

$r_2 : p_2 : q_2 = 4.0455 : 4.2573 : 1;$ $\mu\ 62°13';$ $p_0'\ 1.0741,\ q_0\ 0.2655,\ x_0'\ 0.5269$

Forms:[3]

		ϕ	ρ	ϕ_2	$\rho_2 = B$	C	A
c	001	90°00′	27°47′	62°13′	90°00′	.....	62°13′
b	010	0 00	90 00	.....	0 00	90°00′	90 00
a	100	90 00	90 00	0 00	90 00	62 13	......
τ	160	33 59½	90 00	0 00	33 59½	74 53½	56 00½
ρ	150	38 58½	90 00	0 00	38 58½	72 57	51 01½
ν	140	45 19½	90 00	0 00	45 19½	70 38½	44 40½
λ	130	53 26½	90 00	0 00	53 26½	68 00½	36 33½
ι	120	63 41½	90 00	0 00	63 41½	65 18	26 18½
ϵ	110	76 07	90 00	0 00	76 07	63 05½	13 53
S	021	44 46½	36 48	62 13	64 50½	25 09½	65 02½
Q	031	33 29	43 41	62 13	54 50	35 10	67 36
M	051	21 39	55 00	62 13	40 25	49 35	72 24½
L	061	18 18	59 12½	62 13	35 21½	54 38½	74 21
J	081	13 56	65 25½	62 13	28 01½	61 58½	77 21
s :	101	90 00	58 00½	31 59½	90 00	30 13½	31 59½
n :	$\bar{1}01$	−90 00	28 41½	118 41½	90 00	56 28½	118 41½
W	$\bar{3}32$	−69 50	49 07	137 19	74 53½	75 37	135 12½
p	$\bar{2}12$	−76 22	29 23	118 41½	83 21½	56 43½	118 28½
i	$\bar{1}21$	−45 51½	37 19½	118 41½	65 01½	59 57	115 47½
l	$\bar{1}31$	−34 29½	44 01	118 41½	55 03½	63 04½	113 10½
n	$\bar{1}41$	−27 15½	50 04	118 41½	47 01½	66 09½	110 33½
t	$\bar{1}61$	−18 57½	59 18	118 41½	35 35	71 15	106 13½
U	$\bar{3}12$	−83 01	47 31½	137 19	84 51½	75 09½	137 04

Structure cell.[4] Space group $P2_1/m$; a_0 8.89 ± 0.03, b_0 31.65 ± 0.03, c_0 8.40 ± 0.02, β 118°21′ ± 0°30′; contains $Pb_{27}As_{14}S_{48}$.

Habit. Tabular {010}, with strong zonal developments [001], [100], and [101] producing pseudohexagonal outlines. Rarely reniform.

Twinning. (a) On {001}, most common and often lamellar; (b) on {$\bar{2}01$}, common; (c) on {$\bar{1}01$}, rare; (d) on {101}, very rare. Gliding on (a) {001} in direction [$\bar{1}01$] and (b) on {100} in direction [101].[5]

P h y s. Cleavage {010} very perfect; parting {001} parallel to twin lamellae. Fracture conchoidal. Brittle. H. 3. G. 6.38 ± 0.05,[6] 6.49 (calc.). Luster metallic. Color lead-gray. Frequently tarnished; iridescent. Streak black. Opaque. In polished section[7] anisotropic and pleochroic. Reflection percentages: green 39, orange 32.5, red 29.5.

C h e m.[8] Lead arsenic sulfide, possibly $Pb_{14}As_7S_{24}$.

Anal.

	1	2	3	4	5	6	7
Pb	69.20	68.72	68.67	70.80	70.19	68.89	69.56
As	12.46	12.39	12.46	9.90	11.37	12.40	10.32
S	18.34	18.31	18.81	17.06	18.22	18.24	19.44
Rem.	.....	.....	.....	1.87	.....	.....	0.45
Total	100.00	99.42	99.94	99.63	99.78	99.53	99.77
G.	6.54	6.413	5.484?				6.451

1. $Pb_{14}As_7S_{24}$. 2. Binnental. Average of two analyses.[9] 3. Binnental. Bright

crystals.[10] 4. Nagyág. Material containing a little galena. Rem. is Sb.[11] 5. Blei-Scharley mine. Average of two analyses.[12] 6. Blei-Scharley mine.[7] 7. Yunosawa mine, Aomori, Japan. Rem. is Fe 0.45 (reniforite).[13]

Tests. F. 1. Decomposed by HNO_3 with separation of $PbSO_4$.

Occur.[14] Fine crystals are found in the cavities of a crystalline dolomite at Imfeld, in the Binnental, Valais, Switzerland, associated with other rare sulfosalts, tennantite, and sphalerite. Found with sphalerite and galena at Nagyág, Transylvania, and in cavities in gray dolomite, with sphalerite and galena, at the Blei-Scharley mine, near Beuthen, Upper Silesia. In Japan, at the Yunosawa mine, Aomori (reniforite), as reniform masses on barite crystals.

N a m e. After Dr. Jordan of Saarbrück.

RENIFORITE. Kawai (Geol. Soc. Tokyo, J., **32**, 106, 1925), has been shown to be the same as jordanite.[15]

Ref.

1. First referred to monoclinic symmetry by Baumhauer, Ak. Berlin, Ber., 697, 1891.
2. Angles of Baumhauer (1891), orientation and unit of Berry in Peacock and Berry, Univ. Toronto Stud., Geol. Ser., **44**, 47 (1940), p. 59, for jordanite, derived from an x-ray study, which gave an orientation preferred to that of Palache and Richmond, Am. Min., **23**, 821 (1938). Transformations: Baumhauer to Berry $\bar{1}0\frac{1}{2}/0\bar{1}0/001$; Baumhauer to Palache $\bar{1}03/0\bar{4}0/101$. Palache to Berry $00\bar{2}/010/101$.
3. Forms of Solly, Min. Mag., **12**, 290 (1900), and Palache (1938), with some by the former omitted because vicinal. Less common and rare:

Ω 1·16·0	μ 520	t : 102	Θ 141	j $\bar{4}$14	Z : $\bar{1}$·27·1
Ξ 1·15·0	T 012	r : 201	Λ 151	h $\bar{3}$13	V $\bar{3}$22
Ψ 1·11·0	m 011	o : $\bar{1}$02	Π 161	d $\bar{3}$23	X $\bar{3}$42
ξ 1·10·0	R 052	m : $\bar{3}$02	Σ 171	f $\bar{2}$32	d : $\bar{2}$11
ψ 190	P 072	Y $\bar{2}$01	Υ 181	k $\bar{2}$52	f : $\bar{2}$31
χ 180	O 041	p : $\bar{3}$01	M : $\bar{1}$43	g $\bar{2}$72	g : $\bar{2}$41
φ 170	N 092	U : 112	N : $\bar{1}$53	o $\bar{2}$92	h : $\bar{2}$51
σ 2·11·0	K 071	Φ 111	o : $\bar{1}$63	r $\bar{1}$51	i : $\bar{2}$61
ω 290	H 091	F : $\bar{1}$12	D : $\bar{1}$22	s $\bar{2}$·11·2	j : $\bar{2}$71
γ 270	G 0·10·1	e $\bar{1}$11	G : $\bar{1}$32	u $\bar{1}$71	k : $\bar{2}$81
ζ 380	F 0·11·1	e : $\bar{2}$21	T : $\bar{1}$42	v $\bar{1}$81	l : $\bar{2}$91
κ 250	E 0·12·1	V : 122	L : $\bar{1}$52	w $\bar{1}$91	Φ : $\bar{3}$21
η 370	D 0·13·1	W : 152	P : $\bar{1}$62	x $\bar{1}$·10·1	
θ 780	C 0·14·1	X : 162	S : $\bar{1}$72	y $\bar{1}$·11·1	
δ 320	B 0·17·1	Δ 121	H : $\bar{2}$53	z $\bar{1}$·14·1	
π 210	A 0·18·1	Γ 131	I : $\bar{2}$73	q $\bar{1}$·17·1	

4. Berry in Peacock and Berry (1940).
5. Goetze, Cbl. Min., 65, 1919.
6. An average of four determinations, two by Solly (1900) and one by Palache (1938) and one by Berry (1940). The value, 5.484, by Guillemain (cited in Solly, 1900) is obviously erroneous.
7. Schneiderhöhn and Ramdohr (2, 443, 1931).
8. The old formula $Pb_4As_2S_7$ is not close to Berry's (1940) formula for the unit cell contents, nor does it conform closely enough with the chemical analysis. The formula here given, by Richmond, in Palache and Richmond (1938), is most closely in conformity with the composition and x-ray data. Fisher, Am. Min., **25**, 297 (1940), suggests the formula $Pb_{14}As_7S_{23}$. In this connection see also Schneiderhöhn and Ramdohr (2, 443, 1931) on the inclusions seen in jordanite in polished section.

9. Jackson anal. in Solly (1900).
10. Guillemain anal. (quoted in Solly [1900]).
11. Luding, *Min. Mitt.*, 216, 1873.
12. Sache, *Cbl. Min.*, 723, 1904.
13. Kawai, *Geol. Soc. Tokyo, J.*, 32, 110 (1925) — Harada (244, 1936).
14. A general account of the occurrence of jordanite is given in Bader, *Schweiz. min. Mitt.*, 14, 319 (1934).
15. Watanabe and Nakamo, *J. Japanese Assoc. Min., Petr., Econ. Geol.*, 15, 216 (1936).

339   Guitermanite [$Pb_{10}As_6S_{19}$].   *Hillebrand* (*Colorado Sc. Soc., Proc.*, 1, 129, 1884).

Massive, compact. Fracture uneven. Brittle. H. 3. G. 5.94. Luster metallic. Color and streak bluish gray. Opaque. Composition approximately $Pb_{10}As_6S_{19}$.

Anal.

	Pb	Cu	Fe	As	S	Total
1	65.99	0.19	....	14.33	19.49	100.00
2	64.32	....	1.61	13.85	[19.76]	99.54

1. Zuni mine, Colo. Recalculated after deduction of 2.61 $PbSO_4$, 0.59 free S, and 0.88 Fe (as pyrite).[1] 2. Zuni mine, Colo. Recalculated after deduction of 22.22 per cent zunyite.[2]

Found in the Zuni mine, near Silverton, San Juan County, Colorado, intimately associated with zunyite and pyrite. In part altered to anglesite and sulfur. Named after Frank Guiterman, metallurgist and chemist, of Denver, Colorado. Possibly a mixture.[3]

Ref.

1. Hillebrand (1884).
2. Millosevich anal. in Ferrari and Curti, *Per. Min.*, 5, 154 (1934), p. 166.
3. In polished section found by Ramdohr, *Zbl. Min.*, 208, 1937, to be a mixture of a mineral apparently jordanite with a rather similar, unidentified, mineral. X-ray powder photographs of guitermanite from the original locality (anal. 2) and of jordanite from the Lengenbach, Switzerland, were found by Ferrari and Curti (1934) to be identical. Neither of these identifications, however, is definite. Peacock, *Univ. Toronto Stud., Geol. Ser.*, 44, 52 (1940), finds on x-ray powder study that guitermanite and baumhauerite are identical.

33.10   Goongarrite [$Pb_4Bi_2S_7$]. *Simpson* (*Roy. Soc. Western Australia, J.*, 10, 65, 1924).

Supposedly monoclinic.[1] Usually in irregular to platy masses, in part subfibrous and slightly radiating. Good cleavage.[2] H. 3. G. 7.29. Luster metallic. Opaque. A sulfide of bismuth and lead, $Pb_4Bi_2S_7$. Analysis gave: Pb 54.26, Bi 28.81, S 15.24, rem. 1.63 (includes Zn,Fe,Ag,Sb,Se), total 99.94. Found at Lake Goongarrie, Comet Vale Township, Western Australia, associated with native gold in a quartz vein, in amphibolite. Alters to bismutite, with some cerussite and anglesite.

WARTHAITE.   *Krenner* (*Mat. Termés, Ért.*, 42, 4, 1926), is said to be orthorhombic.[3] Habit acicular, in radial aggregates. G. 7.12 ± 0.05.[4] Luster metallic. Steel-gray. Opaque. A sulfide of bismuth and lead, $Pb_4Bi_2S_7$, identical in composition with goongarrite (see above). Analysis gave: Pb 54.53, Bi 28.18, S 15.31, rem. 2.23 (includes Fe,Ag,Cu), total 100.25. Occurs at Vaskö, Roumania, in crystalline limestone, associated with sphalerite, pyrite, and hematite. Named after Professor Vincze Wartha (1844–?), chemist, of Budapest.

Warthaite is probably identical with goongarrite, but the data for neither are adequate to establish the relationship.

Ref.

1. The measurements given by Simpson (1924) are based on poor material.
2. It is not clear from the description whether there are two different cleavages or a single, nonpinacoidal, cleavage.
3. Palache (priv. comm., 1939) measured some warthaite crystals but they were of such poor quality that no conclusions as to symmetry or similarity with goongarrite could be drawn.
4. An average of 7.163 by Loczka (1926) and 7.07 (Berman, priv. comm., 1939).

33·11 MENEGHINITE [$Pb_{13}Sb_7S_{23}$]. *Bechi* (*Am. J. Sc.*, **14**, 60, 1852). Feather-ore pt.

Cryst. Orthorhombic dipyramidal — $2/m\, 2/m\, 2/m$.[1]

$$a : b : c = 0.4736 : 1 : 0.1715;^2 \quad p_0 : q_0 : r_0 = 0.3621 : 0.1715 : 1$$

$$q_1 : r_1 : p_1 = 0.4736 : 2.7617 : 1; \quad r_2 : p_2 : q_2 = 5.8309 : 2.1114 : 1$$

Forms:[3]

		ϕ	ρ	ϕ_1	$\rho_1 = A$	ϕ_2	$\rho_2 = B$
			0°00′	0°00′	90°00′	90°00′	90°00′
c	001	....	90 00	90 00	90 00	....	0 00
b	010	0°00′	90 00	....	0 00	0 00	90 00
a	100	90 00					
S	130	35 08	90 00	90 00	54 52	0 00	35 08
T	120	46 33	90 00	90 00	43 27	0 00	46 33
m	110	64 39½	90 00	90 00	25 20½	0 00	64 39½
d	021	0 00	18 56	18 56	90 00	90 00	71 04
v	041	0 00	34 27½	34 27½	90 00	90 00	55 32½
n	101	90 00	19 54½	0 00	70 05½	70 05½	90 00
u	111	64 39½	21 50	9 44	70 21½	80 05½	80 50½
t	121	46 33	26 30½	18 56	71 05½	80 05½	72 07½
r	141	27 49½	37 48½	34 27½	73 22½	80 05½	57 10½

Less common and rare:

e	160	i	780	W	403	p	241	σ	24·24·11
R	140	h	520	V	201	δ	0·24·13	ρ	24·48·11
l	380	k	310	β	221	ϕ	0·24·11	ψ	24·48·13
f	5·12·0	y	032	s	131	q	24·0·11	X	24·72·13
g	340	o	083	μ	211	λ	24·24·13	π	24·96·13
								ω	7·21·1

Structure cell.[4] Orthorhombic; a_0 11.29, b_0 23.78, c_0 4.12; $a_0 : b_0 : c_0 = 0.4750 : 1 : 0.1733$; contains $Pb_{13}Sb_7S_{23}$.

Habit. Slender prismatic [001], striated [001]. Also massive, fibrous to compact.

Phys. Cleavage {010} perfect but interrupted, {001} difficult. Fracture conchoidal. Brittle. H. 2½. G. 6.36 ± 0.01;[5] 6.391 (calc.). Luster bright metallic. Color blackish lead-gray. Streak black, shining.

Opaque. In polished section[6] white in color, with high anisotropism and weak pleochroism.

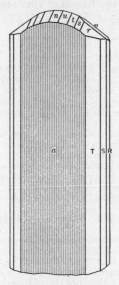

Bottino, Italy.

C h e m. Lead antimony sulfide, $Pb_{13}Sb_7S_{23}$,[7] with Cu in small amounts reported in analyses and doubtless due to impurities.

Anal.

	1	2	3	4	5
Pb	62.88	61.47	59.21	62.45	60.09
Cu	.....	0.39	3.54	1.21	1.56
Fe	.....	0.23	0.35	0.07	0.25
Sb	19.91	18.37	19.28	18.94	19.11
S	17.21	16.97	17.52	17.47	18.22
Rem.	.....	0.82	.....	0.05	.....
Total	100.00	98.25	99.90	100.19	99.23
G.		6.391	6.36		6.43

1. $Pb_{13}Sb_7S_{23}$. 2. Bottino, Tuscany. Rem. is insol.[8] 3. Bottino, Tuscany.[9] 4. Hellfors, Sweden. Rem. is Ag trace, insol. 0.05.[10] 5. Schwarzenberg, Saxony.[11]

Tests. F. 1. Oxidized by concentrated HNO_3 with separation of antimony oxide and lead sulfate.

O c c u r. The most important occurrence is at Bottino, near Seravezza, Tuscany, where it is found in complex crystals associated with galena, chalcopyrite, sphalerite, boulangerite, jamesonite, and albite. Also found in Tuscany in the Val di Castello near Pietrasanta. From the Ochsenkopf south of Schwarzenberg, Saxony, disseminated through emery; from Goldkronach in the Fichtelgebirge, Bavaria; from Hellfors, Sweden. Also reported with quartz and dolomite as a vein in gneiss at Marble Lake, Barrie Township, Frontenac County, Ontario.

A r t i f.   Reported by the fusion of PbS and Sb_2S_3 in H_2S.[12]

N a m e.   After Professor Meneghini (1811–89) of Pisa, who first observed the species.

Ref.

1. The work of Krenner, *Földt. Közl.*, **13**, 297, 350 (1883) and of Miers, *Min. Mag.*, **5**, 325 (1883), established the orthorhombic symmetry.   The earlier interpretation of vom Rath, *Ann. Phys.*, **132**, 372 (1867), who made the mineral monoclinic, was shown to be in error.   The recent morphological study of Palache, *Am. Min.*, **23**, 821 (1938), and of Richmond (in Palache, 1938) by x-ray methods, confirm the orthorhombic symmetry.

2. Elements from Goldschmidt (238, 1897), who took the average of Miers (1883) and Krenner (1883).   Orientation of Palache (1938).   Transformations: Miers to Palache $\frac{1}{4}00/010/00\frac{1}{4}$; Krenner to Palache $\frac{1}{2}00/010/00\frac{1}{4}$.   Since Dana (142, 1892) interchanged a and b of Miers, the transformation Dana to Palache is $0\frac{1}{4}0/100/00\frac{1}{4}$.

3. Forms as given in Palache (1938).   The " aberrant " forms have not yet been satisfactorily explained.   Palache (1938) points out their radial displacement with respect to simpler forms of the crystal.   Ungemach, *Zs. Kr.*, **58**, 158 (1923), has discussed the form series.

4. Richmond in Palache (1938).   Berry and Moddle, *Univ. of Toronto, Geol. Ser.*, **46**, 5 (1941), double the c_0 axis.

5. vom Rath (1867).   Average of two measurements on crystals, checked by Berman (priv. comm.) on a crystal from Bottino.

6. Schneiderhöhn and Ramdohr (**2**, 445, 1931).

7. The previously given formula $Pb_4Sb_2S_7$ is not consistent with the x-ray data and specific gravity, but the composition fits the old formula as well as the newer one of Palache (1938).   Berry and Moddle (1941) propose a slightly different formula.

8. vom Rath (1867).

9. Bechi, *Am. J. Sc.*, **14**, 60 (1852).

10. Mauzelius anal. in Flink, *Ark. Kemi*, **3** [35] (1910).

11. Frenzel, *Ann. Phys.*, **141**, 443 (1870).

12. Sommerlad, *Zs. anorg. Chem.*, **18**, 440 (1898).

33·12   **L I L L I A N I T E** $[Pb_3Bi_2S_6]$.   *Keller* (*Zs. Kr.*, **17**, 67, 1889).   Kobellite pt.

C r y s t.   Orthorhombic.

$$a : b : c = 0.8002 : 1 : 0.5433;^1 \qquad p_0 : q_0 : r_0 = 0.6790 : 0.5433 : 1$$

$$q_1 : r_1 : p_1 = 0.8002 : 1.4729 : 1; \qquad r_2 : p_2 : q_2 = 1.8406 : 1.2497 : 1$$

Forms:[2]

		ϕ	$\rho = C$	ϕ_1	$\rho_1 = A$	ϕ_2	$\rho_2 = B$
b	010	0°00′	90°00′	90°00′	90°00′	.....	0°00′
a	100	90 00	90 00	.....	0 00	0°00′	90 00
m	110	51 20	90 00	90 00	38 40	0 00	51 20
l	320	61 55½	90 00	90 00	28 04½	0 00	61 55½
n	210	68 11½	90 00	90 00	21 48½	0 00	68 11½
k	830	73 18	90 00	90 00	16 42	0 00	73 18
e	011	0 00	28 31	28 31	90 00	90 00	61 29

Habit.   Crystals rare: prismatic [001].   Usually massive granular; also radiating fibrous [001].

P h y s.   Cleavage {100} very good, {010} less so, probably also {001}. H. 2–3.   G. 7.0–7.2.   Luster metallic.   Color steel-gray.   Streak black.

Opaque.   In polished section[3] white in color with distinct anisotropism and very weak pleochroism.   Reflection percentages: green 51.5, orange 45, red 43.5.

C h e m.   A lead bismuth sulfide, $Pb_3Bi_2S_6$.   Se, in small amounts, and Sb, up to about 50 atomic per cent, may substitute for Bi (anal. 7).

Anal.

	1	2	3	4
Pb	50.46	47.62	48.21	48.05
Cu	.....	0.20	1.12	0.69
Fe	.....	0.47	.....	0.16
Bi	33.93	34.60	34.36	33.84
Sb	.....	.....	.....	.....
Se	.....	0.35	.....	.....
S	15.61	15.89	15.79	15.92
Rem.	.....	0.83	.....	0.50
Total	100.00	99.96	99.48	99.16
G.			7.14	7.0–7.07

1. $Pb_3Bi_2S_6$.   2. Bodvik Mine, Svärdsjö, Sweden.   Rem. is Zn 0.52 and insol. 0.31.[4] 3. Gladhammar, Sweden.   Average of two analyses.[5]   4. Gladhammar, Sweden.   Rem. is Zn 0.05 and insol. 0.45.[6]

	5	6	7	8	9
Pb	48.21	43.83	50.66	50.50	48.78
Cu	1.74	2.65	1.46	.....	.....
Fe	trace	1.23	1.70		1.55
Bi	33.23	26.43	17.89	18.02	20.52
Sb	0.24	5.30	10.14	10.25	10.43
Se	.....	2.97	.....	.....	.....
S	15.73	15.93	17.62	17.41	17.47
Rem.	.....	1.37	.....	2.96	.....
Total	99.15	99.71	99.47	99.14	98.75
G.	7.09	7.22		6.535	6.145

5. Gladhammar, Sweden.[7]   6. Jillijärvi, Finland.   Rem. is Ag 0.88 and Zn 0.49.[8] 7. Unstated locality.   Contains chalcopyrite.[9]   8. Vena, Sweden.   Contains chalcopyrite.[10]   9. Vena, Sweden.   After deducting 5.61 cobaltite and 3.67 chalcopyrite.[11]

O c c u r.   In Sweden at the Bodvik mine, Svärdsjö, Delarne;   with cobaltite and chalcopyrite at Gladhammar, Kalmar;   and at Vena, near Askersund.   From Jillijärvi, Finland.

N a m e.   From the supposed occurrence in the Lillian mine, on Printerboy Hill, Leadville, Colorado.

Needs verification.[12]

Ref.

1. Flink, *Ark. Kemi*, **3** [35], 10 (1910).   Berry, *Am. Min.*, **25**, 726 (1940), points out that Flink's ratio, when *c* is halved, is nearly identical with the ratio of the structural cell of galenobismutite ($a_0 : b_0 : c_0 = 0.807 : 1 : 0.280$).
2. Flink (1910) and Johansson, *Ark. Kemi*, **9** [8], 13 (1924).
3. Schneiderhöhn and Ramdohr (2, 640, 1931).
4. Johansson (1924).
5. Mauzelius anal. in Flink (1910).
6. Lindström, *Geol. För. Förh.*, **11**, 171 (1889).

7. Todd anal. in Walker and Thomson, *Univ. Toronto Stud., Geol. Ser.*, 1921, 11.
8. Borgström, *Geol. För. Förh.*, **32**, 1525 (1910).
9. Genth anal. in Rammelsberg (100, 1875).
10. Mauzelius anal. in Flink, *Ark. Kemi*, **5**, 1 (1915) — *Jb. Min.*, **27**, 1916.
11. Rammelsberg (100, 1875).
12. The material from the original locality in the Lillian mine, Leadville, Colo., has been shown by Emmons, Irving, and Loughlin, *U. S. Geol. Sur., Prof. Pap. 148*, 170, 1927, to be a mixture of galena, bismuthinite, and argentite. Analyses of material from the Lillian and other mines at Leadville are close to argentian lillianite in ratio, and the mixture may have resulted from the breakdown of a homogeneous mineral. Berry (1940) found from x-ray powder and polished section study that a specimen of so-called lillianite from Gladhammar, Sweden, was a mixture of galenobismutite and galena. The uniformity with which the reported analyses of lillianite approach the ratio $A_3X_2S_6$, however, makes the interpretation of lillianite as a chance mixture seem unlikely.

3411   **B O U R N O N I T E** [PbCuSbS$_3$].   Ore of Antimony (from Endellion) *Rashleigh* (**1**, 34, pl. xix, 1797).   Triple Sulphuret of Lead, Antimony and Copper *Bournon* (*Roy. Soc. London, Phil. Trans.*, 30, 1804); *Hatchett* (*Roy. Soc. London, Phil. Trans.*, 63, 1804).   Bournonite, Antimonial Lead Ore *Jameson* (**2**, 579, 1805; **3**, 372, 1816). Spiessglanzblei *Karsten* (in *Klaproth* [**4**, 82, 1807; and 68, 1808]).   Plomb sulfuré antimonifère *Haüy* (1809).   Endellione *Bournon* (409, 1813).   Schwarz Spiessglanzerz *Werner*.   Schwarzspiessglanzerz, Antimonbleikupferblende *Germ.*   Antimoine sulfuré plumbocuprifère *Haüy* (**4**, 1822).   Radelerz, Rädlerz [= wheel-ore] *Kapnik miners*.   Tripelglanz *Breithaupt* (270, 1832).   Endellionite *Zippe* (213, 1859). Cañutillo *Span., S.A.*   Cog-wheel ore, Wheel-ore *Eng. miners*.

Prismatischer Spiesglas-Glanz *Mohs* (**2**, 559, 1822).   Prismatoidischer Kupfer-Glanz *Mohs* (**2**, 559, 1824).   Antimonkupfer-Glanz *Breithaupt* (270, 1832).   Wölchit *Haidinger* (564, 1845).   Nickelbournonite, Bournonit-Nickelglanz *Rammelsberg* and *Zinken* (*Ann. Phys.*, 77, 251, 1843).

C r y s t.   Orthorhombic;   dipyramidal — $2/m\ 2/m\ 2/m$.

$$a : b : c = 0.9380 : 1 : 0.8969;^1 \qquad p_0 : q_0 : r_0 = 0.9562 : 0.8969 : 1$$

$$q_1 : r_1 : p_1 = 0.9380 : 1.0458 : 1; \qquad r_2 : p_2 : q_2 = 1.1150 : 1.0661 : 1$$

Forms:[2]

		ϕ	$\rho = C$	ϕ_1	$\rho_1 = A$	ϕ_2	$\rho_2 = B$
c	001	.....	0°00′	0°00′	90°00′	90°00′	90°00′
b	010	0°00′	90 00	90 00	90 00	.....	0 00
a	100	90 00	90 00	.....	0 00	0 00	90 00
f	120	28 03½	90 00	90 00	61 56½	0 00	28 03½
m	110	46 50	90 00	90 00	43 10	0 00	46 50
e	210	64 52½	90 00	90 00	25 07½	0 00	64 52½
n	011	0 00	41 53½	41 53½	90 00	90 00	48 06½
x	102	90 00	25 33	0 00	64 27	64 27	90 00
h	203	90 00	32 31	0 00	57 29	57 29	90 00
o	101	90 00	43 43	0 00	46 17	46 17	90 00
z	201	90 00	62 23½	0 00	27 36½	27 36½	90 00
u	112	46 50	33 15	24 09	66 26	64 27	67 58½
y	111	46 50	52 40	41 53½	54 33½	46 17	57 03
s	212	64 52½	46 34	24 09	48 54	46 17	72 02½
p	121	28 03½	63 48½	60 51½	65 02	46 17	37 38½

Less common forms:

d	160	k	540	κ	013	ν	304	p	223	π	122
i	130	Δ	430	γ	023	δ	301	χ	334	Γ	211
α	230	l	320	t	104	ζ	401	μ	332	ξ	214
w	340	η	310	ϵ	103	ϕ	113	g	221	ω	346
								λ	144	O	213

Structure cell.[3] Space group $Pnmm$; a_0 8.10 ± 0.05, b_0 8.65 ± 0.05, c_0 7.75 ± 0.05; $a_0 : b_0 : c_0 = 0.936 : 1 : 0.896$; contains $Pb_4Cu_4Sb_4S_{12}$.

Habit. Usually short prismatic to tabular [001]. Crystals often subparallel aggregates. Faces $\{hkO\}$ striated [001], $\{h01\}$ striated [010], $\{100\}$ lustrous and striated [010], $\{010\}$ usually smooth and lustrous. Also massive; granular to compact. Common forms: $c\,a\,b\,m\,f\,o\,u\,y$.

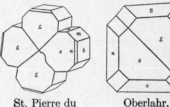

St. Pierre du Mésage.　　Oberlahr.

Twinning. On $\{110\}$, very common; often repeated, forming cruciform or wheel-like aggregates. Twin gliding: $x_1\{110\}$, $\sigma_2[110]$.[6]

P h y s. Cleavage $\{010\}$ imperfect, $\{100\}$ and $\{010\}$ less good. Fracture subconchoidal to uneven. Rather brittle. H. $2\frac{1}{2}$–3. G. 5.83 ± 0.03,[4] 5.68 (Pomacancha, Peru[5]); 5.93 (calc.). Luster metallic, often

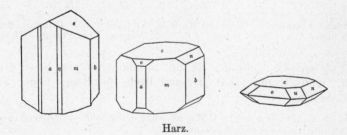

Harz.

brilliant. Color and streak steel-gray, inclining to blackish lead-gray or iron-black. Opaque. In polished section[7] white in color with weak anisotropism and very weak pleochroism; usually exhibits polysynthetic twinning on $\{110\}$, in part due to deformation. Reflection percentages: green 33.5, orange 30, red 29.

C h e m. A lead copper antimony sulfide, $PbCuSbS_3$. As substitutes for Sb, to about Sb : As $= 4 : 1$ (anal. 9). The role of Ag, Fe, Zn, Mn, and Ni, frequently reported in small amounts, is uncertain. High Fe, Ni, and Mn[9] are undoubtedly due to admixture.

Anal.[10]

	1	2	3	4	5
Pb	42.40	43.18	42.34	42.75	43.25
Fe	.....	.....	0.27	.....	.....
Ag	.....	.....	.....	trace	.....
Zn	.....	.....	0.04	.....	.....
Cu	13.01	13.14	12.80	12.77	12.86
Sb	24.91	25.03	24.44	24.76	24.53
As	.....	.....	.....	.....	.....
S	19.68	19.59	19.58	19.40	19.17
Rem.	.....	.....	0.37	.....	.....
Total	100.00	100.94	99.84	99.68	99.81
G.	5.93	5.829		5.85	5.81

1. $PbCuSbS_3$. 2. Park City, Utah.[11] 3. Kisbánya, Hungary. Rem. is insol. 0.37.[12] 4. Najolnig Krjasch, Donetz Basin, U.S.S.R.[13] 5. St. Kreuz, Lebertal, Alsace.[14]

	6	7	8	9
Pb	43.62	39.37	40.21	43.85
Fe	0.74	0.31	0.35	0.51
Ag	.....	1.69	.....	.....
Zn	.....	0.09	0.35	0.20
Cu	12.95	13.52	15.12	12.87
Sb	22.22	24.74	18.99	18.42
As	0.03	.....	2.81	3.18
S	20.40	19.94	20.04	20.22
Rem.	0.38	.....	1.67	0.26
Total	100.34	99.66	99.54	99.51
G.	5.766		[5.84]	5.766

6. Trepča, Yugoslavia. Rem. is Mn 0.38, Ni trace.[15] 7. Příbram, Bohemia.[16] 8. Boggs mine, Ariz. Rem. is insol. 1.67.[17] 9. Nagyág, Transylvania. Rem. is Mn 0.26.[18]

Var. *Arsenian.* Contains As up to about Sb : As = 4 : 1. From Nagyág, Transylvania (anal. 9), and from the Boggs mine, Yavapai County, Arizona (anal. 8).

Tests. F. 1. Decomposed by HNO_3, affording a blue solution and leaving a residue of S and a white powder containing Sb and Pb.

Occur. Bournonite is one of the commonest of the sulfosalts. It typically occurs in hydrothermal veins formed at moderate temperatures, associated with galena, tetrahedrite, sphalerite, chalcopyrite, pyrite, siderite, quartz and, less often, with stibnite, zinkenite, feather ores, rhodochrosite, dolomite, and barite. Frequently noted as microscopic inclusions in galena.

Oriented growths have been found of galena upon bournonite,[19] and of bournonite upon galena.[20]

Only those localities important because of quantity or for fine specimens from which data for the species have been derived are listed here. Many others have been reported.[21] In Germany in the Harz Mountains at Clausthal, Andreasberg, Wolfsberg and, in particular, at Neudorf (including the Meiseberg localities); in the Rhine province at Horhausen and Oberlahr; at Bräunsdorf, Saxony; at Altenberg, Silesia, with boulangerite; in Carinthia at Hüttenberg with barite, and in partly altered crystals at Olsa near Friesach and Wölch near St. Gertraud (*wölchite*); in pockets in dolomitic marble at Lengefeld, Saxony, with jamesonite (?) and sulfides. From Přibram, Bohemia; in Roumania at Felsöbánya, Kapnik, and at Nagyág with rhodochrosite; at Offenbánya and Oradna in Transylvania; at Luciabánya and Rozsnýo, Hungary.

In Italy at a number of localities in Torino and Lucca provinces; in Sicily at Novara with feather-ores; at Brosso, Piedmont. In Spain in the Sierra Almagrera, Almeria Province, Andalusia; from Hiendelaencina, Guadalajara; also in Castile, and with cinnabar at Almadenejos, Almaden. In France at the mines of Pontgibaud, Puy-de-Dôme; at Corbières, Aveyron, and at Avesne and nearby localities in Hérault; at the lead mines in the neighborhood of Alais, Gard; and near Servoz, Haute-Savoie. In England in fine specimens from the Herodsfoot mine, Liskeard, Cornwall; also from mines in St. Endellion parish. A common mineral in the silver and silver-tin veins of Bolivia; notable crystals (up to 10 cm. in size) occur at the Vibora mine, Machacamarca, with tetrahedrite, augelite, and argentite; also at Chorolque with bismuthinite and galena, at Pulacayo and at Colquechaca, at the Pacuani mine, Patacamaya, with feather ores, marcasite and galena, and at Oruro. In Peru in the Recuay district, Huarás, at Casapalca, and at other localities. From Huasco, Atacama, and elsewhere in Chile. In Australia from Broken Hill, New South Wales, and from Steiglitz and Ballarat, Victoria. From the Naguila mine, Sonora, Mexico, with sphalerite, arsenopyrite, and galena.

In the United States, in large crystals with siderite and sphalerite at Park City, Utah; at the Boggs mine, Big Bug district, Yavapai County, Arizona, with pyrite, chalcopyrite, siderite, and byssolite as masses in quartz and as crystals; at the Cerro Gordo mine, Inyo County, California; from Austin, Nevada; reported in the Silverton district and elsewhere in Colorado, and from Montgomery County, Arkansas, with tetrahedrite and galena; from Emery, Montana. In Canada in Marmora township, Hastings County, and Darling, Lanark County, Ontario.

Alter. To bindheimite and antimony ochres; also to cerussite, malachite, azurite, and linarite. Galena, pyrite, chalcopyrite, and marcasite have been noted as pseudomorphs or alteration products of bournonite; also incrustation pseudomorphs of quartz (Cornwall). Bournonite has been found as pseudomorphs after or as an alteration product of galena, tetrahedrite, and nagyagite. Wölchite is a partly altered bournonite.

Artif.[22] Reported by gently heating a mixture of the chlorides or oxides of Pb, Cu, and Sb in H_2S; obtained in crystals when finely powdered bournonite is heated in water containing sodium sulfide in a sealed tube at 80°.

Name. After Count J. L. de Bournon (1751–1825), French crystallographer and mineralogist. *Endellionite* from the locality where it was first found, at Wheal Boys, Endellion, Cornwall. *Wheel-ore* (Rädelerz, *Germ.*) in allusion to the form of aggregation of twinned groups.

WÖLCHITE. Prismatoidischer Spieglas-Glanz *Mohs* (1820). Prismatoidischer Kupfer-Glanz *Mohs* (**2**, 559, 1824). Antimonkupfer-Glanz *Breithaupt* (270, 1832). Wölchit *Haidinger* (564, 1845).

A partly altered bournonite[23] from Wölch, near St. Gertraud, and from Olsa, near Friesach, in Carinthia, Germany, early thought to be a distinct species.

Ref.

1. Brooke and Miller (201, 1852).
2. In Goldschmidt (**1**, 217, 1913).   Also Loew and Tokody, *Cbl. Min.*, **A**, 105, 1928.
Rare and uncertain forms:

190	750	108	445	134	22·11·34
150	530	105	20·20·21	123	314
140	950	207	12·12·11	368	50·66·59
270	720	205	554	275	454
3·10·0	18·5·0	504	14·14·11	5·7·12	232
5·16·0	410	907	443	7·8·15	131
380	610	705	17·17·12	7·2·14	918
6·13·0	0·1·14	503	17·17·11	316	322
350	014	502	885	7·4·14	743
580	012	601	11·11·3	326	11·3·4
450	034	114	441	19·20·38	321
560	032	449	881	132	431
780	021	10·10·19	1·18·19	325	11·1·11
970	031	559	1·12·13	355	
11·8·0	1·0·13	558	1·10·9	568	

3. Oftedal, *Zs. Kr.*, **83**, 157 (1932), on crystals from Horhausen and Cornwall by the oscillation method.
4. From best values in literature and the following measurements (Frondel, priv. comm., 1939): Boggs mine, Arizona, 5.84; Felsöbánya, 5.83; Horhausen 5.80.
5. Two identical determinations on crystals (Frondel, priv. comm., 1939).
6. Mügge, *Jb. Min.*, 31, 1920.
7. Schneiderhöhn and Ramdohr (**2**, 425, 1931); see Head and Loofbourow, *Econ. Geol.*, **24**, 301 (1934), for microchemical tests.
8. Up to 5 per cent Fe has been reported (Lovisato, *Zs. Kr.*, **40**, 98 [1910], and Rammelsberg [79, 1860]), but the validity of these analyses is doubtful.
9. Tschermak, *Ak. Wien, Ber.*, **53**, 518 (1866).
10. For additional analyses see Doelter (4 [1], 469, 1926).
11. Veazey anal. in Van Horn and Hunt, *Am. J. Sc.*, **40**, 145 (1915).
12. Vavrinecz, *Magyar Chem. Foly.*, **39**, 54 (1933) — *Min. Abs.*, **5**, 379 (1933).
13. Samojlov, *Zs. Kr.*, 46, 289 (1909).
14. Dürr anal. in Bücking, *Geol. Landesanst. Elsass-Löthringen, Mitt.*, **8** [2], 203 (1913).
15. Gagarin and Pavlovic, *Geol. Ann. Penin. Balkan*, 14, 199 (1937) — *Jb. Min.*, 561, 1938.
16. Helmhacker, *Berg- u. hütten. Jb.*, **13**, 377 (1864).
17. Schaller, *U. S. Geol. Sur., Bull. 262*, 132, 1905.
18. Sipöcz, *Zs. Kr.*, 11, 218 (1886).
19. Miers, *Min. Mag.*, 11, 268 (1897), with galena {100}, [110] ‖ bournonite {010}, [100].
20. Hintze, *Zs. Kr.*, 11, 606 (1886), with bournonite [001] ‖ galena {100}, [100], and [110].
21. For additional localities see Hintze (1 [1], 1126, 1904) and Schneiderhöhn and Ramdohr (1931).
22. Doelter, *Zs. Kr.*, 11, 38 (1885); *Ak. Wien, Anz.*, 101, 1890.
23. Hintze (1904).

3412 SELIGMANNITE [PbCuAsS₃]. *Baumhauer (Ak. Berlin, Ber.*, 110, 1901; 611, 1902).

C r y s t. Orthorhombic; dipyramidal — $2/m\,2/m\,2/m$.

$a : b : c = 0.9233 : 1 : 0.8734;$[1] $p_0 : q_0 : r_0 = 0.9459 : 0.8734 : 1$

$q_1 : r_1 : p_1 = 0.9233 : 1.0572 : 1;$ $r_2 : p_2 : q_2 = 1.1450 : 1.0830 : 1$

Forms:[2]

		ϕ	$\rho = C$	ϕ_1	$\rho_1 = A$	ϕ_2	$\rho_2 = B$
c	001	....	0°00′	0°00′	90°00′	90°00′	90°00′
b	010	0°00′	90 00	90 00	90 00	....	0 00
a	100	90 00	90 00	....	0 00	0 00	90 00
i	130	19 51	90 00	90 00	70 09	0 00	19 51
m	110	47 17	90 00	90 00	42 43	0 00	47 17
e	210	65 13	90 00	90 00	24 47	0 00	65 13
n	011	0 00	41 08	41 08	90 00	90 00	48 52
o	101	90 00	43 24½	0 00	46 35½	46 35½	90 00
u	112	47 17	32 46	23 35½	66 34	64 41½	68 27½
y	111	47 17	52 10	41 08	54 32	46 35½	57 36½
s	212	65 13	46 10½	23 35½	49 05	46 35½	72 24
v	211	65 13	64 22	41 08	35 03½	27 51½	67 48

Less common and rare:

θ	180	q	510	t	104	r	441	ω	121	Z	261	π	972
α	160	E	610	d	103	Ψ	122	L	131	S	713	γ	541
Φ	140	κ	013	x	102	II	132	K	161	X	14·3·6	μ	561
f	120	g	025	h	203	τ	1·10·2	β	181	Q	733	V	12·1·2
ψ	450	z	021	I	201	ι	213	U	413	C	311	P	611
k	540	ϵ	031	G	601	M	233	Y	312	ξ	341	J	651
l	320	F	061	Γ	229	O	313	D	322	δ	752	λ	781
η	310	B	071	ϕ	113	N	323	R	533	W	431		
A	410	Δ	105	Ξ	331	σ	232	T	613	ζ	451		

Structure cell.[3] Space group *Pnmm*; a_0 8.04, b_0 8.66, c_0 7.56 (all ±0.05); $a_0 : b_0 : c_0 = 0.928 : 1 : 0.873$; contains $Cu_4Pb_4As_4S_{12}$.

Habit. Equant; short prismatic [001] to tabular {001}. {110} often with multiple striae (Binnental) ‖ [001], [1̄10], [1̄1̄1]. Common forms: *c a b e m o v u y.*

Twinning. On {110}, very common.

P h y s. Cleavage very poor on {001}, {100}, and {010}.[4] Fracture conchoidal. Brittle. H. 3. G. 5.44 (Binnental), 5.38 (Bingham[5]); 5.54 (calc.). Lus-

Bingham, Utah.

ter metallic. Color dark lead-gray to black. Streak chocolate-brown to purple-black. Opaque. In polished section[6] rose-white in color with strong anisotropism; frequently exhibits polysynthetic twinning.

C h e m. A lead and copper arsenic sulfide, $PbCuAsS_3$.

Anal.

	Pb	Fe	Zn	Ag	Cu	Sb	As	S	Total	G.
1	46.89	....	....	....	14.38	....	16.99	21.74	100.00	
2	46.34	0.06	0.27	0.11	13.09	0.64	16.88	21.73	99.12	5.44

1. $PbCuAsS_3$. 2. Binnental.[7]

O c c u r. From the Lengenbach quarry in the Binnental, Valais, Switzerland, in cavities in dolomite associated with tennantite, dufrenoysite, rathite, and baumhauerite, and formed later than those species. From Bingham, Utah, deposited upon tennantite, sphalerite, and pyrite. Reported from Butte and from Emery, Montana, and from Kalgoorlie, Western Australia.

N a m e. After Gustav Seligmann (1849–1920), a private mineral collector of Coblenz, Germany.

Ref.

1. Solly, *Min. Mag.*, **13**, 337 (1903).
2. Palache, *Am. Min.*, **13**, 402 (1928). Solly (1903). Solly, *Min. Mag.*, **14**, 186 (1906); **16**, 282 (1912).
3. Frondel, *Am. Min.*, **26**, 25 (1941), by Weissenberg method on material from Bingham, Utah, described by Palache (1928).
4. Solly (1903) observed no cleavage, nor did Palache (1928). The cleavages were later reported by Solly (1912).
5. Frondel (1941).
6. Schneiderhöhn and Ramdohr (**2**, 494, 1931).
7. Prior, *Min. Mag.*, **15**, 385 (1910). A second analysis on probably impure material is also given, with G. 5.48.

3413   **A I K I N I T E** [PbCuBiS₃]. Nadelerz *Mohs* (3, 726, 1804). Bismuth sulfuré plumbo-cuprifère *Haüy* (105, 1809). Needle-ore; Acicular Bismuth; Cupreous Bismuth. Aikinite *Chapman* (127, 1843). Patrinite *Haidinger* (568, 1845). Belonit *Glocker* (27, 1847). Aciculite *Nicol* (487, 1849). (Not the Aikinite [= wolframite] of *Levy* in *Greg* and *Lettsom* [354, 1858].)

C r y s t. Orthorhombic $(2/m\,2/m\,2/m$ or $m\,m\,2).^1$

$$a : b : c = 0.9708 : 1 : 0.3436^1$$

Forms:

$$b\{010\} \qquad i\{130\} \qquad f\{120\} \qquad m\{110\} \qquad l\{210\}$$

Structure cell.[1] Space group *Pnam* or *Pna2*; a_0 11.30 ± 0.03, b_0 11.64 ± 0.03, c_0 4.00 ± 0.02; $a_0 : b_0 : c_0 = 0.9708 : 1 : 0.3436$; contains Pb₄Cu₄Bi₄S₁₂.

Habit. Prismatic to acicular and striated [001]. Also massive.

P h y s. Cleavage {010} (?) very indistinct. Fracture uneven. H. 2–2½. G. 7.07 ± 0.01;[2] 7.22 (calc.). Luster metallic. Color blackish lead-gray; tarnishes brown or copper-red, sometimes with a yellowish green coating. Streak grayish black. Opaque. In polished section[3] cream-white in color with distinct anisotropism; pleochroic: ∥ [001] cream-white, ⊥ [001] either pure white or light brown. Reflection percentages: green 44, orange 37.5, red 38.

C h e m. A lead and copper bismuth sulfide, PbCuBiS₃.

Anal.[4]

	1	2	3
Pb	35.98	35.15	36.01
Cu	11.03	11.11	10.90
Bi	36.29	36.25	36.20
S	16.70	16.56	16.60
Total	100.00	99.07	99.71

1. PbCuBiS₃. 2, 3. Beresovsk, Urals.[5]

Tests. F. 1. Decomposed by HNO₃ with separation of S and PbSO₄.

O c c u r. In the veins of the Beresovsk district, near Ekaterinburg, Ural Mountains, U.S.S.R., with native gold and galena in white quartz. Reported from the mine of Gardette, near Bourg d'Oisans, Isère, France, with gold and pyrite in quartz; also reported from Tasco and Huitzuco, Guerro, Mexico. Said to occur at Dundas, Tasmania. In the United States possibly occurs at Gold Hill, Rowan County, North Carolina; in Idaho in the Seven Devils district, Adams County, and in the St. Louis mine, Butte County; at the Sells mine, Alta, Utah.

A l t e r. To a bismuth ocher, probably largely bismutite, often green from admixed malachite and containing particles of native gold.

N a m e.[6] After Dr. Arthur Aikin (1773–1854), a founder, and for many years secretary, of the Geological Society of London.

Ref.

1. From an x-ray study by Peacock (*Univ. of Toronto Stud., Geol. Ser.*, **47**, 63 [1942]) on material from Beresovsk. The partial morphological ratio of Miers, *Min. Mag.*, **8**, 206 (1889), is $a : b = 0.9719 : 1$, in agreement with the x-ray ratio.
2. Peacock (1940); Frick, *Ann. Phys.*, **31**, 529 (1834), gives 6.757 and Chapman, *Phil. Mag.*, **31**, 541 (1847), gives 6.10.
3. Schneiderhöhn and Ramdohr (**2**, 429, 1931).
4. For additional analyses see Hintze (4 [1], 1139, 1904). Spectroscopic data in de Gramont, *Bull. soc. min.*, **18**, 265 (1895).
5. Guillemain (Inaug. Diss., Breslau, 1898 — *Zs. Kr.*, **33**, 75 [1900]).
6. Hintze (1904) states that the origin of the name is not clear, and proposes a Greek derivation.

342   **Berthonite** [$Pb_2Cu_7Sb_5S_{13}$]. *Buttgenbach* (*Soc. géol. Belgique, Ann.*, **46**, 212, 1923).

Massive, fine granular. No cleavage. Brittle. H. 4–5. G. 5.49. Luster metallic. Color gray-black, streak black. Opaque. In polished section[1] gray in color and anisotropic.

C h e m. A lead and copper antimony sulfide, possibly $Pb_2Cu_7Sb_5S_{13}$.[2]
Anal.

	Pb	Cu	Sb	S	Total
1	21.98	23.61	32.30	22.11	100.00
2	21.83	23.68	32.45	[22.17]	100.13

1. $Pb_2Cu_7Sb_5S_{13}$.   2. Tunis.

Tests. F. 1. Decomposed by HNO_3 with separation of sulfur and $PbSO_4$.

O c c u r. Associated with galena in veinlets in the iron ore deposits of Slata, Tunis.

A l t e r. To chrysocolla, malachite, cerussite, and bindheimite (?).
N a m e. After Mr. Berthon, mining engineer.
Needs further study.

Ref.

1. Short (46, 1934); see also Sampson in Foshag, *Am. Min.*, **9**, 173 (1924).
2. Formula of Fleischer (priv. comm., 1939). Buttgenbach (1923) erroneously derived the formula $Pb_5Cu_{18}Sb_{14}S_{35}$.

DÜRFELDTITE.   *Raimondi* (125, 1878).
In masses with indistinct fibrous structure, also in fine (orthorhombic ?) needles.

H. 2.5. G. 5.40. Color light gray. Luster metallic. Analysis (after deduction of 31.3 per cent quartz): Pb 25.81, Ag 7.34, Cu 1.86, Fe 2.24, Mn 8.08, Sb 30.52, S 24.15, total 100.00, yielding an approximate formula $Pb(Ag,Cu,Fe)MnSb_2S_6$. From the Irismachay mine, Auquimarca, Province Cajatambo, Peru. Named after Richard Dürfeldt, metallurgist. Probably a mixture.

343 **DIAPHORITE** [$Pb_2Ag_3Sb_3S_8$]. *Zepharovich* (*Ak. Wien, Ber.*, **63** [1], 130, 1871). Freieslebenite pt.

Brongniardite pt. *Damour* (*Ann. mines*, **16**, 227, 1849). Bleisilberantimonit *Groth* (18, 1874).

Cryst. Orthorhombic; dipyramidal — $2/m\ 2/m\ 2/m$.

$a : b : c = 0.4953 : 1 : 0.1840;$[1] $p_0 : q_0 : r_0 = 0.3715 : 0.1840 : 1$

$q_1 : r_1 : p_1 = 0.4953 : 2.6918 : 1;\quad r_2 : p_2 : q_2 = 5.4348 : 2.0190 : 1$

Forms:[2]

		ϕ	$\rho = C$	ϕ_1	$\rho_1 = A$	ϕ_2	$\rho_2 = B$
c	001	.....	0°00′	0°00′	90°00′	90°00′	90°00′
b	010	0°00′	90 00	90 00	90 00	.....	0 00
a	100	90 00	90 00	....	0 00	0 00	90 00
π	130	33 56	90 00	90 00	56 04	0 00	33 56
n	120	45 16	90 00	90 00	44 44	0 00	45 16
m	110	63 39	90 00	90 00	26 21	0 00	63 39
u	021	0 00	20 12	20 12	90 00	90 00	69 48
r	041	0 00	36 21	36 21	90 00	90 00	53 39
w	081	0 00	55 48½	55 48½	90 00	90 00	34 11½
ψ	201	90 00	36 36½	0 00	53 23½	53 23½	90 00
x	401	90 00	56 03½	0 00	33 56½	33 56½	90 00
i	111	63 39	22 31	10 25½	69 56	69 37½	80 13
y	221	63 39	39 39½	20 12	55 07	53 23½	73 32½
O	171	16 05	53 16½	52 10½	77 10	69 37½	39 38
θ	261	33 56	53 04½	47 50	63 29½	53 23½	48 27
e	531	73 27	62 42	28 54	31 35½	28 18	75 20

Less common:

ρ	150	C	331	K	192	P	191	λ	2·14·1
f	0·10·1	E	551	L	283	U	392	ω	311
g	0·12·1	H	132	o	131	ι	281	v	351
B	3·3·2	J	172	N	151	κ	2·10·1	ξ	391

ϕ	712	Δ	621
z	421	ϵ	731
X	4·16·1	θ	841
Z	511		

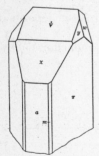

Přibram, Bohemia.

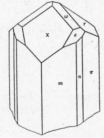

Felsöbánya.

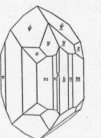

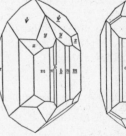

Bräunsdorf, near Freiberg, Saxony.

Structure cell.[3] Space group $Cmma$; a_0 15.83, b_0 32.23, c_0 5.89; $a_0 : b_0 : c_0 = 0.491 : 1 : 0.183$; contains $Pb_{16}Ag_{24}Sb_{24}S_{64}$.

Habit. Prismatic [001]. Often striated [001]. Sometimes highly complex crystals (Freiberg).

Twinning. (a) On {120}. (b) On {241}.

P h y s. Cleavage none. Fracture subconchoidal to uneven. Brittle. H. $2\frac{1}{2}$–3. G. 6.04;[4] 5.97 (calc.). Luster metallic. Color steel-gray. Opaque.

C h e m. A lead and silver antimony sulfide, $Pb_2Ag_3Sb_3S_8$.

Anal.

	1	2	3
Pb	30.48	28.67	31.06
Ag	23.78	23.44	23.36
Sb	26.87	26.43	25.92
S	18.87	20.18	18.51
Rem.	......	1.40	.....
Total	100.00	100.12	98.85
G.		5.73?	6.04

1. $Pb_2Ag_3Sb_3S_8$. 2. Přibram. Rem. is Fe 0.67, Cu 0.73.[6] 3. Přibram. The Pb and Ag are average of two determinations.[7]

Tests. F. 1. B.B. fuses easily, giving the white and yellow sublimates of Pb and Sb oxides. Soluble in HNO_3 with separation of $PbSO_4$.

O c c u r. At Přibram, Bohemia, with sphalerite, galena, quartz, and siderite. At Freiberg, Saxony, in the Alte Hoffnung Gottes mine, Voigtsberg, as highly complex crystals, sometimes with a core of galena, and at the Neues Hoffnung Gottes mine, Bräunsdorf. Reported from Santa Maria de Catorze, San Luis Potosí, Mexico, with miargyrite, sphalerite, pyrite, dolomite, and quartz. Said to occur at Zancudo, Colombia, with sphalerite. In the United States reported from Lake Chelan district, Okanogan County, Washington, with galena, pyrargyrite, quartz, and dolomite.

N a m e. From διαφορά, *difference*, because distinct from freieslebenite, a supposed dimorphous form.

Ref.
1. Palache, *Am. Min.*, **23**, 821 (1938), on crystals from Freiberg. Transformation: Zepharovich (1871) to Palache 100/010/00$\frac{1}{4}$.
2. Palache (1938) and Zepharovich (1871). The following forms of Zepharovich were not found by Palache: {1·11·0}, {5·12·0}, {0·20·3}, {141}, {241}. Rare forms (noted less than three times on 8 crystals) Palache:

170	210	112	1·11·1	251	711
160	310	441	1·13·1	2·14·1	971
140	011	133	312	3·13·1	10·2·1
230	061	173	352	431	16·2·1
320	0·14·1	2·22·3	211	641	

3. Winchell in Palache (1938).
4. The best determinations were made by Vrba, *Zs. Kr.*, **2**, 161 (1878), on crystals from Přibram. Three determinations gave 6.039, 6.044, and 6.038.
5. Earlier formulas proposed (in Dana [124, 1892]) were based on the supposed chemical identity with freieslebenite.
6. Helmhacker anal. in Kenngott (294, 1865 — Dana [124, 1892]).
7. Morawski anal. in Vrba (1878).

Ultrabasite.　Rosický and Štěrba-Böhm (Ak. Česká Roz. **25**, 45, 1916; Zs. Kr., **55**, 430, 1920).

From the Himmelfürst mine in Freiberg, Saxony.　The crystallography and physical description of the species clearly refer to diaphorite,[1] so that the validity of the species can rest only on the complex composition.[2]　No statement of homogeneity is given.

C h e m.　Supposedly a lead, silver, germanium, and antimony sulfide, Pb_{28}-$Ag_{22}Sb_4Ge_3S_{53}$.　Analysis gave (average of two):

Pb	Ag	Sb	Cu	Fe	Ge	S	Total
54.16	22.35	4.60	0.47	0.25	2.20	16.16	100.18

Ref.

1. The described crystals are similar to diaphorite in habit, development of common forms, and density.　The angular relations, when transformed to the diaphorite unit are in complete agreement.　Transformation: ultrabasite to diaphorite $200/040/00\frac{1}{2}$. Palache and Berman (priv. comm., 1939).

2. A portion of the type material, kindly supplied by Rosický (June, 1940), gave no spectrographic test for germanium.　The piece tested came from the freshest portion of a crystal, and appeared to be homogeneous.　The original analysis sample may have had an inhomogeneity not found on our fragment.　The specific gravity and x-ray powder pattern of this material is identical with the specific gravity and pattern of diaphorite (Berman, priv. comm., 1941).

344　　F R E I E S L E B E N I T E　[$Pb_3Ag_5Sb_5S_{12}$].　Mine d'antimoine grise tenant argent (Himmelsfürst) de Lisle (35, 1773; 3, 54, 1783).　Dunkles Weissgültigerz (known since 1720) Klaproth (**1**, 173, 1795).　Schilf-Glaserz Freiesleben (**6**, 97, 1817). Basitom-Glanz Breithaupt (267, 1832).　Antimonial Sulphuret of Silver, Sulphuret of Silver and Antimony.　Argent sulfuré antimonifère et cuprifère Lévy (1837). Donacargyrite Chapman (128, 1843).　Freieslebenite Haidinger (569, 1845A).

C r y s t.　Monoclinic; prismatic — $2/m$.

$a : b : c = 0.5871 : 1 : 0.4638;$[1] $\beta\ 92°14';\ p_0 : q_0 : r_0 = 0.7900 : 0.4634 : 1$

$r_2 : p_2 : q_2 = 2.1577 : 1.7046 : 1;\ \mu\ 87°46';\ p_0'\ 0.7906,\ q_0'\ 0.\ 4638,\ x_0'\ 0.0390$

Forms:[2]

		ϕ	ρ	ϕ_2	ρ_2	C	A
c	001	90°00'	2°14'	87°46'	90°00'	.....	87°46'
b	010	0 00	90 00	.....	0 00	90°00'	90 00
a	100	90 00	90 00	0 00	90 00	87 46	.....
m	110	59 36	90 00	0 00	59 36	88 04½	30 24
β	210	73 39	90 00	0 00	73 39	87 51½	16 21
u	011	4 48½	24 58	87 46	65 08	24 52	87 58½
r	021	2 24½	42 52½	87 46	47 10	42 50	88 21½
x	201	90 00	58 19	31 41	90 00	56 05	31 41
ξ	2̄01	−90 00	57 02½	147 02½	90 00	59 16½	147 02½
y	111	60 47½	43 33	50 19	70 21½	41 36½	53 02
φ	1̄11	−58 19½	41 27	126 56	69 39	43 22½	124 17½
z	211	74 01½	59 19	31 41	76 18½	57 10½	34 13½

Less common:

q	810	l	560	k	120	p	130	d	052	f	221
t	310	σ	450	n	350	i	150	v	031	h	412
s	430	o	230	π	250	ρ	032	w	041	g	311

Structure cell.[3] Space group $P2_1/a$; a_0 7.53, b_0 12.79, c_0 6.88; a_0: $b_0 : c_0 = 0.589 : 1 : 0.460$; β 92°14′; contains $Pb_3Ag_5Sb_5S_{12}$.

Habit. Prismatic and striated [001].

Twinning. On {100}.

P h y s. Cleavage {110} imperfect. Fracture subconchoidal to uneven. Rather brittle. H. 2–2½. G. 6.04–6.23,[4] 6.27 (calc.). Luster metallic. Color and streak light steelgray inclining to silver-white or to lead-gray. Opaque. In polished section[5] anisotropic and showing twin lamellae. Reflection percentages: green 37.5, orange 30.5, red 30.

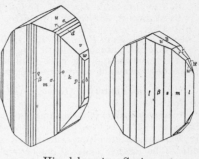

Hiendelaencina, Spain.

C h e m.[6] A lead and silver antimony sulfide, $Pb_3Ag_5Sb_5S_{12}$. It is not clear whether the small amounts of Cu and Fe are constituents of the mineral.

Anal.[7]

	1	2	3	4	5	6
Pb	28.85	31.90	31.38	30.77	30.08	30.00
Ag	25.03	22.45	23.31	23.08	23.76	22.18
Sb	28.26	26.83	25.64	27.11	27.05	27.72
S	17.86	17.60	18.90	18.41	18.71	18.77
Rem.	......	.....	0.13	0.63	.....	1.33
Total	100.00	98.78	99.36	100.00	99.60	100.00
G.	6.27		6.040	6.230		

1. $Pb_3Ag_5Sb_5S_{12}$. 2. Spain.[8] 3. Spain. Rem. is Cu.[9] 4. Příbram. Rem. is Fe.[10] 5. Freiberg.[11] 6. Freiberg. Rem. is Cu 1.22, Fe 0.11.[11]

Tests. F. 1. B.B. gives a coating of Sb and Pb, leaving a globule of Ag.

O c c u r. In the Himmelfürst mine at Freiberg, Saxony, with argentite, siderite, and galena. Reported at Příbram in Bohemia. Good crystals at Hiendelaencina, Spain, with argentite, ruby silver, galena, and siderite. Reported from Kapnik and Felsöbánya in Roumania.

N a m e. After Johann Karl Freiesleben (1774–1846), Mining Commissioner of Saxony.

Ref.

1. Angles and orientation of Brooke and Miller (208, 1852), unit of Winchell (in Palache, *Am. Min.*, **23**, 821 [1938], p. 835). Transformation: Miller to Winchell 100/010/00½.
2. In Dana (124, 1892); Goldschmidt (4, 20, 1918). Uncertain forms: {140}, {510}, {233}.
3. Winchell in Palache (1938).
4. Vrba, *Zs. Kr.*, **2**, 153, 1878 — p. 160, obtained 6.04 as average of three measurements on crystals from Hiendelaencina. Winchell gives 6.20 for material from the same locality. Berman (priv. comm., 1939) obtained 6.15 on crystal fragments. Payr, *Jb. Min.*, 579, 1860, gave 6.230 for an analyzed sample from Příbram (anal. 4).
5. Schneiderhöhn and Ramdohr (2, 411, 1931).

6. Winchell, in Palache (1938), has shown that the older formula $(Pb,Ag_2)_5Sb_4S_{11}$ as given in Dana (125, 1892) is not consistent with the cell dimensions.

7. The analysis by Eakins, *Am. J. Sc.*, **36**, 452 (1888), of supposed freieslebenite from Colorado is placed with boulangerite, since it obviously represents that mineral.

8. Escosura anal., *Rev. min.*, **6**, 358 (1855), *Ann. mines*, **8**, 495 (1855).

9. Morawski, *Zs. Kr.*, **2**, 161 (1878).

10. Payr, *Jb. Min.*, 579 (1860).

11. Wöhler, *Ann. Phys.*, **46**, 153 (1839).

12. Crystallographic evidence is necessary to distinguish between freieslebenite and diaphorite, because of the close similarity between the two in chemical and physical properties. Some of the reported occurrences, such as Freiberg, may be of diaphorite.

BRONGNIARDITE. *Damour* (*Ann. mines*, **16**, 227, 1849). Bleisilberantimonit *Groth* (18, 1874).

A supposed silver and lead antimony sulfide, $Ag_2PbSb_2S_5$, found massive and in octahedra at Potosí, Bolivia,[1] and in cubes at Cueva de Plata, Sierra Nevada, Spain. The crystallized material from Bolivia has been shown to be identical with stannian argyrodite. The massive material has been placed with diaphorite.[3] Some supposed brongniardite has been found to be a mixture or to be argentian jamesonite.[4]

Ref.

1. The original locality is sometimes erroneously given as Mexico.

2. Prior and Spencer, *Min. Mag.*, **12**, 11 (1900). The cubical crystals from Spain (Navarro, *Soc. españ. hist. nat.*, *Acta*, **24**, 94 [1895]) are probably argentite.

3. Spencer, *Am. J. Sc.*, **6**, 316 (1898).

4. Murdoch (37, 1916).

345 **KLAPROTHITE** [$Cu_6Bi_4S_9$]. Kupferwismutherz, Wismuthkupfererz pt. (Not the klaprothite [= lazulite] of *Beudant* [464, 1824].) Klaprothit *Petersen* and *Sandberger* (*Jb. Min.*, 415, 1868). Klaprotholite *Brush* (in *Dana* [2, 1878]).

Cryst.[1] Orthorhombic; dipyramidal — $2/m\,2/m\,2/m$ (?).

$a : b : c = 0.7420 : 1 : 0.6429;$ $p_0 : q_0 : r_0 = 0.8664 : 0.6429 : 1$

$q_1 : r_1 : p_1 = 0.7420 : 1.1542 : 1;$ $r_2 : p_2 : q_2 = 1.5555 : 1.3476 : 1$

Forms:[1]

		ϕ	$\rho = C$	ϕ_1	$\rho_1 = A$	ϕ_2	$\rho_2 = B$
c	001	.....	0°00′	0°00′	90°00′	90°00′	90°00′
b	010	0°00′	90 00	90 00	90 00	.....	0 00
a	100	90 00	90 00	.....	0 00	0 00	90 00
m	110	53 25½	90 00	90 00	36 34½	0 00	53 25½
n	540	59 18½	90 00	90 00	30 41½	0 00	59 18½
o	210	69 38½	90 00	90 00	20 21½	0 00	69 38½
w	011	0 00	32 44	32 44	90 00	90 00	57 16
x	021	0 00	52 07½	52 07½	90 00	90 00	37 52½
h	102	90 00	23 25½	0 00	66 34½	66 34½	90 00
j	201	90 00	60 00½	0 00	29 59½	29 59½	90 00
q	121	33 58½	57 11	52 07½	61 59½	49 05½	45 49
r	211	69 38½	61 35	32 44	34 27	29 59½	72 11
s	231	41 56	68 54½	62 35½	51 25½	29 59½	46 03
t	321	63 40½	70 58½	52 07½	32 04½	21 02½	65 13

Habit. Prismatic [001] to thick tabular {001}. Massive.

Phys. Cleavage {100} distinct. Fracture uneven. Brittle. H. $2\frac{1}{2}$. G. 6.01.[2] Luster metallic. Color steel-gray, tarnishing to brass-yellow or iridescent. Streak black. Opaque. In polished section[3] gold-white to gray-white in color, with strong anisotropism and distinct pleochroism. Reflection percentages: ($\parallel$ to c[001]) green 39, orange 35.5, red 33; ($\perp$ elongation) green 35, orange 33.5, red 33.

C h e m.   Copper bismuth sulfide, $Cu_6Bi_4S_9$.

Anal.

	1	2	3	4	5
Bi	55.51	53.87	53.21	51.62	51.40
Cu	25.33	23.96	24.91	30.48	28.82
Fe	.....	1.70	....	trace	0.91
S	19.16	18.66	18.12	17.64	18.69
Rem.	.....	.....	1.16	.....	.....
Total	100.00	98.19	97.40	99.74	99.82
G.			6.456		

1. $Cu_6Bi_4S_9$.   2. Daniel mine, Wittichen, Baden.   Average of three analyses.[4]
3. Imooka, Japan.   Rem. is SiO_2 1.16.   Fe not det.[5]   4. Hadé, Japan.[6]   5. Daniel mine, Wittichen, Baden.   Average of two analyses.[7]

Tests.   F. 1.   On charcoal fuses to a steel-gray button which with Na_2CO_3 gives a dark yellow sublimate of bismuth oxide and a silver-white metallic bead (an alloy of copper and bismuth).   Slowly soluble in HCl, more rapidly in HNO_3.

O c c u r.   With other bismuth minerals, especially emplectite, and with cobaltian tetrahedrite, chalcopyrite, and barite at the Daniel and Neuglück mines, near Wittichen, Baden, and in nearby localities of the Black Forest region; in the Spessart, Bavaria; with siderite, bismuth, and bismuthinite in the Siegen district, Westphalia.   Reported from copper veins in granite at Imooka and Hadé, Okayama prefecture, Japan.   Reported from Butte, Montana, associated with bornite, chalcocite, and enargite, and may not be uncommon in enargite and chalcocite ores.[8]

A l t e r.   To malachite and bismutite; chalcopyrite has been found as pseudomorphs after klaprothite.

A r t i f.   Reported formed by fusion of the constituents.[9]

N a m e.   After the German mineralogist, M. H. Klaproth (1743–1817). The name klaprothite was first given to lazulite; hence a change to klaprotholite for this species was proposed.   However, the earlier use has now definitely been dropped and no reason exists for the continuance of the latter name.

Ref.

1. Crystals were measured by Wolfe (priv. comm., 1939) from a typical specimen, labeled from the Schapbachthal, Baden (Harvard, 82409).   A polished section verified the authenticity of the material.   Angles by Wolfe, orientation by Sandberger, *Jb. Min.*, 415 (1868).   The forms are by Wolfe.
2. Measured on a 7-mg. sample from Schapbachthal, Baden (Frondel, priv. comm., 1940).   The old value, 4.6, given by Petersen (1868), is obviously too low, as was pointed out by Phillips, *Nature*, **130**, 998 (1932), who calculated 6.4 from the reflectivity and measured 6.3 on artificial material supposedly the same as klaprothite.
3. Schneiderhöhn and Ramdohr (**2**, 399, 1931).
4. Petersen, *Ann. Phys.*, **134**, 96 (1868).
5. Hukuzawa anal. in Harada (242, 1936).
6. Kamiyama anal. in Harada (242, 1936).

7. Schneider, *Ann. Phys.*, **127**, 309 (1866).

8. Schneiderhöhn and Ramdohr (**2**, 401, 1931); see also Krieger, *Econ. Geol.*, **35**, 687 (1940).

9. Phillips (1932); Gaudin and Dicke, *Econ. Geol.*, **34**, 214 (1938).

351   BOULANGERITE [$Pb_5Sb_4S_{11}$]. Plomb antimonié sulfuré *Boulanger* (*Ann. mines*, **7**, 575, 1835). Schwefelantimonblei, Antimonbleiblende *Germ.* Sulphuret of Antimony and Lead. Boulangerit *Thaulow* (*Ann. Phys.*, **41**, 216, 1837); *Hausmann* (*Ann. Phys.*, **46**, 281, 1839). Embrithite, Plumbostib *Breithaupt* (*J. pr. Chem.*, **10**, 442, 1837). Feather ore pt. Jamesonite pt.

Epiboulangerit pt. *Websky* (*Zs. geol. Ges.*, **21**, 747, 1869). Mullanite *Shannon* (*Am. J. Sc.*, **45**, 66, 1918).

Plumosite *Haidinger* (569, 1845). Plumites *Glocker* (30, 1847). Biegsames Federerz *Germ.*

C r y s t.[1] Monoclinic; prismatic — $2/m$.

$a : b : c = 0.9158 : 1 : 0.3456;$[1] $\beta\ 100°39\frac{1}{2}';$ $p_0 : q_0 : r_0 = 0.3774 : 0.3396 : 1$

$r_2 : p_2 : q_2 = 2.9443 : 1.1111 : 1;$ $\mu\ 79°20\frac{1}{2}';$ $p_0'\ 0.3840,\ q_0'\ 0.3456,\ x_0'\ 0.1882$

Forms:[2]

		ϕ	ρ	ϕ_2	$\rho_2 = B$	C	A
a	100	90°00′	90°00′	0°00′	90°00′	79°20$\frac{1}{2}$′	.....
q	130	20 19$\frac{1}{2}$	90 00	0 00	20 19$\frac{1}{2}$	86 19	69°40$\frac{1}{2}$′
m	110	48 01	90 00	0 00	48 01	82 06	41 59
n	210	65 46$\frac{1}{2}$	90 00	0 00	65 46$\frac{1}{2}$	80 17$\frac{1}{2}$	24 13$\frac{1}{2}$
f	031	10 17$\frac{1}{2}$	46 30	79 20$\frac{1}{2}$	44 28	45 32	82 33$\frac{1}{2}$
g	041	7 45	54 22	79 20$\frac{1}{2}$	36 21$\frac{1}{2}$	53 38$\frac{1}{2}$	83 42$\frac{1}{2}$
D	441	51 16$\frac{1}{2}$	65 39	30 07	55 15$\frac{1}{2}$	57 33	44 42
α	$\bar{2}$21	−39 59$\frac{1}{2}$	42 03$\frac{1}{2}$	120 06$\frac{1}{2}$	59 07$\frac{1}{2}$	49 27	115 30
E	121	39 37	41 54	60 13$\frac{1}{2}$	59 02$\frac{1}{2}$	35 53	64 47$\frac{1}{2}$
G	141	22 29	56 14$\frac{1}{2}$	60 13$\frac{1}{2}$	39 48$\frac{1}{2}$	52 46$\frac{1}{2}$	71 27$\frac{1}{2}$
M	211	70 07$\frac{1}{2}$	45 28$\frac{1}{2}$	46 17	75 58$\frac{1}{2}$	36 03	47 53$\frac{1}{2}$
R	251	28 57$\frac{1}{2}$	63 08$\frac{1}{2}$	46 17	38 41	58 24$\frac{1}{2}$	64 24$\frac{1}{2}$
ϵ	$\bar{1}$21	−15 49	35 41$\frac{1}{2}$	101 04$\frac{1}{2}$	55 51	39 45$\frac{1}{2}$	99 09
ϕ	$\bar{1}$31	−10 41$\frac{1}{2}$	46 32	101 04$\frac{1}{2}$	44 30	49 22$\frac{1}{2}$	97 44$\frac{1}{2}$
ρ	$\bar{2}$51	−18 33	61 15	120 06$\frac{1}{2}$	33 47	65 05$\frac{1}{2}$	106 11$\frac{1}{2}$
τ	$\bar{3}$21	−54 21	49 52	133 56$\frac{1}{2}$	63 32$\frac{1}{2}$	58 46	128 24$\frac{1}{2}$
Δ	$\bar{4}$21	−68 09$\frac{1}{2}$	61 42$\frac{1}{2}$	30 07	70 52$\frac{1}{2}$	51 54	35 11
Λ	$\bar{6}$51	−50 45$\frac{1}{2}$	69 53$\frac{1}{2}$	154 42	53 33$\frac{1}{2}$	78 16	136 39$\frac{1}{2}$

Less common forms:

001	021	$\bar{2}$01	551	151	341	541	$\bar{2}$31	$\bar{4}$11
010	051	111	$\bar{3}$31	231	361	$\bar{1}$41	$\bar{2}$41	$\bar{4}$21
120	061	221	$\bar{4}$41	311	411	$\bar{1}$51	$\bar{3}$11	$\bar{6}$31
011	101	331	131	321	531	$\bar{2}$11	$\bar{3}$51	$\bar{6}$41

Structure cell.[3] Monoclinic, space group $P2_1/a;$ $a_0\ 21.52 \pm 0.03,$ $b_0\ 23.46 \pm 0.03,$ $c_0\ 8.07 \pm 0.02,$ $\beta\ 100°48' \pm 30';$ $a_0 : b_0 : c_0 = 0.917 : 1 : 0.344;$ contains $Pb_{40}Sb_{32}S_{88}$.

Habit. Long prismatic to acicular, and deeply striated [001]. Plumose, fibrous, often in compact fibrous masses. Sometimes as schistose masses.

P h y s. Cleavage {100} good.[4] Brittle; thin fibers flexible. H. 2$\frac{1}{2}$–3. G. (for $Pb_5Sb_4S_{11}$ from Mullan) 6.23, 6.21 (calc.); (from Stevens

County, Washington), 5.98 ± 0.02. Luster metallic. Color bluish lead-gray, often covered with yellow spots from oxidation. Streak brownish gray to brown. Opaque. In polished section[5] gray-white in color, with distinct anisotropism and weak pleochroism. Reflection percentages: green 38, orange 34.5, red 33.

C h e m.[6] A lead antimony sulfide, $Pb_5Sb_4S_{11}$.

Anal.[7]

	1	2	3	4	5	6	7
Pb	50.57	51.00	53.33	54.34	54.44	55.05	55.08
Sb	29.49	27.82	24.67	25.33	24.55	25.71	24.38
S	19.91	18.99	18.11	18.51	18.98	18.82	18.65
Rem.	.....	2.54	2.11	0.83	1.50	0.25	1.10
Total	99.97	100.35	98.22	99.01	99.47	99.83	99.21
G.		5.99	6.407?			6.274	

1. " Plumosite," Caspari mine, near Arnsberg, Westphalia. Crystals.[8] 2. " Plumo-site," Trepča, Kapaonik Mountains, Serbia. Rem. is Fe 0.16, Mn 0.14, Zn 0.47, CaO 0.43, CO_2 0.30, insol. 1.14.[9] 3. " Mullanite," Gold Hunter mine, Mullan, Id. Rem. is Fe 1.47, As 0.64. Fe and loss due to siderite in sample.[10] 4. Peru. Rem. is Fe 0.47, Ag trace, insol. 0.36. The 1 per cent loss is probably CO_2 and MnO.[10] 5. Ober-Lahr, near Linz, Germany. Rem. is insol.[10] 6. Iron Mountain mine, Superior, Mont. Aver. of two analyses. Rem. is As 0.25, Fe trace.[10] 7. Příbram, Bohemia. Rem. is insol., Fe trace.[10]

	8	9	10	11	12	13	14
Pb	55.22	55.34	55.52	57.23	58.58	59.01	55.42
Sb	25.54	25.30	23.63	23.82	22.69	22.76	25.69
S	18.91	18.08	19.36	18.23	18.76	18.22	18.89
Rem.	0.29	0.92	1.49	.....	......	.....	.....
Total	99.96	99.64	100.00	99.28	100.03	99.99	100.00
G.	6.185						

8. Sala, Sweden. Rem. is Zn 0.06, insol. 0.23.[11] 9. Cleveland mine, Stevens Co., Wash. Rem. is insol. 0.40, Fe 0.52.[12] 10. North Star mine, Wood River district, Id. Rem. is Fe 0.43, As 1.06, Ag trace. Computed to 100 per cent after deducting 10.86 per cent gangue.[10] 11. Betzdorf a.d. Sieg, Germany.[8] 12. Ober-Lahr, near Linz.[8] 13. San Antonio, Lower California.[8] 14. $Pb_5Sb_4S_{11}$.

Tests. F. 1. Incompletely decomposed in HNO_3; soluble in hot HCl with forma-tion of H_2S.

O c c u r. In hydrothermal vein deposits formed at low or at moderate temperatures. Associated with other lead sulfosalts, stibnite, galena, sphalerite, pyrite, arsenopyrite, quartz, and carbonates, particularly sider-ite. Little reliability can be placed on any reported occurrence unless a chemical analysis or x-ray study is given.

Found at Nertschinsk, Transbaikalia. In crystals from Sala, Våstman-land, and from Nasafjeld, Lappland, in Sweden. In Germany in the Rhineland at Ober-Lahr near Altenkirchen, and at Horhausen and Betz-dorf; at Silbersand near Mayen in the Eifel; at Wolfsberg in the Harz; from Altenberg, Silesia, and Arnsberg, Westphalia. At Trepča, in the Kapaonik Mountains, Serbia. From Bottino, Tuscany, with meneghinite and jamesonite; from Příbram, Bohemia. In France originally found, in considerable quantity, at Molières, Gard. From Guerrouma, Algeria.

Reported from Tampillo and several other localities in Peru, in part as large felted masses. In the El Triunfo and San Antonio districts, Lower California.

In the United States in the Coeur d'Alene and Wood River districts in Idaho; from the Iron Mountain mine, Superior, Montana, with sphalerite; and from Rocker Gulch, Montana; from Augusta Mountain, Gunnison County, Colorado, with pyrite and sphalerite. In the Echo district, Union County, Nevada. At the Cleveland mine, Stevens County, Washington, as columnar to fibrous masses with sphalerite, arsenopyrite, galena, and siderite.

Alter. To bindheimite.

Artif.[13] Compounds having the composition $Pb_2Sb_2S_5$ and $Pb_5Sb_4S_{11}$ have been reported in the system $PbS-Sb_2S_3$.

Name. After C. L. Boulanger (1810–49), a French mining engineer. *Plumosite* in allusion to the often plumose form of the fibrous aggregates.

MULLANITE. *Shannon (Am. J. Sc.*, 45, 66, 1918), from the Iron Mountain mine, Superior, Montana, and the Gold Hunter mine, Mullan, Idaho, is identical with boulangerite.[14]

EPIBOULANGERITE. *Websky (Zs. geol. Ges.*, 21, 747, 1869), approximately $Pb_3Sb_2S_8$, from Altenberg, Silesia, and Superior, Montana,[15] is probably boulangerite or a mixture of boulangerite and galena.[16]

Ref.

1. On crystals from Rocker Gulch, Montana; Gold Hunter mine, Mullan, Idaho; and from Stevens Co., Washington, by Palache and Berman, *Am. Min.*, 27, 552 (1942). These have all been shown to be identical in x-ray powder pattern by Berry, *Univ. Toronto, Geol. Ser.*, 44, 5 (1940). The angles of Sjögren, *Geol. För. Förh.*, 19, 153 (1897), on crystals from Sala, Sweden, regarded by him as orthorhombic, correspond well with those of Palache and Berman. Transformation: Sjögren to Palache 04$\overline{1}$/800/002. The elements of Sjögren in the Palache orientation are $a : b : c = 0.9315 : 1 : 0.3383$, $\beta\ 100°27\frac{1}{2}'$. Shannon, *Am. J. Sc.*, 1, 423 (1921), apparently bases his morphology on that of Sjögren, but his data (on crystals from Wood River) were unsatisfactory and no correlation with the new ratio can be established.
2. Palache and Berman (1942), mainly on Rocker Gulch crystals. Sjögren (1897) on Sala crystals found {130}, {120}, {110}, {210} and {140}, {310}, {410}, {510}, {710}, {102}; the last six mentioned were not found by Palache.
3. Berry (1940) on crystals from Mullan, Idaho. Hurlbut (priv. comm., 1939) obtained essentially the same values on a crystal from Rocker Gulch, Montana (from material of anal. 2). Hiller's data, *Zs. Kr.*, 100, 128 (1938), are not consistent with that given here.
4. Palache and Berman (1942) on crystal from Rocker Gulch. Shannon, *Am. J. Sc.*, 45, 66 (1918), observed cleavages on {001}, {010} and possibly {110}, on Mullan crystals, but no angular measurements are given.
5. Schneiderhöhn and Ramdohr (2, 409, 1931).
6. A number of older analyses of boulangerite (see Doelter 4 [1], 442, 1926) agree with the formula $Pb_5Sb_4S_{11}$, as do the more recent ones of Shannon (1921), *U. S. Nat. Mus. Proc.*, 58, 594 (1920). The so-called plumosite, which differs in none of its physical properties (except density) from boulangerite, gives quite accurately the formula $Pb_2Sb_2S_5$ but this may be due to analytical error. Most of the analyses cited are fairly recent.
7. For other analyses see Doelter (4 [1], 437, 439, 442, 1926).
8. Guillemain (Inaug. Diss., Breslau, 1898 — *Zs. Kr.*, 33, 74 [1900]).
9. Baric anal., *Bull. soc. sc., Skoplje*, 9, 88 (1931).

10. Shannon (1920).
11. Mauzelius anal. in Sjögren, *Geol. För. Förh.*, **19**, 153 (1897).
12. Shannon, *Washington Ac. Sc., J.*, **15**, 195 (1925).
13. Iitsuka, *Kyoto Univ., Mem. Coll. Sc.*, **4**, 51 (1919), and Sommerlad, *Zs. anorg. Chem.*, **18**, 439 (1898); see also Jaeger and van Klooster, *Zs. anorg. Chem.*, **78**, 263 (1912), and Doelter (1926).
14. Shannon (1920).
15. Shannon, *Am. Min.*, **2**, 131 (1917).
16. Guillemain (1898). Short (104, 1931) states that etch tests (on material of unstated locality) are identical with those of boulangerite.

352   **Owyheeite** [$Pb_5Ag_2Sb_6S_{15}$]. Argentiferous jamesonite *Burton* (*Am. J. Sc.*, **45**, 34, 1868). Silver-jamesonite *Shannon* (*U. S. Nat. Mus., Proc.*, **58**, 601, 1920). Owyheeite *Shannon* (*Am. Min.*, **6**, 82, 1921).

As acicular needles or massive with an indistinct fibrous structure. Cleavage perpendicular to elongation. Brittle. H. $2\frac{1}{2}$. G. 6.03. Luster metallic. Color light steel-gray to silver-white, tarnishing yellowish. Streak on paper gray, on porcelain reddish brown. Opaque. In polished section[1] gray-white in color with strong anisotropism and distinct pleochroism.

C h e m.   A lead and silver antimony sulfide, probably $Pb_5Ag_2Sb_6S_{15}$.
Anal.

	1	2	3
Pb	42.18	40.77	43.86
Ag	8.80	7.40	6.14
Cu	.....	0.75	1.55
Fe	.....	0.46	0.05
Sb	29.41	30.61	29.26
S	19.61	20.81	19.06
Total	100.00	100.80	99.92
G.			6.03

1. $Pb_5Ag_2Sb_6S_{15}$. 2. Poorman mine, Owyhee Co., Id.[2] 3. Sheba mine, Star City, Nev. Average of two analyses.[3]

Tests.   F. 1.   Soluble in hot concentrated HCl.

O c c u r.   At the Poorman mine, Silver City district, Owyhee County, Idaho, associated with pyrargyrite, sphalerite, and quartz. Said to occur in the Banner district, Boise County, Idaho, with galena, pyrargyrite, and tetrahedrite. From the Sheba mine, Star City, Nevada, with sphalerite and tetrahedrite.

N a m e.   From the locality, Owyhee County, Idaho.

Ref.

1. Ramdohr, *Zbl. Min.*, 208, 1937.
2. Shannon (1920).
3. Burton, *Am. J. Sc.*, **45**, 36 (1868).

353   **Schirmerite** [PbAg$_4$Bi$_4$S$_9$].   *Genth* (*Am. Phil. Soc., Proc.*, **14**, 230, 1874; *J. pr. Chem.*, **10**, 355, 1874). (Not the schirmerite (a mixture) of *Endlich* [*Eng. Mining J.*, Aug. 29, 1874].)

Massive, finely granular. Cleavage none.[1] Fracture uneven. Brittle. H. 2. G. 6.737. Luster metallic. Color lead-gray inclining to iron-black. In polished section[2] white in color with weak anisotropism.

C h e m.   A silver and lead bismuth sulfide, perhaps PbAg$_4$Bi$_4$S$_9$.

Anal.

	1	2	3
Ag	24.47	24.75	22.82
Pb	11.75	12.76	12.69
Bi	47.41	[47.27]	46.91
S	16.37	15.02	14.41
Rem.	.....	0.20	0.11
Total	100.00	100.00	96.94

1. PbAg$_4$Bi$_4$S$_9$. 2. Treasury lode, Colo. Recalc. after deduction of 1.07 per cent quartz. Rem. is Zn 0.13 and Fe 0.07. 3. Treasury lode, Colo. After deduction of 1.00 per cent quartz. Rem. is Zn 0.08 and Fe 0.03.

O c c u r.   Found in quartz at the Treasury lode, Geneva district, Park County, Colo. Said to occur in the Magnolia district, Boulder County, and at Lake City, Hinsdale County, in Colorado.

N a m e.[3]   After J. H. L. Schirmer, formerly Superintendent of the United States Mint at Denver, Colorado.

Ref.

1. An indistinct cleavage in polished section is mentioned by Ramdohr, *Zbl. Min.*, 295, 1937.
2. Ramdohr (1937); Murdoch (141, 1916).
3. Genth (1874) states that the material from the Red Cloud mine, Boulder Co., Colo., named schirmerite by Endlich, *Eng. Mining J.*, Aug. 29, 1874, is a mixture of a telluride and pyrite.

354   **M I A R G Y R I T E** [AgSbS$_2$]. Fahles Rotgiltigerz *Hausmann* (*Hercyn. Archiv*, **4**, 680, 1805; 224, 1813). Hemiprismatische Rubin-Blende (from Bräunsdorf) *Mohs* (606, 1824). Miargyrit *Rose* (*Ann. Phys.*, **15**, 469, 1829). Hypargyrite, Hypargyron-Blende (from Clausthal) *Breithaupt* (286, 333, 1832). Kenngottite (from Felsöbánya) *Haidinger* (*Ak. Wien, Ber.*, **22**, 236, 1856). Silberantimonglanz *Germ.*

C r y s t.   Monoclinic; prismatic — 2/m.

$a : b : c = 2.9945 : 1 : 2.9095$; $\beta\ 98°37\frac{1}{2}'$;[1] $p_0 : q_0 : r_0 = 0.9716 : 2.8767 : 1$
$r_2 : p_2 : q_2 = 0.3476 : 0.3378 : 1$; $\mu\ 81°22\frac{1}{2}'$; $p_0'\ 0.9827$, $q_0'\ 2.9095$, $x_0'\ 0.1517$

Forms:[2]

		ϕ °	ρ	ϕ_2	$\rho_2 = B$	C	A
c	001	90°00′	8°37½′	81°22½′	90°00′	0°00′	81°22½′
b	010	0 00	90 00	.....	0 00	90 00	90 00
a	100	90 00	90 00	0 00	90 00	81 22½	0 00
β	013	8 53½	44 28	81 22½	46 12	43 48	83 47
ω	011	2 59	71 03½	81 22½	19 10	70 50	87 10½
m	101	90 00	48 36	41 24	90 00	39 58½	41 24
o	$\overline{1}$01	−90 00	39 43½	129 43½	90 00	48 21	129 43½
h	113	26 18	47 15	64 23½	48 49½	43 57	71 01
t	111	21 18	72 14½	41 24	27 28	69 18½	69 45½
A	$\overline{1}$11	−15 56½	71 42½	129 43½	24 05	74 16	105 07
k	124	15 19½	56 27	68 19	36 29½	54 35½	77 18
s	211	36 03	74 28	25 16½	38 50	69 31½	55 27½
d	311	46 49	76 46	17 52½	48 14	70 33½	44 47
ϕ	411	54 31½	78 43	13 45½	55 18½	71 43½	37 00
f	922	57 32½	79 33	12 20	58 08½	72 19	33 55
x	$\overline{1}$22	− 6 39½	71 09	108 44½	19 57	72 21½	96 17½
ξ	$\overline{2}$13	−27 26	47 32	116 43½	49 05½	51 56½	109 51½
γ	$\overline{4}$14	−48 48	47 50	129 43½	60 46½	54 32½	123 53½
g	$\overline{3}$13	−40 35	51 56	129 43½	53 16½	57 48½	120 48½
χ	$\overline{2}$12	−29 44	59 10	129 43½	41 47	63 42½	115 12
σ	$\overline{2}$11	−31 55½	73 44	151 07	35 26	78 25	120 30
i	$\overline{3}$11	−43 52	76 05	160 19	45 35	82 07½	132 16

Less common:

Δ	210		n	301		z	137		r	121		ϵ	522		τ	$\overline{8}$18
W	1·0·12		T	$\overline{1}$06		K:	236		P	524		F	511		p	$\overline{6}$16
G	105		M	$\overline{1}$03		Γ	133		S	312		η	611		π	$\overline{5}$15
κ	104		u	$\overline{2}$03		X	122		U	322		D	711		α	$\overline{5}$44
θ	103		R	$\overline{2}$01		I	315		i	533		C	811		ψ	$\overline{4}$13
B	205		N	$\overline{3}$01		J	233		V	623		ζ	$\overline{2}$15		Z	$\overline{9}$13
λ	102		K	112		O	324		Y	11·5·5		W	$\overline{2}$33		q	$\overline{12}$·1·3
L	703		l	$\overline{1}$13		E	212		Q	733		G:	$\overline{3}$14		H	$\overline{4}$11

Structure cell.[3] Space group $C2/c$; a_0 13.17, b_0 4.39, c_0 12.83; $a_0 : b_0 : c_0 = 3.000 : 1 : 2.923$; $\beta\ 98°37\frac{1}{2}′$; contains $Ag_8Sb_8S_{16}$.

Habit. Crystals usually thick tabular {001} or {100}, less commonly {$\overline{1}$01}. Faces in the zones [010] and [0$\overline{1}$1] often deeply striated parallel to the zone axes; hence {100} shows two sets of striations ‖ [0$\overline{1}$1] and less uniformly ‖ [010]. Also massive. Commonest forms: $c\ a\ o\ s\ t\ d\ g\ \omega$.

P h y s. Cleavage {010} imperfect, {100} and {101} in traces.[4] Fracture subconchoidal to uneven. Brittle. H. 2½. G. 5.25 ± 0.05; 5.26 (Oruro[5]); 5.29 (calc.). Luster metallic adamantine. Color iron-black to steel-gray. Streak cherry-red. Nearly opaque; in thin splinters translucent and deep blood-red in color. Translation gliding (?) on {100} ‖ [010].[6]

O p t. In polished section[7] white in color with strong anisotropism; pleochroic. By transmitted light[8] deep blood-red. $\beta > 2.72_{\text{Li}}$. B_x positive (+). Birefringence very strong. $2V$ medium.

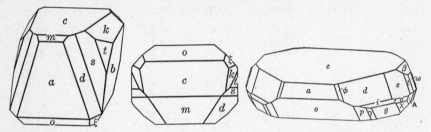

Bräunsdorf, Saxony.   Nagybánya, Hungary.

C h e m. Silver antimony sulfide, $AgSbS_2$. Cu substitutes in small amounts for Ag; the role of Pb, reported in some analyses, is uncertain. As substitutes for Sb in amounts less than 1 per cent by weight.

Anal.[9]

	1	2	3	4	5	6
Fe	.....	.....	trace	0.56	1.0	0.19
Cu	.....	.....	.....	0.02	2.6	0.51
Pb	.....	.....	.....	0.95	0.6	4.01
Ag	36.72	37.06	36.71	36.20	33.9	32.77
Sb	41.45	41.13	41.15	42.46	40.5	40.68
As	.....	0.79	.....	trace	trace	.....
S	21.83	21.50	21.68	19.27	21.9	21.80
Rem.	.....	.....	.....	0.80	.....	.....
Total	100.00	100.48	99.54	100.26	100.5	99.96
G.	5.29		5.077?		5.20	5.298

1. $AgSbS_2$. 2. Andreasberg, Harz.[10] 3. Příbram, Bohemia.[11] 4. Randsberg district, Calif. Rem. is insol. 0.80.[12] 5. Tatasi, Bolivia.[13] 6. Felsöbánya, Roumania. Average of two analyses.[14]

Var. Arsenian? Arsen-miargyrite *Raimondi* (58, 1878). Arsenomiargyrite *Doelter* (4 [1], 258, 1926). Highly arsenian material has been reported but is probably a mixture; the usual range of substitution of As appears to be less than 1 per cent by weight.[15]

Tests. F. 1. C.T. decrepitates. Decomposed by HNO_3 with separation of sulfur and antimony trioxide.

O c c u r. Found in hydrothermal vein deposits formed at low temperatures, associated usually with other silver sulfosalts, galena, pyrite, sphalerite, calcite, barite, and quartz.

At Bräunsdorf, near Freiberg, Saxony, in complex crystals; at Andreasberg with ruby silvers, native arsenic, galena, and calcite and at Clausthal (*hypargyrite*) in the Harz Mountains; at Příbram, Bohemia, and at Felsöbánya, Roumania (*kenngottite*). Reported from Hiendelaencina, Guadalajara, Spain. In Chile from Tres Puntas, Atacama, and from Huantajaya,

Tarapacá. In Bolivia, department of Potosí, at Aullagas with native silver, argyrodite and pyrargyrite, at Tatasi, and with pyrite at the Itos mine, Oruro. In Mexico from Parenos and Catorze, San Luis Potosí, and from Sombrerete, Zacatecas, and Molinares.

In the United States in Idaho with ruby silvers in the Silver City district and with sphalerite and tetrahedrite in the Flint district in Owyhee County. Abundantly in the Randsburg district, California.

A l t e r. Pseudomorphs of pyrite or marcasite after miargyrite have been noted.

A r t i f. Obtained from melts in the system Ag_2S-Sb_2S_3;[15] also reported[16] by heating a mixture of AgCl and Sb_2S_3, or by heating AgCl and $KSbO_3$ in H_2S or in water containing Na_2CO_3 and H_2S.

N a m e. From μείων, *less*, and ἄργυρος, *silver*, in allusion to the fact that it contains less silver than the ruby silvers.

Ref.

1. Angles of Lewis, *Zs. Kr.*, **8**, 545 (1884), recalculated to new elements by Dana (116, 1892).
2. Goldschmidt (**6**, 35, 1920), and Murdoch and Ungemach (unpublished notes). For best treatment of the form series see Rosický, *Ac. sc. Bohême, Bull.*, **17**, 26 (1912). Rare and uncertain forms (see also Rosický):

$\overline{7}02$	843	$\overline{1}\cdot2\cdot10$	$\overline{12}\cdot5\cdot20$	$\overline{6}13$
139	$15\cdot2\cdot2$	$\overline{2}33$	$\overline{12}\cdot1\cdot15$	$\overline{15}\cdot2\cdot6$
235	$15\cdot1\cdot1$	$\overline{3}19$	$\overline{4}15$	$\overline{5}22$
				$\overline{12}\cdot7\cdot1$

3. Hoffman, *Preuss. ak., Ber.*, **55**, 111 (1938) — *Jb. Min.*, 562, 1938.
4. Lewis (1884).
5. On crystal weighing 26 mg. from the Itos mine, Oruro, Bolivia (Frondel, priv. comm., 1939).
6. Mügge, *Jb. Min.*, I, 100, 1898.
7. Schneiderhöhn and Ramdohr (**2**, 385, 1931).
8. Larsen (110, 1921).
9. For additional analyses see Doelter (1926).
10. Jenkins anal. in Weisbach, *Jb. Min.*, II, 109, 1880.
11. Andreasch, *Min. Mitt.*, **4**, 185 (1881).
12. Shannon, *U. S. Nat. Mus., Proc.*, **74**, art. 21, 1 (1929).
13. Prior anal. in Spencer, *Min. Mag.*, **14**, 340 (1907).
14. Sipöcz, *Min. Mitt.*, 215, 1877.
15. Jaeger and van Klooster, *Zs. anorg. Chem.*, **78**, 264 (1912), prepared a compound $AgAsS_2$ from melts in the system Ag_2S-As_2S_3; also prepared by Sommerlad, *Zs. anorg. Chem.*, **15**, 173 (1897); **18**, 420 (1898), by heating AgCl and As_2S_3; reported also by Berzelius, *Ann. Phys.*, **7**, 150 (1826), by reaction of water solutions of $AgNO_3$ and Na_3AsS_4. None of these preparations have been shown to be closely related to miargyrite or smithite.
16. In Doelter (1926).

355   **A R A M A Y O I T E**   [Ag(Sb,Bi)S₂].   Spencer (*Min. Mag.*, **21**, 156, 1926).

C r y s t.   Triclinic; pinacoidal — $\overline{1}$.

$a : b : c = 0.8753 : 1 : 0.9406$;[1] α $100°22'$, β $90°00'$, γ $103°54'$

$p_0 : q_0 : r_0 = 1.0889 : 0.9690 : 1$; λ $79°19'$, μ $87°24\frac{1}{2}'$, ν $75°52'$

p_0' 1.1081, q_0' 0.9861; x_0' $0°00'$, y_0' 0.1887

Forms:[2]

		ϕ	ρ	A	B	C	Z^*
c	001	0°00′	10°41′	87°24½′	79°19′	.....	90°00′
b	010	0 00	90 00	75 52	......	79°19′	......
a	100	75 52	90 00	......	75 52	87 24½	0 00
M	1$\bar{1}$0	123 39½	90 00	47 47½	123 39½	95 54	180 00
u	012	0 00	34 17	82 05½	55 43	23 36	90 00
v	023	0 00	40 14	80 55½	49 46	29 33	90 00
w	011	0 00	49 35½	79 17	40 24½	38 54½	90 00
E	$\bar{2}$01	−99 19	65 20½	154 54	98 27½	67 29½	−24 57
Φ	$\bar{1}$21	−29 37	65 18	104 02	37 50	56 09	137 03½
s	$\bar{1}$2$\bar{1}$	−152 23	66 40	127 41½	144 27	76 12½	−42 56½

* Coordinate from (100) when (010) is polar; B or its supplement is other coordinate.

Less common:

m	110	W	0$\bar{1}$1	ρ	1$\bar{1}$2	Σ	$\bar{3}$32	P	$\bar{1}\bar{1}$1	Ψ	$\bar{2}$11	R	$\bar{2}\bar{1}$2	Y	$\bar{3}\bar{1}$1
n	320	D	$\bar{1}$01	π	$\bar{1}$11	T	$\bar{2}$21	γ	1$\bar{3}$2	Q	1$\bar{2}$2	o	$\bar{2}$11	X	$\bar{3}$21
L	2$\bar{3}$0													

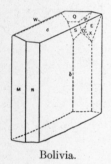

Bolivia.

Structure cell.[3] Triclinic; a_0 7.76, b_0 8.79, c_0 8.34; $a_0 : b_0 : c_0 = 0.8829 : 1 : 0.9488$; α 100°22′, β 90°00′, γ 103°54′; contains $Ag_6(Sb,Bi)_6S_{12}$.

Habit. Thin plates {010} striated [100] and [001].

Twinning. On [$\bar{1}$01] with {$\bar{1}$01} near composition plane.[2]

P h y s. Cleavage {010} perfect, {100} fair, {001} poor. Parting {$\bar{1}$01} frequent.[2] Pliable but not elastic. Sectile. Luster metallic. Color iron-black. Streak black. H. 2½. G. 5.602, 5.624 (calc.). Nearly opaque. Deep red by transmitted light. Extinction 4° to {010}.

C h e m. Silver antimony sulfide, $Ag(Sb,Bi)S_2$, with Bi substituting for Sb in part.

Anal.

	Ag	Cu	Bi	Sb	S	Total	G.
1	34.77	....	14.02	30.55	20.66	100.00	5.624
2	34.74	0.53	13.75	29.95	20.87	99.84	5.602

1. $Ag(Sb,Bi)S_2$ with Sb : Bi $\sim$ 5 : 1.   2. Animas mine, Bolivia.   Also Fe trace.[4]

O c c u r. At the Animas mine, Chocaya, Sud-Chichas, Potosí, Bolivia, as aggregates of broad plates associated with pyrite, tetrahedrite, and stannite.

N a m e. After Don Felix Avelino Aramayo, formerly Managing Director of the Compagnie Aramayo de Mines en Bolivie.

Ref.

1. Angles, unit and orientation of Berman and Wolfe, *Min. Mag.*, **25**, 466 (1939). The original crystallography of Spencer (1926) was incomplete because of the poor

quality of the crystals. Yardley, *Min. Mag.*, **21**, 163 (1926), derived a triclinic unit, from x-ray study, not consistent with the morphology of Berman and Wolfe. Transformation: Yardley to Berman and Wolfe $\overline{1}10/\frac{1}{2}0\frac{3}{2}/\overline{1}10$. Yardley ratio $a_0 : b_0 : c_0 =$ 0.9972 : 1 : 0.9886, $\alpha\ 86°55'$, $\beta\ 90°53'$, $\gamma\ 93°18'$.

2. Berman and Wolfe (1939).

3. Berman and Wolfe (1939). The Yardley (1926) values are $a_0\ 5.672$, $b_0\ 5.688$, $c_0\ 5.623$.

4. Mountain anal. in Spencer (1926).

356 **MATILDITE** [AgBiS₂]. Silberwismuthglanz *Rammelsberg* (*Zs. deutsche geol. Ges.*, **29**, 80, 1877). Matildite *D'Achiardi* (**1**, 136, 1883). Morocochite *Heddle* (*Enc. Brit.*, **16**, 394, 1883). Peruvite *Pflücker y Rico* (*An. esc. de minas, Peru*, **3**, 62, 1883). Argentobismutite *Genth* (*Am. Phil. Soc. Proc.*, **23**, 35, 1885).

Wismutisches Silber *Selb* (*Crell's Ann.*, **1**, 10, 1793). Wismuthbleierz. Schapbachit *Kenngott* (118, 1853); *Sandberger* (**1**, 90, 1882).

Plenargyrite *Sandberger* (**1**, 96, 1882).

C r y s t.[1] Orthorhombic (?). Inverts at ca. 210° to an isometric modification.

Structure cell.[2] Orthorhombic; $a_0\ 8.14$, $b_0\ 7.87$, $c_0\ 5.69$; $a_0 : b_0 : c_0 =$ 1.03 : 1 : 0.723; contains $Ag_4Bi_4S_8$.

Habit. Rarely as indistinct prismatic crystals, striated [001]. Massive, granular.

P h y s. Cleavage none. Fracture uneven. Brittle. H. $2\frac{1}{2}$. G. $\sim$ 6.9; 6.90 (calc.). Luster metallic. Color iron-black to gray. Streak light gray. Opaque. In polished section[2] white in color with weak anisotropism and weak pleochroism.

C h e m. Silver bismuth sulfide, AgBiS₂.

Anal.[3]

	1	2	3	4
Ag	28.33	28.76	26.39	21.86
Bi	54.84	54.50	52.89	58.50
S	16.83	17.24	[16.66]	16.28
Rem.	.....	.....	4.06	3.36
Total	100.00	100.00	100.00	100.00
G.		6.92		

1. AgBiS₂. 2. Morococha, Peru. Average of three analyses, after deduction of galena.[4] 3. Lake City, Colo. Rem. is Pb 4.06, possibly present as galena.[5] 4. Nishizawa mine, Japan. Recalc. after deduction of gangue. Rem. is Au 0.84, Se 2.52.[6]

Tests. F. 1. Soluble in HNO₃ with separation of sulfur and, usually, some lead sulfate.

O c c u r. Occurs associated with galena, pyrite, chalcopyrite, arsenopyrite, sphalerite, and tetrahedrite in deposits formed at moderate to high temperatures. Usually found as a microscopic oriented intergrowth with galena, and apparently resulting from the breakdown of an argentian and bismuthian galena stable at higher temperatures.[2]

From Schapbach, in the Black Forest, Baden, intimately associated with galena, pyrite, and chalcopyrite (*schapbachite*), in part as small indistinct crystals (*plenargyrite*). Reported from Gondo, Switzerland, with pyrite in a gold-quartz vein; from Bustarviejo, near Madrid, Spain, in pegmatite with chalcopyrite, cassiterite, and arsenopyrite; and from Ivigtut, Greenland, with cryolite and chalcopyrite. At the Nishizawa mine, near Nikkō, Kuriyamamura, Totizi, Japan. From the Matilda mine, near Morococha, Province of Junin, Peru, with tetrahedrite, sphalerite, and pyrite, and at the Nueva Verdun mine, near Colquechaca, Bolivia. In the United States near Lake City, Hinsdale County, Colorado, as striated needle-shaped crystals in quartz, and at the Mayflower mine, Boise Basin region, Boise County, Idaho. At the O'Brien mine, Cobalt, Ontario, with native silver, tetrahedrite, chalcopyrite, and galena.

A r t i f. A compound of the composition $AgBiS_2$ has been reported by fusion of the reaction product of an ammoniacal solution of $AgNO_3$ and $KBiS_2$;[7] also as octahedral crystals (high-$AgBiS_2$?) by reaction of Ag_2S with molten bismuth and extraction of excess Bi in acid.[8] Heated to between 204° and 239° matildite inverts to an isometric modification with $a_0 = 5\ 64 \pm 0.02$ Å.

N a m e. *Matildite, morocochite,* and *peruvite* from the original locality at the Matilda mine, near Morococha, Peru. *Schapbachite* from the locality, Schapbach, Baden. *Plenargyrite* in allusion to the fact that it contains less silver than miargyrite. The name matildite is established through usage and is here retained for the species, although schapbachite and plenargyrite have priority.

SCHAPBACHITE. Wismutisches Silber *Selb* (*Crell's Ann.*, **1**, 10, 1793). Wismuthbleierz. Schapbachit *Kenngott* (118, 1853); *Sandberger* (**1**, 90, 1882). A supposed silver and lead bismuth sulfide, $PbAg_2Bi_2S_5$, from Schapbach, Baden. Shown[2] to be a mixture of matildite and galena.

PLENARGYRITE. *Sandberger* (**1**, 96, 1882). A silver bismuth sulfide, approximately $AgBiS_2$, from Schapbach, Baden, supposed to be dimorphous with matildite. In indistinct crystals and crystalline groups, apparently like miargyrite in form. Shown[2] to be identical with matildite.

Ref.

1. From x-ray study in Ramdohr, *Ak. Berlin, Ber.*, 71, 1938.
2. In Ramdohr (1938), by powder pictures, on type material (?). A high-temperature modification, formed by heating to 204–239°, has a rock-salt type structure with a_0 5.64 and contains $Ag_2Bi_2S_4$, according to Ramdohr.
3. For analyses of so-called schapbachite and plenargyrite, and additional analyses of matildite see Hintze (**1** [1], 991, 992, 1035, 1901).
4. Rammelsberg, *Ak. Berlin, Monatsh.*, 701, 1876.
5. Genth, *Am. Phil. Soc., Proc.*, **23**, 35 (1885).
6. Codera anal. in Wada (74, 1904).
7. Schneider, *J. pr. Chem.*, **41**, 414 (1890).
8. Roessler, *Zs. anorg. Chem.*, **9**, 48 (1895).

357   **S M I T H I T E** [AgAsS_2]. *Solly* (*Min. Mag.*, **14**, 74, 1905).

C r y s t. Monoclinic; prismatic — $2/m$.

$a : b : c = 2.2206 : 1 : 1.9570$;[1] $\beta\ 101°12'$; $p_0 : q_0 : r_0 = 0.8813 : 1.9197 : 1$

$r_2 : p_2 : q_2 = 0.5209 : 0.4591 : 1$; $\mu\ 78°48'$; $p_0'\ 0.8984$, $q_0'\ 1.9570$, $x_0'\ 0.1980$

Forms:[2]

		ϕ	ρ	ϕ_2	$\rho_2 = B$	C	A
c	001	90°00'	11°12'	78°48'	90°00'	0°00'	78°48'
a	100	90 00	90 00	0 00	90 00	78 48	0 00
l	320	34 33	90 00	0 00	34 33	83 40½	55 27
h	102	90 00	32 54½	57 05½	90 00	21 42½	57 05½
e	101	90 00	47 38	42 22	90 00	36 26	42 22
d	$\bar{1}$01	−90 00	35 00½	125 00½	90 00	46 12½	125 00½
p	111	29 15½	65 58½	42 22	37 10½	60 55	63 29
P	$\bar{1}$11	−19 41½	64 18½	125 00½	31 57½	68 31	107 40½
q	211	45 33	70 18½	26 37½	48 45	62 32½	47 46
r	311	55 55½	74 01½	19 04	57 24½	64 52½	37 13
Q	$\bar{2}$11	−39 15	68 24½	147 58½	43 56½	75 43	126 02
R	$\bar{3}$11	−51 55	72 30½	158 10½	53 58	81 25½	138 39

Less common:

b	010	k	013	δ	$\bar{5}$03	C	215	α	15·7·7
u	140	o	011	i	$\bar{2}$01	y	213	A	522
w	130	ϵ	308	r	$\bar{5}$02	π	355	s	411
v	120	ζ	305	κ	$\bar{1}\bar{1}$·0·3	θ	759	t	511
m	110	g	301	j	$\bar{4}$01	z	313	O	$\bar{2}$14
n	210	η	501	χ	113	D	121	ρ	$\bar{1}$22
ν	520	β	10·0·1	J	$\bar{4}$41	ξ	413	τ	$\bar{2}$33
G	0·1·10	λ	$\bar{4}$03	H	3·1·10	B	322	σ	$\bar{3}$44

Z	$\bar{3}$13
Ξ	$\bar{4}$13
S	$\bar{4}$11
T	$\bar{5}$11
U	611

Habit. Equant; tabular {100}. The tabular crystals appear hexagonal due to strong zonal developments nearly 60° apart. Commonest forms: $a\,e\,c\,d\,q\,p\,P\,Q$.

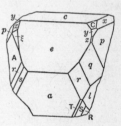

Binnental.

Phys. Cleavage {100} perfect. Fracture conchoidal. Brittle. H. 1½–2. G. 4.88. Luster adamantine. Color light red, changing to orange-red on exposure to light. Streak vermilion. In thin splinters transmits red light.

Opt.[3]

$$Y = b \left.\begin{matrix} \\ \end{matrix}\right\} \quad \text{some} \quad \left.\begin{matrix} \\ \end{matrix}\right\}$$
$$Z \wedge c = 6\tfrac{1}{2}° \quad \text{pleochroism}$$

n_{Na} 3.27   ±0.09

Bx neg. (−).
$2V$ 65°±.
Biref. very strong.

Chem. Silver arsenic sulfide, $AgAsS_2$.
Anal.

	Ag	As	Sb	S	Total
1	43.69	30.34	...	25.97	100.00
2	43.9	28.9	0.4	26.0	99.2

1. $AgAsS_2$. 2. Binnental.[4]

Occur. In the Binnental, Valais, Switzerland, associated with other arsenic sulfosalts, sphalerite, pyrite, realgar, and orpiment.

Artif.[5] The so-called arsenomiargyrite,[6] an artificial compound, has the composition of smithite, but the relationship to the natural mineral is not known.

N a m e.   After G. F. Herbert Smith, crystallographer, of the British Museum.

Ref.

1. Unit and orientation of Solly (1905), angles of Smith and Prior, *Min. Mag.*, **14**, 293 (1907).
2. Solly (1905); Smith and Prior (1907).
3. Smith and Prior (1907). Larsen (144, 1921) gives the optical properties of a supposed smithite formed by heating trechmannite, as follows: Bx neg. $(-)$. $2V$ moderate. $r > v$ strong. nX_{Li} 2.48 ± 0.02, nY_{Li} 2.58 ± 0.02, nZ_{Li} 2.60 ± 0.02.
4. Smith and Prior (1907).
5. Larsen (144, 1921) obtained what he thought might be smithite by inversion from trechmannite when heated. Gaudin and McGlashan, *Econ. Geol.*, **33**, 143 (1938), state that they have prepared smithite and studied its properties, but they give no description of their compound nor any comparison with the natural mineral.
6. Jaeger and van Klooster, *Zs. anorg. Chem.*, **78**, 265 (1912).

358   **Trechmannite.**   *Solly* (*Min. Mag.*, **14**, 283, 1907), p. 300. (Not the trechmannite (undescribed) of *Koechlin, Min. Mitt.*, **23**, 552 [1904].)

C r y s t.   Hexagonal — R; rhombohedral — $\bar{3}$.

$$a : c = 1 : 0.6530$$

Forms:[1]

| c | 0001 | 111 | a | $11\bar{2}0$ | $10\bar{1}$ | e | $10\bar{1}2$ | 411 | v | $12\bar{3}1$ | $52\bar{4}$ | z | $24\bar{6}1$ | $31\bar{3}$ |
| m | $10\bar{1}0$ | $2\bar{1}\bar{1}$ | r | $10\bar{1}1$ | 100 | p | $11\bar{2}3$ | 210 | x | $13\bar{4}1$ | $21\bar{2}$ | n | $14\bar{5}3$ | $32\bar{2}$ |

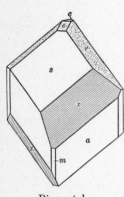

Binnental.

Habit.   Short prismatic. Equant. Sometimes irregular.

P h y s.   Cleavage $\{10\bar{1}1\}$ good, $\{0001\}$ distinct. Fracture conchoidal. Brittle. H. $1\frac{1}{2}$–2. Luster adamantine. Color and streak scarlet-vermilion. In transmitted light[2] shows faint pleochroism with O pale reddish, E clear and nearly colorless. Uniaxial negative $(-)$. Extreme birefringence.

C h e m.   Qualitative tests indicate the presence of Ag, As, and S.

O c c u r.   At the Lengenbach quarry in the Binnental, Valais, Switzerland, with seligmannite, pyrite, fuchsite, and usually deposited upon tennantite.

N a m e.   After Dr. C. O. Trechmann (1851–1917), crystallographer.

TRECHMANNITE-α.   *Solly* (*Min. Mag.*, **18**, 363, 1919). Supposedly isomorphous with trechmannite because of the close crystallographic relations. Cleavage $\{0001\}$, and probably $\{10\bar{1}1\}$. Rhombohedral, with 21 reported forms. Lead gray, with a chocolate-colored streak. From the Binnental, Valais, Switzerland, with sartorite. Needs investigation.

Ref.

1. Smith and Prior, *Min. Mag.*, **14**, 283 (1907), p. 300. Rare forms:

$14\bar{5}0$	$10\bar{1}5$	$50\bar{5}1$	$1 \cdot 12 \cdot \overline{13} \cdot 4$	$4 \cdot 9 \cdot \overline{13} \cdot 4$	$35\bar{8}1$	$34\bar{7}1$
$13\bar{4}0$	$20\bar{2}7$	$40\bar{4}1$	$1 \cdot 11 \cdot \overline{12} \cdot 5$	$6 \cdot 13 \cdot \overline{19} \cdot 8$	$23\bar{5}5$	$45\bar{9}2$
$25\bar{7}0$	$20\bar{2}1$	$2 \cdot 29 \cdot \overline{31} \cdot 9$	$26\bar{8}1$	$35\bar{8}4$	$23\bar{5}4$	

2. Larsen (144, 1921). On heating, the trechmannite inverts to a biaxial form, probably smithite.

3591 **CHALCOSTIBITE** [CuSbS$_2$]. Kupferantimonglanz *Zinken* (*Ann. Phys.*, **35**, 357, 1835). Sulphuret of Copper and Antimony, Antimonial Copper. Rosit *Huot* (**1**, 197, 1841). Chalkostibit *Glocker* (32, 1847). Wolfsbergite *Nicol* (484, 1849). Guejarite *Cumenge* (*Bull. soc. min.*, **2**, 201, 1879). Chalcostibite *Dana* (85, 1868).

C r y s t. Orthorhombic; dipyramidal — $2/m\ 2/m\ 2/m$.

$$a : b : c = 0.4153 : 1 : 0.2606;^1 \qquad p_0 : q_0 : r_0 = 0.6275 : 0.2606 : 1$$

$$q_1 : r_1 : p_1 = 0.4153 : 1.5936 : 1; \qquad r_2 : p_2 : q_2 = 3.8373 : 2.4079 : 1$$

Forms:[2]

		ϕ	$\rho = C$	ϕ_1	$\rho_1 = A$	ϕ_2	$\rho_2 = B$
c	001	.....	0°00′	0°00′	90°00′	90°00′	90°00′
b	010	0°00′	90 00	90 00	90 00	.....	0 00
a	100	90 00	90 00	.....	0 00	0 00	90 00
y	160	21 52	90 00	90 00	68 08	0 00	21 52
z	150	25 43	90 00	90 00	64 17	0 00	25 43
j	140	31 03	90 00	90 00	58 57	0 00	31 03
h	130	38 45	90 00	90 00	51 15	0 00	38 45
d	120	50 17½	90 00	90 00	39 42½	0 00	50 17½
m	110	67 27	90 00	90 00	22 33	0 00	67 27
u	011	0 00	14 36½	14 36½	90 00	90 00	75 23½
t	031	0 00	38 01	38 01	90 00	90 00	51 59
s	051	0 00	52 29½	52 29½	90 00	90 00	37 30½
l	101	90 00	32 06½	0 00	57 53½	57 53½	90 00
τ	111	67 27	34 11½	14 36½	58 44	57 53½	77 33
γ	221	67 27	53 39	27 31½	41 56½	38 33	72 00½
ρ	131	38 45	45 04½	38 01	63 41½	57 53½	56 29
π	151	25 43	55 20½	52 29½	69 05½	57 53½	42 10½
ν	161	21 52	59 18½	57 24	71 19	57 53½	37 03½
p	372	45 54	52 39½	42 22	55 11	46 44	56 24½
g:	392	38 45	56 22½	49 32½	48 35	46 44	49 30½
r:	251	43 55½	61 04	52 29½	52 37	38 33	50 55½
q	431	72 42	69 10½	38 01	26 49½	21 43½	73 51½
x:	521	80 34	72 33	27 31½	19 46	17 40½	81 00½
χ	721	83 14	77 15½	27 31½	14 24	12 49½	83 24

Less common:

N	1·12·0	B	210	Σ	401	X	121	o:	493	t:	411
Δ	190	g	053	Λ	501	ψ	141	ω	694	u:	421
χ	2·15·0	n	094	i:	132	Y	171	Γ	382	v:	511
A	170	o	073	w:	253	r	2·15·2	θ	231	Θ	531
M	290	v	052	η	374	K	181	p:	241	y:	541
k	270	f	061	j:	475	a:	191	I	311	Ξ	5·10·1
C	250	f:	071	k:	5·14·6	l:	1·10·1	κ	371	z:	651
D	350	h:	091	V	10·3·10	n:	1·12·1	s:	381	b:	711
E	790	Ψ	201	d:·	323	q:	1·14·1	O	3·10·1	φ	761
										Φ	911

Structure cell.[3] Orthorhombic; space group *Pnam*; a_0 6.01 ± 0.01, b_0 14.46 ± 0.03, c_0 3.78 ± 0.01; $a_0 : b_0 : c_0 = 0.4156 : 1 : 0.2614$; contains $Cu_4Sb_4S_8$.

Habit. Blade-shaped crystals, flattened {010}. Often elongated and striated [001]. Massive.

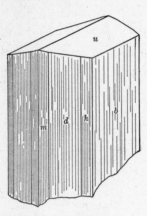

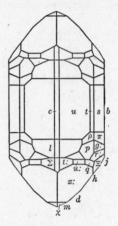

Guejar, Spain.   Rar el Anz, Morocco.

Twinning. On {104}, with composition plane {104}.

P h y s. Cleavage {010} perfect, {001} and {100} less so. Fracture subconchoidal. Brittle. H. 3–4. G. 4.95 ± 0.05;[4] 5.011 (calc.). Luster metallic. Color between lead- and iron-gray, sometimes with a blue or green alteration coating. Opaque. In polished section anisotropic. Reflection percentages: green 42, orange 35, red 34.[5]

C h e m. Copper antimony sulfide, $CuSbS$, with minor amounts (less than one per cent) of Pb and Fe reported, but probably as impurities.

Anal.

	1	2	3
Cu	25.48	26.20	24.72
Sb	48.81	48.60	48.45
S	25.71	25.20	26.20
Rem.	.....	1.00	.....
Total	100.00	101.00	99.37
G.	5.011	4.96	

1. $CuSbS_2$. 2. Guejar (*guejarite*). Average of two analyses of crystals, with the Cu and Sb determined on three portions. Rem. is Pb 0.45, Fe 0.46, Zn 0.09.[6] 3. Huanchaca, Bolivia. Crystals.[6]

Tests. F. 1. In C.T. decrepitates and then fuses. Decomposed by HNO_3 with separation of sulfur and antimony trioxide.

O c c u r. At Rar el Anz, wadi of Cherrat, east of Casablanca, Morocco, large crystals, partially altered to azurite and malachite (?), are found in veins in a dolomitic limestone. Originally from Wolfsberg (*wolfsbergite*) in the Harz Mountains, where it occurs in vugs in quartz with chalcopyrite and jamesonite.   In Granada, Spain, from Guadix and from the district of Guejar (*guejarite*[7]).   Found at various localities in Bolivia, mainly at the Pulcaya mine, Huanchaca, on pyrite and quartz; at Colquechaca, southeast of Oruro, associated with tetrahedrite, andorite, stannite, pyrite, and quartz; at Machacamarca with bournonite; also reported from the Tapi mine, near Almona, and from Huarojolla near Cotagaita, both in the Tupiza district; from the Terremoto mine, Bustillos, as large crystals in a quartz vein, associated with stibnite; as small crystals in the cavities of a quartz-pyrite vein at Vita Purisima, Oruro.

A l t e r.   A thin alteration skin of azurite and malachite (?) is found on some crystals (Rar el Anz).

A r t i f.   A compound of the composition of chalcostibite has been reported in the system $Cu_2S-Sb_2S_3$.[8]

N a m e.   From χαλκός, *copper*, and στίβι, *antimony*.

Ref.

1. New elements from angles of Penfield and Frenzel, *Am. J. Sc.*, **4**, 27 (1897), on crystals from Huanchaca, Bolivia; orientation of Friedel, *Bull. soc. min.*, **2**, 203 (1879), unit of Hofmann, *Zs. Kr.*, **84**, 177 (1933), from the x-ray study.   Goldschmidt (367, 1897) adopted another position, and was followed in this by Ernst, *Jb. Min., Beil.-Bd.*, **56A**, 275 (1927).   Ungemach, *Zs. Kr.*, **58**, 159 (1923), and *Bull. soc. min.*, **57**, 186 (1934), set the striated zone as [100].   Transformations: Penfield and Frenzel to new elements 300/006/010; Goldschmidt to new elements 010/300/001; Ungemach to new elements 010/001/100; Hofmann to new elements 100/001/010.

2. Forms from Goldschmidt (9, 91, 1923), Ungemach (1923) modified by Palache (priv. comm., 1939), and Ernst (1927).   Rare and uncertain:

1·36·0	230	101	313	9·30·5
1·27·0	560	331	252	412
2·33·0	320	187	4·33·4	261
1·14·0	13·6·0	1·24·2	674	271
2·27·0	032	497	12·24·7	7·21·3
3·14·0	041	233	24·49·14	562
5·21·0	092	283	12·30·7	582
5·12·0	0·27·4	3·26·4	12·36·7	321
3·7·0	0·11·1	18·49·21	48·147·28	12·7·3
13·18·0	301	414	9·24·5	5·25·1

3. Hofmann (1933) on crystals from Wolfsberg, Harz.   The b_0 and c_0 directions are interchanged here, according to the transformation for the new setting (see above).
4. On crystals from Bolivia (Berman, priv. comm., 1939).   The value 5.32 by Ahlfeld and Moritz, *Jb. Min., Beil.-Bd.*, **66**, 179 (1933) is obviously wrong.
5. Schneiderhöhn and Ramdohr (**2**, 379, 1931).
6. Frenzel anal. in Penfield and Frenzel (1897).
7. Shown to be identical with chalcostibite by Penfield and Frenzel (1897).
8. Guertler and Meissner, *Met. Erz*, **18**, 358 (1921).   See also Parravano and Cesaris, *Acc. Linc., Rend.*, **21**, 798 (1912) — *Zs. Kr.*, **55**, 276 (1915), and Gaudin and Dicke, *Econ. Geol.*, **39**, 49 (1939).

3592   **E M P L E C T I T E** [CuBiS₂].   Wismuth-Kupfererz *Selb* (**11**, 441, 451, 1817). Kupferwismuthglanz *Schneider* (*Ann. Phys.*, **90**, 166, 1853).   Emplektit *Kenngott* (125, 1853).   Tannenite *Dana* (73, 1854).   Hemichalcit *Kobell* (600, 1864). Emplectite *Dana* (86, 1868).   Cuprobismutite pt. *Hillebrand* (*Am. J. Sc.*, **27**, 355, 1884; *Dana* [110, 1892]).

C r y s t. Orthorhombic; dipyramidal — $2/m\,2/m\,2/m$.

$a : b : c = 0.4223 : 1 : 0.2698;$[1] $p_0 : q_0 : r_0 = 0.6389 : 0.2698 : 1$

$q_1 : r_1 : p_1 = 0.4223 : 1.5652 : 1;$ $r_2 : p_2 : q_2 = 3.7064 : 2.3681 : 1$

Forms:[2]

		ϕ	$\rho = C$	ϕ_1	$\rho_1 = A$	ϕ_2	$\rho_2 = B$
c	001	.....	0°00′	0°00′	90°00′	90°00′	90°00′
b	010	0°00′	90 00	90 00	90 00	.....	0 00
a	100	90 00	90 00	.....	0 00	0 00	90 00
k	011	0 00	15 06	15 06	90 00	90 00	74 54
l	021	0 00	28 21	28 21	90 00	90 00	61 39
d	031	0 00	38 59	38 59	90 00	90 00	51 01
s	051	0 00	53 27	53 27	90 00	90 00	36 33
h	201	90 00	51 57	0 00	38 03	38 03	90 00
n	601	90 00	75 23	0 00	14 37	14 37	90 00
u	111	67 06½	34 44½	15 06	58 20	57 25½	77 11½
y	221	67 06½	54 12½	28 21	41 38½	38 03	71 36½
x	121	49 49	39 54	28 21	60 39	57 25½	65 33

Less common:

j	140	i	120	f	061	o	132	q	392
g	130	m	110	v	071	p	131	w	211
r	250	e	041	t	112	z	141	α	321

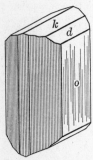

Johanngeorgenstadt, Saxony.

Structure cell.[3] Space group $Pnam$; a_0 6.125 ± 0.01, b_0 14.512 ± 0.03, c_0 3.890 ± 0.01; $a_0 : b_0 : c_0 = 0.4221 : 1 : 0.2681$; contains $Cu_4Bi_4S_8$.

Habit. Prismatic, striated [001], flattened {010}. Commonest forms: $b\,K\,d\,u\,x\,y$.

Twinning. Contact twins reported as observed in polished section, but twin law unknown.[4]

P h y s. Cleavage {010} perfect, {001} less so. Fracture conchoidal to uneven. Brittle. H. 2. G. 6.38;[5] 6.426 (calc.). Luster metallic. Color grayish to tin-white. Opaque. In polished section[4] strongly anisotropic. Reflection percentages: green 37.5, orange 35, red 35.

C h e m. Copper bismuth sulfide, $CuBiS_2$.

Anal.[6]

	Cu	Bi	S	Total	G.
1	18.88	62.08	19.04	100.00	6.426
2	18.80	61.95	19.16	99.91	

1. $CuBiS_2$. 2. Tannenbaum, Saxony. Average of two analyses.[7]

Tests. F. 1. Fuses with frothing and spurting B.B. Decomposed by HNO_3 with separation of sulfur.

O c c u r. At Schlaggenwald, Bohemia, with chalcopyrite, pyrite, sphalerite, fluorite, and apatite. In Saxony occurs embedded in quartz at Tannenbaum, near Schwarzenberg, and on the Schreckenberg at Annaberg, in the cobalt-nickel-bismuth ores, associated with chalcopyrite, siderite, and fluorite; also in the tin veins at Sadisdorf, southwest of Dippoldis-walde, with wolframite, molybdenite, and chalcopyrite. Fine crystals, partly filmed with limonite from Johanngeorgenstadt in Saxony, have been measured. Reported from near Freudenstadt in the Black Forest, Würt-temberg. At the Aamdal copper mines, Telemarken, Norway. In Chile from Cerro Blanco, near Copiapó.

Alter. To bismite (?).

Artif. Reported in the system Cu-Bi-S.[8]

Name. From ἔμπλεκτος, *entwined, interwoven,* in allusion to its inti-mate association with quartz.

Ref.

1. Angles of Palache and Peacock, *Am. Min.*, **18**, 277 (1933) on crystals from Johann-georgenstadt, in a new preferred orientation (Palache, priv. comm., 1939), differing only from the x-ray cell of Hofmann, *Zs. Kr.*, **84**, 177 (1933), by an interchange of the $b[010]$ and $c[001]$ directions. The orientation of Ungemach, *Bull. soc. min.*, **57**, 186 (1934), differs as shown in the transformation below.

Palache and Peacock to Palache   010/300/001
Hofmann to Palache   100/001/010
Ungemach to Palache   010/001/100

2. Palache and Peacock (1933). Ungemach (1934).
3. Hofmann (1933) transformed to the new position as given above, on a crystal from Schwarzenberg, Saxony. Full structural data are presented, and a discussion of cleavage and uncertain twinning is given in terms of the structure. Relations to chalcostibite are pointed out.
4. Schneiderhöhn and Ramdohr (**2**, 381, 1931).
5. Specific gravity on Johanngeorgenstadt crystal of 10 mg. (Berman, priv. comm., 1940).
6. Older analyses in Dana (113, 1892).
7. Guillemain anal. (Inaug. Diss., Breslau, 1898 — *Zs. Kr.*, **33**, 75, 1900).
8. Guertler and Meisner, *Met. Erz.*, **18**, 351 (1921).

CUPROBISMUTITE. *Hillebrand (Am. J: Sc.,* **27**, 355, 1884). Cuprobismutite *Dana* (110, 1892).

A copper bismuth sulfide, supposedly $Cu_6Bi_8S_{15}$, from Hall's Valley, Park County, Colorado. Shown to be a mixture of bismuthinite and emplectite.[1] A reported[2] occur-rence at Arnsberg, Westphalia, may be a new mineral but pertinent data are lacking.

Ref.

1. Short (104, 1931) examined the type material. Palache, *Am. Min.*, **25**, 611 (1940), has shown that both bismuthinite and emplectite crystals are in the type specimen.
2. Schneiderhöhn and Ramdohr (**2**, 378, 1931) report a mineral differing from emplec-tite, but no evidence is given that the composition is that previously assigned to cuprobis-mutite. Gaudin and Dicke, *Econ. Geol.*, **34**, 214 (1939), claim to have produced a com-pound of this composition in a melt.

35·10 **LORANDITE** [$TlAsS_2$]. *Krenner (Mat. Termés. Ért.,* **12**, 473, 1894; **13**, 258, 1895; *Zs. Kr.,* **27**, 98, 1897).

Cryst. Monoclinic; prismatic — $2/m$.

$a : b : c = 1.0873 : 1 : 0.5390;$ $\beta\ 104°16';$ $p_0 : q_0 : r_0 = 0.4957 : 0.5224 : 1$

$r_2 : p_2 : q_2 = 1.9143 : 0.9490 : 1;$ $\mu\ 75°44';$ $p_0'\ 0.5115,\ q_0'\ 0.5390,\ x_0'\ 0.2543$

Forms:[2]

		ϕ	ρ	ϕ_2	$\rho_2 = B$	C	A
m	110	43°30′	90°00′	0°00′	43°30′	80°14′	46°30′
q	210	62 13	90 00	0 00	62 13	77 24½	27 47
p	011	25 15½	30 47½	75 44	62 25	27 35	77 23
C	201	90 00	51 56½	38 03½	90 00	37 40½	38 03½
A	$\bar{2}01$	−90 00	37 33	127 33	90 00	51 49	127 33
s	$\bar{1}11$	−25 30½	30 51	104 25½	62 26	38 57½	102 45½
v	$\bar{3}11$	−67 10	54 15	142 00½	71 38½	67 33	138 25
l	$\bar{3}21$	−49 54	59 08½	142 00½	56 26	70 24½	131 03

Less common:

c	001	u	140	ϵ	320	β	$\bar{1}05$	k	121	w	$\bar{2}41$
b	010	M	130	n	045	y	111	ζ	$\bar{1}22$	i	$\bar{7}22$
a	100	e	120	z	021	r	221	α	$\bar{4}32$	f	$\bar{4}11$

Structure cell.[3] Space group $P2/x$ or $P2_1/x$; glide component $x = \frac{1}{2}(a + 2c)$; a_0 12.25, b_0 11.32, c_0 6.10; β 104°12′; $a_0 : b_0 : c_0 = 1.083 : 1 : 0.539$; contains $Tl_8As_8S_{16}$.

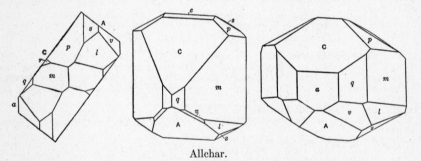

Allchar.

Habit. Short prismatic {110} and striated [001]; also prismatic {$\bar{2}$01}, {201}; tabular {201}.

P h y s. Cleavage {100} excellent, {$\bar{2}$01} very good, {001} good. Flexible, separating easily into cleavage lamellae and fibers. H. 2–2½. G. 5.53; 5.53 (calc.). Luster metallic adamantine. Color cochineal- to carmine-red, often dark lead-gray on the surface and frequently covered with an ocher-yellow powder. Streak cherry-red. Translucent to transparent in small crystals and deep red in color. Translation gliding on {100} in direction [010].[4]

O p t. In polished section[5] bluish gray-white in color with strong anisotropism and weak pleochroism; shows internal reflections. Reflection percentages: green 29.5, orange 23, red 20. In transmitted light:[6]

ORIENTATION	PLEOCHROISM	
X nearly $\perp$ {100}		Bx pos. (+)?　$2V$ large.
Y	Purple-red	Elong. pos. (+) on cleav-
$Z = b$	Orange-red	age fragments.　$n_{Li} > 2.72$
		Biref. extreme.

C h e m. A thallium arsenic sulfide, $TlAsS_2$.

Anal.

	1	2	3	4	5
Tl	59.46	59.40	59.76	58.75	59.08
As	21.87	[21.60]	22.30	21.65	21.32
S	18.67	19.00	18.99	19.26	18.75
Rem.	......	......	......	0.08	0.12
Total	100.00	100.00	101.05	99.74	99.27

1. $TlAsS_2$. 2, 3. Allchar.[7] 4, 5. Allchar. Rem. is gangue.[8]

Tests. F. 1. In C.T. fuses to a black globule and yields sublimates of black TlS, orange AsS and white As_2O_3. Soluble in HNO_3 with separation of S.

Occur. At Allchar, near Rozsdan, northwest of Salonika, Macedonia, with realgar and stibnite. At the Rambler mine, near Encampment, Wyoming, with orpiment, realgar and barite, incrusting massive pyrite.

Artif. A compound of the composition $TlAsS_2$ was found in the system Tl_2S-As_2S_3.[9] Reported also by reaction of H_2S, $TlSO_4$, and H_3AsO_3 in acid (H_2SO_4) solution, or of Tl flue dust with $Na_2S_2O_4$ solution.[10]

Name. After the physicist Eotvös Lorand of Budapest.

Ref.

1. Angles from Goldschmidt, Zs. Kr., **30**, 272 (1898), on crystals from Allchar, unit and orientation of Peacock (priv. comm., 1939). The unit corresponds to the x-ray cell of Hoffmann, Fortschr. Min., **17**, 46 (1932), and the orientation yields the shortest identity periods using Hoffmann's data. Ungemach, Zs. Kr., **58**, 155 (1923), had another orientation. Transformations: Krenner to Peacock $\overline{2}02/0\overline{2}0/101$; Goldschmidt to Peacock $\overline{2}0\overline{2}/0\overline{2}0/001$; Hoffmann to Peacock $\overline{1}0\overline{2}/0\overline{1}0/001$; Ungemach to Peacock $\overline{1}0\overline{1}/010/100$. Tokody, Zs. Kr., **59**, 83 (1923), has discussed the crystallographic relations of lorandite and miargyrite.
2. Goldschmidt (1898). Uncertain forms: $\{\overline{8}55\}$, $\{\overline{1}0\cdot8\cdot5\}$, $\{\overline{9}\cdot13\cdot4\}$, $\{\overline{18}\cdot5\cdot5\}$, $\{\overline{16}\cdot3\cdot3\}$, $\{\overline{15}\cdot4\cdot4\}$.
3. Values given are those of Hoffmann (1932) transformed according to the formula of reference. Hoffmann's data: a_0 15.023, b_0 11.315, c_0 6.102; β 127°45′.
4. Mügge, Jb. Min., I, 99, 1898.
5. Schneiderhöhn and Ramdohr (**2**, 384, 1931).
6. Larsen (102, 1921) and Tokody, Zs. Kr., **59**, 83 (1923).
7. Loczka, Zs. Kr., **39**, 523 (1904). Analysis 2 was given erroneously in Krenner (1895).
8. Jannasch, Zs. Kr., **39**, 123 (1904).
9. Canneri and Fernandes, Acc. Linc., Att., **1**, 671 (1925).
10. Gunning, Jahresber. Chem. for 1868, 247, 1870.

35·11 **TEALLITE** [$PbSnS_2$]. Prior (Min. Mag., **14**, 21, 1904). Pufahlite Ahlfeld (Met. Erz., **22**, 135, 1925).
　　　Zinc-teallite Ahlfeld (Cbl. Min., 388, 1926).

Cryst. Orthorhombic; dipyramidal — $2/m\ 2/m\ 2/m$.

$$a : b : c = 0.971 : 1 : 2.670;^1 \qquad p_0 : q_0 : r_0 = 2.7498 : 2.670 : 1$$

$$q_1 : r_1 : p_1 = 0.971 : 0.3637 : 1; \qquad r_2 : p_2 : q_2 = 0.3745 : 1.0299 : 1$$

Forms:[2]

		ϕ	$\rho = C$	ϕ_1	$\rho_1 = A$	ϕ_2	$\rho_2 = B$
c	001	.....	0°00'	0°00'	90°00'	90°00'	90°00'
B	205	90°00'	47 43½	0 00	42 16½	42 16½	90 00
d	102	90 00	53 58	0 00	36 02	36 02	90 00
e	101	90 00	70 01	0 00	19 59	19 59	90 00
p	111	45 50½	75 22½	69 28	46 02	19 59	47 37

Less common:

$$m\{110\} \qquad f\{012\} \qquad c\{3\cdot0\cdot10\} \qquad o\{112\}$$

Structure cell.[3] Space group $Pnma$; a_0 4.04, b_0 4.28, c_0 11.33; $a_0 : b_0 : c_0 = 0.944 : 1 : 2.647$; contains $Pb_2Sn_2S_4$.

Habit. Thin tabular $\{001\}$ with nearly square outline; lateral faces striated $\|$ intersection with $\{001\}$; $\{001\}$ striated [110]. Usually massive aggregates of thin graphite-like foliae with ir-regular boundaries; crystals often warped or bent.

[Mt. Cerillos, Bolivia.

Twinning. Observed only in polished sec-tion.[4]

P h y s. Cleavage $\{001\}$ perfect.[5] Flexible but not elastic. Somewhat malleable. H. 1½; soils paper. G. 6.36; 6.57 (calc.). Luster metallic; may tarnish dull or iridescent. Color grayish black. Streak black. Opaque. Transla-tion gliding on $\{010\}$.[4] In polished section[4] white in color with distinct anisotropism; weakly pleochroic: $\|$ $\{001\}$ white with a light golden tint, [001] pure white. Reflection percentages: green 41, orange 38.5, red 36.

C h e m. A lead tin sulfide, $PbSnS_2$. Ge and Bi have been reported spectroscopically.[6]

Anal.

	1	2	3
Pb	53.05	52.98	52.09
Fe	.....	0.20	0.17
Sn	30.51	30.39	30.55
S	16.44	16.29	16.91
Total	100.00	99.86	99.72
G.		6.36	

1. $PbSnS_2$. 2. "Bolivia." Average of two analyses.[7] 3. Santa Rosa mine, Mon-serrat, Bolivia. Recalculated after deduction of 1.08 Zn as ZnS. Spectrographically shown to contain 0.001 ± per cent Zn.[8]

Tests. In C.T. does not melt, and affords a sublimate of S. Easily decomposed by hot concentrated HCl or HNO_3.

O c c u r.[9] Sometimes found in large amounts in the silver-tin veins of Bolivia. At the Santa Rosa and El Salvador mines, Monserrat (Ante-quera), with wurtzite, cassiterite, galena, sphalerite, and pyrite; in the veins of Mount Cerillos near Carquaicollo in the Cordillera de los Frailes with wurtzite; in the Lipez Huaico mine, Ocuri, with cassiterite, stannite, pyrite, and sphalerite; also reported from the San Alfredo mine, Colquiri, from the Aliada mine, Colquechaca, and from the Porvenir mine, Huanuni, with franckeite and sphalerite. Said to occur at the Himmelsfürst mine, Freiberg, Saxony.

Alter. To cassiterite, the crystals or masses of this mineral often arranged along {001} of the teallite; also to franckeite and to oxidized Pb and Zn minerals.

Name. After Dr. J. J. Harris Teall (1849–1924), formerly Director-General of the Geological Survey of Great Britain and Ireland.

PUFAHLITE. *Ahlfeld (Met. Erz*, **22**, 135, 1925). Zinc-teallite *Ahlfeld (Cbl. Min.*, 388, 1926).

A supposed zincian teallite from Carquaicollo and from the Ichocollo mine, Monserrat, Bolivia. Analyses gave 6–11 per cent Zn. Shown[6] to be a mixture of teallite and wurtzite or sphalerite. Named after Professor Otto Pufahl (1855–1924), metallurgist, formerly of the Technical High School, Charlottenberg, Berlin.

Ref.

1. Angles of Ahlfeld, Himmel, and Kleber, *Zbl. Min.*, 225, 1935, unit of Hoffmann, *Zs. Kr.*, **92**, 161 (1935), orientation of Prior (1904). Transformation: Ahlfeld, Himmel, and Kleber, also Prior, to Hoffmann 100/010/002. The crystals measured are generally poor, and the agreement between the x-ray work of Hoffmann and the crystallographic measurements is not good.
2. Prior (1904), Ahlfeld, Himmel, and Kleber (1935). Uncertain forms: {100}, {017}, {011}, {114}, {212}.
3. Hoffmann (1935). The structure is similar to that of herzenbergite, SnS, with Pb substituting for half of the Sn atoms.
4. Schneiderhöhn and Ramdohr (**2**, 479, 1931).
5. An indistinct parting or cleavage ∥ {110} (?) is sometimes noted (Hintze [676, 1938]).
6. Moritz, *Jb. Min., Beil.-Bd.*, **66**, 203 (1933).
7. Prior (1904).
8. Krüll anal. in Moritz (1933).
9. The originally described material was labeled as coming from " Bolivia," without specific locality designation.

35·12 **Benjaminite** [Pb(Cu,Ag)Bi$_2$S$_4$?]. *Shannon (U. S. Nat. Mus., Proc.*, **65**, art. 24, 1, 1924).

Granular massive, with a fair cleavage in one direction. H. $3\frac{1}{2}$. G. 6.34.[1] Luster metallic. Color gray, tarnishing dull or yellow to coppery red. Streak dull lead-gray. Opaque. In polished section gray in color and strongly anisotropic.

Chem. A lead, copper, and silver bismuth sulfide of uncertain formula, perhaps Pb(Cu,Ag)Bi$_2$S$_4$.[2]

Anal.

	Pb	Cu	Ag	Bi	S	Total
1	24.91	5.10	4.32	50.25	15.42	100.00
2	25.18	4.69	3.51	50.78	15.84	100.00

1. Pb(Cu,Ag)Bi$_2$S$_4$ with Cu : Ag = 2 : 1. 2. Nevada. Average of four analyses after deducting quartz, molybdenite, and chalcopyrite as impurities.

Tests. In C.T. a sublimate of sulfur, and in O.T. fumes of sulfur dioxide. Soluble in hot concentrated HNO$_3$ or HCl.

Occur. At the Outlaw mine, 12 miles north of Manhattan, Nye County, Nevada, associated with muscovite, fluorite, chalcopyrite, molybdenite, and pyrite in a quartz vein near the contact of a soda-granite and an intrusive rhyolite.

Name. After Dr. Marcus Benjamin (1857–1932), editor, of the U. S. National Museum.

Ref.

1. On a 25-mg. sample (Frondel, priv. comm., 1939).
2. An x-ray powder photograph of benjaminite was found to be similar to that of cosalite (Frondel, priv. comm., 1939).

35·13 Hammarite [$Pb_2Cu_2Bi_4S_9$?]. *Johansson* (*Ark. Kemi*, **9** [8], 11, 1924).

Cryst. Monoclinic? $a : b = 1.048 : 1$.

Forms:

		ϕ	ρ				ϕ	ρ
b	010	0°00′	90°00′		K	230	32°57′	90°00′
a	100	90 00	90 00		m	110	44 12	90 00
n	120	25 56	90 00		l	210	62 47	90 00

Habit. Short prismatic to acicular [001], flattened {010}, without terminal faces; faces curved.

Phys. Cleavage {010} poor.[1] Fracture flat conchoidal. H. 3–4. Luster metallic. Color steel-gray with red tone. Streak black. Opaque.

Chem. A lead and copper bismuth sulfide, possibly $Pb_2Cu_2Bi_4S_9$.[2]

Anal.

	Pb	Cu	Bi	S	Insol.	Total
1	24.87	7.63	50.18	17.32	....	100.00
2	27.40	7.60	47.59	17.01	0.04	99.64

1. $Pb_2Cu_2Bi_4S_9$. 2. Gladhammar.

Occur. In crystals grown upon drusy quartz at Gladhammar, Kalmar, Sweden.

Name. From the locality, Gladhammar, Sweden.

Needs further study.

Ref.

1. One crystal showed an obscure parting parallel to the supposed base.
2. Foshag, *Am. Min.*, **10**, 157 (1925). Johansson (1924) erroneously derived the formula $Pb_5Bi_6S_{14}$.

361 DUFRENOYSITE [$Pb_2As_2S_5$]. *Damour* (*Ann. chim. phys.*, **14**, 379, 1845). Gotthardit *Rammelsberg* (229, 256, 1847). Arsenomelan and Scleroclase pt. *von Waltershausen* (*Ann. Phys.*, **94**, 115, 1855). Binnit *Heusser* (*Ann. Phys.*, **94**, 334, 1855). Dufrenoysite pt. *Des Cloizeaux* (*Ann. mines*, **8**, 389, 1855). Scleroklas *Petersen* (*Offenbacher Ver. Naturkunde*, **7**, 13 1866; *Jb. Min.*, 203, 1867). Bleiarsenit *Groth* (18, 1874). Plumbobinnite *Weisbach* (42, 1880).

Cryst. Monoclinic; prismatic — $2/m$.[1]

$a : b : c = 0.6510 : 1 : 0.6126$; $\beta\ 90°33\frac{1}{2}'$;[2] $p_0 : q_0 : r_0 = 0.9941 : 0.6227 : 1$

$r_2 : p_2 : q_2 = 1.6325 : 1.5362 : 1$; $\mu\ 89°26\frac{1}{2}'$; $p_0'\ 0.9410$, $q_0'\ 0.6126$, $x_0'\ 0.0097$

Forms:[3]

		ϕ	ρ	ϕ_2	$\rho_2 = B$	C	A
c	001	90°00′	0°33½′	89°26½′	90°00′	.....	89°26½′
b	010	0 00	90 00	......	0 00	90°00′	90 00
a	100	90 00	90 00	0 00	90 00	89 26½	......
F	120	37 31½	90 00	0 00	37 31½	89 39½	52 28½
K	230	45 41	90 00	0 00	45 41	89 36	44 19
m	110	56 56	90 00	0 00	56 56	89 32	33 04
s	210	71 58	90 00	0 00	71 58	89 28	18 02
ν	012	1 49½	17 02½	89 26½	72 58	17 02	89 28
k:	034	1 13	24 41	89 26½	65 19½	24 40½	89 29½
L:	056	1 05½	27 03	89 26½	62 57	27 02½	89 30
k	011	0 54½	31 29½	89 26½	58 31	31 29	89 31½
N:	054	0 44	37 26½	89 26½	52 33½	37 26½	89 33½
P:	032	0 36½	42 35	89 26½	47 25	42 35	89 35½
T:	074	0 31½	46 59½	89 26½	43 00½	46 59½	89 37
W:	021	0 27½	50 47	89 26½	39 13	50 47	89 39
a:	052	0 22	56 51½	89 26½	33 08½	56 51½	89 41½
c:	031	0 18	61 27	89 26½	28 33	61 27	89 44
e	101	90 00	43 33	46 27	90 00	42 59½	46 27
π	$\bar{1}11$	6 40	48 06½	132 58	65 51	48 34½	128 27½
t	212	72 08½	44 58	46 27	77 29	44 26	47 43½
t:	232	45 58½	52 54	46 27	66 20½	52 30	55 00½
η	$\bar{2}32$	−45 23	52 36½	132 58	66 05	53 00½	124 26½
ζ	$\bar{1}21$	−37 14½	56 59	132 58	48 07	57 19½	120 29½

Less common forms:

C 130	O 560	A: 410	S: 0·17·10	f: 092	χ $\bar{2}01$	o: 432
D 250	P 670	G: 014	V: 0·15·8	g: 051	p 111	ϕ $\bar{2}52$
G 590	S 760	H: 013	X: 0·11·5	k: 081	q 121	μ $\bar{4}52$
H 470	T 430	M: 076	b: 0·11·4	x 201	n: 412	Π $\bar{2}31$
I 350	W 530	O: 043	d: 0·7·2	ι $\bar{1}02$	u 211	y $\bar{5}22$
N 450	Y 310	R: 053	e: 041	ϵ $\bar{1}01$		

Habit. Tabular {010} and somewhat elongated [100]; also elongated [010] and striated [100].

Twinning. On {001}.[4]

Phys. Cleavage {010} perfect. Fracture conchoidal. Brittle. H. 3. G. 5.53 ± 0.03. Luster metallic. Color lead-gray to steel-gray. Streak reddish brown. Subtranslucent and dark red-brown in transmitted light. $n_{Li} > 2.72$, with very strong birefringence.[5] In polished section[6] white in color, sometimes with deep red internal reflections, with strong anisotropism and very weak pleochroism.

Chem. Lead arsenic sulfide, $Pb_2As_2S_5$.

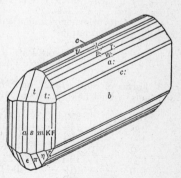

Binnental.

Anal.[7]

	1	2	3
Pb	57.20	57.42	57.38
As	20.68	20.89	21.01
S	22.12	22.55	21.94
Total	100.00	100.86	100.33
G.		5.52	

1. $Pb_2As_2S_5$. 2. Binnental. Crystal.[8] 3. Binnental. Surficial portion of crystal.[9]

Tests. F. 1. In O.T. an odor of SO_2 but not of As; in upper portion of tube a sublimate of S, and in lower portion of As_2O_3. On charcoal decrepitates, affording in R.F. a white sublimate of lead arsenate, volatilizing with continued heating with an odor of As and leaving a lead button.

O c c u r. In druses in saccharoidal dolomite at Imfeld in the Binnental, Valais, Switzerland. Reported from Hall, Tirol, Germany, with sphalerite, realgar, and orpiment in gypsum, and from Dundas, Tasmania, with tetrahedrite and chalcopyrite. Said to occur in the Wood River and Banner districts, Idaho, and in the Cerro Gordo district, Inyo County, California.

A r t i f.[10] Compounds of this composition have been reported from melts in the system $PbS-As_2S_3$, from the fusion of $PbCl_2$ with As_2S_3, and from the reaction of solutions of a lead salt and sodium sulfarsenite.

N a m e. After P. A. Dufrénoy (1792–1857), Professor of Mineralogy in the École des Mines, Paris. The name was also applied to other Binnental minerals because of crystallographic uncertainties concerning the species.[1]

Ref.

1. The material of the original crystallographic description by Damour, *Ann. chim. phys.*, **14**, 379 (1845), was later shown to be tennantite by von Waltershausen, *Ann. Phys.*, **94**, 115 (1855). The crystals called dufrenoyite by Des Cloizeaux, *Ann. mines*, **8**, 389 (1855), were sartorite and jordanite according to Solly, *Min. Mag.*, **13**, 151 (1902). vom Rath, *Ann. Phys.*, **122**, 373 (1864), made the mineral orthorhombic, but his material according to Solly (1902) was not well authenticated. The monoclinic character of dufrenoysite was finally established by Solly (1902), but an unconventional setting, with the angle β acute, that is, with {001} sloping back in the normal position, has been corrected by Palache (priv. comm., 1939), after checking Solly's original crystal (British Museum spec., 1912, 542).

2. Elements from angles and orientation of Solly (1902), unit of Palache (priv. comm., 1939). Transformations:

> vom Rath to Palache   001/100/010
> Solly to Palache $\bar{1}00/010/001$

3. Forms of Solly (1902), and *Min. Mag.*, **16**, 282 (1912), with revision and some additions by Palache (priv. comm., 1939). Rare forms (seen only once):

150	320	035	0·11·1	373	$\bar{4}34$	$\bar{3}62$
270	740	0·11·7	221	252	$\bar{6}56$	$\bar{5}93$
490	720	0·11·6	$\bar{3}32$	131	$\bar{4}54$	$\bar{7}84$
580	610	094	$\bar{2}21$	452	$\bar{1}31$	$\bar{4}12$
570	14·1·0	073	414	231	$\bar{2}72$	$\bar{2}11$
340	019	0·11·2	313	$\bar{2}14$	$\bar{1}41$	$\bar{8}54$
11·12·0	016	061	525	$\bar{1}42$	$\bar{1}51$	$\bar{6}43$
12·11·0	015	071	535	$\bar{4}14$	$\bar{5}24$	$\bar{4}32$
750	025	091	343	$\bar{2}12$	$\bar{5}44$	$\bar{5}12$

Doubtful forms:

1·14·0	$\bar{7}04$	322	543	321	$\bar{5}33$	$\bar{5}42$
$\bar{5}04$	$\bar{3}02$	533	542	331	$\bar{5}43$	$\bar{3}21$
						$\bar{3}31$

4. Solly (1912).
5. Larsen (70, 1921).
6. Schneiderhöhn and Ramdohr (2, 488, 1931).
7. Additional anal. in Bader, *Schweiz. min. Mitt.*, **14**, 319 (1934), p. 397. For spectroscopic traces of Tl and Cu, see Brun, *Bull. soc. min.*, **40**, 110 (1917), and de Gramont, *ibid.*, **18**, 292 (1895).
8. König anal. in Baumhauer, *Zs. Kr.*, **24**, 86 (1895).
9. Guillemain (Inaug. Diss. Breslau, 1898 — *Zs. Kr.*, **33**, 73 [1900]).
10. Wagemann, *Metall.*, **9**, 518 (1908); Sommerlad, *Zs. anorg. Chem.*, **18**, 445 (1898); and much earlier Berzelius, *Ann. Phys.*, **7**, 147 (1826).

3621   **C O S A L I T E** [$Pb_2Bi_2S_5$].   *Genth* (*Am. J. Sc.*, **45**, 319, 1868).   Ett nytt vis-mutsvafladt svafvelbly *Lundström* (*Geol. För. Förh.*, **2**, 178, 1874).   Bleibismutit *Groth* (18, 1874).   Bjelkite *Sjögren* (*Geol. För. Förh.*, **4**, 107, 1878).

C r y s t.   Orthorhombic;   dipyramidal — $2/m\ 2/m\ 2/m$ (?).[1]

$a : b : c = 0.800 : 1 : 0.170$;[2] $p_0 : q_0 : r_0 = 0.2125 : 0.1700 : 1$

$q_1 : r_1 : p_1 = 0.8000 : 4.706 : 1$; $r_2 : p_2 : q_2 = 5.882 : 1.250 : 1$

Forms:[3]

		ϕ	$\rho = C$	ϕ_1	$\rho_1 = A$	ϕ_2	$\rho_2 = B$
c	001	.....	0°00′	0°00′	90°00′	90°00′	90°00′
b	010	0°00′	90 00	90 00	90 00	.....	0 00
a	100	90 00	90 00	.....	0 00	0 00	90 00
n	130	22 37	90 00	90 00	67 23	0 00	22 37
e	120	32 00½	90 00	90 00	57 59½	0 00	32 00½
r	230	39 48½	90 00	90 00	50 11½	0 00	39 48½
m	110	51 20½	90 00	90 00	38 39½	0 00	51 20½
u	320	61 55½	90 00	90 00	28 04½	0 00	61 55½
d	210	68 12	90 00	90 00	21 48	0 00	68 12
i	032	0 00	14 18½	14 18½	90 00	90 00	75 41½
f	301	90 00	33 31	0 00	56 29	56 29	90 00
h	332	51 20½	22 12½	14 18½	72 50	72 19	76 20½

Also:

| j | 160 | l | 140 | o | 380 | q | 250 | s | 340 | t | 430 | k | 3·12·2 | g | 632 |

Structure cell.[4]   Space group *Pbnm*; a_0 19.04, b_0 23.81, c_0 4.05; $a_0 : b_0 : c_0 = 0.800 : 1 : 0.170$;   contains $(Pb,Cu)_{16}Bi_{16}S_{40}$, with Pb : Cu = 14 : 2.

Habit.   Prismatic [001], frequently elongated to needle-like and capillary forms.   Usually massive, in radiating prismatic, fibrous, or feathery aggregates; also dense, with an indistinct crystalline structure.   Common forms: *b a n e m d*.

Bjelke, Sweden.

Phys.   Fracture uneven.[5]   H. 2½–3.   G. 6.76, 6.86 (calc.).   Luster metallic.   Color lead-gray to steel-gray. Streak black.   Opaque.   In polished section[6] white in color with very weak pleochroism and anisotropism.

Chem. A lead bismuth sulfide, essentially $Pb_2Bi_2S_5$, but containing small amounts of Cu, Ag, and Fe, the role of which in the formula is not yet clear.

Anal.[7]

	1	2	3	4	5	6	7
Pb	41.75	39.55	38.68	37.88	37.68	36.23	34.54
Cu	.....	2.71	2.02	1.24	3.41	3.41	1.19
Ag	.....	.....	.....	1.67	0.32	1.50	0.82
Fe	.....	0.25	.....	1.79	0.68	0.19	......
Bi	42.10	40.21	42.38	39.21	41.75	42.34	46.44
S	16.15	17.20	16.59	15.76	15.92	16.33	17.01
Rem.	.....	0.78	.....	2.46	.....	.....	.....
Total	100.00	100.70	99.67	100.01	99.76	100.00	100.00
G.	6.86	6.63	6.76	6.55	6.776	7.13	

1. $Pb_2Bi_2S_5$. 2. Vaskö, Hungary. Rem. is Sb 0.04 and insol. 0.74.[8] 3. McElroy Township, Ont. Crystals.[9] 4. Cobalt, Ont. Rem. is Ni 0.05, Co 0.44, As 1.47, Sb 0.36, insol. 0.14. Probably contains a small amount of cobaltite.[9] 5. Vaskö, Hungary.[10] 6. Vaskö, Hungary.[11] 7. Deer Park, Stevens Co., Wash. Recalculated after deduction of insol. 2.19 and H_2O 0.17.[12]

Tests. F. 1. On charcoal the argentian varieties give a small button of Ag. Slowly attacked by HCl, and soluble in HNO_3 with separation of lead sulfate.

Occur. A not uncommon mineral, found in hydrothermal deposits formed at moderate temperatures, in contact metamorphic deposits (Vaskö, Rézbánya, Fahlun, and Nordmark), and in pegmatites. In Sweden occurs at the Bjelke mine, Nordmark (*bjelkite*) with calcite, diopside, and epidote, and reported at Fahlun, with bismuthinite. From Rézbánya, Roumania, with sphalerite, chalcopyrite, calcite, and tremolite. Found at Vaskö, Hungary, with ankerite and chalcopyrite. From the Forno glacier, Switzerland, in smoky quartz. Reported from Duckmaloi, Kingsgate, and Deepwater, in the New England range, New South Wales, and from a pegmatite at Amparindravato, Madagascar. In Mexico with cobaltite and quartz in a silver mine at Cosala, Sinaloa; a supposedly argentian variety occurs at Candameña, Chihuahua.

In the United States found at Deer Park, Stevens County, Washington, in quartz veins with huebnerite and pyrite. In Colorado occurs with bornite, enargite, stromeyerite, sphalerite, and other sulfides in the Yankee Girl and Genesee mines in the Red Mountain district,[13] San Juan County; also at the Comstock mine, near Comstock City, La Plata County, and at the Gladiator mine and the Alaska mine, in Poughkeepsie Gulch, Ouray County. In Ontario, Canada, at Boston Creek, McElroy Township, with calcite and bismuth, and at Cobalt with smaltite and cobaltite; from the Ireland Mountain and Cariboo Gold Quartz mines, Cariboo district, British Columbia.

Alter. To bismutite.

Name. From the occurrence at the Cosala mine, Sinaloa, Mexico.

Ref.

1. Evidence for dipyramidal symmetry is the doubly terminated crystal figured by Flink, *Ak. Stockholm, Öfv. Bihang.*, **12** [2], 2, 6, (1886).
2. Berry, *Univ. Toronto Stud., Geol. Ser.*, **42**, 23 (1939), from an x-ray study of material from McElroy Township, Ont., earlier used by Walker, *Univ. Toronto Stud., Geol. Ser.*, **12**, 5 (1921), for a morphological description. The ratio of Flink (1886) is based on poor measurements. Walker (1921) adopted Flink's ratio. Transformation: Flink to Berry 003/600/010. In the transformed position Flink's ratio becomes $a : b : c = 0.795 : 1 : 0.181$.
3. Forms from Flink (1886) and Walker (1921).
4. Berry (1939).
5. An indistinct prismatic cleavage is remarked by Hugi, *Schweiz. min. Mitt.*, **11**, 163 (1931), on crystals from Forno, Switzerland.
6. Tokody and Vavrinecz, *Földt. Közl.*, **65**, 301 (1935); Hugi (1931); Schneiderhöhn and Ramdohr (**2**, 405, 1931).
7. Older analyses in Doelter (4 [1], 459, 1926).
8. Vavrinecz anal. in Tokody and Vavrinecz (1935).
9. Todd anal. in Walker (1921).
10. Koch, *Cbl. Min.*, 51, 1930.
11. Loczka, *Mat. Termés. Ért.*, **42**, 20 (1926) — *Min. Abs.*, **3**, 7 (1926–28).
12. Wells anal. in Bancroft, *U. S. Geol. Surv., Bull. 430*, 214, 1910.
13. For a description of the occurrences in the Red Mountain district see Bastin, *U. S. Geol. Surv., Bull. 735d*, 65, 1923.

3622   **Kobellite** [$Pb_2(Bi,Sb)_2S_5$]. Kobellit *Sätterberg* (*Ak. Stockholm, Handl.*, 188, 1839; *Jahresber. Chem. Min.*, **20**, 215, 1840).

Massive, fibrous or radiated, also fine granular. Cleavage prismatic.[1] H. $2\frac{1}{2}$–3. G. 6.334.[2] Color blackish lead-gray to steel-gray. Streak black. In polished section[1] white in color with distinct anisotropism and weak pleochroism. Reflection percentages: green 37.5, orange 33.5, red 32.

C h e m.[3] Lead bismuth sulfide, possibly $Pb_2(Bi,Sb)_2S_5$, with Bi : Sb = 2 : 1, approximately. Some Cu and Ag is reported.

Anal.

	1	2	3
Pb	44.37	40.74	38.95
Cu	.....	0.88	0.97
Bi	29.87	28.37	30.61
Sb	8.57	9.38	8.13
S	17.19	18.61	17.76
Rem.	......	2.02	3.58
Total	100.00	100.00	100.00

1. $Pb_2(Bi,Sb)_2S_5$, with Bi : Sb = 2 : 1.   2. Vena, Sweden. Rem. is Fe 2.02.[4] 3. Silver Bell mine, Ouray, Colo. Rem. is Ag 3.58. Average of four analyses, recalc. after deduction of sphalerite, chalcopyrite, and gangue.[5]

Tests. F. 1; decrepitates. Soluble in concentrated HCl with evolution of H_2S.

O c c u r. At the Vena cobalt mines near Askersund, Örebro, Sweden, as radiated masses with cobaltite, cobaltian arsenopyrite, chalcopyrite, and actinolite. In Colorado at the Silver Bell mine, Ouray, associated with barite and chalcopyrite. Said to occur at San José de Amparo, near San Rafael, Sierra de Tapalpa, Jalisco, Mexico.

N a m e. After the Bavarian mineralogist and poet, Franz von Kobell (1803–82).

Needs confirmation.

Ref.

1. Observed in polished sections of material from Vena, Sweden, by Schneiderhöhn and Ramdohr (**2**, 431, 1931).
2. Keller, *Zs. Kr.*, **17**, 67 (1889).
3. Rammelsberg (100, 1875) rejected the original analyses of Sätterberg (1839), and on the basis of analyses by himself and Genth deduced the composition $Pb_3(Bi,Sb)_2S_6$. Keller (1889), however, analyzed material with the approximate composition $Pb_2(Bi,Sb)_2S_5$, to which Sätterberg's analysis conforms, and to the other gave the name lillianite. Flink, *Ark. Kemi*, **5** [10], 2 (1914), however, considered kobellite to be the antimonian analogue of lillianite, but this appears unwarranted. The original formula, $Pb_2(Bi,Sb)_2S_5$, here given, is that of an antimonian cosalite, to which mineral kobellite is similar in physical properties. The validity of both lillianite and kobellite is open to some doubt.
4. Sätterberg (1839). Recalculated by Rammelsberg (100, 1875) from newer atomic weights.
5. Keller (1889).

363   **F R A N C K E I T E** [$Pb_5Sn_3Sb_2S_{14}$]. Lepidolamprite, Schuppenglanz *Breithaupt* (in *Hintze* [**1** [1], 1198; 1904]). Franckeït *Stelzner* (*Jb. Min.*, II, 114, 1893). Llicteria *Bolivian miners*.

   Plumbostannite *Raimondi* (187, 1878).

C r y s t. Orthorhombic.

$a : b : c = 0.5811 : 1 : 0.5531;^1$ $p_0 : q_0 : r_0 = 0.9518 : 0.5531 : 1$

$q_1 : r_1 : p_1 = 0.5811 : 1.0506 : 1;$ $r_2 : p_2 : q_2 = 1.8080 : 1.7209 : 1$

Forms:[1]

		ϕ	$\rho = C$	ϕ_1	$\rho_1 = A$	ϕ_2	$\rho_2 = B$
c	001	.....	0°00′	0°00′	90°00′	90°00′	90°00′
b	010	0°00′	90 00	90 00	90 00	.....	0 00
a	100	90 00	90 00	.....	0 00	0 00	90 00
j	150	18 59½	90 00	90 00	71 00½	0 00	18 59½
m	110	59 50½	90 00	90 00	30 09½	0 00	59 50½
y	012	0 00	15 27½	15 27½	90 00	90 00	74 32½
f	011	0 00	28 57	28 57	90 00	90 00	61 03
S	041	0 00	65 40½	65 40½	90 00	90 00	24 19½
D	051	0 00	70 07	70 07	90 00	90 00	19 53
M	101	90 00	43 35	0 00	46 25	46 25	90 00
N	201	90 00	62 17	0 00	27 43	27 43	90 00
o	111	59 50½	47 45	28 57	50 12½	46 25	68 10
R	232	48 55½	51 37½	39 41	53 46½	46 25	59 00

Habit. Thin tabular {010}, elongated [100]; {010} striated [001], and less markedly [100]. Usually massive, radial, or foliated; often in spherical, rosette- or cauliflower-like aggregates of thin plates. Crystals often warped or bent.

Twinning. Complex twinning has been observed.[1]

P h y s. Cleavage {010} perfect. Flexible, but not elastic. Slightly malleable. H. 2½–3. G. 5.90.[2] Luster metallic, sometimes tarnished iridescent. Color and streak grayish black. Opaque. Translation gliding on {010}.[3] In polished section[3] gray-white in color with weak anisotropism and very weak pleochroism. Reflection percentages: green 37.5, orange 32.5, red 31.

Huanuni, Bolivia.

C h e m. A lead and tin antimony sulfide, possibly $Pb_5Sn_3Sb_2S_{14}$.[4] The Fe and Zn reported are apparently due to impurities.[5] Ge, Cu, Ag, and Bi have been reported spectrographically.[4]

Anal.

	1	2	3	4	5	6
Pb	49.71	50.57	48.02	46.23	46.11	49.80
Fe	.....	2.48	2.74	2.69	2.55	.....
Zn	.....	1.22	.....	0.57	0.79	.....
Ag	.....	.....	0.99	0.97	0.88	0.94
Sn	17.09	12.34	13.89	17.05	16.08	17.36
Sb	11.69	10.51	13.06	11.56	10.98	11.87
S	21.51	21.04	20.82	21.12	21.14	19.28
Rem.	.....	0.71	.....	.....	0.72	.....
Total	100.00	98.87	99.52	100.19	99.25	99.25
G.			5.92	5.88		

1. $Pb_5Sn_3Sb_2S_{14}$. 2. Chocaya. Rem. is gangue 0.71. Contains ca. 0.1 Ge.[6] 3. Poopó.[7] 4. Poopó.[7] 5. Porvenir mine, Huanuni. Rem. is gangue 0.72.[8] 6. Anal. 5 recalculated after deduction of Zn as ZnS and Fe as FeS_2.

Tests. F. 1. Decomposed in HNO_3 with separation of the oxides of Sn, Sb; soluble in aqua regia with separation of S.

O c c u r. A common mineral in the silver-tin veins of Bolivia, sometimes found in large amounts. At the Trinacria and other mines, Poopó, with wurtzite, cassiterite, cylindrite, galena, pyrite, and feather-ore; at several mines at Oruro, with cassiterite, plagionite, and zinkenite (?); abundantly at Llallagua, with pyrite, pyrrhotite and marcasite; in the Descubridora and Aliadas mines, Colquechaca, with sphalerite and galena; in the veins of Chocaya, with wurtzite and galena; abundantly in the Porvenir and Francisca veins, Huanuni, with cylindrite, lead antimony sulfides, wurtzite, arsenopyrite, sphalerite, pyrite and siderite; reported also from Aullagas, Chorolque, and elsewhere in Bolivia.

N a m e. After the mining engineers Carl and Ernest Francke. Llic-teria from the Quechua Indian name *llicta*, applied to a kneaded-together chewing mixture of cocoa and the ashes of certain plants, in allusion to the form of aggregation.

PLUMBOSTANNITE. *Raimondi* (187, 1878).

A lead-gray scaly to granular material, approximately $Pb_2Fe_2Sn_2Sb_2S_{11}$, from the Moho district, Huancane, Peru. Associated with cassiterite and sphalerite. Malleable, H. 2. G. 4.5 (on material containing much quartz). Similar to franckeite in chemical tests. Probably a mixture, in large part franckeite.[9]

Ref.

1. Ahlfeld, Himmel, and Kleber, *Zbl. Min.*, 292, 1935. Transformation Ahlfeld, Himmel, and Kleber to new elements in the preferred position 100/001/010. Doubtful forms: {140}, {130}, {120}, {043}, {021}, {122}, {121}.
2. Average of 5.88 and 5.92 of Prior, *Min. Mag.*, 14, 24 (1904).
3. Schneiderhöhn and Ramdohr (2, 482, 1931).
4. Moritz, *Jb. Min., Beil.-Bd.*, 66, 205 (1933).
5. Moritz (1933). The nearly constant amount of Fe reported in the analyses suggests the constitutive role of this element (cf. Prior, *Min. Mag.*, 14, 24 [1904], who derives $Pb_5FeSn_3Sb_2S_{14}$), but spectrographic examination of material from Huanuni (anal. 5) shows <0.1 per cent Fe.
6. Winkler anal. in Stelzner (1893).
7. Prior (1904).
8. Brendler anal. in Moritz (1933).
9. Stelzner (1893), see also de Gramont, *Bull. soc. min.*, 18, 340 (1895).

364   **F I Z E L Y I T E** [$Pb_5Ag_2Sb_8S_{18}$?].   *Krenner* and *Loczka* (*Mat. Termés. Ért.*, 42, 18, 1926 — *Min. Abs.*, 3, 8, 1926).

In small deeply striated prisms without terminal faces. Cleavage {010}. Brittle. H. 2. Luster metallic. Color dark lead- or steel-gray. Streak dark gray.

C h e m. A lead and silver antimony sulfide, perhaps $Pb_5Ag_2Sb_8S_{18}$. *Anal.*

	Pb	Ag	Fe	Sb	As	S	Insol.	Total
1	36.96	7.70	....	34.75	....	20.59	....	100.00
2	37.48	7.70	0.62	34.02	0.32	20.10	0.30	100.54

1. $Pb_5Ag_2Sb_8S_{18}$. 2. Kisbánya.

O c c u r. At Kisbánya, Hungary, associated with semseyite, galena, pyrite, sphalerite, pyrrhotite, quartz, and dolomite.

N a m e. After Sandor Fizély, mining engineer, who discovered the mineral.

Needs further study.

365   **R A M D O H R I T E** [$Pb_3Ag_2Sb_6S_{13}$].   *Ahlfeld* (*Cbl. Min.*, 365, 1930).

In long prismatic or thick lance-shaped crystals. Fracture uneven. Brittle. H. 2. G. 5.43.[1] Luster metallic. Color and streak gray-black. Opaque. In polished section[2] white in color with moderate anisotropism and very weak pleochroism; exhibits lamellar twinning.

C h e m. A lead and silver antimony sulfide, possibly $Pb_3Ag_2Sb_6S_{13}$. Bi apparently substitutes in small amounts for Sb.

Anal.

	1	2	3
Pb	31.32	30.6	30.3
Fe	.....	n.d.	0.3
Cu	.....	0.3	0.3
Ag	10.87	9.6	10.1
Sb	36.81	32.8	31.1
Bi	.....	n.d.	2.5
S	21.00	20.4	20.1
Rem.	.....	6.6	5.5
Total	100.00	100.3	100.2

1. $Pb_3Ag_2Sb_6S_{13}$. 2. Bolivia. Rem. is SiO_2 6.6.[3] 3. Bolivia. Rem. is SiO_2 5.5.[4]

O c c u r. From the Colorado vein, Chocaya, Potosí, Bolivia, embedded in quartz. Associated with tetrahedrite, stannite, pyrite, cassiterite, and sphalerite; often intergrown with jamesonite needles.

N a m e. After Professor Paul Ramdohr, University of Berlin.

Needs further study.

Ref.

1. Measured on 17-mg. sample of type material (Frondel, priv. comm., 1939). Ahlfeld (1930) gives 4.18.
2. Ramdohr, *Zbl. Min.*, 293, 1937.
3. Huegel anal. in Ahlfeld (1930).
4. Brendler anal. in Ahlfeld (1930).

366   Wittite [$Pb_5Bi_6(S,Se)_{14}$?]. *Johansson* (*Ark. Kemi*, 9 [9], 2, 1924).

Orthorhombic or monoclinic.[1] Resembles molybdenite in appearance. One good cleavage. Cleavage surfaces show striations at $57°$ to $57\frac{1}{2}°$. H. $2-2\frac{1}{2}$. G. 7.12. Luster metallic. Color light lead-gray. Streak black. Opaque.

C h e m. A lead bismuth sulfide, possibly $Pb_5Bi_6(S,Se)_{14}$, with S : Se approximately 11 : 3. Analysis gave:

	Pb	Bi	S	Se	Ag	Cu	Fe	Zn	Insol.	Total
1	35.98	43.55	12.25	8.22	....	....	....	....	....	100.00
2	33.85	43.33	12.14	8.46	0.19	0.08	0.28	0.26	0.54	99.13

1. $Pb_5Bi_6(S,Se)_{14}$, with S : Se = 11 : 3. 2. Gladhammar.

O c c u r. At Fahlun, Kopparberg, Sweden, with quartz, magnetite, and cordierite in an amphibole rock.

N a m e. After Th. Witt, Swedish mining engineer.

Needs further study.

Ref.

1. Aminoff in Johansson (1924), from x-ray Laue photograph.

367   J A M E S O N I T E [$Pb_4FeSb_6S_{14}$]. Gray antimony pt. *Jameson* (3, 390, 1820). Axotomous Antimony Glance *Jameson* (285, 1821). Axotomer Antimon-Glanz *Mohs* (586, 1824). Jamesonite *Haidinger* (1, 451, 1825; 3, 26, 1825). Bleischimmer *Pfaff* (*Schweigger's J.*, **27**, 1, 1819). Pfaffite *Huot* (**1**, 192, 1841). Antimonialisk Fädererz pt., Minera antimonii plumosa pt. *Wallerius* (1747). Federerz *Germ.* Mine d'antimoine au plumes *Fr.* Feather-ore, Plumose Antimonial ore pt. (rest mostly stibnite) *through eighteenth cent.* Antimoine sulfuré capillaire pt. [or var. of stibnite] *Haüy* (1801). Haarförmiges Grauspiessglanzerz pt. *Karsten* (52, 1800). Haarförmiges Antimonglanz *Mohs* (1824); *Leonhard* (1826). Federerz of Wolfsberg *Rose* (*Ann. Phys.*, **15**, 471, 1829); *Beudant* (**2**, 425, 1832). Federerz, var. of Jamesonite, *von Kobell* (**2**, 175, 1831). Wolfsbergite *Huot* (**1**, 193, 1841). Plumosite pt. Heteromorphit pt. Bleiantimonit *Groth* (18, 1874). Querspiessglanz, *Germ.*

Zundererz pt. *Lehmann* (*Ak. Berlin, Mem.*, 20, 1758); Bergzundererz pt., Lumpenerz pt., Tinder-ore pt. Comuccite *Doelter* (4 [1], 481, 1926). Cornuccite. Warrenite pt. *Eakins* (*Am. J. Sc.*, **36**, 450, 1888; **39**, 74, 1890). Domingite pt. *Groth* (30, 1889).

C r y s t. Monoclinic; prismatic — $2/m$.

$a : b : c = 0.8316 : 1 : 0.2130$; $\beta\ 91°24'$;[1] $p_0 : q_0 : r_0 = 0.2562 : 0.2129 : 1$

$r_2 : p_2 : q_2 = 4.6962 : 1.2033 : 1$; $\mu\ 88°36'$; $p_0'\ 0.2563$, $q_0'\ 0.2130$, $x_0'\ 0.0244$

Forms:[2]

		ϕ	ρ	ϕ_2	$p_2 = B$	C	A
c	001	90°00′	1°24′	88°36′	90°00′	0°00′	88°36′
b	010	0 00	90 00	.....	0 00	90 00	90 00
a	100	90 00	90 00	0 00	90 00	88 36	0 00
n	120	31 02	90 00	0 00	31 02	89 16½	58 58
m	110	50 16½	90 00	0 00	50 16½	88 55½	39 43½
l	210	67 26	90 00	0 00	67 26	88 42½	22 34
f	011	6 32½	12 06	88 36	77 59	12 01	88 38
e	021	3 17	23 06½	88 36	66 56	23 04	88 42½
d	2̄01	−90 00	26 01½	116 01½	90 00	27 25½	116 01½
t	111	52 48½	19 24½	74 19	78 24½	18 19	74 39
o	221	51 34½	34 25½	61 46	69 25½	33 20½	63 42½
r	1̄11	−47 26	17 28½	103 03½	78 16½	18 32	102 46½
v	1̄31	−19 57	34 12½	103 03½	58 06	34 42½	101 03½
z	3̄52	−34 04	32 44	109 48	63 23½	33 32	107 38
q	2̄11	−66 25½	28 02½	116 01½	79 10	29 20	115 31½
s	2̄31	−37 23	38 48½	116 01½	60 08	39 40	112 21½

Structure cell.[3] Space group $P2_1/a$; $a_0\ 15.68 \pm 0.05$, $b_0\ 19.01 \pm 0.05$, $c_0\ 4.03 \pm 0.01$, $\beta\ 91°48' \pm 0°30'$; $a_0 : b_0 : c_0 = 0.8247 : 1 : 0.2120$; contains $Pb_8Fe_2Sb_{12}S_{28}$.

Habit. Acicular to fibrous [001] and striated ‖ [001]. In felted masses of needles; also massive, fibrous to columnar; sometimes radial or plumose. In subparallel aggregates of prismatic crystals, forming a columnar mass.

Twinning. On {100}.[4]

P h y s. Cleavage {001} good; also possibly {010} and {120}.[5] Brittle. H. $2\frac{1}{2}$. G. 5.63;[6] 5.67 (calc.). Luster metallic. Color and streak gray-black; sometimes tarnished iridescent. Opaque. In polished section[7] white in color with strong anisotropism and distinct pleochroism.

C h e m. A lead and iron antimony sulfide, probably $Pb_4FeSb_6S_{14}$.[8] Cu, up to 3.5 per cent, Zn, up to 6 per cent, and small amounts of Ag and Bi have been reported, but it has not been shown that these are constituents of the mineral.

Anal.

	1	2	3	4	5	6	7	8
Pb	40.16	42.79	40.47	40.32	40.14	40.08	39.97	39.05
Fe	2.71	2.83	2.68	3.68	2.64	2.79	3.63	2.00
Cu	....	1.01	0.50	....	0.18	0.22	....	3.45
Sb	35.39	31.94	n.d.	32.92	34.25	34.70	32.62	32.00
S	21.74	20.86	21.35	21.40	22.34	21.37	21.78	21.75
Rem.	....	1.84	5.82	1.24	....	0.13	1.48	2.16
Total	100.00	101.27	70.82	99.56	99.55	99.29	99.48	100.41
G.		5.48–5.72				5.56	5.546		5.54

1. $Pb_4FeSb_6S_{14}$. 2. Selkethal, Harz. Rem. is Zn 1.84.[10] 3. Selkethal, Harz. Rem. is Zn 5.82.[10] 4. Slate Creek, Idaho. Rem. is insol. 1.24.[11] 5. Cornwall. Average of three analyses.[12] 6. Cerro de Ubina, Bolivia. Rem. is Ag 0.13.[13] 7. Valencia d'Alcantara, Spain. Rem. is Bi 1.06, Zn 0.42.[14] 8. Sierra de los Angulos, Argentina. Rem. is Zn 0.62, As 0.20, Ag 1.34.[15]

Tests. F. 1. Decomposed by HNO_3 with separation of Sb_2O_3 and $PbSO_4$.

O c c u r. Found in druses and massive in hydrothermal veins formed at low to moderate temperatures. Associated with other lead sulfosalts, pyrite, sphalerite, galena, tetrahedrite, and stibnite. Common gangue minerals are quartz and siderite, also dolomite, calcite, and rhodochrosite. Only the more important localities are cited below, and it is probable that some of these may represent other feather-ores in part or entirely.[16]

In Cornwall, England, at Endellion and elsewhere, as columnar masses. In the Harz, Germany, at Selkethal, and reported from Wolfsberg, Andreasberg and other localities. Reported from Přibram, Bohemia, and from Schemnitz; also from Felsöbánya and Aranyidka, Roumania. At Mount Avala, near Belgrad, Serbia. From Valencia d'Alcantara, Estramadura, Spain. In Bolivia from the Cerro de Ubina, east of Huanchaca, Potosí, with pyrite and tetrahedrite, at the Socovon de la Virgin, Oruro, at Machacamarca near Potosí, and reported from other localities. From the Sierra de los Angulos, Argentina. Said to occur in Tasmania at Mount Bischoff.

In the United States in Sevier County, Arkansas, with stibnite, zinkenite, and bindheimite. At Slate Creek and Mackay, Custer County, and reported from elsewhere in Idaho. In the Park City district, Utah. Reported also from various localities in California, Nevada, and Colorado. Reported in Canada at Fredericton, New Brunswick, in dolomite near Barrie, Frontenac County, Ontario, and in British Columbia in the East Kootenay and other districts.

A l t e r. Commonly to bindheimite; also to ill-defined antimony ochres. Reported pseudomorphous after plagionite.

N a m e. The name jamesonite, after the mineralogist Robert Jameson (1774–1854), of Edinburgh, was first applied specifically to the Cornwall mineral with the good end cleavage {001}, and this usage is here retained.

The presence of iron was early noted (see anal. 5) but was ascribed to pyrite impurity. A similar mineral without iron was later described[17] as federerz (feather-ore) and was finally called plumosite. A supposed dimorphous form of jamesonite was found at about this time[18] and was given the name heteromorphite, in allusion to the difference between it and jamesonite. In 1860[19] what had been known as three distinct species were united under the name jamesonite with the formula $Pb_2Sb_2S_5$. More recent examination,[20] however, has again separated these species, since iron is a constituent part of jamesonite and heteromorphite is of definitely different form,[21] belonging to the plagionite group.[22]

The term feather-ore (federerz *Germ.*) early embraced all the lead antimony sulfides occurring as plumose or felted aggregates of needle-like crystals. The so-called flexible feather-ores included zinkenite, boulangerite, meneghinite, and plumosite. Jamesonite, however, because of its cross cleavage, was, along with capillary stibnite, called brittle feather-ore. The term feather-ore has little scientific usefulness.

ZUNDERERZ. Lehmann (*Ak. Berlin, Mem.*, 20, 1758). Pilite *Schulze* (29, 1895). Bergzundererz, Lumpenerz *Germ.* Tinder-ore.

A felted or acicular material which is soft like tinder and dark, dirty red in color. From Andreasberg, Clausthal, and Wolfsberg in the Harz, Germany. Largely an impure or altered jamesonite or feather-ore, sometimes mixed with ruby-silver or other minerals, in part stibnite[23] or metastibnite.

WARRENITE. Eakins (*Am. J. Sc.*, 36, 450, 1888). Domingite *Groth* (30, 1889). Warrenite *Eakins* (*Am. J. Sc.*, 39, 74, 1890).

A supposed lead antimony sulfide, $Pb_3Sb_4S_9$, from the Domingo mine, Gunnison County, Colorado. Occurs as matted, wool-like aggregates of acicular crystals in cavities in a siliceous rock mixed with calcite. Shown[24] to be a mixture of jamesonite and zinkenite.

COMUCCITE. Comucci (*Ac. Linc., Att.*, 25, II, 111, 1916). Comuccit *Doelter* (4 [1], 481, 1926). Cornuccite.

A fibrous lead antimony sulfide from San Giorgio, Sardinia. Analysis gave: Pb 37.86, Fe 3.99, Sb 36.01, S 21.54, total 99.40. G. 5.65. Stated[25] to be identical with jamesonite.

Ref.

1. Angles from Slavík, *Cbl. Min.*, 7, 1914, on crystals from Kasejovik, Bohemia, identified only by qualitative tests and by the typical cross cleavage. In general the angles are in agreement with the less accurate measurements of Spencer on analyzed crystals from Cerro de Ubina, Bolivia, *Min. Mag.*, 14, 308 (1907). The unit chosen here (Berman, priv. comm., 1939) conforms with the x-ray data (see ref. 3). Transformation Slavík to Berman: 100/010/00$\frac{1}{2}$. Crystal class from x-ray study of Berry, *Min. Mag.*, 25, 597 (1940).

2. Slavík (1914).

3. Berry (1940) by Weissenberg method on material from the Itos mine, Oruro, Bolivia. Hiller, *Zs. Kr.*, 100, 144 (1938), gives values completely inconsistent with these data or Slavík's (1914) ratio.

4. Recognized by Berry (1940) in x-ray study of material from the Itos mine, Oruro, Bolivia.

5. Shannon, *Am. Min.*, 10, 197 (1925), on crystals from Slate Creek, Idaho. The cleavages had earlier been given as {001}, {010}, and {110} by Mohs (586, 1824). Spencer (1907) was unable to verify {010} and {110}.

6. Berry (1940) by pycnometer on material from Oruro.

7. Short in Shannon, *Am. Min.*, **10**, 194 (1925); Schneiderhöhn and Ramdohr (**2**, 402, 1931); Berry (1940).

8. The formula of jamesonite has long been controversial, owing largely to the use of unauthenticated or impure specimens for analysis. Analysis of material known by cross cleavage to be jamesonite invariably shows an iron content of 2–3 per cent. The iron, which long had been ascribed to admixed pyrite or other iron minerals, is held to be constitutional by Spencer (1907) and Schaller, *Zs. Kr.*, **48**, 562 (1910).

9. Only those analyses made on material known to be jamesonite by the presence of the basal cleavage are cited here. For other analyses, on material which may or may not be jamesonite, see Hintze (**1** [1], 1024, 1898) and Doelter (**4** [1], 434, 1926).

10. Zinken and Rammelsberg, *Ann. Phys.*, **77**, 242 (1849). Different figures are given in Rammelsberg (71, 1860).

11. Shannon (1925).

12. Rose, *Ann. Phys.*, **8**, 100 (1826); **15**, 470 (1829).

13. Prior anal. in Spencer (1907).

14. Schaffgotsch, *Ann. Phys.*, **38**, 403 (1836).

15. Siewert anal. in Stelzner, *Tschermak's Min. Mitt.*, 248, 1873.

16. Additional localities, many of uncertain authenticity, are given by Hintze (**1** [1], 1026, 1898).

17. Rose, *Ann. Phys.*, **15**, 471 (1829), called the mineral with the composition $Pb_2Sb_2S_5$ *federerz from Wolfsberg*, Huot (**1**, 193, 1841) called it *wolfsbergite*, and Haidinger (569, 1845) gave it the name *plumosite*.

18. Zinken and Rammelsberg, *Ann. Phys.*, **77**, 240 (1849).

19. Rammelsberg (71, 1860).

20. Spencer (1907) and Schaller (1910).

21. Pisani, *C. R.*, **83**, 747 (1876).

22. See references under plagionite group discussion.

23. Dana (123, 1892) and Luedecke (128, 1896).

24. Spencer, *Min. Mag.*, **14**, 207 (1907).

25. Short (104, 1931).

368 **R A T H I T E** [$Pb_{13}As_{18}S_{40}$]. *Baumhauer* (*Zs. Kr.*, **26**, 593, 1896). Rathite-α *Solly* (*Min. Mag.*, **16**, 121, 1911). Wiltshireite *Lewis* (*Zs. Kr.*, **49**, 514, 1910). Arsenomelane pt. *von Waltershausen* in *Uhrlaub* and *Nason* (*Ann. Phys.*, **100**, 540, 1857).

C r y s t. Monoclinic; prismatic — $2/m$.

$a : b : c = 3.1544 : 1 : 1.0698$; $\beta\ 98°43\frac{1}{2}'$;[1] $p_0 : q_0 : r_0 = 0.3391 : 1.0574 : 1$

$r_2 : p_2 : q_2 = 0.9457 : 0.3207 : 1$; $\mu\ 81°16\frac{1}{2}'$; $p_0'\ 0.3431$, $q_0'\ 1.0698$; $x_0'\ 0.1535$

Forms:[2]

		ϕ	ρ	ϕ_2	$\rho_2 = B$	C	A
c	001	90°00′	8°43½′	81°16½′	90°00′	.....	81°16½′
a	100	90 00	90 00	0 00	90 00	81°16½′	......
f	110	17 47	90 00	0 00	17 47	87 20½	72 13
m	210	32 40½	90 00	0 00	32 40½	85 18	57 19½
s	310	43 53½	90 00	0 00	43 53½	83 57½	46 06½
r	410	52 04	90 00	0 00	52 04	83 07½	37 56
F	510	58 03	90 00	0 00	58 03	82 36½	31 57
l	610	62 32½	90 00	0 00	62 32½	82 16	27 27½
θ	10·1·0	72 41	90 00	0 00	72 41	81 40½	17 18
z	101	90 00	26 24½	63 35½	90 00	17 40	63 35½
y	301	90 00	49 47	40 13	90 00	41 03½	40 13
p	111	24 54	49 42½	63 35½	46 13½	46 32	71 16
σ	$\bar{2}11$	−26 28	50 04½	118 02½	46 38½	54 22½	109 59½
g	$\bar{3}11$	−39 18½	54 07½	131 12½	51 10½	59 54½	120 53
e	$\bar{4}11$	−48 43½	58 20½	140 38	55 50½	65 03½	129 24½

Structure cell.[3] Monoclinic $P2_1/n$. a_0 25.00 ± 0.03, b_0 7.91 ± 0.03, c_0 8.42 ± 0.03, β 99°00′ ± 0°30′; $a_0 : b_0 : c_0 = 3.160 : 1 : 1.064$, contains $Pb_{13}As_{18}S_{40}$ (?).

Habit. Prismatic to short prismatic and striated [001].

Twinning.[4] (a) On {100} producing polysynthetic pseudo-orthorhombic crystals; (b) On {$\bar{3}$01}.

Phys. Cleavage {100} perfect. Parting on {010}. Fracture conchoidal. H. 3. G. 5.37 ± 0.04; 5.31 (calc.). Color lead-gray; often tarnished iridescent. Streak chocolate-brown. In polished section[5] white, with deep red internal reflections. Strongly anisotropic and pleochroic. Shows polysynthetic twin lamellae of irregular thickness.

Chem. Lead arsenic sulfide, $Pb_{13}As_{18}S_{40}$,[6] with perhaps some Sb substituting for the As (anal. 5).

Anal.[7]

	1	2	3	4	5
Pb	50.59	51.51	51.62	52.43	52.98
Fe	.....	.....	.....	0.33	0.56
As	25.32	24.62	24.91	21.96	17.21
Sb	.....	.....	.....	0.43	4.53
S	24.09	23.41	23.62	24.11	23.72
Total	100.00	99.54	100.15	99.26	99.00
G.		5.412	5.421		5.32

1. $Pb_{13}As_{18}S_{40}$. 2, 3, 4. Binnental.[8] 5. Binnental.[9]

Occur. Found only in the dolomite of the Binnental, Valais, Switzerland, associated with liveingite, baumhauerite, sartorite, hutchinsonite, and the other rare sulfarsenides of the locality.

Alter. Said to alter along the cleavages and twin lamellae to baumhauerite and other arsenic sulfides.

Name. After G. vom Rath (1830–88), Professor of Mineralogy at Bonn, Germany. Wiltshireite after Professor Thomas Wiltshire (1826–1902), Professor of Mineralogy at King's College, London.

WILTSHIREITE and RATHITE-α[10] were shown to be the same as rathite, the former an untwinned habit which revealed for the first time the true symmetry of rathite.

An unnamed mineral[11] supposedly of the same composition as rathite, but with a needle-like habit and angular relations close to dufrenoysite has been found at the Binnental. There is a good cleavage. G. 5.453. Color lead-gray. Streak chocolate-brown. Composition $Pb_3As_4S_9$. Analysis gave: Pb 51.11, As 23.37, S 23.22, rem. 2.28, total 99.98. Rem. is Ag, Cu, Tl, Fe, Sb, and insol.

Ref.

1. Angles of Lewis, *Min. Mag.*, **16**, 197 (1912), who first demonstrated the monoclinic symmetry; unit and orientation of Berry in Berry and Peacock, *Univ. Toronto Stud., Geol. Ser.*, **44**, 47 (1940), p. 63. Baumhauer (1896), in the original description, assigned a complex unit to the supposedly orthorhombic mineral. Solly, *Min. Mag.*, **13**, 77 (1901), changed the orientation but retained the orthorhombic symmetry; in his rathite-α he had a still different orientation. Transformations: Baumhauer to Berry 0·$\bar{5}$·28/14·0·0/0·10·0; Solly to Berry 0$\bar{3}\bar{1}$/200/002; Rathite-α to Berry 300/010/00$\bar{1}$; Lewis to Berry $\bar{2}0\bar{1}$/010/00$\bar{1}$.

2. Lewis (1912), Solly (1901), Baumhauer (1896).   Rare and uncertain forms:

010	320	710	012	201	$\bar{1}01$	$\bar{5}01$	$\bar{1}11$	412	$\bar{4}12$
120	520	810	011	501	$\bar{2}01$	$\bar{7}01$	212	211	$\bar{5}22$
450	720	910	103	$\bar{1}02$	$\bar{3}01$	112	312	311	$\bar{2}12$	$\bar{5}11$

Also some very complex forms by Solly and Baumhauer reported in the orthorhombic interpretation.

3. Berry in Peacock and Berry (1940).
4. Lewis (1912).   Solly's twin planes become $\{\bar{3}\bar{3}\cdot0\cdot8\}$ and $\{\bar{2}\bar{3}\cdot0\cdot1\}$.
5. Guisca, *Schweiz. min. Mitt.*, **10**, 152 (1930).
6. Formula here given is derived from the cell contents (by Berry).   Other less likely alternatives are given.   The old formula, $Pb_3As_4S_9$ fits the analysis better but is inconsistent with the x-ray results.
7. An old analysis by Petersen, *Jb. Min.*, 203, 1867, agrees with the rathite composition.   See Solly and Jackson, *Min. Mag.*, **12**, 282 (1900), p. 284.   Also a more recent analysis is given by Ferrari and Curti, *Per. Min.*, **5**, 155 (1934).
8. Jackson anal. in Solly and Jackson, *Min. Mag.*, **12**, 282 (1900).
9. Börner anal. in Baumhauer (1896).
10. Lewis (1912) and Solly, *Min. Mag.*, **16**, 121 (1911).
11. Solly, *Min. Mag.*, **18**, 360 (1919).

3711   **A N D O R I T E** [PbAgSb₃S₆].   *Krenner* (*Mat. Termés. Ért.*, **11**, 119, 1892 — *Zs. Kr.*, **23**, 497, 1894).

Sundtite *Brögger* (*Zs. Kr.*, **21**, 193, 1893).   Webnerite *Stelzner* (*Zs. Kr.*, **24**, 125, 1894).

C r y s t.   Orthorhombic;   dipyramidal — $2/m\ 2/m\ 2/m$.

$a : b : c = 0.6771 : 1 : 0.4458;^1$ $p_0 : q_0 : r_0 = 0.6584 : 0.4458 : 1$

$q_1 : r_1 : p_1 = 0.6771 : 1.5188 : 1;$ $r_2 : p_2 : q_2 = 2.2432 : 1.4769 : 1$

Forms:²

		ϕ	$\rho = C$	ϕ_1	$\rho_1 = A$	ϕ_2	$\rho_2 = B$
c	001	.....	0°00′	0°00′	90°00′	90°00′	90°00′
b	010	0°00′	90 00	90 00	90 00	.....	0 00
a	100	90 00	90 00	.....	0 00	0 00	90 00
k	120	36 26½	90 00	90 00	53 33½	0 00	36 26½
l	230	44 33½	90 00	90 00	45 26½	0 00	44 33½
m	110	55 54	90 00	90 00	34 06	0 00	55 54
n	210	71 18	90 00	90 00	18 42	0 00	71 18
x	011	0 00	24 01½	24 01½	90 00	90 00	65 58½
π	032	0 00	33 46	33 46	90 00	90 00	56 14
γ	021	0 00	41 43	41 43	90 00	90 00	48 17
y	031	0 00	53 13	53 13	90 00	90 00	36 47
h	102	90 00	18 13½	0 00	71 46½	71 46½	90 00
f	101	90 00	33 21½	0 00	56 38½	56 38½	90 00
v	112	55 54	21 41	12 34	72 11	71 46½	78 03
p	111	55 54	38 29½	24 01½	58 59	56 38½	69 34½
q	221	55 54	57 50½	41 43	45 29½	37 13	61 40
w	132	26 12½	36 42	33 46	74 41½	71 46½	57 34½
r	121	36 26½	47 56½	41 43	63 50	56 38½	53 19½
β	131	26 12½	56 08½	53 13	68 29	56 38½	41 50

Less common:

j	160	X	410	H	092	e	302	B	441	δ	364	E	261
z	150	ψ	510	S	061	Ω	201	g:	661	n:	3·12·4	t:	281
I	140	ϕ	610	Δ	0·15·2	λ	301	h:	1·12·4	o:	141	N	632
J	270	w	035	t	091	V	401	ζ	2·21·7	p:	463	A	321
u	130	R	023	Θ	0·10·1	μ	902	L	122	ξ	312	K	361
g	250	Y	065	Λ	0·12·1	d	601	i:	142	ϵ	362	u:	391
T	450	ν	043	Ψ	0·18·1	d:	335	α	162	O	392	v:	421
Q	760	τ	095	θ	305	χ	223	P	427	q:	3·12·2	w:	481
i	430	Γ	0·13·6	σ	203	e:	334	k:	365	s	211	x:	962
o	320	F	052	κ	405	f:	667	l:	395	r:	231	M	631
U	830	G	072	Π	506	Z	332	m:	233	D	241	y:	691
W	310	η	041	Σ	605	ρ	331	C	243	s:	251	z:	961

Habit. Stout prismatic and striated [001]; thick tabular {100}, or less commonly thin tabular {010}. Also massive. Commonest forms: $b\ q\ k\ y\ p\ x\ r\ l\ v\ \beta\ n\ m\ \pi$.

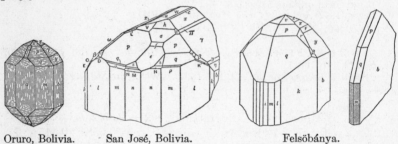

Oruro, Bolivia.   San José, Bolivia.   Felsöbánya.

Twinning. Said to be on {110}.[3]

Phys. No cleavage.[4] Fracture smooth conchoidal. Brittle. H. 3–$3\frac{1}{2}$. G. 5.35 ± 0.02. Luster metallic; sometimes tarnished yellow or iridescent. Color dark steel-gray. Streak black. Opaque. In polished section[5] white in color with weak anisotropism. Reflection percentages: green 31.5, orange 27.5, red 25.5.

Chem. A silver and lead antimony sulfide, $PbAgSb_3S_6$. Cu apparently substitutes for Ag in amounts less than 2 per cent by weight. The relatively large amounts of Fe reported in some analyses are probably due to admixed pyrite.

Anal.[6]

	1	2	3	4	5
Pb	23.75	24.10	21.81	25.06	22.25
Ag	12.36	10.94	11.73	12.98	10.90
Cu	.....	0.68	0.73	.....	0.96
Fe	.....	0.30	1.45	.....	0.75
Sb	41.87	41.31	41.76	40.41	40.75
S	22.02	22.06	22.19	21.55	24.26
Rem.	.....	.....	.....	.....	0.31
Total	100.00	99.39	99.67	100.00	100.18
G.		5.38	5.33		

1. $PbAgSb_3S_6$. 2. Oruro.[7] 3. "Hungary."[7] 4. Morey district, Nev. Recalc. after deduction of Zn 3.56 and Fe 1.55 as ferrian sphalerite.[8] 5. Felsöbánya, Roumania. Rem. is Zn 0.31.[9]

Tests. F. 1. In C.T. decrepitates and melts. Soluble in HCl with separation of S and Sb_2O_3.

Occur. At Felsöbánya, Roumania, with stibnite, sphalerite, barite, fluorite, siderite, and quartz; also with jamesonite (?). In Bolivia at the Itos and other mines, Oruro, with cassiterite, arsenopyrite, stannite, zinkenite (?), tetrahedrite, pyrite, and alunite; at the Santa Rita and other mines, Potosí, with cassiterite, tetrahedrite, jamesonite (?), and ruby silver; reported also from Machacamarca with zinkenite (?), and from the Gallofa vein, Colquechaca. From the Keyser mine, Morey district, Nye County, Nevada, with sphalerite, pyrargyrite, stephanite, rhodochrosite, and quartz.

Alter. Material from the Morey district, Nevada, is altered to an unidentified fibrous sulfantimonide of lead and silver.[10]

Name. After Andor von Semsey (died 1923). The mineral semseyite was named after the same person.

SUNDTITE *Brögger* (*Zs. Kr.*, **21**, 193, 1893), and WEBNERITE *Stelzner* (*Zs. Kr.*, **24**, 125, 1894), both from the Itos mine, Oruro, Bolivia, are identical with andorite.[11]

Ref.

1. Brögger, *Zs. Kr.*, **21**, 193 (1893), slightly modified by Palache (priv. comm., 1939), on Oruro crystals.
2. Goldschmidt (**1**, 39, 1913). Ungemach (unpublished notes), verified by Palache (priv. comm., 1939). Also Koch, *Cbl. Min.*, **28**, 1928, and Laszkiewicz, *Min. Soc. Warsaw, Arch.*, **8**, 109 (1932) — *Jb. Min.*, 493, 1935.
3. Laszkiewicz in Kozlowski and Jaskolski, *Min. Soc. Warsaw, Arch.*, **8**, 1 (1932) — *Jb. Min.*, 578, 1934. See also Schneiderhöhn and Ramdohr (**2**, 390, 1931).
4. A good cleavage {010} was stated by Krenner (1892) but has not been verified by Spencer, *Min. Mag.*, **11**, 286 (1897), and other observers.
5. Schneiderhöhn and Ramdohr (1931).
6. Additional analyses in Spencer (1897).
7. Prior anal. in Spencer (1897).
8. Shannon, *U. S. Nat. Mus., Proc.*, **60**, art. 16, 1 (1922).
9. Endrédy anal. in Koch, *Cbl. Min.*, 34, 1928.
10. Shannon (1922), with analyses.
11. Spencer (1897).

3712 **LINDSTROMITE** [$PbCuBi_3S_6$]. Lindströmit *Johansson* (*Ark. Kemi*, **9** [8], 14, 1924).

Cryst. Orthorhombic?.

$$a : b = 0.6827 : 1.^1$$

Forms:

		ϕ	ρ				ϕ	ρ
b	010	0°00′	90°00′		g	250	30°22′	90°00′
a	100	90 00	90 00		k	230	44 19	90 00
ϵ	2·15·0	11 03	90 00		m	110	55 40½	90 00
μ	160	13 43	90 00		l	430	62 53	90 00
e	290	18 01½	90 00		λ	210	71 09	90 00
f	4·15·0	21 20	90 00		v	830	75 38½	90 00
n	130	26 21½	90 00					

Habit. Prismatic [001], without terminal faces; striated [001].

Phys. Cleavage {100} and {010} good, also {230}. Fracture small conchoidal to uneven. H. $3-3\frac{1}{2}$. G. 7.01. Luster metallic. Color lead-gray. Streak black. Opaque.

Chem. A lead and copper bismuth sulfide, $PbCuBi_3S_6$.

Anal.

	Pb	Cu	Fe	Bi	S	Insol.	Total
1	19.05	5.85	..	57.40	17.70	....	100.00
2	18.95	5.84	tr.	57.13	[17.88]	0.20	100.00

1. $PbCuBi_3S_6$. 2. Gladhammar.

Occur. At Gladhammar, Kalmar, Sweden, in crystals several millimeters thick and 1 cm. long on quartz.

Name. After G. Lindström (1838–1916), mineral analyst, of the Riksmuseet, Sweden.

Needs further study.

Ref.

1. In order to bring the orientation into agreement with the prism zone angles of andorite, a presumably related mineral, the a and b directions of the original orientation have been interchanged and a new unit chosen. Transformation: Johansson to new orientation 020/300/001 (LaForge, priv. comm., 1935).

372   **BAUMHAUERITE** [$Pb_4As_6S_{13}$]. *Solly* (*Min. Mag.*, **13**, 151, 1903 — *Zs. Kr.*, **37**, 321, 1903).

Cryst. Monoclinic; prismatic — $2/m$.

$a : b : c = 2.7374 : 1 : 0.9472;^1$ $\beta\ 97°17'$; $p_0 : q_0 : r_0 = 0.3460 : 0.9396 : 1$
$r_2 : p_2 : q_2 = 1.0643 : 0.3683 : 1$; $\mu\ 82°43'$; $p_0'\ 0.3488$, $q_0'\ 0.9472$, $x_0'\ 0.1278$

Forms:[2]

		ϕ	ρ	ϕ_2	$\rho_2 = B$	C	A
c	001	90°00′	7°17′	82°43′	90°00′	.....	82°43′
b	010	0 00	90 00	.....	0 00	90 00	90 00
a	100	90 00	90 00	0 00	90 00	82 43	0 00
H	410	55 49½	90 00	0 00	55 49½	83 59	34 10½
K	310	47 51	90 00	0 00	47 51	84 36½	42 09
O	210	36 22½	90 00	0 00	36 22½	85 41½	53 37½
m	110	20 13	90 00	0 00	20 13	87 29½	69 47
k	011	7 41	43 42½	82 43	46 47	43 13	84 42
Λ	101	90 00	25 29	64 31	90 00	18 12	64 31
Ψ	201	90 00	39 32	50 28	90 00	32 15	50 28
ρ	301	90 00	49 35	40 25	90 00	42 18	40 25
q:	$\bar{2}$01	−90 00	29 40½	119 40½	90 00	36 57½	119 40½
z:	$\bar{4}$01	−90 00	51 43½	141 43½	90 00	59 00½	141 43½
n	111	26 42½	46 40½	64 31	49 28	43 46½	70 55
o	$\bar{2}$11	−31 02	47 52	119 40½	50 33	51 54	112 28½

Also:

F	510	Σ	102	ξ	401	κ	601	g:	$\bar{1}$02	t:	$\bar{3}$01	C:	$\bar{5}$01	N	$\bar{1}$11
Φ	103	Π	203	μ	501	ι	701	l:	$\bar{1}$01	w:	702	E:	$\bar{6}$01	p	211

Structure cell.[3] Space group $P2_1/m$; a_0 22.68, b_0 8.32, c_0 7.92; β 97°17′; $a_0 : b_0 : c_0 = 2.7263 : 1 : 0.9524$; contains $Pb_{12}As_{18}S_{39}$.

Habit. Short prismatic [010]; tabular {100}; striated on {100} ‖ [010] and on {010} ‖ [001]. Some crystals are appreciably rounded, as if by etching.

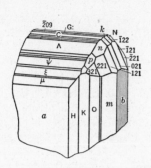 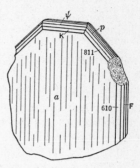

Binnental.

Twinning. On {100}, polysynthetic, with visible twin lamellae.

P h y s. Cleavage {100} perfect. Fracture conchoidal. H. 3. G. 5.329; 5.66 (calc.). Luster metallic. Color lead- to steel-gray; sometimes tarnished iridescent. Streak chocolate-brown. Opaque. In polished section[4] white, with deep red internal reflections. Anisotropic.

C h e m. Lead arsenic sulfide, $Pb_4As_6S_{13}$[5].

Anal.

	Pb	As	S	Total	G.
1	48.90	26.51	24.59	100.00	
2	48.86	26.42	24.39	99.67	5.329

1. $Pb_4As_6S_{13}$. 2. Binnental.[6]

O c c u r. In the Binnental, Valais, Switzerland, at the Lengenbach quarry associated with other lead sulfarsenides in the sugary dolomite.

N a m e. After H. A. Baumhauer (1848–1926), Professor of Mineralogy in the University of Freiburg, Switzerland.

Ref.

1. Angles and orientation from Solly (1903) modified by Palache, *Am. Min.*, **23**, 821 (1938), unit of Hurlbut (priv. comm., 1939) from x-ray study. Transformation: Solly to Hurlbut 200/010/001.
2. Solly (1903), Palache (1938).

Less common and rare forms:

S	120	Θ	504	δ	15·0·1	j:	304	F: 13·0·2	z	321
M	320	Δ	302	γ	17·0·1	k:	405	G: 701	y	511
L	940	Γ	805	β	18·0·1	m:	10·0·9	H: 801	W	20·3·3
J	18·5·0	ω	503	α	19·0·1	n:	403	J: 901	w	811
G	17·4·0	χ	13·0·6	Z	25·0·1	o:	302	K: 10·0·1	V	32·3·3
E	16·3·0	φ	703	U	38·0·1	p:	503	L: 11·0·1	v	122
D	610	τ	803	P	50·0·1	r:	502	M: 12·0·1	R	121
C	20·3·0	σ	14·0·5	I	60·0·1	s:	803	N: 14·0·1	t	322
B	22·3·0	π	26·0·7	a:	1·0·10	u:	16·0·5	O: 15·0·1	X	311

A	11·1·0	ν	13·0·3	b:	$\bar{1}$·0·6	v:	$\bar{10}$·0·3	P:	16·0·1	u	$\bar{4}$11
l	012	λ	26·0·5	c:	$\bar{1}$04	x:	$\bar{11}$·0·3	q	221	Y	$\bar{5}$11
j	021	θ	801	d:	$\bar{2}$07	y:	$\bar{26}$·0·7	Q	$\bar{2}$21	Z	$\bar{6}$11
Ω	209	η	901	e:	$\bar{1}$03	A:	$\bar{22}$·0·5	r	121		
Υ	207	ζ	10·0·1	f:	$\bar{4}$·0·11	B:	$\bar{9}$·0·2	T	8·10·5		
Ξ	405	ϵ	13·0·1	h:	$\bar{2}$03	D:	$\bar{11}$·0·2	x	311		

3. Hurlbut (priv. comm., 1939).
4. Schneiderhöhn and Ramdohr (2, 490, 1931).
5. The preferred formula of Bader, *Schweiz. min. Mitt.*, 14, 320, 1934 — p. 396, $Pb_5As_8S_{17}$, has no support either from the chemistry or the x-ray cell dimensions.
6. Jackson anal. in Solly (1903).

373   **Liveingite** [$Pb_5As_8S_{17}$].   *Solly* and *Jackson* (*Cambridge Phil. Soc., Proc.*, 11, 239, 1901).

Monoclinic; β 90°14$\frac{1}{2}$'.   Twinned on {100}. H. 3. G. 5.3. In polished section[1] material supposed to be liveingite is anisotropic with deep red internal reflections and irregular twin lamellae.   Analysis of one of the two known crystals yielded the formula $Pb_5As_8S_{17}$.[2] Analysis gave: Pb 47.58, As 26.93, S 24.91, total 99.42.

From the Binnental, Valais, Switzerland.   Named after G. D. Liveing (1827–1924), Professor of Chemistry in the University of Cambridge, England.

Ref.

1. Guisca, *Schweiz. min. Mitt.*, 10, 164 (1930).
2. Solly, *Min. Mag.*, 13, 160 (1902).

PLAGIONITE GROUP

Fuloppite	$Pb_3Sb_8S_{15}$	1.1184 : 1 : 1.4085,	β 94°49'
Plagionite	$Pb_5Sb_8S_{17}$	1.1318 : 1 : 1.6878,	β 107°13'
Heteromorphite	$Pb_7Sb_8S_{19}$		
Semseyite	$Pb_9Sb_8S_{21}$	1.1356 : 1 : 2.0436,	β 105°46'

The members of this group form a supposed morphotropic series,[1] but full data are not yet available for an adequate discussion.   The unit cell dimensions of plagionite and semseyite[2] show that the a and b axial lengths remain more or less constant, and the c axial length changes in accordance with change in the composition.   All the minerals of the group are of much the same habit, short prismatic to tabular, and in this respect they are in striking contrast to the acicular and fibrous minerals, jamesonite, plumosite, boulangerite, meneghinite, and zinkenite, which are also sulf-antimonides of lead.   A cleavage {112} is found in all members of the group with the exception of fuloppite.   The hardness and other physical properties are the same.   A systematic increase in specific gravity with an increase in Pb content affords a quick means of distinction between members of the group.

The name heteromorphite was first applied[3] to a mineral not certainly of this group, but later work[4] has clearly separated this species from plumosite or jamesonite, both of which are acicular in habit and of a different composition.

Ref.

1. Spencer, *Min. Mag.*, **12**, 55 (1899), Zambonini, *Riv. min.*, **41**, 338 (1912); Smith, *Min. Mag.*, **18**, 354 (1919), de Finály and Koch, *ibid.*, **22**, 179 (1929).
2. Wolfe (priv. comm., 1939).
3. Zinken and Rammelsberg, *Ann. Phys.*, **77**, 240 (1849).
4. Pisani, *C. R.*, **83**, 747 (1876), and Spencer (1899).

3741　**F U L O P P I T E** [$Pb_3Sb_8S_{15}$].　Fülöppite *de Finály* and *Koch* (*Min. Mag.*, **22**, 179, 1929).

C r y s t.　Monoclinic; prismatic — $2/m$.

$a : b : c = 1.1184 : 1 : 1.4085;$　β 94°49′;[1]　$p_0 : q_0 : r_0 = 1.2594 : 1 : 1.4035$

$r_2 : p_2 : q_2 = 0.7125 : 0.8973 : 1;$　μ 85°11′, p_0' 1.2640, q_0' 1.4085, x_0' 0.0843

Forms:

		ϕ	ρ	ϕ_2	ρ_2	C	A
c	001	90°00′	4°49′	85°11′	90°00′	0°00′	85°11′
a	100	90 00	90 00	0 00	90 00	85 11	0 00
d	$\bar{1}02$	−90 00	28 42½	118 42½	90 00	23 53½	118 42½
e	114	48 40	28 04	68 11	71 54	24 38	69 19
p	112	45 29	45 07½	54 23	60 12½	41 48	59 38½
t	$\bar{1}13$	−35 40½	30 01½	108 37½	66 01	33 03	106 58
o	$\bar{1}12$	−37 52½	41 44	118 42½	58 18	44 49½	114 07½
s	$\bar{1}11$	−39 57	61 26½	139 42½	47 40½	64 36	124 20

Habit.　Pyramidal and short prismatic [201]; {$\bar{1}12$} striated ‖ [110]; {100} striated ‖ [0$\bar{1}$0].　Rarely thick tabular {001}.　Crystals often curved.　Commonest forms: *c a o*.

P h y s.　Fracture uneven.　Brittle.　H. 2½.　G. 5.23.　Luster metallic.　Color lead-gray, sometimes tarnished steel-blue or bronzy.　Streak reddish gray.　Opaque.　In polished section white in color.

C h e m.　A lead antimony sulfide, $Pb_3Sb_8S_{15}$.

Anal.

	1	2
Pb	29.93	28.29
Sb	46.91	49.90
S	23.16	24.10
Rem.	. . . . . .	0.19
Total	100.00	100.08

1. $Pb_3Sb_8S_{15}$.　2. Nagyág.　Rem. is SiO_2 0.19.

Tests.　F. 1.　In O.T. fuses, yielding sulfurous odors and a sublimate of Sb_2S_3.　Not attacked by concentrated HCl or concentrated HNO_3.

Occur. In the Kereszthegy mine, Nagyág, Roumania, associated with sphalerite, dolomite, and zinkenite.

Name. After Dr. Bela Fülöpp, a Hungarian mineral collector.

Ref.

1. Recalculated elements from angles of de Finály and Koch (1929), unit of Berman (priv. comm., 1939) to conform with other members of the plagionite group.

3742 **PLAGIONITE** [$Pb_5Sb_8S_{17}$]. Ein neues Spiessglanzerz *Zinken* (*Ann. Phys.*, **22**, 492, 1831). Plagionit *Rose* (*Ann. Phys.*, **28**, 421, 1833). Rosenite *Zinken* (*Ann. Phys.*, **35**, 357, 1835).

Cryst. Monoclinic; prismatic — $2/m$.

$a : b : c = 1.1318 : 1 : 1.6878$; $\beta\,107°13'$;[1] $p_0 : q_0 : r_0 = 1.4913 : 1.6122 : 1$
$r_2 : p_2 : q_2 = 0.6203 : 0.9250 : 1$; $\mu\,72°47'$; $p_0'\,1.5613$, $q_0'\,1.6878$, $x_0'\,0.3099$

Forms:[2]

		ϕ	ρ	ϕ_2	$\rho_2 = B$	C	A
c	001	90°00′	17°13′	72°47′	90°00′	0°00′	72°47′
m	110	42 46	90 00	0 00	42 46	78 24½	47 14
γ	310	70 11	90 00	0 00	70 11	73 50	19 49
d	021	5 14½	73 34	72 47	17 14	72 46	84 58
g	$\bar{1}01$	−90 00	51 22½	141 22½	90 00	68 35½	141 22½
j	115	61 31	35 17½	58 06½	74 00½	21 34½	59 29
e	114	58 55½	39 16	55 00	70 56	25 50½	57 10½
l	113	55 53	45 05	50 18	66 35½	32 00½	54 06½
n	112	52 16	54 03	42 31	60 18	41 23	50 11½
x	111	47 57	68 21½	28 07	51 30	56 10½	46 21
k	$\bar{1}12$	−29 09	44 01	115 12½	52 38	54 04½	109 47

Less common:

b	010	η	023	λ	2·2·11	E	$\bar{1}18$	N	$\bar{2}23$	v	421
a	100	ρ	011	A	223	F	$\bar{1}16$	V	137	S	10·1·2
o	150	u	102	y	332	G	$\bar{1}15$	α	314	W	$\bar{4}23$
q	130	f	$\bar{1}02$	B	221	s	$\bar{1}14$	β	313	σ	$\bar{3}12$
ξ	013	p	118	C	331	h	$\bar{1}13$	H	914	τ	$\bar{5}12$
ζ	025	L	116	D	$\bar{1}19$	t	$\bar{2}25$	ψ	311	Ξ	$\bar{3}11$
Ω	012									ϵ	$\bar{5}11$

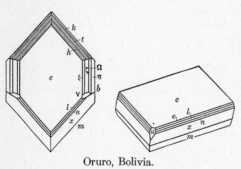

Oruro, Bolivia.

Structure cell.[3] Monoclinic; a_0 13.4, b_0 11.9, c_0 19.77; $a_0 : b_0 : c_0 = 1.126 : 1 : 1.66$, β 107°13′; contains $Pb_{20}Sb_{32}S_{68}$.

Habit. Thick tabular {001}, sometimes short prismatic [20$\bar{1}$]. Striated [$\bar{1}$10]. Also massive granular to compact.

Phys. Cleavage {112} very good. Fracture conchoidal to uneven. Brittle. H. 2.5.

G. 5.56 ± 0.02;[4] 5.60 (calc.). Luster metallic. Color and streak black-ish lead-gray. Opaque. In polished section[5] anisotropic. Reflection percentages: green 33, orange 29, red 27.5.

C h e m. Lead antimony sulfide, $Pb_5Sb_8S_{17}$.

Anal.[6]

	1	2	3	4
Pb	40.55	41.24	40.28	44.20
Sb	38.12	37.35	38.30	34.40
S	21.33	21.10	21.43	20.70
Rem.	......	.....	0.18	1.22
Total	100.00	99.69	100.19	100.52
G.	5.533	5.50	5.54	5.60

1. $Pb_5Sb_8S_{17}$. 2. Wolfsberg, Harz.[7] 3. Oruro, Bolivia. Rem. is Ag.[8] 4. Oruro, Bolivia. Rem. is Sn 0.62, insol. 0.60, Cu trace.[9]

Tests. F. 1. Decrepitates. Soluble in hot HCl with evolution of H_2S and separation of lead chloride on cooling.

O c c u r. Found with other lead sulfosalts at Wolfsberg, in the Harz Mountains, Germany. Reported from Arnsberg, Westphalia, and from the antimony mine at Leyraux, Cantal, France. In Bolivia at Oruro, with cassiterite and franckeite in pyrite.

A l t e r. Observed superficially altered to kermesite; a pseudomorph of boulangerite (?) after plagionite has also been noted.

A r t i f. A compound of the composition of plagionite is said to be formed in the system $PbS-Sb_2S_3$.[10]

N a m e. In allusion to the obliquity of the crystals, from πλάγιος, oblique.

Ref.

1. New elements from average of elements of Luedecke, *Jb. Min.*, II, 112, 1883, and of Zambonini, *Riv. min.*, **41**, 338 (1912); orientation of Luedecke, unit of Zambonini. Goldschmidt (**2**, 479, 1890) and Federov, *Ac. sc. St. Pétersbourg*, **14** [2], 23 (1903), chose other orientations. Transformations: Luedecke to Zambonini 100/010/004, Goldschmidt to Zambonini 100/010/002, Federov to Zambonini 110/1$\overline{1}$0/002.
2. Zambonini (1912), and some additional forms from unpublished notes of Ungemach, modified by Palache (priv. comm., 1939). Uncertain forms: {053}, {706}, {$\overline{7}$04}, {$\overline{7}$02}, {$\overline{15}$·0·4}, {117}, {335}, {$\overline{1}$·1·11}, {$\overline{2}$29}.
3. Crystal from Oruro, Bolivia, by Wolfe (priv. comm., 1939) with Weissenberg and rotation x-ray pictures.
4. Three determinations on crystals from Oruro, Bolivia (Berman, priv. comm., 1939).
5. Schneiderhöhn and Ramdohr (**2**, 397, 1931).
6. Earlier analyses in Dana (118, 1892).
7. Prior anal. in Spencer, *Min. Mag.*, **12**, 55 (1899).
8. Zambonini, *Riv. min.*, **41**, 338 (1912).
9. Pisani anal. in Kozlowski and Jaskólski, *Min. Soc. Warsaw, Arch.*, **8**, 1 (1932) — p. 118.
10. Jaeger and van Klooster, *Zs. anorg. Chem.*, **78**, 245 (1912), Sommerlad, *ibid.*, **18**, 441 (1898).

3743 **H E T E R O M O R P H I T E** [$Pb_7Sb_8S_{19}$]. *Pisani* (*C. R.*, **83**, 747, 1876). (Not certainly the heteromorphite of *Zinken* and *Rammelsberg*, *Ann. Phys.*, **77**, 240 [1849]).

C r y s t. Monoclinic.[1]

Habit. Pyramidal, somewhat elongated in the direction of the pyramid edges. Striated and rounded ∥ [1$\bar{1}$0]; often distorted or twisted and composed of subparallel individuals. Also massive. Common forms: *c a p e n.*

P h y s. Cleavage {112} good. Fracture uneven. Brittle. H. 2$\frac{1}{2}$–3. G. 5.73. Luster metallic. Color iron-black. Streak black. Opaque.

C h e m. A lead antimony sulfide, $Pb_7Sb_8S_{19}$.[2]

Anal.

	1	2	3	4
Pb	47.81	47.86	48.89	48.48
Zn	.....	0.60	0.18	.....
Sb	32.11	● 31.20	31.08	32.98
S	20.08	19.90	19.36	20.32
Rem.	.....	.....	0.10	....
Total	100.00	99.56	99.61	101.78
G.		5.59–5.73	5.73	5.68

1. $Pb_7Sb_8S_{19}$. 2. Arnsberg. Another Pb determination gave 48.1.[3] 3. Arnsberg. Rem. is Cu 0.10.[4] 4. Heteromorphite (?), Wolfsberg.[5]

O c c u r. At the stibnite mines of Arnsberg, Westphalia, in part as crystals with sphalerite lining cavities in the massive mineral.

N a m e. From ετερος, *different*, and μορφή, *form*, in allusion to the difference in form between this species and the supposed dimorphous feather-ore from Wolfsberg. See also under discussion of plagionite group.

Ref.

1. The approximate measurements of Spencer, *Min. Mag.*, **12**, 55 (1899), on analyzed material from Arnsberg establishes this species as monoclinic, related to other members of the plagionite group. The x-ray powder data of supposed heteromorphite from Wolfsberg by Hiller, *Zs. Kr.*, **100**, 149 (1938), has little significance, since the material was not analyzed, nor was it of the stout tabular habit typical of heteromorphite in the sense here adopted, following Spencer. The common forms given here correspond to similar forms in plagionite, but the angles are only approximately known, and an angle table was consequently not prepared.
2. The formula given is that of Pisani (1876), here adopted because it agrees with the analyses about as well as the others proposed by Rammelsberg (138, 1886) and by Spencer (1899), and fits into the formula type of the plagionite group.
3. Pisani (1876).
4. Prior anal. in Spencer (1899).
5. Poselger anal. in Zinken and Rammelsberg (1849). This is the original heteromorphite of Zinken and Rammelsberg. Compare Rammelsberg (71, 1860) where different figures are given; a second analysis is also given, which agrees more closely with $Pb_2Sb_2S_5$.

3744   **S E M S E Y I T E** [$Pb_9Sb_8S_{21}$]. *Krenner* (*Ak. Magyar Értes*, **15**, 111, 1881; *Ungarischer Revue*, 367, 1881; *Zs. Kr.*, **8**, 532, 1883).

C r y s t. Monoclinic; prismatic — 2/m

$a : b : c = 1.1356 : 1 : 2.0436$; β 105°46′; $p_0 : q_0 : r_0 = 1.7996 : 1.9667 : 1$

$r_2 : p_2 : q_2 = 0.5085 : 0.9150 : 1$; μ 74°14′; p_0' 1.8699, q_0' 2.0436, x_0' 0.2823

Forms:[2]

		ϕ	ρ	ϕ_2	ρ_2	C	A
c	001	90°00′	15°46′	74°14′	90°00′	0°00′	74°14′
a	100	90 00	90 00	0 00	90 00	74 14	0 00
γ	310	69 59	90 00	0 00	69 59	75 12½	20 01
g	101	90 00	65 04½	24 55½	90 00	49 18½	24 55½
G	$\bar{1}01$	−90 00	57 47½	147 47½	90 00	73 33½	147 47½
ρ	011	7 52	64 08½	74 14	26 57	63 03	82 55½
e	114	55 44	42 13	53 08	67 46	30 16½	56 16
n	112	49 59½	57 49½	39 24	57 02	46 28½	49 35½
x	111	46 29	71 23	24 55½	49 16	60 24	46 35½
k	$\bar{1}12$	−32 34	50 29	123 08	49 27	60 02	114 32
X	$\bar{1}11$	−37 50½	68 53	147 47½	42 33	78 58½	124 54½
σ	$\bar{3}12$	−67 57	69 49½	158 22½	69 22	84 31	150 27½

Less common:

$$d\{021\} \qquad f\{102\} \qquad l\{113\} \qquad \Delta\{\bar{2}29\} \qquad s\{\bar{1}14\}$$

Structure cell.[3] Space group $C2/c$; a_0 13.48, b_0 11.87, c_0 24.48; β 105°45′; $a_0 : b_0 : c_0 = 1.1356 : 1 : 2.0623$; contains $Pb_{36}Sb_{32}S_{84}$.

Habit. Tabular $\{001\}$, often prismatic [010] (resembling plagionite and heteromorphite). Also prismatic $[\bar{4}01]$ and $[\bar{2}01]$ (Wolfsberg). Crystals often twisted and composed of subparallel individuals; in globular aggregates and rosette-like groups.

Phys. Cleavage $\{112\}$ perfect. Brittle. H. $2\frac{1}{2}$. G. 6.08 (Kisbánya[4]); 6.15 (calc.). Luster metallic, tarnishing dull. Color gray to black. Streak black. Opaque. In polished section[5] white in color, with strong anisotropism and very weak pleochroism. Reflection percentages: green 40, orange 35, red 31.5.

Chem. A lead antimony sulfide, $Pb_9Sb_8S_{21}$.

Anal.[5]

	1	2	3	4	5	6	7	8
Pb	53.10	54.27	53.21	52.9	52.49	52.37	51.88	51.84
Sb	27.73	26.17	26.95	24.8	28.34	25.49	27.20	28.62
S	19.17	18.99	19.90	18.7	18.93	18.81	19.73	19.42
Rem.	......	0.26	0.08	1.6	0.46	3.14	1.82	.....
Total	100.00	99.69	100.14	98.0	100.22	99.81	100.63	99.88
G.	6.15			5.82	6.105	5.92		5.92

1. $Pb_9Sb_8S_{21}$. 2. Kisbánya. Rem. is Ag 0.25 and insol. 0.01.[7] 3. Rodna. Rem. is insol. 0.08, Cu trace.[8] 4. Oruro. Crystals. Rem. is Ag, which may be present as andorite.[9] 5. Kisbánya. Rem. is Ag 0.13, Cu 0.06, Fe 0.06, insol. 0.21.[10] 6. Glendinning, Dumfriesshire, Scotland. Rem. is Fe 0.67, insol. 0.81, CaCO₃ 1.66.[11] 7. Kisbánya. Rem. is Ag 0.56, Cu 0.11, Fe trace and insol. 1.15.[8] 8. Wolfsberg.[12]

Occur. In Roumania at Felsöbánya upon corroded galena, associated with bournonite, diaphorite, sphalerite and siderite, at Rodna, also upon corroded galena and in part as incrustation pseudomorphs after that mineral, and at Kisbánya. From Wolfsberg, in the Harz Mountains, Germany, associated with jamesonite and bournonite. From Montlucon, France. At Glendinning, Eskdale, Dumfriesshire, Scotland, with stibnite, sphalerite, pyrite, and carbonates. From Oruro, Bolivia, with felted boulangerite (?) and pyrite.

A r t i f. Compounds with ratios close to semseyite have been reported in the system $PbS-Sb_2S_3$.[13]

N a m e. After Andor von Semsey (died 1923), a Hungarian nobleman who was much interested in minerals.

Ref.

1. Angles and orientation of Smith, *Min. Mag.*, **18**, 354 (1919) on crystal from Dumfriesshire (anal. 6), unit of Wolfe (priv. comm., 1939), based on an x-ray study of a Kisbánya crystal. Transformation: Smith to Wolfe 100/010/002. The possible morphotropic relation between semseyite, heteromorphite and plagionite is discussed by Spencer, *Min. Mag.*, **12**, 55 (1899); Smith (1919); and Zambonini, *Riv. min.*, **41**, 338 (1912). de Finály and Koch, *Min. Mag.*, **22**, 179 (1929), have included fuloppite in the morphotropic relation. See also the discussion of this relationship under the discussion of the plagionite group.
2. Smith (1919), Koch, *Ak. Magyar, Értes*, **48**, 800 (1931); Wolfe (priv. comm., 1939). Vicinal forms: $\{\bar{5}\cdot5\cdot12\}$, $\{\bar{9}\cdot9\cdot19\}$.
3. Wolfe (priv. comm., 1939) by Weissenberg method.
4. Berman (priv. comm., 1939) on 10-mg. crystal.
5. Schneiderhöhn and Ramdohr (**2**, 407, 1931).
6. For additional analyses see Doelter (4 [1], 454, 1926).
7. de Finály anal. in Koch (1931).
8. Endredy anal. in Koch (1931).
9. Prior anal. in Spencer, *Min. Mag.*, **14**, 308 (1907).
10. Loczka, *Mat. Termés Ért.*, **42**, 20 (1926) — *Min. Abs.*, **3**, 7 (1926).
11. Prior anal. in Smith, *Min. Mag.*, **18**, 354 (1919).
12. Prior anal. in Spencer, *Min. Mag.*, **12**, 55 (1899).
13. Iitsuka, *Kyoto Univ., Mem. Coll. Sc.*, 4, 51 (1919).

381 **H U T C H I N S O N I T E** $[(Pb,Tl)_2(Cu,Ag)As_5S_{10}?]$. *Solly* (*Cambridge Phil. Soc., Proc.*, **12**, 277, 1904; *Min. Mag.*, **14**, 72, 1905).

C r y s t. Orthorhombic.

$$a : b : c = 0.6119 : 1 : 0.4619;^1 \quad p_0 : q_0 : r_0 = 0.7549 : 0.4619 : 1$$

$$q_1 : r_1 : p_1 = 0.6119 : 1.3247 : 1; \quad r_2 : p_2 : q_2 = 2.1649 : 1.6343 : 1$$

Forms:[2]

		ϕ	$\rho = C$	ϕ_1	$\rho_1 = A$	ϕ_2	$\rho_2 = B$
c	001	.....	0°00′	0°00′	90°00′	90°00′	90°00′
b	010	0°00′	90 00	90 00	90 00	.....	0 00
a	100	90 00	90 00	.....	0 00	0 00	90 00
l	470	43 02½	90 00	90 00	46 57½	0 00	43 02½
k	230	47 27	90 00	90 00	42 33	0 00	47 27
i	450	52 35½	90 00	90 00	37 24½	0 00	52 35½
m	110	58 32½	90 00	90 00	31 27½	0 00	58 32½
h	430	65 21	90 00	90 00	24 39	0 00	65 21
f	210	72 59½	90 00	90 00	17 00½	0 00	72 59½
g	410	81 18	90 00	90 00	8 42	0 00	81 18
d	011	0 00	24 47½	24 47½	90 00	90 00	65 12½
v	031	0 00	54 11	54 11	90 00	90 00	35 49
p	111	58 32½	41 30½	24 47½	25 34½	52 57	69 46
r	212	72 59½	38 17½	13 00½	53 40	52 57	79 33½
q	232	47 27	45 42	34 43	58 10½	52 57	61 03½
o	121	39 15	50 02	42 44	60 59½	52 57	53 36

Less common:

H 380	J 012	X 073	e 102	x 254	Q 131	t 432
G 370	V 034	w 041	A 332	C 132	R 141	T 472
F 120	W 032	Y 051	N 221	O 414	s 412	
K 520	U 021	Z 061	θ 285	P 252	n 211	

Habit. Prismatic to acicular [001]. Dominant prism {410}. Sometimes in radiating tufts.

Phys. Cleavage {010} good. Fracture conchoidal. Brittle. H. $1\frac{1}{2}$–2. G. 4.6. Adamantine luster. Color and streak scarlet-vermilion to deep cherry-red. In thin splinters transmits red light.

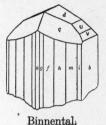

Binnental.

Opt.[3]

ORIENTATION	$n_{589(Na)}$	$n_{656(C)}$	Bx. neg. (−)
X = a	3.078 ± 0.018 (calc.)	2.779 ± 0.06 (calc.)	$2V_{Na}$ 37°24′.
Y = b	3.176 ± 0.003	3.063 ± 0.003	$2V_{(C)}$ 19°44′.
Z = c	3.188 ± 0.003	3.073 ± 0.003	$r < v$, extreme.

In polished section[4] strongly anisotropic, with marked carmine-red internal reflections. Reflection percentage: orange 29.

Chem. Composition uncertain, possibly $(Pb,Tl)_2(Cu,Ag)As_5S_{10}$.
Anal.

	Pb	Tl	Ag	Cu	Fe	As	Sb	S	Total
1	$12\frac{1}{4}$	25	9	..	..	$30\frac{1}{4}$	..	26	103
2	16	18	2	3	$\frac{1}{2}$	$29\frac{1}{2}$	2	$26\frac{1}{2}$	$97\frac{1}{2}$

1. Binnental. On 0.0184 gm., deep red crystals with scarlet streak.[3] 2. Binnental. On 0.0664 gm., crystals with cherry-red streak.[3]

Occur. At Lengenbach in the Binnental, Valais, Switzerland, in the dolomite with other arsenic sulfides, sphalerite, pyrite, realgar, and orpiment. Sometimes as a coating on sartorite and rathite, and then with the prism edge in parallel position with the underlying crystal edges.

Name. After Dr. Arthur Hutchinson (1866–1937), Professor of Mineralogy in the University of Cambridge.

Ref.

1. Angles and unit of Smith and Prior, *Min. Mag.*, **14**, 283 (1907), new orientation in preferred orthorhombic position. Transformations: Smith and Prior to new orientation 010/100/001. Solly (1905) to new orientation: 010/200/001.
2. Solly (1905). Smith and Prior (1907).
3. Smith and Prior (1907).
4. Guisca, *Min. Mitt.*, **10**, 170 (1930).

HISTRIXITE. Petterd (*Roy. Soc. Tasmania, Proc.*, 18, 1902; 95, 1906).
Orthorhombic? In radiating groups of prismatic crystals, striated longitudinally and showing indistinct acute terminations, also massive with foliated structure. H. 2. Slightly sectile. Luster metallic, tarnishing iridescent. Color and streak steel-gray.
Chem. Possibly $Cu_5Fe_5Bi_4Sb_{14}S_{32}$ or $(Cu,Fe)(Bi,Sb)_2S_3$.

Anal.

	Fe	Cu	Bi	Sb	S	Total
1	5.18	6.86	55.93	10.08	24.05	102.10
2	5.44	6.12	56.08	9.33	23.01	99.98

O c c u r. Found associated with chalcopyrite, pyrite, and bismuthinite in a massive body of tetrahedrite at the Curtin-Davis mine, Ringville, Tasmania. Named from ὕστριξ, *a porcupine.*

Needs confirmation.

  DOGNACSKITE. *Krenner (Földt. Közl.,* **14,** 564, 1884).

Described as a gray, cleavable, "wismuthkupfererz," approximately $Cu_2Bi_4S_7$. G. 6.79. Analyses gave:

		1	2	3
	Cu	10.70	10.04	12.28
	Bi	70.40	71.88	71.79
	S	18.90	17.91	15.75
	Total	100.00	99.83	99.82
	G.		6.79	

1. $Cu_2Bi_4S_7$. 2. Dognácska.[1] 3. Dognácska.[2]

From Dognácska, Hungary, with gold, pyrite, chalcocite, and bismuth ocher. Stated[3] to be a mixture of bismuthinite, chalcocite, and other copper sulfides.

Needs further study.

Ref.

1. Neugebauer, *Min. Mitt.,* **24,** 323 (1905); another analysis, in Koechlin, *ibid.,* **24,** 117 (1905), is close to wittichenite.
2. Maderspach anal. in Krenner (1884).
3. Short (104, 1931); see also Murdoch (135, 1916).

382 **Rezbanyite** [$Pb_3Cu_2Bi_{10}S_{19}$]. *Frenzel (Min. Mitt.,* **5,** 175, 1883).

P h y s. Massive, fine granular to compact. Cleavage indistinct, fracture uneven. H. $2\frac{1}{2}$. G. 6.24 ± 0.15 (Rezbánya), 6.89 (Vaskö). Color light lead-gray, tarnishing dull. Streak black. Opaque. In polished section[1] white, with strong anisotropism.

C h e m. A lead and copper bismuth sulfide, possibly $Pb_3Cu_2Bi_{10}S_{19}$.[2]

	1	2
Pb	18.03	18.24
Cu	3.69	4.13
Fe	.....	0.44
Bi	60.62	59.25
S	17.66	17.86
Rem.	.....	0.06
Total	100.00	99.98
G.		6.89

1. $Pb_3Cu_2Bi_{10}S_{19}$. 2. Vaskö. Average of two analyses. Rem. is SiO_2.[3]

O c c u r. At Rezbánya, Roumania, intimately mixed with chalcopyrite and calcite; also with quartz. At Vaskö, Hungary, with dolomite and quartz.

N a m e. From the locality. The same name was given[4] to a lead-gray bismuth ore from Rezbánya, which was probably an impure cosalite.

Needs further study.

Ref.

1. Short (25, 1934), Murdoch (136, 1916). No certainty exists as to the authenticity of the material described by these writers.
2. Formula of Koch, *Cbl. Min.*, 52, 1930. The original formula of Frenzel (1883), $Pb_4Bi_{10}S_{19}$, was derived from analyses (in Dana [111, 1892]) made on impure material. The formula was later written by Wherry and Foshag, *Washington Ac. Sc., J.*, 11, 1 (1921), as $Pb_2Bi_6S_{11}$ and the mineral placed with keeleyite, the latter subsequently shown to be invalid as a species.
3. Koch (1930).
4. Herman, *J. pr. Chem.*, 75, 450 (1859).

383 **G A L E N O B I S M U T I T E** [$PbBi_2S_4$]. *Sjögren (Geol. För. Förh.*, 4, 109, 1878). Bleiwismuthglanz *Groth* (25, 1882). Bismutoplagionite *Shannon (Am. J. Sc.*, 49, 106, 1920; *U. S. Nat. Mus., Proc.*, 58, 589, 1920). Cannizzarite *Zambonini, de Fiore* and *Carobbi (Acc. Napoli, Rend.*, 31, 24, 1925; *Osserv. Vesuviano*, 1, 31, 1924).

C r y s t.[1] Orthorhombic; dipyramidal — $2/m\ 2/m\ 2/m$.

$a : b : c = 0.8050 : 1 : 0.2828;$ $p_0 : q_0 : r_0 = 0.3513 : 0.2828 : 1$

$q_1 : r_1 : p_1 = 0.8050 : 2.8463 : 1;$ $r_2 : p_2 : q_2 = 3.5359 : 1.2423 : 1$

Forms:[2]

		ϕ	ρ	ϕ_1	ρ_1	ϕ_2	ρ_2
a	100	90°00′	90°00′	.....	0°00′	0°00′	90°00′
h	140	17 15	90 00	90°00′	72 45	0 00	17 15
m	110	51 10	90 00	90 00	38 50	0 00	51 10
Q	210	68 04½	90 00	90 00	21 55½	0 00	68 04½
S	410	78 37½	90 00	90 00	11 22½	0 00	78 37½
y	810	84 15	90 00	90 00	5 45	0 00	84 15
w	011	0 00	15 47½	15 47½	90 00	90 00	74 12½
x	031	0 00	40 18½	40 18½	90 00	90 00	49 41½
d	201	90 00	35 05½	0 00	54 54½	54 54½	90 00
p	111	51 10	24 16½	15 47½	71 19½	70 38½	75 03½
g	211	68 04½	37 08½	15 47½	55 56½	54 54½	76 58½

Less common:

c	001	j	120	N	750	U	510	Z	16·1·0
b	010	k	230	P	320	V	11·2·0	e	232
o	190	l	560	R	310	W	6·1·0	f	121
i	130	O	430	T	920	Y	15·2·0	G	311

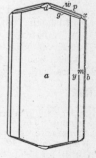

Vulcano.

Structure cell.[3] Space group *Pnam*; a_0 11.73, b_0 14.47, c_0 4.076; $a_0 : b_0 : c_0 = 0.8106 : 1 : 0.2817$; contains $Pb_4Bi_8S_{16}$.

Habit. Lathlike, elongated [001] and flattened {100}; needles [001]; striated [001]. Sometimes extremely thin plates {100} Usually massive, columnar to fibrous, or compact.

P h y s. Cleavage {110} good.[2] Flexible; crystals frequently bent and twisted. H. $2\frac{1}{2}$–$3\frac{1}{2}$. G. 7.04;[4] 7.19 (calc.). Luster metallic. Color light gray to tin-white; lead-gray; sometimes tarnished yellow or iridescent.

Streak black. Opaque. In polished section[4] white in color and strongly anisotropic.

Chem. A lead bismuth sulfide, $PbBi_2S_4$. Sb substitutes in small amounts for Bi.

Anal.

	1	2	3	4	5	6
Pb	27.50	27.18	27.65	23.93	31.33	33.02
Fe	.....	trace	trace	0.39	0.27	.....
Cu	.....	.....	.....	1.73	.....	.....
Sb	.....	.....	.....	2.56	0.19	3.05
Bi	55.48	54.13	54.69	53.59	51.25	46.83
S	17.02	16.78	17.35	[17.80]	17.16	[17.10]
Total	100.00	98.09	99.69	100.00	100.20	100.00
G.	7.19		6.88		4.8	5.35

1. $PbBi_2S_4$. 2, 3. Nordmark, Sweden.[5] 4. Quartzburg district, Id.[6] 5. Vulcano, Lipari Islands, Italy (cannizzarite).[7] 6. Wickes, Montana (*bismutoplagionite*). Recalc. to 100 per cent after deduction of 18.8 insol. and 1.25 FeS_2.[8]

Tests. F. 1. Soluble in hot HCl.

Occur. In Sweden at the Ko mine, Nordmark, and at Gladhammar. In the deeper part of fumaroles (temp. 550–610°) on Vulcano, Lipari Islands, Italy (*cannizzarite*) associated with acicular bismuthinite, with which it may easily be confused. In the United States from Wickes, Jefferson County, Montana (*bismutoplagionite*) as indistinctly fibrous aggregates and minute acicular crystals associated with pyrite, tetrahedrite, galena, chalcopyrite, quartz, and sericite; at the Belzazzar mine, Quartzburg district, Idaho, with pyrite and quartz. In Canada from the Caribou mine, Cariboo district, British Columbia, with cosalite and native gold in quartz.

Name. Galenobismutite in allusion to the composition. Cannizzarite after the Italian chemist, Stanislao Cannizzaro (1826–1910). Bismutoplagionite in allusion to a supposed relation to plagionite.

CANNIZZARITE. *Zambonini, de Fiore* and *Carobbi* (*Acc. Napoli, Rend.*, **31**, 24, 1925; *Osserv. Vesuviano*, **1**, 31 1924).

A supposed lead bismuth sulfide, $Pb_3Bi_5S_{11}$, found as a sublimation product on Vulcano, Lipari Islands, Italy. Identical with galenobismutite.[9]

BISMUTOPLAGIONITE. *Shannon* (*Am. J. Sc.*, **49**, 106, 1920; *U.S. Nat. Mus., Proc.*, **58**, 589, 1920).

A lead bismuth sulfide, supposedly $Pb_5Bi_8S_{17}$, from Wickes, Montana. Shown to be identical with galenobismutite.[10]

Ref.

1. Wolfe, *Am. Min.*, **23**, 790 (1938), on crystals of so-called cannizzarite from Vulcano. The measurements by Zambonini, de Fiore and Carobbi (1925) on so-called cannizzarite were apparently made on associated crystals of bismuthinite. Berry, *Am. Min.*, **25**, 726 (1940), notes that the morphological data of Flink, *Ark. Kemi*, **3** [1], (1910), for lillianite from Gladhammar, Sweden, may refer to galenobismutite.

2. Wolfe (1938).

3. Wolfe (1938) by Weissenberg method on so-called cannizzarite from Vulcano (anal. 5). Berry (1940) reports on type galenobismutite of Sjögren from Nordmark: a_0 11.72 ± 0.03, b_0 14.52 ± 0.03, c_0 4.07 ± 0.02.

4. Berry (1940).
5. Sjögren (1878).
6. Shannon, *Washington Ac. Sc., J.*, **11**, 298 (1921).
7. Gonyer anal. in Wolfe (1940).
8. Shannon, *Am. J. Sc.*, **49**, 106 (1920).
9. Peacock (priv. comm., 1940), who pointed out the identity in cell dimensions, space group, and physical properties reported by Wolfe (1938) for cannizzarite and by Berry (1940) for galenobismutite. The apparent differences in composition of the two materials is attributed to inhomogeneities in the analyzed samples of cannizzarite.
10. Wolfe (priv. comm., 1939), by x-ray powder study; the patterns are identical with the exception of a difference in intensity of one line.

The validity and interrelations of the following four minerals are uncertain.

384   **Weibullite** [$PbBi_2(S,Se)_4$].   Selenhaltiger Galenobismutite *Weibull* (*Geol. För. Förh.*, **7**, 657, 1885).   Seleniferous Galenobismutite *Genth* (*Am. Phil. Soc., Proc.*, **23**, 34, 1885).   Selenbleiwismuthglanz *Groth* (**28**, 1889; **33**, 1898).   Weibullite *Flink* (*Ark. Kemi*, **3**, 4, 1910).

In indistinct prismatic crystals.[1]   Usually massive, prismatic to fibrous, or foliated.

P h y s.   One good cleavage, parallel the elongation.   Very brittle.[2] Flexible, but not elastic.   H. 2–3.   G. 6.97, 7.145.[2]   Luster metallic. Color steel-gray; streak somewhat darker.   Opaque.   In polished section[3] white in color with strong anisotropism and pleochroism.

C h e m.   A lead bismuth sulfide, with Se substituting for S in about the ratio 3 : 5; possibly $PbBi_2(S,Se)_4$.[4]

Anal.

	1	2	3
Pb	25.15	27.88	25.37
Ag	.....	0.33	.....
Bi	50.74	49.88	51.24
Se	14.38	12.43	14.03
S	9.73	9.75	9.36
Total	100.00	100.27	100.00
G.		7.145	6.97

1. $PbBi_2(S,Se)_4$, with Se : S = 3 : 5.   2. Fahlun.   Average of five analyses from which 4 to 9 per cent quartz, chalcopyrite, and pyrrhotite have been deducted.[2]   3. Fahlun.   Recalc. to 100 after deduction of Cu 0.77 and Fe 0.61 as chalcopyrite.

O c c u r.   At Fahlun, Sweden, with gold, chalcopyrite, native bismuth, pyrrhotite, and quartz in a hornblende rock.

N a m e.   After Mats Weibull (1856–1923), who first described the mineral.

Needs verification.[4]

Ref.

1. Weibull (1885) gives approximate measurements to the cleavage of a number of faces.
2. Genth (1885).
3. Schneiderhöhn and Ramdohr (**2**, 397, 1931).

4. Weibullite has been variously classed as a selenian galenobismutite or as a distinct species, as in Flink, *Ark. Kemi*, **3**, 4 (1910), but the mineral is insufficiently characterized to permit a definite decision. Walker and Thomson, *Univ. Toronto Stud., Geol. Ser.*, **12**, 12 (1921), found by microscopic examination and analysis (by Todd) that a specimen from Fahlun was a mixture of cosalite, bismuthinite, and guanajuatite; see also Schneiderhöhn and Ramdohr (1931). Genth (35, 1885), Nordström, *Geol. För. Förh.*, **4**, 268 (1879), and Atterberg, *Geol. För. Förh.*, **2**, 76 (1874), have also analyzed selenian material (Se 1.15 to 5.11 per cent) from Fahlun, doubtless mixtures of lead bismuth sulfides, native bismuth, or bismuthinite and guanajuatite (?). See also Peacock and Berry, *Univ. Toronto Stud., Geol. Ser.*, **44**, 47 (1940).

385   **Platynite** [PbBi$_2$(Se,S)$_3$]. *Flink (Ark. Kemi*, **3** [35], 5, 1910).

C r y s t.[1] Hexagonal — R; $a : c = 1 : 1.226$.
Habit. Only as thin plates or foliae.
P h y s. Cleavage {0001} good, {10$\bar{1}$1} fair. H. 2–3. G. 7.98. Luster metallic; in part dull. Color iron-black to dark steel-gray, like that of graphite. Streak black, shining. Opaque.
C h e m. A lead bismuth selenide, essentially PbBi$_2$(Se,S)$_3$.[2]
Anal.

	Pb	Bi	Se	S	Total
1	25.44	51.16	19.45	3.95	100.00
2	26.45	50.22	19.20	4.13	100.00

1. PbBi$_2$(Se,S)$_3$, with Se : S = 2 : 1. 2. Fahlun. Recalculated after deduction of Cu 0.32 and Fe 0.30, as chalcopyrite, and insol. 0.36.[3]

O c c u r. In quartz with chalcopyrite at Fahlun, Sweden.
N a m e. From πλατύγω, *to broaden*, in allusion to the platy structure. Needs further study.

Ref.
1. Ratio from measurements to rhombohedral cleavage from basal cleavage by Flink (1910). {0001} ∧ {10$\bar{1}$1} = 54°46'.
2. The formula is erroneously given as PbS · Bi$_2$S$_3$ in Dana-Ford (446, 1932).
3. Mauzelius anal. in Flink (1910).

386   **Chiviatite** [Pb$_3$Bi$_8$S$_{15}$?]. *Rammelsberg (Ann. Phys.*, **88**, 320, 1853).

In foliated or columnar aggregates, with three cleavages[1] parallel the elongation. H. 2–3. G. 6.92 (Chiviato), 7.15 (Fahlun). Luster metallic. Color lead-gray. Opaque.
C h e m. A lead bismuth sulfide, possibly Pb$_3$Bi$_8$S$_{15}$.[2] Cu apparently substitutes in small part for Pb, and Se may substitute for S (anal. 3).
Anal.

	1	2	3
Pb	22.41	16.73	17.39
Cu	.....	2.42	1.20
Fe	.....	1.02	0.29
Ag	.....	trace	0.15
Bi	60.26	60.95	56.72
S	17.33	18.00	11.48
Se	.....	.....	12.28
Rem.	.....	0.59	0.57
Total	100.00	99.71	100.04
G.		6.92	7.15

1. Pb$_3$Bi$_8$S$_{15}$. 2. Chiviato.[3] 3. Fahlun. Rem. is Zn 0.35, insol. 0.22.[4]

Var. *Selenian.* *Johansson* (*Ark. Kemi*, **9** [9], 3, 1924). From Fahlun, Sweden, with S : Se approximately 2 : 1 (anal. 3).

Occur. From Chiviato, Peru, with pyrite and barite; reported also from Chicla, San Mateo, Huarochiri,[5] in Peru. From Fahlun, Sweden, as columnar aggregates 3–4 cm. long with quartz in a cordierite-bearing amphibole rock.

Name. From the locality, Chiviato, Peru.

Needs confirmation.[6]

Ref.

1. Cleavages on crystals from Fahlun were designated by Johansson, *Ark. Kemi*, **9** [9], 3 (1924), as $b\{010\}$, $m\{110\}$, and $n\{130\}$, with $bm \sim 46°40'$ and $bn \sim 19°37'$. Miller, *Ann. Phys.*, **88**, 320 (1853), gives similar data for crystals from Chiviato.
2. See Johansson (1924) and Doelter (4 [1], 465, 1926) for a discussion of the formula.
3. Rammelsberg (1853).
4. Johansson (1924).
5. Raimondi (176, 1878) with analyses.
6. Specimens from Chiviato examined by Short (104, 1931) were a mixture of bismuthinite and copper sulfides.

387   **Alaskaite** [$Pb(Ag,Cu)_2Bi_4S_8$?]. *Koenig* (*Am. Phil. Soc.*, 19, 472, 1881).

Massive, compact or with a foliated structure.

Phys. Indistinct cleavage.[1] Brittle. H. 2.[2] G. 6.83 ± 0.05. Luster metallic; may tarnish bronzy. Color light lead-gray. Streak gray. Opaque. In polished section[3] white in color with distinct anisotropism and very weak pleochroism. Reflection percentages: green 43.5, orange 40, red 37.5.

Chem. A lead, silver, and copper bismuth sulfide. Formula uncertain,[4] possibly $Pb(Ag,Cu)_2Bi_4S_8$; anal. 6 affords $Pb(Cu,Ag)Bi_3S_6$.

Anal.

	1	2	3	4	5	6
Pb	13.95	14.41	15.4	11.79	12.02	19.02
Ag	9.68	9.07	11.7	8.74	7.80	3.26
Cu	2.85	2.68	1.6	3.46	5.11	4.07
Zn	....	....	....	0.79	0.34	0.22
Bi	56.26	56.11	55.3	56.97	53.39	55.81
S	17.26	17.73	16.0	17.63	17.98	17.62
Rem.	....	....	....	0.62	2.64	....
Total	100.00	100.00	100.0	100.00	99.28	100.00
G.		6.23?		[6.878]	6.782	6.878

1. $Pb(Ag,Cu)_2Bi_4S_8$, with Ag : Cu = 2 : 1. 2. Bolivia. Recalc. to 100 from original total of 98.45 per cent.[5] 3. Silverton district, Colo. Recalculated after deduction of 7.3 insol. and 5.4 Fe as FeS_2.[6] 4. Alaska mine, Colorado. Rem. is Sb 0.62. Average of two analyses recalculated after deduction of 2.28 per cent chalcopyrite and 15.00 per cent barite.[7] 5. Alaska mine, Colorado. Rem. is Fe 0.84, insol. 1.80. Pb average of 11.88 and 12.16. Fe present as chalcopyrite.[8] 6. Alaska mine, Colo. Average of three analyses recalculated after deduction of 4.71 per cent chalcopyrite and 2.83 per cent barite.[7]

Tests. F. 1. In C.T. melts without formation of a sublimate. Soluble in hot concentrated HCl with the separation of AgCl.

O c c u r. From the Alaska and Saxon mines, Poughkeepsie Gulch, Silverton district, San Juan County, Colorado, associated with pyrite, tetrahedrite, cosalite, sphalerite, barite, and quartz; in part intimately admixed with chalcopyrite. In Sur-Lipez Province, Bolivia, about 75 km. south-southwest of Esmoraca, with chalcopyrite and bismuthinite in a vein cutting Paleozoic graywacke.

N a m e. From the occurrence in the Alaska mine, Colorado. Needs further study.

Ref.

1. Also noted in polished section by Brown, *Am. Min.*, **12**, 21 (1927) who found two cleavage directions in material from the Saxon mine, Colorado, and by Schneiderhöhn and Ramdohr (**2**, 391, 1931) who found one cleavage direction in material from Bolivia.
2. Brown (1927); Ahlfeld, *Cbl. Min.*, 390, 1926, gives H. $3\frac{1}{2}$ for the Bolivian mineral.
3. Schneiderhöhn and Ramdohr, (**2**, 391, 1931) on the Bolivian material, see Brown (1927) and Short (43, 1934) for data on material from Colorado.
4. Alaskaite has been variously classed as an argentian galenobismutite, as in Dana (114, 1892), or as a distinct species, but the mineral is not sufficiently characterized to permit a definite opinion. Liweh, *Zs. Kr.*, **10**, 488 (1885) considered it identical with tetrahedrite, from measurements of supposed alaskaite crystals, but this was denied by Koenig, *Zs. Kr.*, **14**, 254 (1888), by reason of the low (*ca.* 0.6 per cent) Sb content.
5. Herzenberg anal. in Ahlfeld, *Cbl. Min.*, 390, 1926.
6. Fairchild anal. in Short (87, 1931).
7. Koenig (1881).
8. Koenig, *Am. Phil. Soc., Proc.*, **22**, 211 (1885).

388　　**Z I N K E N I T E** [$Pb_6Sb_{14}S_{27}$]. Zinkenit, Zinckenit *Rose* (*Ann. Phys.*, **7**, 91, 1826). Bleiantimonglanz *Groth* (25, 1882). Feather-ore pt. Warrenite pt. *Eakins* (*Am. J. Sc.*, **39**, 74, 1890). Keeleyite *Gordon* (*Ac. Nat. Sc. Philadelphia, Proc.*, **74**, 101, 1922).

C r y s t. Hexagonal.[1]

$$a : c = 1 : 0.1938;^2 \qquad p_0 : r_0 = 0.2238 : 1$$

Forms:

		ϕ	ρ	M	A_2
m	$10\bar{1}0$	30°00′	90°00′	60°00′	90°00′
r	$10\bar{1}1$	30 00	12 37	83 44	90 00

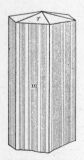

Wolfsberg, Harz.

Structure cell.[3] Space group $C6_3$ or $C6_3/m$; a_0 44.06, c_0 8.60; $a_0 : c_0 = 1 : 0.195$. The unit cell contains $Pb_{72}Sb_{168}S_{324}$ ($= 12(Pb_6Sb_{14}S_{27})$) or, less likely, $Pb_{81}Sb_{162}S_{324}$ ($= 81(PbSb_2S_4)$).

Habit. Crystals seldom distinct; thin prismatic, and striated [0001] in part due to subparallel aggregation. In columnar to radial fibrous aggregates and massive.

P h y s. Cleavage indistinct $\{11\bar{2}0\}$.[4] Fracture uneven. H. $3-3\frac{1}{2}$. G. 5.30 ± 0.05, 5.33 (Wolfsberg[5]); 5.22 (calc. for $Pb_{72}Sb_{168}S_{324}$). Luster metallic. Color and streak steel-gray. Sometimes tarnished iridescent. Opaque. In polished section[6] gray-white in color with distinct anisotropism and weak pleochroism. Reflection percentages: green 37.5, orange 33, red 31.

C h e m. A lead antimony sulfide, probably $Pb_6Sb_{14}S_{27}$.[7] As has been reported replacing Sb in small amounts.[8] The small amounts of Fe, Cu, and Ag frequently reported may be due to impurities.

Anal.[9]

	1	2	3	4	5	6
Pb	32.60	34.33	32.77	31.84	29.80	29.33
Cu	.....	0.70	1.20	0.42	0.64	.....
Fe	.....	0.06	0.02	.....	0.84	0.08
Sb	44.70	42.15	35.00	44.39	43.32	46.17
As	.....	.....	5.64	.....	0.27	.....
S	22.70	22.63	22.50	22.58	23.02	23.10
Rem.	.....	.....	1.58	.....	2.54	0.94
Total	100.00	99.87	98.71	99.23	100.43	99.62
G.	5.22		5.21			5.22

1. $Pb_6Sb_{14}S_{27}$. 2. Wolfsberg, Harz.[10] 3. Red Mountain district, Colo. Rem. is Ag 0.23, gangue 0.59, CaO 0.31, alk. 0.45.[11] 4. Wolfsberg, Harz. Probably contains some stibnite.[12] 5. San José mine, Oruro, Bolivia (*keeleyite*). Rem. is insol. 0.60, Ag 0.52, Zn 1.24, Sn 0.18.[13] 6. Nagyág, Roumania. Contains some native sulfur, jamesonite (?) and possibly stibnite.[14]

Var. *Arsenian.* Contains as much as 5.64 per cent by weight of As (anal. 3).

Tests. F. 1. Decrepitates. Soluble in hot HCl with evolution of H_2S and separation of $PbCl_2$ on cooling.

O c c u r. Found in vein deposits formed at low to moderate temperatures, associated with stibnite, jamesonite, boulangerite, bournonite and other sulfosalts, sphalerite, galena, pyrite, carbonates, and quartz.

At Wolfsberg, in the Harz Mountains, Germany, with plagionite and other sulfosalts, as crystals and as columnar to fibrous radiated masses. At Adlersbach in the Kinzigthal, Baden. Said to occur at Bräunsdorf, near Freiberg, at Niederreinsberg, Saxony, and at Kuttenberg, Bohemia. At Nagyág, Roumania, with fuloppite and sphalerite. In France at Peschadoire near Pontigibaud, Puy-de-Dôme. In the San José, Itos, and other mines in Oruro, Bolivia, with cassiterite, stannite, andorite, pyrite, and lead sulfosalts. An argentian variety is said to occur in the Magnet mine, Dundas, Tasmania.

In the United States an arsenian variety occurs at the Brobdignag mine, Red Mountain district, San Juan County, Colorado. Said to occur in Sevier County, Arkansas and in Nevada at Morey, Nye County, and Eureka, Eureka County.

A l t e r. To bindheimite.

A r t i f. A compound with the formula $PbSb_2S_4$ has been obtained from melts in the system $PbS-Sb_2S_3$;[15] also by fusion of $PbCl_2$ and Sb_2S_3.[16]

N a m e. After J. K. L. Zinken (1798–1862), mineralogist and mining geologist. The name has also been written Zincken.

KEELEYITE. *Gordon* (*Ac. Nat. Sc. Philadelphia, Proc.*, **74**, 101, 1922). A lead antimony sulfide, supposedly $Pb_2Sb_6S_{11}$. Found as acicular crystals in quartz, associated with stannite and pyrite, at the San José mine, Oruro, Bolivia. Shown[17] to be identical with zinkenite. Named after Frank J. Keeley, formerly curator of the Vaux collection, Academy of Natural Sciences, Philadelphia.

Ref.

1. Vaux and Bannister, *Min. Mag.*, **25**, 221 (1938), assign hexagonal symmetry to zinkenite on the basis of x-ray evidence. The orientation of Dana (112, 1892), from measurements by Rose, *Ann. Phys.*, **7**, 91 (1826), made the direction of elongation [010], in order to show the supposed relation to sartorite. Luedecke (121, 1896) made this the [001] axis, with orthorhombic symmetry. Goldschmidt (**9**, 107, 1923) interchanged the *a* and *b* of Dana (1892), and also considered the mineral orthorhombic.

2. Elements from angles of Berman (priv. comm., 1939) on Wolfsberg crystals. The terminal form value is an average of 7 measurements on two crystals with a deviation from 12°06' to 14°00'. The prism zone of one crystal gave excellent agreement with the required 60° angle.

3. Vaux and Bannister, *Min. Mag.*, **25**, 221 (1938), on crystals from Wolfsberg. The earlier rotation measurements of Ferrari and Curti, *Per. Min.*, **5**, 173 (1935), with a_0 6.37, b_0 3.81 and c_0 14.53, are not in agreement with the work of Vaux and Bannister. Hiller, *Zs. Kr.*, **100**, 137 (1938), obtained by the powder method an unlikely orthorhombic cell with a_0 12.29, b_0 8.66, c_0 13.76; $a_0 : b_0 : c_0 = 1.4192 : 1 : 1.5889$; and containing $Pb_8Sb_{16}S_{32}$.

4. Vaux and Bannister (1938).

5. Measured on 22-mg. crystal (Berman, priv. comm., 1939).

6. Schneiderhöhn and Ramdohr (**2**, 393, 1931).

7. The earlier formula (in Dana, 1892, and elsewhere), $PbSb_2S_4$, does not agree so well with the analyses. However, a unit cell of the dimensions given, with $81(PbSb_2S_4)$ gives a calculated specific gravity of 5.35, in better agreement with observation.

8. As has also been found spectroscopically in the material from Wolfsberg by de Gramont, *Bull. soc. min.*, **18**, 312 (1895).

9. For additional analyses see Doelter (4 [1], 449, 1926).

10. Guillemain (Inaug. Diss., Breslau, 1898 — *Zs. Kr.*, **33**, 73 (1900).

11. Hillebrand, *Sc. Soc. Colorado, Proc.*, **1**, 121 (1884).

12. Rose, *Ann. Phys.*, **8**, 199 (1826).

13. Shannon anal. in Shannon and Short, *Am. Min.*, **12**, 405 (1927).

14. de Finály and Koch, *Min. Mag.*, **22**, 183 (1929).

15. Iitsuka, *Kyoto Univ., Mem. Coll. Sc.*, 4, 61 (1920), and Fournet, *J. pr. Chem.*, **2**, 490 (1834). See also Jaeger and van Klooster, *Zs. anorg. Chem.*, **78**, 260 (1912).

16. Sommerlad, *Zs. anorg. Chem.*, **18**, 436 (1898); **15**, 179 (1897).

17. Vaux and Bannister (1938) from x-ray study of type keeleyite and authentic zinkenite from Wolfsberg. The mineral had earlier been considered by Shannon and Short (1927), on a basis of etch tests and a new analysis (which yielded the formula $PbSb_2S_4$), to differ from zinkenite (the formula of which was suggested to be $Pb_2Sb_6S_{11}$ or $Pb_3Sb_8S_{15}$). Wherry, *Am. Min.*, **13**, 29 (1928), however, disagreed with these conclusions and considered that keeleyite was an impure zinkenite.

389   **SARTORITE** [$PbAs_2S_4$].   Skleroklas + Arsenomelan *Walterhausen* (*Ann. Phys.*, **94**, 115, 1855; **100**, 537, 1857). Skleroklas *Rath* (*Ann. Phys.*, **122**, 380, 1864). Binnit *Heusser* (*Ann. Phys.*, **94**, 335, 1855; **97**, 120, 1856). (Not the binnite (= tennantite) of *Des Cloizeaux, Ann. mines*, **8**, 389 [1855].) Dufrenoysite pt. *Dufrénoy* (pl. 235, Fig. 66, 1856); *Des Cloizeaux* (*Ann. mines*, **8**, 389, 1855). Arseno-melan pt. *Petersen* (*Offenbach Ver., Ber.*, **7**, 13, 1866). Sartorite *Dana* (87, 1868). Bleiarsenglanz *Groth* (22, 1882).

C r y s t. Monoclinic.[1]

$a : b : c = 1.276 : 1 : 1.195; \quad \beta\ 102°12'; \quad p_0 : q_0 : r_0 = 0.9365 : 1.168 : 1$

$r_2 : p_2 : q_2 = 0.8562 : 0.8018 : 1; \quad \mu\ 77°48'; \quad p_0'\ 0.9582,\ q_0'\ 1.195,\ x_0'\ 0.2162$

Forms:[3]

		ϕ	ρ	ϕ_2	$\rho_2 = B$	C	A
c	001	90°00′	12°12′	77°48′	90°00′	....	77°48′
a	100	90 00	90 00	0 00	90 00	77°48′	.....
N	120	21 51	90 00	0 00	21 51	85 29½	55 57
m	110	38 43½	90 00	0 00	38 43½	82 24	39 04½
K	320	50 15½	90 00	0 00	50 15½	80 39	27 32½
d	101	90 00	49 35	40 25	90 00	37 23	40 25
D	$\bar{1}$01	−90 00	36 34½	126 34½	90 00	48 46½	126 34½
E	$\bar{5}$04	−90 00	44 28	134 28	90 00	56 40	134 28
F	$\bar{9}$05	−90 00	56 27½	146 27½	90 00	68 39½	146 27½
G	$\bar{2}$01	−90 00	59 32	149 32	90 00	71 44	149 32
H	$\bar{4}$01	−90 00	74 32½	164 32½	90 00	86 44½	164 32½
r	111	44 30	59 10	40 25	52 14	51 05½	52 59½
M	443	43 09½	65 24	33 48	48 27	57 26	51 32½
o	441	40 16	80 56	13 52½	41 06½	73 12½	50 20½
n	322	54 08½	63 53	31 10	58 16	54 16½	43 18
u	$\bar{1}$23	− 7 23	38 46½	95 53½	51 36½	41 50½	94 37
ε	$\bar{2}$45	− 9 55	44 08½	99 29	46 41	47 27½	96 53
h	$\bar{1}$22	−12 24½	50 44½	104 44	40 52	54 18½	99 34½

Structure cell.[4] Monoclinic, a_0 58.38, b_0 7.79, c_0 83.30; β 90°; $a_0 : b_0 : c_0 = 7.49 : 1 : 10.69$; contains $Pb_{240}As_{480}S_{960}$.

Habit. Prismatic and deeply striated [010]. Terminal forms often rounded and interrupted, sometimes cavernous. Parallel and subparallel groupings common.

Twinning.[5] On {100}, often repeated to produce lamination of the crystals.

Phys. Cleavage {100} fair. Fracture conchoidal. Extremely brittle, often breaking with a snap. H. 3. G. 5.10 ± 0.02;[6] 5.07 (calc. for pseudocell). Luster metallic. Color dark lead-gray. Streak chocolate-brown. Opaque. In polished section[7] shows twin lamellae, sometimes bent; weakly anisotropic; deep red internal reflection.

Chem. Lead arsenic sulfide, $PbAs_2S_4$.

Anal.

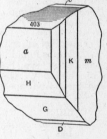

Binnental.

	1	2	3	4
Pb	42.70	43.63	42.93	41.92
As	30.87	30.46	31.11	29.59
S	26.43	25.51	25.32	[25.49]
Rem.	.....	......	.....	0.04
Total	100.00	99.60	99.36	97.04
G.	5.07	4.980		

1. $PbAs_2S_4$. 2. Binnental. Average of three analyses.[8] 3. Binnental.[9] 4. Binnental. Rem. is insol. On 0.1-gm. sample.[10]

Occur.[11] In the sugary dolomite of the Binnental at Lengenbach, Valais, Switzerland, often as large crystals several centimeters long, principally with tennantite, pyrite, dufrenoysite, and realgar. When found in the vugs sometimes yields terminated crystals.

Name. After Sartorius von Waltershausen (1809–1876), who first announced the species. Skleroclase is from σκληρός, *hard, violent,* and κλαν, *to break,* in allusion to its brittle character.

SARTORITE-α. *Smith* and *Solly* (*Min. Mag.*, **18**, 259, 1919), p. 312. Apparently of the same composition as sartorite, but with different crystallographic properties.[12]

Ref.

1. Monoclinic symmetry established by Trechmann, *Min. Mag.*, **14**, 212 (1907), confirmed by Bannister, Pabst, and Vaux, *ibid.*, **25**, 264 (1939). The triclinic interpretation of Smith and Solly, *ibid.*, **18**, 259 (1919) is involved and complicated, and their data are not consistent with other observations on the symmetry of the species.

2. Trechmann (1907). The relation between the Trechmann orientation and that of Smith and Solly (1919) is not simple. The latter have proposed, in addition to a monoclinic lattice, three other triclinic lattices, to explain the morphology of sartorite. Their measurements of different crystals, however, yield very different elements, so that little significance can be attached to the exceedingly complex form indices presented. Furthermore, the large cell proposed by Bannister, Pabst, and Vaux (1939) on the basis of an x-ray study, shows no simple correlation with the Smith and Solly interpretation, nor with the Trechmann angles. Some of the crystals studied have been reexamined by Palache (priv. comm., 1940) and found to be, for the most part, in agreement with Trechmann's results. The forms falling on the offset triclinic lattices of Smith and Solly are usually poor and uncertain in angular position, and may even be part of other crystals in subparallel or inclined position with the principal crystal.

3. Forms found by Trechmann (1907), verified by Palache (priv. comm., 1940), on some of the type crystallographic specimens from the British Museum. The forms of Smith and Solly, referred by them to the offset lattices are not given here. Other rare and uncertain forms are:

010	310	041	$\bar{4}$03	$\bar{1}$11	21·14·3
2·13·0	720	207	$\bar{3}$02	$\bar{4}$41	12·1·1
140	410	304	$\bar{8}$05	122	$\bar{1}$66
130	920	11·0·12	$\bar{5}$02	5·10·8	$\bar{2}$43
540	510	706	$\bar{8}$03	2·4·3	$\bar{3}$44 or $\bar{7}$99
430	11·2·0	403	$\bar{2}\bar{1}$·0·5	645	$\bar{1}$21
11·7·0	20·1·0	401	902	211	$\bar{4}$83
210	023	$\bar{2}$07	$\bar{8}$01	643	$\bar{3}$22
11·5·0	045	$\bar{4}$07	901	241	$\bar{2}$11
940	011	$\bar{2}$03	113	321	$\bar{2}$41
520	065	$\bar{7}$·0·10	445	722	$\bar{7}$22
11·4·0	085	$\bar{1}$9·0·20	221	411	$\bar{6}$11
					$\bar{6}$41

4. Bannister, Pabst, and Vaux (1939). They also recognized an orthorhombic pseudocell, with diffraction spots due mainly to the Pb atoms, having the dimensions a_0 19.46, b_0 7.79, c_0 4.17; $a_0 : b_0 : c_0 = 2.498 : 1 : 0.535$. Space group $P2_12_12_1$; containing $Pb_4As_8S_{16}$. The true cell has a complex relationship to the crystallographic elements previously proposed, and the forms reported have very complex indices when referred to the x-ray unit. Ferrari and Curti, *Per. Min.*, **5**, 155 (1934), on the basis of x-ray powder pictures of sartorite and other lead sulfosalts from the Binnental, have concluded that these minerals form an isomorphous series. The evidence, however, is not good.

5. Smith and Solly, *Min. Mag.*, **18**, 259 (1919) state that twinning is invariably found. Schneiderhöhn and Ramdohr (**2**, 491, 1931) have found twin lamellae in polished

section. Bannister, Pabst, and Vaux (1939), however, state that the crystal used for x-ray work (one of the crystals studied by Smith and Solly) was not twinned.

6. An average of 6 determinations by Berman (priv. comm., 1939), on fragments. Solly, *Min. Mag.*, **12**, 282 (1900), obtained 4.98.

7. Schneiderhöhn and Ramdohr (1931).

8. Jackson anal. in Solly (1900).

9. Jackson anal. in Lewis, *Min. Mag.*, **13**, XXXIV (1903).

10. Ferrari and Curti (1934).

11. Bader, *Schweiz. min. Mitt.*, **14**, 319 (1934), discusses the paragenesis of the deposit and gives detailed descriptions of the minerals. See also Guisca, *ibid.*, **10**, 152 (1930), and Niggli, Koenigsberger, and Parker (**1**, 251, 1940).

12. Bannister, Pabst, and Vaux (1939) find that sartorite-α gives x-ray diffraction effects identical with those of sartorite, but the morphology is definitely not the same, as shown by the measurements of Smith and Solly (1919) and of Palache (priv. comm., 1939).

38·10 **BERTHIERITE** [FeSb$_2$S$_4$].   Haidingerite *Berthier* (*Ann. chim. phys.*, **35**, 351, 1827; *Ann. Phys.*, **11**, 478, 1827).   Berthierit *Haidinger* (*Edinburgh J. Sc.*, **7**, 353, 1827).   Eisenantimonglanz *Groth* (16, 80, 1874).

Anglarite, Martourite, Chazellite *Nordenskiöld* (*Atom. chem. Mineralsyst.*, 1848).

C r y s t.   Orthorhombic;   dipyramidal — $2/m\,2/m\,2/m$.[1]

Structure cell.[1]   Space group *Pnam*; a_0 11.44, b_0 14.12, c_0 3.76; a_0 : $b_0 : c_0 = 0.810 : 1 : 0.266$;   contains Fe$_4Sb_8S_{16}$.

Habit.   Prismatic on, and striated ∥, [001].   Prismatic to fibrous massive, plumose or radial; granular.

P h y s.   Cleavage prismatic, rather indistinct.   Brittle.   H. 2–3. G. 4.64;[2] 4.66 (calc.).   Luster metallic.   Color dark steel-gray, often tarnished iridescent or pinchbeck brown.   Streak dark brownish gray. Opaque.   In polished section[3] gray in color with very strong anisotropism and marked pleochroism.   Reflection percentages: (∥ b) green 27.5, orange 26.5, red 26.5; (∥ c) green 39, orange 34.5, red 34.

C h e m.   An iron antimony sulfide, FeSb$_2$S$_4$.   Mn apparently substitutes for Fe up to about 4 weight per cent.

Anal.[4]

	1	2	3	4	5	6	7
Fe	13.21	13.43	13.42	13.38	12.61	13.54	10.09
Mn	.....	.....	.....	.....	0.31	.....	3.56
Sb	56.55	56.06	57.02	57.44	55.96	56.11	56.61
S	30.24	29.46	29.56	29.18	29.28	30.12	29.12
Rem.	.....	0.33	.....	.....	1.29	0.23	.....
Total	100.00	99.28	100.00	100.00	99.45	100.00	99.38
G.	4.66	4.65			4.622		4.06

1. FeSb$_2$S$_4$.   2. Kisbánya, Roumania.   Rem. is 0.33 insol., Mn trace.[5]   3. Honigoutte, Charbes, Alsace.   Recalc. to 100 per cent after deduction of 5.29 per cent quartz.[6] 4. Bohutin, near Příbram, Bohemia.   With Pb trace.   Recalculated to 100 per cent after deduction of 19.96 per cent quartz.[7]   5. Felsöbánya, Roumania.   Rem. is Pb 0.94, Cu 0.06, Zn 0.24, insol. 0.05.[8]   6. Bräunsdorf, Saxony.   Recalc. after deduction of 1.30 per cent quartz.[9]   7. San Antonio, Lower California.[10]

Tests.   Easily fusible to a weakly magnetic globule.   Soluble in HCl, giving off H$_2$S.

O c c u r.   In low-temperature hydrothermal veins, usually intimately associated with quartz and stibnite.   In Germany from Bräunsdorf and elsewhere in the Freiberg district with stibnite and silver sulfosalts.   At

Bohutin, south of Přibram, Bohemia, and with jamesonite and stibnite at Aranyidka, Hungary. Originally described from the district of Pontigibaud, Puy-de-Dôme, France; also from Anglar, Creuse, and near Charbes, Val de Villé, Alsace, in the veins of Honigoutte and Trou-du-Loup. At Padstow, Cornwall, England. Reported from various localities in Peru, Chile and Bolivia. From San Antonio, Lower California, Mexico. With stibnite at Nullamanna, near Inverell, New South Wales. From the stibnite deposit near Lake George, southwest of Fredericton, New Brunswick, Canada.

A r t i f. Early reported by fusion of FeS and Sb_2S_3.[11]

N a m e. After the French chemist, Pierre Berthier (1782–1861).

Ref.

1. From x-ray study of Buerger, *Am. Min.*, **21**, 442 (1936); **21**, 205 (1936), on analyzed material from Kisbánya (anal. 2).
2. Average of 4.65 and 4.622 by Zsivny and Zomboro, *Min. Mag.*, **23**, 566 (1934), and Krenner, *Cbl. Min.*, 265, 1928. Older values in the literature give 4.0 ± 0.1.
3. Schneiderhöhn and Ramdohr (2, 394, 1931).
4. For additional analyses see Doelter (4 [1], 586, 1926) and Stillwell, *Min. Mag.*, **21**, 83 (1926). The older analyses show wide variations, probably because of admixed stibnite, and several varietal names (*martourite, anglarite, chazellite*) have been based on analyses of impure material. See Loczka, *Zs. Kr.*, **37**, 379 (1902), and Stillwell (1926).
5. Loczka anal. in Zsivny and Zomboro (1934).
6. Ungemach, *Bull. soc. min.*, **29**, 266 (1906).
7. Vambera anal. in Hoffmann, *Böhm. Ges., Ber.*, **19** (1897) — *Zs. Kr.*, **31**, 527 (1899).
8. Loczka anal. in Krenner, *Cbl. Min.*, 265, 1928.
9. Loczka (1902).
10. Freese anal. in Rammelsberg (86, 1875).
11. Berthier, *Ann. Phys.*, **11**, 482 (1827).

38·11 C Y L I N D R I T E [$Pb_3Sn_4Sb_2S_{14}$]. Kylindrit *Frenzel* (*Jb. Min.*, II, 125, 1893). Cylindrite *Dana* (21, 1899).

Massive, in cylindrical forms[1] separating under pressure into smooth concentric shells. Also in spherically grouped aggregates.

P h y s. Good circular separation ‖ elongation of cylinders, and a poorer one across the elongation. Slightly malleable. H. $2\frac{1}{2}$. G. 5.46 ± 0.03. Luster metallic. Color blackish lead-gray. Streak black. Opaque. In polished section[2] gray-white in color with distinct anisotropism; extremely weak pleochroism: ‖ elongation gray-white, ⊥ elongation darker gray-white. Reflection percentages: green 41, orange 38.5, red 35.

C h e m. A lead, tin, antimony sulfide, possibly $Pb_3Sn_4Sb_2S_{14}$.[3] The Fe reported apparently is due to impurities. Ge, Au, Cu, Bi, and Fe have been reported spectrographically.[3]

Anal.

	1	2	3	4	5
Pb	34.76	35.41	35.24	34.58	36.74
Fe	.....	3.00	2.81	2.77	.....
Ag	.....	0.62	0.50	0.28	0.41
Sb	13.61	8.73	12.31	12.98	13.32
Sn	26.54	26.37	25.65	25.10	26.71
S	25.09	24.50	23.83	23.88	22.79
Total	100.00	98.63	100.34	99.59	99.97
G.		5.22	5.46	5.49	

1. $Pb_3Sn_4Sb_2S_{14}$. 2. Poopó.[4] 3, 4. Poopó.[5] 5. Average of anal. 3 and 4 recalc. after deduction of Fe as FeS_2.

Tests. F. 1. Unattacked by cold acids. Slowly soluble in hot HCl; also in hot HNO$_3$ with separation of S and the oxides of Sn and Sb.

O c c u r. In Bolivia in the Trinacria and other mines at Poopó, with franckeite, pyrite, and sphalerite; at the Porvenir and Francisca mines, Huanuni, with franckeite; reported from the Nueva Virginia vein, Colquechaca, and from the Purisima vein, Oruro.

A l t e r. To cassiterite, usually in finely divided dispersed particles, and to cerussite.

A r t i f. Cylindrical forms have been observed in some artificial Sn-Sb-As alloys.

N a m e. From κύλινδρος, *a roll*, in allusion to the cylindrical form of aggregation.

Ref.

1. Stead, *J. Inst. Met.*, **22**, 127 (1919), has observed cylindrical forms in Sn-Sb-As alloys.
2. Schneiderhöhn and Ramdohr (**2**, 484, 1931).
3. Moritz, *Jb. Min., Beil.-Bd.*, **66**, 205 (1933). The nearly constant amount of Fe in the analyses, as with franckeite, suggests the constitutive role of this element. Prior, *Min. Mag.*, **14**, 25 (1904), derives Pb$_3$FeSn$_4$Sb$_2$S$_{14}$. Spectrographic and microscopic examination (Moritz, 1933), however, indicates the Fe to be due to impurities.
4. Frenzel (1893).
5. Prior (1904).

38·12   **Gladite** [PbCuBi$_5$S$_9$]. *Johansson* (*Ark. Kemi*, **9** [8], 17, 1924).

C r y s t.   Orthorhombic?.

$$a : b = 0.9859 : 1$$

Forms:

		ϕ	ρ
a	100	90°00′	90°00′
b	010	0 00	90 00
l	250	22 05	90 00
m	110	45 25½	90 00

Habit.   Prismatic [001], without terminal faces.

P h y s.   Cleavage {010} good, {100} fair. H. 2–3. G. 6.96. Luster metallic. Color lead-gray. Streak black. Opaque.

C h e m.   A lead and copper bismuth sulfide, PbCuBi$_5$S$_9$.

Anal.

	Pb	Fe	Cu	Bi	S	Insol.	Total
1	12.92	....	3.96	65.14	17.98	....	100.00
2	12.40	0.19	3.98	64.96	18.04	0.12	99.69

1. PbCuBi$_5$S$_9$.   2. Gladhammar.

O c c u r. At Gladhammar, Kalmar, Sweden, as crystals (2 cm. long and 2–6 mm. thick) with quartz and lead bismuth sulfides.

N a m e. From the locality, Gladhammar, Sweden.

Needs further study.

38·13 **V R B A I T E** [TlAs₂SbS₅].   *Jezek (Ak. Böhmen, Roz.,* **21,** 1912; *Zs. Kr.,* **51,** 365, 1912).   Urbaite.

C r y s t.   Orthorhombic; dipyramidal — $2/m\,2/m\,2/m$.

$a : b : c = 0.5657 : 1 : 0.4836;^1$ $p_0 : q_0 : r_0 = 0.8548 : 0.4836 : 1$

$q_1 : r_1 : p_1 = 0.5657 : 1.1699 : 1$; $r_2 : p_2 : q_2 = 2.0678 : 1.7676 : 1$

Forms:

		ϕ	ρ	ϕ_1	ρ_1	ϕ_2	$\rho_2 = B$
c	001	.....	0°00′	0°00′	90°00′	90°00′	90°00′
b	010	0°00′	90 00	90 00	90 00	.....	0 00
a	100	90 00	90 00	.....	0 00	0 00	90 00
f	035	0 00	16 11	16 11	90 00	90 00	73 49
e	021	0 00	44 02½	44 02½	90 00	90 00	45 57½
d	041	0 00	62 40	62 40	90 00	90 00	27 20
q	112	60 30	26 09	13 35½	67 26½	76 24½	77 28
p	111	60 30	44 29	25 48½	52 25	49 28½	69 49
o	331	60 30	71 15	55 25½	34 29½	21 18	62 12½
r	131	30 30½	59 17½	55 25½	64 07½	49 28½	42 12

Structure cell.² Space group *Cmca*; a_0 13.35, b_0 23.32, c_0 11.23 (all ± 0.05); $a_0 : b : c_0 = 0.5725 : 1 : 0.4815$; contains Tl₂₁(As,Sb)₆₃S₁₀₅.

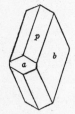 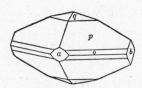

Habit.   Crystals small, tabular {010} or pyramidal {111}.   In groups.

P h y s.   Cleavage {010} good.   Fracture uneven to conchoidal. Brittle.   H. 3½.   G. 5.30 ± 0.03;   5.29 (calc.).   Luster submetallic to metallic.   Color dark gray-black with a bluish tint; in small crystals or thin splinters translucent and dark red.   Streak light red with a yellow tone.   In polished section³ bluish white in color, with red internal reflections.

C h e m.   Thallium arsenic-antimony sulfide, Tl(As,Sb)₃S₅, with As : Sb nearly 2 : 1.

Anal.

	Tl	Fe	Sb	As	S	Total
1	32.12	....	19.14	23.55	25.19	100.00
2	29.52	1.85	18.34	24.06	25.20	98.97

1. TlAs₂SbS₅.   2. Allchar.⁴

Tests.   F. 1.   Insoluble in HCl but soluble in concentrated H₂SO₄ and in HNO₃ with separation of sulfur.

O c c u r. Found intergrown with realgar and orpiment at Allchar, near Rozsdan, northwest of Salonika, Macedonia.

A r t i f. The compound $TlAs_3S_5$ has been obtained from melts in the system $Tl_2S-As_2S_3$.[5]

N a m e. After the Bohemian mineralogist, Karl Vrba (1845–1922).

Ref.

1. The a value here given is slightly different from that of Jezek (1912), but corresponds better with the angular values.
2. Frondel, *Am. Min.*, **26**, 25 (1941), by Weissenberg method.
3. Murdoch (115, 1916).
4. Křehlik, *Zs. Kr.*, **51**, 379 (1912).
5. Canneri and Fernandes, *Acc. Linc., Att.*, **1**, 671 (1925).

EICHBERGITE.   *Grosspietsch (Cbl. Min.*, 433, 1911).

Massive. Fracture uneven. H. $6\frac{1}{2}$. G. 5.36. Color iron-gray. Composition possibly $(Cu,Fe)(Bi,Sb)_3S_5$. Analysis gave:

Cu	Fe	Bi	Sb	S	Total
3.62	1.45	51.53	30.00	12.74	99.34

Known in a single specimen from the magnesite deposit on the Eichberg, Semmering Mountains, Styria, Germany. Superficially altered to gray-green and golden ocherous material.

Needs confirmation.

391   **L I V I N G S T O N I T E** [$HgSb_4S_7$]. *Barcena (Naturaleza*, **3**, 35, 172, 1874; **4**, 268, 1879 — *Am. J. Sc.*, **8**, 145, 1874; **9**, 64, 1875).

C r y s t.[1] Monoclinic; prismatic — $2/m$.

$a : b : c = 3.7572 : 1 : 5.3660;$ $\beta\ 104°10';$ $p_0 : q_0 : r_0 = 1.4282 : 5.2028 : 1$
$r_2 : p_2 : q_2 = 0.1922 : 0.2745 : 1;$ $\mu\ 75°50';$ $p_0'\ 1.4730,\ q_0'\ 5.3660,\ x_0'\ 0.2524$

Forms:[2]

		ϕ	ρ	ϕ_2	$\rho_2 = B$	C	A
c	001	90°00′	14°10′	75°50′	90°00′	0°00′	75°50′
a	100	90 00	90 00	0 00	90 00	75 50	0 00
d	101	90 00	59 54½	30 05½	90 00	45 44½	30 05½
e	$\bar{1}01$	−90 00	50 40½	140 40½	90 00	64 50½	140 40½
p	$\bar{1}11$	−12 49	79 42	140 40½	16 23	83 06½	102 36½
q	122	10 26½	79 37	45 19	14 41	77 23	79 44

Structure cell.[1] Space group $P2_1/c$; $a_0\ 15.14$, $b_0\ 3.98$, $c_0\ 21.60$; $\beta\ 104°$; $a_0 : b_0 : c_0 = 3.80 : 1 : 5.43$; contains $Hg_4Sb_{16}S_{28}$.

Habit. Minute needles elongated [010]. Also columnar to fibrous massive; in globular masses of interlaced needles.

Huitzuco, Mexico.

P h y s. Cleavage {001} perfect, {010}, and {100} poor.[3] Flexible. H. 2. G. 5.00;[4] 4.79 (calc.). Luster adamantine to metallic. Color blackish gray. Streak red. Nearly opaque. In thin splinters translucent and red in color. Translation gliding:[3] $T\{001\}$, $t[010]$; probably also twin gliding.[5]

O p t.   In polished section[6] white in color with strong anisotropism and weak pleochroism; deep red internal reflections.   Reflection percentages: green 37, orange 32.5, red 30.   In transmitted light red.[7] n_{Li} much above 2.72.   Probably optically negative $(-)$. $Z = [010]$.   Pleochroism moderate in red with $X > Z$.   Birefringence extreme.

C h e m.   A mercury antimony sulfide, probably $HgSb_4S_7$.

Anal.[8]

	1	2	3
Hg	22.00	22.61	22.52
Sb	53.40	52.21	53.75
S	24.60	24.50	23.73
Rem.	.....	0.68	.....
Total	100.00	100.00	100.00
G.	4.79	4.06	4.41

1. $HgSb_4S_7$.   2. Guadalcázar.   Rem. is Fe 0.68.   Recalc. after deduction of 37.6 per cent impurities.[9]   3. Huitzuco.   Average of two analyses.   Recalc. after deduction of 13–16 per cent impurities.[10]

Tests.   F. 1.   Insoluble in cold HNO_3, but dissolved by warm HNO_3 with separation of Sb_2O_3.

O c c u r.   In Mexico at Huitzuco, Guerrero, associated with cinnabar, stibnite, sulfur, and valentinite in a matrix of calcite and gypsum; also at Guadalcázar, San Luis Potosí, with gypsum and sulfur.

A l t e r.   Cinnabar has been reported as pseudomorphs after livingstonite; livingstonite also alters to a black material,[11] apparently a mixture of metacinnabar and antimony oxide.

A r t i f.   Not found in the system $HgS-Sb_2S_3$.[12]

N a m e.   After David Livingstone (1813–73), the African explorer and missionary.

Ref.

1. Richmond, *Am. Min.*, **21**, 719 (1936), on crystals from Huitzuco.   Uncertain forms: {11·1·0}, {011}, {111}, {Ī22}.
2. Berman in Richmond (1936).
3. Berman (priv. comm., 1939).
4. Measured on 19-mg. fragment from Huitzuco (Frondel, priv. comm., 1939). Older values in literature are lower.
5. Orcel, *Bull. soc. min.*, **51**, 202 (1928); Schneiderhöhn and Ramdohr (**2**, 376, 1931).
6. Schneiderhöhn and Ramdohr (1931).
7. Larsen (101, 1921).
8. For additional analyses see Barcena (1874, 1879).
9. Page, *Chem. News*, **42**, 195 (1880).
10. Venable, *Chem. News*, **40**, 186 (1879).
11. Page (1880), with analysis.
12. Pelabon, *C. R.*, **140**, 1389 (1905); see also Baker, *Chem. News*, **42**, 196 (1880).

Allcharite.   *Jezek* (*Zs. Kr.*, **51**, 275, 1912).

C r y s t.   Orthorhombic.

$a : b : c = 0.9283 : 1 : 0.6080;$ $p_0 : q_0 : r_0 = 0.6550 : 0.6080 : 1$

$q_1 : r_1 : p_1 = 0.9283 : 1.5267 : 1;$ $r_2 : p_2 : q_2 = 1.6447 : 1.0773 : 1$

Forms:

		ϕ	$\rho = C$	ϕ_1	$\rho_1 = A$	ϕ_2	$\rho_2 = B$
b	010	0°00′	90°00′	90°00′	90°00′	. . . . .	0°00′
m	110	47 08	90 00	90 00	42 52	0°00′	47 08
n	210	65 06	90 00	90 00	24 54	0 00	65 06
u	011	0 00	31 18	31 18	90 00	90 00	58 42
z	101	90 00	33 13½	0 00	56 46½	56 46½	90 00
p	111	47 08	41 47	31 18	60 46	56 46½	63 02½

Habit. Small crystals, prismatic [001].

Known only crystallographically. Said to resemble stibnite in color and luster. Found with vrbaite, realgar and orpiment at Allchar, Macedonia. Named after the locality.

Hatchite. *Solly* and *Smith* (*Min. Mag.*, 16, 287, 1912).

Cryst. Triclinic.

$$a : b : c = 0.9787 : 1 : 1.1575; \quad \alpha\ 116°53\tfrac{1}{2}', \quad \beta\ 85°12', \quad \gamma\ 113°44\tfrac{1}{2}'$$

$$p_0 : q_0 : r_0 = 1.4487 : 1.2601 : 1; \quad \lambda\ 62°41', \quad \mu\ 83°04\tfrac{1}{2}', \quad \nu\ 65°46'$$

$$p_0'\ 1.6363, \quad q_0'\ 1.4232, \quad x_0'\ 0.0839, \quad y_0'\ 0.5195$$

Forms:

c	001	m	110	M	$\bar{1}10$	f	$0\bar{2}1$	μ	$2\bar{2}1$	o	$11\bar{1}$	q	256
b	010	n	$\bar{2}10$	g	$0\bar{1}2$	d	103	s	$\bar{1}12$	i	$2\bar{5}1$	v	$12\bar{1}$
a	100	l	$\bar{3}20$	e	$0\bar{1}1$	r	$1\bar{1}1$	p	$\bar{1}11$	j	$13\bar{6}$	w	$32\bar{1}$

Phys. Color lead-gray. Streak chocolate colored.

Chem. Undetermined, but supposed to be a lead arsenic sulfide.

Occur. Five small crystals deposited upon a crystal probably of rathite were found at the Lengenbach quarry, Binnental, Valais, Switzerland.

Name. After Dr. Frederick Henry Hatch (1864–1932), mining engineer and geologist.

Ref.

1. Solly and Smith (1912). Their orientation is retained although unconventional.

Marrite. *Solly* (*Min. Mag.*, 14, 76, 1905; 14, 188, 1906).

Cryst. Monoclinic; prismatic — $2/m$.

$$a : b : c = 0.5763 : 1 : 0.4739; \quad \beta\ 91°15', \quad p_0 : q_0 : r_0 = 1.2161 : 0.5748 : 1$$

$$r_2 : p_2 : q_2 = 1.7356 : 2.1107 : 1; \quad \mu\ 88°45'; \quad p_0'\ 1.2164, \quad q_0'\ 0.4739, \quad x_0'\ 0.0218$$

Forms:

		ϕ	ρ	ϕ_2	$\rho_2 = B$	C	A
c	001	90°00′	1°15′	88°45′	90°00′	.....	88°45′
b	010	0 00	90 00	.....	0 00	90°00′	90 00
a	100	90 00	90 00	0 00	90 00	88 45	.....
k	120	46 32	90 00	0 00	46 32	89 05½	43 28
m	110	64 39	90 00	0 00	64 39	88 52	25 21
K	210	76 40½	90 00	0 00	76 40½	88 47	13 19½
ϵ	011	2 10	29 58½	88 45	60 03	29 57	88 55
ξ	021	1 05	49 03½	88 45	40 57	49 03	89 11
e	201	90 00	67 50	22 10	90 00	66 35	22 10
E	$\overline{2}01$	−90 00	67 28½	157 28½	90 00	68 43½	157 28½
p	111	65 02½	53 47½	38 55½	70 05½	52 39½	42 59½
P	$\overline{1}11$	−64 15	52 59	140 04	69 42	54 07	135 59
w	211	76 47	68 22	22 10	77 44	67 09	25 11

Less common:

f	170	l	230	β	013	ι	031	N	$\overline{1}12$	t	131	v	312
g	160	L	320	γ	012	κ	072	O	$\overline{2}23$	u	151	x	271
h	150	J	310	δ	023	λ	041	Q	$\overline{2}33$	R	$\overline{2}12$	W	$\overline{2}11$
i	140	I	720	η	073	d	101	r	212	S	$\overline{1}21$	Y	$\overline{2}31$
j	130	α	015	θ	083	D	$\overline{1}01$	s	121	T	$\overline{1}31$	

Habit. Equant, to tabular {010}. Striated [001].

P h y s. Cleavage none. Fracture conchoidal. Brittle H. 3. Luster brilliant metallic. Color lead- to steel-gray, often with iridescent tarnish. Streak black with chocolate tinge.

C h e m. Presumably a sulfosalt, but no chemical data are available.

O c c u r. Sparingly in the white dolomite at Lengenbach, Binnental, Valais, Switzerland, associated with lengenbachite and rathite.

N a m e. After Dr. John E. Marr of Cambridge, England.

UNNAMED MINERAL. *Smith* (*Min. Mag.*, **19**, 40, 1920).

C r y s t. Triclinic[1]?

$a : b : c = 3.3425 : 1 : 3.5536;$ $\beta\ 102°08′;$ $p_0 : q_0 : r_0 = 1.063 : 3.474 : 1$

$r_2 : p_2 : q_2 = 0.298 : 0.306 : 1;$ $\mu\ 77°52′;$ $p_0'\ 1.087,\ q_0'\ 3.554,\ x_0'\ 0.210$

Forms:[2]

010	10$\overline{9}$	10$\overline{1}$	11$\overline{5}$	5$\overline{1}$5	4$\overline{1}\overline{4}$	21$\overline{2}$
103	10$\overline{3}$	111	311	6$\overline{1}$2	5$\overline{1}\overline{1}$	61$\overline{2}$
801	50$\overline{9}$	$\overline{1}11$	3$\overline{1}5$	2·3·10	515	

Color steel-gray. Streak black. G. 4.2. The chemical composition is unknown. Known only as a single loose crystal (in the British Museum collection) from the Binnental, Switzerland.

Ref.

1. Smith (1920) considered the mineral triclinic, class unknown, but his elements are monoclinic, with α and γ both 90°00′. The equivalent monoclinic projection elements are given here.
2. The face poles are given in the positions observed by Smith, since the crystal class is unknown.

SIMPLE OXIDES

This section contains the simple oxides, that is, compounds of one metal and oxygen. These minerals are, for the most part, not complex in composition or structure, and the crystallochemical relations between them are fairly well understood.[1] The ratio $A : X$ varies from $2 : 1$ (cuprite) to $1 : 2$ (rutile, etc.) and most of the minerals found here can be expressed by a simple formula.

The most important group of the AX type is the periclase group, where A = Mg, Ni, Mn, Cd, Ca. All these possess the NaCl structure, as indicated by the radius ratio R_A/R_X. The zincite group has the wurtzite structure. Litharge (and palladinite) has a distorted rock-salt structure. The other minerals of the AX type, such as tenorite, are less simple.[2] Paramelaconite may be a defect structure, with O deficient in the lattice.

In the A_2X_3 type the most important group is the hematite group, in which the oxygen atoms are approximately in hexagonal closest packing and the metal ions lie between 6 oxygens forming an octahedron. In ilmenite the symmetry of the hematite structure is diminished to $R\bar{3}$ because one of the Fe ions of hematite is replaced by Ti.

Valentinite, Sb_2O_3, and senarmontite are dimorphous, as are claudetite, As_2O_3, and arsenolite. The structure of valentinite indicates that it is a molecular compound with indefinitely long chains of Sb_2O_3 in the direction of the c-axis. In senarmontite the molecular grouping has the composition Sb_4O_6 and no chains are found. Presumably the claudetite-arsenolite relationship may be the same. Little is known of the structures of other A_2X_3 minerals.

The most important simple oxides of the AX_2 type are members of the rutile group in which the coordination is $6 : 3$ and the ratio $R_A : R_X = 0.732$ to 0.414.[1] Many other oxides not found as minerals have this structure, and some of the multiple oxides containing columbium and tantalum, such as tapiolite with $A + B/X = 1 : 2$, also have a closely similar structure. The other polymorphous titanium oxides, anatase and brookite, are more complex in structure.

The simple oxides or hydrous oxides of antimony, bismuth, vanadium and tungsten are little known, chiefly because they are poorly crystallized and inhomogeneous.

489

4 SIMPLE OXIDES

41 A_2X TYPE

| 411 | Cuprite | Cu_2O |
| 413 | Water | H_2O |

42 AX TYPE

421	PERICLASE GROUP	
4211	Periclase	MgO
4212	Bunsenite	NiO
4213	Manganosite	MnO
4214	Cadmium oxide	CdO
4215	Lime	CaO

422	ZINCITE GROUP	
4221	Zincite	ZnO
4222	Bromellite	BeO

| 423 | Tenorite | CuO |
| 424 | Paramelaconite | $Cu^2_{1-2x}Cu^1_{2x}O_{1-x}$ |

| 425 | Montroydite | HgO |

| 426 | Litharge | PbO |

| 427 | Massicot | PbO |

43 A_3X_4 TYPE

| 431 | Minium | Pb_3O_4 |

44 A_2X_3 TYPE

441	HEMATITE GROUP	
4411	Corundum	Al_2O_3
4412	Hematite	Fe_2O_3
	Ilmenite series	
4413	Ilmenite	$FeTiO_3$
4414	Geikielite	$MgTiO_3$
4415	Pyrophanite	$MnTiO_3$
4416	Senaite	$(Fe,Mn,Pb)TiO_3$

442	ARSENOLITE GROUP	
4421	Arsenolite	As_2O_3
4422	Senarmontite	Sb_2O_3

| 443 | Claudetite | As_2O_3 |
| 444 | Valentinite | Sb_2O_3 |

| 445 | Bixbyite | $(Mn,Fe)_2O_3$ |

| 446 | Braunite | $(Mn,Si)_2O_3$ |

45 AX_2 TYPE

451	RUTILE GROUP	
4511	Rutile	TiO_2
4512	Pyrolusite	MnO_2
4513	Wad	
4514	Todorokite	
4515	Cassiterite	SnO_2
4516	Plattnerite	PbO_2

452	Anatase	TiO_2
453	Brookite	TiO_2
454	Tellurite	TeO_2
455	Selenolite	SeO_2

456	Cervantite	Sb_2O_4?
457	Stibiconite	$Sb_3O_6(OH)$?

447	Bismite	Bi_2O_3
448	Sillenite	Bi_2O_3

46 A_mX_n TYPE

461	Vanoxite	$V_4V_2O_{13} \cdot 8H_2O$?
462	Corvusite	$V_2V_{12}O_{34} \cdot nH_2O$
463`	Ilsemannite	$Mo_3O_8 \cdot nH_2O$?
464	Russellite	$(Bi_2W)O_3$
465	Tungstite	$WO_3 \cdot H_2O$?

Ref.

1. See Evans (168, 1939).
2. Tunell, Posnjak, and Ksanda, *Zs. Kr.*, **90**, 120 (1935).
3. Goldschmidt, *Vidensk. Skr. Oslo, Mat.-Nat. Kl.*, **1**, 17 (1926).

411   **CUPRITE** [Cu_2O]. Aes caldarium rubro-fuscum *Germ.* Lebererzkupfer *Agricola* (334, 1546A; 462, 1546B). Minera cupri calciformis pura et indurata, colore rubro, vulgo Kupferglas, Kupfer Lebererz *Cronstedt* (173, 1758). Cuprum tessulatum nudum *Linnaeus* (176, tab. viii, 1756); Cuprum cryst. octaëdrum *Linnaeus* (1768). Octahedral Copper Ore, Red Glassy Copper Ore *Hill* (1771). Mine rouge de cuivre *Sage* (1772). Mine de cuivre vitreuse rouge *de Lisle* (1772, 1783). Rothes Kupferglas *Pallas* (*Nord. Beiträge*, **5**, 283, 1793). Rothkupfererz *Germ.* Cuivre oxidulé *Fr.* Oxydulated Copper. Ziguéline *Beudant* (**2**, 713, 1832). Ruberite *Chapman* (63, 1843). Cuprit *Haidinger* (548, 1845). Kupferoxydul, Kupferroth, Kupferbraun *Hausmann* (370, 1847). Ruby Copper.

Ziegelerz = Tile Ore; Kupferlebererz; Hepatinerz. Ziguelina *Ital.* Ziegelite. Haarförmiges Rothkupfererz. Cuivre oxidulé capillaire *Haüy.* Kupferblüthe *Hausmann.* Capillary Red Oxide of Copper. Chalkotrichit *Glocker* (369, 1839). Plush Copper Ore.

Vanadic Ocher, Vanadic Acid *Teschemacher* (*Am. J. Sc.*, **11**, 233, 1851). Cuprocuprite pt. *Vernadsky* (**1** [3], 416, 1910).

Cryst. Isometric; gyroidal — 4 3 2.[1]

Forms:[2]

a 001	δ 016	f 013	n 112	χ 334	r 233	F 689
d 011	η 015	e 012	σ 335	q 133	D 245	G 10·12·13
o 111	h 014	m 113	β 223	p 122	E 467	

Structure cell.[3] Space group $Pn3m$; a_0 4.252 ± 0.002; contains Cu_4O_2.

Habit.[4] Octahedral, less often dodecahedral or cubic; occasionally highly modified. Plagiohedral forms rare. Sometimes as cubes greatly elongated [001] into capillary shapes (*chalcotrichite*). Also massive, granular or earthy. Commonest forms: *o d a n p e.*

Wheal Phoenix, Cornwall:

P h y s. Cleavage {111} interrupted, {001} rare.[5] Fracture conchoidal to uneven. Brittle. H. $3\frac{1}{2}$–4. G. 6.14;[6] 6.15 (calc.). M.P. 1235°. Luster adamantine or submetallic to earthy. Color red of various shades, particularly cochineal-red; sometimes almost black. Streak several shades of brownish red, shining.

O p t. In polished section[7] bluish white in color with blood-red internal reflections; usually exhibits anomalous anisotropism and pleochroism. Reflection percentages: green 30, orange 22.5, red 21.5. In transmitted light, red or cochineal-red in thick sections becoming orange-yellow, yellow and lemon-yellow with decreasing thickness. Isotropic. n_{red} 2.849.[8]

C h e m. Cuprous oxide, Cu_2O. Cu 88.82, O 11.18, total 100.00. Traces of Se[9] and I[10] reported are probably due to admixture. No modern analyses are available.[11]

Var. (*a*) *Capillary*; Chalcotrichite; Plush Copper Ore. In plushlike or matted aggregates of capillary or acicular crystals (cubes greatly elongated [001][12]), early thought to be an orthorhombic modification of Cu_2O.

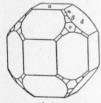

(*b*) *Earthy*. Tile Ore, Ziegelerz *Germ.* Hydrocuprite pt. Brick red or reddish brown and earthy; often mixed with hematite, limonite, and clayey material, also tenorite; color sometimes black. The hepatinerz and kupferlebererz, or liver-ore, has a liver-brown color.

Arizona.

Tests. Unaltered in C.T. B.B. fusible at about 1200°. Soluble in HCl, and a concentrated solution when cooled and diluted with cold water yields a heavy white precipitate of Cu_2Cl. Soluble also in NH_4OH, concentrated NaOH, HNO_3, H_3PO_4, and H_2SO_4.

O c c u r. A common mineral in the oxidized zone of copper deposits. Often impure through admixture with iron oxides, ferruginous clay, tenorite, and secondary copper minerals. Associated minerals are commonly native copper, malachite, azurite, chalcocite, chrysocolla, tenorite, " copperpitch " and limonite; the crystals are often grown upon or contain native copper. Associated calcite is sometimes tinted red through admixed, finely divided, cuprite.

Oriented growths have been found of cuprite upon native copper.[13]

Cuprite is widespread in its occurrence, and only some of the more notable localities are listed here.[14] From Bogoslovsk, Nizhne Tagilsk, and Ekaterinburg, Urals, Russia. In Germany at Rheinbreitbach near Linz, and in the neighborhood of Siegen, Westphalia. At Szaszka and elsewhere in the Banat, Hungary. A notable occurrence at Chessy, near Lyon, France, as octahedral and dodecahedral crystals and combinations, up to 3 cm. in diameter; the crystals occur in clay and are usually altered to malachite, rarely to azurite or limonite. In England in fine specimens in the oxidized ores of the tin and copper veins in Cornwall at Redruth, Liskeard, the Lizard district and other places. In Australia at Broken Hill and Cobar, New South Wales; at Burra-Burra, South Australia. At Mount Lyell, Tasmania. In Africa at Mindouli, French Congo; at Katanga, Belgian Congo, and at Tsumeb, near Otavi, South-West Africa, sometimes as sharp crystals as large as a centimeter on a side. In Japan at Arakawa, Ugo. In South America in Chile at Chuquicamata, in part pseudomorphous after fibrous antlerite, at Andaxollo, south of Coquimbo, and in Atacama Province; in Bolivia at Coro-Coro. In Mexico at Cananea, Sonora.

In the United States, cuprite is widespread in the copper deposits of the southwest and sometimes is an important ore (Bisbee); the mineral often occurs at the upper limit of the chalcocite zone and in these instances probably is a product of alteration of the chalcocite. In Arizona in important amounts at Bisbee as earthy masses and as crystalline aggregates and fine crystals often penetrated by dendritic masses of native copper; also at Morenci, Ray, Clifton, Globe, and Jerome. In New Mexico abundant in the Santa Rita district; at Fierro. In Nevada at Ely, and in the Bullion district, Elko County. In California in Del Norte, Mono, and other counties in unimportant amounts. In Idaho from the Mackay district, Custer County, and with azurite, malachite, and chrysocolla in concentric rings around residual cores of tetrahedrite at the Caledonian mine, near Wardner, Shoshone County. In Colorado near Garfield, Chaffee County, and formerly mined in small amounts at many other places. In Pennsylvania at the South Mountain copper mines, Lehigh County, at Cornwall, Lebanon County, and elsewhere. At Ducktown, Tennessee, and in other copper deposits of the southern Appalachians.

Alter. Most commonly to malachite pseudomorphs; often to native copper and, less commonly, to tenorite, atacamite, and other oxidized copper minerals. Also to pyrrhotite,[15] and as substitution pseudomorphs in limonite. Cuprite is commonly found as an alteration product of, or as pseudomorphs after tetrahedrite, chalcopyrite and other copper sulfides, antlerite, brochantite, atacamite and, rarely, malachite. Frequently noted as a coating or crystals on ancient copper or bronze objects.[16]

Artif.[17] Observed in slags from copper refining processes. Readily obtained as crystals in a variety of ways based on the reduction of cupric salts in alkaline solution or fusion; also by heating metallic copper in air, by heating a mixture of precipitated Cu_2O with Cu, and by the electrolysis under certain conditions of $CuSO_4$ solutions.

N a m e. From *cuprum, copper,* in allusion to the composition. Chalcotrichite from θρίξ, *hair,* and χαλκός, *copper.*

HYDROCUPRITE. *Genth* (46, 1875). An ill-defined, supposedly amorphous, form of Cu_2O with an indefinite amount of water, found as a thin orange-yellow to orange-red raglike coating on magnetite at Cornwall, Pennsylvania. Also said to occur at Schapbach, Baden, and at Chessy, France. Reported from the Arlington copper mine, New Jersey, as orange-red aggregates of birefringent fibers.

VANADIC OCHER, VANADIC ACID. *Teschemacher (Am. J. Sc.,* 11, 233, 1851), from Lake Superior, has been shown to be cuprite.[18]

Ref.

1. Gyroidal symmetry established on morphological grounds by Miers, *Phil. Mag.,* 18, 127 (1884), verified by Schroeder, *Cbl. Min.,* 353 (1934), and others. The structure, derived from x-ray studies by Bragg and Bragg (155, 1915), Greenwood, *Phil. Mag.,* 48, 654 (1924), and Niggli, *Zs. Kr.,* 57, 253 (1922), is holohedral. Etch figures, studied by Honess (75, 1927), Royer, *C. R.,* 202, 1346 (1936), and earlier by Traube, *Jb. Min., Beil.-Bd.,* 10, 455 (1895), confirm the x-ray results.

2. From Kleber and Schroeder, *Jb. Min., Beil.-Bd.,* 69A, 364 (1935). No precise definition of the forms is given in terms of the gyroidal symmetry.

3. The structure derived is holohedral, according to Niggli (1922) and others. Cell dimensions from Neuburger, *Zs. Kr.,* 77, 169 (1931), on artificial Cu_2O by precision powder methods.

4. See Kleber and Schroeder (1935) for discussion of frequency and size of forms.

5. Miers (1884).

6. Average of 6.12 (Cornwall) and 6.16 (Fierro, New Mexico) by Frondel (priv. comm., 1939); Haidinger (in Dana [206, 1892], gives 5.992. The earthy varieties yield lower values due, no doubt, to porosity of the sample.

7. Schneiderhöhn and Ramdohr (2, 550, 1931); see also Pavlovitch, *Bull. soc. min.,* 55, 125 (1932), for reflectivity data.

8. Fizeau in Des Cloizeaux (520, 1867) by the prism method on a crystal from Chessy.

9. Kobell and Rammelsberg in Rammelsberg (126, 1875).

10. In Doelter (3 [2], 82, 1926).

11. For old analyses see Doelter (1926).

12. Kenngott (101, 1861) and Knop, *Jb. Min.,* 521, 1861; x-ray study by Böhm, *Zs. Kr.,* 64, 550 (1926).

13. In Mügge, *Jb. Min., Beil.-Bd.,* 16, 333 (1903).

14. For further localities see Hintze (1 [2A], 1905, 1908); also Schrader, Stone, and Sanford, *U.S. Geol. Sur., Bull. 624,* 1916, for localities in the United States. For Chessy see Lacroix (3, 305, 1901).

15. Jeremejew, *Russ. Min. Ges., Vh.,* 31, 398 (1894).

16. In Hintze (1 [2A], 1918, 1908).

17. In Hintze (1908) and Doelter (3, 2, 89, 1926).

18. Schaller, *Am. J. Sc.,* 39, 404 (1915).

412　　**W A T E R** [H₂O].　Wasser *Germ.* Vatten *Swed.* Eau *Fr.* Acqua *Ital.* Aqua *Span.*

Water exists in three states: (*a*) a solid, *ice,* at or below 0°; (*b*) a liquid, *water* proper, between 0 and 100°);[1] (*c*) a gas, *steam* and *aqueous vapor,* the former at 100°, under a pressure of 760 mm., or at higher or lower temperatures with requisite increase or decrease of pressure, the latter in the atmosphere at all temperatures.

I C E.　Eis *Germ.* Is *Swed.* Glace *Fr.* Ghiaccio *Ital.*

C r y s t.　Hexagonal — *R*; ditrigonal pyramidal — $3m$.[2]

Forms:[3]

	LOWER	UPPER	
	$\bar{c}$	c	0001
		m	$10\bar{1}0$
		a	$11\bar{2}0$
	$\bar{x}$	x	$h0\bar{u}l$
		y	$0kil$

Structure cell. Space group possibly $C6mc$;[4] a_0 7.82, c_0 7.36; $a_0 : c_0 = 1 : 0.942$; a_{rh} 5.148, α 98°51′; contains $12H_2O$ in the hexagonal unit.

Habit. Usually, as snow crystals, in compound six-rayed stellate forms of great variety and delicacy, flattened {0001}. Occasionally, as hail, as hexagonal crystals projecting from a solid nucleus or, rarely, in distinct quartzoids; also in rounded bodies with a concentric or helical internal structure. As skeletal hexagonal prisms with mazelike internal partitions.[6] As lathlike crystals, sometimes greatly elongated, by crystallization on the surface of water; in delicate skeletal forms or hopper-shaped prisms as hoar frost.

Twinning.[7] Twin plane (a) {0001}, and (b) {000$\bar{1}$}.

P h y s. (For *ice*). Fracture conchoidal. Brittle at low temperatures, but somewhat less so near the melting point. H. $1\frac{1}{2}$.[8] G. 0.9167.[9] M.P. 0°. Luster vitreous. Colorless in thin layers, pale blue to greenish blue in thick layers; usually white, from included gas bubbles or flaws. Streak colorless. Transparent. Diamagnetic. Glides readily on {0001}.[10] Electrical conductivity very low.

(For *water*). Maximum density, at 3.98°, 0.999973 gm./cm.³ Colorless in thin layers, greenish blue in thick layers. Compared to other liquids the specific heat, surface tension (ca. 75 dynes per cm.) and dielectric constant are abnormally high; the electrical conductivity is very low.

O p t. Uniaxial. Optically positive (+). Refractive indices:

ICE ($-1°$ to -4.5)[11]

	λ	O	E
	690.7	1.30655	1.30794
Li	670.8	1.30693	1.30832
Na	589.3	1.30907	1.31052
	504.7	1.31855	1.32006

WATER [12]

λ	n	λ		n
214.45	1.40397	Na	589.31	1.33299
267.61	1.36902	H	656.29	1.33114
308.23	1.35672	Li	670.82	1.33079
396.85	1.34352		768.24	1.32888
434.07	1.34032		871	1.3270
486.14	1.33714		1028	1.3245
535.05	1.33488		1256	1.3210

C h e m. Water, H_2O. O 88.81, H 11.19, total 100.00.

Water usually contains inorganic and organic material in solution or suspension. Fresh water is a vague term applied to a potable natural water. Hard waters contain calcium and magnesium carbonates and sulfates in solution.

Sea water and, in particular, the waters of closed basins in arid regions contain a relatively large proportion of soluble salts, varying in amount with the rate of evaporation, the incidence of fresh water from tributaries or rainfall, etc. The total content and composition of soluble salts in some sea waters and lakes are given in the accompanying table.

	1	2	3	4
Cl	55.292	55.48	32.27	65.86
Br	0.188	.....	0.04	1.13
SO_4	7.692	6.68	0.13	0.39
CO_3	0.207	0.09	22.47	0.02
B_4O_7	......	.....	5.05	....
Na	30.593	33.17	38.10	13.73
K	1.106	1.66	1.52	2.36
Ca	1.197	0.16	0.03	4.19
Mg	3.725	2.76	0.35	12.32
Rem.	......	.....	0.04	....
Total	100.00	100.00	100.00	100.00
Salinity, in per cent	3.30–3.74	20.349	7.656	18.8453

1. Average of 77 analyses of ocean water from many localities. Also, in traces, I, F, N, NH_4, Au, Mn, etc.[13] 2. Great Salt Lake, Utah.[14] 3. Borax Lake, Calif. Also PO_4 0.02, SiO_2 0.01, $(Al,Fe,Mn)_2O_3$ 0.01.[15] 4. Dead Sea. Also I trace, $(Al,Fe)_2O_3$ trace.[16]

Rain water is relatively low in impurities, but as a carrier of ammonia, nitric acid, sulfuric acid, and chlorides, it performs a function of the highest agricultural and geological significance. Evaporated to dryness, rain water gives about 0.003 per cent of solid matter, largely NaCl, organic matter and mineral dusts, but these constituents vary in amount and kind with respect to nearness to cities, the ocean, etc. Dissolved gases, notably nitrogen (ca. 0.013 per cent), oxygen (ca. 0.0064 per cent) and carbon dioxide (ca. 0.0013 per cent) are also present.

Spring waters vary widely in the kind and concentration of their dissolved substances and in temperature, according to the local geological conditions and admixture with waters of other types and origins. Vadose or meteoric spring waters, of surface origin, as a rule contain carbonates of lime, magnesium and ferrous iron, chlorides and sulfates, rarely sodium carbonate, and are usually cold to tepid. Juvenile waters, of deep-seated, magmatic origin, on the whole carry sodium carbonate, alkaline silicates, sodium chloride, CO_2, H_2S, and heavy metals as chief constituents, less often with sulfates, boric and other free acids, and, rarely, alkaline earth carbonates. These waters are often tepid to hot, and are confined to regions of recent or Tertiary volcanic activity.

The amount and kind of dissolved matter in river and lake waters is markedly influenced, particularly in smaller streams, by the nature of the rocks and soil in the drainage area, vegetation, climatic conditions, and other factors. Carbonate waters, with Ca as the dominant metal, characterize regions of abundant rainfall and vegetation, while sulfate and chloride waters, of relatively high salinity, are found in arid regions.

The solubilities of some common minerals in water follow.

SOLUBILITY GIVEN IN GRAMS PER 100 GRAMS WATER AT THE TEMPERATURE CITED

Anglesite	0.0028	0°	Fluorite	0.0016	18°
	0.0056	40°		0.0017	26°
Anhydrite	0.298	0°	Galena	0.000086	18°
	0.1619	100°	Gypsum	0.241	0°
Aragonite	0.00153	25°		0.222	100°
	0.00190	75°	Halite	35.7	0°
Barite	0.00023	18°		39.8	100°
	0.00039	100°	Nahcolite	6.9	0°
Calcite	0.0014	25°		16.4	60°
	0.0018	75°	Natron	21.52	0°
Cerussite	0.00011	20°		421.	104°
Chalcanthite	31.6	0°	Quartz	No true solubility?	
	203.3	100°	Siderite	0.0067	25°
Chalcocite	0.0005	18°	Smithsonite	0.001	15°
Cinnabar	0.000001	18°	Soda niter	73.	0°
Covellite	0.000033	18°		180.	100°
Epsomite	71.	20°	Sphalerite	0.000065	18°
	91.	40°	Sylvite	34.7	20°
				56.7	100°

Occur. Ice is formed as a coating over ponds, lakes, rivers, etc., at low temperatures; also direct from water vapor in the atmosphere as snow, often in crystals of great beauty and complexity of form; also as frost, hail, etc. Forming permanent fields of snow at definite altitudes, depending upon the latitude; under favorable conditions changed into solid ice and descending as glaciers far below the snow line; also, when the latter reach the sea, forming icebergs carried by ocean currents into lower latitudes; as permanent ice under Arctic tundras.

Artif. A vitreous modification has been reported[17] as forming by condensation from vapor below −110°. Other modifications have been made at high pressures.[18] An isometric form has been reported at ordinary pressures.[19]

Ref.

1. So-called heavy water contains the heavy isotope of hydrogen (deuterium) or the heavy isotope of oxygen (O = 18). It is present in small amounts in natural waters and concentrates have recently been prepared. B.P. 101.42°. G. (at 20°) 1.1059.
2. Crystal class from Dobrowolski, *Ark. Kemi*, 6 [7], 1916, who reviews the evidence of morphology, twinning, polar solution, and other physical properties. See also Adams, *Roy. Soc. London, Proc.*, **128**, 588 (1930), and Mügge, *Cbl. Min.*, 187, 1918, in support of the polar character of the c-axis. Bernal and Fowler, *J. Chem. Phys.*, **1**, 515 (1933), in their structure study of the physical properties of ice and water show that ice is polar with the probable crystal class 6*mm*, and not holohedral as proposed by Barnes, *Roy. Soc. London, Proc.*, **125**, 670 (1929), who gives the crystal class as 6/*m* 2/*m* 2/*m*.
3. Dobrowolski (1916); Adams (1930); Steinmetz, *Zs. Kr.*, **57**, 558 (1922).
4. The space group given by Bernal and Fowler (1933); a rhombohedral space group, however, is not excluded by the x-ray evidence. See Brandenberger, *Zs. Kr.*, **73**, 429 (1930). The cell dimensions are from Bernal and Fowler; Barnes (1929) gives a cell containing 4H$_2$O and rotated 30° with respect to the Bernal and Fowler cell. The Barnes cell is not compatible with a rhombohedral interpretation.
5. For a discussion of the relation between the habit of ice and temperature, and on the orientation of ice crystals in a thermal gradient see Kalb, *Cbl. Min.*, 129, 1921, and Barnes, *Nature*, **83**, 276 (1910). See also Bentley, *Snow Crystals*, New York, 1931; U. S. Weather Bureau *Monthly Weather Review*, August to December, 1907; *Ann. Summary*, 1902, for a large collection of photographs of ice crystals; and Dobrowolski (1916).

6. Fermor, *Min. Mag.*, **17**, 150 (1914).
7. Adams (1930) and Dobrowolski (1916).
8. Recent work by Blackwelder, *Am. J. Sc.*, **238**, 61 (1939), has shown that the hardness of ice may increase with decreasing temperature to about 6 at $-78.5°$.
9. Bunsen, *Ann Phys.*, **141**, 7 (1870).
10. Tammann and Salge, *Jb. Min., Beil.-Bd.*, **57**, 117 (1928).
11. Ehringhaus, *Jb. Min., Beil.-Bd.*, **41**, 364 (1917).
12. Doelter (3 [1], 880, 1918), average of values in literature.
13. Dittmar anal. in Challenger Rep., " Phys. and Chem.," **1**, 203 (1884).
14. Bailey anal. in Clarke (157, 1924).
15. Melville anal. in Becker, *U.S. Geol. Sur., Monog. 13*, 265, 1888.
16. Fresenius, *Zs. anorg. Chem.*, 1991, 1912.
17. Burton and Oliver, *Roy. Soc. London Proc.*, **153**, 166, (1935).
18. Tammann, *Zs. phys. Chem.*, **72**, 609 (1910), and Bridgman, *Am. Ac. Arts Sc., Proc.*, **47**, 439 (1912). See also McFarlan, *J. Chem. Phys.*, **4**, 60, 253 (1936), for x-ray data on ice II and ice III.
19. In Dobrowolski (1916).

PERICLASE GROUP

ISOMETRIC HEXOCTAHEDRAL — $4/m\,\bar{3}\,2/m$

		a_0	G.
Periclase	MgO	4.203	3.56
Bunsenite	NiO	4.171	6.89
Manganosite	MnO	4.436	5.36
Cadmium oxide	CdO	4.689	8.2
Lime	CaO	4.797	3.3

Periclase has been found in nature in a number of localities and manganosite in three places, but the other members of the group are mineralogical rarities, reported but once and not completely authenticated. However, these as well as other[1] oxides of the rock-salt type have been prepared artificially and studied in detail. Although comparatively little solid solution between the natural members of the group is observed, many of the artificial systems have been shown to form complete series, and some have partial or no substitution.[2] Oriented inclusions of zincite in manganosite and of manganosite in periclase suggest that the minerals consisted of mixed oxides at the higher temperature of formation and that the inclusions are the result of exsolution.[3]

Periclase, manganosite, and lime are found in high-temperature metamorphic deposits; the others of the group are apparently secondary oxidation products. The name iozite has been proposed for supposed FeO reported from basaltic glass.

Ref.

1 Members of the type not found in nature are SrO, BaO, CoO, FeO, TiO, and VO.
2. Complete series have been shown between MgO and CoO, NiO and FeO; between CoO and NiO and MnO; between CaO and CdO. Partial series are between MnO and MgO, CaO, NiO and CdO. No series have been found between CaO and CoO, NiO and MgO, or between CdO and CoO or NiO. See Holgersson and Karlsson, *Zs. anorg. Chem.*, **182**, 255 (1929); Natta and Passerini, *Gazz. chim. ital.*, **59**, 129 (1929); Passerini, *ibid.*, **60**, 535 (1930); Bowen and Schairer, *Am. J. Sc.*, **29**, 194 (1935).
3. Frondel, *Am. Min.*, **25**, 534 (1940).

4211 **PERICLASE** [MgO]. Periclasia *Scacchi* (1841). Periklas *Germ.* Periclasite.

C r y s t. Isometric; hexoctahedral — $4/m\,\bar{3}\,2/m$.

Forms:[1]

$$a\{001\} \qquad d\{011\} \qquad o\{111\}$$

Structure cell. Space group $Fm3m$; a_0 4.203;[2] contains Mg_4O_4.

Habit. Often octahedral, less often cubo-octahedral or cubic, rarely dodecahedral (Crestmore). Usually in irregular or rounded grains.

Twinning. Spinel twins, twin plane $\{111\}$, have been noted in artificial crystals.[3]

P h y s. Cleavage $\{001\}$ perfect, $\{111\}$ imperfect; sometimes exhibits parting $\{011\}$ on glide faces. H. $5\frac{1}{2}$. G. 3.56 ± 0.01 (artif.); 3.58 (calc.). Luster vitreous. Colorless to grayish white; also yellow, brownish yellow (containing Fe), green or black (in part due to inclusions). Transparent. Streak white. In transmitted light colorless with n_{red} 1.7298, n_{Na} 1.7350, n_{blue} 1.7460.[4] Translation gliding: $T\{011\}$, $t[110]$.[5]

C h e m. An oxide of magnesium, MgO. Mg 60.32, O 39.68, total 100.00. Fe (anal. 1) and apparently also Zn (anal. 2) may substitute for Mg in part. Mn has been reported but is due to microscopic oriented inclusions of manganosite.[6]

Anal.[7]

	1	2
MgO	93.86	87.38
FeO	5.97	0.19
MnO	.....	9.00
ZnO	.....	2.52
Total	99.83	99.09
G.	3.674	3.90

1. Monte Somma.[8] 2. Nordmark. Contains manganosite.[9]

Var. Ferrian. Magnesio-wüstite (artif.) *Bowen* and *Schairer* (*Am. J. Sc.*, **29**, 194, 1935). Periclase from Monte Somma contains up to about 8.5 per cent FeO by weight. Artificial MgO forms a complete series with FeO.[10]

Tests. B.B. infusible; the manganian variety becomes dark colored. Easily soluble in dilute HCl or HNO_3. The finely powdered mineral gives an alkaline reaction when moistened with water.

O c c u r. Periclase is a high-temperature metamorphic mineral found in marbles and formed by the dissociation (dedolomitization) of dolomitic limestones. Found disseminated and in spots of small clustered crystals in ejected blocks of white limestone on Monte Somma, Vesuvius, Italy, associated with forsterite and earthy magnesite or hydromagnesite. At Teulada, Sardinia, with brucite in a contact zone between Silurian limestone and granite. In marble in the neighborhood of Predazzo, Tirol, in part altered to a calcite-brucite rock. At Leon, Spain. In Sweden at Nordmark, in dolomitic marble with hausmannite; also at Långban. In Moravia at Novýmlýn near Strážek, associated with other contact minerals in metamorphic limestone.

In the United States in California at Crestmore, containing minute oriented octahedra of magnetite[11] and in part altered to brucite and hydromagnesite, with chondrodite, wilkeite and spinel; also at Riverside. Found with forsterite in the dolomite xenoliths of the Organ Mountains batholith of New Mexico.

Alter. Easily altered to fibrous or scaly brucite, and further to hydromagnesite; also to serpentine, as in the pseudomorphs of the Tilly Foster mine, Brewster, New York, where the cubic parting of the serpentine is perhaps due to replaced periclase.[12]

The rock names *predazzite* and *pencatite* (originally applied to the then supposed mineral species) refer to calcite-brucite rocks, often with hydromagnesite, which have been formed by the alteration of periclase marbles. These have been found in the Skye and Assynt districts in Scotland; Carlingford, Scotland; Ben Bullen, New South Wales; Nordmark, Sweden; the Nantei mine, Suian, Korea; the Mountain Lake mine, near Salt Lake City, Utah; the Phillipsburg quadrangle, Montana.

Artif.[13] Obtained in crystals by fusion of magnesium borate and lime; by decomposing $MgCl_2$ at red heat in the presence of HCl, CaO, or H_2O; by slowly cooling a fusion of MgO and KOH: from molten MgO.

Name. From περικλάω, *to break around*, in allusion to the cleavage.

Ref.

1. A general form $\{hkl\}$ is noted on artificial crystals by Otto and Kloos, *Ber.*, **24**, 1480 (1891).
2. Wyckoff, *Am. J. Sc.*, **10**, 107 (1925).
3. Seifert, *Cbl. Min.*, 305, 1926.
4. Sommerfeldt, *Cbl. Min.*, 213, 1907, by prism method on artificial crystals. The Monte Somma material has n_{Na} 1.745 (Berman, priv. comm., 1939). In the artificial system MgO-FeO the refractive index increases from $n_{Na} = 1.736$ to 2.32 (extrapolated) with the increase in FeO content.
5. Mügge, *Jb. Min.*, 24, 1920.
6. Frondel, *Am. Min.*, **25**, 534 (1940), oriented with the crystallographic axes parallel. The intergrowth may be due to exsolution, so that periclase may contain considerable Mn at elevated temperatures; MnO has been found to form a partial series with MgO in the artificial system (see Passerini, *Gazz. chim. ital.*, **60**, 535 [1930]).
7. For additional analyses see Doelter (3 [2], 286, 1926).
8. Damour, *Bull. soc. geol.*, **6**, 311 (1849).
9. Lindström anal. in Sjögren, *Geol. För. Förh.*, **9**, 527 (1887).
10. Bowen and Schairer, *Am. J. Sc.*, **29**, 194 (1935).
11. Rogers, *Am. Min.*, **14**, 466 (1929), in parallel orientation.
12. Dana, *Am. J. Sc.*, **8**, 375 (1874); Mügge, *Jb. Min.*, *Beil.-Bd.*, **16**, 366 (1903).
13. In Mellor (4, 282, 1923).

4212	**Bunsenite** [NiO]. Nickeloxydul *Bergemann* (*J. pr. Chem.*, **75**, 243, 1858; *Jb. Min.*, 450, 1859). Bunsenite *Dana* (134, 1868).

Cryst. Isometric; hexoctahedral — $4/m\,\bar{3}\,2/m$.

Forms:

$$a\{001\} \qquad d\{011\} \qquad o\{111\}$$

Structure cell.[1]   Space group $Fm3m$; a_0 4.171 ± 0.003;[2] contains Ni_4O_4.

Habit.   Octahedral, sometimes with modifying dodecahedron or cube.
Twinning.   Observed on natural crystals.[3]
P h y s.   H. $5\frac{1}{2}$.   G. 6.898,[4] 6.7 ± 0.1 (artif.);   6.79 (calc.).   Luster vitreous.   Color dark pistachio green.   Streak brownish black.   Transparent. n_{Li} 2.37.[5]
C h e m.   An oxide of nickel, NiO.   Ni 78.58, O 21.42, total 100.00. No analyses have been reported of the natural crystals.

Tests.   B.B. infusible.   Difficultly soluble in acids.

O c c u r.   With native bismuth and nickel and cobalt arsenates, largely annabergite, in the oxidized portion of a nickel-uranium vein at Johanngeorgenstadt, Saxony.
A r t i f.[6]   Observed in slags.   Easily prepared by heating the metal, the hydroxide, or a salt of the metal and a volatile acid in air.   Obtained in octahedral or cubic crystals by fusing nickel borate with lime or nickel phosphate with potassium sulfate, by fusing the oxide in borax, and in other ways.
N a m e.   After R. W. Bunsen (1811–99), German chemist, who had observed artificial crystals of NiO.

Ref.

1. In Bragg (92, 1937).
2. Ksanda, *Am. J. Sc.*, **22**, 131 (1931), on artificial NiO; the x-ray powder pattern of the natural crystals is stated to be identical with that of the artificial material.
3. Ksanda (1931) on the material from Johanngeorgenstadt, but the twin law is not stated.
4. Bergemann, *Jb. Min.*, 450, 1859; the value 6.398 in Dana (208, 1892) and in Hintze (1 [2], 1891, 1908) probably is a misprint.
5. Merwin in Ksanda (1931).   Kundt, *Ak. Berlin, Ber.*, 255, 1888, gives n_{red} 2.18, n_{white} 2.23 and n_{blue} 2.39, from a prism of oxidized metal.
6. Mellor (15, 374, 1936).

4213   **M A N G A N O S I T E** [MnO].   *Blomstrand (Geol. För. Förh.*, **2**, 179, 1874).

C r y s t.   Isometric;   hexoctahedral — $4/m \, \bar{3} \, 2/m$.

Forms:

$a\{001\}$ $d\{011\}$ $o\{111\}$

Structure cell.[1]   Space group $Fm3m$; a_0 4.436 ± 0.002;[2] contains Mn_4O_4.
Habit.   Octahedral, sometimes modified by cube or dodecahedron. Usually in irregular grains or masses.
P h y s.   Cleavage $\{001\}$ fair, with a fibrous break; sometimes exhibits parting $\{111\}$ (from Franklin, due to zincite inclusions).   H. $5\frac{1}{2}$.   G. 5.364,[3] 5.0–5.4 (artif.);   5.36 (calc.).   Luster vitreous.   Color emerald green on fresh fracture, becoming black on exposure.   Streak brown. Transparent.

O p t. In polished section[4] gray in color and isotropic, with emerald green internal reflections. In transmitted light, emerald green with n_{green} 2.19 and n_{red} 2.16.[5]

C h e m. An oxide of manganese, MnO. Mn 77.44, O 23.56, total 100.00. The Fe, Mg, and Zn reported are possibly substituting for Mn, with Zn in part due to inclusions.

Anal.

	1	2	3
MnO	93.33	94.59	98.04
ZnO	4.89	3.41	.....
FeO + Fe$_2$O$_3$	0.23	0.26	0.42
MgO	0.61	0.11	1.71
Rem.	1.05	2.08	0.16
Total	100.11	100.45	100.33
G.		5.364	

1. Franklin. Rem. is MnO$_2$.[6] 2. Franklin. Rem. is MnO$_2$ 1.30, H$_2$O 0.78.[7] 3. Långban. Average of two analyses. Rem. is CaO 0.16.[8]

Tests. B.B. blackens, but not sensibly fusible. Dissolves with difficulty in strong HCl or HNO$_3$ to a colorless solution.

O c c u r. In Sweden at Långban, with pyrochroite and manganite in dolomite, and at Nordmark with pyrochroite, hausmannite, garnet, and periclase in dolomite. At Franklin, New Jersey, in octahedral crystals and irregular masses, often with octahedral parting planes upon which are oriented zincite plates,[9] associated with franklinite, willemite, and zincite.

A l t e r. To hausmannite or pyrochroite, and probably to pyrolusite.

A r t i f.[10] By heating manganous carbonate or hydroxide out of contact with air, and by the reduction at red heat of higher oxides or salts of manganese. Obtained in octahedral or cubo-octahedral crystals by fusing manganese borate with lime, by heating to redness MnCl$_2$ in water vapor in a nonoxidizing atmosphere; by melting together MnO and SiO$_2$.

N a m e. In allusion to the composition.

Ref.

1. In Wyckoff (215, 1931).
2. Ellefson and Taylor, *J. Chem. Phys.*, **2**, 58 (1934).
3. Palache (37, 1935).
4. Ramdohr, *Cbl. Min.*, 133, 1938.
5. Ford, *Am. J. Sc.*, **38**, 502 (1914), by the prism method.
6. Bauer anal. in Palache (37, 1935).
7. Steiger anal. in Palache, *Am. J. Sc.*, **29**, 178 (1910).
8. Blomstrand (1874).
9. Frondel, *Am. Min.*, **25**, 534 (1940), oriented with manganosite {111} [110] ‖ zincite {0001}[10$\bar{1}$0].
10. In Mellor (**12**, 220, 1932).

4214 Cadmium Oxide [CdO]. Cadmiumoxyd *Wittich* and *Neumann* (*Cbl. Min.*, 549, 1901).

C r y s t. Isometric; hexoctahedral — $4/m\ \bar{3}\ 2/m$.

Forms: $c\{001\}$, $o\{111\}$; also $d\{011\}$ and $\{112\}$(?) on artificial crystals.

Structure cell.[1] Space group *Fm3m*; a_0 4.689 ± 0.003;[2] contains Cd_4O_4.

Habit. Octahedral, sometimes with modifying cube. Also pulverulent.

Twinning. Penetration twins of unknown twin law have been observed.

P h y s. Cleavage {111}[3] (?). H. 3. G. 8.1–8.2 (artif.); 8.21 (calc.).[4] Color black,[5] lustrous. Transparent. In transmitted light, red to orange brown with n_{Li} 2.49.[6]

C h e m. An oxide of cadmium, CdO.

Anal.

	Cd	O	Total
1	87.54	12.46	100.00
2	87.5	[12.5]	100.0

1. CdO. 2. Sardinia.

Tests. B.B. infusible. Soluble in dilute acids.

O c c u r. At Genarutta, near Iglesias, Sardinia, as a coating over hemimorphite.

A r t i f.[7] Observed in the muffles of zinc ovens. Readily prepared by heating the metal, the hydroxide or a salt of the metal and a volatile acid in air; obtained in octahedral or cubic crystals by heating the metal or the oxide in oxygen, by fusing the oxide in borax; also as colloidally dispersed dodecahedral crystals by arcing Cd electrodes in air.[8]

Ref.

1. In Bragg (92, 1937).
2. Ksanda, *Am. J. Sc.*, **22**, 131 (1931), on artificial CdO.
3. Wittich and Neumann (1901), on artificial crystals.
4. The value 6.146 given for natural material by Wittich and Neumann (1901) is obviously in error.
5. The artificial material is yellow-brown, red-brown, brown-black, etc., depending on impurities and on particle size.
6. Merwin in Ksanda (1931).
7. Mellor (4, 508, 1923).
8. Walmsley, *Proc. Phys. Soc. London*, **40**, 87 (1928).

4215   Lime [CaO]. Calcium Oxide. Calce *Scacchi* (12, 1883).

Said to occur at Vesuvius in blocks of calcareous rocks enveloped in the lava.[1] Artificial[2] CaO is isometric hexoctahedral, with a rock-salt type structure[3] and a_0 4.797; G. 3.3, H. $3\frac{1}{2}$, cleavage {001} perfect and parting {011}; n 1.838.[4]

Ref.

1. Zambonini (58, 1935).
2. In Mellor (3, 660, 1923).
3. In Wyckoff (215, 1931).
4. Larsen and Berman (59, 1934).

IOZITE. *Brun* (*Arch. sc. phys. nat.*, **6**, 253, 263, 1924; *C.R. soc. phys. hist. nat. Genève*, **41**, 94, 1924; *Schweiz. min. Mitt.*, 4, 355, 1924). Iosidérite. Jozite *Germ.* A name given to supposed FeO present as minute black magnetic grains around trichites of feldspar and pyroxene in basaltic or trachytic glass.[1] Also as a generic term includes gradations to magnetite containing supposedly an excess of FeO. Artificial[2] FeO (" wüstite ") has a rock-salt structure with a_0 4.29,[3] G. 6.00 (calc.).

Name from *ίός*, *rust*.

Ref.

1. It has not been fully demonstrated that these bodies are not magnetite. Cf. Foshag, *Am. Min.*, **11**, 77 (1926).
2. In Mellor (13, 709, 1934).
3. Wyckoff (215, 1931).

ZINCITE GROUP

DIHEXAGONAL PYRAMIDAL — 6mm

		a_0	c_0	c_0/a_0	G.	H.
Zincite	ZnO	3.258	5.239	1.608	5.66	4
Bromellite	BeO	2.68	4.36	1.627	3.017	9

Zincite and bromellite resemble wurtzite, ZnS, in structure.[1] The polar characteristics of zincite are shown both in the crystal habit and in the structure. The cleavage is $\{10\bar{1}0\}$ in both minerals. The hardness difference between zincite and bromellite is noteworthy.[2] A number of artificial compounds of the AX type are of this structure.[1]

Ref.

1. Wyckoff (216, 1931).
2. For a discussion of hardness relative to structure and atomic dimensions see Stillwell (225, 1938).

4221 **Z I N C I T E** [ZnO].   Red Oxide of Zinc *Bruce* (*Am. Min. J.*, **1** [2], 96, 1810). Zinkoxyd. Rothzinkerz *Germ.* Zinc oxydé *Fr.* Red Zink Ore. Zinkit *Haidinger* (548, 1845A). Spartalite *Brooke* and *Miller* (218, 1852). Sterlingite *Alger* (565, 1844). Ruby zinc *Alger* (*Boston Soc. Nat. Hist., Proc.*, **6**, 145, 1861). (Not the ruby zinc = sphalerite of American and English miners.)

Calcozincite pt. *Shepard* (*Am. J. Sc.*, **12**, 231, 1876).

C r y s t. Hexagonal — P; dihexagonal pyramidal — 6mm.

$$a : c = 1 : 1.5870;^1 \qquad p_0 : r_0 = 1.8325 : 1$$

Forms:[2]

LOWER	UPPER		ϕ	ρ	M	A_2
c	c	0001	. . . .	0°00′	90°00′	90°00′
	m	10$\bar{1}$0	30°00′	90 00	60 00	90 00
	s	10$\bar{1}$3	30 00	31 25	74 53½	90 00
	α	40$\bar{4}$5	30 00	55 42	65 36	90 00
	p	10$\bar{1}$1	30 00	61 22½	63 58	90 00
	β	50$\bar{5}$4	30 00	66 25	62 43½	90 00

Structure cell.[3] Space group *C6mc*; a_0 3.242, c_0 5.176; $a_0 : c_0 = 1 : 1.596 \pm 0.004$; contains Zn_2O_2.

Habit. Natural crystals rare; hemimorphic pyramidal with a large negative base $\{000\bar{1}\}$; often rounded and corroded. Usually massive, foliated; also compact, granular, and in rounded irregular masses. Artificial crystals often prismatic [0001].

Twinning. (a) On {0001}, composition plane always {000$\bar{1}$}.[4]

Artificial.
$f\{20\bar{2}1\}$, $\bar{B}\{21\bar{3}3\}$.

P h y s. Cleavage {10$\bar{1}$0} perfect, but difficult; parting on {000$\bar{1}$} sometimes distinct.[5] Fracture conchoidal. Brittle. H. 4. G. 5.66 ± 0.02,[6] 5.684;[7] 5.699 (calc.). M.P. 1670° ± 10° (material of anal. 4), decreasing with addition of Mn or Fe.[16] Luster subadamantine. Color orange-yellow to deep red, rarely yellow;[8] in artificial crystals colorless to yellow and, rarely, orange-red or red. Streak orange-yellow. Artificial material is fluorescent in ultraviolet light. Transparent in thin pieces.

O p t.[9] Deep red to yellow by transmitted light.

	n_{Hg}	n_{Na}	n_{Li}	
λ	546	589	670	Uniaxial pos. (+).
O	2.032	2.013	1.990	Nonpleochroic. Often
E	2.048	2.029	2.005	shows inclusions.

In polished section[10] light rose-brown in color, and weakly anisotropic. Reflection percentages: green 11, orange 10, red 8.

C h e m. Zinc oxide, ZnO. Zn 80.34, O 19.66, total 100.00. Contains varying but minor amounts of Mn; also some Fe. Traces of other elements have been reported.[11]

Anal.[12]

	1	2	3	4	5	6
ZnO	99.63	96.20	94.85	93.14	93.06	91.47
MnO	0.27	3.33	4.83	6.20	5.46	.....
FeO	0.01	.....	.....	.....	1.14	.....
Rem.	0.08	0.43	0.30	0.72	0.24	8.34
Total	99.99	99.96	99.98	100.06	99.90	99.81

1. Sterling Hill, N. J. Rem. is SiO_2.[13] 2. Franklin, N. J. Rem. is Fe_2O_3.[14] 3. Franklin, N. J. Rem. is Fe_2O_3.[15] 4. Franklin, N. J. Rem. is Fe_2O_3 0.38, Mn_3O_4 0.34.[16] 5. Franklin, N. J. Rem. is Fe_2O_3.[16] 6. Olkusz mine, Poland. Rem. is Fe_2O_3 0.11, PbO 5.26, CO_2 2.85, insol. 0.12.[17]

Tests. Infusible. In C.T. blackens, but on cooling resumes original color. Soluble in acids.

O c c u r. Zincite is rare except at the unusual zinc deposits at Franklin and Sterling Hill, New Jersey. Here it occurs, sparingly, together with willemite and franklinite in calcite (about 1 per cent of the ore). The zincite occurs in the granular ore, and also as broad plates; an early occurrence was as corroded, irregular, masses, sometimes club-shaped, in calcite. Crystals are rare and are found only in the secondary calcite veins cutting the main ore body.

Also reported from Olkusz in Kielce, Poland; from Bottino, near Saravezza, Tuscany; near Paterna, Almeria, Spain; and at the Heazlewood mine, Tasmania.

A r t i f.[18] Frequently observed as a furnace product. Prepared by burning the metal in air, by calcining various zinc salts, and in other ways. Much of the zinc mined is converted to the oxide.

CALCOZINCITE.   *Shepard* (*Am. J. Sc.*, **12**, 231, 1876) is a mixture of zincite and calcite.[11]

FERROZINCITE.   *Adam* (38, 1869) contains Fe_2O_3 and ZnO.   Probably invalid.

Ref.

1. Palache, *Am. J. Sc.*, **29**, 177 (1910); 38, 1935, on natural crystals of superior quality. The old ratio in Dana (208, 1892) is high. Traube, *Jb. Min., Beil.-Bd.*, **9**, 147 (1874), obtained a slightly higher ratio (1.6077) for artificial crystals. The best x-ray ratio, by Barth, *Norsk Geol. Tidskr.*, **9**, 317 (1927), is close to Traube's value.

2. Palache (1910) on the natural crystals only. The following are additional forms observed on artificial crystals:

$11\bar{2}0$	$20\bar{2}5$	$30\bar{3}5$	$80\bar{8}9$	$20\bar{2}1$	$11\bar{2}3$	$11\bar{2}1$	$21\bar{3}3$
$10\bar{1}8$	$10\bar{1}2$	$20\bar{2}3$	$80\bar{8}5$	$11\bar{2}4$	$11\bar{2}2$	$21\bar{3}3$	$31\bar{4}1$

See Rath, *Ann. Phys.*, **122**, 406 (1864); Busz, *Zs. Kr.*, **15**, 621 (1889); Hutchinson, *Min. Mag.*, **9**, 5 (1890); Cesáro, *Soc. géol. Belgique, Ann.*, **19**, 271 (1892) — *Zs. Kr.*, **24**, 618 (1895); Ries, *Am. J. Sc.*, **48**, 256 (1894); Traube, *Jb. Min., Beil.-Bd.*, **9**, 147 (1894); Sachs, *Cbl. Min.*, **54**, 1905.

3. Structure in Bragg (91, 1937); dimensions from Barth (1927). Finch and Wilman, *J. Chem. Soc. London*, 751, 1934, on artificial material obtained values leading to a calculated specific gravity of 5.576.

4. vom Rath, *Ann. Phys.*, **144**, 580 (1871), found the additional twin plane {80$\bar{8}$9} on artificial crystals.

5. The plane {0001} is sometimes given as a cleavage plane, but it is more likely a plane of separation due to twinning or to intergrown inclusions.

6. On natural crystal fragments of the material of anal. 1. Average of four measurements (Draisin, priv. comm., 1939).

7. Blake in Brush, *Am. J. Sc.*, **31**, 371 (1861) on analyzed material of high purity.

8. The deep red color is presumably due to Mn. See Dana (136, 1868), and Dittler, *Zs. anorg. Chem.*, **148**, 332 (1925) — in Palache (38, 1935), who heated natural crystals in air and hydrogen to obtain color changes; the Mn is supposedly present as Mn_3O_4. The earlier contention of Hayes, *Am. J. Sc.*, **9**, 424 (1850); **4**, 146 (1872) that zincite is colored by hematite scales has been shown to be invalid. Pyramidal natural crystals (with the new form {10$\bar{1}$3}) of a deep yellow color have recently been found (Palache, priv. comm., 1939).

9. Berman, *Am. Min.*, **12**, 168 (1927) on material of anal. 1.

10. Schneiderhöhn and Ramdohr (2, 523, 1931).

11. In Palache (38, 1935).

12. Earlier analyses in Palache (38, 1935).

13. Bauer anal. in Berman (1927).

14. Schütz anal. in Grosser, *Zs. Kr.*, **20**, 354 (1892).

15. Bauer anal. in Palache (38, 1935).

16. Dittler (1925).

17. Antipov, *Russ., Ges. Min. Vh.*, **38**, 41 (1900) — *Zs. Kr.*, **36**, 176 (1901).

18. A more detailed account of the preparation of ZnO may be found in Doelter (3 [2], 299, 1922) and in Mellor (4, 504, 1923).

4222   **B R O M E L L I T E** [BeO].   *Aminoff* (*Zs. Kr.*, **62**, 113, 1925).

C r y s t. Hexagonal — *P*; dihexagonal pyramidal — *6mm*.[1]

$$a : c = 1 : 1.6288;^2 \quad p_0 = 1.8808$$

Forms:[3]

LOWER	UPPER		ϕ	ρ	M	A_2
c	c	0001	....	0°00′	90°00′	90°00′
	m	$10\bar{1}0$	30°00′	90 00	60 00	90 00
$\bar{r}$	r	$10\bar{1}1$	30 00	62 00	63 48	90 00
$\bar{h}$	h	$11\bar{2}2$	0 00	58 27	90 00	64 47

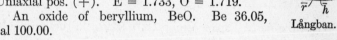

Structure cell.[2] Space group $C6mc$; a_0 2.68, c_0 4.36; $a_0 : c_0 = 1 : 1.627$; contains Be_2O_2.

Habit. Prismatic [0001] with large $\{000\bar{1}\}$ and $\{10\bar{1}0\}$ and small $\{10\bar{1}1\}$.

P h y s. Cleavage $\{10\bar{1}0\}$ distinct. H. about 9. G. 3.017; 3.044 (calc.). Color white. Transparent.

O p t. Uniaxial pos. (+). E = 1.733, O = 1.719.

C h e m. An oxide of beryllium, BeO. Be 36.05, O 63.95, total 100.00.

Långban.

m

r

$\bar{r}$ $\bar{h}$

Anal.

BeO	CaO	BaO	MgO	MnO	Sb_2O_3	Al_2O_3	Ign.	Total	G.
98.02	1.03	0.55	0.07	trace	0.29	0.17	0.85	100.98	3.017

Tests. B.B. infusible. Slowly soluble in hot concentrated HCl or HNO_3, and more readily in concentrated H_2SO_4.

O c c u r. At Långban, Sweden, as minute crystals associated with swedenborgite, richterite, and manganophyllite in a calcite vein in a skarn-forming hematite rock.

A r t i f.[4] Obtained in hexagonal prisms by fusing BeO and silica with potassium carbonate, potassium sulfate or borax; by fusing BeO with alkali sulfides, or beryllium pyrophosphate with potassium sulfate; by strongly heating beryllium sulfate or ammonium beryllium carbonate; also by sublimation (at ca. 2400°).

N a m e. After the Swedish physician and mineralogist, Magnus von Bromell (1679–1731).

Ref.

1. Crystal class from habit of crystals examined by Berman and Wolfe (priv. comm., 1941). Also inferred from crystal structure and similarity with zincite.
2. Aminoff (1925); earlier measurements by Mallard, *Ann. mines*, **12**, 427 (1887) — *Zs. Kr.*, **15**, 650 (1889), gave c = 1.6305, for poor artificial crystals.
3. Berman and Wolfe (priv. comm., 1941).
4. Mellor (4, 221, 1923).

423 **T E N O R I T E** [CuO]. Kupferschwärze *Werner (Bergm. J.,* 1789). Melaconite *Huot* (326, 1841). Tenorite *Semmola (Opere Minori,* 45, Napoli, 1841; *Soc. géol, France, Bull.,* **13**, 206, 1841–42). Melaconisa *Scacchi (Distrib. Sist. Min.,* 40, Napoli 1842). Melaconite *Dana* (518, 1850). Black Copper; Black Oxide of Copper. Schwarzkupfer, Kupferoxyd, Melakonit *Germ.* Cuivre oxydé noir *Fr.* Nero rame *Ital.* Cobre negro *Span.*

Marcylite pt. *Shepard (Marcy's Expl. Red River,* 135, 1854 — Dana [137, 1868]). Melanochalcite pt. *Koenig (Am. J. Sc.,* **14**, 404, 1902). Copper Pitch Ore pt. Kupferpecherz pt. *Germ.*

C r y s t. Monoclinic; prismatic — $2/m$.[1]

$a : b : c = 1.498 : 1 : 1.365$;[2] $\beta\ 99°29'$; $p_0 : q_0 : r_0 = 0.9112 : 1.3463 : 1$

$r_2 : p_2 : q_2 = 0.7428 : 0.6768 : 1$; $\mu\ 80°31'$; $p_0'\ 0.9238$, $q_0'\ 1.365$; $x_0'\ 0.1670$

Forms:[3]

	ϕ	ρ	ϕ_2	$\rho_2 = B$	C	A
c {001}	90°00'	9°29'	80°31'	90°00'	....	80°31'
a {100}	90 00	90 00	0 00	90 00	80°31'	....
f {011}	6 58½	53 58½	80 31	36 36	53 24	84 21½
x {601}	90 00	80 04	9 56	90 00	70 35	9 56
ϵ {101}	−90 00	37 07	127 07	90 00	46 36	127 07
p {111}	38 37½	60 13	42 31	47 18½	54 36½	57 11½
d {$\bar{1}$11}	−29 00½	57 21	127 07	42 34½	62 18	114 06
z {611}	76 33½	80 20	9 06	76 45	71 07	16 30½

Structure cell.[4] Space group $C2/c$ ($A2/a$ in the morphological orientation); $c_0\ 5.108$, $b_0\ 3.410$, $a_0\ 4.653$, all ±0.010; $c_0 : b_0 : a_0 = 1.498 : 1 :$ 1.365, $\beta\ 99°29' \pm 0°20'$; contains Cu_4O_4.

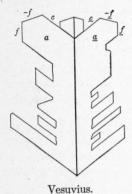

Vesuvius.

Habit. Paper-thin twinned aggregates and laths ‖ {100} and elongated [011] (Vesuvius); striated [010] on {100}. Curved plates. Thin shining flexible scales. Stellate groups. Also earthy or pulverulent.

Twinning.[5] (a) Common on {011}, producing dovetail reentrants and feather-like forms as seen on {100}; also stellate groups and complex dendritic patterns. (b) On {100}?.

P h y s. Cleavages[6] in zones [011] and [0$\bar{1}$1]. Fracture conchoidal to uneven. Brittle. Thin scales are flexible and elastic. H. 3½. G. 5.8–6.4; 6.45 (artif.); 6.57 (calc.). Luster metallic. Color steel- or iron-gray to black. Brown by transmitted light in very thin scales.

O p t. In polished section[7] light gray-white with a golden tint; strongly anisotropic and distinctly pleochroic; sometimes shows lamellar twinning. By transmitted light[8] thin scales are brown in color.

ORIENTATION	n_{red}	n_{blue}[9]	ABSORPTION	
$Y = b$	2.63	3.17	Light brown	Bx. $2V$ large.
Z near c			Dark brown	Sign unknown.

C h e m. An oxide of copper, CuO. Cu 79.89, O 20.11, total 100.00. Modern analyses are not available. A sample from Copper Harbor, Michigan, gave[10] 99.45 per cent CuO, with G. 5.952; crystals from Cornwall gave[11] 98.12 per cent CuO and 1.72 per cent gangue, with G. > 6.

Var. Massive. Melaconite. Melakonit *Germ.* Marcylite pt. *Shepard* (*Marcy's Expl. Red River*, 135, 1854 — Dana [137, 1868]). Melanochalcite pt. *Koenig* (*Am. J. Sc.*, **14**, 404, 1902). Copper Pitch Ore pt. Kupferpecherz pt. *Germ.* Dull earthy, pulverulent, or compact masses or coatings; also lustrous and pitchlike with conchoidal fracture; sometimes reniform or colloform. G. 4.0–5.0.[12] Commonly admixed with oxide of iron or manganese, and then grading toward limonite or wad, or with copper silicates, malachite, colloidal silica (melanochalcite) and forming part of the material loosely designated as copper pitch ore.

Tests. B.B. infusible. Easily soluble in dilute HCl or HNO₃.

O c c u r. The massive variety, melaconite, is a common mineral in the oxidized portion of copper deposits, but is less abundant than cuprite. Usually associated with cuprite, limonite, manganese oxides, chrysocolla, malachite, and azurite; also chalcocite, cerussite, and other secondary minerals. Also in crystals on lavas as a product of sublimation. Only a few occurrences can be mentioned here.

Found at Siegen and Daaden, Westphalia; Joachimstal, Bohemia; at Oravicza and Rézbánya, Roumania. At Bogoslowsk and Nizhne Tagilsk, in the Urals, U.S.S.R. In Spain at Rio Tinto, Huelva, at Linares, Andalusia, and in large amounts at Huerta Arriba, Burgos. At Chessy, Rhône, and near Toulon, Var, in France. In clustered aggregates of thin scales on lava at Mount Vesuvius, Italy, associated with alkali chlorides, cotunnite, copper chlorides, and thought to be the product of reaction of volatilized copper chloride and water vapor. Occurs similarly at Mount Etna. In Cornwall, England, in distinct crystals at Lostwithiel, and at many other localities; at Leadhills, Scotland. At Tsumeb, South-West Africa. At Cobija, Bolivia, and at Chuquicamata, Chile.

In the United States at many of the copper deposits of the southwest, notably Bisbee, where it constituted an ore, and also Globe and Morenci, in Arizona; Eureka, Nevada; and Santa Rita, New Mexico. In Oregon in the Waldo district, Josephine County. At Bingham, Utah, in the chalcocite ores, and at Butte, Montana. Formerly abundant at Copper Harbor, Keweenaw Point, Michigan. At Ducktown, Tennessee.

A l t e r. Often found as alteration shells or pseudomorphs after cuprite; also as an alteration product of tetrahedrite, chalcopyrite, bournonite, chalcocite, and other copper minerals. Found at Vesuvius altered to a basic chloride of copper (*atelite*) by the action of HCl fumes in a fumarole.

A r t i f.[13] Obtained in crystals by slowly cooling a fusion of CuO in NaOH, KOH or KF; also by heating CuCl₂ in water vapor or CuCl in oxygen. Observed near a flue in roasting copper matte with NaCl. Powdery or granular black cupric oxide is formed by heating finely divided Cu or Cu₂O in oxygen, by calcining cupric salts and by electrolysis.

N a m e. After the Neapolitan botanist, M. Tenore (1780–1861). Melaconite from μέλας, *black*, and κόνις, *dust*. Melanochalcite from μέλας, *black*, and χαλκός, *copper*.

MELANOCHALCITE. *Koenig* (*Am. J. Sc.*, **14**, 404, 1902). A lustrous black pitchlike material from Bisbee, Arizona, supposed to have the formula

$Cu_2(Si,C)O_4 \cdot Cu(OH)_2$. Very brittle. H. 4, G. 4.1–4.7. Streak brown to brownish black. Forms alteration shells around kernels or nodules of cuprite, with hematite, chrysocolla, and other minerals. Shown[14] to be a mixture largely of tenorite, with chrysocolla and malachite.

Ref.

1. Monoclinic symmetry assigned by Story-Maskelyne, *British Assoc., Rep.*, **35**, 33 (1865); *Russ. Min. Ges.,Vh.*, **1**, 147 (1866); verified by Tunell, Posnjak, and Ksanda, *Zs. Kr.*, **90**, 120 (1935). The orthorhombic interpretation of Jenzsch, *Ann. Phys.*, **107**, 647 (1859), was shown to be in error by Scacchi, *Acc. Napoli, Att.*, **6** [9], 12 (1875), who recalculated Jenzsch's measurements in the orientation of Story-Maskelyne.
2. Orientation and unit of Story-Maskelyne (1865), values from Tunell, Posnjak, and Ksanda (1935) on artificial crystals by x-ray method. In the x-ray study the a- and c-axes are interchanged with respect to crystallographic usage.
3. Story-Maskelyne (1865) on Cornwall crystals.
4. Tunell, Posnjak, and Ksanda (1935).
5. Twinning on $\{011\}$ is the common law. Story-Maskelyne reports $\{100\}$ as twin plane. The figures given by Scacchi (1875) are obviously of twin groups with more than one twin law, $\{011\}$ and perhaps $\{001\}$.
6. Tunell, Posnjak, and Ksanda (1935) give only the traces of the cleavage planes on $\{100\}$ (morphological orientation). Story-Maskelyne (1865) gives $\{\bar{1}11\}$ and $\{001\}$. Jenzsch (1859) gives $\{\bar{1}11\}$ and $\{\bar{1}01\}$ (in our orientation).
7. Schneiderhöhn and Ramdohr (**2**, 553, 1931).
8. Tunell, Posnjak, and Ksanda (1935).
9. Kundt, *Ak. Berlin, Ber.*, 255, 1387; 1888.
10. Joy anal. in Rammelsberg, *Ann. Phys.*, **80**, 286 (1850).
11. Church, *Chem. News*, **11**, 122 (1865); CuO average of two determinations.
12. The low values for the specific gravity are probably due to inhomogeneities of the material.
13. In Mellor (**3**, 131, 1923); also Duboin, *C.R.*, **186**, 1133 (1928).
14. Hunt and Kraus, *Am. J. Sc.*, **41**, 211 (1916), by chemical and optical study, and also Guild, *Am. Min.*, **14**, 315 (1929). The x-ray powder pattern is identical with tenorite (Frondel, priv. comm., 1939).

HYDROTENORITE. *de Leenheer (Bull. soc. belge géol.*, 47, 215, 1937).
A black, massive material interbanded with chrysocolla at the Star of the Congo mine, Katanga, Belgian Congo. Thought to be $4CuO \cdot H_2O$, but later shown[1] to be a mixture of tenorite with chrysocolla and adsorbed water.

Ref.

1. Billiet and Vandendriessche, *Bull. soc. belge géol.*, **48**, 333 (1938), by x-ray study; also de Leenheer, *ibid.*, **48**, 343 (1938).

424 **PARAMELACONITE** $[Cu^2_{1-2x}Cu^1_{2x}O_{1-x}]$. *Koenig (Ac. Nat. Sc. Philadelphia, Proc.*, 284, 1891).

Cryst.[1] Tetragonal; ditetragonal dipyramidal — $4/m\,2/m\,2/m$.

$$a : c = 1 : 1.695; \qquad p_0 : r_0 = 1.695 : 1$$

Forms:[2]

		ϕ	ρ	A	$\overline{M}$
c	001	....	....	90°00′	90°00′
a	010	0°00′	90°00′	90 00	45 00
d	011	0 00	59 28	90 00	52 29

Structure cell.[3] Space group $I4/amd$; a_0 5.83, c_0 9.88; $a_0 : c_0 = 1 : 1.695$; cell contents $(Cu^2_{16-2x}C^1_{2x})_{16}O_{16-x}$ where $x = 1.85$.
Habit. Stout prismatic [001]. $\{010\}$ striated [100].

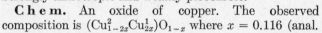

Etch figures.[2] Artificial etch pits and hillocks conform to ditetragonal dipyramidal symmetry.

P h y s. No cleavage. Fracture flat conchoidal. H. $4\frac{1}{2}$. G. 6.04;[2] 6.106 (calc. for $x = 1.85$). Luster brilliant metallic adamantine. Color on fracture surfaces pitch black; on natural faces black with a faint purplish tone. Streak brownish black. Opaque. In polished section[2] white with a pinkish brown tint. Strongly anisotropic and weakly pleochroic.

C h e m. An oxide of copper. The observed composition is $(Cu^2_{1-2x}Cu^1_{2x})O_{1-x}$ where $x = 0.116$ (anal. 3). The ideal composition may be CuO. Spectrographic analysis[2] has shown Al, Mn, Si, Mg, Ba (<0.1 per cent); Ca, Pb, Zn, Mo, Ti, Zr (<0.01 per cent); Sn, V (<0.001 per cent); also Fe.

Anal.

	1	2	3
Cu	. . . . .	. . . .	81.80
O	. . . . .	. . . .	[18.20]
CuO	87.66	77.94	[78.62]
Cu₂O	[11.70]	19.45	[21.38]
Fe₂O₃	0.64	2.70	0.00
Total	100.00	100.09	100.00

1. Bisbee. Cu_2O calculated from excess summation of total Cu determined as Cu_2S. The analyzed sample contained cuprite and probably much tenorite.[4] 2. Bisbee. Cu_2O and CuO determined directly by KH tartrate method. Fe_2O_3 present as impurity.[5] 3. Bisbee. Total Cu determined directly by electrolytic method.[5]

Tests.[2] Fusible with difficulty in strong O.F. Melts easily and yields metallic copper in R.F. Readily soluble in cold dilute mineral acids and in dilute NH_4OH and NH_4Cl solution. Becomes coated by metallic copper and black cupric oxide in extremely dilute HNO_3 or H_2SO_4. On heating breaks down at a measurable rate below 190°, and more rapidly with increasing temperature, to a mixture of tenorite and cuprite.

O c c u r. A secondary mineral, found at the Copper Queen mine, Bisbee, Arizona, as fine crystals associated with cuprite, goethite, tenorite, connellite, and malachite. Only two specimens are known.

A l t e r. To tenorite.

N a m e. From παρά, *near*, and *melaconite*, because near melaconite in composition.

Ref.

1. Frondel, *Am. Min.*, **26**, 657 (1941), on the original specimens of Koenig (1891). The x-ray ratio is taken in preference to the morphological ratio, $a : c = 1 : 1.6709$, obtained from the average (59°6') of the best angular measurements on {011}.
2. Frondel (1941).
3. Frondel (1941) by the x-ray Weissenberg method.
4. Koenig (1891).
5. Gonyer anal. in Frondel (1941).

425 **M O N T R O Y D I T E** [HgO]. *Moses (Am. J. Sc., 16, 259, 1903).*

C r y s t. Orthorhombic; dipyramidal — $2/m \, 2/m \, 2/m$.

$a : b : c = 0.6375 : 1 : 0.5989$;[1] $p_0 : q_0 : r_0 = 0.9395 : 0.5989 : 1$

$q_1 : r_1 : p_1 = 0.6375 : 1.0644 : 1$; $r_2 : p_2 : q_2 = 1.5686 : 1.6697 : 1$

Forms:[2]

	φ	ρ = C	φ₁	ρ₁ = A	φ₂	ρ₂ = B
b 010	0°00′	90°00′	90°00′	90°00′	....	0°00′
a 100	90 00	90 00	....	0 00	0°00′	90 00
m 110	57 29	90 00	90 00	32 31	0 00	57 29
v 011	0 00	30 55	30 55	90 00	90 00	59 05
y 043	0 00	38 36½	38 36½	90 00	90 00	51 23½
z 021	0 00	43 46½	43 46½	90 00	90 00	46 13½
g 101	90 00	43 12½	0 00	46 47½	46 47½	90 00
d 201	90 00	61 58½	0 00	28 01½	28 01½	90 00
n 301	90 00	70 28	0 00	19 32	19 32	90 00
q 401	90 00	75 06	0 00	14 54	14 54	90 00
u 601	90 00	79 56½	0 00	10 03½	10 03½	90 00
s 111	57 29	48 05½	30 55	51 08	46 47½	66 25
o 221	57 29	65 50	50 08½	39 42½	28 01½	60 38
i 441	57 29	77 21	67 20½	34 38	14 54	58 22
x 661	57 29	81 29½	74 27	33 29½	10 03½	57 53
α 263	27 36	53 30½	50 08½	68 08	51 13½	44 34
t 121	38 06½	56 42	50 08½	58 57	46 47½	48 53
e 131	27 36	63 45	60 54	65 26½	46 47½	37 22
ρ 14·6·13	74 43	46 22	15 27	45 43½	44 40	79 00
r 421	72 19	75 46½	50 08½	22 33	14 54	72 53
w 621	78 00	80 09½	50 08½	15 28½	10 03½	78 11

Less common:

l 1·10·0	*j* 410	*β* 0·12·1	*A* 112	*δ* 10·10·1	*R* 343	*ω* 10·1·6
h 120	*k* 085	*E* 203	*B* 223	*P* 323	*Z* 373	*φ* 631
ξ 310	*L* 041	*M* 403	*D* 443	*V* 545	*N* 4·12·3	

Structure cell.[3]　Space group $Pmmn$; a_0 3.296, b_0 3.513, c_0 5.504, all ±0.006; $b_0 : c_0 : a_0 = 0.6383 : 1 : 0.5988$; contains Hg_2O_2.

Habit.[4]　Crystals long prismatic [001]; also equant or, rarely, flattened {111}. Terminal forms frequently striated; on {011} ‖ [100], on {201} ‖ [101], the pyramids often with several sets of striae. As wormlike, tubular, or spherical aggregates consisting usually of minute prismatic crystals. Also massive, powdery, or banded. Crystals often bent or twisted.

Phys.　Cleavage {010} perfect.[5] Sectile. Very flexible, but not elastic; somewhat brittle when bent on [010]. H. 2½. G. 11.23,[6] 11.2 ± 0.1 (artif.); 11.22 (calc.). Luster .vitreous, inclining to adamantine. Color deep red, inclining toward brownish red and brown in smaller crystals. Streak yellow-brown. Transparent in thin pieces. Crystals glide[7] readily: bend-gliding and twist-gliding with T{010} and t[001]; also other, unidentified, gliding elements.

Opt.[8]　In transmitted light, orange-red to pale yellow with decreasing thickness.

Orientation	n_{Li}		
X = a?	2.37 ± 0.02	Bx pos. (+).	2V large.
Y = b?	2.5		
Z = c	2.65 ± 0.02		

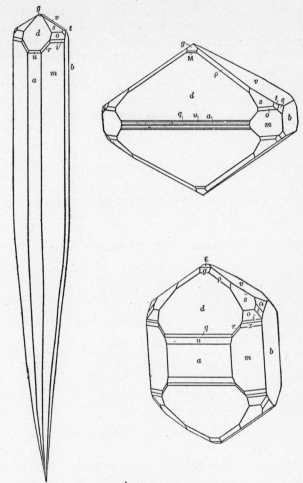

Terlingua, Texas.

In thick sections pleochroic in deep orange-red and in yellowish brown.

Chem. Mercuric oxide, HgO.

Anal.

	1	2	3
Hg	92.61	92.87	92.74
O	7.39	7.13	7.49
Total	100.00	100.00	100.23
G.	11.22		

1. HgO. 2. Terlingua. O by loss on heating.[9] 3. Terlingua. O from volumetric determination.[10]

Tests. In C.T. volatilizes completely, yielding a sublimate of metallic mercury. Readily soluble in cold HCl, HNO$_3$, and in solutions of alkali or alkaline earth chlorides and in KI.

O c c u r. At Terlingua, Brewster County, Texas, upon or embedded in calcite, with terlinguaite, native mercury and, rarely, calomel, eglestonite, and gypsum. Found about two miles west of Redwood City, San Mateo County, California, with eglestonite, calomel, native mercury, cinnabar, and dolomite.

A r t i f.[11] By heating native mercury in air or with an oxidizing agent, and by calcining mercuric or mercurous nitrates.

N a m e. After Montroyd Sharp, one of the owners of the Terlingua mine.

Ref.

1. Orientation and angles of Schaller, in Hillebrand and Schaller, *U.S. Geol. Sur., Bull. 405*, 47, 1909; unit of Zachariasen, *Zs. phys. Chem.*, **128**, 421 (1927), from an x-ray study of artificial material. Schaller's *c*-axis is halved by Zachariasen.

2. Schaller, in Hillebrand and Schaller (1909). Rare forms:

350	320	031	4·12·5	483	623	231	821
230	510	469	627	342	643	541	

3. Zachariasen (1927) by powder method on artificial material. The space group symbol in the morphological orientation is *Pmnm*. The supposed yellow and red modification of artificial HgO have been shown by x-ray study to be identical by Levi, *Gazz. chim. ital.*, **54**, 709 (1924), Zachariasen (1927), and others. For x-ray powder data see also Bird, *Am. Min.*, **17**, 541 (1932).

4. See Hillebrand and Schaller (1909) for a detailed description of the habit and forms of aggregation.

5. Moses (1903) mentions a cleavage oblique to the length, but this was not verified by Hillebrand and Schaller (1909).

6. Frondel (priv. comm., 1939) on 22-mg. Terlingua crystal.

7. Frondel (priv. comm., 1939), on Terlingua crystals. See also Hillebrand and Schaller (1909) for remarks on gliding properties.

8. Larsen (113, 1921); Hillebrand and Schaller (1909).

9. Moses (1903).

10. Hillebrand and Schaller (1909).

11. Mellor (4, 771, 1923).

426　L I T H A R G E [PbO]. Goldglätte *Germ.* Lithargite *Wherry* (*Am. Min.*, **2**, 19, 1917). α-PbO.

C r y s t. Tetragonal; probably ditetragonal dipyramidal — $4/m \ 2/m \ 2/m$.[1]

$$a : c = 1 : 1.258; \qquad p_0 : r_0 = 1.258 : 1$$

Forms:[2]

	ϕ	ρ	$\overline{M}$	A
c 001	.....	0°00′	90°00′	90°00′
a 010	0°00′	90 00	45 00	90 00
m 110	45 00	90 00	90 00	45 00
r 011	0 00	51 31	56 23½	90 00

Structure cell. Space group probably $P4/nmm$; a_0 3.986, c_0 5.011;[3] $a_0 : c_0 = 1 : 1.257$; contains Pb_2O_2.

Habit. Found as alteration borders on scales or tablets of massicot. Also as crusts. Artificial crystals are tabular {001}.

P h y s. Cleavage {110}.[4] H. 2. G. 9.14 (artif.[1]); 9.25 (calc.). Luster greasy to dull. Color red. Transparent.

O p t.[5] In transmitted light, red to orange-red in color with decreasing thickness. Uniaxial negative $(-)$. O_{Li} 2.665; E_{Li} 2.535.

C h e m. A monoxide of lead, PbO. Pb 92.83, O 7.17, total 100.00. Analyses of natural material shown to be litharge are not available.[6]

Tests. F. 2. Soluble in HCl and HNO_3; decomposed by H_2SO_4 with the formation of Pb_2SO_4. Slowly soluble in alkalies.

O c c u r. Reported[7] as borders on scales or tablets of massicot (and derived therefrom by paramorphism). Probably more common in oxidized lead deposits than hitherto supposed. In the United States in California at Cucamonga Peak, San Bernardino County, and at Fort Tejon, Kern County. In the Mineral Hill district, near Hailey, Blaine County, Idaho, with native lead and leadhillite.[8] Probably at the Zashuran River, Kurdistan, with massicot (?), orpiment, realgar and cerussite.

A l t e r. Observed as paramorphs after massicot. Inverts, on heating to about 530°C, to massicot, β-PbO.[9]

A r t i f.[10] Obtained in crystals by slow cooling from solutions of PbO in strong KOH or from fusion in KOH; with fast cooling massicot is formed. By calcining lead hydroxide or lead salts of volatile acids in air at relatively low temperatures, and by heating lead in air and superheated steam at about 250°. Much commercial and other artificial so-called litharge is a mixture of litharge and massicot.

N a m e. Litharge is derived from λιθάργυρος, the name given by Dioscorides to a material obtained in the process of separating lead from silver by fire metallurgy.[11]

Ref.

1. Applebey and Powell, *J. Chem. Soc. London*, 2821, 1931, on artificial crystals.
2. Applebey and Powell (1931) and Luedecke, *Zs. Kr.*, **8**, 82 (1884), on artificial crystals.
3. Darbyshire, *J. Chem. Soc. London*, 211, 1932, by the powder method on artificial crystals; see also Dickinson and Friauf, *J. Am. Chem. Soc.*, **46**, 2457 (1924).
4. Michel, *Bull. soc. min.*, **13**, 56 (1890). Shannon, *Econ. Geol.*, **22**, 826 (1927), notes a perfect cleavage with two other cleavages at right angles to this and to each other, in material from Idaho.
5. Larsen and Berman (94, 1934).
6. Scott, *Min. Mag.*, **17**, 143 (1914), gives an analysis of supposed litharge from Zashuran River, Kurdistan, but the material is, in part, optically orthorhombic (with $n_\beta = 1.735 \pm 0.005$, which is much too low for an oxide of lead) and, in part, apparently uniaxial; possibly a mixture of litharge and massicot.
7. Larsen (105, 1921).
8. Shannon (1927).
9. Rencker and Bassière, *C.R.*, **202**, 765 (1936).
10. In Mellor (7, 638, 1927); also Applebey and Powell (1931) and Rencker and Bassière (1936).
11. For a discussion of the history of the name see Mellor (1927) and Hintze (1 [2A], 1934, 1910).

PALLADINITE. Palladiumoxydul *Johnson* and *Lampadius* (*J. pr. Chem.*, **11**, 311, 1837). Palladinite *Shepard* (408, 1857). Palladiumocker *Rammelsberg* (1004, 1860).

A brown ocherous coating found on palladian gold (*porpezite*) from Brazil, and considered to be PdO. Artificial[1] PdO is tetragonal[2] with a_0 3.029, c_0 5.314; G. 8.70, 8.31 (calc.).

Ref.

1. In Mellor (**15**, 655, 1936).
2. Zachariasen, *Zs. phys. Chem.*, **128**, 412 (1927).

427   **M A S S I C O T** [PbO].   *Huot* (346, 1841).   Massicottite *D'Achiardi* (**1**, 221, 1883).   Lead ocher, Plumbic ochre, Lead oxide.   Bleiglätte, Silberglätte, Bleioxyd *Germ.*   Chrysitin *Weisbach* (54, 1875).   Plomb oxidé jaune *Fr.*   Piombo ossidato *Ital.*   Litarjirio nativo *Span.*, *Domeyko* (1879).   β-PbO.

C r y s t.[1]   (Artif.) Orthorhombic; dipyramidal — $2/m\ 2/m\ 2/m$.
Structure cell.   Space group probably *Cmmm*; a_0 5.459, b_0 4.723, c_0 5.859;[2] $a_0 : b_0 : c_0 = 1.156 : 1 : 1.240$; contains Pb_4O_4.
Habit.   Massive, earthy to scaly.   Artificial crystals are tabular {100}.
Twinning.   Observed on artificial crystals.[3]
P h y s.   Cleavage {100}, {010}, and in traces on {110}.[4]   Crystals flexible but not elastic.   H. 2.   G. 9.56 (artif.[5]); 9.75 (calc.).   Luster greasy to dull.   Color between sulfur- and orpiment-yellow, sometimes with a reddish tint.   Streak somewhat lighter than the color.   Transparent in very thin pieces.
O p t.[6]   In transmitted light nearly colorless to pale yellow.

ORIENTATION	n_{Li}	ABSORPTION	
X	2.51		Bx. pos. (+). $2V = 90\pm$.
Y = a?	2.61	Light sulfur yellow	Bx. neg. (−) for blue.
Z	2.71	Deep yellow	Disp. strong.

C h e m.   A monoxide of lead, PbO.   Pb 92.83, O 7.17, total 100.00. No modern analyses have been reported.[7]

Tests.   F. 2, to a yellow glass.   Soluble in HCl and HNO_3; decomposed by H_2SO_4 with the formation of $PbSO_4$.   Slowly soluble in alkalies.

O c c u r.   Massicot is a product of oxidation of galena and other primary lead minerals.   Associated with cerussite, litharge, and other secondary lead or copper minerals, limonite, and antimony oxides.   May easily be confused with bindheimite or other yellow ocherous lead or antimony minerals.

In Germany at Badenweiler, Baden; Freiberg, Saxony; Greifenstein, Nassau; and at Kis-Almás and Oláhláposbánya in Bohemia.   In Roumania at Rézbánya and Boinick.   As a product of oxidation of ancient lead slags at Laurion, Greece.   In Italy in Sardinia in the Oreddo valley with leadhillite, cerussite, caledonite and other secondary minerals, and near Portotorres.   In France at Malmes, Gard, with cerussite; near Ally, Haute-Loire; at La Gardette, Isère; with malachite, azurite, and cerussite at Montchonay, Rhône; at the lead mines of La Croix-aux-Mines, Vosges. In the Transvaal, Africa, in the Marico district with minium, vanadinite, wad, and pyromorphite, and elsewhere.   In Mexico reported from the volcanoes of Popocatepetl and Jztaccituall, and found along the streams between Ceralvo Monterey in Chihuahua and Coahuila provinces; also from Perote, Zomelahuacán district, Vera Cruz, and from Carachilas, Lower California. In Bolivia at Caracoles. From Melrose, New South Wales. In the United States at Austin's mines, Wythe County, Virginia. Reported from Colorado from near Rico, Dolores County; Leadville, Lake County. In Nevada from the Redemption mine, near Hornsilver, Esmeralda County. In California at Cucamonga Peak, San Bernardino County, and from Fort Tejon, Kern County.

Alter. As an alteration crust upon galena; also by the oxidation of bournonite, boulangerite, and other primary lead minerals. Observed as a product of alteration of lead pipes in the thermal springs of Plombières and Bourbon-les-Bains, France. Alters to the paramorph, litharge. Massicot is the stable form of PbO above 530°.[8]

Artif.[9] Obtained in crystals by the action of fused KOH or water solutions of KOH or NaOH on PbO. Formed as a powder by direct oxidation of lead, and by calcining salts of lead with volatile acids at moderate temperatures. Observed as a furnace product.

Name. Massicot is derived from a French name for oxide of lead.[10]

Ref.

1. The crystallography, both morphological and structural, is based on artificial material. The structural elements of Darbyshire, *J. Chem. Soc.*, London, 211, 1932, and of Halla and Pawlek, *Zs. phys. Chem.*, **128**, 49 (1927), are not in agreement with the morphological measurements of Mitscherlich, *Ak. Berlin, Ber.*, 11, 1840, and Nordenskiöld, *Ann. Phys.*, **114**, 619 (1861). The latter gave $a : b : c = 0.6706 : 1 : 0.9764$, with the forms: $c\{001\}$, $a\{100\}$, $d\{h01\}$, $t\{233\}$, $s\{455\}$, $r\{111\}$.
2. Darbyshire (1932) by powder method on artificial material; Halla and Pawlek (1927) give a_0 5.50, b_0 4.68, c_0 5.88.
3. Termier, *Bull. soc. min.*, **18**, 376 (1895).
4. Grailich, *Ak. Wien, Ber.*, **28**, 282 (1858).
5. Applebey and Powell, *J. Chem. Soc. London*, 2821, 1931.
6. Larsen and Berman (147, 1934); see also Grailich (1858) and Michel, *Bull. soc. min.*, **13**, 56 (1890).
7. For old analyses see Dana (136, 1868).
8. Rencker and Bassière, *C.R.*, **202**, 765 (1936).
9. Mellor (7, 638, 1927) and Hintze (1 [2A], 1937, 1910).
10. See Mellor (1927) and Hintze (1910) for a discussion of the history of massicot.

431   **M I N I U M** [Pb_3O_4]. Mennige *Germ.* Plomb oxidé rouge *Haüy.* Minio, Piombo ossidato rosso *Ital.* Azarcon nativo *Span.* Red-lead.

Cryst. Found only massive, earthy, or pulverulent; in microscopic crystalline scales. Minium has been investigated by the x-ray powder method,[1] but the cell dimensions and the symmetry are unknown.

Phys. H. $2\frac{1}{2}$. G. 8.9–9.2 (artif.[2]). Luster faint greasy or dull. Color scarlet-red or brownish red, sometimes with a yellowish tint. Streak orange-yellow.

Opt.[3] In transmitted light, red in color. Strong pleochroism: X deep reddish brown, Z nearly colorless. Elongation neg. $(-)$. Extinction parallel. n_{Li} 2.42 $\pm$ 0.02. Birefringence weak. Abnormal green interference colors are characteristic.

Chem. An oxide of lead, Pb_3O_4. Pb 90.67, O 9.33, total 100.00.

Anal.

	Pb₃O₄	Fe₂O₃	V₂O₅	Insol.	Total
1	91.39	0.80	0.52	7.51	100.22

1. Leadville. Pb_3O_4 calc. from Pb determination. Insol. includes PbS 5.08, CaO 0.28, $(Fe,Al)_2O_3$ 0.41, SiO_2 2.00.[4]

Tests. F. 1. In C.T. gives off oxygen. On heating, the color darkens and becomes black, but the original color is restored on cooling. Soluble in excess HCl with evolution of chlorine; decomposed by dilute HNO_3, forming lead nitrate and a brown residue of PbO_2.

Occur. Minium is a secondary mineral found in small amounts at many localities, usually as an alteration product of galena or cerussite.

Only a few of the known localities can be mentioned here.[5] At Schlangenberg (Smeyewskaja-Gora) in the Altai Mountains, Siberia, in part with barite. In Germany, notably at Badenweiler, Baden; also at Bleialf and at many other localities in the Eifel, and at Horhausen, Mayen, Bleiberg, and elsewhere in the Rhine province; at Brilon, Westphalia; at Weilmünster and Runkel, Nassau; at Biberwier, Tirol. In Italy at Sarrabus, Sardinia. At Långban, Sweden, with native lead. In England at Leadhills, Scotland, and in Weardale, Yorkshire. Found in Mexico at the Santa Fé mine, Bolaños, with massicot and cerussite, and at Zimapan.

In the United States at Austin's mine, Wythe County, Virginia. In Idaho in the Jay Gould mine, Alturas County, with native lead and galena, in the Texas Creek district and with plattnerite near Gilmore, in Lemhi County, and at other localities. In many of the oxidized ores of the Leadville district, Colorado, enclosing residual particles of galena and admixed with cerussite and iron oxide. At Mineral Point, Wisconsin, incrusting galena. In Utah in the Godiva mine, Tintic district. Reported from near Fort Tejon, Kern County, and in the Felix fluorite mine, near Azusa, Los Angeles County, in California.

Alter. Commonly found as an alteration crust upon, or as complete pseudomorphs after, galena and cerussite. The pseudomorphs often retain the cleavages of the original mineral. Also pseudomorphs after calcite and as an alteration product of native lead. Observed incrusting ancient leaden objects. Minium apparently inverts to a black modification at 389°.[6]

Artif.[7] By heating PbO in air at dull red heat; formed more slowly at ordinary temperatures. In minute crystals by fusion of $PbCO_3$ in a mixture of K and Na nitrates, and by heating lead oxide or carbonate in hot concentrated KOH solution.

Name. The name minium was originally applied to cinnabar. The cinnabar was adulterated with red-lead and in time the adulterant alone received the name.[8]

Ref.

1. Darbyshire, *J. Chem. Soc. London*, 211, 1932.
2. The values 4.55 and 4.59 given by Hawkins, *Am. J. Sc.*, **39**, 42 (1890), for natural material from Leadville are obviously much too low.
3. Larsen (111, 1921); Larsen and Berman (216, 1934).

4. Hawkins (1890).
5. For additional localities see Hintze (**1** [3A], 3586, 1929).
6. LeBlanc and Eberius, *Zs. phys. Chem.*, **160**, 69 (1932).
7. Mellor (**7**, 672, 1927), and Milbauer, *Chem.-Ztg.*, **38**, 477 (1914).
8. See Hintze (1929) for a discussion of the history of the term.

HEMATITE GROUP

		Symmetry	$c/2a$	G.	a_{rh}
Corundum	Al_2O_3	$\bar{3}\,2/m$	1.3638	4.02	5.12Å
Hematite	Fe_2O_3	$\bar{3}\,2/m$	1.3652	5.26	5.42
Ilmenite series					
Ilmenite	$FeTiO_3$	$\bar{3}$	1.3846	4.72	5.52
Geikielite	$MgTiO_3$	$\bar{3}$	1.3855	4.05	5.54
Pyrophanite	$MnTiO_3$	$\bar{3}$	1.3980	4.54	5.62
Senaite	$(Fe,Mn,Pb)TiO_3$	$\bar{3}$?		5.30 ?	

All the minerals of this group are rhombohedral, but the members of the ilmenite series are of a lower symmetry than corundum and hematite because the nonequivalent cations in ilmenite eliminate a glide plane in the corundum structure.[1] The unit rhombohedral cell contains A_4X_6. The well-established morphological unit has the c-axis half of the structural c-axis length, but the former has been retained here for the sake of convenience. Crystals of the group are inclined to be tabular {0001}. They usually have a parting plane {0001} due to twinning on the base. Other twinning planes and partings are less often encountered.

Ilmenite forms a series with more or less complete miscibility between the Fe and Mg members, and between Fe and Mn. Hematite shows little solid solution with the other members,[2] and corundum still less. Analyses of ilmenite often show considerable amounts of Fe_2O_3 but examination in polished section[3] of such material usually shows hematite or magnetite intergrowths. Presumably not more than about 6 per cent of Fe_2O_3 can remain in solid solution at normal temperatures, and exsolution is responsible for the observed intergrowths. High Ti ilmenites are likewise found to contain intergrowths of rutile.

The minerals of the group are generally formed at high temperatures, and frequently are found as accessory minerals in igneous rocks or as large concentrations closely affiliated with magmatic sources.

Senaite is not too well known but it may be a member of the ilmenite series.

Ref.

1. Barth and Posnjak, *Zs. Kr.*, **88**, 265 (1934); Posnjak and Barth, *Zs. Kr.*, **88**, 271 (1934).
2. Ramdohr (*Sonderdruck Festschr. Bergak.*, Clausthal, 307, 1925).
3. Ramdohr (1925); Warren, *Econ. Geol.*, **13**, 419 (1918).

4411   **CORUNDUM** [Al$_2$O$_3$]. Corindon (= sapphire, corundum, and emery united) *Haüy* (*Ann. Phys.*, **20**, 187, 1805); *Lucas* (**1**, 257, 1806).

Corundum. Adamas Siderites *Pliny* (**37**, 15, A.D. 77). Karund *Hindustan.* Corinindum, Corinendum *Woodward* (1714, 1725). Adamantine spar *Black* (1780) (in *Greville, Roy. Soc. London, Phil. Trans.*, 1798, and in *Klaproth, Ak. Berlin, Mem.*, 1786–87). Demantspath *Klaproth* (*Ak. Berlin, Mem.*, 1786–87; 17, 1795); *Werner* (*Bergm. J.*, **1**, 375, 390, 1789). Spath adamantin *Delamétherie* (*J. phys.*, **30**, 12, 1787); *Haüy* (*J. phys.*, **30**, 193, 1787). Corundum *Greville* (*Roy. Soc. London, Phil. Trans.*, 1798). Corindon *Haüy* (1801). Corindon harmophane *Haüy.* Corindon adamantin *Brongniart* (**1**, 429, 1807). Korund *Germ.*

Sapphire. 'Γάκινθos. Hyacinthos *Pliny* (**37**, 44, A.D. 77). Asteria *Pliny* (**37**, 49 A.D. 77). Jacut *Arab.* ''Ανθραξ pt *Theophrastus* (ca. 315 B.C.). Carbunculus, Lychnis pt. *Pliny* (**37**, 25, 29, A.D. 77). Saphir, Sapphirus *Wallerius* (116, 1747). Orientalisk Rubin *Wallerius* (117, 1747). Télésie *Haüy* (1801). Corindon hyalin *Haüy* (1805). Salamstein *Werner* (in *Hoffmann* [**1**, 547, 541, 1811]).

Emery. 'Ακονη 'εξ 'Αρμθνίαs [= Armenian Whetstone] *Theophrastus.* Σμῦρις *Dioscorides* (ca. A.D. 50). Naxium, Naxium ex Armenia *Pliny* (**36**, 10, A.D. 77). Pyrites virus (?) *Pliny* (**36**, 30, A.D. 77). Smyris, Smiris *Agricola* (1546). Smergel, Smiris ferrea *Wallerius* (267, 1747). Smirgel, Schmirgel *Germ.* Emeril *Haüy* (1801). Corindon granuleux *Haüy* (1805). Taosite (?) *de Lapparent, C.R.*, **201**, 154 (1935).

Cryst. Hexagonal — R; scalenohedral — $\overline{3}\,2/m.$

$a : c = 1 : 1.3638;$[1] $\alpha\ 85°45';$ $p_0 : r_0 = 1.5747 : 1;$ $\lambda\ 93°57'$

Forms:[2]

			ϕ	ρ	A_1	A_2
c	0001	111	.....	0°00'	90°00'	90°00'
m	10$\overline{1}$0	2$\overline{1}\overline{1}$	30°00'	90 00	30 00	90 00
a	11$\overline{2}$0	10$\overline{1}$	0 00	90 00	60 00	60 00
r	10$\overline{1}$1	100	30 00	57 35	43 01$\frac{1}{2}$	90 00
s	02$\overline{2}$1	11$\overline{1}$	−30 00	72 23	90 00	34 22
n	22$\overline{4}$3	31$\overline{1}$	0 00	61 11$\frac{1}{2}$	64 01	64 01
w	11$\overline{2}$1	41$\overline{2}$	0 00	69 52	62 00	62 00
v	44$\overline{8}$3	51$\overline{3}$	0 00	74 37$\frac{1}{2}$	61 10$\frac{1}{2}$	61 10$\frac{1}{2}$
X	5·5·$\overline{10}$·3	61$\overline{4}$	0 00	77 35$\frac{1}{2}$	60 46	60 46
z	22$\overline{4}$1	71$\overline{5}$	0 00	79 36$\frac{1}{2}$	60 32$\frac{1}{2}$	60 32$\frac{1}{2}$
λ	7·7·$\overline{14}$·3	81$\overline{6}$	0 00	81 04	60 24	60 24
θ	8·8·$\overline{16}$·3	91$\overline{7}$	0 00	82 10$\frac{1}{2}$	60 18$\frac{1}{2}$	60 18$\frac{1}{2}$
E	33$\overline{6}$1	10·1·$\overline{8}$	0 00	83 02	60 14$\frac{1}{2}$	60 14$\frac{1}{2}$
ν	44$\overline{8}$1	13·1·$\overline{11}$	0 00	84 46	60 08$\frac{1}{2}$	60 08$\frac{1}{2}$
ω	14·14·$\overline{28}$·3	15·1·$\overline{13}$	0 00	85 30$\frac{1}{2}$	60 06	60 06

Less common:

f	71$\overline{8}$0(5$\overline{2}\overline{3}$)	R	01$\overline{1}$2(110)	Y	10·10·$\overline{20}$·9(13·3·$\overline{7}$)	ξ	31$\overline{2}$2(30$\overline{1}$)
e	52$\overline{7}$0(4$\overline{1}\overline{3}$)	η	01$\overline{1}$1(22$\overline{1}$)	k	7·7·$\overline{14}$·6(9$\overline{2}\overline{5}$)	l	21$\overline{3}$1(20$\overline{1}$)
γ	10$\overline{1}$5(744)	A	05$\overline{5}$2(77$\overline{8}$)	u	11·11·$\overline{22}$·6(13·2·$\overline{9}$)	σ	20·5·$\overline{25}$·9(18·$\overline{2}$·$\overline{7}$)
δ	10$\overline{1}$3(522)	β	07$\overline{7}$2(33$\overline{4}$)	$\jmath$	10·10·$\overline{20}$·3(11·1·$\overline{9}$)	L	12$\overline{3}$1(52$\overline{4}$)
d	10$\overline{1}$2(411)	P	05$\overline{5}$1(22$\overline{3}$)	ϵ	11·11·$\overline{22}$·3(12·1·$\overline{10}$)	Σ	5·20·$\overline{25}$·9(13·8·$\overline{12}$)
x	30$\overline{3}$2(8$\overline{1}\overline{1}$)	π	11$\overline{2}$3(210)	ψ	7·4·$\overline{11}$·9(92$\overline{2}$)	ϕ	32$\overline{5}$1(30$\overline{2}$)
α	50$\overline{5}$2(4$\overline{1}\overline{1}$)	o	22$\overline{4}$5(11·5·$\overline{1}$)	ρ	2·8·$\overline{10}$·9(75$\overline{3}$)	T	11·8·$\overline{19}$·3(11·0·$\overline{8}$)
b	70$\overline{7}$2(65$\overline{5}$)	M	11$\overline{2}$2(52$\overline{1}$)	D	28·4·$\overline{32}$·27(29·1·$\overline{3}$)	χ	2·4·$\overline{6}$·1(31$\overline{3}$)
p	50$\overline{5}$1(11·$\overline{4}$·$\overline{4}$)	ζ	7·7·$\overline{14}$·9(10·3·$\overline{4}$)	H	16·4·$\overline{20}$·15(17·1·$\overline{3}$)		
q	70$\overline{7}$1(5$\overline{2}\overline{2}$)	B	44$\overline{8}$5(17·5·$\overline{7}$)	τ	41$\overline{5}$3(40$\overline{1}$)		

Etch figures. Natural etch and accessory growth figures conform with the symmetry.[3]

Structure cell. Space group $R\bar{3}c$; a_{rh} 5.120,[4] α 55°17'; a_0 4.751, c_0 12.97; $c_0/2 : a_0 = 1.365 : 1$; contains Al_4O_6 in the rhombohedral unit.

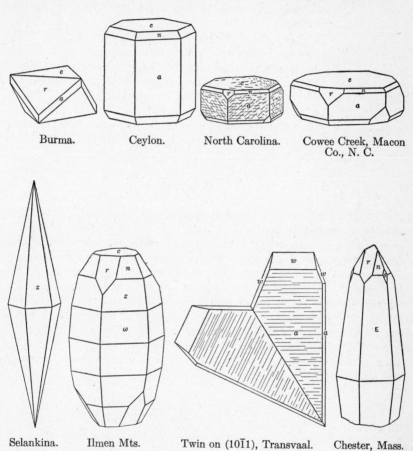

Burma.   Ceylon.   North Carolina.   Cowee Creek, Macon Co., N. C.

Selankina.   Ilmen Mts.   Twin on (10$\bar{1}$1), Transvaal.   Chester, Mass.

Habit. Often steep pyramidal on w, z, E, or ω. Also rough and rounded, barrel-shaped crystals, sometimes of considerable size, varying from short prismatic [0001] with a large base to steep pyramidal (Transvaal). More rarely flat tabular {0001} (Montana), or rhombohedral (Burma). Striae on {0001} ‖ [01$\bar{1}$0]; sometimes lines in direction [11$\bar{2}$0] divide the base into six sectors. Pyramidal and prism faces frequently show horizontal striae due to oscillations. Large blocks showing rhombohedral and basal parting are frequently observed (Georgia). Massive granular (emery); in rounded grains.

Twinning.[5] (*a*) Common {10ī1}; usually lamellar and producing a lamellar structure and striae on *c* and *r*; less commonly penetration twins or, rarely, arrowhead twins (South Africa) with crystals tabular {11ō0}. (*b*) On {0001}, less common.

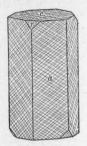

Burma.

Pressure twinning produced on {10ī1},[6] and on {0001}.[7]

P h y s. Cleavage none.[8] Fracture uneven to conchoidal. Parting {0001} sometimes perfect, but interrupted, and frequently having a pearly luster; also on {10ī1} due to twin lamination, often prominent (Georgia). Brittle; very tough when compact. H. 9.[9] G. 4.022,[10] 4.0–4.1; 3.98 (calc.). Luster adamantine to vitreous; on {0001} sometimes pearly. Color various: shades of blue (sapphire) to colorless, yellow to golden, rarely purple to violet, green; pink to deep pigeon-blood red (ruby); sometimes blue in daylight and reddish in artificial light (alexandrite-sapphire). The same crystal sometimes shows differences in depth of color,[11] or has color zoning with blue and red (Georgia) or other banding; some natural and artificial crystals have color zones parallel to a pyramid,[12] or are more intensely pigmented toward the apices. On heating[13] ruby changes to green and then to colorless; on cooling these changes are reversed. Sapphire changes to pale yellow at 1300° and on cooling becomes greenish blue. Some sapphires and rubies are phosphorescent and fluorescent in ultraviolet light, and especially so in a cathode-ray stream; radium emanations commonly change the colors of sapphire. M.P. 2050° (artif.[14]). Streak uncolored. Transparent in gem varieties, others transparent in thin pieces. Specific heat 0.1981;[15] thermal expansion, $\alpha = 6.2 \parallel c$, $54 \perp c$, with $\alpha = (10^6/l) \cdot (dl/dt)$, at 40°.[16] Coefficient of elasticity[17] 5.2×10^7.

O p t.[18] Uniaxial negative (−). Often, however, shows an anomalous biaxial character, due perhaps to twinning,[18] with $2V$ to 58°. Indices:

	C	*D*	*F*
O	1.7653	1.7686	1.7760
E	1.7573	1.7604	1.7677

Pleochroic in the deeper-colored crystals, with absorption $O > E$.

	O	*E*
Ceylon	Indigo blue	Lighter blue
Australia[19]	Blue	Emerald green to yellow-green
India, ruby[20]	Deep purple	Light yellow

Asterism is frequently noted (star-ruby and star-sapphire) and is due to oriented needle-like inclusions, perhaps of rutile,[21] or to colloidal or other material deposited in oriented tubules.[22] The center of the " star " coincides with the *c*-axis and the six rays are in conformity with the symmetry of the crystal. Hematite also occurs as minute oriented inclusions in corundum,[35] and macroscopic inclusions of garnet,[36] spinel, ilmenite, rutile are sometimes found.

C h e m. Aluminum oxide, Al_2O_3, with Al 52.91, O 47.09, total 100.00. Minor amounts of Fe^3 (1 per cent or less) and possibly Ti may be present. Spectrographic examination has shown the presence of Cr (in ruby[23]). Lesser spectrographic amounts of other elements have been reported. The color of ruby is apparently due to the small Cr content, and the color of the sapphire presumably to Fe or Ti.[23] Emery contains much Fe, but mostly as admixed iron minerals.

Anal.[24]

	1	2	3
Al_2O_3	99.27	99.39	99.30
Fe_2O_3	0.99	0.91	0.98
Total	100.26	100.30	100.28

1. Siam, ruby. Average of three analyses.[25] 2. Burma, ruby. Average of two analyses.[25] 3. Ceylon, sapphire. Average of three analyses.[25]

Var.[26] *Ordinary.* Corundum. Adamantine spar (India). Armenian stone (?). Here are included the non-gem varieties of pure corundum.

Gems. Sapphire. Ruby. Oriental topaz (yellow); oriental emerald (green); oriental amethyst (purple). Alexandrite-sapphire. Star-ruby. Star-sapphire (asteriated = asteria of *Pliny*). Chlor-sapphire. Carbunculus, Lychnis (of *Pliny*). Salamstein (of *Werner*). Barklyite. Here are included all the gem varieties, usually transparent and of deep color.

Emery. Schmirgel *Germ.* Granular black to grayish black; contains magnetite or hematite and spinel intimately admixed, the corundum forming only a part of the total. Not properly a mineralogical variety.

Tests. Infusible. Slowly soluble in borax or salt of phosphorus to a clear glass. Insoluble in acids. Converted to a soluble compound when fused with potassium bisulfate.

O c c u r.[27] Corundum is widespread and diversified in occurrence. It is found as an accessory mineral in some igneous rocks and as an important primary constituent in silica-deficient rocks such as nepheline syenites (Bancroft, Ontario) and syenites (Craigmont, Ontario). As a recrystallization product of aluminous xenoliths in igneous rocks. Concentrations are found in nepheline pegmatites (Bancroft) and in feldspar pegmatites and veins (plumasite of California). The genesis of some of these bodies is still a matter of dispute, but they all occur in association with silica-deficient rocks. Emery deposits (Chester, Massachusetts; Naxos, Greece) are made up principally of granular corundum and are found in limestones or aluminous sediments as the result of contact metamorphism and metasomatism; also in metamorphosed bauxite deposits. Some of the finest gems are found in recrystallized limestones (Burma) as isolated crystals. Placer deposits (Ceylon) have yielded most of the sapphires used in industry.

Minerals associated with corundum are: anorthite or oligoclase in the feldspar corundum dikes; hematite, magnetite, spinel, cordierite, hoegbomite, garnet in the emery deposits; chlorites, tourmaline, margarite, kyanite in the southern Appalachian occurrences; zircon, spinel, and other hard gem minerals in the Ceylon and other placer deposits.

The best rubies have come since early times from the mines of Upper Burma. The area covers 25 to 30 square miles. It includes Mogok, the center, and Mainglon state, Manyetseik, and Sagyin. The rubies are found principally in the soil of the hillsides and in the gravels of the Irrawaddy River, but some have been found *in situ* in the crystalline limestone of the region. A Burmese ruby in the British Museum weighs 690 gm. In Ceylon large quantities of rolled pebbles and crystals of various colors and quality are found in the placer deposits of the Ratnapura and Rakwana districts. In Siam fine cornflower blue sapphires and some rubies come from the region southeast of Bangkok, near Bottambang in Cambodia and Chantabun. In India found extensively: in Madras as large coarse crystals in the Carnatic district and in Malabar; in Salem as an anorthite-corundum vein; in Kangayan in Coimbatore as a corundum syenite, with zircon, spinel, and chrysoberyl; in Mysore; as pale blue crystals in Kashmir, northern India. Rubies have been mined in the limestone at Jagdalak, Afghanistan. Prismatic and tabular blue and gray crystals have been found at Takayama Mino, Japan.

In Madagascar large coarse crystals in mica schist and rolled pebbles in alluvial deposits are found at Vatondrangy and other localities southeast of Antsirabe. In Queensland gem material is found at Anakie, mostly in the streams but also in basalt. Large opaque crystals are found at Steinkopf, Namaqualand, in the Cape Province, South Africa; also in the Transvaal, at Zoutpansberg and Pietersberg as large crystals (one of which weighed 335 lb.) loose in the soil or in pegmatites.

In the Urals, principally at Kyschtym as large masses in an anorthite-corundum dike at the contact between serpentine and gneiss; some of the specimens show central cores of corundum with successive zones of spinel, labradorite, and hornblende. Also from Zlatoust and Miask. In Switzerland at Ticino, and in red or blue crystals in dolomite at Campolongo. In Italy in white compact feldspar in a contact deposit at Mosso St. Maria, northeast of Biella, Piedmont. At Naxos, Samos, and other Greek islands large emery deposits have long been mined. In Asia Minor at several localities in the neighborhood of Smyrna and at Aidin. In France in the basalt at Le Croustet. Large coarse pyramidal crystals occur near Gellivare, Norbotten, Sweden; a nepheline-corundum pegmatite occurs at Seiland, Finmarken, Norway.

In the United States an emery deposit has been worked at Chester, Massachusetts. Reported from Barkhamsted, Connecticut, with kyanite in schist. In Orange County, New York, bluish and pink crystals occur with spinel and rutile in crystalline limestone at Warwick. Large deposits of emery occur at the contact of aluminous schists with basic intrusive rocks in the neighborhood of Peekskill, Westchester County, New York. In New Jersey at Franklin and Newton as blue and red crystals associated with hornblende, phlogopite, spinel, chondrodite in limestone, and at Vernon as red crystals, some several inches long.   In Pennsylvania, formerly abundant in large crystals at Corundum Hill, near Unionville, Chester County; as large crystals loose in the soil at Shimersville, Lehigh County; in Alston Township, Delaware County.

In the southern Appalachians a belt of corundum-bearing feldspar veins in basic rocks (dunites) near the contact with schists extends from Virginia through North and South Carolina, Georgia, and Alabama.   Especially abundant in Mitchell, Madison, Buncombe, Haywood, Jackson, Macon, Clay, and Burke counties in North Carolina; prior to 1905 mining at Corundum Hill, near Franklin, Macon County, was extensive.   Also at Laurel Creek, Georgia.   Large blocks showing parting are common in the region.   Some specimens from Clayton, Georgia, show zoning of sapphire and ruby with an outer alteration shell of margarite.   In Colorado small blue crystals occur in mica schist near Salida, Chaffee County; also with dumortierite and sillimanite at Canyon City, Fremont County.   In Montana sapphires occur in an andesite dike in limestone at Yogo Gulch on the Judith River; near Helena, in gold washings; near Salesville, Gallatin County, as corundum syenite.   In Plumas County, California, an orthoclase-corundum dike (plumasite) cuts serpentinized peridotite.

Abundant in Ontario, Canada, especially at Craigmont, Raglan Township, Renfrew County, as a large corundum-syenite deposit; in Hastings County in the nepheline syenite and in the nepheline pegmatites at Bancroft; as pseudomorphs after spinel in Bathurst Township, Lanark County.

Alter.   Corundum alters[37] readily to other aluminous minerals, including zoisite, sillimanite, kyanite, and in particular margarite and damourite; less commonly to diaspore, gibbsite, andalusite, spinel, chloritoid, muscovite, tourmaline, kayserite.   Found pseudomorphous after spinel.   Crystals often show a pearly luster on {0001}, perhaps due to alteration.[28]

Artif.[29]   There are presumably four[30] modifications of alumina, of which only one (α-alumina), the most stable form, is found in nature. β-alumina is hexagonal;[31] γ-alumina is isometric[32] and forms an isomorphous series with synthetic spinel. Δ-alumina is said to be rhombohedral.[33]

Large amounts of artificial corundum for abrasives (alundum) are produced by melting bauxite in an electric furnace.   Artificial rubies and sapphires are produced by melting and recrystallizing alumina in an oxy-hydrogen flame.   The so-called "boules" thus produced are clear and transparent.   When colored by chromium salts they are ruby-red, and by cobalt and titanium salts they show the various sapphire colors.   Well-made artificial gems are not easily distinguished from the natural stones.

Name.   Sapphire as applied by the ancients referred to lazurite; the word is of unknown origin, possibly Hebraic.[34]   Corundum is probably from the Indian name of the mineral, *Kauruntaka*.   Schmirgel *Germ.*, from the locality, Smyrna.

TAOSITE.   *de Lapparent* (*C. R.*, **201**, 154, 1935).

A supposedly Fe- and Ti-rich corundum, found as inclusions parallel the octahedral faces of spinel in the emery of Samos, Greece.   Uniaxial negative $(-)$, E clear yellow, O reddish yellow-brown.

Ref.

1. Value from average of Miller (242, 1852); Goldschmidt (5, 37, 1918); Melczer, *Zs. Kr.*, **35**, 561 (1902).

2. Goldschmidt and Schroeder, *Min. Mitt.*, **29**, 461 (1910), give statistics on the form frequency. The letters here used conform in great part to those of Dana (211, 1892), with revision in order to avoid duplication. Rare and uncertain forms:

70$\bar{7}$6	11·11·$\overline{22}$·10	8·8·$\overline{16}$·5	11·11·$\overline{22}$·3
70$\bar{7}$4	11·11·$\overline{22}$·9	27·27·$\overline{54}$·16	15·15·$\overline{30}$·4
5·5·$\overline{10}$·9	5·5·$\overline{10}$·4	15·15·$\overline{30}$·8	17·17·$\overline{34}$·2
4·4·$\bar{8}$·7	11·11·$\overline{22}$·8	13·13·$\overline{26}$·6	14·14·$\overline{28}$·1
7·7·$\overline{14}$·8	13·13·$\overline{26}$·9	9·9·$\overline{18}$·4	37·37·$\overline{74}$·2
17·17·$\overline{34}$·18	33$\bar{6}$2	5·5·$\overline{10}$·2	62$\bar{8}$7

3. See Bauer, *Jb. Min.*, II, 213, 1896. Also Melczer (1902) and Brauns, *Jb. Min.*, 47, 1906. Seebach, *Jb. Min.*, *Beil.-Bd.*, **54**, 420 (1926), showed that etchings produced on a sphere showed scalenohedral symmetry.

4. Pauling and Hendricks, *Am. Chem. Soc.*, *J.*, **47**, 781 (1925). The x-ray unit is not used for the morphological discussion because (*a*) the form series becomes somewhat more complex, (*b*) the twin plane and prominent rhombohedron also must be given more complex indices, and (*c*) well-established usage would necessarily be modified with little gain.

5. Arrowhead twins from the Transvaal described by Spencer, *Min. Mag.*, **21**, 329 (1927). For other twin laws proposed see Bowman, *ibid.*, **12**, 355 (1900), Hintze (1 [2A], 1740, 1907).

6. Mügge, *Jb. Min.*, 147, 1886.

7. Veit, *Jb. Min.*, *Beil.-Bd.*, **45**, 121 (1921).

8. Judd, *Min. Mag.*, **11**, 49 (1895), demonstrated that the supposed cleavages in corundum are due to twinning and to alteration along definite planes of the crystal.

9. Jaggar, *Am. J. Sc.*, 4, 411 (1897), used a microsclerometer to obtain a hardness of 188,808 on the rhombohedron, on the basis of topaz 28,867 and quartz 7648. Hodge and McKay, *Am. Min.*, **19**, 161 (1934) obtained 5300, with quartz 2700 on the same scale. See also Rosiwal, *Min. Mitt.*, **34**, 69 (1917).

10. Fremy (*Synthèse du Rubis*, Paris, 1891). Darker crystals have a slightly higher specific gravity. See also Loczka in Melczer (1902) and Church, *Geol. Mag.*, **2**, 321 (1875).

11. Jeremejev, *Zs. Kr.*, **15**, 536 (1889).

12. Schroeder, *Zbl. Min.*, 129, 1936.

13. Weigel, *Jb. Min.*, *Beil.-Bd.*, **48**, 274 (1923).

14. Kanolt, *Washington Ac. Sc.*, *J.*, **3**, 315 (1913).

15. Joly, *Zs. Kr.*, **15**, 523 (1889).

16. Fizeau (from *Int. Crit. Tables*, **3**, 43, 1928).

17. Auerbach, *Ann. Phys.*, **58**, 381 (1896).

18. See Melczer, *Zs. Kr.*, **35**, 561 (1902); earlier, Bertrand, *Bull. soc. min.*, **1**, 95 (1878), who measured $2V = 58°$ in a ruby from Siam. Tschermak, *Min. Mitt.*, **1**, 362 (1878), found that highly colored material from Kyschtym had greater $2V$ than the colorless crystals. The indices of refraction are an average of measurements on 12 crystals by Melczer (1902) from Burma and Ceylon, mostly colorless and blue. Another lot yielded a higher average, with O 1.7697$_C$, 1.7732$_D$, 1.7803$_F$. Brauns, *Cbl. Min.*, 234 (1929), and Vogel, *Jb. Min.*, *Beil.-Bd.*, **68**, 401 (1934), have studied the optical properties of artificial crystals.

19. Brauns, *Cbl. Min.*, 588, 1905.

20. Judd, *Min. Mag.*, **11**, 59 (1897), from Pipra, India.

21. Tschermak (1878); see also Walcott, *Field Mus. Chicago, Geol. Ser.*, **7**, 39 (1937).

22. Klemm and Wild, *Jb. Min.*, *Beil.-Bd.*, **53**, 266 (1926).

23. Wild and Klemm, *Cbl. Min.*, 273, 1925.

24. Older analyses in Doelter (3 [2], 436, 1922).

25. Pfeil anal., *Cbl. Min.*, 143, 1902.

26. The varieties here given are subdivisions recognized in the arts, and until early in the nineteenth century regarded as species. Haüy (1805) first formally united them.

27. For general treatment of the occurrence of corundum, especially in Ontario, see Barlow, *Geol. Sur. Canada, Mem.*, **57**, *Geol. Ser.*, 50, 1915. For Australia and Ceylon see Brauns, *Cbl. Min.*, 588, 1905; for the United States see Pratt, *U. S. Geol. Sur., Bull. 269*, 1906, and Finley, *J. Geol.*, **15**, 479 (1907); for Africa see Hall, *Geol. Sur. South Africa, Mem.*, **15** (1920); for India see Dunn, *Geol. Sur. India, Mem.*, **52**, 145 (1929). Larsen, *Econ. Geol.*, **23**, 398 (1928), discusses the origin of certain corundum bodies by hydrothermal activity.

28. Judd (1895).

29. For more details see Doelter (**3** [2], 445, 1922), Hintze (**1** [2A], 1777, 1908), Michel (*Die Kunst. Edelsteine*, Leipzig, 1926).

30. Beevers and Ross, *Zs. Kr.*, **97**, 59 (1937), state that the supposed β-Al₂O₃ has a composition NaAl₁₁O₁₇.

31. Rankin and Merwin, *Am. Chem. Soc., J.*, **38**, 568 (1916).

32. Ulrich, *Norsk. Geol. Tidskr.*, **8**, 122 (1925); also Beljankin and Dilaktorsky, *Cbl. Min.*, 229, 1932, and Kordes, *Zs. Kr.*, **91**, 193 (1935).

33. Parravano and Montoro, *Acc. Linc., Att.*, **7**, 885 (1928).

34. See Hintze (**1** [2A], 1747, 1907); also see, *Min. Abs.*, **6**, 245 (1936).

35. See Bray, *Am. Min.*, **24**, 162 (1939).

36. Judd and Hidden, *Min. Mag.*, **12**, 139 (1899).

37. Genth, *Am. Phil. Soc., Proc.*, **13**, 361 (1873); **20**, 381, (1882); *Am. J. Sc.*, **39**, 47 (1890).

4412   **H E M A T I T E** [Fe₂O₃]. 'Αιματίτης [= Blood-stone] pt. *Theophrastus* (325 B.C.); *Dioscorides* (**5**, 143, A.D. 40). Haematites pt. *Pliny* (**36**, 28, 38, A.D. 77). Galenae genus tertium omnis metalli inanissimum, Eisenglanz, Haematites pt., *Germ.* Blutstein, Glaskopf *Agricola* (465, 468, 1546). Speglande Jernmalm, Minera ferri specularis, Haematites ruber, Ochra rubra *Wallerius* (259–266, 1747). Rotheisenstein. Järnmalm tritura rubra, Speglande Eisenglimmer, Haematites ruber, Ochra pt. *Cronstedt* (178–185, 1758). Specular Iron; Red Hematite. Red Ocher. Specularite. Fer speculaire, Hematite rouge, Sanguine *Fr.* Eisenglanz, Roth Eisenstein, Rother Glaskopf, Rother Eisenrahm *Werner* (*Bergm. J.*, 1789). Iron Glance, Red Iron Ore, Red Oxide of Iron, Micaceous Iron Ore. Fer oligiste, Fer oxydé rouge *Haüy* (1801). Basonomelane pt. *Kobell* (318, 1838). Hämatit *Hausmann* (in *Haidinger* [552, 1845A]); *Hausmann* (232, 1847). Jernglanz, Röd Jernmalm, Blodsten, Rödmalm *Swed.* Ematite rossa, Oligisto, Ferro specolare *Ital.* Hematita rojo, Hierro oligisto *Span.* Hematogelite *Tučan* (*Cbl. Min.*, **65**, 1913). Hematitogelite.

Martite *Breithaupt* (*Schweigger's J.*, **54**, 158, 1828; 233, 1832); Eisenoxyd *Haidinger* (*Ann. Phys.*, **11**, 188, 1827). Turgite *Hermann* (*J. pr. Chem.*, **33**, 96, 1844). Hydrohämatit *Breithaupt* (846, 1847).

C r y s t.   Hexagonal — *R*;   scalenohedral — $\bar{3}\,2/m$.

$a : c = 1 : 1.3652;$ $\alpha\ 85°42\frac{1}{2}';^1$ $p_0 : r_0 = 1.5764 : 1;$ $\lambda\ 93°59\frac{1}{2}'$

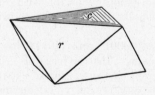
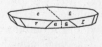

(*Upper*) Binnental.
(*Lower*) Vesuvius.

Forms:[2]

			ϕ	$\rho = C$	A_1	A_2
c	0001	111	....	0°00'	90°00'	90°00'
m	10$\bar{1}$0	2$\bar{1}$$\bar{1}$	30°00'	90 00	30 00	90 00
a	11$\bar{2}$0	10$\bar{1}$	0 00	90 00	60 00	60 00
μ	01$\bar{1}$5	221	−30 00	17 30	90 00	74 54½
u	10$\bar{1}$4	211	30 00	21 30½	71 29	90 00
e	01$\bar{1}$2	110	−30 00	38 14½	90 00	57 35
r	10$\bar{1}$1	100	30 00	57 36½	43 00½	90 00
η	01$\bar{1}$1	22$\bar{1}$	−30 00	57 36½	90 00	43 00½
s	02$\bar{2}$1	11$\bar{1}$	−30 00	72 24	90 00	34 21½
π	11$\bar{2}$3	210	0 00	42 18½	70 20	70 20
n	22$\bar{4}$3	31$\bar{1}$	0 00	61 13	64 00½	64 00½
p	24$\bar{6}$7	53$\bar{1}$	−10 53½	50 00	75 28½	59 54
i	42$\bar{6}$5	51$\bar{1}$	10 53½	59 03½	55 50½	73 44
x	12$\bar{3}$2	21$\bar{1}$	−10 53½	64 23	72 50	53 49½
f	62$\bar{8}$1	5$\bar{1}$3	16 06	84 58½	44 07½	76 09½

Less common:

h	41$\bar{5}$0	3$\bar{1}$2	d	10$\bar{1}$2	411	ψ	12$\bar{3}$5	320
λ	1·0·1·16	655	T	30$\bar{3}$5	11·2·2	O	52$\bar{7}$6	61$\bar{1}$
y	01$\bar{1}$8	332	θ	20$\bar{2}$1	5$\bar{1}$$\bar{1}$	m_2	62$\bar{8}$7	71$\bar{1}$
τ	10$\bar{1}$6	855	m:	40$\bar{4}$1	3$\bar{1}$$\bar{1}$		8·2·$\bar{10}$·9	91$\bar{1}$
J	01$\bar{1}$6	774	X	44$\bar{8}$3	51$\bar{3}$	K	21$\bar{3}$1	20$\bar{1}$
e:	20$\bar{2}$5	311	z	22$\bar{4}$1	71$\bar{5}$			

Structure cell.[3] Space group $R\bar{3}c$; a_{rh} 5.420 α 55°17'; a_0 5.029, c_0 13.73; $a_0 : c_0/2 = 1 : 1.365$;[4] contains Fe_4O_6 in the rhombohedral unit.

Habit. Thick to thin tabular {0001} often as subparallel growths on {0001} or as rosettes (Switzerland); {0001} often striated [01$\bar{1}$0]; {1$\bar{1}$04} frequently striated and rounded over to produce convex forms (Dognácska). Rhombohedral {10$\bar{1}$1} to produce pseudocubic crystals; more rarely prismatic [0001]; rarely scalenohedral. Commonest forms: *c r n a e m i s.*

Sometimes micaceous to platy. Also compact columnar, fibrous, and frequently radiating; in reniform masses with smooth fracture (*kidney ore*), and in botryoidal or stalactitic shapes. Commonly earthy, ocherous (*reddle, red chalk*) and frequently admixed with clay and other impurities (*clay iron-stone, argillaceous hematite*); also granular, friable to compact. Concretionary, oolitic (*lenticular iron ore, fossil ore*).

Twinning. (*a*) On {0001} as penetration twins, or with {10$\bar{1}$0} as composition plane.[5] (*b*) On {10$\bar{1}$1} usually lamellar, and showing twin striae on base and rhombohedron.[6]

Phys. Cleavage none. Parting on {0001} and {10$\bar{1}$1} due to twinning.[7] Fracture subconchoidal to uneven. Brittle (crystals); soft and sometimes unctuous in the loosely coherent earthy varieties; elastic in thin laminae. H. 5–6. G. 5.26 (crystals;[8]) 5.256 (calc.). Luster metallic to submetallic to dull (earthy and impure varieties). Color steel-gray (crystals) and sometimes iridescent (Elba).   In thin splinters deep blood-red by transmitted light or internal reflections.   Earthy and compact material dull red to bright red.   Streak cherry-red or reddish brown, and when heated turns black, reverting on cooling.[9]   M.P. 1350–1360°.[10]

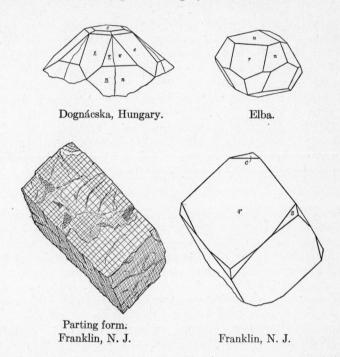

Dognácska, Hungary.   Elba.

Parting form.
Franklin, N. J.   Franklin, N. J.

Other physical properties:[11] compressibility, $B = 0.60 \times 10^{-6}$ at 0° and 125 megabaryes. Thermal expansion, $\alpha^{40°} = 7.61 \parallel c$, $7.71 \perp c$, where $\alpha^{t} = (10^{6}/l) \cdot (dl/dt)$. Thermal conductivity ratio $a/c = 1.20$. Intensity of magnetization (I) in a magnetic field of intensity H is as follows: H 36, $I \perp c$-axis 1.71, $I \parallel c$-axis 0.025 (on the basis of I 250, H 50, along the a-axis of magnetite). Specific heat 0.1683.[12]

O p t. Uniaxial negative (−). Dispersion strong. Absorption $O > E$.[13] Refractive indices:[14]

λ	759	719	686	656	589[15]	DICHROISM
O	2.904	2.949	2.988	3.042	3.22	Brownish red
E	2.690	2.725	2.759	2.797	2.94	Yellowish red

In polished section[16] anisotropic and weakly pleochroic. Reflection percentages: green 26, orange 25, red 21. Shows red internal reflections, and frequently exhibits a lamellar twinning on $\{10\bar{1}1\}$.

C h e m. Ferric oxide, Fe_2O_3, with Fe 69.94, O 30.06, total 100.00. Some Ti is usually present, but the high Ti analyses are undoubtedly due to admixed ilmenite.[17]　The supposed deficiency in O in some analyses is probably due to admixed magnetite, perhaps by alteration.[18]　Up to several per cent H_2O may be present in the fibrous or ocherous varieties.

Var.　The varieties are on the basis of texture and habit of the material, as follows.

1. *Specular.*　Luster metallic, and crystals often splendent, whence the name *specular iron* (*Glanzeisenerz, Germ.*).　When the structure is foliated or micaceous, the ore is called *micaceous hematite* (Eisenglimmer, *Germ.*); some of the micaceous varieties are soft and unctuous (Eisenrahm, *Germ.*).

2. *Compact columnar*; or fibrous.　(Red hematite[19]).　The masses often long radiating; luster submetallic to metallic; color brownish red to iron-black.　Often in reniform masses with smooth fracture, called *kidney ore* (rother Glaskopf, Blutstein, Eisenniere, *Germ.*).

3. *Ocherous.*　Reddle or Ruddle (Röthel, *Germ.*).　Red and earthy. Often mixed with clay (Reddle, red chalk), sand or other impurities and grading into clay iron-stone or argillaceous hematite.

Tests.　Infusible.　Becomes magnetic in R.F.　Soluble in concentrated HCl.

O c c u r.[20]　The huge hematite deposits worked as a source of iron (Lake Superior; the Clinton formation in the Appalachians) are mainly of sedimentary origin with some subsequent concentration of the iron presumably by meteoric waters.　Hydrated iron oxides, iron carbonate, and magnetite, as well as iron silicates, are associated, and part of the hematite at least has been derived by the alteration of these minerals.　Igneous rocks frequently contain hematite as an accessory mineral.　It is found as a sublimate of thin crystals due to volcanic activity (Vesuvius).　Metamorphosed sediments often contain important hematite deposits (the *itabiryte* of Brazil).　It is found in contact metamorphic deposits (Persberg, Sweden) associated with magnetite, and occurs as a minor constituent of high-temperature hydrothermal veins.　Hematite is a common weathering product of siderite, limonite, magnetite ("martite"), and other iron-bearing minerals.　In the gossan of metalliferous veins.　There is an almost universal distribution of hematite (and limonite) in small quantities as a pigmenting agent of sedimentary and other rocks, and the (adventitious) pigmenting matter in many red or reddish brown minerals is finely divided hematite.

Oriented intergrowths of hematite and ilmenite are common, and may be due to exsolution phenomena;[21] rutile is frequently found in oriented position upon hematite;[22] and muscovite often contains dendritic or broad lathlike or latticelike oriented inclusions of hematite.[23]　Magnetite and spinel also are found in oriented relation to hematite, with magnetite {111} [110] ‖ hematite {0001} [10$\bar{1}$0]; also hematite upon calcite with calcite {11$\bar{2}$0} ‖ hematite {11$\bar{2}$0}.[24]　Minute oriented exsolved plates of hematite are often dispersed in oligoclase or other feldspar, giving rise to aventurine effects,[26] and also occur in carnallite, sylvite, pyroxene, olivine, and other species.

Only those occurrences of special importance because of concentrations in commercial quantities, or because of exceptional specimens, can be given here. In the Urals fine crystals have been found at Ekaterinburg. In Bohemia massive, at Platten. In Roumania at Dognácska, rounded pyramidal crystals are found, and at Kakuk-Berg in the Hargitta Mountains, very thin crystal plates. In the Zillerthal, Austria. In Saxony at Altenberg and Johanngeorgenstadt. Especially fine rosettes of thin plates forming radial aggregates, sometimes with rutile prisms oriented on the plates, are found in Switzerland, notably at St. Gotthard, Cavradi, Val Tavetsch, Grisons; also in crystals in the Binnental. In Italy as a sublimate at Vesuvius and Etna in twinned aggregates of thin platy crystals; at Stromboli, Lipari Islands; notable crystals and groups come from Elba, often with a brilliant luster and iridescent tarnish. In France fine crystals are found at Framont, Alsace, and in Puy-de-Dôme on Mont Dore, especially in the trachyte of Puy de la Tâche. In Sweden at Harstig in pyramidal crystals; at Långban and Persberg; in Norway at Kragerö. Crystals are found on Ascension Island in the South Atlantic. In England especially fine crystals come from Cleator Moor, Cumberland, and concentric massive material (kidney ore) from Ulverstone, Lancashire.

In Brazil in metamorphosed sediments (itabiryte) in Minas Geraes, and as large rosettes of thick crystals (much like the Swiss " iron-roses ") at the Burnier iron mines. In Mexico crystals containing cassiterite and partly altered to that mineral have been described from Mina del Diablo, Durango. In Cuba vast residual iron-laterites are mined in Oriente Province; in the Mayari and Moa districts where the ore is mostly hematite and limonite; near Santiago a contact metamorphic deposit contains hematite.

In the United States the great Lake Superior deposits yield about 50 million tons a year, most of which is hematite, with small amounts of limonite and magnetite. In some parts of the pre-Cambrian sediments the thickness of the hematite ores is as great as 1000 ft. The ore varies from a hard specular hematite to soft earthy varieties. The most important deposits are along the southern and northeastern shores of Lake Superior; the various districts are as follows: the Marquette and Menominee Ranges in northern Michigan, the Penokee-Gogebic in northern Wisconsin, the Mesabi, Vermilion, and Cuyuna in Minnesota. Farther north, in Canada, is the Michipicoten district. Another extensive source of hematite is the Clinton formation of Upper Silurian age, consisting of oolitic ores and mixed with clay, goethite, lepidocrocite, and limonite. These sediments extend from New York, in Herkimer, Madison, and Wayne Counties, through Pennsylvania to Alabama, and as far west as Wisconsin; prominent mines are near Birmingham, Alabama. An oolitic ore is also mined at Wabana, Newfoundland, where the hematite is associated with chamosite. At Franklin, New Jersey, specimens showing fine parting planes have been found. In Pennsylvania at Cornwall, in part as an alteration of magnetite. In New York at Edwards, Gouverneur, and Antwerp in crystallized specimens. In Missouri at Iron Mountain, Iron County, with apatite. In

Colorado at Pikes Peak, as pseudomorphs after siderite. In Wyoming, in the schist at Hartville.

In Canada, as previously noted, in the Michipicoten district of Lake Superior. Tabular crystals are reported from Leeds in Quebec; also from various localities in Ontario, in Leeds, Hastings and Renfrew counties, and as pseudomorphs after magnetite (martite) from the Dalhousie iron mine, Lanark County.

A l t e r. Magnetite alters readily to hematite (see *martite*, below). Pseudomorphs or alterations after the following minerals have also been observed: siderite, goethite, pyrite, marcasite, calcite, fluorite; also sphalerite, galena, pharmacosiderite, pyromorphite, cuprite, manganite, quartz, aragonite, dolomite, barite, anhydrite, gypsum, garnet, chrysolite, ilvaite, biotite, bronzite, feldspar, and others less commonly. Magnetite, limonite, siderite and pyrite have been found as pseudomorphs after or as alterations of hematite; less frequently rutile, cassiterite, chlorite, manganite.

A r t i f.[25] Produced by (a) sublimation, as by the reaction of ferric chloride vapors and steam, (b) in melts, as by heating iron oxide in borax, and in silicate melts of high iron content, and (c) in a wet way, as by heating iron hydrate with water in a closed tube.

N a m e. Hematite is from $\alpha\iota\mu\alpha$, *blood*, it seeming, says Theophrastus, as if formed of concreted blood. This early Greek author also mentions a second kind of hematite ('$A\iota\mu\alpha\tau\iota\tau\eta s$ $\xi\alpha\nu\theta\delta s$) of a yellowish white color, probably a yellow ocher, or limonite, long called brown hematite.

MARTITE. Eisenoxyd *Haidinger* (*Ann. Phys.*, **11**, 188, 1827). Martit *Breithaupt* (*Schweigger's J.*, **54**, 158, 1828; 233, 1832).

A name applied to Fe_2O_3 (hematite[27]) occurring in octahedral or dodecahedral crystals and pseudomorphous after magnetite; perhaps in part also after pyrite.[28] Color iron-black, with a dull to splendent submetallic luster, and with a reddish or purplish brown streak. Sometimes feebly magnetic and containing FeO, due to residual magnetite. Notable localities include Twin Peaks, near Kanosh, Millard County, Utah, where octahedrons up to 9 cm. on an edge occur with apatite and pyroxene in veins in rhyolite. In the Marquette and other districts in the Lake Superior iron region. In fine crystals in the Cerro de Mercado, Durango, Mexico, in a large deposit. In Nova Scotia at Digby Neck, Digby County. In Minas Geraes, Brazil.

TURGITE. *Hermann* (*Bull. soc. nat. Moscou*, **18**, 252, 1845; *J. pr. Chem.*, **33**, 96, 1844). Hydrohämatit *Breithaupt* (846, 1847). Hydrohematite. Turjit. Turyite. Turite.

A supposed hydrous iron oxide with the formula $2Fe_2O_3 \cdot H_2O$. Analyses[29] of material referred to turgite varied widely in water content. Described as compact fibrous and divergent; often botryoidal and stalactitic; earthy, ocherous. Color reddish black to dark red; bright red or orange-red when earthy. Streak red. G. 4.2–4.7. Originally came from the Turginsk (properly Turjinsk) copper mine on the Turja river near Bogoslovsk, Urals. Hydrohematite originally was found in Germany at Hof, Bavaria, and Siegen, Westphalia. Both materials were later reported from many additional localities.

Identical with hematite.[30]   In part a metacolloid with adsorbed and capillary water, $Fe_2O_3 \cdot nH_2O$; probably also as a more or less complete alteration of goethite.

Ref.

1. Elements from average of closely agreeing values principally of Melczer, *Zs. Kr.*, **37**, 580 (1903), and Biäsch, *Zs. Kr.*, **70**, 1 (1929).

2. Forms from compilation of Biäsch (1929), with common and less common forms on the basis of his frequency data. See also Goldschmidt (**3**, 86, 1916) and Gonnard, *Bull. soc. min.*, **37**, 113 (1914). Rare and uncertain forms listed below. Many are probably vicinal forms, but the list is complete for sake of record.

$9 \cdot 5 \cdot \overline{14} \cdot 0$	$50\bar{5}8$	$11\bar{2}4$	$14 \cdot 10 \cdot \overline{24} \cdot 1$	$42\bar{6}3$	$41\bar{5}5$
$21\bar{3}0$	$02\bar{2}3$	$22\bar{4}5$	$5 \cdot 7 \cdot \overline{12} \cdot 19$	$8 \cdot 4 \cdot \overline{12} \cdot 1$	$41\bar{5}3$
$31\bar{4}0$	$05\bar{5}7$	$16 \cdot 16 \cdot \overline{32} \cdot 27$	$32\bar{5}4$	$12\bar{3}8$	$8 \cdot 2 \cdot \overline{10} \cdot 3$
$71\bar{8}0$	$0 \cdot 8 \cdot \bar{8} \cdot 11$	$11\bar{2}2$	$6 \cdot 4 \cdot \overline{10} \cdot 5$	$3 \cdot 6 \cdot \bar{9} \cdot 10$	$24 \cdot 6 \cdot \overline{30} \cdot 5$
$0 \cdot 1 \cdot \bar{1} \cdot 23$	$04\bar{4}5$	$44\bar{8}7$	$32\bar{5}1$	$12\bar{3}3$	$2 \cdot 8 \cdot \overline{10} \cdot 25$
$0 \cdot 1 \cdot \bar{1} \cdot 16$	$60\bar{6}7$	$33\bar{6}5$	$23\bar{5}8$	$7 \cdot 14 \cdot \overline{21} \cdot 20$	$2 \cdot 8 \cdot \overline{10} \cdot 15$
$0 \cdot 1 \cdot \bar{1} \cdot 12$	$0 \cdot 24 \cdot \overline{24} \cdot 23$	$11\bar{2}1$	$23\bar{5}5$	$10 \cdot 20 \cdot \overline{30} \cdot 27$	$13 \cdot 3 \cdot \overline{16} \cdot 4$
$0 \cdot 1 \cdot \bar{1} \cdot 11$	$06\bar{6}5$	$10 \cdot 10 \cdot \overline{20} \cdot 9$	$4 \cdot 6 \cdot \overline{10} \cdot 7$	$24\bar{6}5$	$26 \cdot 6 \cdot \overline{32} \cdot 7$
$1 \cdot 0 \cdot \bar{1} \cdot 10$	$50\bar{5}4$	$33\bar{6}2$	$23\bar{5}2$	$7 \cdot 14 \cdot \overline{21} \cdot 18$	$9 \cdot 2 \cdot \overline{11} \cdot 10$
$10\bar{1}9$	$05\bar{5}4$	$5 \cdot 5 \cdot \overline{10} \cdot 3$	$11 \cdot 7 \cdot \overline{18} \cdot 22$	$24\bar{6}1$	$10 \cdot 2 \cdot \overline{12} \cdot 11$
$2 \cdot 0 \cdot \bar{2} \cdot 15$	$04\bar{4}3$	$7 \cdot 7 \cdot \overline{14} \cdot 3$	$11 \cdot 7 \cdot \overline{18} \cdot 10$	$21 \cdot 10 \cdot \overline{31} \cdot 26$	$51\bar{6}1$
$10\bar{1}7$	$0 \cdot 19 \cdot \overline{19} \cdot 14$	$8 \cdot 8 \cdot \overline{16} \cdot 3$	$10 \cdot 6 \cdot \overline{16} \cdot 7$	$15 \cdot 7 \cdot \overline{22} \cdot 2$	$1 \cdot 5 \cdot \bar{6} \cdot 11$
$01\bar{1}7$	$03\bar{3}2$	$33\bar{6}1$	$3 \cdot 5 \cdot \bar{8} \cdot 13$	$11 \cdot 5 \cdot \overline{16} \cdot 3$	$15\bar{6}8$
$0 \cdot 2 \cdot \bar{2} \cdot 13$	$27 \cdot 0 \cdot \overline{27} \cdot 17$	$44\bar{8}1$	$17 \cdot 10 \cdot \overline{27} \cdot 22$	$14 \cdot 6 \cdot \overline{20} \cdot 17$	$15\bar{6}5$
$11 \cdot 0 \cdot \overline{11} \cdot 64$	$05\bar{5}3$	$16 \cdot 16 \cdot \overline{32} \cdot 3$	$7 \cdot 4 \cdot \overline{11} \cdot 9$	$14 \cdot 6 \cdot \overline{20} \cdot 5$	$11 \cdot 2 \cdot \overline{13} \cdot 12$
$4 \cdot 0 \cdot \bar{4} \cdot 21$	$70\bar{7}4$	$25 \cdot 24 \cdot \overline{49} \cdot 37$	$7 \cdot 4 \cdot \overline{11} \cdot 6$	$7 \cdot 3 \cdot \overline{10} \cdot 1$	$11 \cdot 2 \cdot \overline{13} \cdot 10$
$0 \cdot 5 \cdot \bar{5} \cdot 26$	$16 \cdot 0 \cdot \overline{16} \cdot 9$	$24 \cdot 25 \cdot \overline{49} \cdot 57$	$14 \cdot 8 \cdot \overline{22} \cdot 19$	$10 \cdot 4 \cdot \overline{14} \cdot 9$	$12 \cdot 2 \cdot \overline{14} \cdot 13$
$10\bar{1}5$	$20 \cdot 0 \cdot \overline{20} \cdot 9$	$13 \cdot 12 \cdot \overline{25} \cdot 19$	$18 \cdot 10 \cdot \overline{28} \cdot 23$	$10 \cdot 4 \cdot \overline{14} \cdot 3$	$16\bar{7}1$
$5 \cdot 0 \cdot \bar{5} \cdot 23$	$50\bar{5}2$	$9 \cdot 8 \cdot \overline{17} \cdot 3$	$9 \cdot 5 \cdot \overline{14} \cdot 14$	$25\bar{7}6$	$13 \cdot 2 \cdot \overline{15} \cdot 14$
$01\bar{1}4$	$05\bar{5}2$	$\mathbf{8 \cdot 9 \cdot \overline{17} \cdot 14}$	$9 \cdot 5 \cdot \overline{14} \cdot 13$	$3 \cdot 1 \cdot \bar{4} \cdot 32$	$7 \cdot 1 \cdot \bar{8} \cdot 32$
$0 \cdot 4 \cdot \bar{4} \cdot 15$	$03\bar{3}1$	$7 \cdot 6 \cdot \overline{13} \cdot 10$	$5 \cdot 9 \cdot \overline{14} \cdot 23$	$31\bar{4}2$	$1 \cdot 7 \cdot \bar{8} \cdot 32$
$20\bar{2}7$	$04\bar{4}1$	$54\bar{9}7$	$5 \cdot 9 \cdot \overline{14} \cdot 20$	$12 \cdot 4 \cdot \overline{16} \cdot 5$	$14 \cdot 2 \cdot \overline{16} \cdot 15$
$02\bar{2}7$	$09\bar{9}2$	$18 \cdot 14 \cdot \overline{32} \cdot 1$	$15 \cdot 8 \cdot \overline{23} \cdot 25$	$13\bar{4}7$	$29 \cdot 4 \cdot \overline{33} \cdot 31$
$3 \cdot 0 \cdot \bar{3} \cdot 10$	$50\bar{5}1$	$20 \cdot 16 \cdot \overline{36} \cdot 27$	$15 \cdot 8 \cdot \overline{23} \cdot 22$	$13\bar{4}4$	$16 \cdot 2 \cdot \overline{18} \cdot 17$
$4 \cdot 0 \cdot \bar{4} \cdot 13$	$05\bar{5}1$	$21 \cdot 16 \cdot \overline{37} \cdot 29$	$15 \cdot 8 \cdot \overline{23} \cdot 19$	$26\bar{8}5$	$2 \cdot 17 \cdot \overline{19} \cdot 30$
$10\bar{1}3$	$70\bar{7}1$	$8 \cdot 6 \cdot \overline{14} \cdot 11$	$8 \cdot 15 \cdot \overline{23} \cdot 19$	$26\bar{8}3$	$10 \cdot 1 \cdot \overline{11} \cdot 1$
$01\bar{1}3$	$07\bar{7}1$	$43\bar{7}4$	$9 \cdot 17 \cdot \overline{26} \cdot 28$	$13\bar{4}1$	$1 \cdot 10 \cdot \overline{11} \cdot 3$
$02\bar{2}5$	$80\bar{8}1$	$8 \cdot 6 \cdot \overline{14} \cdot 7$	$19 \cdot 10 \cdot \overline{29} \cdot 24$	$31 \cdot 10 \cdot \overline{41} \cdot 6$	$2 \cdot 20 \cdot \overline{22} \cdot 3$
$40\bar{4}9$	$1 \cdot 1 \cdot \bar{2} \cdot 10$	$43\bar{7}1$	$21\bar{3}5$	$3 \cdot 10 \cdot \overline{13} \cdot 8$	$23 \cdot 2 \cdot \overline{25} \cdot 24$
$8 \cdot 0 \cdot \bar{8} \cdot 15$	$11\bar{2}9$	$3 \cdot 4 \cdot \bar{7} \cdot 11$	$42\bar{6}9$	$72\bar{9}8$	$7 \cdot 84 \cdot \overline{91} \cdot 156$
$0 \cdot 16 \cdot \overline{16} \cdot 29$	$11\bar{2}8$	$6 \cdot 8 \cdot \overline{14} \cdot 13$	$21\bar{3}4$	$72\bar{9}5$	$1 \cdot 15 \cdot \overline{16} \cdot 4$
$05\bar{5}9$	$2 \cdot 2 \cdot \bar{4} \cdot 15$	$34\bar{7}5$	$42\bar{6}7$	$14 \cdot 4 \cdot \overline{18} \cdot 11$	$43 \cdot 2 \cdot \overline{45} \cdot 44$
$40\bar{4}7$	$11\bar{2}7$	$6 \cdot 8 \cdot \overline{14} \cdot 1$	$16 \cdot 8 \cdot \overline{24} \cdot 25$	$25 \cdot 7 \cdot \overline{32} \cdot 42$	$72 \cdot 1 \cdot \overline{73} \cdot 73$
$04\bar{4}7$	$11\bar{2}6$	$35 \cdot 48 \cdot \overline{83} \cdot 59$	$21\bar{3}3$	$22 \cdot 6 \cdot \overline{28} \cdot 25$	
$7 \cdot 0 \cdot \bar{7} \cdot 12$	$11\bar{2}5$	$11 \cdot 8 \cdot \overline{19} \cdot 15$	$10 \cdot 5 \cdot \overline{15} \cdot 12$	$8 \cdot 2 \cdot \overline{10} \cdot 25$	

3. Pauling and Hendricks, *Am. Chem. Soc., J.*, **47**, 781 (1925).

4. The c_0 is halved in the ratio to conform with the morphological cell. See also under corundum.

5. Haidinger in Mohs (**2**, 406, 1825).

6. Bauer, *Deutsche Zs. geol. Ges.*, **26**, 186 (1874). See also Mügge, *Jb. Min.*, 216, 1884; 35, 1886.

7. Mügge (1884, 1886). Jeremejev, *Zs. Kr.*, **28**, 521 (1897), observed striae indicating another parting plane $\{01\bar{1}2\}$.

8. Given specific gravity is an average of 6 measurements of small crystal fragments from various localities (Berman, priv. comm., 1940). The less compact varieties yield low values due to the state of aggregation of the material.

9. van der Kolk, *Cbl. Min.*, 80, 1901.

10. Doelter, *Min. Mitt.*, **22**, 316 (1903).

11. *Int. Crit. Tab.*, **3**, 5, 6, 1928, 1929.

12. Joly, *Zs. Kr.*, **15**, 523 (1889).

13. Rinne, *Jb. Min.*, 193, 1890.

14. Wülfing, *Min. Mitt.*, **15**, 68 (1895), using a prism of an Elba crystal. Refractive and absorption indices have been calculated from reflection measurements by Försterling, *Jb. Min., Beil.-Bd.*, **25**, 359 (1907).

15. H. E. Merwin (priv. comm.).

16. Schneiderhöhn and Ramdohr (**2**, 525, 1931).

17. See particularly Ramdohr (*Sonderdruck, Festschr., Bergak.*, 307, Clausthal, 1925); at higher temperatures hematite may carry appreciable Ti but on cooling this exsolves in the form of oriented ilmenite plates.

18. Greig, Posnjak, Merwin, and Sosman, *Am. J. Sc.*, **30**, 239 (1935), have demonstrated by experiments on synthetic material that hematite will carry only very small amounts of magnetite in solid solution.

19. The early mineralogists included in the name hematite the fibrous, stalactitic, and other massive varieties, as well as the hydrated iron ores (limonite).

20. For many additional occurrences see Hintze (**1** [2A], 1800, 1908); an extended review of the sedimentary hematites may be found in Lindgren (271, 295, 1933).

21. Ramdohr (1925) believes that hematite may contain considerable amounts of Ti at elevated temperatures and that the intergrowths observed in polished section are due to exsolution.

22. Goldschmidt and Schröder, *Beitr. Kryst. Min.*, **2**, 110 (1923), found the orientation is rutile {100}[010] ∥ hematite {0001}[0001].

23. Frondel and Ashby, *Am. Min.*, **22**, 104 (1937).

24. See Mügge, *Jb. Min., Beil.-Bd.*, **16**, 374 (1903).

25. Greig, Posnjak, Merwin, and Sosman (1935) have studied artificial hematite in the system Fe_3O_4-Fe_2O_3-O. See also Doelter (3 [2], 633, 1924) and Hintze (1 [2A], 1849, 1908) for lengthy accounts of the synthesis of hematite.

26. Andersen, *Am. J. Sc.*, **40**, 351 (1915).

27. Shown to be hematite by the x-ray studies of Aminoff, *Geol. För. Förh.*, **41**, 407 (1919), and Zachariasen, *Zs. Kr., Strukturber.*, 266, 1931; early recognized as Fe_2O_3 by Haidinger and others and thought by some to be dimorphous with hematite.

28. Gorceix, *C.R.*, **90**, 316 (1880), Lavenir, *Bull. soc. min.*, **12**, 49 (1889).

29. See Dana (168, 1868), Fischer, *Zs. anorg. Chem.*, **66**, 37 (1910), Posnjak and Merwin, *Am. J. Sc.*, **47**, 311 (1919), Doelter (3 [2A], 764, 1926).

30. Shown by x-ray powder study by Posnjak and Merwin, *Am. Chem. Soc., J.*, **44**, 1965 (1922), Böhm, *Zs. Kr.*, **68**, 572 (1928), and Frondel (priv. comm., 1940) on material from Salisbury, Conn. The indices are variable (see Posnjak and Merwin [1919] and Larsen [147, 1921]) and on the whole are greater than those of lepidocrocite and goethite, but less than those of hematite (owing to the physical nature of the material). For dehydration data see Fischer (1910); Spencer, *Min. Mag.*, **18**, 339 (1919); Posnjak and Merwin (1919); Kurnakow and Rode, *Zs. anorg. Chem.*, **169**, 57 (1928). The data differ from those of goethite and lepidocrocite, and indicate hematite with loosely held water.

RAPHISIDERITE. Rafisiderite *Scacchi* (*Acc. Napoli, Att., Mem. 3*, read Dec. 1, 1888). Raphisiderite *Dana* (217, 1892).

A form of ferric oxide occurring in the tufa of Pianura and Fiano, Campania, Italy; it appears in minute acicular crystals for which an orthorhombic form is suggested. This possible dimorphous modification of ferric oxide has not been confirmed.

4413   I L M E N I T E [FeTiO₃]. Specular Iron pt., Eisensand pt., Menachanite (Cornwall) *McGregor* (*J. phys.*, **72**, 152, 1791; *Chem. Ann.*, 1791; Kirwan, 1796). Eisenhaltige Titanerz, Menakanit (Cornwall) *Klaproth* (**2**, 226, 232, 235, 1797). Titane oxydé ferrifère *Haüy* (1801). Mänaken *Karsten* (74, 1808). Titaneisenstein, Titaneisen *Germ.* Titanic or Titaniferous Iron. Crichtonite (= Craitonite) *Bournon* (430, 1813). Axotomous Eisenerz (Gastein) *Mohs* (**2**, 462, 1824), the Kibdelophan of *Kobell* (*J. Chem. Phys.*, **64**, 1832). Ilmenit *Kupffer* (*Arch. Nat.*, **10**, 1, 1827). Mohsite (Dauphiné) *Levy* (*Phil. Mag.*, **1**, 221, 1827). Hystatisches Eisenerz. Hystatite (Arendal) *Breithaupt* (64, 1830; 236, 1832). Haplotypite *Breithaupt.* Basonomelane (St. Gothard Eisenrose pt.) *Kobell* (318, 1838). Washingtonite *Shepard* (*Am. J. Sc.*, **43**, 364, 1842). Titanoferrite *Chapman* (1843)

Paracolumbite *Shepard* (*Am. J. Sc.*, **12**, 209, 1851). Uddevallite *Dana* (144, 1868).
Parailmenite *Shepard* (*Am. J. Sc.*, **20**, 56, 1880). Picrotitanite *Dana* (144, 1868).
Picroilmenite *Groth* (143, 1898). Picrocrichtonite *Lacroix* (3, 284, 1901). Guadarramite *Muñoz del Castillo* (*Boll. soc. españ. hist. nat.*, **6**, 479, 1906). Manganilmenite *Simpson* (*Roy. Soc. Western Australia, J.*, **15**, 103, 1929). Magnetoilmenite *Ramdohr* (*Jb. Min., Beil.-Bd.*, **54**, 345, 1926). Titanjern, Titanjernmalm *Swed.*

4414   **G E I K I E L I T E** [MgTiO₃]. *Fletcher* (*Nature*, **46**, 620, 1892).
4415   **P Y R O P H A N I T E** [MnTiO₃]. *Hamberg* (*Geol. För. Förh.*, **12**, 598, 1890).

C r y s t.   Hexagonal — *R*; rhombohedral — $\bar{3}$.[1]

Ilmenite $a : c = 1 : 1.3846$;[2] $\alpha\ 85°08'$; $p_0 : q_0 = 1.5988 : 1$;
                                       $\lambda\ 94°29'$

Geikielite $a : c = 1 : 1.3855$; $\alpha\ 85°06\frac{1}{2}'$; $p_0 : q_0 = 1.5998 : 1$;
                                      $\lambda\ 94°30\frac{1}{2}'$

Pyrophanite $a : c = 1 : 1.3980$; $\alpha\ 84°44\frac{1}{2}'$; $p_0 : q_0 = 1.6143 : 1$;
                                      $\lambda\ 94°49'$

Ilmenite forms:[3]

			ϕ	ρ	A_1	A_2
c	0001	111	.....	0°00′	90°00′	90°00′
m	10$\bar{1}$0	2$\bar{1}\bar{1}$	30°00′	90 00	30 00	90 00
a	11$\bar{2}$0	10$\bar{1}$	0 00	90 00	60 00	60 00
δ	21$\bar{3}$0	5$\bar{1}$4	10 53½	90 00	49 06½	70 53½
u	10$\bar{1}$4	211	30 00	21 47	71 15	90 00
ζ	20$\bar{2}$5	311	30 00	32 36	62 11	90 00
r	10$\bar{1}$1	100	30 00	57 58½	42 45½	90 00
l	50$\bar{5}$2	4$\bar{1}\bar{1}$	30 00	75 57	32 50½	90 00
e	01$\bar{1}$2	110	−30 00	38 38½	90 00	57 16
s	02$\bar{2}$1	11$\bar{1}$	−30 00	72 38	90 00	34 15½
P	05$\dot{5}$1	22$\bar{3}$	−30 00	82 52	90 00	30 45½
n'	22$\bar{4}$3	31$\bar{1}$	0 00	61 33½	63 55	63 55
$'n$	4$\bar{2}\bar{2}$3	3$\bar{1}$1	60 00	61 33½	28 26½	116 05
χ'	44$\bar{8}$3	51$\bar{3}$	0 00	74 50½	61 08½	61 08½
$'\chi$	8$\bar{4}\bar{4}$3	5$\bar{3}$1	60 00	74 50½	15 09½	118 51

Geikielite forms:[4] $c\{0001\}$, $r\{10\bar{1}1\}$, $\phi\{50\bar{5}8\}$?
Pyrophanite forms:[5] $c\{0001\}$, $a\{11\bar{2}0\}$, $g\{10\bar{1}2\}$, $s\{02\bar{2}1\}$

Avigliana, Italy.

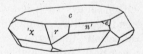

Bearpaw, Mont.

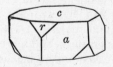

Litchfield, Conn.

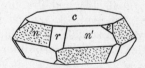

Binnental.

Ilmenite

Structure cell.[6]　Space group $R\bar{3}$.　Cell dimensions:

	a_{rh}	α	a_0	c_0	$a_0 : c_0/2$
Ilmenite	5.52	54°50′	5.083	14.04	1 : 1.380
Geikielite	5.54	54°39′	5.086	14.093	1 : 1.3855
Pyrophanite	5.62	54°16′	5.126	14.333	1 : 1.3980

Contains $(Fe,Mg,Mn)_2Ti_2O_6$ in the rhombohedral unit.

Habit. Commonly thick tabular {0001} (ilmenite), to fine scaly (pyrophanite). Sometimes in thin laminae; also acute rhombohedral (ilmenite). Compact massive; as embedded grains; loose in sand. Commonest forms (ilmenite): *c m a n e r s.*

Twinning. Ilmenite (*a*) On {0001}; (*b*) On {10$\bar{1}$1}, lamellar.

P h y s. Cleavage: on ilmenite, none; on geikielite, {10$\bar{1}$1}; on pyrophanite, {02$\bar{2}$1} perfect, {10$\bar{1}$2} less so. Parting (ilmenite) {0001}, {10$\bar{1}$1} due to twinning (?). Fracture conchoidal to subconchoidal. H. 5–6. Specific gravities as follows.

	OBSERVED	CALCULATED
Ilmenite	4.72 ± 0.04[7]	4.79
Geikielite	4.05	4.03
Pyrophanite	4.54	4.58

Color iron-black (ilmenite) to brownish black (geikielite) to deep blood-red (pyrophanite). Luster metallic to submetallic. Streak black (ilmenite) to brownish red to ochre yellow (pyrophanite) with greenish tinge. Opaque, except in thin splinters which transmit only red light.

O p t. Uniaxial negative (−). Transmits only red light.

	O	E	Color	Absorption
Ilmenite	Biref. very strong		Deep red	
Geikielite[8]	2.31	1.95	Purplish red	$E > O$ faint
Pyrophanite	2.441$_{Li}$			
	2.481$_{Na}$	2.21$_{Na}$	Yellowish red	Nonpleochroic

In polished section[9] (ilmenite) grayish white and only weakly pleochroic. Anisotropic. Often shows twin lamellae and undulatory extinctions; also regularly arranged, exsolved, inclusions of magnetite, hematite, rutile.[10] Percentage of reflection: for various colors, 18.

C h e m. Essentially iron, magnesium, and manganese titanium oxide, $(Fe,Mg,Mn)TiO_3$. Ilmenite is $FeTiO_3$ with as much as 54 atomic per cent of Mg (anal. 13) and grading into geikielite, $(Mg,Fe)TiO_3$, with Mg : Fe = 8 : 1 in anal. 18; pyrophanite is $MnTiO_3$ with Mn : Fe = 5 : 7 in some analyses (anal. 20). Only limited amounts of Fe_2O_3 can enter into the composition of ilmenite at ordinary temperatures, and more than about 6 per cent by weight is presumably present as admixed hematite or magnetite.[11] Excess TiO_2 reported in some analyses may be due to admixed rutile, which is known to occur with ilmenite in intimate admixture.

Anal.   The following are a selection of modern analyses.[12]

	1	2	ʼ3	4	5	6	7	8
TiO$_2$	52.66	52.73	52.50	51.32	54.20	48.64	50.02	52.42
FeO	47.34	45.83	44.32	42.38	42.85	41.76	40.87	40.80
MgO	.....	1.25	0.79	.....	.....	0.88	1.72	.....
MnO	.....	.....	1.36	3.37	.....	1.10	0.48	0.22
Fe$_2$O$_3$	.....	.....	.....	2.10	2.58	5.57	6.03	6.82
Rem.	.....	.....	0.06	0.36	.....	1.66	1.08	.....
Total	100.00	99.81	99.03	99.53	99.63	99.61	100.20	100.26
G.	4.79		4.755	4.711			4.68	4.751

1. FeTiO$_3$.   2. Mt. Ruwenzori, Belgian Congo.[13]   3. Sundsvale, Sweden.   Rem. is CaO.[14]   4. Ambatofotsikely, Madagascar.   Rem. is SiO$_2$ 0.16, U$_3$O$_8$ 0.20.   Total 100.53 in original.[15]   5. Chibinsky Tundra, Siberia.[16]   6. Sasso di Chiesa, Val Malenco, Lombardy.   Rem. SiO$_2$ 0.60, Al$_2$O$_3$ 0.91, H$_2$O 0.15.[17]   7. Val Devero, Ossola, Italy, crystals.   Rem. SiO$_2$ 0.76, Al$_2$O$_3$ 0.20, H$_2$O 0.12.[17]   8. Ferenczfalva, Komitat Krassó-zörény, Carpathians.[18]

	9	10	11	12	13	14	15	16
TiO$_2$	56.43	48.88	57.29	56.08	57.64	64.03	63.94	63.77
FeO	33.91	25.44	24.15	24.40	16.57	12.14	10.09	6.34
MgO	2.10	6.26	15.97	14.18	15.56	24.66	25.79	28.50
MnO	.....	2.60	1.10	.....	.....	.....	.....	.....
Fe$_2$O$_3$	7.16	8.94	1.87	5.43	10.17	.....	0.25	1.93
Rem.	.....	7.68	0.37	.....	.....	.....	.....	.....
Total	99.60	99.80	100.75	100.09	99.94	100.83	100.07	100.54
G.		4.44	4.345	4.25	4.17	4.11	4.01	

9. Chibinsky Tundra, Siberia.[16]   10. Pelotas, Brazil.   Grains.   Rem. SiO$_2$ 5.30, CaO 2.38.[19]   11. Layton's Farm, Warwick, N. Y.   Rem. is SiO$_2$.   Average of two analyses on a crystal.[20]   12. "Picroilmenite."   Balangoda district, Ceylon.[21]   13. "Picroilmenite."   Balangoda district, Ceylon.[21]   14–17. Geikielite.   Ceylon.[21]

	17	18	19	20	21	22
TiO$_2$	64.41	67.74	66.46	51.79	50.49	52.97
FeO	5.44	3.81	.....	21.27	.....	.....
MgO	27.90	28.73	33.54	.....	.....	.....
MnO	.....	.....	.....	14.40	46.92	47.03
Fe$_2$O$_3$	2.77	.....	.....	12.12	1.16	.....
Rem.	.....	.....	.....	0.80	2.06	.....
Total	100.52	100.28	100.00	100.38	100.63	100.00
G.	3.97		4.03	4.63	4.537	4.58

18. Geikielite.   Ceylon.[22]   19. MgTiO$_3$.   20. "Manganilmenite."   Woodstock, Australia.   Rem. SiO$_2$.[23]   21. Pyrophanite.   Pajsberg, Sweden.   Rem. SiO$_2$ 1.58, Sb$_2$O$_3$ 0.48.[24]   22. MnTiO$_3$.

Var.

A. ILMENITE

1. *Ordinary.*   Crichtonite *Bournon* (430, 1813).   Kibdelophane *von Kobell* (*Schweigger's J.*, **64**, 1832).   Essentially FeTiO$_3$ with only minor amounts of Mg and Mn and with a low Fe$_2$O$_3$ content.

2. *Ferrian.*   Menaccanite.   Hystatite *Breithaupt* (**64**, 1830; 236, 1832).   Washingtonite *Shepard* (*Am. J. Sc.*, **43**, 364, 1842).   Uddevallite *Dana* (144, 1868).   Magnetoilmenite *Ramdohr* (*Jb. Min. Beil.-Bd.*, **54**, 345, 1926).   Material supposedly of a high Fe$_2$O$_3$ content has been reported, but prob-

ably is a mixture.[12]   Possibly not more than about 6 per cent by weight of Fe_2O_3 is found in homogeneous ilmenite at ordinary temperatures.

3. *Magnesian.* Magnesian menaccanite. Picrotitanite *Dana* (144, 1868). Picroilmenite *Groth* (143, 1898). Picrocrichtonite *Lacroix* (**3**, 284, 1901). Probably a complete series is formed between ilmenite and geikiel-ite, the latter being the name for the Mg end-component (see analyses).

4. *Manganoan.* Manganilmenite *Simpson* (*Roy. Soc. Western Australia*, **15**, 103, 1929). Probably a complete series is formed between ilmenite and pyrophanite, the latter being the name for the Mn end-component (see analyses).

B. GEIKIELITE

1. *Ferroan.* Contains a considerable amount of Fe in substitution for Mg (anal. 14, 15).

C. PYROPHANITE

1. *Ferroan.* Contains a considerable amount of Fe in substitution for Mn (anal. 20).

Tests. B.B. infusible in O.F., but slightly rounded on edges in R.F. (ilmenite). Slowly soluble in hot HCl.

O c c u r. Ilmenite occurs principally in close association with gabbros, diorites, and anorthosites, as veins and disseminated deposits, sometimes of large extent,[25] and presumably of magmatic origin, or as high-temperature vein deposits.[26] Often large masses are found as dikes cutting anorthosite (Iron Mountain, Wyoming). Ilmenite is common as an accessory mineral in rocks. Ore veins carrying copper minerals (Engels, California) have ilmenite and magnetite in association with chalcopyrite, bornite, and hema-tite. Found often in pegmatites (Quincy, Massachusetts), especially those of intermediate or basic composition, and also in massive quartz (Washing-ton, Connecticut). The heavy black beach sands sometimes contain extensive ilmenite deposits (Florida; India).

Intergrowths of ilmenite and hematite in parallel position with the base as contact face are common.[27] Magnetite and ilmenite intergrowths are also common, with magnetite {111} [$\bar{1}\bar{1}1$] ∥ ilmenite {0001} [$\bar{1}2\bar{1}0$]. These growths are in part due to exsolution phenomena.[28]

In India ilmenite occurs in veins in syenite at Kishengark State; as beach deposits at Travancore, southern India. In Western Australia at Woodstock (manganoan ilmenite). In the Urals at Miask; in the Ilmen Mountains; in gabbro at Oirotia, western Siberia. Found in the crystal-line schists of the southern Carpathians. In Norway particularly at Krägero as large crystals in veins in diorite; at Ekersund as large dikes in anorthosite and norite, and associated with plagioclase and hypersthene; at Arendal and Snarum. In northern Sweden large masses are associated with pyrrhotite in an altered gabbro at Routivare. As crystals in the

Binnental, Switzerland. In France, crystals at St. Cristophe near Bourg d'Oisans, Isère. In Italy at Val Malenco, Lombardy, and at Val Devero, Piedmont. In Cornwall, England, in the sands at Menaccan.

In the United States at Chester, Massachusetts, as crystals; at Quincy in the granite pegmatites. In Rhode Island, at Cumberland, with magnetite. In Connecticut at Washington, Waterford, and Litchfield in quartz. In New York at Elizabethtown and Lake Sanford in gabbro, and associated with magnetite, garnet, apatite, and spinel; crystals in serpentine and limestone at Warwick, Amity, and Monroe, Orange County, associated with spinel, chondrodite, and rutile. In Pennsylvania at Chester, Texas, and elsewhere. Extensive deposits are found in Virginia, principally at Roseland as massive dikes containing ilmenite, rutile, and apatite. In Kentucky in a peridotite dike in Elliott County. In the black sands of Boise County, Idaho. In Florida extensive beach deposits containing ilmenite, zircon, and rutile occur on the east coast between St. Johns River and St. Augustine inlet. In Wyoming a huge solid ilmenite-magnetite dike occurs in anorthosite at Iron Mountain. In California at the Engels copper mine, Plumas County, with magnetite, bornite, chalcopyrite; in Mariposa County with dolomite; along the coast in beach sands. In Quebec at St. Urbain, Charleroix, as veinlets and disseminated in the anorthosite, with intergrown hematite, also sapphirine, rutile, spinel, and biotite.

Geikielite is found in the gem gravels of the Rakwana and Balangoda district, Ceylon.

Pyrophanite is found at the Harstig mine, Pajsberg, near Persberg, Vermland, Sweden, associated with ganophyllite, garnet, and manganophyllite in cavities later filled with calcite. Said to occur at Queluz, southwest of Ouro Preto, Minas Geraes, Brazil.

Alter. Ilmenite is relatively stable under conditions of ordinary chemical attack, and may be concentrated by weathering and detrital action. The most frequent alteration is to a dull white, yellowish, or brown opaque substance (the so-called leucoxene or titanomorphite, which see) for the most part identical with rutile, anatase, or sphene. Also to perovskite, anatase, rutile, and as pseudomorphs after perovskite. Hydroilmenite[29] is a partially altered ilmenite, hydrated and in part with a whitish crust of rutile (?). Geikielite alters to rutile (?), limonite.

Artif. Ilmenite and pyrophanite are produced by heating the oxides in sealed evacuated silica glass tubes to about 1200° for a number of hours.[30] Geikielite, and pyrophanite, by fusing $MgCl_2$ or $MnCl_2$ with TiO_2.[31]

Name. Ilmenite is after the locality in the Ilmen Mountains. Geikielite is after Sir Archibald Geikie (1835–1924), Director of the Geological Survey of Great Britain.

Pyrophanite is from πῦρ, *fire*, and φαίνεσθαι, *to appear*, in allusion to its red color.

GUADARRAMITE. *Muñoz del Castillo* (*Boll. soc. españ. hist. nat.* **6**, 479, 1906).
A supposed radioactive variety of ilmenite from the Sierra de Guadarrama, Castile, Spain.

Ref.

1. The lower symmetry of the ilmenite minerals as compared with hematite is explained by the nonequivalent Fe and Ti in the structure. See Barth and Posnjak, *Zs. Kr.*, **88**, 265 (1934).

2. Angles and unit of Koksharov (6, 350, 1874) in Dana (219, 1892) on crystals from Miask. The geikielite ratio is from the x-ray work of Posnjak and Barth, *Zs. Kr.*, **88**, 275 (1934), with their c-axis halved to conform with the standard treatment here of members of the hematite group. Artificial pyrophanite as given by them has the axial ratio $a : c = 1 : 2.7960$, which is not in close agreement with the ratio by Hamberg, *Geol. För. Förh.*, **12**, 598 (1890). There may be a variation in the axial ratio with Fe_2O_3 content, but the work of Doby and Melczer, *Zs. Kr.*, **39**, 526 (1904), is inconclusive because the homogeneity of their material was not known.

3. Forms in Goldschmidt (8, 138, 1922). Rare and uncertain forms:

$41\bar{5}0$	$0\cdot5\cdot\bar{5}\cdot13$	$04\bar{4}5$	$11\bar{2}5$	$2\cdot3\cdot\bar{5}\cdot14$	$21\bar{3}1$
$10\bar{1}9$	$10\bar{1}2$	$03\bar{3}2$	$5\cdot5\cdot\overline{10}\cdot24$	$24\bar{6}7$	$12\bar{3}1$
$0\cdot3\cdot\bar{3}\cdot11$	$40\bar{4}7$	$05\bar{5}2$	$11\bar{2}3$	$12\bar{3}2$	$36\bar{9}2$
$02\bar{2}7$	$05\bar{5}7$	$30\bar{3}1$	$7\cdot7\cdot\overline{14}\cdot6$	$6\cdot4\cdot\overline{10}\cdot5$	$24\bar{6}1$
$0\cdot3\cdot\bar{3}\cdot10$	$30\bar{3}4$	$40\bar{4}1$	$5\cdot5\cdot\overline{10}\cdot3$	$31\bar{4}2$	
$0\cdot7\cdot\bar{7}\cdot20$	$03\bar{3}4$	$11\bar{2}6$	$8\cdot8\cdot\overline{16}\cdot3$	$23\bar{5}2$	

4. On geikielite from Ceylon, by Sustschinsky, *Zs. Kr.*, **37**, 57 (1902).
5. On pyrophanite, by Hamberg (1890).
6. Ilmenite in Barth and Posnjak (1934); geikielite and pyrophanite data on artificial material by Posnjak and Barth (1934).
7. Averages of recent values on analyzed material with small amounts of Fe_2O_3. Many earlier values in Doelter (3 [1], 45, 1913), and Dana (218,1892) undoubtedly refer to impure material.
8. Larsen (78, 1921).
9. Schneiderhöhn and Ramdohr (2, 539, 1931); also Warren, *Econ. Geol.*, **13**, 419 (1918).
10. Schneiderhöhn and Ramdohr (1931).
11. See Ramdohr, *Sonderdruck Festschr. Bergak. Clausthal*, 1925, 307, who maintains that much more Fe_2O_3 may be in solid solution at elevated temperatures with consequent exsolution at ordinary temperatures. See in this connection Greig, *Econ. Geol.*, **27**, 25 (1932), and Warren (1918).
12. Older analyses in Hintze (1 [2A], 1876, 1908); Doelter (3 [1], 45, 1913); and Dana (218, 1892).
13. Colomba, *Zs. Kr.*, **50**, 512 (1912).
14. Chernik, *J. phys. chim. russe*, **36**, 712 (1904) — *Zs. Kr.*, **43**, 78 (1906).
15. Duparc, Sabot, and Wunder, *Bull. soc. min.*, **37**, 19 (1914).
16. Labuntzov, *Ac. sc. St. Pétersbourg, Trav. Mus. Min.*, **1**, 35 (1926) — *Jb. Min.*, ref., **97**, 1928.
17. Bianchi, *Soc. sc. Milano, Att.*, **60**, 127, 149 (1921) — *Jb. Min.*, ref., **33**, 1924.
18. Vendl anal., *Cbl. Min.*, **1**, 1924.
19. Azema, *Bull. soc. min.*, **34**, 29 (1911).
20. Penfield and Foote, *Am. J. Sc.*, **4**, 108 (1897).
21. Crook and Jones, *Min. Mag.*, **14**, 160 (1906).
22. Dick, *Min. Mag.*, **10**, 145 (1893).
23. Simpson, *Roy. Soc. Western Australia, J.*, **15**, 99 (1929).
24. Hamberg (1890).
25. For occurrences see Lindgren (786, 1933), Warren (1918), Ramdohr (1925), Watson, *Am. Min.*, **7**, 186 (1922).
26. Ramdohr (1925) and Greig (1932). The latter maintains that Ramdohr's temperature estimates are in error.
27. See Schneiderhöhn and Ramdohr (1931); Lacroix, *C.R.*, **171**, 481 (1920), on Madagascar intergrowths; Warren (1918) on polished sections showing intergrowths.
28. See particularly Ramdohr (1925), who designates the hypothetical high-temperature solid solution of magnetite and ilmenite as " magnetoilmenite."
29. Hydroilmenite was described by Blomstrand, *Minneskrift Fys. Sällsk., Lund*, **3**, 4 (1878) from Småland, Sweden. See also Dana (219, 1892) and Hussak, *Min. Mitt.*, **18**, 348, 358 (1899).

30. Posnjak and Barth (1934); see also Hintze (1 [2A], 1876, 1908).
31. In Doelter (1913).

ISERINE. Iserin *Klaproth* (5, 208, 1810). Titaneisenstein pt. Magnetischer Eisen-Sand pt. *Werner.* Iserin *Werner* (26, 52, 1817); *Hoffmann* (4, 258, 1817). Oktaëdrisches Titaneisen-Oxyd *Werner.* Iserin *Breithaupt* (51, 1820). Hexaëdrisches Eisen-Erz *Mohs* (436, 1839). Iserite pt. (Not Iserite *Janovsky, Ak. Wien, Ber.*, 80, 39 [1880] = rutile.)

A supposed[1] isometric form of $FeTiO_3$. Found as rounded octahedral crystals and grains in the sands of the Iserwiese, Bohemia, associated with detrital grains of ilmenite, corundum and ferroan(?) rutile (*iserite*). Probably magnetite with intergrown ilmenite, or simply ilmenite if the octahedra reported are regarded as a combination of a rhombohedron with basal truncations.

Ref.

1. See Hintze (1 [2A], 1861, 1864, 1908) for a historical survey and for analyses.

SILICOILMENITE. *Pilipenko* (*Mineralnoe Syre*, 5, 981, 1930 — *Min. Abs.*, 4, 499, 1931).

A red-brown mineral intergrown with ilmenite from the Ilmen Mountains, Ural, thought to represent a solid solution of silicate or silica in ilmenite.

4416   **Senaite** [(Fe,Mn,Pb)TiO_3. *Hussak* and *Prior* (*Min. Mag.*, 12, 30, 1898).

C r y s t. Said to be rhombohedral — $\bar{3}$; with $a : c = 1 : 1.011$,[1] and related to ilmenite, but the given crystallography is very different. Forms: $c\{0001\}, r\{10\bar{1}1\}, S\{20\bar{2}1\}, Z\{40\bar{4}1\}$. Found as rough crystals and rounded fragments.

P h y s. Fracture conchoidal. H. 6 +. G. 5.301 (crystals). Luster submetallic. Color black. Streak brownish black. In transmitted light through very thin splinters oil-green to greenish black. Uniaxial neg. $(-)$. O_{Li} 2.50.[2] Birefringence low to moderate; nonpleochroic.

C h e m. Presumably a lead and manganese-bearing ilmenite, (Fe,Mn,Pb)TiO_3, but the state of oxidation of the Fe is not clearly known. *Anal.*

	1	2	3	4
TiO_2	57.21	52.11	50.32	49.91
Fe_2O_3	20.22	.....	.....	.....
FeO	4.14	26.97	21.99	25.44
PbO	10.51	10.86	9.62	12.01
MnO	7.00	10.42	17.58	11.88
MgO	0.49	0.32	.....	.....
Rem.	0.11	.....	0.84	0.68
Total	99.68	100.68	100.35	99.92

1. Dattas, Brazil. Rem. is SnO_2 0.11.[3]   2. Dattas, Brazil. Crystals. Average of two analyses.[4]   3. Curralinho, Brazil. Average of two analyses. Rem. is ZrO_2 0.84.[4]   4. Diamantina, Brazil. Rem. is ZrO_2 0.68.[5]

Tests. Infusible. Decomposed by HF and boiling H_2SO_4.

O c c u r. As rounded fragments and rough crystals in the diamond-bearing sands at Dattas and Curralinho near Diamantina, Minas Geraes, Brazil.

A l t e r. Observed superficially altered to limonite and rutile (?).

N a m e. After Professor Joachim da Costa Sena, of Ouro Preto, Brazil.

Ref.

1. The axial ratio of Hussak and Prior is $a : c = 1 : 0.997$. A better average leads to the value given here. The form $p\{05\bar{5}1\}$, reported by Hussak and Reitinger, *Zs. Kr.*, **37**, 574 (1903), does correspond with a form in ilmenite.
2. Larsen (133, 1921).
3. Prior anal. in Hussak and Prior (1898).
4. Reitinger anal. in Hussak and Reitinger (1903).
5. Freise, *Chem. Erde*, **6**, 66 (1930).

DAVIDITE. *Mawson* (*Trans. Proc. Roy. Soc. South Australia*, **30**, 191, 1906).

A name given to a supposed new mineral from Radium Hill, Olary, South Australia. Apparently a mixture[1] largely of ilmenite, with rutile, magnetite, carnotite, and a rare-earth mineral similar to chevkinite. Named after Professor T. W. E. David (1858–1934), Australian geologist.

Ref.

1. Crook and Blake, *Min. Mag.*, **15**, 279 (1910). Analyses are given by Cooke, *Trans. Proc. Roy. Soc. South Australia*, **40**, 267 (1916), and by Crook and Blake (1910). See also Mawson, *ibid.*, **40**, 262 (1916), and Cook, *ibid.*, **30**, 193 (1906).

SEFSTROMITE. *Crook* and *Blake* (*Min. Mag.*, **15**, 281, 1910). Seffstromite.

A name applied by mineral dealers to a supposed new mineral from Radium Hill, Olary, South Australia. Apparently a mixture largely of ilmenite and similar to davidite. Named after N. G. Sefström (1787–1845), Swedish chemist who discovered vanadium.

UNNAMED MINERAL. *Dürrfeld* (*Zs. Kr.*, **47**, 246, 1910).

Cryst. Monoclinic; domatic — m (?).[1]

$$a : b : c = 0.6056 : 1 : 0.6105; \qquad \beta\ 74°47'$$

Forms:

	LOWER	UPPER	
		$-m$	$\bar{1}10$
		w	011
		q	$21 \cdot 20 \cdot 1$
	r		166

Habit. Short prismatic [001] (or a distorted pyramid); sometimes aggregated into groups.

Phys. H. about 6. G. > 3.2. Luster pitchy, bright. Color black.

Chem. Qualitative tests indicate that the mineral is essentially a magnesium titanium oxide; not enough for analysis was found.

Tests. Insoluble in acids. Dissolved by fused Na_2CO_3.

Occur. A few crystals found with microcline, quartz, albite, topaz, and apatite in drusy cavities in granite at Epprechtstein in the Fichtelgebirge, Bavaria.

Ref.

1. The crystallography, as given by Dürrfeld, is open to question. The crystals might also be considered orthorhombic with the forms $\{011\}$ and $\{\bar{1}10\}$ becoming together $\{111\}$. The other forms deviate slightly from the unit pyramidal position. Transformation, Dürrfeld to orthorhombic elements: $101/010/\bar{1}01$. Orthorhombic elements, $a : b : c = 0.9643 : 1 : 0.7385$ (Wolfe, priv. comm., 1941).

4421 **ARSENOLITE** [As$_2$O$_3$]. Arsenicum nativum farinaceum, Arsenicum nativum crystallinum *Wallerius* (224, 1747). Arsenicum calciforme *Cronstedt* (207, 1758). Arsenicum cubicum, etc. *Linnaeus* (1768). White arsenic *Hill* (1771). Natürlicher Arsenikkalk. Arsenikblüthe *Karsten* (79, 1800). Arsenic oxide *Haüy*. Arsenit *Haidinger* (487, 1845). Arsenolite *Dana* (139, 1854). White arsenic, Arsenious acid, Arsenious oxide. Arsenige Säure *Germ*. Arsenikblomma *Swed*. Acide arsenieux, Arsenic blanc natif *Fr*. Arsenico bianco *Ital*. Arsenico blanco, Acido arsenioso *Span*.

C r y s t. Isometric; hexoctahedral — $4/m\ \bar{3}\ 2/m$.[1]

Forms:

$$o\{111\}; \quad \text{less commonly } d\{011\}$$

Structure cell.[2] Space group $Fd3m$; a_0 11.0457 ± 0.0002 (artif.); contains As$_{32}$O$_{48}$.

Habit. Octahedral. Usually in minute octahedra or capillary crystals or as stellar aggregates or crusts. Also botryoidal and stalactitic; earthy to pulverulent. Sometimes skeletal octahedra (artif.).

P h y s. Cleavage {111}. Fracture conchoidal. H. $1\frac{1}{2}$. G. 3.87 ± 0.01;[3] 3.88 (calc.). Luster vitreous to silky. Color white, occasionally with a bluish, yellowish, or reddish tinge. Streak white, pale yellowish. Transparent. Taste astringent, sweetish.

O p t. In transmitted light, colorless. Isotropic, but sometimes exhibits anomalous birefringence[4] (analogous to senarmontite). n_{Na} = 1.755; n_{Li} = 1.748.[5]

C h e m. Arsenic trioxide, As$_2$O$_3$, dimorphous with claudetite. As 75.74, O 24.26, total 100.00. Analyses of natural material are lacking.

Tests. In C.T. sublimes, condensing above in small octahedrons. Slightly soluble in hot water.

O c c u r. A secondary mineral formed by the oxidation of arsenopyrite, native arsenic, enargite, tennantite, smaltite, and other arsenic minerals. Associated with claudetite, erythrite, realgar, orpiment. Found as a sublimate in mine fires and burning coal seams.

Occurs in Germany at Wittichen, Baden, as an alteration of smaltite, and in Saxony as an alteration of native arsenic at Lauta near Marienbad, at Johanngeorgenstadt, and at Graul. With erythrite as an alteration of smaltite at Joachimstal, and as crusts upon arsenopyrite at Kuttenberg, in Bohemia. Found as paramorphs after claudetite at Schmölnitz, Hungary. At Sondalo, Sondrio, and Borgofranco, in Torino, Italy, as alteration of native arsenic. Found as a sublimation product in burning coal seams at localities in the departments of Aveyron, Loire, and Sâone-et-Loire, France. At Morococha, Tarma, Peru, with realgar and orpiment.

In the United States found as an alteration of native arsenic at the Ophir mine, Nevada. In California at the Armagosa mine, San Bernadino County, and as an alteration of enargite at the Exchequer and Monitor mines, Alpine County. With native arsenic on the Saline River, Ellis

County, Kansas. In Canada on Watson Creek, British Columbia, and near Lake Wanapitei, Sudbury district, Ontario.

A l t e r. Found as paramorphs after claudetite, and reported superficially altered to realgar. The blackish or grayish crust or powder often found upon native arsenic is a mixture of the oxide with unoxidized particles of the metal.

A r t i f.[6] Obtained in crystals by sublimation with rapid and marked cooling. Also by crystallization from pure or alkaline water solutions, and by the devitrification of As_2O_3-glass. Claudetite is the stable modification of As_2O_3 at an unknown temperature above 100°.

N a m e. In allusion to the composition.

Ref.

1. Some crystals of arsenolite show optical anomalies and this material (like senarmontite) may be of lower symmetry and only pseudoisometric at ordinary temperatures.
2. Bozorth, *Am. Chem. Soc., J.*, **45**, 1621 (1923), on artificial crystals; cell dimensions from Lihl, *Zs. Kr.*, **81**, 142 (1931).
3. From values 3.884 of Filhol, *Ann. chim. phys.*, **21**, 415 (1847), and 3.865 at 25° of Baxter and Hawkins, *Am. Chem. Soc., J.*, **38**, 266 (1916), on artificial material.
4. Grosse-Bohle, *Zs. Kr.*, **5**, 233 (1881).
5. Des Cloizeaux (513, 1867).
6. See Hintze (1 [2A], 1229, 1915).

4422   S E N A R M O N T I T E [Sb_2O_3]. Antimoine oxydé octaédrique *de Senarmont* (*Ann. chim. phys.*, **31**, 504, 1851). Senarmontite *Dana* (*Am. J. Sc.*, **12**, 209, 1851).

C r y s t. Pseudoisometric; hexoctahedral — $4/m\,\bar{3}\,2/m$.[1]

Forms:[2]

$$a\{001\} \qquad d\{011\} \qquad o\{111\}$$

Structure cell.[3] Space group $Fd3m$; a_0 11.14; contains $Sb_{32}O_{48}$.

Habit. Octahedral; also granular massive and as crusts.

P h y s. Cleavage $\{111\}$ in traces. Fracture uneven. Brittle. H. 2–2½. G. 5.50;[4] 5.56 (calc.). Luster resinous inclining to subadamantine. Colorless or grayish white. Streak white. Transparent.

O p t. In transmitted light, colorless. Shows strong anomalous birefringence[5] often arranged in zones or pyramidal segments (like boracite); becomes isotropic above 460°. n_{Na} 2.087; n_{Li} 2.073.[6]

C h e m. Antimony trioxide, Sb_2O_3 (dimorphous with valentinite). Sb 83.54, O 16.48, total 100.00. Modern analyses are lacking.

Tests. In C.T. fuses and partially sublimes. Easily soluble in HCl.

O c c u r. A secondary mineral, formed by the oxidation of stibnite, native antimony, and other antimony minerals. Associated with valentinite, kermesite, and antimony ochers.

Found in Germany at Arnsberg, Westphalia, and with kermesite at Pernek, Hungary. At Nieddoris, Sardinia, Italy. In France at Auzat-le-Luguet, Puy-de-Dôme. Found abundantly and well crystallized at Hamimat, 60 km. southwest of Guelma, Constantine, Algeria; associated with kermesite, valentinite, hemimorphite, cerussite, cinnabar, calcite, barite as an alteration product of stibnite in veins and cavities in a bituminous marly sediment; crystals from this locality range up to 3 cm. along an axis. In Canada at South Ham, Wolfe County, Quebec, with valentinite and kermesite as an alteration of stibnite and native antimony.

Alter. Observed superficially altered to stibnite, and also completely altered, as paramorphs, to valentinite.

Artif.[7] Obtained by fusing precipitated Sb_2O_3 at a temperature below 570° (above which temperature valentinite is stable[8]), and by sublimation in an inert gas at relatively low temperatures. Obtained in crystals by reaction in solution of alkali antimonyl tartrates and alkalies, and by digesting $SbOCl$ in sodium carbonate solution.

Name. After Henri de Sénarmont (1808–1862), Professor of Mineralogy in the School of Mines in Paris, who first described the species.

Ref.

1. The x-ray study of Bozorth, *Am. Chem. Soc., J.*, **45**, 1621 (1923) and the morphology are in accord with isometric symmetry, but Hocart, *Bull. soc. min.*, **57**, 90 (1934), has concluded from study of the optical anomalies that at ordinary temperatures the mineral is triclinic and pseudoisometric by twinning.
2. Goldschmidt (**8**, 36, 1922).
3. Bozorth (1923) on crystals from Constantine, Algeria; see also Dehlinger, *Zs. Kr.*, **66**, 108 (1927).
4. Frondel (priv. comm. 1940) by microbalance on 19- and 14-mg. single crystals from Algeria; the values 5.22–5.30 are given in the literature.
5. For description and literature see Hocart (1934).
6. Des Cloizeaux (520, 1867; **2**, 330, 1893) by prism method.
7. See Hintze (**1** [2A], 1234, 1915).
8. Fenwick and Roberts, *Am. Chem. Soc., J.*, **50**, 2134 (1928).

443   CLAUDETITE [As_2O_3]. Prismatic Arsenious Acid *Claudet* (*Chem. News*, **22**, 128, 1868). Claudetite *Dana* (796, 1868). Rhombarsenite *Adam* (41, 1869). Arsenphyllite *Breithaupt* (39, 1832). Acide arsénieux prismatique *Fr.*

Cryst. Monoclinic; prismatic — $2/m$.[1]

$a : b : c = 0.4093 : 1 : 0.3493; \quad \beta\ 94°20';$[2] $\quad p_0 : q_0 : r_0 = 0.8535 : 0.3483 : 1$

$r_2 : p_2 : q_2 = 2.8711 : 2.4505 : 1; \quad \mu\ 85°40'; \quad p_0'\ 0.8559, \quad q_0'\ 0.3493, \quad x_0'\ 0.0758$

Forms:[3]

		ϕ	ρ	ϕ_2	$\rho_2 = B$	C	A
b	010	0°00′	90°00′	. . . .	0°00′	90°00′	90°00′
a	100	90 00	90 00	0°00′	90 00	85 40	. . . .
s	130	39 14½	90 00	0 00	39 14½	87 15½	50 45½
r	120	50 47	90 00	0 00	50 47	86 38½	39 13
m	110	67 48	90 00	0 00	67 48	85 59½	22 12
γ	011	12 15	19 40½	85 40	70 39½	19 12½	85 54½
β	021	6 11½	35 05½	85 40	55 08½	34 51½	86 27
d	101	90 00	42 58½	47 01½	90 00	38 38½	47 01½
q	1̄01	−90 00	37 57½	127 57½	90 00	42 17½	127 57½
o	111	69 27	44 51½	47 01½	75 40	40 49	48 40
g	1̄11	−65 53	40 31½	127 57½	74 36	44 30½	126 22½

Structure cell.[4]   Space group $P2_1/n$; a_0 5.25, b_0 12.87, c_0 4.54, β 93°49′; $a_0 : b_0 : c_0 = 0.408 : 1 : 0.353$; cell contents As_8O_{12}.

Habit.   Crystals thin plates on {010} and elongated [001] with {111} and {$\bar{1}$11} prominent, resembling gypsum.

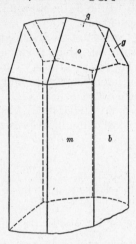
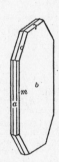

Imperial Valley, Calif.   Schmöllnitz, Hungary.

Twinning.[1]   On {100} as penetration or contact twins, common.

P h y s.   Cleavage {010} perfect, with a fibrous fracture parallel {110}. Very flexible.   H. $2\frac{1}{2}$.   G. 4.15;[5] 4.26 (calc.).   Luster vitreous, on cleavage surfaces pearly.   Colorless to white.   Transparent.

O p t.[6]   In transmitted light, colorless.

	ORIENTATION		n_{Na}	
X	∧ c	84°±	1.871 ± 0.005	
Y	b		1.92 ± 0.02	Bx pos. (+).
. Z	∧ c	6°±	2.01 ± 0.01	$r < v$

C h e m.   Arsenic trioxide, As_2O_3 (dimorphous with arsenolite).
Anal.

	As	O	Insol.	Total
1	75.74	24.26	....	100.00
2	75.99	[23.84]	0.17	100.00

1. As_2O_3.   2. Schmölnitz, Hungary.   Average of two analyses.[7]

Tests.   In C.T. sublimes, condensing above in small octahedrons (arsenolite). Soluble in hot alkaline water solutions.

O c c u r.   A secondary mineral, formed by the oxidation of realgar, arsenopyrite, or other arsenic minerals.   Associated with arsenolite, realgar, orpiment, native sulfur.   Frequently observed as a sublimation product of fires in coal or metalliferous mines.

Found at Schmölnitz, Hungary, well crystallized as a sublimation product, and similarly at the San Domingo mines, Portugal, and with native sulfur and orpiment at the Lasalle mine, Decazeville, Aveyron, France. In Spain at Calañas, Andalusia. In the United States occurs as an alteration of realga: in Imperial County, California, about 35 miles north of Yuma, Arizona.[8] Observed as a sublimation product in the fire zone of the United Verde mine, Jerome, Arizona. As crusts in the oxidized zone of the pyrrhotite deposit at Island Mountain, Trinity County, California. Reported from Butte, Montana.

Alter. Observed changed to arsenolite (Schmölnitz).

Artif.[9] Found as a sublimate in ore roasting ovens (Freiberg, Schwarzenfels Hesse). In crystals by sublimation (in a closed tube arsenolite forms in the cooler regions [ca. 200°] and the glassy modification in the hotter portions [ca. 400°]). Also obtained in crystals from NH_4OH or KOH solutions, by supersaturating a concentrated solution of arsenic acid with arsenious acid, and from solutions of silver arsenite in HNO_3.

Name. After F. Claudet, a French chemist who first described the natural mineral.

Ref.

1. Schmidt, Zs. Kr., 14, 577 (1888).
2. Unit and orientation of Schmidt (1888); angles of Palache, Am. Min., 19, 194 (1934).
3. In Goldschmidt (2, 161, 1913); Palache (1934). Rare or uncertain: {001}, {1·10·0}, {150}, {250}, {041}, {171}, {121}.
4. Buerger (priv. comm., 1941) by Weissenberg method on material from Jerome, Arizona.
5. Groth, Ann. Phys., 137, 416 (1869); a check value of 4.14 (average of two determinations) on material from Jerome, was obtained by Berman (priv. comm., 1941).
6. Indices from Larsen (58, 1921) on material from Schmöllnitz; other data from Des Cloizeaux, Bull. soc. min., 10, 306 (1887). Schmidt (1888) gives $r > v$, with $2H_{Li} = 66°14'$ and $2H_{Na} = 65°21'$, and optically neg. (−).
7. Loczka, Zs. Kr., 39, 525 (1903).
8. Kelley, Am. Min., 21, 137 (1936).
9. Hintze (1 [2A], 1233, 1915).

444   VALENTINITE [Sb_2O_3]. Chaux d'antimoine native (from Chalanches) *Mongez* (J. phys., 23, 66, 1783); (from Příbram) *Rössler* (Crell's Ann., 1, 334, 1787). Antimonium spatosum album *Hacquet* (Crell's Ann., 1, 523, 1788). Weiss-Spiesglaserz *Werner, Hoffman* (Bergm. J., 385, 398, 1789). Weiss-Spiess-glanzerz *Klaproth* (Crell's Ann., 1, 9, 1789; 3, 183, 1802). Antimoine oxydé *Haüy* (4,1801). White Antimonial Ore *Kirwan* (1, 251, 1796). Antimonblüthe *von Leonhard* (160, 1821). Antimonphyllit *Breithaupt* (39, 1832). Exitèle *Beudant* (615, 1832). Exitelite *Chapman* (39, 1843). Valentinit *Haidinger* (506, 1845). White Antimony, Antimonious acid, Antimony trioxide. Antimonige Säure, Antimonspath *Germ.* Antimonblomma *Swed.* Acide antimonieux *Fr.* Antimonio bianco *Ital.* Antimonio blanco *pt. Span.*

Cryst. Orthorhombic; dipyramidal — $2/m\ 2/m\ 2/m$.[1]

$a : b : c = 0.3939 : 1 : 0.4339;$[2] $p_0 : q_0 : r_0 = 1.1016 : 0.4339 : 1$

$q_1 : r_1 : p_1 = 0.3939 : 0.9078 : 1;$ $r_2 : p_2 : q_2 = 2.3046 : 2.5388 : 1$

Forms:[3]

		ϕ	$\rho = C$	ϕ_1	$\rho_1 = A$	ϕ_2	$\rho_2 = B$
b	010	0°00′	90°00′	90°00′	90°00′	. . . . .	0°00′
m	110	68 30	90 00	90 00	21 30	0°00′	68 30
μ	210	78 51½	90 00	90 00	11 08½	0 00	78 51½
π	310	82 31	90 00	90 00	7 29	0 00	82 31
i	011	0 00	23 27½	23 27½	90 00	90 00	66 32½
X	021	0 00	40 57	40 57	90 00	90 00	49 03
p	031	0 00	52 28	52 28	90 00	90 00	37 32
r	112	68 30	30 37½	12 14½	61 42½	61 09	79 14½

Structure cell.[4] Space group $Pccn$; a_0 4.92, b_0 12.46, c_0 5.42; $a_0 : b_0 : c_0 = 0.395 : 1 : 0.435$; contains Sb_8O_{12}.

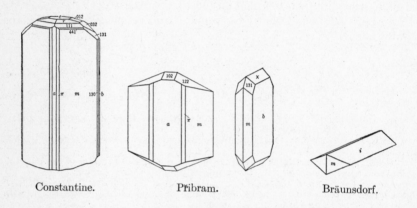

Constantine.   Pŕibram.   Bräunsdorf.

Habit.   Commonly prismatic either [001] or [100]; also tabular {010}. The prism faces usually are rounded by striations ‖ [001], and the brachy-domes are striated [100].   Crystals often aggregated in fan-shaped or stellate groups, in bundles and druses and as aggregates of thin plates. Also massive, with lamellar, columnar, or granular structure.

P h y s.   Cleavage {110} very perfect, {010} imperfect.[5]   Brittle. H. $2\frac{1}{2}$–3.   G. 5.76;[6] 5.76 (calc.).   Luster adamantine, often pearly on cleavage surfaces.   Colorless to snow-white, occasionally yellowish, red-dish, and ash gray to brownish.   Streak white.   Transparent.

O p t.[7]   In transmitted light, colorless.   Axial plane ‖ {001} for red and yellow, and ‖ {010} for green and blue.   When heated to 75° the axial angle for red decreases somewhat and for blue increases.

		n_{Na}[8]	n_{red}	n_{green}	
X	a	2.18	a	a	Bx. neg. (−). $2V$ very small; essen-
Y	b	2.35	c	b	tially uniaxial for yellow. $r < v$,
Z	c	2.35	b	c	marked (sometimes $r > v$?).

C h e m.   Antimony trioxide, Sb_2O_3 (dimorphous with senarmontite).

Anal.

	1	2
Sb	83.54	82.79
O	16.46	[17.21]
As	.....	trace
Total	100.00	100.00
G.	5.76	5.76

1. Sb_2O_3.   2. Tatasi, Bolivia.[9]

Tests. Fuses easily in C.T. and gives slight sublimate. Soluble in HCl. Colored brown and slowly dissolved by ammonium sulfide solution.

O c c u r. A common secondary mineral resulting from the oxidation of stibnite, native antimony, kermesite, tetrahedrite and other antimony minerals. Associated with kermesite, stibiconite, cervantite, and other more or less well-defined antimony oxides. Only a few localities are given here.

Originally found at Chalanches near Allemont, Dauphiné, France, and derived in large part from native antimony and allemontite. At Bräunsdorf, near Freiberg, Saxony, Germany. At Přibram, Bohemia, and in Roumania at Felsöbánya and with kermesite at Pernek, near Bösing. Found in Italy at Cetina, Sienna, and at Ballao, Nieddoris and Su Suergiu in Sardinia. In the Sanza mine, Constantine, and elsewhere in Algeria. In Bolivia at Huanini and Tatasi, and in Brazil from Hargreaves, between Ouro Preto and Burnier. In the United States valentinite occurs well crystallized in the Ochoco district, Crook County, Oregon. In Idaho at the Stanley stibnite mine, Shoshone County. With stibnite at the Picahotes mine, San Benito County, California. In Canada at South Ham, Wolfe County, Quebec, and at the Prince William mine, New Brunswick.

A l t e r. Found as paramorphs after senarmontite, and said to occur altered to native antimony.

A r t i f.[10] Readily prepared in crystals by sublimation, and by crystallization from hot-water solutions (and then usually accompanied by slow transformation to the stable modification, senarmontite). Also by quenching melts heated above 570°; by the action of water vapor on metallic antimony at elevated temperatures; by the reaction of acid $SbCl_3$ solutions with alkali carbonates. Observed in cavities in slags, and as an oven product.

N a m e. After Basil Valentine, an alchemist of the fifteenth century, who discovered the properties of antimony.

Ref.

1. Crystal class established by Buerger and Hendricks, *Zs. Kr.*, **98**, 1 (1937).
2. Unit and orientation of Brezina, *Ann. Mus. Wien*, **1**, 145 (1886), ratio of Schaller, *Am. Min.*, **22**, 651 (1937). Transformation: Laspeyres (and Dana [199, 1892]) to Brezina: 100/0$\frac{4}{3}$0/00$\frac{1}{4}$.
3. In Goldschmidt (**9**, 45, 1923); also Cesaro, *Ac. Belgique, Mém.*, **8** [4], (1925); Schaller (1937); Ungemach, *Bull. soc. min.*, **35**, 539 (1912). Rare and uncertain forms:

001	340	10·7·0	720	045	041	178
100	450	14·9·0	410	065	051	133
160	10·9·0	530	510	0·11·8	061	378
130	760	950	910	032	102	122
120	540	730	012	053	111	131
350	430	830	034	072	441	361

4. Buerger and Hendricks (1937) by Weissenberg method on crystals from Su Suergiu, with analysis of structure.
5. Ungemach (1912) states that no cleavage || {010} was noted by him.
6. Spencer, *Min. Mag.*, 14, 308 (1907), on crystals from Tatasi, Bolivia.
7. Des Cloizeaux (568, 1867; 2, 332, 1893); Spencer (1907).
8. Larsen (152, 1921) on crystals from Algeria. The indices (for Na) $X = 2.352$, $Y = 2.358$ of Cavinato, *Acc. Linc., Rend.*, 25, 140 (1937) — *Jb. Min.*, I, 584, 1937, are for an optically positive mineral.
9. Prior anal. in Spencer (1907).
10. See Doelter (3 [1], 762, 1926); Fenwick and Roberts, *Am. Chem. Soc., J.*, 50, 2134 (1928).

445   **B I X B Y I T E** [$(Mn,Fe)_2O_3$]. *Penfield* and *Foote* (*Am. J. Sc.*, 4, 105, 1897). Sitaparite *Fermor* (*Geol. Sur. India, Rec.*, 37, 199, 1909; *Geol. Sur. India, Mem.*, 37, 49, 1909). Partridgeite *de Villiers* (*Am. Min.*, 28, 336, 468, 1943).

C r y s t.   Isometric; diploidal — $2/m \bar{3}$.[1]

Forms:[2]

$a\{001\}$ $o\{111\}$ $n\{112\}$

Utah.

Structure cell.[3] Space group $Ia3$; a_0 9.365 ± 0.020; contains $(Mn,Fe)_{32}O_{48}$.

Habit. Cubic, sometimes modified by {112}; the crystals occasionally are deeply pitted.

Twinning. On {111} as penetration twins.[4]

P h y s. Cleavage {111} in traces.[5] Fracture irregular. H. 6–6½. G. 4.945; 5.068 (calc. for Mn : Fe = 1 : 1).[5] Luster metallic to sub-metallic. Color and streak black. Opaque. In polished section isotropic.[6]

C h e m. Essentially iron manganese oxide, $(Mn,Fe)_2O_3$, with some Ti. Fe substitutes for Mn and a series exists from nearly pure Mn_2O_3 up to at least 59 weight per cent Fe_2O_3.

Anal.[7]

	Fe_2O_3	Mn_2O_3	TiO_2	Rem.	Total	G.
1	47.98	46.43	1.70	3.84	99.95	4.945
2	49.85	46.04	2.05	0.51	98.45	4.853

1. Utah. Rem. is MgO 0.10, SiO_2 1.21, Al_2O_3 2.53; average of two analyses. 2. Patagonia.[8]

Tests. F. 4. B.B. fuses to a magnetic globule. Difficultly soluble in HCl with evolution of Cl.

O c c u r. In cavities in rhyolite, associated with topaz, garnet, pink beryl, and hematite in the northeast section of the Thomas Range, Utah.[9] Reported from the Valle de las Plumas, Patagonia, and from Ribes, Girona,

Spain; also said to occur in South Rhodesia. At Sitapár, Chhindwara district, Central Provinces, India (*sitaparite*) associated with braunite and hollandite. In metamorphosed manganese ores at Langban and near Murjek, Sweden. A nearly iron-free variety occurs at Postmasburg, South Africa (*partridgeite*).

Observed from the Utah locality as oriented growths[10] upon topaz, with bixbyite {010}[100] || topaz {023}[100].

A r t i f. MnO_2 heated for 5 hours at dull red heat produced Mn_2O_3 with the bixbyite structure.[11]

N a m e. After the late Maynard Bixby of Salt Lake City, Utah.

SITAPARITE. *Fermor* (*Geol. Sur. India, Rec.*, **37**, 199, 1909; *Geol. Sur. India, Mem.*, **37**, 49, 1909).

Massive, with good cleavage {111} (?) H. 7. G. 4.93–5.09. Color deep bronze-gray. Analysis gave BaO 0.10, CaO 6.14, MgO 1.02, MnO 26.89, MnO_2 36.79, Fe_2O_3 27.60, Al_2O_3 1.02, SiO_2 1.17, H_2O 0.09, total 100.82. From Sitapár, Central Provinces, India. Shown to be identical with bixbyite.[12]

PARTRIDGEITE. *de Villiers* (*Am. Min.*, **28**, 336, 468, 1943).

An unnecessary name proposed for varieties of bixbyite containing less than 10 weight per cent Fe_2O_3, originally applied to material from Postmasburg, South Africa.

Ref.

1. Symmetry established from the x-ray structural work of Pauling and Shappell, *Zs. Kr.*, **75**, 128 (1930). Cortelezzi, Himmel, and Schroeder, *Cbl. Min.*, 129, 1934, reported a higher symmetry in their study, but their material may not have been authentic. The latter find striae on {001} indicating a possible twin lamination, in which case the mineral investigated by them may be pseudoisometric.
2. Cortelezzi, Himmel, and Schroeder (1934) report the forms {011} and {123} on the Patagonian crystals.
3. Pauling and Shappell (1930).
4. Montgomery, *Am. Min.*, **19**, 82 (1934).
5. Cortelezzi, Himmel, and Schroeder (1934) report a perfect {001} cleavage, and no {111} cleavage in Patagonian crystals. This has not been verified on Utah crystals (Berman, priv. comm., 1940).
6. Orcel and Pavlovitch, *Bull. soc. min.*, **54**, 108 (1932). See also Schneiderhöhn and Ramdohr (**2**, 572, 1931) and de Villiers (1943).
7. See also Mason (*Geol. För. Förh.*, **64**, 117, 1942) and de Villiers (*Am. Min.*, **28**, 336, 468, 1943). The structure deduced by Pauling and Shappell (1930) indicates the equivalence of Fe and Mn.
8. Analysis by de Mouzo [Cortelezzi], *Jb. Min.*, ref. [1], 133, 1931. Analytical results given as FeO and MnO_2.
9. Montgomery (1934) has described what is presumably the original locality.
10. Pabst, *Am. Min.*, **23**, 342 (1938).
11. Zachariasen, *Zs. Kr.*, **67**, 455 (1928).
12. Mason (1942).

---

446 **B R A U N I T E** [(Mn,Si)$_2O_3$]. Brachytypous Manganese-Ore, Braunite *Haidinger* (*Edinburgh J. Sc.*, **4**, 48, 1826; *Roy. Soc. Edinburgh, Trans.*, **11**, 137, 1827). Hartbraunstein *Hausmann* (222, 1847). Marceline *Beudant* (**2**, 188, 1832). Heteroklin *Breithaupt* in *Evreinov* (*Ann. Phys.*, **49**, 204, 1840). Leptonematite, Pesillite *Adam* (75, 1869).

C r y s t. Tetragonal; ditetragonal dipyramidal — $4/m\ 2/m\ 2/m$.

$$a : c = 1 : 1.4070;^1 \qquad p_0 : r_0 = 1.4070 : 1$$

Forms:[2]

		φ	ρ	A	$\overline{M}$
c	001	.....	0°00'	90°00'	90°00'
a	010	0°00'	90 00	90 00	45 00
m	110	45 00	90 00	45 00	90 00
τ	013	0 00	25 07½	90 00	72 31½
e	011	0 00	54 36	90 00	54 48
s	021	0 00	70 26	90 00	48 13
n	112	45 00	44 51	60 05	90 00
p	111	45 00	63 19	50 49	90 00
y	133	18 26	56 00½	74 48	68 14
x	131	18 26	77 20	72 02	64 07½

Less common:

γ	012	l	221	D	177	i	134	λ	5·11·13	f	344	η	151
o	338	r	331	g	135	u	153	v	122	ε	353	j	241
q	5·5·12	b	441	σ	155	t	378	d	142	w	121		

Structure cell. Space group $I4/acd$; a_0 13.44, c_0 18.93, $a_0 : c_0 = 1 : 1.408$; contains $(Mn,Si)_{128}O_{192}$ with Mn : Si = 7 : 1.[3]

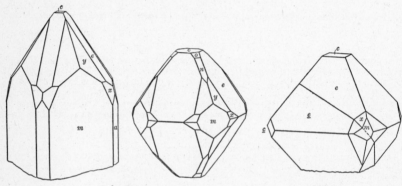

Långban.   Nágpur.

Nágpur.

Habit. Pyramidal {011} and {131}. Striated on {001} and {201} ‖ [010]. Also granular massive. Commonest forms: .

Twinning. On {112} producing a combination with only a small reentrant (0°18') on e{011}.

Phys. Cleavage {112} perfect. Fracture uneven to subconchoidal. Brittle. H. 6–6½. G. 4.72–4.83;[4] 4.67 (calc. for Mn : Si = 7 : 1). Luster submetallic. Color dark, brownish black to steel-gray. Streak same. Weakly magnetic. Opaque. In polished section[5] anisotropic. Reflection percentages: (for λ465) ‖ [001] 21.7, ‖ [100] 20.4.

Chem. Essentially an oxide of manganese and silicon, Mn_7SiO_{12} or $3Mn_2O_3 \cdot MnSiO_3$; possibly

$(Mn,Si)_2O_3.$[6] Some Fe substitutes for Mn, with the ratio Mn : Fe = 5 : 1 in anal. 5. Ba is often present, in amounts up to several per cent; also Ca and Mg in small amounts.

Anal.[7]

	1	2	3	4	5
MnO	82.13	80.40	78.91	74.40	66.89
O	7.94	8.35	7.35	7.50	6.27
Fe_2O_3	.....	0.30	.....	3.80	15.39
FeO	.....	.....	3.81	.....	.....
CaO	.....	1.20	0.34	0.50	0.06
SiO_2	9.93	8.15	9.89	9.80	9.90
Rem.	.....	1.35	0.15	4.30	1.59
Total	100.00	99.75	100.45	100.30	100.10
G.	4.67	4.83	4.720	4.76	4.729

1. Mn_7SiO_{12}. 2. Öhrenstock, Swarzburg-Sonderhausen. Rem. is CuO, PbO, BaO, alkalies, H_2O 0.75, gangue 0.60.[8] 3. Långban. Rem. is MgO 0.15. MnO + O given as Mn_3O_4 84.77; direct determination of O is higher, as given; Fe_2O_3 4.23 as given.[9] 4. St. Marcel, Piedmont. Fe_2O_3 includes Al_2O_3. Rem. is MgO 1.00; gangue 2.60; PbO, CuO, BaO, alkalies, H_2O 0.70.[8] 5. Spiller manganese mine, Texas. Rem. is MgO 0.19, H_2O 0.73, insol. 0.67.[10]

Var. Ferrian. The maximum Fe : Mn ratio is 1 : 5 (anal. 5).

Tests. Infusible. Soluble in HCl with evolution of Cl. Leaves a residue of gelatinous silica.

O c c u r. Braunite is nearly always associated with other manganese minerals, including psilomelane, manganite, polianite, hausmannite, jacobsite, manganian epidote; also barite. Found in veins and lenses as the result of metamorphism of manganese oxides and silicates; and with pyrolusite, wad, psilomelane as a secondary mineral formed under weathering conditions. Many localities are known. At Öhrenstock and Elgersburg, near Ilmenau, Thuringia, as crystals and massive in veins in porphyry; at Ilfeld in the Harz Mountains. From St. Marcel, Piedmont, as crystals up to 5 cm. in size and as granular masses with polianite, quartz, and manganese silicates. In Norway at Botnedalen, Telemark; in Sweden from the manganese mines at Jacobsberg in the Nordmark district, also from Långban and the Gläkarn mine, Linde. In India at Kacharwaki, Nágpur district, in fine crystals, and in other districts. In Brazil at Miguel Burnier, near Ouro Preto, Minas Geraes. In Panama with pyrolusite and psilomelane at Nombre de Dios and several other places. In the United States at the Spiller manganese mine, 15 miles northeast of Mason, Mason County, Texas, as lenses in quartzite; in the Batesville district, Arkansas; at Cartersville, Georgia.

N a m e. After Kammerath Braun of Gotha.

Ref.

1. Orientation of Goldschmidt (78, 1897), values of Switzer, *Am. Min.*, **23**, 649 (1938) on Nágpur crystals. Goldschmidt gives a c value of 1.4032 which fits measurements of crystals from other localities quite well. The orientation of Dana (232, 1892) is not retained. Transformation: Dana to Goldschmidt: $110/\bar{1}10/002$.

2. In Switzer (1938) based on earlier work of Koechlin, *Ann. Mus. Wien.*, **27**, 159 (1913). Rare and uncertain forms: {175}, {343}, {8·14·3}, {351}, {571}, {11·13·1}.

3. Aminoff, *Ak. Stockholm Handl.*, **9** [5], 14 (1931) on Långban crystals, confirmed by Switzer (1938).

4. The specific gravity variation may be due to a variation in the Mn/Si ratio.

5. Orcel and Pavlovitch, *Bull. soc. min.*, **54**, 108 (1931), on Indian crystals.

6. The role of Si in this mineral is not well understood.   The simplest interpretation indicates a substitution of Mn by Si in the oxide.

7. Other, less complete and older, analyses are cited in Dana (233, 1029, 1892), Doelter (3 [2], 896, 1926), Fermor, *Geol. Sur. India, Mem.*, **37** (1909).

8. Gorgeu, *Soc. chim. bull.*, **9**, 656 (1893) — *Zs. Kr.*, **25**, 314 (1896).

9. Flink, *Ak. Stockholm, Bihang.*, **16** [2], 1 (1891) — Dana (1029, 1892).

10. Schaller anal. in Hewett and Schaller, *Am. Min.*, **22**, 785 (1937).

RUTILE GROUP

DITETRAGONAL DIPYRAMIDAL — $4/m\,2/m\,2/m$

		c/a	a_0	c_0	G
Rutile	TiO_2	0.6442	4.58	2.95	4.23
Pyrolusite	MnO_2	0.6647	4.38	2.85	5.06
Cassiterite	SnO_2	0.6723	4.72	3.17	7.00
Plattnerite	PbO_2	0.6828	4.931	3.367	9.42

Members of the rutile group show little variation in composition, and little tendency to form series between the species, this latter perhaps because of the considerable variation in the ionic radii of the A ions.

Crystals are often elongated in [001] and also pyramidal. Striae are nearly always found ‖ [001]. The minerals of the group have rather imperfect cleavages (except the {110} of pyrolusite). Most of the species are nearly always twinned on {101} and less often on {301}, with the latter twin law more common in pyrolusite. The minerals have a high refractive index; they are uniaxial positive with a moderate to high birefringence.

Rutile and cassiterite occur in granitic rocks, and presumably form at a fairly high temperature. Rutile is especially widespread as an accessory mineral. Pyrolusite forms at much lower temperatures. The members of the group, therefore, have little in common in their paragenesis.

Certain structural and crystallographic similarities are found between the AX_2 minerals of this group and the multiple oxide tapiolite, the fluoride sellaite, the silicate zircon, and the phosphate xenotime. The fundamental similarity between all these is the ratio of the metal elements to oxygen, and the limited range of radius ratio.

4511 RUTILE [TiO_2]. Schorl rouge *de Lisle* (**2**, 421, 1783), *von Born* (**1**, 168, 1790).   Rother Schorl pt., Titankalk *Klaproth* (**1**, 233, 1795).   Red Schorl *Kirwan* (**1**, 271, 1794).   Titanite *Kirwan* (**2**, 239, 1796).   [Not Titanite *Klaproth* (1794) = Sphene.] Schorl rouge, Sagenite *Saussure* (**4**, §1894, 1796).   Crispite *Delametherie* (**2**, 333, 1797).   Rutile *Werner* (1800); Ludwig's ed. of *Werner* (**1**, 55, 1803).   Titane oxydé, Titane oxydé chromifère *Haüy* (1801).   Ilmenorutile, Naumannite *Koksharov* (**2**, 352, 1854).   Edisonite *Hidden* (*Am. J. Sc.*, **36**, 272, 1888).   Dicksbergite *Igelström* (*Geol. För. Förh.*, **18**, 231, 1896).   Strüverite *Zambonini* (*Acc. Napoli, Rend.*, **8** [3], 35, 1907); *Prior* and *Zambonini* (*Min. Mag.*, **15**, 78, 1908).   Strueverite.   Chromrutile (?) *Gordon* and *Shannon* (*Am. Min.*, **13**, 69, 1928).

Schwarzer Granat *Lampadius* (**2**, 119, 1797). Eisenhaltiges Titanerz *Klaproth* (**2**, 235, 1797) = Nigrin *Karsten* (**56**, 79, 1800). Leucoxene pt. *Gümbel* (*Die paläolith. Eruptivgest. Fichtelgebirg.* **22**, 1874). Iserite *Janovsky* (*Ak. Wien, Ber.,* **80**, 34, 1886). Paredrite *Farrington* (*Am. J. Sc.,* **41**, 356, 1916).

C r y s t. Tetragonal; ditetragonal dipyramidal — $4/m\, 2/m\, 2/m$.

$$a : c = 1 : 0.6442;^1 \qquad p_0 : r_0 = 0.6442 : 1$$

Forms:[2]

		ϕ	ρ	A	$\overline{M}$
c	001	.....	0°00′	90°00′	90°00′
a	010	0°00′	90 00	90 00	45 00
m	110	45 00	90 00	45 00	90 00
u	170	8 08	90 00	81 52	53 08
x	140	14 02	90 00	75 58	59 02
l	130	18 26	90 00	71 34	63 26
h	120	26 34	90 00	63 26	71 34
r	230	33 41½	90 00	56 18½	78 41½
e	011	0 00	32 47½	90 00	67 29
v	031	0 00	62 38½	90 00	51 06
w	051	0 00	68 47½	90 00	48 45½
s	111	45 00	42 20	61 33½	90 00
ρ	221	45 00	61 14½	51 41½	90 00
t	133	18 26	34 10½	79 46	75 27
L	131	18 26	63 51½	73 30½	66 20
f	233	33 41½	37 45	70 09	83 05½
Z	231	33 41½	66 42½	59 22	79 36½

Structure cell.[3] Space group $P4/mnm$; $a_0\, 4.58$, $c_0\, 2.95$; $a_0 : c_0 = 1 : 0.644$; contains Ti_2O_4.

Habit. Commonly prismatic, often slender to acicular [001]. Prism zone vertically striated or furrowed. Usually terminated by {101} or {111}; {001} rare. Rarely pyramidal. Also granular massive, coarse to fine. Common forms: *a m l h e s t z.*

Twinning.[4] (*a*) On {011} common. Often geniculated; also contact twins of very varied habit, sometimes sixlings and eightlings, occasionally polysynthetic. The twins sometimes are distorted by extension of a pair of faces of {011}. Twin gliding also observed in this plane.[11] (*b*) On {031}, rare. As contact twins, often distorted by extension of a pair of prism faces. Also found in combination with twins on {011}. (*c*) On {092}, as twin gliding plane.

Oriented growths. Oriented overgrowths have been found of rutile upon hematite,[5] magnetite,[6] ilmenite,[7] brookite, and anatase. Oriented microscopic needles of rutile are of frequent occurrence in corundum,[8] pseudobrookite, phlogopite,[9] and quartz. The asterism of phlogopite, quartz,

Modriach.

and, in part, of corundum is due to these inclusions.

Rutile $\{010\}[10\bar{1}]\parallel$ hematite $\{0001\}[10\bar{1}0]$

Rutile $\{010\}[10\bar{1}]\parallel$ magnetite $\{111\}$ $[101]$

Rutile $\{010\}[10\bar{1}]\parallel$ ilmenite $\{0001\}[10\bar{1}0]$

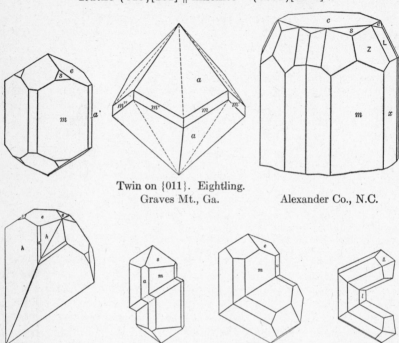

Twin on $\{011\}$. Eightling.
Graves Mt., Ga.

Alexander Co., N.C.

Twin on $\{031\}$
Cerrado Frio, Brazil.

Twins on $\{011\}$

St. Yrieix, France.

Phys. Cleavage $\{110\}$ distinct, $\{100\}$ less so, $\{111\}$ in traces. Part-

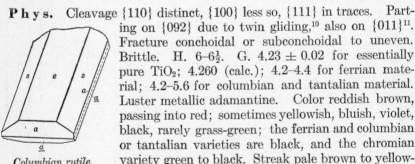

ing on $\{092\}$ due to twin gliding,[10] also on $\{011\}$[11].
Fracture conchoidal or subconchoidal to uneven.
Brittle. H. 6-6½. G. 4.23 ± 0.02 for essentially
pure TiO_2; 4.260 (calc.); 4.2-4.4 for ferrian material; 4.2-5.6 for columbian and tantalian material.
Luster metallic adamantine. Color reddish brown,
passing into red; sometimes yellowish, bluish, violet,
black, rarely grass-green; the ferrian and columbian
or tantalian varieties are black, and the chromian

Columbian rutile.
Black Hills.
Distorted twin on $\{011\}$

variety green to black. Streak pale brown to yellowish; grayish or greenish black (in the black Cb-Ta
varieties) Transparent in small pieces; the varie-
ties containing much Fe^3, Cb, or Ta are transparent only in very thin
splinters. Photosensitive.[33]

Opt. In transmitted light, usually red or brownish red. The depth of the color[12] increases with increasing content of Fe^3. The columbian and tantalian varieties are deep brown to green, or opaque.

Uniaxial positive (+). An anomalous biaxial character is sometimes observed,[13] as in crystals that have been mechanically deformed. Pleochroism distinct, in shades of red, brown, yellow, green. Thick grains, especially of varieties containing Fe^3, Cb, or Ta, may be opaque in the position of maximum absorption. Absorption $E > O$.

The indices of refraction decrease markedly with increasing temperature at constant wavelength, but E much more rapidly so that the birefringence decreases. O apparently reaches a minimum at about 700°. With increasing wavelength at constant temperature the refractive indices decrease markedly, but E much more rapidly so that the birefringence decreases.

$n_{589.3}$ at Varying Temperature[14]

	25°	75°	110°	150°	300°	450°
O	2.6124	2.6092	2.6087	2.6062	2.5992	2.5953
E	2.8993	2.8943	2.8920	2.8888	2.8770	2.8679

$n_{25°}$ at Varying Wavelength[14]

	546.07	579.07	607.27	623.43	671.63	690.75
O	2.6505	2.6211	2.6001	2.5890	2.5643	2.5555
E	2.9467	2.9085	2.8842	2.8712	2.8397	2.8294

Chem. Essentially titanium dioxide, TiO_2. Important amounts of Cb, Ta, Fe^2, Fe^3 are reported. Smaller amounts[15] of Sn, Cr, and V are also given. Sc has been found by the spectrograph. The formula for the Fe^2, Cb, and Ta members may be written $Fe_x^2(Cb,Ta)_{2x} Ti_{1-3x}O_2$, where x does not exceed about 0.2.[16] In this connection the structural relations between rutile and tapiolite, $Fe(Ta,Cb)_2O_6$, are significant.[3] The presence of Fe^3 in many analyses indicates a possible further complication of the formula of rutile.[17]

Anal.[18]

	1	2	3	4	5	6	7	8	9
FeO	0.78	.....	.....	.....	15.84	8.27	11.38	10.56	12.29
SnO_2	.....	.....	1.40	.....	0.05	2.67	.....	.....	.....
Fe_2O_3	.....	2.62	6.68	11.03	.....	.....	.....	.....	.....
TiO_2	98.96	97.46	91.96	89.49	71.15	45.74	41.20	53.04	54.57
Cb_2O_5	.....	.....	.....	.....	.....	6.90	23.48	21.73	32.15
Ta_2O_5	.....	.....	.....	.....	10.14	35.96	23.48	14.70	.....
Rem.	0.54	.....	.....	0.45	1.80	0.70	0.68	trace	0.11
Total	100.28	100.08	100.04	100.97	98.98	100.24	100.22	100.03	99.12
G.	4.264		4.249	4.41	4.91	5.30	5.54–5.59	5.14	4.64

1. Prilepec, Serbia. Rem. is Cr_2O_3 0.03, V_2O_3 0.13, H_2O 0.38.[19] 2. Graves Mt., Georgia. Average of three analyses.[20] 3. Ferrian rutile. West Cheyenne Canyon, Colo. 0.7 per cent quartz deducted.[21] 4. Ferrian rutile (*nigrin*). Bernau, Bavaria.[22] 5. Tantalian rutile (*strüverite*). Ampangabé, Madagascar. Rem. is Al_2O_3 1.80.[23] 6. Tantalian rutile (*strüverite*). Perak, Malaya. Rem. is H_2O 0.50, SiO_2 0.20, MnO trace.[24] 7. Columbian rutile. Craveggia, Piedmont, Italy. Rem. is CaO 0.51, MgO 0.17, MnO trace. Average of two analyses.[25] 8. Columbian rutile (*ilmenorutile*). Ilmen Mts., Russia. Rem. is CaO.[25] 9. Columbian rutile (*ilmenorutile*). Iveland, southern Norway. Rem. is CaO 0.11, MgO trace.[25]

Var. *Ordinary.* Color brownish red and other shades, not black. G. 4.23 ± 0.02. *Sagenite* is the complexly reticulated, twinned, intergrowth of acicular crystals.[26] Dark smoky quartz penetrated with acicular rutile is apparently the *Veneris crinis* of Pliny (Flêches d'amour *Fr.* or Venus' hair-stone).

Ferrian.[17] Schwarzer Granat *Lampadius* (2, 119, 1797). Eisenhaltiges Titanerz *Klaproth* (2, 235, 1797) = Nigrin *Karsten* (56, 79, 1800). Color black. G. 4.2–4.4. Contains Fe^3 up to about 11 per cent (anal. 4) in substitution (?) for Ti (without significant amounts of [Ta,Cb]).

Tantalian. Strüverite *Hess* and *Wells* (*Am. J. Sc.*, 31, 432, 1911); *Crook* and *Johnstone* (*Min. Mag.*, 16, 224, 1912); *Lacroix* (*Bull. soc. min.*, 35, 194, 1912). Color black. G. 4.2–5.3. Contains Ta and usually Cb together with Fe^2 (anal. 6). Fe^2 is usually present in amounts approximately half the atomic (Ta + Cb) content.

Columbian. Ilmenorutile *Koksharov* (2, 352, 1854). Strüverite *Zambonini* (*Acc. Napoli, Rend.*, 8 [3], 35, 1907); *Prior* and *Zambonini* (*Min. Mag.*, 15, 78, 1908). Color black. G. 4.2–5.6. Contains Cb and usually Ta, with Cb > Ta in this variety (anal. 7, 8, 9). Fe^2 usually is present, in amounts approximately half the atomic (Cb + Ta) content.

Ferroan.? Iserite *Janovsky* (*Ak. Wien, Ber.*, 80, 34, 1886). Supposedly contains Fe^2, without significant amounts of (Ta, Cb), in substitution for Ti. Highly ferroan material has been reported. The validity of this variety is doubtful.

Tests. B.B. infusible. Turns black on heating to ca. 700° and the color is retained on cooling.[27] Insoluble in acids. Decomposed by fusion with an alkali or an alkali carbonate. Most material reacts for iron, also, less commonly, Ta, Cb, Cr, and Sn.

Occur.[28] Rutile is much more common than either anatase or brookite. The mineral is typically formed at high temperatures. Widespread in gneiss and schist, both as a minor rock constituent and especially as drusy crystals in veins of the so-called Alpine type. As an accessory mineral in igneous rocks, especially in plutonic rocks rich in hornblende; also in anorthosite (Roseland, Virginia). Also found in basic or granitic pegmatites; in crystalline limestones formed by regional or contact metamorphism; in high-temperature apatite veins (Norway) and in quartz veins and masses; in quartzite with kyanite, pyrophyllite, lazulite (Graves Mountain, Georgia). The so-called blue quartz[29] found in metamorphic and other rocks has a structural color, produced by minute needles of rutile. Microscopic needle-like crystals of rutile are extremely common as a product of reconstitution processes in clay and shales. A common detrital mineral. Some of the more notable localities are listed below.

In Norway in large amounts in apatite veins, especially at Fogne and other localities in the region of Gjerstadvand and Vegaardsheien; a columbian variety occurs in granite pegmatite at Evje, Iveland, and Tvedstrand in southern Norway; at Kragerö. At Horrsjöberg, Wermland, Sweden, with lazulite, pyrophyllite, and kyanite in quartzite. In the

Ekaterinburg district, Urals, in mica schist with beryl, phenakite, and chrysoberyl; a chrome-bearing rutile occurs with kammererite in chromite near Kassli, Urals; a columbian variety (*ilmenorutile*) is found with topaz, phenakite, albite, and microcline in pegmatite at several places in the neighborhood of Miask in the Ilmen Mountains. A ferroan (?) variety (*iserite*) is found in the black sands of the Iserwiese, Bohemia, and a ferrian variety (*nigrin*) at Bernau, Bavaria, and Oláhpian, Transylvania. In Styria especially at Modriach. Finely crystallized rutile has been found at many localities in the Alpine region of Switzerland, France, Italy, and in Germany. The mineral occurs as drusy crystals in crevice and vein deposits, mostly in metamorphic rocks, associated with quartz, epidote, adularia, albite, hematite, anatase, brookite, sphene, mica, chlorite, siderite, calcite, fluorite. Notable localities in Switzerland include Cavradi in Tavetsch; the Binnental, especially on Lercheltini Alp, in Valais; St. Gotthard, Uri. A tantalian and columbian variety occurs in pegmatite near Craveggia, Val Vigesso, Piedmont, Italy. In France in the region of Saint-Yrieix, Haute-Vienne, and at Gourdon, Saône-et-Loire. Found as rolled pebbles in the diamond gravels of Minas Geraes and Bahia, Brazil, including much of the material designated as "*favas*" (see beyond). In Madagascar near Ambatofinandrahana; tantalian varieties occur in pegmatite at Fefena and Ampangabé. At N'Dacire, French Congo. Tantalian rutile occurs with cassiterite in the Federated Malay States.

In the United States found in large amounts, in part well crystallized, and in pseudomorphs after brookite, at Magnet Cove, Arkansas. Fine specimens, including large multiple twins, have been obtained at Graves Mountain, Georgia, with lazulite, kyanite, and pyrophyllite in quartzite. Important deposits of rutile occur in central Virginia in Amherst and Nelson counties, notably at Roseland; the mineral is found disseminated in anorthosite, and with ilmenite and apatite in a pegmatite-like rock (nelsonite). Abundant in quartz veins on Shooting Creek, North Carolina; also well crystallized in pegmatites at many localities, especially at Stony Point, Alexander County, with green spodumene (hiddenite), dolomite, muscovite, apatite, beryl. Tantalian rutile containing tin occurs in pegmatite near Keystone, South Dakota. In the Red Ledge chromite mine, Washington district, Nevada County, California, containing chromium; at the andalusite mine near Laws, California, fine large crystals in pyrophyllite. At St. Urbain, near Baie St. Paul, Quebec, with sapphirine in an ilmenite-hematite deposit in anorthosite. Fine specimens of rutilated quartz come from West Hartford, Vermont, and Alexander County, North Carolina; Minas Geraes, Brazil; Madagascar; Val Tavetsch, Grisons, and elsewhere in Switzerland.

Alter. Observed as an alteration product of other titanium minerals, especially sphene and ilmenite, perovskite, and titanian magnetite; also, less commonly chevkinite, geikielite, hornblende, phlogopite, and titanian hematite. The yellowish to brown earthy material loosely designated as *leucoxene* (see beyond) is for the most part composed of rutile. Rutile occurs as paramorphs after both anatase and brookite, and has been observed altered to sphene and, in one instance, anatase.

Artif.[30]   A large number of syntheses have been reported. Obtained in crystals by the decomposition of $TiCl_4$ or TiF_4 at red heat, and by fusion of TiO_2 in borax, salt of phosphorus, or sodium tungstate; anatase or brookite may form instead at somewhat lower temperatures. Rutile is formed by ageing of gelatinous hydrous TiO_2 precipitated by hydrolysis of $TiCl_4$ or $Ti(NO_3)_4$; anatase ordinarily is formed by precipitation of tetravalent titanium salts by alkalies. Both anatase and brookite invert to rutile at high temperatures.[31]

Name.   Rutile from *rutilus, red, reddish,* in allusion to the usual color. Nigrin in allusion to the black color of this variety. Strüverite after Giovanni Strüver (1842–1915), Professor of Mineralogy in the University of Rome. Sagenite from σαγήνη, *net,* in allusion to the netlike character of the intergrown needles. Ilmenorutile from the occurrence in the Ilmen Mountains. Edisonite, a supposed orthorhombic polymorph of TiO_2, after the American inventor, Thomas A. Edison (1847–1931).

LEUCOXENE.   *Gümbel (Die paläolith. Eruptivgest,* Fichtelgebirg. 22, 1874).

A name loosely applied to dull, fine grained, yellowish to brown alteration products high in titanium. Found as an alteration product of sphene, ilmenite, perovskite, titanian magnetite, or other titanium minerals. The material consists in most instances of rutile;[32] also, less commonly, of anatase (which see), or sphene.

CHROMRUTILE.   *Gordon* and *Shannon (Am. Min.,* 13, 69, 1928).

Tetragonal (dipyramidal ?), with $c = 0.611$. Crystals prismatic or equant, with {001}, {010}, {110}, {120}, {111}, {114}, {144}. Color black, brilliant. Analysis gave: CaO 0.76, MgO 5.52, Al_2O_3 0.57, Fe_2O_3 0.80, Cr_2O_3 16.61, SiO_2 5.51, TiO_2 69.71, ign. loss 1.48, total 100.96. Found with kammererite in crevices in chromite at the Red Ledge mine, Washington district, Nevada County, California.

The analysis apparently represents a mixture of a chromian rutile with a silicate.

Ref.

1. Miller, *Phil. Mag.,* 17, 268 (1840). Prior and Zambonini, *Min. Mag.,* 15, 78 (1908) obtained $a : c = 1 : 0.6456$ with {010}, {110}, {111} on columbian and tantalian material from Italy; Ungemach, *Bull. soc. min.,* 39, 5 (1916), obtained $a : c = 1 : 0.6469$ on tantalian material from Madagascar.

2. Goldschmidt (7, 167, 1922), Siedel, *Jb. Min., Beil.-Bd.,* 38, 759 (1915); Palache, Davidson, and Goranson, *Am. Min.,* 15, 280 (1930). Rare or uncertain forms:

180	20·49·0	20·37·0	092	229	998	155	351
290	5·12·0	350	071	227	554	3·10·10	561
270	7·16·0	340	118	112	331	255	
380	490	450	117	223	441	122	
250	5·11·0	058	115	334	158	899	

3. Vegard, *Phil. Mag.,* 32, 65 (1916). See also Goldschmidt, *Vidensk. Skr., Mat.-Nat. Kl.,* no. 1, 17, 1926, for a discussion of the similarities in the structures of rutile and tapiolite.

4. See especially Rose, *Ann. Phys.,* 115, 643 (1862); Des Cloizeaux (2, 197, 1874), *Ann. chim. phys.,* 13, 436 (1845); vom Rath, *Niederrh. Ges. Bonn, Ber.,* 158, 1886, *Zs. Kr.,* 1, 13 (436); Haidinger, *Ak. Wien, Ber.,* 39, 5 (1860); Palache, Davidson, and Goranson (1930); on the structural interpretation of the twinning see Gliszczynski, *Zbl. Min.,* 181, 1940; on twinning in a tantalian variety from Madagascar see Lacroix, *Bull.*

soc. min., **35**, 185 (1912), and Ungemach (1916). On mechanical deformation and twinning see Mügge, *Jb. Min.*, **1**, 221 (1884); **1**, 147 (1886); **1**, 231 (1889).

5. See Goldschmidt and Schröder, *Beitr. Kryst. Min.*, **2**, 110 (1923), and Mügge, *Jb. Min., Beil.-Bd.*, **16**, 376 (1903).

6. Seligmann, *Zs. Kr.*, **1**, 340 (1877).

7. Pelikan, *Min. Mitt.*, **21**, 226 (1902).

8. See Mügge (1903).

9. See Pogue, *U. S. Nat. Mus. Proc.*, **39**, 571 (1911), and Mügge (1903); many different positions of orientation are developed.

10. Mügge (1884, 1886, 1889); *Cbl. Min.*, **72**, 1902.

11. Grün and Johnsen, *Cbl. Min.*, 366, 1917; see also Weber, *ibid.*, 353, 1919.

12. For data on the color and composition of rutile see Traube, *Jb. Min., Beil.-Bd.*, **10**, 472 (1895); Wöhler and Kraatz-Koschlau, *Min. Mitt.*, **18**, 447 (1899).

13. Mallard, *Ann. mines*, **10**, 134 (1876); von Lasaulx, *Zs. Kr.*, **8**, 67 (1883).

14. Schröder, *Zs. Kr.*, **67**, 485 (1928) by prism method on unanalyzed material from an unknown locality. Determinations of the indices by the prism method also have been made by Barić, *Glas. Hrvatsh. Priro. Drustva*, 101, 1929–36 — *Jb. Min.*, **1**, 472, 1936; Bärwald, *Zs. Kr.*, **7**, 168 (1882); Lincio, *Acc. Torino Att.*, **39**, 995 (1904); Ites (Inaug. Diss., Göttingen, 1903); Brun, *Bull. soc. min.*, **54**, 191 (1931); Taubert (Inaug. Diss., Jena, 1905) — *Zs. Kr.*, **44**, 313 (1907). Larsen gives O (?) $= 2.50 \pm 0.03$ for a tantalian rutile analyzed by Hess and Wells, *Am. J. Sc.*, **31**, 432 (1911).

15. For Sn see Hess and Wells, *Am. J. Sc.*, **31**, 432 (1911), Friedel and Grandjean, *Bull. soc. min.*, **32**, 52 (1909); for Cr see Quensel, *Geol. För. Förh.*, **34**, 490 (1912); Ekeberg, *Ak. Stockholm, Handl.*, 46, 1803, Arzruni, *Zs. Kr.*, **8**, 330 (1883), Watson, *Am. Min.*, **7**, 185 (1922), Gordon and Shannon, *Am. Min.*, **13**, 69 (1928); for V see Quensel (1912), Hasselberg, *Astrophys. J.*, **6**, 22 (1897), **9**, 143 (1899), Deville, *C. R.*, **53**, 161 (1861), Watson (1922); for Sc see Fowler in Crook and Johnstone, *Min. Mag.*, **16**, 224 (1912).

16. Some analyses clearly have an excess of FeO; with $X = 0.2$ there is about 12 per cent of FeO (see anal. 9). See also Eakins anal. in Smith, *Colorado Sc. Soc., Proc.*, **2**, 175 (1887); Janovsky (1886); Müller, *J. pr. Chem.*, **58**, 183 (1853). Since the purity of analysis material is often not stated, some of the FeO may be due to admixed ilmenite. See further, Watson, *Am. Min.*, **7**, 185 (1922), and von Lasaulx, *Zs. Kr.*, **8**, 54 (1883).

17. The Fe^3 may be held in a defect lattice; if the O is deficient the formula is $Ti_{1-x}Fe^3_2O_{(4-x)/2}$; if the O remains fixed, the formula is $Ti_{(4-3x)/4}Fe^3_2O_2$ with $Ti + Fe > 1$.

18. For additional analyses see Doelter (3 [1], 16, 1918).

19. Barić (1936).

20. Pfeil (Inaug. Diss., Heidelberg, 1901) — *Cbl. Min.*, 144, 1902.

21. Genth anal. in Genth and Penfield, *Am. J. Sc.*, **44**, 381 (1892).

22. Rammelsberg (169, 1875).

23. Pisani anal. in Lacroix, *Bull. soc. min.*, **35**, 194 (1912).

24. Johnstone anal. in Crook and Johnstone (1912).

25. Prior anal. in Prior and Zambonini (1908).

26. The name sagenite is also given to transparent quartz containing acicular or capillary crystals of rutile.

27. Schröder (1928).

28. For lengthy list of additional occurrences see Hintze (1 [2A], 1592, 1906).

29. Jaydraman, *Proc. Indian Ac. Sc.*, **9**, 265 (1939).

30. See Doelter (3 [1], 23, 1918), Weiser, **2**, 257 (1934); Chudoba and Wisfeld, *Cbl. Min.*, 323, 1933; Merwin and Hostetter, *Am. Min.*, **4**, 126 (1919).

31. Schröder (1928); Bunting, *J. Res. Nat. Bur. Stand.*, **11**, 719 (1933).

32. Tyler and Marsden, *J. Sed. Petrol.*, **8**, 55 (1938); also Frondel (priv. comm., 1941) from an x-ray powder study of numerous specimens.

33. See Williamson, *Min. Mag.*, **25**, 513 (1940).

FAVA is a miner's term for various minerals found in the diamond gravels of Brazil as rolled pebbles resembling a bean in size and shape. (The name is derived from the Portuguese word for a bean.) Most favas consist of rutile, others of baddeleyite, zircon, or various phosphates. The name *paredrite* was proposed[1] to designate those favas composed of TiO_2 (often with a little water). The so-called *captivos*[2] from Brazil and the Urals are favas consisting of rutile as paramorph after anatase. Both names are given in allusion to the association with diamonds, paredrite from πάρεδρος, *sitting beside*, and *captivos* because they accompany the diamond as slaves do a master.

Ref.

1. Farrington, *Am. J. Sc.*, **41**, 356 (1916).
2. For descriptions of captivos and other favas see Bauer, *Jb. Min.*, I, 232, 1891; Hussak, *Min. Mitt.*, **18**, 335 (1899); Damour, *Soc. géol. France Bull.*, **13**, 550 (1856).

DOELTERITE. *Lacroix* (*Nouv. arch. mus. hist. nat. Paris*, **5** [5], 334, 1913).
A colloidal hydrous form of TiO_2 supposedly present in laterite.[1] Named after Cornelio August Doelter (1850–1930), mineral chemist, and formerly Professor of Mineralogy at the universities of Graz and Vienna.

Ref.

1. For description of colloidal hydrous TiO_2 see Weiser (**2**, 257, 1935).

MICAULTITE. *de Limur* (*Cat. minéraux du Morbihan*, 38, Vannes, 1883 — *Min. Mag.*, **16**, 404, 1907).
An earthy, brick-red, decomposition product of rutile, which is suggested may be an aluminous hydrorutile. Presumably named after Victor Micault, of Paris.

4512 P Y R O L U S I T E [MnO_2]. Lapis manganensis pt. *Caesalpinus* (*Metall.*, 1596). Brunsten = Magnesia pt. *Wallerius* (268, 1747); Manganese pt. *Wallerius* (1, 483, 1753). Manganaise grise pt. *Forster* (1772). Molybdaenum Magnesii *Linnaeus*. Grau Braunstein pt. *Werner* (*Bergm. J.*, 386, 1789), *Hausmann* (288, 1813). Gray Oxyd of Manganese pt.; Anhydrous Binoxyd of Manganese. Mangan Hyperoxyd *Leonhard* (204, 1826). Pyrolusite, Prismatic Manganese-Ore *Haidinger* (*Roy. Soc. Edinburgh, Trans.*, **11**, 136, 1827). Weichbraunstein, Weichmangan *Germ.* Peroxide of manganese. Manganese dioxide. Varvicite *Phillips* (*Phil. Mag.*, **6**, 281, 1829; **7**, 284, 1830). Lichtes Graumanganerz *Breithaupt* (231, 1832). Polianite *Breithaupt* (*Ann. Phys.*, **61**, 191, 1844). Pseudomanganite *Fermor* (*Geol. Sur. India, Mem.*, **37** [I], 78, 1909). Manganomelane pt. *Klockmann* (422, 1922).

C r y s t. Tetragonal; ditetragonal dipyramidal — $4/m\ 2/m\ 2/m$.[1]

$$a : c = 1 : 0.6647;^2 \qquad p_0 : r_0 = 0.6647 : 1$$

Forms:[2]

		ϕ	ρ	A	$\overline{M}$
a	010	0°00′	90°00′	90°00′	45°00′
m	110	45 00	90 00	45 00	90 00
h	120	26 34	90 00	63 26	71 34
e	011	0 00	33 36½	90 00	66 57½
g	021	0 00	53 03	90 00	55 35½
s	111	45 00	43 14	61 02	90 00
n	221	45 00	61 59½	51 22	90 00
z	231	33 41½	67 21	59 12½	79 33½

Structure cell.[3] Space group $P4/mnm$; a_0 4.38, c_0 2.85; $a_0 : c_0 = 1 : 0.651$; contains Mn_2O_4.

Habit. Rarely in large well-developed crystals (polianite), long to short prismatic [001] or equant. In composite subparallel groupings of minute crystals, resulting in a rough large crystal; also forming the outer shell of crystals of manganite Usually massive columnar or fibrous and often divergent (pyrolusite); in reniform coatings and in concretionary forms; granular to powdery massive; as dendritic growths on fracture surfaces or enclosed in chalcedony (moss agate). Pseudomorphs after manganite are common.

Twinning.[5] Rare, repeated twins with twin planes {031} and {032}. Polysynthetic twinning has been observed in polished section.

P h y s. Cleavage {110}, perfect. Fracture uneven. Brittle. H. 6–6½ (crystals), 2–6 (massive). The fibrous or pulverulent material often soils the fingers. G. 5.06 ± 0.02 (crystals), 4.4–5.0 (massive); 5.24 (calc.). Luster metallic. Color light steel-gray or iron-gray in crystals, inclining to dark steel-gray or iron-black, sometimes bluish, in massive material. Streak black or bluish black, sometimes submetallic. Opaque.

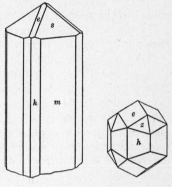

Platten, Bohemia.

In polished section[6] cream-white in color with distinct anisotropism and very weak pleochroism. Reflection percentages (crystal from Platten): green 34, orange 32.5, red 27.5. Sometimes exhibits polysynthetic twinning.

C h e m. Manganese dioxide, MnO_2. Mn 63.19, O 36.81, total 100.00. Capillary and adsorbed water is usually present in amounts up to several per cent.[7] Mn^2 is often reported in pseudomorphs after manganite (anal. 3) and no doubt is due to unaltered residua of that mineral. Small amounts of heavy metals, PO_4, alkalies (see lithiophorite and ebelmenite) and alkaline earths, notably Ba, may be present as adsorbed or admixed impurities. Ba, especially when present in amounts over a per cent or so, may be due to mechanically admixed psilomelane or hollandite. Massive varieties frequently contain admixed limonite, clay, silica, or other manganese minerals.

Anal.[8]

	1	2	3	4
MnO_2	98.72	.....	94.30	.....
MnO	.....	80.35	2.25	78.20
O	.....	17.75	.....	17.40
Fe_2O_3	} 0.09	} 0.35	0.22	.....
Al_2O_3			0.14	.....
BaO	.....	.....	0.33	0.95
CaO	.....	0.25	0.08	0.30
MgO	.....	0.05	.....	0.05
SiO_2	.....	.....	0.64	.....
P_2O_5	.....	trace	0.52	0.10
H_2O	0.91	0.35	1.75	1.70
Rem.	0.23	0.90	.....	1.60
Total	99.95	100.00	100.23	100.30
G.	4.91	5.08	4.748	4.96

1. Platten, Bohemia (polianite). Rem. is insol. 0.23.[9] 2. Platten, Bohemia (polianite). Rem. is insol. 0.25, SO_3 0.30, CO_2 0.10, alkalies 0.20, PbO and CuO 0.05.[10]

3. Woodstock, Va. (pseudomorph after manganite). H₂O includes $H_2O + 1.53$, $H_2O - 0.22$.[11] 4. Giessen, Germany (radial fibrous). Rem. is insol. 0.90, CO_2 trace, alkalies 0.10, PbO and CuO 0.60.[10]

Var. *Ordinary.* (Pyrolusite.) Massive; fibrous or columnar; in concretionary forms; pseudomorphs; etc.

Crystallized. (Polianite.) Coarsely crystallized material (from Platten, Bohemia). Relatively hard with superior density, and anhydrous.

O c c u r.[12] Pyrolusite is one of the most common manganese minerals. It is apparently always formed under highly oxidizing conditions. The chief types of occurrence are as a bog, lacustrine, or shallow marine deposit, in the oxidized zone of manganiferous ore deposits and rocks, and as deposits formed by circulating meteoric waters. Colloidal processes undoubtedly play a major role in the transportation and deposition of pyrolusite. Bacterial action also is important.[13] Associated minerals are other manganese and iron oxides and hydrous oxides, and include hausmannite, manganite, braunite, psilomelane, chalcophanite, limonite, hematite, goethite.

Only a few of the more important localities can be mentioned. In Germany mined at Elgersburg, Thuringia, and at Vorderehrensdorf, near Mährisch-Trübau, Moravia; at Siegen as an alteration of manganoan siderite and with manganite at Horhausen, Rhine Province; at Giessen and in the Odenwald, Hesse; at Johanngeorgenstadt, Saxony. Large crystals (*polianite*) occur at Platten, Bohemia. At Macskamezö, Transylvania, as fine pseudomorphs after manganite. At several localities in Andalusia and Catalonia, Spain. With rhodochrosite at Las Cabesses, Ariège, France, and on the island Groix, Morbihan. Many large deposits are found in the U.S.S.R., notably at Kutais, Transcaucasus, where the pisolitic mineral occurs interbedded in Eocene marine sediments. Pyrolusite ores formed by combined weathering and replacement of pre-Cambrian rocks containing manganese silicates are extensively distributed in India,[14] and similar deposits occur on the Gold Coast, Africa, and in Minas Geraes and São Paulo, Brazil. Residual manganese deposits are widely scattered in Cuba and Central America.

In the United States small deposits mostly of the bog ore type are widely distributed in New England: localities include Brandon, Bennington, Monkton, and Irasberg in Vermont; Conway, Plainfield, and West Stockbridge, Massachusetts; Salisbury and Kent, Connecticut; Winchester, New Hampshire. Residual deposits occur at a number of localities in the Appalachian region. In Virginia notably at the Crimora and Old Dominion mines in Augusta County, and in a large deposit, partly as pseudomorphs after manganite, at Powells Fort, Shenandoah County. In Georgia in the Cartersville district, Bartow County, and in the Cave Spring district. In Tennessee near Elizabethton, Carter County. High-grade residual ores occur in the Batesville district, Arkansas. Small deposits occur in central Texas in Mason, Llano, and San Saba counties as weathering products of schists containing manganese silicates. Pyrolusite ores derived by the weathering of manganoan siderite were worked in the oxidized zone at Leadville, Colorado. In the Phillipsburg district, Montana, and in the oxidized zone at Butte, Silver Bow County, where the mineral was derived from manganiferous carbonates. At Happy Creek, Warren County, Nevada. In the Cuyuna range, Minnesota, with manganite. Found disseminated in sandstone at Argyle, Custer County, South Dakota. In the Tres Hermanos district, New Mexico. A large bog ore deposit occurs at Hillsborough, New Brunswick, Canada, and deposits are found elsewhere in New Brunswick and in Nova Scotia.

Alter. Manganite alters readily to pyrolusite, and perfect pseudomorphs after crystals of manganite are common. Some pyrolusite deposits are largely secondary after manganite. Also observed as an alteration product of rhodonite, alabandite, manganosite, hausmannite, braunite, huebnerite, rhodochrosite, and manganoan siderite and calcite. Pseudomorphs are often observed of pyrolusite after calcite, dolomite, rhodochrosite, and siderite; also, less commonly, after fluorite, aragonite, barite, smithsonite.

Artif. Obtained in small crystals by slow decomposition of $Mn(NO_3)_2$ at $154°$ and reduced pressure.[15] Also as a fine powder by oxidation of manganous salts with oxidizing agents such as $KClO_3$, HNO_3 or ozone; by reduction of permanganates with H_2O_2, K oxalate, etc., and by hydrolysis of tetravalent manganese salts.

Colloidal hydrous MnO_2 is easily prepared.[16] The sol is negatively charged and readily peptized by dilute alkalies. Humic acids and other organic materials have a protecting effect.

Name. Pyrolusite from πῦρ, *fire*, and λούειν, *to wash*, because used to discharge the brown and green (FeO) tints of glass. Polianite, from πολιαίνεσθαι, *to become gray*, refers to the color.

Ref.

1. The symmetry of polianite was established as tetragonal by Dana and Penfield, *Am. J. Sc.*, **35**, 243 (1888), and was later confirmed as such by the x-ray studies of Ferrari, *Acc. Linc., Att.*, **3**, 224 (1926), and others. The identity of polianite and pyrolusite, long-considered distinct species, is proven by the x-ray studies of St. John, *Phys. Rev.*, **21**, 389 (1923), Ferrari (1926) and Vaux, *Min. Mag.*, **24**, 521 (1937), and by the convergence of physical and chemical properties attending variation in crystal size. See also Koechlin, *Cbl. Min.*, 108, 1932, Schneiderhöhn and Ramdohr (**2**, 508, 1931), Orcel and Pavlovitch, *Bull. soc. min.*, **54**, 123 (1931), and Lacroix (**3**, 235, 1911).
2. Dana and Penfield (1888) on polianite from Bohemia.
3. Ferrari (1926). A dimorphous modification of MnO_2 has been reported by Dubois, *Ann. chim. phys.*, **5**, 411 (1936), as an artificial product.
4. See Watson and Wherry, *Washington Ac. Sc., J.*, **8**, 550 (1918) and Koechlin, *Min. Mitt.*, **9**, 34 (1887); *Cbl. Min.*, 108, 1932.
5. Rosati and Steinmetz, *Zs. Kr.*, **53**, 394 (1914).
6. Schneiderhöhn and Ramdohr (1931), Orcel and Pavlovitch (1931), Thiel, *Econ. Geol.*, **19**, 107 (1924).
7. Vapor pressure studies indicate that MnO_2 does not form definite hydrates, and that the water content is a function of the physical character, age and conditions of drying of the material; see Weiser (**2**, 323, 1935).
8. For many additional analyses see Dana (243, 1892) and Doelter (**3** [2], 854, 1926). In the past many analyses of pyrolusite have been classed under psilomelane.

9. Krüll, *Chem. Erde*, **7**, 473 (1932).
10. Gorgeu, *Bull. soc. min.*, **16**, 96 (1893).
11. Gooch anal. in Watson and Wherry, *Washington Ac. Sc., J.*, **8**, 550 (1918).
12. The conditions of solution, transportation and deposition of manganese minerals in nature are discussed by Savage, *Econ. Geol.*, **31**, 278 (1936).
13. Thiel, *Econ. Geol.*, **20**, 301 (1925).
14. See Fermor, *Geol. Sur. India, Mem.*, **37**, 1909.
15. Gorgeu, *Zs. Kr.*, **4**, 408 (1880).
16. See Weiser (**2**, 323, 1935).

CALVONIGRITE. *Laspeyres* (*J. pr. Chem.*, **13**, 226, 1876).

A black finely fibrous stalactitic material. Streak brownish black. H. $5\frac{1}{2}$. G. 4.36.
Analysis gave: MnO 67.87, O 13.66, MgO 0.20, CaO 0.10, CoO 0.47, CuO 1.15, BaO 0.20, Al$_2$O$_3$ 6.32, Fe$_2$O$_3$ 3.77, SiO$_2$ 0.36, K$_2$O 0.38, Na$_2$O 0.39, Li$_2$O 0.21, H$_2$O 6.42, total 101.50. Found at Kalteborn, near Eiserfeld, Siegen, Germany. The name is a latinization of the German term *Schwarzer Glaskopf*.

Probably a mixture of pyrolusite with hydrous iron and aluminum oxides.

4513 **WAD**

The name *wad* is here applied as a field or generic term to substances whose chief constituent is a hydrous manganese oxide and whose true identity is unknown. Wad thus stands much in the same relation to the well-defined manganese oxides that limonite has to the iron oxides and bauxite has to the aluminum oxides. The substances included under the name are largely mixtures, probably chiefly of pyrolusite and, in Ba-rich material, psilomelane.

A. **Ordinary.** Bog Manganese. Magnesia friabilis terriformis *Cronstedt* (105, 1758). Earthy Ocher of Manganese, Black Wad pt. *Kirwan* (1784, 1796). Schwarz Braunsteinerz, Manganschaum *Karsten* (1808). Brauner Eisenrahm *Werner*. Ouatite *Huot* (241, 1841). Groroilite *Berthier* (*Ann. chim. phys.*, **51**, 19, 1832). Pelagite *Church* (*Min. Mag.*, **1**, 50, 1876). Vod *Ital.* Schwarzer Glaskopf pt. *Germ.* Manganomelane pt., *Klockmann* (422, 1922). Hydrohausmannite, Hydromanganite, Hydrobraunite, Hydroxybraunite, etc. *Boldyrev* (97, Pt. 2, 1928).

B. **Cobaltian.** Asbolite. Asbolan. Cobaltum nigrum *Agricola* (459, 1529). Svart Kobolt-Jord, Minerale Cobalti terrea fuliginea *Wallerius* (235, 1747). Kobalt-Mulm, Ochra Cobaltea nigra *Cronstedt* (211, 1758). Kobolt-Erde, Schwarzer Erdkobalt, Russkobalt, Kobaltmanganerz *Germ.* Earthy Cobalt, Black Cobalt Ocher. Cobalt oxydé noir *Haüy* (4, 1801). Kakochlor *Breithaupt* (240, 1832; 896, 1847). Asbolan *Breithaupt* (332, 1847). Aithalite *Adam* (78, 1869). Cupro-asbolane *de Leenheer* (*Ann. Service Mines*, Katanga, **8**, 32, 1938).

C. **Cuprian.** Lampadite. Kupfermangan *Lampadius* (**2**, 70, 1817). Kupfermanganerz *Breithaupt* (in *Hoffmann* [**4b**, 201, 1818]). Cupreous Manganese. Kupferschwärze pt. *Germ.* Pelokonit *Richter* (*Ann. Phys.*, **21**, 591, 1831). Lampadite *Huot* (238, 1841). Lepidophäit *Weisbach* (*Jb. Min.*, II, 109, 1880); Schaumiges Wad. Lubeckite *Morozewicz* (*Ak. Krakau, Int. Bull.* [A], 185, 1918).

D. **Ferrian.** Reissacherit *Haidinger* (*Geol. Reichsanst., Jb.*, **7**, 609, 1856). Rhabdionit, Rabdionit *von Kobell* (*Ak. München, Ber.*, 46, 1870). Anomalite *Koenig* (*Am. Inst. Min. Eng.*; 1876). Skemmatite *Ford* and *Bradley* (*Am. J. Sc.*, **36**, 169, 1913). Brostenite *Poni* (*Ann. Sc. Univ. Jassy*, **1**, 15, 1900 — *Zs. Kr.*, **36**, 198, 1902); *Butureanu* (*Ann. Sc. Univ. Jassy*, **5**, 1908; **7**, 1912; *Bull. soc. min.*, **40**, 164, 1917).

E. **Aluminian.** Manganoxydaluminit *Lehmann* (*Taschenb. theor. Chem.*, 132, 1851).

F. **Plumbian.** Wackenrodite *Adam* (76, 1869); *Wackenroder* (*Kastner's Arch.*, **14**, 269, 1828).

***G.* Lithian.** Allophytin *Breithaupt.* Lithiophorite *Frenzel* (*J. pr. Chem.*, **2**, 203, 1870; **4**, 353, 1871; *Jb. Min.*, 55, 1879). Lithionpsilomelane *Laspeyres* (*J. pr. Chem.*, **13**, 2, 1876).

P h y s. Found in earthy or compact masses; reniform, concretionary, also incrusting or as stains. Ordinarily without internal structure, but sometimes fine fibrous, banded or scaly. Usually very soft, soiling the fingers; less often hard to H. $6\frac{1}{2}$. G. 2.8–4.4; but often loosely aggregated, or porous, and feeling very light to the hand. Luster dull. Color black, bluish or brownish black. Streak black, bluish or brownish black, reddish brown, liver-brown.

C h e m. No single or definite composition can be attributed to the materials here loosely grouped. Predominantly an oxide of manganese, with from ca. 3 to 25 per cent water and with BaO up to 10 per cent or more. Commonly admixed with the hydrous oxides of Co, Cu, Fe[3], Al and sometimes with constitutional or adsorbed alkalies, especially Li; V is present in some wads. Analyses are chiefly of technical interest.[1]

Anal.

	1	2	3	4	5	6	
K_2O	0.61	....	....	.....	.....	.....	.....
Na_2O	0.31	1.22	....	.....	.....	.....	.....
Li_2O	....	....	....	.....	.....	.....	.....
CaO	1.32	6.69	....	0.32	0.75	.....	.....
MgO	0.54	0.66	....	0.24	2.33	.....	.....
BaO	9.53	0.37	....	.....	0.55	.....	.....
CuO	0.05	....	....	0.17	18.68	11.48	14.0
CoO	0.10	....	....	8.33	4.70	.....	5.1
NiO	0.10	....	....	2.82	.....	.....	.....
MnO	3.59	4.62	62.4	49.93	26.31	9.59	7.61
MnO_2	61.38	62.03	....	.....	.....	58.77	.....
O	....	....	12.8	11.09	5.16	.....	.....
Al_2O_3	2.91	0.27	} 6.0	6.28	.....	.....	1.4
Fe_2O_3	5.86	3.59		4.39	8.10	.....	45.0
SiO_2	3.40	....		1.79	.....	.....	.....
H_2O	9.85	11.21	15.8	11.51	19.40	21.05	13.5
Insol.	....	9.75	3.0	.....	15.60	.....	.....
Rem.	0.491	....	....	.....	.....	.....	13.0
Total	100.041	100.41	100.0	96.87	101.58	100.89	99.61
G.					2.95	2.95	2.80

1. Wad. Kodur, Vizagapatam district, India. Rem. is ZnO 0.15, TiO_2 0.02, S 0.048, P_2O_5 0.261, As_2O_5 0.012.[2] 2. Wad. Kertsch Peninsula, U.S.S.R.[3] 3. Groroilite. Groroi, Mayenne, France.[4] 4. Cobaltian wad. New Caledonia.[5] 5. Cuprian wad. Chile.[6] 6. Lepidophaeite. Kamsdorf, Silesia.[7] 7. Rhabdionite. Nizhne Tagilsk, Urals. Rem. is Mn_2O_3.[8]

	8	9	10	11	12	13	14
K_2O	0.44	3.38	0.73	.....	.....	.....	.....
Na_2O	1.20	0.84	.....	.....	.....	.....	.....
Li_2O	0.35	0.48	1.23	.....	.....	.....	.....
CaO	trace	0.26	trace	.....	6.10	0.8	.....
MgO	.....	0.08	.....	.....	1.00	.....	.....
BaO	3.12	.....	2.78	.....	.....	.....	.....
CuO	.....	0.08	1.74	.....	1.56	5.41	20.79
CoO	1.76	0.12	}2.42	.....	17.30	1.4	.....
NiO	0.32	trace		.....	.....	11.8	.....
MnO	5.84	75.74	55.12	11.88	40.50	.....	}38.67
MnO_2	56.54	.....	.....	35.06	.....	23.6	
O	.....	14.66	10.28	.....	10.04	.....	
Al_2O_3	7.83	2.53	10.54	.....	}2.50	9.8	} 5.04
Fe_2O_3	2.20	0.17	1.48	9.22		2.7	
SiO_2	7.68	0.13	.....	.....	.....	.....	.....
H_2O	11.40	3.76	12.64	12.46	19.12	24.5	11.51
Insol.	.....	.....	.....	.....	2.20	2.95	6.88
Rem.	1.38	.....	trace	30.28	.....	14.7	13.40
Total	100.06	102.23	98.96	98.90	100.32	97.66	96.29
G.	4.2–4.3	4.328	3.36	3.51		2.985	2.37

8. Lithian wad. Appalachian Park, Tenn. Rem. is P_2O_5 0.49, SO_3 0.89.[9] 9. Lithian wad. Salm Chateau, Belgium. Average of 2 analyses.[10] 10. Lithian wad (lithiophorite). Schneeberg region, Saxony. Rem. is Bi_2O_3 trace.[11] 11. Plumbian wad. Sardinia. Rem. is PbO.[12] 12. Cobaltian wad. Lemhi Co., Id.[16] 13. Wad. Kara-Chagyr, Fergana, U.S.S.R. Rem. is ZnO 10.4, V_2O_5 4.3, H_2O^+ 19.9, H_2O^- 4.6.[18] 14. Cupro-asbolane. Kambove, Katanga, Belgian Congo. Rem. is Co_2O_3. Mn given as Mn_2O_3.[19]

The following are the chief varieties based on the nature of the accessory elements.

A. Ordinary. Bog Manganese. Consists mainly of hydrous manganese oxide (anal. 1–3).

Pelagite is a name given to manganese nodules found in deep sea deposits.[17] Structure concretionary, consisting of concentric layers with a nucleus composed of clay, pumice, teeth, or bone fragments. Fragile. Color brownish black. The analyses vary widely, and the material often is largely admixed with clay.

Groroilite (anal. 3) was found as roundish cavernous masses of a brownish black color and chocolate streak at Groroi (Grazay), Mayenne, France.

B. Cobaltian. Asbolite. Asbolan. Wad containing CoO, often together with NiO and CuO (anal. 4, 5, 7, 10, 12, 13), and grading presumably through admixture into heterogenite or other cobalt oxides.

Kakochlor from Rengersdorf, Silesia, also contains Li_2O and relatively large amounts of Fe_2O_3 and Al_2O_3.

Asbolan originally came from Kamsdorf, Thuringia. The name has since been more or less generally applied to cobaltian wads.

Cupro-asbolane is a cobaltian and cuprian wad from Katanga, Belgian Congo (anal. 14).

C. Cuprian. Lampadite. Wad containing CuO, sometimes up to 25 per cent, and often CoO and Fe_2O_3 also (anal. 5, 6, 7, 10, 13). The CuO in most instances is no doubt due to admixed tenorite, and with increasing admixture the material graduates into melaconite.

Pelokonite (anal. 5) is a brownish black material with a liver-brown streak found with malachite at Tierra Amarilla and Remolinos, Chile.

Lepidophaeite (anal. 6) is a very soft, fine fibrous or scaly material with a silky or dull luster. Color and streak reddish brown. From Kamsdorf, Silesia.

Lubeckite, from Miedzianka, Poland, is a cuprian and cobaltian wad found with malachite and native silver. In black spherules or botryoidal aggregates.

Lampadite originally came from Schlaggenwald, Bohemia. The name has since been extended to cuprian wads in general.

D. Ferrian. Small amounts of Fe_2O_3 are usually present in wad, and with increasing admixture the material grades into goethite or limonite.

Reissacherite is a radioactive and rather flocculent wad from Gastein, Salzburg, Tirol.

Rhabdionite (anal. 7) was found as soft black stalactitic and rodlike forms at Nizhne Tagilsk, Urals, and contains rather large amounts of CuO and CoO.

Anomalite is a name applied to pithlike pseudomorphs of iron and manganese oxides, with minor cobalt and nickel oxide, after jeffersonite at Sterling Hill, New Jersey.

Skemmatite is a mixture of iron and manganese oxides found as an alteration product of pyroxmangite near Iva, Anderson County, South Carolina, and Ada County, Idaho.

Brostenite occurs as irregular masses or coating derived by the alteration of carbonates of iron and manganese at various places near Brosteni, Sucéva, Roumania. Analyses[13] and physical properties indicate that the material is largely pyrolusite, admixed with iron oxide and undecomposed manganoan and ferroan carbonates.

E. Aluminian. Wad containing relatively large amounts of Al_2O_3 (cf. anal. 4, 8, 10), presumably due to admixture with gibbsite or other hydrous aluminum oxides.

F. Plumbian. *Wackenrodite* from Schapbach, Baden, contains ca. 12 per cent Pb. A similar substance (anal. 11) occurs between Bosa and Montresta, Sardinia.

G. Lithian. Alkalian. Wad containing a per cent or so of Li_2O, usually with Na_2O and K_2O in addition, has often been reported (cf. anal. 8, 9, 10). Some of this material contains relatively large amounts of Al_2O_3.

Lithiophorite (anal. 10) was originally found at various localities in the Schneeberg district, Saxony. It occurred as fine scales, also compact, botryoidal. H. 3. G. 3.14–3.36. Luster dull to metallic. Color bluish black. Streak blackish gray.

H. Tungstenian. Wad formed as a hot spring deposit near the Uncia tin mine, central Bolivia, contains BaO and ca. 0.5 per cent WO_3; a similar hot spring deposit near Golconda, Nevada, contains several per cent BaO and 2.78 per cent WO₃.[14]

Occur. Wad is formed under oxidizing conditions at ordinary temperatures and pressures as a direct chemical or biogenic precipitate or as an alteration product of manganese minerals. Colloidal processes doubtlessly play an important role in the formation of the material. Wad occurs typically as a bog or lake deposit, in clays and in shallow marine sediments, in the oxidized portions of ore deposits, and as a residual weathering product in areas of manganiferous rocks.

Wad is a common substance and includes many of the occurrences formerly ascribed to pyrolusite and psilomelane. Only a few localities will be mentioned here. In Germany in the manganese ore region of Ilmenau and Elgersburg-Öhrenstock in Thuringia; at Ilfeld in the Harz; at a number of localities in the Siegen region, Rhine Province; at Hüttenberg and Lölling, Carinthia; in the region of Heidelberg, in the Black Forest; at Gastein in the Tirol (*reissacherite*). In Norway at Flatdal, Telemarken, and at Idsö east of Stavanger. In the region of Smyrna, Turkey. Large deposits occur in the U.S.S.R. in the Government Kutais, Transcaucasus, in Eocene marine sediments; a wad containing V, Cu, Ni, and Zn (anal. 13) occurs with a nickel vanadate at Kara-Chagyr, Fergana, U.S.S.R. In France at Romanèche, Saône-et-Loire, and at Groroi (Grazay), Mayenne (*groroïlite*). At Leadhills, Scotland. Wad is widely distributed in the manganese deposits of the Central Provinces and elsewhere in India. Abundantly in the Queluz district, Minas Geraes, Brazil. In Cuba at numerous localities in Santiago de Cuba, Oriente, Santa Clara and other provinces. Deposits of wad are widely distributed in the United States.[15] Many deposits are found in the Piedmont and Appalachian regions, notably in the James River-Staunton River regions of Virginia, in the Shady Valley and Newport regions of northeastern Tennessee, and the Cave Spring and Cartersville districts of Georgia. Large deposits are found in the Batesville district, Arkansas. Found abundantly in oxidized ores in the Leadville district, Colorado, and in the Wickes area and Butte district, Montana. In California in the Livermore-Tesla district. In Mason, Llano, and San Saba counties, Texas. In Canada abundant at Hillsborough, New Brunswick, and in the Minas Basin, Nova Scotia.

Cobaltian wad often occurs associated with erythrite, annabergite, and ill-defined hydrous oxides of Co and Ni as an alteration product of smaltite and other cobalt and nickel minerals. Found in Germany at Schweina and Kamsdorf, Thuringia; at Gerbstadt, Harz; abundantly in the Schneeberg region, Saxony; at Rengersdorf, near Görlitz, Silesia (*kakochlor*); at Markirch, Alsace. On Capo Calamita, Elba. At Chalanches, France. In Russia at Nizhne Tagilsk (*rhabdionite*) and Reoda, in Siberia. Cobaltian wad occurs abundantly in New Caledonia, associated with garnierite as residual deposits on peridotite containing disseminated Co and Ni minerals. At Katanga, Belgian Congo (*cupro-asbolane*). At Ambatafangehana, Madagascar. Found in the United States at Mine la Motte, Missouri (sometimes with ca. 11 per cent NiO); at Silver Bluff, South Carolina (ca. 24 per cent CoO); in the Blackbird district, Lehmi County, Idaho.

Cuprian wad is commonly associated with tenorite, chrysocolla, malachite, and azurite. Found in Germany at Kamsdorf, Thuringia (*lepidophaeite*); at Lauterberg in the Harz; at Schlaggenwald, Bohemia (*lampadite*). At Tierra Amarilla and Remolinos (*pelokonite*) in Atacama, and at Huiquintipa, Tarapaca, in Chile. At Miedzianka, west of Kielce, Poland (*lubeckite*).

Lithian wad is not uncommon. Lithian and cobaltian wad occurs near Saalfeld, Thuringia, and Rengersdorf, Silesia. In the Erzebirge, Saxony, at Eibenstock, Schneeberg and Andreasberg; at Epprechtstein, Vordorf and Köhlerloh in the Fichtelgebirge; at Trochenberg, near Tarnowitz, Silesia. In Belgium at Salm Chateau, and in the United States at Appalachian Park, Virginia.

Alter. Wad (see also under psilomelane) is a common alteration product of rhodochrosite, manganoan siderite, rhodonite, tephroite, spessartite, and other manganese minerals. The material has been found pseudomorphous after calcite, dolomite, rhodochrosite, manganite, fluorite, barite, and, rarely, after mimetite, pharmacosiderite, franklinite.

Name. *Wad* is an English name of uncertain origin. *Lampadite* after W. H. Lampadius (1772–1842), Professor of Chemistry and Metallurgy at the Mining Academy at Freiberg, Saxony. *Wackenrodite* after H. W. F. Wackenroder (1798–1854), a German chemist and apothecary who analyzed the material. *Rhabdionite* (less properly written rabdionite) from ῥάβδεον, *a little rod*, in allusion to the form of aggregation. *Skemmatite* from σκέμμα, *a question*, alluding to the questionable species validity of the mineral. *Pelokonite* from πελός, *dark-colored*, and κόνις, *powder*, in allusion to the liver-brown streak. *Asbolite* from ἀσβόλη, *soot* (and *asbolan* from ἀσβολᾶν, *to soil like soot*).

Ref.

1. For additional analyses see Doelter (3 [2], 876, 1926) and Hintze (1 [3A], 3641, 1929). Commercial analyses of manganese ores are widely scattered through the literature; see also Harder, *U. S. Geol. Sur., Bull. 427*, 1910.
2. Pattinson anal. in Fermor, *Geol. Sur. India, Mem.*, **37**, 119 (1907).
3. Popoff, *Ac. Sc. St. Pétersbourg, Trav. Mus. géol.*, **4**, 99 (1910) — *Zs. Kr*, **52**, 613 (1913).
4. Berthier, *Ann. chim. phys.*, **51**, 91 (1832).
5. Kurnakow and Podkopajew, *Russ. Ges. Min., Vh.*, **39**, 15 (1901) — *Zs. Kr.*, **37**, 415 (1903).
6. Frenzel, *Jb. Min.*, 801, 1873.
7. Jenkins anal. in Weisbach, *Jb. Min.*, II, 109, 1880.
8. von Kobell, *Ak. München, Ber.*, 46, 1870.
9. Whitfield anal. in Wherry, *U. S. Nat. Mus., Proc.*, **51**, 84 (1916).
10. Laspeyres, *J. pr. Chem.*, **13**, 16 (1876).
11. Winkler anal. in Frenzel, *Jb. Min.*, 219, 1872.
12. Rimatori, *Acc. Linc., Rend.*, **10**, 230 (1901) — *Jb. Min.*, II, 344, 1902.
13. See Doelter (1926).
14. Lindgren, *Econ. Geol.*, **17**, 201 (1922).
15. See Harder, *U. S. Geol. Sur., Bull. 427*, 1910.
16. Shannon (212, 1926).

17. For discussion and literature see Beyschlag, Krusch and Vogt (**2**, 477, 1913).
18. Saukov, *C.r. ac. sc. U.R.S.S.*, 77, 1926.
19. de Leenheer, *Ann. Service Mines, Katanga*, **8**, 32 (1938), with 5 additional analyses of similar material from Katanga.

TUNNERITE.   Zinkmanganerz *Brunlechner* (*Jb. nat. Landes-Mus., Klagenfurt*, **23**, 194, 1893).   Tunnerit *Cornu* (*Zs. Chem. Ind. Koll.*, 4, 297, 1909).
An ill-defined massive dark brown or gray material found associated with hemimorphite at Bleiberg, Carinthia, Germany.   Stated to be a hydrous oxide of Zn and Mn.   Possibly a zincian wad.

RANCIEITE.   Chaux de manganèse argentin pt. *de Lisle*.   Manganèse oxydé argentin pt. (?) *Haüy*.   Ranciérite *Leymérie* (**2**, 329, 1859).   Ranciéite *Lacroix* (**4**, 24, 1910).
Originally found at Rancié, near Vicdessos, Ariège, France, in cavities in limonite and later reported from other localities.   Fine lamellar with a black, brownish, or violet color and bright metallic luster.   G. 3.2–3.3.   Transparent in thin splinters with a brown color.

Anal.

	1	2
Na$_2$O	} 0.50	2.89
K$_2$O		1.38
CaO	9.20	8.24
MgO	3.95	.....
FeO	.....	12.06
MnO	15.05	29.56
MnO$_2$	59.75	31.82
Al$_2$O$_3$	.....	0.20
H$_2$O	12.40	14.60
Total	100.85	100.75

1. Fillols, Ariège, France.[2]   2. Villerouge, Aude, France.[3]

Considered[1] to be a calcian psilomelane.   Evidence of homogeneity is lacking.

Ref.

1. Lacroix (1910).
2. Pisani anal. in Lacroix (1910).
3. Haas, *Bull. soc. min.*, 44, 95 (1921).

EBELMENITE.   *Lacroix* (Guide du visiteur à la coll. Min. du Mus. d'Hist. nat. Paris, 29, 1900; **4**, 13, 1910).
A name proposed for a potassium-rich psilomelane.   Analyses of material referred to this species (anal. 1, 2) indicate a mixture[4] of psilomelane and pyrolusite, with constitutional or adsorbed alkali.

Anal.

	1	2	3	4
Na$_2$O	.....	.....	0.18	0.18
K$_2$O	4.05	3.12	2.63	2.33
CaO	.....	0.20	0.47	0.29
BaO	6.55	9.44	2.07	5.16
MgO	1.05	.....	0.16	0.22
MnO	7.68	9.07	6.47	6.61
MnO$_2$	77.10	75.15	82.44	79.87
SiO$_2$	0.60	.....	0.10	0.05
Fe$_2$O$_3$	0.77	0.80	0.50	0.07
H$_2$O	1.67	2.20	3.00	3.05
Rem.	.....	.....	2.131	2.253
Total	99.47	99.98	100.151	100.083
G.	4.24		4.38	4.41

1. Gy, Haute-Saône, France.[1] 2. Gouttes-Pommiers, Allier, France.[2] 3. Tekrasi, Bengal, India. Rem. is CoO 0.35, CuO 0.01, Al_2O_3 0.45, S 0.025, P_2O_5 0.696, NiO 0.05, ZnO 0.55.[3] 4. Tekrasi, Bengal. India. Rem. is CoO 0.20, CuO 0.04, Al_2O_3 0.75, S 0.037, P_2O_5 0.676, NiO 0.15, ZnO 0.40, Cl trace.[3]

Material composed in part of psilomelane and containing notable amounts of K_2O has been found at Gy, Haute-Saône, and Gouttes-Pommiers, Allier, France; in Germany at Heidelberg and Eisenbach near Neustadt in the Black Forest, and Elgersburg and Ilmenau in Thuringia. In India at Tekrasi, in the Singhbhum district, Bengal.

Named after a French chemist, J. J. Ebelmen (1814–52), who early analyzed the material.

Ref.

1. Ebelmen, *Ann. mines*, **19**, 155 (1841).
2. Pisani in Lacroix (1910).
3. Pattinson anal. in Fermor, *Geol. Sur. India, Mem.*, **37**, 100 (1909).
4. Orcel and Pavlovitch, *Bull. soc. min.*, **54**, 165 (1932) state that ebelmenite is a mixture containing pyrolusite.

BELDONGRITE. *Fermor (Geol. Sur. India, Mem.*, **37**, 908, 1909).
An ill-defined material looking very like metallic lead. H. 4. G. 3.22. Analysis gave: K_2O 0.01, Na_2O 0.33, (Ni,Cu,Co)O 0.018, BaO 0.78, CaO 2.31, MgO 0.15, MnO 22.00, MnO_2 36.96, Fe_2O_3 7.49, Al_2O_3 0.40, SiO_2 19.13, P_2O_5 0.05, H_2O 10.37, CO_2 0.11, As_2O_5 0.005, total 100.113.
Found with spessartite at Beldongri, Nágpur district, Central Provinces, India.

ZINCDIBRAUNITE. *Nenadkevic* (Ac. Sc., St. Pétersbourg, Trav. Mus. géol., **5**, 37, 1911 — *Zs. Kr.*, **53**, 609, 1914).
Soft earthy chocolate-colored masses found with calamine at Olkush, U.S.S.R. G. 4.63. Analysis gave: ZnO 23.28, CaO 0.94, BaO trace, CuO trace, CoO trace, PbO 0.54, MnO_2 52.27, PbO_2 6.89, Fe_2O_3 1.28, Al_2O_3 0.12, SiO_2 0.06, $(Tl,K)_2O$ 0.51, H_2O 13.59, total 99.48. The proportion of PbO_2 present is said to vary. Named from a special nomenclature proposed by the author for the salts of hypothetical acids of manganese.
Probably a mixture with adsorbed water.

4514 **Todorokite.** *Yoshimura (Hokkaidô Univ., J. Fac. Sc.*, **2**, 289, 1934).

Occurs as spongy banded and reniform aggregates composed of minute lathlike crystals. Crystals are possibly monoclinic; flattened {010} and elongated [001] with terminal edges inclined ca. 60° and 70° to [001]. Sometimes contact twins with $c \wedge \acute{c}$ about 60°.

P h y s. Cleavage {100} and {010} perfect. Soft; soils paper. G. 3.67. Luster metallic. Color black.

O p t. Brown in transmitted light. Pleochroic in brown with absorption $Z > X$. $Y = b$ with L near or parallel c. $n > 1.74$.

C h e m. A hydrous oxide of Mn^2, alkaline earths and Mn^4. Formula uncertain, possibly $(Mn,Ba,Ca,Mg)Mn_3O_7 \cdot H_2O$. Analysis gave: K_2O 0.54, Na_2O 0.21, MgO 1.01, CaO 3.28, BaO 2.05, Al_2O_3 0.28, Fe_2O_3 0.20, MnO 65.89, O 12.07, H_2O^+ 9.72, H_2O^- 1.56, SiO_2 0.45, TiO_2 trace, CO_2 trace, P_2O_5 0.42, SO_3 0.28, insoluble 1.28, total 99.24.

Tests. Infusible. Soluble in HCl with evolution of Cl. Easily soluble in acidified H_2O_2.

O c c u r. Found as an alteration of inesite with rhodochrosite and opal at the Todoroki mine, Hokkaidô, Japan.
N a m e. From the locality.
Needs further study.

4515 **C A S S I T E R I T E** [SnO₂]. Ore of the Κασσίτερος *Greeks, Romans, Herodotus;* Plumbum album *Pliny* (34, 47, 77) (not ore of the Stannum [= a pewter-like alloy] of *Pliny*). Zinnsten, Stannum ferro et arsenico mineralisatum *Wallerius* (303, 1747). Mine d'Étain *Wallerius* (1753). Stannum calciforme (Oxide of Tin) *Bergmann* (**2**, 436, 1780); *Klaproth* (**2**, 245, 1797). Zinnstein *Werner.* Zinnerz *Leonhard* (218, 1821). Tin Ore. Tin Stone. Wood-tin. Zinnstein, Zinnerz, Zinnsand, Holzzinn *Germ.* Étain oxydé *Fr.* Cassiterite *Beudant* (**2**, 618, 1832). Kassiterit *Germ.* Tennmalm *Swed.* Stagno ossidata *Ital.* Ainalite *Nordenskiöld* (162, 1855; 26, 1863). Stannite *Breithaupt* (**3**, 772, 1847). Silesite *Pauly* (*Cbl. Min.*, 44, 1926).

C r y s t. Tetragonal; ditetragonal dipyramidal — 4/m 2/m 2/m.

$$a : c = 1 : 0.6723;^1 \qquad p_0 : r_0 = 0.6723 : 1$$

Forms:[2]

		ϕ	ρ	A	$\overline{M}$
c	001	.....	0°00′	90°00′	90°00′
a	010	0°00′	90 00	90 00	45 00
m	110	45 00	90 00	45 00	90 00
h	120	26 34	90 00	63 26	71 34
r	230	33 41½	90 00	56 18½	78 41½
e	011	0 00	33 55	90 00	66 46
s	111	45 00	43 33½	60 50½	90 00
i	552	45 00	67 11	49 19½	90 00
t	133	18 26	35 19½	79 28	75 01
z	231	33 41½	67 35	59 09	79 32

Less common forms:

l	140	w	051	q	221	H	8·13·4	N	241	u	16·19·7
γ	130	x	114	ƺ	1·3·12	K	6·10·3	O	492	T	7·8·3
ρ	570	y	335	b	122	L	472	R	13·17·6	ν	572
k	340	S	223	f	233	M	8·15·4	Y	11·14·5		

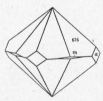
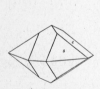

Stoneham, Me.   Greenwood, Me.

Structure cell.[3] Space group P4/*mnm*; a_0 4.72, c_0 3.17; $a_0 : c_0$ = 1 : 0.672; contains Sn₂O₄.

Habit.[4] Untwinned crystals usually short prismatic [001] with {110} and {100} prominent; sometimes long prismatic [001], or with acute terminations due to development of a steep pyramid (needle-tin). Less commonly pyramidal. Faces {001} and {110} frequently uneven; faces in zone [10ī] as also those in zone [001] often striated parallel their intersections. Common forms: *s m e a r z h c.* Also massive, in radially fibrous botryoidal crusts or concretionary masses (wood-tin); granular, coarse to fine.

Twinning. (a) On {011}, very common. Both contact and penetration twins; often repeated producing complex forms, sometimes stellate fivelings. (b) Reported on {031}.[5]

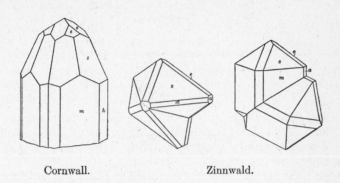

Cornwall.   Zinnwald.

Oriented growths. Oriented overgrowths have been found of cassiterite upon nordenskioldine[6] and of quartz upon cassiterite:[7]

$$\text{Quartz } \{10\bar{1}0\}[0001] \parallel \text{Cassiterite } \{111\}[\bar{1}\bar{1}2]$$

P h y s. Cleavage {100} imperfect, {110} indistinct, with a more or less distinct parting[8] on {111} or {011}. Fracture subconchoidal to uneven. Brittle. H. 6–7. G. 6.99 (Cornwall[9]), (values down to ca. 6.1 for some fibrous massive materials, but these values are not representative); 7.02 ± 0.02 (artificial);[10] 7.04 (calc.). Luster adamantine to metallic adamantine and usually splendent; inclining to greasy on fracture surfaces. Color ordinarily yellowish or reddish brown to brownish black, occasionally red, yellow, gray, or white; very rarely colorless (needle-tin). The color may be unequally distributed within the crystals in growth bands, parallel to the bounding faces or in segments subjacent to particular forms;[11] also in irregular areas. Streak white, grayish, brownish. Light-colored material quite transparent; in dark-colored material transparent only in thin splinters.

Twin gliding[12] with K_1 {011}, σ_2 [013].

O p t. In transmitted light, colorless to brown to red, yellow, orange, green. May exhibit an irregular zonal or segmental distribution of color in thin section. Pleochroic haloes have been observed.[13] Uniaxial positive (+). Dichroic[14] in yellow, green, brown, etc.; the dichroism is usually weak, or absent, but sometimes is strong; absorption $E > O$. Sometimes shows optical anomalies and then distinctly biaxial[15] with dispersion $v > r$. Birefringence increases with increasing wavelength. At constant wavelength the indices increase with increasing temperature and the birefringence decreases.

n_{210} at Varying Wavelengths[16]

λ	O	E
440.0	2.0475	2.1397
496.1	2.0239	2.1188
585.1	2.006	2.0972
653.0	1.9899	2.0874
715.2	1.9836	2.0818

n_{578} at Varying Temperature[16]

t	16°	324°	533°	824°	1014°
O	2.0007	2.0173	2.0316	2.0545	2.0702
E	2.0980	2.1135	2.1275	2.1489	2.1658

In polished section[17] light gray with strong anisotropism and very weak pleochroism. May exhibit lamellar twinning on {011} and, especially after etching, also zonal growth banding. White to brownish internal reflections are noticeable in dark colored material.

C h e m. Tin dioxide, SnO_2. Fe^3 is usually present in substitution for Sn, to about Fe : Sn = 1 : 6 (anal. 2), but this may be too high; material with ca. 13 weight per cent Fe_2O_3 has been reported[19] but evidence of homogeneity is lacking. Ta and Cb are often present in small amounts, and substitute for Sn to (Ta, Cb) : Sn = 1 : 30[20] (anal. 5). Small amounts of Zn (due to admixture),[19] W and Mn also have been reported. Ge, Sc, Cb, Ta, Zr, Ga, Be, Hf, In, V, and other elements have been found present in minute amounts by spectrum analysis.[21]

Anal.[22]

	1	2	3	4	5
Fe_2O_3	3.42	8.08	0.86	.....	2.04
SnO_2	94.89	91.92	94.00	93.36	88.95
Ta_2O_5	0.24	.....	4.64	6.53	8.78
Rem.	1.42	.....	0.53	0.84	0.78
Total	99.97	100.00	100.03	100.73	100.55
G.	6.609		6.91–7.0	7.5	6.6–6.8

1. Irish Creek, Rockbridge Co., Va. Rem. is MgO 0.03, CaO 0.24, SiO_2 0.76, ign. loss 0.39.[23] 2. Ferrian cassiterite. Monte Feital, Portugal. Recalculated after deduction of quartz.[24] 3. Tantalian cassiterite. Niriella, Ceylon. Rem. is Mn_2O_3 0.03, CaO 0.50.[25] 4. Tantalian cassiterite. Department of Potosí, Bolivia. Ta_2O_5 includes Cb_2O_5 2.82. Rem. is H_2O 0.35, TiO_2 0.49.[26] The accuracy of the analysis is uncertain. 5. Tantalian cassiterite (ainalite). Pennikoja, Finland. Rem. is CuO.[27]

Var. Ordinary. Tin-stone. Zinnerz, Zinnstein *Germ.* In crystals or massive. The acute pyramidal and long prismatic habits have been called *sparable tin* (Sperlings Schnabel, *Germ.*) and *needle-tin ore* (Nadelzinnerz *Germ.*). The twinned groups have been called by the German miners *Zwitter, Zinngraupen, Visirerz.* Stream tin (Zinnsand) is the ore as sand or pebbles in alluvial deposits.

Wood-tin. Holzzinnerz *Germ.* In botryoidal and reniform shapes, concentric in structure, and radiated fibrous internally, although very compact, with a brownish color of various shades, looking somewhat like dry wood.[28] *Toads'-eye tin* is the same on a smaller scale. The measured specific gravity is somewhat less than that of the crystals, and the material is more or less admixed with hematite and silica.

Ferrian. Contains Fe^3 in substitution for Sn to about Fe : Sn = 1 : 6 (anal. 2) or perhaps more. The color of the mineral apparently is not directly related to the iron content.[29]

Tantalian. Ainalite *Nordenskiöld* (162, 1855; 26, 1863). Tantalum cassiterite. Contains Ta and Cb in substitution for Sn to at least (Ta,Cb) : Sn = 1 : 30 (anal. 5). Ta and Cb probably are more commonly present in cassiterite than has been generally supposed.

Tests. B.B. infusible. Only slowly attacked by acids, but decomposed by fusion in alkalies, KF or KHF_2. Fragments of cassiterite when placed in dilute HCl with metallic zinc become coated with a dull gray deposit of metallic tin which turns bright on friction.

Occur.[30] Cassiterite is the most important ore of tin and one of the few tin minerals. The mineral characteristically occurs in high-temperature hydrothermal veins or metasomatic deposits that are genetically closely associated with highly siliceous igneous rocks, usually granite or quartz porphyry. Found associated with wolframite, tourmaline, topaz, quartz, fluorite, arsenopyrite, muscovite, lepidolite, bismuthinite, native bismuth, molybdenite, and less abundantly with pyrrhotite, pyrite, chalcopyrite, galena, and sphalerite. The name greisen is given to coarse-grained rocks containing cassiterite, topaz, tourmaline, coarse muscovite, lepidolite, and fluorite formed by hydrothermal alteration usually along fissures. Cassiterite also occurs as stockworks and impregnations in acidic igneous rocks; in pipelike pegmatitic bodies cutting limestone or other rock and genetically associated with granitic intrusives (Kinta Valley, Perak); in rhyolite and rhyolite tuff as colloform masses (Lander County, Nevada); rarely in contact metamorphic deposits between limestone and granite (Seward Peninsula, Alaska). Cassiterite often occurs, although usually in relatively small, noncommercial, concentrations, in granite pegmatites. Important amounts occur in moderate-temperature Bi-Pb-Ag sulfide veins in Bolivia together with stannite, cylindrite, and teallite, but the mineral ordinarily is found but rarely and in small amounts in sulfide-rich deposits. A radially fibrous colloform variety of cassiterite (wood-tin) is formed by secondary processes in the zone of oxidation of tin deposits, and also occurs as a hypogene mineral both in deep-seated veins and, in particular, in deposits associated with surface rhyolitic lavas and tuffs. Cassiterite is a common alluvial or eluvial mineral in some areas of granitic rocks. A few of the many known occurrences of cassiterite are given below.

The mining of vein deposits of tin began in central Europe in the early fifteenth century and the production reached its maximum in the seventeenth century.[31] Important deposits in this region were worked at Marienbad, St. Christoph near Breitenbrunn, Ehrenfriedersdorf, Johanngeorgenstadt, and especially Altenberg in Saxony, and at Zinnwald, Graupen, and Schlaggenwald in Bohemia. Found at Campiglia Marittima, Tuscany, with siderite at a limestone-granite contact. A number of small deposits occur in Beira Province, Portugal, and in Galicia and Asturias in Spain. In France in small amounts in greisen at Montebras, Département Creuse (tantalian)[32], and Meymac, Département Corrèze; in notable twinned groups at La Villeder, Morbihan. The great tin deposits of Cornwall, England, were the world's principal source of tin during the eighteenth and much of the nineteenth centuries.[33] Tin was brought from Cornwall to Italy at the time of the invasion of Britain by Julius Caesar, and the Cassiterides (i.e., " Tin-islands ") of the ancient Greek and Roman geographers, vaguely described as islands affording tin ore somewhere near the coasts of western Europe, have been thought to be Cornwall or the Scilly or Channel Islands. The mineral occurs in Cornwall in high-temperature veins and greisen in or adjacent to post-Carboniferous granites that have intruded Paleozoic sediments.[34] In Finland cassiterite occurs in pegmatite at Pitkäranta on the northern shore of Lake Ladoga, and at Pennikoja (ainalite). Large alluvial and eluvial deposits are found in Perak and Selangor on the Malay Peninsula, and on the islands of Sumatra and especially Banka and Billiton[35] in the Dutch East Indies. At Kokieu, Yunnan Province, China, and in Japan at the Taniyama mine, Satsuma Province, and at Takayama, Mino Province. Deposits of cassiterite are widespread in Australia, notably in the Greenbushes and Pilbarra fields in Western Australia, in the Herberton district in Queensland, in pegmatite pipes in the New England range of New South Wales,[36] and in the Mount Bischoff mine in Tasmania. An important ore in many districts in Bolivia in sulfide veins formed at moderate temperatures, associated with bismuthinite, tetrahedrite, wolframite, native bismuth, stannite, teallite, sphalerite, pyrite, galena, and a variety of complex Pb-Bi-Ag-Sn sulfosalts; fluorine and boron-bearing minerals, characteristically associated with cassiterite, are relatively rare in these occurrences. Found at numerous localities in Africa, notably at the Stiepelmann mine, Arandis, South-West Africa, where ore pipes and pegmatites in marble contain pyrrhotite, cassiterite, axinite, and other contact silicates together with many rare species including arandisite, nordenskiöldine, stiepelmannite, danburite; also found abundantly in Nigeria, and pipelike pegmatite deposits occur in the Mutue Fides-Stavoren tin field in the Transvaal.[37] Small deposits are widely distributed in Mexico, and many are associated with rhyolites.

In the United States cassiterite has been mined at a few localities, but with little success. Found at a number of localities in the Appalachian region, notably with wolframite in quartz veins at Irish Creek in Rockbridge County, Virginia, and at the Ross mine, near Gaffney, South Carolina. Cassiterite occurs in very minor amounts in many of the granite pegmatites of the New England states: in Maine at Greenwood, Newry, Hebron, Poland, Paris, Auburn, Stoneham, and elsewhere; in New Hampshire at Lyme and in quartz veins with arsenopyrite, fluorite, tourmaline at Jackson. Found in South Dakota, where unsuccessful efforts to mine cassiterite disseminated in granite pegmatite were made at Tinton, Lawrence County, and at Hill City and Keystone, Pennington County. A small deposit occurs in the Franklin Mountains, El Paso County, Texas. In pegmatite at Silver Hill, near Spokane, Spokane County, Washington. The mineral occurs at a number of places in California, notably at the Temescal mine, near South Riverside in the Santa Ana Mountains, Riverside County. Wood-tin occurs in rhyolite in northern Lander County, Nevada. At Lost River, Seward Peninsula, Alaska, cassiterite occurs in the contact zone of limestone with granite, associated with axinite, danburite, tourmaline, vesuvianite, tremolite, hulsite, paigeite. Found in Canada in pegmatite at New Ross, Nova Scotia, and in southeastern Manitoba; with sperrylite in the Vermilion mine, Sudbury district, Ontario. Wood-tin occurs in placers in the Yukon.

A l t e r. Cassiterite has been found as pseudomorphs after orthoclase,[38] bismuthinite, hematite, and after unidentified monoclinic,[39] hexagonal,[40] and isometric[41] minerals. The reported pseudomorphs of cassiterite after tourmaline and quartz appear to be without foundation. The supposed pseudomorphs after quartz from Cornwall actually are quartz crystals with mechanically enclosed, finely divided, particles of cassiterite; these crystals were early supposed to be a silicate of tin. Deer horns more or less replaced by cassiterite have been found in stream gravels in Cornwall.[38]

A r t i f.[42] Gels or sols of hydrous stannic oxide are formed by precipitating stannic salts with alkalies, and in other ways, and on aging give the x-ray diffraction pattern of cassiterite. The supposed α and β modifications of colloidal SnO_2 are identical, and differ only in particle size and in content of adsorbed water. Macroscopic crystals of cassiterite have been obtained from fusions of SnO_2; by the action of steam on stannic halides at red heat; by the fusion of SnO_2 in borax; and otherwise. Also formed accidentally in metallurgical furnaces, and both cassiterite crystals and masses of wood-tin have been observed formed by the atmospheric weathering of ancient tin slags or masses of metallic tin.

N a m e. Cassiterite from the Greek word, κασσίτερος, for tin. The Cornish term *sparable tin* was given from the resemblance of some crystals to the sparable nail of the shoe cobbler; sparable itself is a corruption of sparrow-bill, which the nail resembles, or the meaning of sparable nail may be simply that which spars or rivets, since Anglo-Saxon " sparriam " means to fasten or rivet. Visirerz or visirgraupen is an old German mining term that refers to the habit of certain twin crystals, in which a small twinned individual projects, with a reentrant, from a terminal corner of a larger prismatic individual, in fancied resemblance to the vizor of head armor. Ainalite from the Finnish word *aina, constant,* and λίθος, *stone,* alluding to its refractory behavior in solvents.

SILESITE. *Pauly (Cbl. Min.,* 44, 1926).

In fine-grained, horny, often fibrous, concretionary aggregates resembling chalcedony. Porous. Color light yellow, H. 6±. G. 5±. Found in the oxidized zone of tin veins in Bolivia. Named after Hernando Siles, a former president of Bolivia. Supposed to be a silicate of tin, but very probably a mixture of wood-tin and colloidal silica.[43]

Ref.

1. Becke, *Min. Mitt.*, 243 (1877).
2. Goldschmidt, **9**, 121 (1923), Candel Vila, *R. soc. española hist. nat., Bolet.*, **26**, 369 (1926), Heilmaier, *Jb. Min., Beil.-Bd.*, **61**, 403 (1927). Rare or uncertain forms:

7·50·0	560	31·32·0	551	1·10·10	181	781
170	670	031	661	154	7·100·7	
350	780	112	771	457	342	
8·11·0	9·10·0	665	12·12·1	14·21·18	341	
790	10·11·0	332	18·18·1	465	11·13·2	
450	13·14·0	331	120·120·1	676	671	

3. Vegard, *Phil. Mag.*, **32**, 65 (1916); **1**, 115 (1920); Williams, *Roy. Soc. London, Proc.*, **93**, 418 (1917); Bragg and Darbyshire, *Trans. Faraday Soc.*, **28**, 522 (1932).
4. On the relation between the habit and genesis see Ahlfeld, *Fortschr. Min.*, **16**, 303 (1931); also Boldyreva, *Mem. soc. russe min.*, **68** [3], 418 (1939).
5. Bourgeois, *Bull. soc. min.*, **11**, 58 (1888).
6. Ramdohr, *Jb. Min., Beil.-Bd.*, **68**, 288 (1934).
7. Ramdohr, *Cbl. Min.*, 200, 1923.
8. Hidden, *Am. J. Sc.*, **20**, 410 (1905), and Johnsen, *Cbl. Min.*, 426, 1908, observed a perfect parting {011} apparently on twin planes. The {111} parting (?) repeatedly has been observed (Ramdohr [1923]) and has been described as a true cleavage. The cleavage {110} also may be a parting (Becke [1877]).
9. Frondel (priv. comm., 1941) from identical measurements by microbalance on two Cornish specimens. A wide range of values (6.6–7.0) has been reported.
10. Stevanovic, *Zs. Kr.*, **37**, 255 (1902).
11. Pelikan, *Min. Mitt.*, **16**, 27 (1897).
12. Johnsen (1908).
13. Ramdohr, *Jb. Min., Beil.-Bd.*, **67**, 63 (1933).
14. See Heide, *Zs. Kr.*, **67**, 33 (1928) for a tabulation of observed pleochroism formulas; see also Heide (1928) and Weinschenk, *Zs. anorg. Chem.*, **12**, 384 (1896) for observations on the variation in pleochroism and color on heating.
15. Madelung, *Zs. Kr.*, **7**, 75 (1882).
16. Ecklebe, *Jb. Min., Beil.-Bd.*, **66**, 47 (1932), on unanalyzed crystals from Araca, Bolivia.
17. Schneiderhöhn and Ramdohr (**2**, 501, 1931).
18. The substitution of Fe^3 for Sn^4 presumably is accompanied by the development of a defect structure unless balanced by a concomitant substitution of (Cb,Ta).[5]
19. See Genth, *Am. Phil. Soc. Proc.*, **24**, 29 (1887).
20. If both Fe^3 and Ta are present in equal atomic amounts the formula AX_2 would be valid. Otherwise a composition defective in O or Sn to a small amount must be postulated.
21. See Geilmann and Brünger, *Zs. anorg. Chem.*, **196**, 312 (1931); Borovick and Gotman, *C. r. ac. sc. U.R.S.S.*, **23**, 351 (1939); Papish and Holt, *J. Phys. Chem.*, **32**, 142 (1928); Goldschmidt and Peters, *Nach. Ges. Göttingen, Math-phys. Kl.*, 257, 1931; Liebisch, *Ak. Berlin, Ber.*, 414, 1911.
22. For additional analyses see Doelter (**3** [1], 177, 1913) and Headden, *Colorado Sc. Soc., Proc.*, **8**, 167 (1906).
23. Brown, *Am. Chem. J.*, **6**, 185 (1883).
24. Winkler anal. in Breithaupt, *Jb. Min.*, 820, 1872.
25. Dunstan, *Jb. Min.*, I, 166, 1906.
26. Thugutt, *Arch. Min. Soc. Warsaw*, **8**, 122 (1932).
27. Nordenskiöld (26, 1863).
28. On the structure of wood-tin see Collins (*Cornish Tin-Stones . . .*, Truro, 1888); Newhouse and Buerger, *Econ. Geol.*, **23**, 185 (1928); Knopf, *ibid.*, **11**, 653 (1916).
29. On the color of cassiterite see Kohlmann, *Zs. Kr.*, **24**, 362 (1895); Traube, *Jb. Min., Beil.-Bd.*, **10**, 474 (1895). The color must in part, at least, be related to the content of (Ta, Cb).

30. See Lindgren (1933) for descriptions of the more important occurrences of cassiterite.
31. For an account of these deposits see especially Stelzner-Bergeat (**2**, 926 [1905–6]).
32. Caron, *C. R.*, **61**, 1064 (1875).
33. For a popular account of the Cornish tin mines see Jenkin (*The Cornish Miner*, London, 351 pp., 1927).
34. For mention of notable specimen localities in Cornwall see especially Collins (*Min. Cornwall and Devon*, 24, 1876; *Cornish Tin-Stones* . . ., 1888; *Min. Mag.*, **4**, 1 [1880]).
35. For an account of the tin industry of Billiton see the Gedenkboek Billiton, 1852–1927,'s-Gravenhage, 2 volumes, 1927.
36. See Andrews, *Rec. Geol. Sur. New South Wales*, pt. V, 239, 1907.
37. See Wagner, *Geol. Sur. South Africa, Mem.*, **16** (1921).
38. See Collins (*Cornish Tin-Stones*, 30, 1888); *Min. Mag.*, **4** (1880).
39. Pearce, *Min. Mag.*, **14**, 345 (1906), from Bolivia.
40. Scrivenor, *Min. Mag.*, **16**, 118 (1911), from Malaya.
41. Genth (1887) from Mexico.
42. See Weiser (**2**, 231, 1935) and Doelter (**3** [1], 184, 1918).
43. Ahlfeld, *Cbl. Min.*, 320 (1927).

4516   **P L A T T N E R I T E** [PbO_2].   Schwerbleierz, Diplasites plumbicus *Breithaupt* (*J. pr. Chem.*, **10**, 508, 1837).   Plattnerit *Haidinger* (504, 1845).   Braunbleioxyd *Hausmann* (202, 1847).

C r y s t.   Tetragonal; ditetragonal dipyramidal — $4/m\,2/m\,2/m$.[1]

$$a : c = 1 : 0.6828;^2 \qquad p_0 : r_0 = 0.6828 : 1$$

Forms:[3]

		ϕ	ρ	A	$\overline{M}$
c	001	. . . .	0°00′	90°00′	90°00′
a	010	0°00′	90 00	90 00	45 00
e	011	0 00	34 19½	90 00	66 30
v	031	0 00	53 47	90 00	55 13
x	332	45 00	55 22½	54 25	90 00

Structure cell.[4]   Space group probably $P4/mnm$; $a_0\ 4.931$, $c_0\ 3.367$; $a_0 : c_0 = 1 : 0.6828$; contains Pb_2O_4.

Habit.   Prismatic [001].   Usually in nodular or botryoidal masses; dense to fibrous, or in concentric shells.

Twinning.[5]   Twin plane {011}, as penetration twins.

P h y s.   No cleavage.[6]   Fracture of masses, small conchoidal, sometimes fibrous.   Crystals brittle.   H. $5\frac{1}{2}$.   G. 9.42 ± 0.02;[7] 8.9–9.36 (artif.); 9.63 (calc.).   Luster bright metallic adamantine, tarnishing and becoming dull on exposure.   Color of crystals jet-black, of massive material iron-black to brownish black.   Streak chestnut-brown.   Opaque.

O p t.   In polished section[8] gray-white in color; anisotropic and pleochroic, with red-brown internal reflections.   Reflection percentages: green 16.5, orange 13, red 11.

In transmitted light[9] cloudy and nearly opaque. $n_{Li}\ 2.30 \pm 0.05$.   No birefringence recognized.   Basal sections may show six biaxial segments.

C h e m.   Lead dioxide, PbO_2.

Anal.

	1	2	3	4
Pb	86.62	.....	.....	83.20
O	13.38	.....	.....	12.93
PbO_2	.....	90.99	91.03	.....
Rem.	.....	8.72	8.93	2.16
Total	100.00	99.71	99.96	98.29
G.	9.63	7.52		8.56

1. PbO_2. 2. You Like lode, Id. Rem. is ZnO 0.07, SiO_2 2.68, Al_2O_3 0.28, Fe_2O_3 5.69.[10] 3. You Like lode, Id. Rem. is ZnO 0.07, insol. 3.00, Fe_2O_3 5.86.[10] 4. You Like lode, Id. Rem. is insol. 0.82, Cu 0.14, Ag trace, (Fe,Al) 1.20. O det. directly as H_2O.[11]

Tests. F. 2. Decomposes to red-lead and oxygen when moderately heated. Easily soluble in HCl with evolution of chlorine; difficultly soluble in HNO_3 with liberation of oxygen; decomposed by H_2SO_4 with formation of $PbSO_4$ and oxygen.

O c c u r. Originally described on specimens probably from Leadhills, Scotland, apparently pseudomorphous after pyromorphite. Later identified from Leadhills with cerussite, leadhillite, and pyromorphite, and also from Wanlockhead, Dumfries, with smithsonite and plumbian calcite. From Tsumeb, South-West Africa, with minium and massicot as coatings.

In the United States, a notable occurrence in the You Like lode of the Morning mine at Mullan, Shoshone County, Idaho; here found as nodules and botryoidal masses, sometimes weighing as much as 200 lb, associated with pyromorphite and botryoidal or ocherous masses of limonite; in part distinctly fibrous, and terminating in cavities in minute crystals. Also in Idaho in the Gilmore district, Lemhi County, and at Mace, Burke, and Wardner in Shoshone County. Reported from South Dakota.

A l t e r. As pseudomorphs after pyromorphite.

A r t i f.[12] As a powder by treating PbO or dissolved lead salts with a strong oxidizing agent; also deposited on the anode in the electrolysis of lead salts. As crystals, admixed with red PbO, by fusing PbO in KOH. An artificial hexagonal modification has been reported but not verified.[13]

N a m e. After K. F. Plattner (1800–58), Professor of Metallurgy and Assaying at Freiburg. Diplasites from διπλάσιος, *double*, because the metal is twice as strongly oxidized as is the case with litharge.

Ref.

1. Originally described as rhombohedral, but presumably these were pseudomorphs after pyromorphite. See Greg and Lettsom (389, 1858). Tetragonal symmetry of the mineral established by Yeates and Ayres, *Am. J. Sc.*, **43**, 407 (1892), on Idaho material, and of the artificial substance by Darbyshire, *J. Chem. Soc.*, 211, 1932, from an x-ray study.
2. Unit of Ayres in Yeates and Ayres (1892); ratio of Darbyshire (1932) on artificial material, by x-ray powder method.
3. Ayres in Yeates and Ayres (1892). Davidson, *Am. Min.*, **26**, 18 (1941), found {230} and {121} on artificial crystals.
4. Darbyshire (1932) by powder method on artificial material. van Arkel, *Physica*, **5**, 162 (1925), gives a_0 4.97, c_0 3.40, c = 0.685, by powder method.
5. Davidson (1941) on artificial crystals.
6. Yeates and Ayres (1892). Michel, *Bull. soc. min.*, **13**, 56 (1890), reports a prismatic cleavage on artificial crystals not certainly shown to be identical with plattnerite.

7. Average of 9.392 and 9.448 of Breithaupt (1837) on Leadhills (?) material, and of 9.411 of Wheeler, *Am. J. Sc.*, **38**, 79 (1889), on Idaho material. Values ranging down to 7.25 have been reported for natural material, due no doubt to impurities and porosity of sample.

8. Schneiderhöhn and Ramdohr (**2**, 507, 1931).
9. Larsen (121, 1921) on Idaho material.
10. Hawkins and Hawkins, *Am. J. Sc.*, **38**, 165 (1885).
11. Yeates anal. in Yeates and Ayres (1892).
12. Mellor (**7**, 682, 1927); see also Davidson (1941).
13. Genther, *Zs. Kr.*, **11**, 107 (1885), in hexagonal tablets in part regularly intergrown with red PbO.

452 **A N A T A S E** [TiO₂]. Schorl bleu indigo (from Oisans) *Bournon* in *de Lisle* (**2**, 406, 1783); Schorl octaedre rectangulaire *Bournon* (*J. phys.*, **30**, 386, 1787). Octaèdrite *Saussure* (§1901, 1796). Oktaedrit *Werner* (1803, **2**, 218, 1804). Oisanite *Delametherie* (**2**, 269, 1797); *Haüy* (*J. mines*, **5**, 273, 1799). Anatase *Haüy* (**3**, 1801). Dauphinit *Glocker* (541, 1831). Octahedrite.

Wiserine *Kenngott* (*Jb. Min.*, 484, 1864). Leucoxene, pt. Xanthitane *Shepard* (*Am. J. Sc.*, **22**, 96, 1856). Xanthotitane. Hydrotitanite *Koenig* (*Ac. Sc. Philadelphia, Proc.*, 82, 1876).

C r y s t. Tetragonal; ditetragonal dipyramidal — $4/m\,2/m\,2/m$.

$$a : c = 1 : 2.5133;^1 \qquad p_0 : r_0 = 2.5133 : 1$$

Forms:[2]

		ϕ	ρ	A	$\bar{M}$
c	001	.....	0°00′	90°00′	90°00′
a	010	0°00′	90 00′	90 00	45 00′
m	110	45 00	90 00	45 00	90 00
v	017	0 00	19 45	90 00	76 10½
z	013	0 00	39 57½	90 00	62 59½
k	012	0 00	51 29½	90 00	56 24½
e	035	0 00	56 27	90 00	53 53½
p	011	0 00	68 18	90 00	48 55½
ϵ	112	45 00	60 38	51 57½	90 00
q	111	45 00	74 17	47 06	90 00

Less common forms:

α	019	f	014	n	023	o	1·1·14	E 441	Δ 142
i	016	ψ	025	w	021	x	116	s 2·3·19	
r	015	χ	037	δ	031	d	332	τ 123	

Structure cell.[3] Space group $I4/amd$; a_0 3.73, c_0 9.37; $a_0 : c_0 = 1 :$ 2.512; contains Ti_4O_8.

Habit. Commonly acute pyramidal {011}. Less commonly obtuse pyramidal, usually with {017} or {013}. Also tabular {001}. Rarely prismatic [001] with {110} or, very rarely, {010}. The crystals are often highly modified. Common forms: $p\,c\,e\,a\,v\,z\,\epsilon\,m$.

Twinning.[4] On {112}, rare.

Oriented growths. Oriented overgrowths and paramorphs of rutile have been observed.[5]

P h y s. Cleavage {001} and {011}, perfect.[6] Fracture subconchoidal. Brittle. H. 5½–6. G. 3.90;[7] 4.04 (calc.). Luster adamantine or metallic adamantine, sometimes splendent. Color various shades of brown, including yellowish and reddish brown, passing into indigo-blue and black; also greenish, blue-green, pale lilac, slate-gray, and, rarely, nearly colorless.

Streak colorless to pale yellow. Transparent; the very deeply colored varieties are transparent only in small fragments. Pyramidal crystals often appear opaque owing to total reflection.[8]

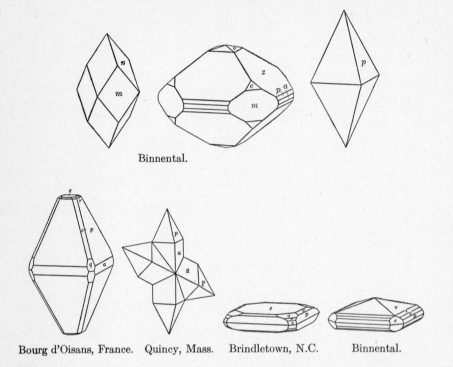

Binnental.

Bourg d'Oisans, France.   Quincy, Mass.   Brindletown, N.C.   Binnental.

Opt. In transmitted light variously colored: brown, yellow brown, greenish, blue. Zonal growth-banding is sometimes observed. Usually uniaxial negative ($-$). Often biaxial with small $2V$, especially in deeply colored crystals. Dichroism usually weak, sometimes strong in the highly colored crystals. Absorption usually $E > O$, sometimes $O > E$.

The optical constants vary markedly with the wavelength and the temperature.[9] At constant wave length and increasing temperature, O decreases markedly while E decreases or increases but slightly so that the birefringence decreases. At constant temperature and increasing wavelength, the indices decrease but O more rapidly so that the birefringence decreases.

n_{589} AT VARYING TEMPERATURE[9]

	25°	150°	300°	450°	600°	750°
O	2.5612	2.5580	2.5545	2.5520	2.5503	2.5486
E	2.4880	2.4872	2.4859	2.4853	2.4853	2.4858

ABSORPTION

Locality	O	E
Binnental[9]	Greenish yellow Yellow Dark yellow Yellow brown	Brownish and reddish yellow Yellowish brown Light liver-brown Reddish brown
Brazil[10]	Light blue Light yellow	Deep blue Dark yellow and orange-red
Abichl-Alp[11] Frossnitz[12]	Deep bluish green Yellowish and bluish green	Sky blue Yellow

C h e m. Titanium dioxide, TiO_2, polymorphous with brookite and rutile.

Anal.[13]

	1	2
Fe_2O_3	1.11	0.25
TiO_2	98.36	99.75
SnO_2	0.20	.....
Total	99.67	100.00
G.	3.857	3.89

1. Brazil.[14] 2. Brazil.[15]

Tests. B.B. infusible. Insoluble in acids. Decomposed by fusion with $KHSO_4$ or by heating with carbon to redness in a stream of Cl gas. The G may increase on heating to redness due to conversion to rutile.

O c c u r. Anatase, like brookite, typically occurs in vein or crevice deposits of the so-called Alpine type in gneiss or schist. The TiO_2 in these deposits is derived through alteration and leaching of the country rock by traversing hydrothermal solutions. In Alpine veins anatase is associated with quartz, brookite, rutile, adularia, hematite, chlorite, and other minerals. Also widespread as a minor constituent of igneous and metamorphic rocks, especially their altered facies. Found occasionally in pegmatites, as a druse mineral in granite and in veinlets in or near diabase, diorite and other igneous rocks. A common detrital mineral.

The following list includes only a few of the many known localities. Found well crystallized in crevices, joint planes and veins of the Alpine type in many localities in the Alps. Notable localities in the Swiss Alps include Santa Brigitta and Cavradi in Tavetsch, Graubünden; numerous places in the Maderanerthal and on St. Gotthard in Uri; the Binnental, Valais. In the French Alps found especially in the region of Bourg d'Oisans, Isère, and in the neighborhood of La Grave, Hautes-Alpes. In the Tirolian Alps anatase is found on the Eicham peak, at Frossnitz near Pregratten and in the Zillerthal. In Salzburg on the Grieswies, Rauris, and on the Abichl-Alp in the Untersulzbachthal. In Italy especially at Sondalo, Lombardy. Occurrences similar to those of the Alps are found in many other regions. In granite pegmatite at Pisek, Bohemia, and in Moravia. As an alteration product of sphene in the apatite veins at Kragerö, Norway. In Cornwall, England, in veins in altered greenstone at Liskeard and at Tintagel Cliffs with adularia· with brookite and chlorite in the Virtuous Lady mine, Tavistock, Devonshire; with brookite and albite at Fronolen near Snowdon and Tremadoc, Wales. Found as detrital crystals in the Urals, U.S.S.R., notably at the Atliansk placers near Miask and in the placers of the Sanarka region, Orenburg. A common mineral in the diamond placers of Minas Geraes and Bahia, Brazil, often more or less altered into rutile; also at Piracuruca, Piauhy, with opal and zircon.

In the United States anatase occurs as detrital grains and crystals in the gold placers of North Carolina, notably at Brindletown, Burke Co. Rarely at Magnet Cove, Arkansas. At Arvon, Buckingham County, Virginia, in joint planes in slate with quartz and pyrite. Found in Massachusetts with brookite and sphene in veinlets in or near diabase dikes at Somerville, and in pockets in granite pegmatite with aegerite, fluorite, and ilmenite in the Fallon quarry, Quincy. With brookite upon quartz at Placerville, Eldorado County, California. Fine blue crystals occur along joint planes in a diorite dike on Beaver Creek, Gunnison County, Colorado. In Canada implanted on quartz at Sherbrooke, Nova Scotia, and as an alteration product of sphene in Henvey Township, Ontario.

Alter. Frequently observed as an alteration product of sphene;[16] also found as an alteration of ilmenite, arizonite, and of titanian magnetite. Anatase often is found more or less completely altered by paramorphism into rutile. Pebbles and crystals of anatase altered to rutile are common in the placers of Brazil and the Sanarka region in the Urals, and form part of the material known as " favas " or " captivos " (see further under rutile).

Artif.[17] Anatase has been obtained in crystals by the reaction of $TiCl_4$ or TiF_4 with water vapor at temperatures below ca. 767°; by heating precipitated hydrous titanium oxide in HCl gas to 700°; from solution in molten salt of phosphorus; and in other ways. Rutile rather than anatase is usually obtained when these syntheses are carried out at somewhat higher temperatures. The gelatinous precipitate obtained by the reaction of bases with tetravalent titanium salts or by the hydrolysis of $Ti(SO_4)_2$ when aged by standing or slight heating consists of anatase with adsorbed water.[18]

When anatase is heated it is said[19] to invert to another modification (α-anatase) at ca. 642° and on further heating this substance inverts to rutile at 915 ± 20°.

Name. Anatase, from ἀνάτασις, extension, was intended to signify that the common pyramid was longer than that of other tetragonal species. Octahedrite in allusion to the common octahedral habit. Oisanite and dauphinite from the locality at Bourg d'Oisans, Dauphiné, France. Wiserine after D. F. Wiser (1802–78), a mineralogist of Zürich, Switzerland. Although octahedrite has priority, the name anatase is here adopted since it is now in almost universal use.

XANTHITANE. *Shepard* (*Am. J. Sc.*, **22**, 96, 1856; *Eakins*, *Am. J. Sc.*, **35**, 418, 1888). Xanthotitane.

A soft, friable, yellow earthy material found as alteration pseudomorphs after sphene at Green River, Henderson County, North Carolina. Identical with anatase.[20]

HYDROTITANITE. *Koenig* (*Ac. Sc. Philadelphia, Proc.*, 82, 1876).

A soft compact, earthy, yellowish to brownish material found as alteration pseudomorphs after columbian perovskite at Magnet Cove, Arkansas. Identical with anatase.[20]

Ref.

1. Angles of Miller in Brooke and Miller (229, 1852) and the orientation of Brezina, *Min. Mitt.*, **2**, 7 (1872), unit of Vegard, *Phil. Mag.*, **32**, 65 (1916); **1**, 1151 (1926). The elements of Miller and of Dana (240, 1892) refer to the face-centered structural cell. The body-centered structural cell of Vegard (1916) is chosen here. Transformations:

$$\text{Miller to Vegard } \tfrac{1}{2}\tfrac{1}{2}0 / \overline{\tfrac{1}{2}}\tfrac{1}{2}0 / 0\,0\,1$$
$$\text{Brezina to Vegard } 100 / 010 / 004$$
$$\text{Lévy (3, 344, 1838) and Des Cloizeaux (2, 200, 1874) to Vegard } 110 / \overline{1}10 / 001$$

2. See Parker, *Zs. Kr.*, **58**, 522 (1923), and Bader, *Schweiz. min. Mitt.*, **14**, 336 (1934), for statistical studies of the form development. On the relation of form to structure see Parker, *Zs. Kr.*, **59**, 1 (1923). Rare and uncertain forms:

0·1·40	049	0·13·2	3·5·32	233
0·1·28	0·5·11	0·19·2	1·2·13	5·19·7
0·1·14	0·7·13	1·1·10	1·3·12	564
0·1·10	059	118	9·81·100	7·18·5
0·5·43	0·31·50	5·5·38	4·7·45	30·33·14
018	058	3·3·20	4·7·44	8·10·3
0·3·20	034	114	2·3·20	35·43·12
0·5·29	0·9·10	113	129	19·21·6
0·2·11	076	221	7·13·60	16·19·5
0·4·21	043	994	158	10·11·3
029	032	883	5·13·24	7·10·2
0·5·19	053	13·13·4	124	37·43·10
027	0·15·8	772	3·7·12	177·183·40
038	0·11·3	1·3·20	6·9·20	7·18·1
0·5·12	051	1·4·20	9·13·24	

3. Vegard (1916; 1926).

4. See Palache, *Rosenbusch Festschr.*, 311, 1906, *Am. Ac. Arts Sc., Proc.*, **47**, 125 (1911), on twins from Somerville and Quincy, Massachusetts. Twins on {112}, {011} and {012} have been reported on artificial crystals by Doss, *Jb. Min.*, **2**, 152 (1894). On the structural interpretation of the twinning see Gliszczynski, *Zbl. Min.*, 181, 1940.

5. See Mügge, *Jb. Min., Beil.-Bd.*, **16**, 392 (1903) and Palache (1906).

6. On the relation of the cleavage to the structure see Tertsch, *Zs. Kr.*, **58**, 293 (1923), and Parker (1923).

7. Schröder, *Zs. Kr.*, **67**, 485 (1928) gives 3.900 ± 0.006 for Binnental crystals. Values in the literature range from 3.82 to 3.97. Schröder's value has been checked (Berman, 1941). Presumably the cell volume is slightly too small, as given.

8. See Joly, *Proc. Roy. Soc. Dublin*, **9**, 475 (1901).

9. See Schröder (1928), who cites earlier work, for a detailed investigation. Prism cut from Binnental crystal.

10. Lasaulx, *Zs. Kr.*, **8**, 54 (1883).

11. Weinschenk, *Zs. Kr.*, **26**, 405 (1896).

12. Pohl, *Min. Mitt.*, **22**, 482 (1903).

13. An analysis by Warren in O'Reilly, *Proc. Roy. Soc. Dublin*, **8**, 732 (1898), of a supposedly aluminian anatase from Shankill, Ireland, with 13.02 per cent Al_2O_3, probably was made on impure material. For analyses of anatase found as "favas" in Brazilian diamond gravels see Florence in Hussak, *Min. Mitt.*, **18**, 336 (1899).

14. Damour, *Ann. chim. phys.*, **10**, 417 (1844).
15. Rose, *Ann. Phys.*, **61**, 517 (1844).
16. See Pough, *Am. Min.*, **19**, 599 (1934).
17. See Mellor (7, 32, 1927); Doss, *Jb. Min.*, II, 152, 1894; and Florence, *ibid.*, II, 130, 1898.
18. Weiser (2, 257, 1935).
19. Schröder (1928).
20. Frondel (priv. comm., 1941), by x-ray powder study.

453   **B R O O K I T E** [TiO$_2$].   Jurinite *Soret* (1822).   Brookite *Lévy* (*Ann. Phil.*, **9**, 140, 1825).

     Arkansite *Shepard* (*Am. J. Sc.*, **2**, 250, 1846).   Eumanite Shepard (*Am. J. Sc.*, **12**, 211, 1851).   Pyromelane *Shepard* (*Am. J. Sc.*, **22**, 96, 1856).

C r y s t.   Orthorhombic; dipyramidal — $2/m\,2/m\,2/m$.

$$a : b : c = 0.5941 : 1 : 0.5611;^1 \qquad p_0 : q_0 : r_0 = 0.9445 : 0.5611 : 1$$

$$q_1 : r_1 : p_1 = 0.5941 : 1.0588 : 1; \qquad r_2 : p_2 : q_2 = 1.7822 : 1.6832 : 1$$

Forms:[2]

		ϕ	$\rho = C$	ϕ_1	$\rho_1 = A$	ϕ_2	$\rho_2 = B$
c	001	.....	0°00′	0°00′	90°00′	90°00′	90°00′
b	010	0°00′	90 00	90 00	90 00	.....	0 00
a	100	90 00	90 00	.....	0 00	0 00	90 00
k	180	11 53	90 00	90 00	78 07	0 00	11 53
l	140	22 49½	90 00	90 00	67 10½	0 00	22 49½
M	120	40 05	90 00	90 00	49 55	0 00	40 05
y	012	0 00	15 40½	15 40½	90 00	90 00	74 19½
x	011	0 00	29 18	29 18	90 00	90 00	60 42
d	403	90 00	51 33	0 00	38 27	38 27	90 00
t	201	90 00	62 06	0 00	27 54	27 54	90 00
χ	112	59 17	28 46½	15 40½	65 33	64 43½	75 46
e	111	59 17	47 41½	29 18	50 31½	46 38	67 48½
n	221	59 17	65 31½	48 17½	38 30½	27 54	62 18
v	133	29 17½	32 45½	29 18	74 39	72 31½	61 50½
z	122	40 05	36 15½	29 18	67 37	64 43½	63 06
ϵ	324	68 23½	37 18	15 40½	55 42½	54 41½	77 06½
Q	344	51 37	42 06	29 18	58 17½	54 41½	65 24
θ	759	67 00½	38 35½	17 19	54 57½	53 42	75 54
o	121	40 05	55 43	48 17½	57 51½	46 38	50 47½
s	131	29 17½	62 36½	59 17	64 15	46 38	39 15
i	231	48 17½	68 26	59 17	46 01½	27 54	51 46½

Structure cell.[3]   Space group *Pcab*; a_0 5.436, b_0 9.166, c_0 5.135; $a_0 : b_0 : c_0 = 0.5931 : 1 : 0.5602$;   contains Ti$_8O_{16}$.

     Habit. Found only as crystals. Usually tabular {010} and elongated [001], with {010} and the prism faces striated [001]; also prismatic [001] with {120} prominent (and sometimes simulating rutile); rarely tabular {001}, or pseudohexagonal with {120} and {111} equally developed; also pyramidal {111}. Common forms: *M b e c t y*. A dark brown to black, rarely blue, hourglass coloration is often seen through {010} as sectors extending from the terminal faces.

Twinning.[4]   Twinning on {120} has been reported but is uncertain.
Oriented growths.[5]   Incrusted by rutile, with

Rutile {110} [001] ‖ brookite {120} [001]
Rutile {110} [001] ‖ brookite {111} [001]]

Rutile also occurs as more or less complete paramorphs after brookite, in part at least oriented, with rutile [001] ‖ brookite [001].

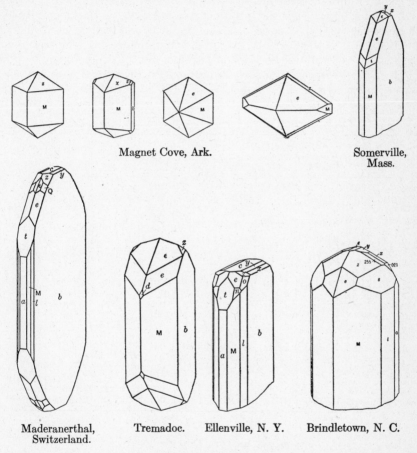

Magnet Cove, Ark.   Somerville,
                                             Mass.

Maderanerthal,   Tremadoc.   Ellenville, N. Y.   Brindletown, N. C.
Switzerland.

P h y s.   Cleavage {120} indistinct, {001} still more so.   Fracture subconchoidal to uneven.   Brittle.   H. $5\frac{1}{2}$–6.   G. 4.14 ± 0.06[6] (highest in dark-colored material); 4.12 (calc.).   Luster metallic adamantine to submetallic.   Color hair-brown, yellowish brown, reddish brown; also dark brown to iron-black.   Streak uncolored to grayish to yellowish.   Transparent in small fragments; in dark brown to black varieties transparent only in thin splinters.

O p t. In transmitted light, yellowish brown, golden brown, reddish brown to brown and dark brown in color. Zonal growth-banding is sometimes observed. Biaxial positive (+). Weakly pleochroic in yellowish, reddish, orange, and brownish tints. Absorption[7] $Z > Y > X$. Dispersion very strong, $r > v$ above ca. 555 mμ, $r < v$ below ca. 555 mμ. The optical properties vary markedly with variation in wavelength and temperature.[8] The effect of variation of the optical properties with variation in composition is unknown.

$Z = b$ for all wavelengths. With decreasing wavelength the optic angle decreases in {001} to 0° at ca. 555.5 mμ (for 25°), and then opens again and increases in {100} (see following tables). With increasing temperature at constant wavelength the optic angle decreases if in {100} and increases if in {001}. The temperature effects are reversed if the crystal is cooled, and $2E$ was reduced from 54° for red at ca. 25° to 26° at −190°.[9]

	$2E$[10]						n at 25°[11]		
λ	Temperature					Optic plane	X	Y	Z
	25°	150°	300°	450°	600°				
480	72°30					100			
491.61	68 16	62°39		56°29		100	2.6717	2.6770	2.809
500	58 33					100			
513.20	47 05		37°58			100			
520	44 58					100			
540	29 39					100			
546.07						100	2.6154	2.6159	2.7402
555.5	0								
570	21 20					001			
579.07	25 48	38 33	44 58	62 43	85°48	001	2.5895	2.5904	2.7091
580	27 48					001			
589.3						001	2.5831	2.5843	2.7004
600	37 33					001			
607.27						001	2.5718	2.5739	2.6882
620	44 57					001			
623.43		58 50	69 39	87 20	109 23	001	2.5627	2.5642	2.6770
640	50 11					001			
660	54 58					001			
671.63						001	2.5404	2.5443	2.6519
680	58 51					001			
690.73	64 02	70 50	84 11	103 30	131 22	001	2.5331	2.5375	2.6429

n_{589} AT VARYING TEMPERATURE[11]

	25°	150°	300°	450°	600°
X	2.5831	2.5856	2.5880	2.5904	2.5924
Y	2.5843	2.5869	2.5897	2.5942	2.5981
Z	2.7004	2.6903	2.6762	2.6675	2.6610

C h e m. Titanium dioxide, TiO_2, polymorphous with rutile and anatase. Small amounts of Fe^3 apparently substitute for Ti. Cb, Ta, W, Ge, and other elements have been reported in traces.[12]

Anal.[13]

	1	2	3
TiO_2	98.78	98.59	94.09
Fe_2O_3	1.43	1.41	4.50
Rem.	.....	.....	1.40
Total	100.21	100.00	99.99
G.		4.13	3.83

1. Magnet Cove, Ark. (arkansite).[14] 2. Snowdon, Wales.[15] 3. Urals. Rem. is ign. loss.[16]

Tests. B.B. infusible. Most specimens give reactions for Fe[3]. Insoluble in acids. The G. may increase on heating to redness, because of conversion to rutile.

O c c u r. Found typically, and often in fine crystals, in veins in gneiss and schist of the so-called Alpine type, associated with anatase, sphene, adularia, quartz, rutile, hematite, albite, muscovite, calcite, chlorite. As an accessory mineral in gneiss, schist, and igneous rocks, especially their hydrothermal alteration facies. Less commonly found as a contact mineral (Magnet Cove, Arkansas); in hydrothermal veinlets in or near diabase (Somerville, Massachusetts); as a very minor constituent accompanying quartz in hydrothermal sulfide deposits (Ellenville, New York); rarely in pegmatites. A common detrital mineral.

Brookite is widespread in the Alps in veins of the Alpine type. Notable localities here include places (including localities given as Amsteg, Lungenthal, Tavetsch, Griesernthal, and Cornera) in or neighboring the Maderanerthal in Uri and Graubünden, where tabular crystals more than two inches across have been found; on the Abichl-Alp in the Untersulzbachthal, Salzburg; near Pregratten, Tirol (including localities given as Frossnitz, Eicham, Virgener Thal, and Pfitsch); on the Tête-Noir on Mont Blanc, Haute Savoy, and notably at Bourg d'Oisans, Dauphiné, Isère, in France; in Italy at Sondalo, Lombardy, and at Beura, Novara, in Piedmont. In volcanic tuff at Biancavilla on Mount Etna. With apatite, tourmaline, and albite in pegmatite at Bobrůvky, Moravia, and in pegmatite at Rabenstein, Silesia. At Kuttenberg, Bohemia, and at Práchnovna, near Kutná Hora. A well-known occurrence at Fronolen near Snowdon and Tremadoc, Wales; in England as a detrital mineral in grit and sandstone in localities in Yorkshire, and as an accessory mineral with rutile and anatase in granite at Dartmoor. Fine crystals came from the Atliansk placers in the region of Miask in the Urals, U.S.S.R.; also from the gold washings of the Sanarka River, Orenburg. In Brazil as a detrital mineral in the diamond placers of Bahia and of Diamantina in Minas Geraes.

In the United States brookite occurs in North Carolina as a detrital mineral in gold placers on Pilot Mountain near Brindletown, Burke County, and similarly in McDowell County (*pyromelane?*) and Rutherford County. A notable occurrence at Magnet Cove, Arkansas (*arkansite*); here the thick crystals are deep brown to black, of variable habit, and often are incrusted by, or more or less completely altered to, rutile. In New York as small crystals upon quartz with galena and chalcopyrite at the Ellenville lead mine, Ulster County, and at Indian Ladder near Meadowdale, Albany County. At Princeton, New Jersey, with ilmenite and analcime in veinlets in Triassic sandstone near diabase intrusions. In Massachusetts at Somerville in quartz-calcite veinlets in diabase dikes, associated with rutile, anatase, sphene, albite, chlorite; in part altered to rutile. Reported from granite pegmatites at Chesterfield, Massachusetts (*eumanite?*) and Paris, Maine. Found in hydrothermal veinlets in nepheline syenite pegmatites in the Rocky Boy stock, Bearpaw Mountains, Montana. With anatase upon quartz near Placerville, El Dorado County, California.

A l t e r. More or less complete paramorphs of rutile after brookite have been found, especially at Magnet Cove, Arkansas. Also pseudomorphs of magnetite after brookite.

A r t i f. Brookite is converted into rutile by heating to temperatures above ca. 700°.[17] The reported[18] syntheses of brookite are not well authenticated.

N a m e. Brookite after the English crystallographer and mineralogist, Henry James Brooke (1771–1857). Arkansite from the locality at Magnet Cove, Arkansas. Jurinite probably after Louis Jurine (1751–1819), physician, naturalist and mineral collector, of Geneva, Switzerland.

Haidinger stated[19] in 1825 that the name jurinite was given to this species by Soret in 1822 and that the original locality was Dauphiné. All record of the original publication (if any) appears to be lost.[20]

PYROMELANE. *Shepard* (*Am. J. Sc.*, **22**, 96, 1856; 253, 1857).

A supposed titanate of iron and aluminum found in a gold placer in McDowell County, North Carolina. Later[21] placed with sphene but probably identical with brookite.[22]

EUMANITE. *Shepard* (*Am. J. Sc.*, **12**, 211, 1851).

A name given to minute crystals occurring with rubellite and microlite in pegmatite at Chesterfield, Massachusetts. Later shown to be in all probability identical with brookite.[23]

Ref.

1. Orientation and unit of Haidinger, *Ann. Phys.*, **5**, 162 (1825), angles of Koksharov (**1**, 61, 1853). Transformations:

Koksharov to Haidinger   010/002/100
Dana (242, 1892) to Haidinger   010/200/001

2. For a discussion of the form development and form list see Holzgang, *Schweiz. min Mitt.*, **10**, 374 (1930) and Arnold, *Zs. Kr.*, **71**, 344 (1929). Rare and uncertain forms:

1·18·0	205	469	13·10·16	211
1·14·0	102	4·18·9	546	472
2·23·0	809	132	252	
1·11·0	101	213	292	241
290	401	11·9·15	10·18·9	742
130	299	15·12·20	685	752
340	236	13·10·17	463	521
110	163	10·8·13	4·10·3	531
065	5·14·14	11·8·14	322	
021	235	11·10·14	11·1·6	
	255			

3. Pauling and Sturdivant, *Zs. Kr.*, **68**, 239 (1928), on a crystal from Riedertobel, Uri, Switzerland, with an analysis of the structure. Transformation: Pauling and Sturdivant to Haidinger: 010/100/001.
4. See Gliszczynski (*Cbl. Min.*, 181, 1940), Hussak, *Jb. Min.*, II, 100, 1898; vom Rath, *Zs. deutsche geol. Ges.*, **14**, 416 (1862).
5. See vom Rath, *Ann. Phys.*, **158**, 407 (1876); *Jb. Min.*, 397, 1876; Bauer, *Jb. Min.*, I, 221, 1891, Mügge, *Jb. Min., Beil.-Bd.*, **16**, 396 (1903). Other positions of orientation are stated to occur but are undefined.
6. Range of best values.
7. For a quantitative measurement of the absorption see Berek and Strieder, *Zs. Kr.*, **86**, 212 (1933).
8. For detailed optical studies see especially Schröder, *Zs. Kr.*, **67**, 485 (1928), Arnold (1929), Des Cloizeaux, *Ann. mines*, 14, 361 (1858); **2**, 11 (1862); **2**, 207, 407 (1874); also in Hintze (**1** [2A], 1546, 1906).
9. Panichi, *Zs. Kr.*, **40**, 89 (1905). Des Cloizeaux (1858) states this relation obtains in many but not all crystals from Bourg d'Oisans and Tremadoc, but the observation needs verification. Also stated by Palache, *Rosenbusch Festschr.*, 311, 1906, for some crystals from Somerville, Mass.
10. Data from Arnold (1929) at 25° on an unanalyzed crystal from the Maderanerthal locality, who summarizes the somewhat diverging earlier measurements; also Schröder (1928), for data at other temperatures, on crystal from unknown locality. The reported wavelengths for uniaxiality range between 546 mμ and 562 mμ.
11. For a detailed investigation of refractive index variation with wavelength and temperature change see Schröder (1928), who worked, however, with an unanalyzed crystal from an unknown locality. See also Wülfing (in Zirkel [**1**, 844, 1893]) Berek and Strieder (1933), who got slightly different values for nX at 25° (again on unanalyzed material).
12. Arnold (1929) and Ulrich, *Ak. Česká, Roz.*, **31**, no. 8 (1922) — *Min. Abs.*, **2**, 141 (1923).
13. For additional analyses see Doelter (**3** [1], 33, 1926).
14. Pfeil (Inaug. Diss., Heidelberg, 1901 — *Cbl. Min.*, 143, 1902).
15. Rose, *Ann. Phys.*, **61**, 515 (1844).
16. Hermann, *J. pr. Chem.*, **46**, 403 (1849).
17. See Schröder (1928).
18. See Doelter (1926).
19. Haidinger (**3**, 82, 1825).
20. The name jurinite does not appear in any of the publications by Soret listed in the *Catalogue of Scientific Literature* of the Royal Society of London. Lacroix (**3**, 172, 1901) also states that he could not find the original paper; his remark that the mineral was discovered in 1827 by Soret on the Tête-Noire, Mont Blanc, appears to be in error.
21. Dana (716, 1892).
22. Foshag, *Am. Min.*, **15**, 204 (1930).
23. Dana, *Am. J. Sc.*, **12**, 211, 397 (1851); **13**, 117 (1852).

TITANIC OXIDE. *Riggs* (*Am. J. Sc.*, **35**, 35, 1888).
A supposed rhombohedral modification of TiO_2 found as microscopic inclusions in tourmaline from Hamburg, Sussex County, New Jersey, and DeKalb, St. Lawrence County, New York. Not subsequently verified.

454   TELLURITE [TeO₂]. Tellurige Säure *Petz* (*Ann. Phys.*, **57**, 478, 1842). Tellurite *Nicol* (429, 1849). Tellurocker *Rammelsberg* (175, 1875).

Cryst. Orthorhombic; dipyramidal — $2/m\ 2/m\ 2/m$.

$a : b : c = 0.4550 : 1 : 0.4647;^1$ $\quad p_0 : q_0 : r_0 = 1.0213 : 0.4647 : 1$
$q_1 : r_1 : p_1 = 0.4550 : 0.9791 : 1;$ $\quad r_2 : p_2 : q_2 = 2.1519 : 2.1978 : 1$

Forms:[2]

		ϕ	$\rho = C$	ϕ_1	$\rho_1 = A$	ϕ_2	$\rho_2 = B$
c	001	....	0°00′	0°00′	90°00′	90°00′	90°00′
b	010	0°00′	90 00	90 00	90 00	....	0 00
a	100	90 00	90 00	.....	0 00	0 00	90 00
s	140	28 47	90 00	90 00	61 13	0 00	28 47
r	120	47 42	90 00	90 00	42 18	0 00	47 42
m	110	65 32	90 00	90 00	24 28	0 00	65 32
N	430	71 09½	90 00	90 00	18 50½	0 00	71 09½
g	034	0 00	19 13	19 13	90 00	90 00	70 47
d	101	90 00	45 36½	0 00	44 23½	44 23½	90 00
p	111	65 32	48 17½	27 41½	47 11½	44 23½	71 59½
e	131	36 13½	59 36½	54 21	59 14	44 23½	45 43
i	10·21·6	46 18	66 59	58 25	48 17	30 26	50 31

Structure cell.[3] Space group *Pcab*; a_0 5.50, b_0 11.75, c_0 5.59; $a_0 : b_0 : c_0 = 0.467 : 1 : 0.476$; contains Te_8O_{16}.

Habit. Acicular [001] and thin laths {010}, often striated [001]. Also grouped in tufts, and in spherical masses with a radiated structure; as a powdery coating.

P h y s. Cleavage {010} perfect. Flexible. H. 2. G. 5.90 ± 0.02; 5.83 (calc.). Luster subadamantine. Color white, yellowish white, honey- or straw-yellow. Transparent.

O p t.[4] Nearly colorless in transmitted light.

	ORIENTATION	n_{LI}	
X	b	2.00 ± 0.05	Bx. pos. (+).
Y	a	2.18 ± 0.02	$r < v$, moderate.
Z	c	2.35 ± 0.02	2V nearly 90°.

C h e m. Tellurium dioxide, TeO_2.
Anal.

	Te	O	Rem.	Total
1	79.94	20.06	....	100.00
2	78.68	[19.58]	1.74	100.00

Cripple Creek, Colo.

1. TeO_2. 2. Good Hope mine, Colo. Rem. is Fe_2O_3 0.70, insol. 1.04, Bi trace.[5]

Tests. When strongly heated in O.F. fuses to brown droplets and sublimes. Easily soluble in HCl, HNO_3, and alkalies, very slightly soluble in H_2O.

O c c u r. As an oxidation product of native tellurium or tellurides. In Transylvania at several mines at Zalathna in the Faczebajer Mountains, and at Nagyág. In the western Altai Mountains, U.S.S.R., in the Nikolaevsky mine. In Japan with tetradymite and nagyagite at the Rendaizi mine, Idu. In Colorado in Boulder County, in the Magnolia district at the Keystone, Smuggler and John Jay mines; in Gunnison County at the Good Hope mine; with emmonsite (?) at Cripple Creek. At Jefferson Canyon, Nye County, Nevada.

A r t i f.[6] In crystals by fusion of TeO_2, and by combustion in air or oxygen of metallic Te. A tetragonal modification not found in nature is obtained by addition of H_2O to a solution of Te in HNO_3 or H_2SO_4.

Name. In allusion to the composition.

Ref.

1. Unit and orientation of Krenner, *Term. Füz.*, **10**, 81, 106 (1886); angles of Kato, Shibata, and Nakamoto, *J. Geol. Soc. Tokyo*, **40**, 233 (1933). Goldschmidt (**8**, 118, 1922) uses another unit. Transformation: Goldschmidt to Kato $\frac{1}{2}00/010/00\frac{1}{2}$.
2. Goldschmidt (1922) and Kato, Shibata, and Nakamoto (1933). Rare or uncertain: $\{3\cdot34\cdot0\}$, $\{3\cdot16\cdot0\}$, $\{4\cdot17\cdot0\}$, $\{430\}$, $\{210\}$, $\{520\}$, $\{094\}$, $\{1\cdot42\cdot1\}$.
3. Ito, *J. Geol. Soc. Tokyo*, **40**, 613 (1933) — *Min. Abs.*, **6**, 43 (1935); the structure is similar to brookite. A dimorphous, tetragonal, modification similar to rutile is described by Zachariasen in Goldschmidt, *Zs. Kr., Strukturber.*, 211, 1931, see also Vrba and Brauner, *Zs. Kr.*, **19**, 1 (1891).
4. Larsen (142, 1921); optic orientation from Krenner, *Termes Füz.*, **10**, 81, 106 (1886) — *Zs. Kr.*, **13**, 70 (1887).
5. Headden, *Colorado Sc. Soc., Proc.*, **7**, 141 (1903). Genth, *Zs. Kr.*, **2**, 7 (1878) found that the ammonia solution of material from Boulder Co., Colo., contained only ammonium tellurate.
6. See Doelter (4 [1], 889, 1926).

455   **Selenolite** [SeO_2]. Acide sélénieux *Bertrand* (*Bull. soc. min.*, **5**, 92, 1882). Selenolite *Dana* (201, 1892).

SeO_2, reported as white needles with cerussite and molybdomenite at Cacheuta, Argentina. Artificial SeO_2 (sublimed) is tetragonal[1] with a_0 8.353, c_0 5.051. Needs verification.

Ref.

1. McCullough, *J. Am. Chem. Soc.*, **59**, 789 (1937).

456   **CERVANTITE** [Sb_2O_4?]. Spiesglanzokker pt. *Karsten* (**1**, 534, 1789; 54, 78, 1800). Antimony Ocher pt. Antimonocker pt. *Germ.* Gelbantimonerz (from Hungary) *Breithaupt* (98, 1823; 224, 1832). Acide antimonieux *Dufrénoy* (**2**, 654, 1845). Antimonous Acid, Antimonosoantimonic Oxide. Cervantite *Dana* (417, 1850). White Antimony *Meneghini* (*Am. J. Sc.*, **14**, 61, 1852).

Cryst. Orthorhombic (?).[1]

Habit. In minute acicular crystals. Usually massive, as a fibrous crust or a powder.

Phys. H. 4–5. G. 6.64 (artificial Sb_2O_4[2]). Luster greasy or pearly, also bright or earthy. Color isabella-yellow, sulfur-yellow, or nearly white; sometimes reddish white. Streak light yellow to white. Transparent.

Opt. In transmitted light, colorless. Optical study[3] of so-called cervantite has shown that the material usually is inhomogeneous, consisting of an isotropic substance (see stibiconite) with a birefringent fibrous material (cervantite?). Observed indices of refraction:

LOCALITY	n	BIREFRINGENCE	ELONGATION
Garfield Co., Utah	1.67	Low	+
Eureka district, Nev.	1.91–1.97	Moderate	
Western Australia	1.91	Strong	+
Fords Creek, New South Wales	1.98	Strong	
Utah	2.05 (β)		

Chem. An anhydrous oxide of antimony. Formula uncertain, perhaps Sb_2O_4.

Anal.

	1	2	3
Sb₂O₄	.....	.....	98.00
Sb	79.19	78.83	.....
O	20.81	19.47	.....
Rem.	.....	2.00	2.95
Total	100.00	100.30	100.95
G.		4.08	5.09

1. Sb_2O_4. 2. Pereta, Tuscany. Rem. is Fe_2O_3 1.25, gangue 0.75.[4] 3. Borneo. Rem. is CaO 2.10, MgO 0.15, H_2O 0.70.[5]

O c c u r. A secondary mineral formed by the oxidation of stibnite and other antimony minerals. Found associated with stibiconite, valentinite, bindheimite, hydrous iron and aluminum oxides, clay. The following partial list of localities includes many occurrences of massive antimony oxides or antimony ochers whose exact identity is uncertain.

In Germany at Goldkronach, Bavaria; in the Siegen region, Westphalia; at Silbersand near Mayen, Rhenish Prussia; as an alteration of bournonite at Olsa and Wölch, Carinthia. Occurs as minute acicular crystals and massive at Pereta, Tuscany, Italy. From Cervantes, Galicia, Spain. In France at Chazelles, Puy-de-Dôme and at Allemont, Isère. At several localities in Cornwall, England. In Algeria with valentinite at Semsa, Constantine, and impregnated with earthy cinnabar at Djebel-Taya near Guelma. Found at many localities in Peru and Bolivia. From Waikare, New Zealand; the Wiluna district, Western Australia; from the Heazlewood district and elsewhere in Tasmania; at Costerfield, Victoria. In pseudomorphs after stibnite from Borneo. In Mexico in the Altar district, Sonora; from the Carmen mine, Zacualpan; at Huitzuco, Guerrero. In the United States reported from Garfield County, and from the Emma mine, Little Cottonwood Canyon, Salt Lake County, in Utah. In the Wood River district, Blaine County, Idaho. In New Mexico in the Central district, Grant County. In California in the Wild Rose district Inyo County, and in the San Emidio mine, Kern County.

A l t e r. Very commonly found as pseudomorphs after stibnite. Also as an alteration product of bournonite, jamesonite, allemontite, and tetrahedrite.

A r t i f.[6] Obtained as a powder by heating Sb, Sb_2O_3 or Sb_2O_5 in air; Sb_2O_4 is the stable oxide between ca. 585° and 775°. Also formed by igniting Sb_3O_6OH at 800–900°.

N a m e. From the supposed locality at Cervantes, Prov. Lugo, Spain.

Ref.

1. Stated by Dana (187, 1868) and others to occur as acicular, orthorhombic crystals but descriptive details are lacking. An artificial orthorhombic modification of Sb_2O_4 has a_0 4.804, b_0 5.424, c_0 11.76, space group *Pna*, according to Dihlstrom, *Zs. anorg. Chem.*, **239**, 57 (1938), but the relation of this material to the natural mineral is unknown.
2. Winkler in Mellor (**9**, 435, 1929), the reported specific gravities of the natural and artificial materials vary widely.

3. Larsen (54, 136, 1921). A number of other specimens from unknown localities were examined by Larsen.
4. Bechi anal. in Meneghini (1852).
5. Frenzel, *Min. Mitt.*, 298, 1877.
6. See Mellor (1929), Dihlström (1938), Dehlinger, *Zs. Kr.*, 66, 108 (1927).

457   S T I B I C O N I T E [Sb₃O₆(OH)?]. Antimony Ocher pt. (syn. under Cervantite). Stibiconise *Beudant* (2, 616, 1832).   Stiblith *Blum* and *Delffs* (*J. pr. Chem.*, 40, 318, 1847). Stibiconite *Brush* (*Am. J. Sc.*, 34, 207, 1862).

C r y s t. Isometric; hexoctahedral (?).[1]
Habit. Massive, compact; also as a powder and in crusts; botryoidal, and in concentric shells.[2]
P h y s. H. 4–5½. G. 5.58 (Arkansas, anal. 3). Luster pearly to earthy; opaline; glassy. Color pale yellow to yellowish white, reddish white. Transparent.
O p t. In transmitted light, colorless to cloudy. Isotropic. The reported[3] indices of refraction (for material of unknown composition but ascribed to stibiconite) vary almost continuously from 1.60 to 2.00. Often admixed with birefringent fibrous material (see cervantite). Observed indices of refraction of the isotropic material:

LOCALITY	n	LOCALITY	n
Kern Co., Calif.	1.605–1.63	Garfield Co., Utah	1.69 ± 0.01
Kern Co., Calif.	1.97–2.00	Pima Co., Ariz.	1.86 ± 0.01
Unionville, Nev.	1.647 ± 0.005	Cornwall, England	1.86–1.90

C h e m. Apparently a basic or hydrated oxide of antimony. Formula uncertain, perhaps Sb₃O₆OH.[1] Contains Ca but its role is uncertain (anal. 5, 6).
Anal.

	1	2	3	4	5	6
Sb₂O₅	.....	.....	......	.....	46.42	58.66
Sb₂O₃	.....	.....	......	.....	43.44	34.96
Sb	76.37	75.83	[76.15]	75.0	[71.23]	[73.35]
O	21.75	19.54	19.85	[20.0]	[18.63]	[20.27]
CaO	.....	.....	......	.....	3.71	0.95
H₂O	1.88	4.63	3.08	5.0	5.75	2.57
Rem.	.....	trace	0.92	.....	0.50	0.59
Total	100.00	100.00	100.00	100.00	99.82	97.73
G.		5.28	5.58	5.07		

1. Sb₃O₆OH. 2. Losacio, Spain. Rem. is As.[4] 3. Sevier Co., Ark. Rem. is insol.[5] 4. Sonora, Mexico.[6] 5. Szalonack, Hungary. Rem. is Fe₂O₃.[7] 6. Oruro, Bolivia (cervantite ?). Rem. is Fe₂O₃.[7]

Tests. In C.T. gives off water but does not fuse. On charcoal decrepitates, fuses with difficulty to a gray slag and gives a white coating.

O c c u r. A secondary mineral formed by the oxidation of stibnite and other antimony minerals. Associated with cervantite and valentinite. Only a few of the many reported localities of so-called antimony ocher are known with any certainty to afford stibiconite, but the mineral probably is common.

Found in Spain at Losacio, Zamora (*stiblith*). In Mexico in the Altar district, Sonora. An alteration product of stibnite from Chayramonte, Cajamarca, Peru, apparently belongs here.[8] Reported from Wiluna, Central Division, Western Australia. From Borneo as an alteration of stibnite. In the United States in Sevier County, Arkansas; from the Black Warrior mine near Unionville, Nevada; as an alteration product of stibnite at Antimony, Garfield County, Utah; from Pima County, Arizona. Reported from the Stanley stibnite mine, Shoshone County, Idaho; also from Little Caliente Springs and on Erskine Creek, Kern County, California. Reported from South Ham, Wolfe County, Quebec, Canada, as an alteration of stibnite.

Alter. Found as pseudomorphs after stibnite.

Artif. The compound Sb_3O_6OH has been formed by heating antimonic acid.[1]

Name. From *stibium*, *antimony*, and κόνις, *powder* or *dust*, because it often occurs as a powder.

Ref.

1. The artificial compound Sb_3O_6OH has the space group $Fd3m$, $a_0 = 10.28$, cell contents $Sb_{24}O_{48}(OH)_8$ and a calculated specific gravity of 5.78 according to Dihlström and Westgren, *Zs. anorg. Chem.*, **235**, 153 (1937), but the relation of this substance to the natural mineral is uncertain. See also Natta and Baccaredda, *Zs. Kr.*, **85**, 271 (1933), who investigated a stibiconite from Szalonack (anal. 5) apparently identical with Sb_3O_6OH.
2. Lewis, *Am. Nat.*, 608, 1882, mentions octahedral crystals in material from Mexico not certainly identified as stibiconite.
3. Larsen (136, 1921). A number of specimens from unknown localities were also examined by Larsen, and these too were very variable.
4. Delffs anal. in Blum and Delffs (1847).
5. Santos, *Chem. News*, **36**, 167 (1877).
6. Sharples, *Am. J. Sc.*, **20**, 423 (1880).
7. Natta and Baccaredda (1933).
8. Raimondi (190, 194, 196, 1878).

The following ill-defined materials probably represent mixtures largely composed of antimony and arsenic oxides. Antimonates or antimonites of Cu, Fe, Ca, etc., also may be represented.

VOLGERITE. Antimony Ocher pt. Hydrous Antimonic Acid. Volgerite *Dana* (142, 1854). Cumengite *Kenngott* (29, 1853). (Not the cumengeite of *Mallard*.) Massive, or as a powder. Color white. Analysis gave: Sb 62.0, O 17.0, H_2O 15.0, Fe_2O_3 1.0, gangue 3.0, total 98.0. Found in the province of Constantine, Algeria. A somewhat similar substance occurs as an alteration product of stibnite at the Stanley mine, near Burke, Idaho.[6] Named after G. H. O. Volger (1822–97); German mineralogist.

STETEFELDITE. *Riotte* (*B. H. Ztg.*, **26**, 253, 1867). Massive. H. $3\frac{1}{2}$–$4\frac{1}{2}$. G. 4.12–4.24. Color black to brown. Streak shining. Analysis gave (mean of two): Sb_2O_4 43.77, S 4.7, Ag 23.74, Cu 12.78, Fe 1.82, H_2O 7.9, total 94.71. From the Empire and Philadelphia districts in southeastern Nevada. Named after C. Stetefeld, mining engineer. A similar material occurs in the Potosi mine, near Huancavelica, Peru;[1] analysis gave: Sb_2O_4 32.93, CuO 32.27, Fe_2O_3 11.14, ZnO 0.50, SO_3 1.00, H_2O (loss at low redness) 18.53, insol. 1.57, total 97.94.

BuddyBISMITE   599

PARTZITE.   *Arents (Am. J. Sc.*, **43**, 362, 1867).
Massive. Fracture conchoidal to even. H. 3–4. G. 3.8.   Color variable: yellowish green to blackish green and black. Analysis gave Sb_2O_4 47.65, CuO 32.11, Ag_2O 6.12, PbO 2.01, FeO 2.33, H_2O 8.29, total 98.51.   The Ag content varies from 4 to 12 per cent, and the material appears to be a mixture[2] consisting largely of a hydrous antimony oxide. Found as an alteration product of antimonial sulfide ores in the Blind Spring district, Mono County, California. Rather similar materials have been found in Peru[3] and elsewhere (see also rivotite).

ARSENSTIBITE.   *Adam* (1869); *Des Cloizeaux* (**2**, 334, 1893).
A name given to a hydrous oxide of As and Sb, possibly from Borneo. Analysis gave As_2O_5 13, Sb_2O_3 64, H_2O 23, total 100.

STIBIOFERRITE.   Stibiaferrite *Goldsmith* (*Ac. Sc. Philadelphia, Proc.*, 366, 1873). Stibioferrite *Dana* (204, 1892).
Found as thin coatings[4] on stibnite. Fracture uneven to conchoidal. Brittle. H. 4. G. 3.598. Luster slightly resinous. Color yellow to brownish yellow. Streak dull yellow. Soluble in HCl. Analysis gave Sb_2O_5 42. 96, Fe_2O_3 31.85, H_2O 15.26, SiO_2 8.84, loss 1.09, total 100.00. Occurs as an alteration product of stibnite in Santa Clara County, California.

RIVOTITE.   *Ducloux* (*C. R.*, **78**, 1471, 1874).
Compact massive. Fragile. Fracture uneven. H. $3\frac{1}{2}$–4. G. 3.55–3.62. Color yellowish green to grayish green. Streak grayish green. Analysis gave: Sb_2O_5 42.00, Ag_2O 1.18, CuO 39.50, CO_2 21.00, CaO tr., total 103.68. Occurs in small irregular masses disseminated through a yellowish white limestone, on the west side of the Sierra del Cadi, Lerida, Spain. Named after L. E. Rivot (1820–69), Professor of Assaying in the School of Mines, Paris.

STIBIANITE.   *Goldsmith* (*Ac. Sc. Philadelphia, Proc.*, 154, 1878).
In porous masses. H. 5. G. 3.67. Luster dull. Color reddish yellow. Streak pale yellow. Analysis gave: Sb_2O_5 81.21, gangue 13.55, H_2O 4.46, total 99.22. An alteration product of stibnite from Victoria, Australia.

ARSENOSTIBITE.   *Quensel* (*Geol. För. Förh.*, **59**, 145, 1937).
As porous yellow coatings. Fracture conchoidal. In transmitted light, yellow in color and isotropic with n 1.670–1.685. Essentially a hydrous oxide of antimony and arsenic, with Fe_2O_3 reported and possibly due to admixture. Analysis gave (after deduction of 18.1 per cent insoluble): Sb_2O_5 55.2, As_2O_5 6.8, Sb_2O_3 5.2, As_2O_3 7.1, Fe_2O_3 7.5, Bi_2O_3 0.4, H_2O (+105°) 8.0, H_2O (−105°) 9.8, total 100.0. Found as an alteration product of allemontite in pegmatite at Varuträsk, about 20 km. southeast of the Boliden mine, in northern Sweden. Named in allusion to the composition.

Ref.

1. Domeyko (in Dana, 1871).
2. Blake, *Am. J. Sc.*, **44**, 119 (1867).
3. Raimondi (**45**, 83, 86, 87, 167, 1878).
4. The morphological data given by Goldsmith (1873) probably refer to altered crystals of stibnite.
5. Dougherty anal. in Goldsmith (1878).
6. Shannon, *Am. Min.*, **3**, 26 (1918).

447   **Bismite** [Bi_2O_3]. Wismuthum terrestre pulverulentum flavescens, Ochra wismuthi (pt. ?) *Wallerius* (**2**, 209, 1753). Mine de bismuth calciforme (pt.?) *de Lisle* (**3**, 113, 1783). Wismuthokker (pt.?) *Emmerling* (**2**, 440, 1796). Bismuth oxydé (pt.?) *Haüy* (**4**, 194, 1801). Bismite *Dana* (185, 1868). Bismite (α-Bi_2O_3) *Frondel* (*Am. Min.*, **28**, 521, 1943). Bismuth trioxide, Bismuth ocher pt. Wismuth-oxyd, Wismuthocker pt., Wismuthblüthe pt. *Germ.* Bismutocra *Ital.*

C r y s t.[1] Monoclinic (pseudo-orthorhombic); prismatic — $2/m$.
Structure Cell.[2] Space group $P2_1/c$; a_0 5.83, b_0 8.14, c_0 7.48; $\beta = 67°4'$; $a_0 : b_0 : c_0 = 0.716 : 1 : 0.919$; contains Bi_8O_{12}.

Habit. Massive; compact granular to earthy and pulverulent.

P h y s. Fracture of massive material uneven to earthy. H. $4\frac{1}{2}$, decreasing in earthy material. G. 8.64 (Bolivia[3]), 9.22 (Meymac, France[4]), 10.4 (calc.). Luster subadamantine to dull, earthy. Color grayish green, greenish yellow to bright yellow. Streak grayish to yellow. Transparent, in very small fragments.

O p t. Biaxial, with high dispersion and refractive indices above 2.42.

C h e m. Bismuth trioxide, Bi_2O_3. Polymorphous with sillenite. The available analyses are on impure material not shown certainly to belong to this species.[5]

O c c u r. A secondary mineral, formed by the oxidation of native bismuth and other bismuth minerals. Found as an alteration crust on water-worn masses of native bismuth at Colavi, Bolivia. Probably occurs in pegmatite at Rincon, San Diego County, California, as microscopic crystals[6] associated with bismutite and pucherite. Material hitherto referred to bismite but not certainly this species has been reported from numerous localities. Here may be mentioned Schneeberg, Schwarzenberg, and Johanngeorgenstadt in Saxony; Siegen, Westphalia; Joachimstal, Bohemia. Also at Meymac, Corrèze, France, with bismutite. At several localities in Cornwall, England. As an alteration of aikinite at Beresov, in the Urals, U.S.S.R. In Tasmania at Mount McDonald. At Tasna and Esmoraca, Bolivia. In Durango, Mexico. In the United States, bismuth oxide has been reported from Petaca, New Mexico; from Beaver County, Utah; and from localities in North Carolina. The supposed rhombohedral bismite from Goldfield, Nevada, is bismoclite.

A r t i f.[7] Four polymorphous modifications of artificial Bi_2O_3 have been described: α-Bi_2O_3 (bismite); a body-centered isometric form (sillenite); and tetragonal and simple cubic modifications not yet found in nature. α-Bi_2O_3, the form stable under ordinary conditions, is obtained by heating or aging the hydrous precipitate formed by the reaction of bismuth nitrate and alkalies in water solution; also, as microscopic crystals, from fusion in KOH or from hot water solutions of KOH.

N a m e. In allusion to the composition. The name hitherto has been applied to material supposedly an oxide of bismuth but in most cases not clearly identified either as such or as a specific polymorph. The name bismite, first given by J. D. Dana in 1868, is here restricted[8] to the monoclinic polymorph, α-Bi_2O_3, known to occur in nature at Colavi, Bolivia. The true nature of the other reported occurrences of bismuth oxide remains to be determined. The early occurrences reported by Wallerius in 1753 and by Lampadius[9] in 1801 probably were of the basic carbonate, bismutite.

Hydrated bismuth oxide. A hydrated oxide or hydroxide of bismuth has been reported[8] from Colavi, Bolivia, and other localities, but evidence of species validity or of distinction from bismite is lacking. Found as earthy, creamy-white to yellow masses as an alteration product of bismuth minerals. $Bi_2O_3 \cdot 3H_2O$ is known as an artificial compound.[10]

Ref.

1. Crystallography based on the x-ray structural study of Sillén, *Ark. Kemi*, **12**, no. 18 (1938), and *Zs. Kr.*, **103**, 274 (1941) on artificial material, shown by Frondel, *Am. Min.*, **28**, 521 (1943) to be identical with natural material from Colavi, Bolivia. The Dana (200, 1892) crystallography was based on the orthorhombic symmetry earlier attributed to the artificial material by Nordenskiöld, *Ann. Phys.*, **114**, 622 (1861).
2. Sillén (1941).
3. Frondel, *Am. Min.*, **28**, 521 (1943) by microbalance on compact massive material.
4. Carnot, *C. R.*, **79**, 478 (1874).
5. See Doelter (3[1], 815, 1926), Stelzner, *Zs. deutsche geol. Ges.*, **49**, 134 (1897), and Schaller, *J. Am. Chem. Soc.*, **33**, 162 (1911).
6. Rogers, *Sch. Mines Q.*, **31**, 208 (1910).
7. Sillén (1938, 1941); Frondel (1943).
8. Frondel (1943).
9. Lampadius, *Handb. chem. anal. Min. Freiberg*, 288, 1801.
10. See Weiser (2, 304, 1935) and Mellor (9, 646, 1929).

448   Sillenite [Bi_2O_3].   *Frondel* (*Am. Min.*, **28**, 521, 1943).

C r y s t.[1] Isometric; hextetrahedral — $\bar{4}\,3\,m$ (?).

Structure Cell.[2] Body-centered isometric; a_0 10.08; contains $Bi_{24}O_{36}$.

Habit. As fine-grained masses; earthy.

P h y s. Soft. G. 8.80 (calc.). Luster waxy to dull, earthy. Color olive drab to grayish green, green, and yellowish green. Transparent in small fragments.

O p t. In transmitted light, yellow to golden yellow. Isotropic. $n > 2.42$.

C h e m. Bismuth trioxide, Bi_2O_3. Polymorphous with bismite. Artificial material has a very small but apparently definite content of Si, Al, or Fe.[3] Analyses of natural material are lacking.[4]

O c c u r. A secondary product found associated with bismutite at Durango, Mexico.

A r t i f.[5] Obtained by the brief fusion and rapid cooling of Bi_2O_3 in a porcelain crucible. Also obtained by the reaction of water solutions of $Bi(NO_3)_3$ and KOH or KCN in glass vessels.

N a m e. After Lars Gunnar Sillén, of Stockholm, who did much work on the bismuth oxides.

Ref.

1. From x-ray structural study of Sillén, *Ark. Kemi*, **12A**, no. 18 (1938) on artificial material, shown by Frondel (1943) by x-ray powder study to be identical with the natural mineral. The crystal class is probably hextetrahedral from the crystallographic observations of Muir and Hutchinson, *J. Chem. Soc.*, London, **55**, 143 (1889), on microscopic artificial crystals.
2. Sillén (1938) on artificial material.
3. The impurity content may act either as a stabilizer of this modification or may be an integral part of the composition. (Cf. Sillén [1938].)
4. Spectrographic analysis of natural material by Rabbitt in Frondel (1943) reveals only Bi, with traces of Si and Al.
5. Sillén (1938); Muir and Hutchinson (1889).

461   Vanoxite [$V_4V_2O_{13}\cdot 8H_2O$?].   *Hess* (*U. S. Geol. Sur., Bull. 750d*, 63, 1925).

In microscopic crystals, sometimes with a rhombohedral section; massive, as a cement in sandstone. Color black. Opaque; extremely thin fragments transmit a brownish color.

C h e m.   A hydrous oxide of vanadium, $V_4V_2O_{13} \cdot 8H_2O$?   (The water content may be higher than is indicated by the formula.)

Anal.

	1	2	3	4	5
V_2O_4	50.44	53.1	50.9	51.60	49.66
V_2O_5	27.65	25.7	29.5	27.03	29.91
UO_3	.....	0.5	0.2	.....	.....
H_2O	21.91	20.7	19.4	21.37	20.43
Total	100.00	100.00	100.00	100.00	100.00

1. $V_4V_2O_{13} \cdot 8H_2O$.   2. Jo Dandy claim.   Analysis recalc. after deduction of 77.55 per cent impurities (quartz, tyuyamunite, gypsum, pyrite, etc.).[1]   3. Jo Dandy claim. Analysis recalc. after deduction of 55.62 per cent impurities.[1]   4. Jo Dandy claim. Analysis recalc. after deduction of unstated amount of quartz, gypsum, carnotite, ferganite, uvanite, etc.[2]   5. Jo Dandy claim. H_2O includes $H_2O + 13.54$, $H_2O - 6.89$ per cent.   Analysis recalc. after deduction of unstated amount of impurities.[2]

O c c u r.   Found on the Jo Dandy claim in Paradox Valley, Montrose County, Colorado, as a cement in sandstone of the McElmo formation (Jurassic?), and as thin coatings along cracks and in masses as a replacement of wood.   Associated with carnotite, gypsum, hewettite, pintadoite, tyuyamunite, pyrite.   Also reported from the Bill Bryan claim, Wild Steer Canyon, Paradox Valley, in concretionary masses in sandstone, and from the Henry Clay claim at Long Park on the northeast side of Paradox Valley, with pascoite as an impregnation of sandstone.   Reported from the Kunkle claim, 6 miles west of Gateway, Colorado.

N a m e.   From *van*adium *ox*ide, in allusion to the composition.

Ref.

1. Schaller anal. in Hess (1925).
2. Schaller anal. in Wells, *U. S. Geol. Sur., Bull. 878*, 93, 1937.

462   Corvusite [$V_2V_{12}O_{34} \cdot nH_2O$?].   *Henderson* and *Hess* (*Am. Min.*, **18**, 195, 1933).

Found only massive.   Fracture conchoidal.   H. $2\frac{1}{2}$–3.   G. 2.82 (?). Color and streak blue-black to brown.   Opaque.

C h e m.   A hydrous oxide of vanadium, perhaps $V_2V_{12}O_{34} \cdot nH_2O$. Fe_2O_3 is reported in analyses, especially in the brown material, and probably is due to admixture.

Anal.

	1	2	3	4
Na_2O	1.44	1.24	not det.	not det.
K_2O	1.06	2.15	not det.	not det.
CaO	1.98	0.40	1.85	1.70
MgO	0.27	2.07	not det.	not det.
Fe_2O_3	5.82	12.20	1.69	0.99
V_2O_4	9.67	7.62	10.26	10.13
V_2O_5	64.89	50.68	69.00	65.24
UO_3	1.71	2.94	1.16	3.12
H_2O	11.68	15.83	13.52	14.09
Insol.	1.08	.....	0.16	0.17
Sol. SiO_2	0.30	4.21	0.63	2.19
MoO_3	not det.	0.28	0.16	0.18
Total	99.90	99.62	98.43	97.81

1. Purple material. Jack claim, La Sal Mts., Grand Co., Utah.[1] 2. Brown material. Jack claim. Recalc. after deduction of 21.52 per cent insol.[1] 3. Purple-black material. Ponto No. 3 claim, Gypsum Valley, San Miguel Co., Colo.[2] 4. Brownish black material. Ponto No. 3 claim.[2]

Tests. Soluble in acids, but before complete decomposition takes place the blue material changes to brown and becomes more slowly soluble. The V_2O_5 is partially extracted in cold water.

O c c u r. Found as an impregnation in sandstone, associated with carnotite, roscoelite, ferganite, asphaltic material, rauvite, vanoxite. Probably widespread in the carnotite region of Utah and Colorado. Described from the Jack claim on the east side of the La Sal Mountains, Grand County, Utah (about 10 miles west of Gateway, Colorado), and from the Ponto No. 3 claim in Gypsum Valley, San Miguel County, Colorado.

N a m e. From *corvus, raven*, in allusion to the color.

Needs further investigation.

Ref.

1. Henderson anal. in Henderson and Hess (1933).
2. Schaller anal. cited in Henderson and Hess (1933).

ALAITE. Alaïte *Nenadkewicz* (*Ac. sc. St. Pétersbourg, Bull.*, **3** [6], 185, 1909). Aloite.

An ill-defined substance, supposedly a hydrated vanadium oxide, $V_2O_5 \cdot H_2O$, found as soft dark blood-red mosslike masses at Tyuya-Muyun in the Alai Mountains, Ferghana, Russian Turkestan. $V_2O_5 \cdot H_2O$ is known as an artificial compound.[1]

Ref.

1. Weiser (**2**, 288, 1935) and Mellor (**9**, 748, 1929).

ROBELLAZITE. *Cumenge* (*Bull. soc. min.*, **23**, 17, 1900).

An ill-defined substance, presumably a mixture, found as black concretions associated with carnotite from Colorado. Contains Cb, Ta, W, V, Al, Fe, Mn. Named after a French engineer, Robellaz, who studied the occurrence.

TANTALIC OCHER. Tantalochra *Nordenskiöld* (27, 1855). Tantalic Ocher *Dana* (188, 1868). Tantalocker *Hintze* (1 [2A], 1259, 1903).

A brown coating occurring on crystals of tantalite at Pennikoja, Somero, Finland. Believed to have the composition Ta_2O_5. Artificial Ta_2O_5 is dimorphous,[1] orthorhombic and isometric (?).

Ref.

1. Nordenskiöld, *Ann. Phys.*, **110**, 642 (1860), and Florence, *Jb. Min.*, II, 132, 1898.

463   Ilsemannite [$Mo_3O_8 \cdot nH_2O$?]. *Höfer* (*Jb. Min.*, 566, 1871). Molybdenum Blue.

Found only as earthy masses or crusts, and as a stain or disseminated pigment. Color black, blue-black or blue, becoming blue on exposure. Readily peptized by water, giving a deep blue sol.

C h e m. The composition of the natural and artificial so-called molybdenum blue is uncertain, and has been variously interpreted as a molybdenum sulfate, $MoO_3 \cdot SO_3 \cdot 5H_2O$,[1] as a molybdyl molybdate[2] and, more probably, as a hydrous oxide, $Mo_3O_8 \cdot nH_2O$.[3] Possibly several different substances are represented among the natural occurrences. Analyses of water extracts of ilsemannite-bearing rocks have been reported.[4]

O c c u r. Ilsemannite is a secondary mineral formed by the oxidation of molybdenite or other molybdenum minerals.[5] Found associated with iron, aluminum, or magnesium sulfates, and often colors crystals of those species blue. Originally described from Bleiberg, Carinthia, Germany, associated with wulfenite, barite, and gypsum; also from Himmelsfürst mine, near Freiberg, Germany. Observed with aluminite in sandstone in the Hlatimbe Valley, Natal, South Africa. At Bamford, Queensland, Australia, as stains in molybdenite-bearing quartz. In the United States found associated with halotrichite and molybdite in sandstone near Ouray, Utah; as an alteration product of molybdenite at Gibson, Shasta County, California; as a pigment in copiapite in a molybdenite deposit near the head of Death Valley, California; reported as stains from a number of localities in Clear Creek and Boulder counties, and found as an alteration product of molybdenite at Cripple Creek, in Colorado. Observed in a mine water in the Lucania tunnel, near Idaho Springs, Colorado.[6]

A r t i f.[7] The deep blue hydrous precipitate or sol known as *molybdenum blue* is readily obtained by reducing a solution of MoO_3 or an acidified molybdate, by oxidizing lower oxides such as MoO_2, and by the reaction of a cold HCl solution of MoO_2 with ammonium molybdate. The sol prepared by reduction of a molybdate solution made acid with HS_2O_4 is negatively charged.

N a m e. After J. C. Ilsemann (1727–1822), a former Mining Commissioner at Clausthal, Harz, who early published (1787) a study of molybdenite.

Ref.

1. Schaller, *Washington Ac. Sc., J.*, **7**, 417 (1917); see also Hess, *U. S. Geol. Sur., Bull. 750A*, 1923.
2. Weiser (**2**, 311, 1935) and Höfer (1871).
3. Dittler, *Cbl. Min.*, 689, 1922; 705, 1923; and Weiser (1935).
4. See Hess (1923) and Dittler (1922, 1923) for a summarizing discussion of the analyses.
5. Details of the occurrences have been summarized by Hess (1923), and the chemistry of formation of ilsemannite is also discussed by Dittler (1922, 1923).
6. Horton, *U. S. Bur. Mines Bull. 111*, 15, 1916, with analysis by Wells.
7. Literature in Weiser (1935).

464   R U S S E L L I T E [$(Bi_2,W)O_3$]. *Hey, Bannister*, and *Russell* (*Min. Mag.*, **25**, 41, 1938).

C r y s t. Tetragonal; scalenohedral — $\bar{4}2/m$; or ditetragonal-dipyramidal — $4/m\ 2/m\ 2/m$.

Structure cell. Space group $I\bar{4}2d$ or $I4/amd$; a_0 5.42 ± 0.03, c_0 11.3 ± 0.3; $a_0 : c_0 = 1 : 2.084$; cell contents $4(Bi_2,W)O_3$.

Habit. Found only as fine-grained compact masses.

P h y s. H. $3\frac{1}{2}$. G. 7.35 ± 0.02; 7.40 (calc. for anal. 2). Color pale yellow to greenish.

C h e m. An oxide of bismuth and tungsten, $(Bi_2,W)O_3$. W substitutes for Bi to W : Bi = 1 : 1.9 in anal. 2.

Anal.

	1	2
Bi_2O_3	68.26	62.3
WO_3	25.50	32.1
As_2O_3	0.26	0.29
Fe_2O_3	trace	n.d.
Insol.	1.60	1.6
Ign. loss	4.86	n.d.
Total	100.48	96.29

1, 2. Castle-an-Dinas, Cornwall. State of oxidation of As not determined.

O c c u r. An alteration product, probably of native bismuth, found with wolframite, topaz, lithia-mica, tourmaline, cassiterite, native bismuth, and bismuthinite at the Castle-an-Dinas mine, St. Columb Major, Cornwall.

A r t i f.[2] An artificial compound with a composition near $Bi_2O_3 \cdot 2WO_3$ has been obtained by fusion of Bi tungstate with excess NaCl at 700–900°. This material is either a member of the same isomorphous series as russellite or has a very closely allied structure.

N a m e. After the British mineralogist, Arthur Russell.

Ref.

1. Possible crystal classes from x-ray study.
2. Zambonini, *Gazz. chim. ital.*, **50** [2], 129, 132 (1920), and Hey, Bannister, and Russell (1938).

465   T U N G S T I T E [$WO_3 \cdot H_2O$?]. Tungstic Ocher *Silliman* (*Am. J. Sc.*, **4**, 52, 1822). Wolframocker *Leonhard* (345, 1826). Wolframsäure *von Kobell* (**2**, 35, 1831). Wolframine *Greg* and *Lettsom* (in Dana [143, 1854, 349, 1858]). Tungstite *Dana* (186, 1868). Wolframocker *Germ.*

Meymacit *Carnot* (*C. R.*, **79**, 639, 1874).

Possibly orthorhombic.[1] Found massive, pulverulent to earthy and as microscopic platy crystals.

P h y s. Cleavage {001} perfect,[2] and {110} imperfect.[3] H. $2\frac{1}{2}$. Luster resinous; on the cleavage pearly. Color bright yellow, golden yellow, yellowish green. Transparent.

O p t. In transmitted light, yellow.

ORIENTATION		n	
X	c	2.09 ± 0.02	Bx. neg. (−). 2V 26°±.[3] Dispersion
Y		2.24 ± 0.02	r < v, rather strong. Absorption strong,
Z		2.26 ± 0.02	Z > Y > X.

C h e m. Composition uncertain. Formerly considered to be WO_3, but probably the monohydrate, $WO_3 \cdot H_2O$.[5] The available analyses[6] are on very impure material.

Tests. B.B. infusible. Soluble in alkalies but not in acids.

O c c u r. An oxidation product of wolframite and other tungsten minerals. In France at La Vilate near Chanteloube, Haute-Vienne, and as an alteration of scheelite at Meymac, Corrèze (*meymacite*). Reported from Genna Gureu, near Orroli, Sardinia. In Cornwall, England, at the Drakewall mine, near Callington, and at the Huel Friendship and other mines in Gwennap; at Carrock Fells, Cumberland. Reported from Ben Lomond, Tasmania. In Bolivia at Oruro and at Tazna, and as an alteration of ferberite at Calacalani near Colquiri. In the United States tungstite occurs at Lanes' mine, Monroe (the original locality) and at Huntington, in Connecticut; in Cabarrus County, North Carolina; as an alteration product of huebnerite at Osceola, Nevada; reported from the Black Hills region, South Dakota, and from Salida, Colorado; also from the Blue Wing district, Lemhi County, Idaho. Found as minute crystals at the Kootenay Belle mine, Salmo, British Columbia, and reported from Marlow, Beauce County, Quebec.

A l t e r. Observed as an alteration product of wolframite, huebnerite, ferberite, and scheelite. Well-formed pseudomorphs after scheelite have been found (meymacite).

A r t i f. Anhydrous WO_3 has been prepared artificially in crystals,[7] and several ill-defined hydrates have been prepared by precipitation from solution.[8]

N a m e. In allusion to the composition.

Needs investigation.

MEYMACITE.   *Carnot* (*C. R.*, **79**, 639, 1874).
A yellow alteration product of scheelite found at Meymac, Corrèze, France. The analyses approximate to $WO_3 \cdot 2H_2O$, but it probably is identical with tungstite.

Ref.

1. The optical data of Walker, *Univ. Toronto Stud.*, *Geol. Ser.*, no. 35, 13, 1933, on the Kootenay Belle material indicate orthorhombic symmetry. Dana (202, 1892) considered the mineral to be identical with an artificial orthorhombic anhydrous modification of WO_3 described by Nordenskiöld, *Ann. Phys.*, **114**, 623 (1861), but Walker, *Am. J. Sc.*, **25**, 305 (1908), has shown that the natural material probably is a monohydrate.
2. Walker (1908) on Kootenay Belle material.
3. Walker (1933) on Kootenay Belle material.
4. Larsen (147, 1921) on Kootenay Belle material.
5. Walker (1908).
6. See Walker (1908), and Carnot, *C. R.*, **79**, 639 (1874) (on meymacite).
7. See Mellor (**11**, 753, 762, 1931).
8. See Weiser (**2**, 315, 1935) and Mellor (1931).

OXIDES CONTAINING URANIUM, THORIUM, AND ZIRCONIUM

Uraninite and thorianite have the fluorite structure and baddeleyite has a distorted fluorite structure.[1] The other minerals containing uranium are more complex and structural studies of them have not, as yet, been made. Since the other uranium minerals of this class are usually derived by alteration from uraninite, they are hydrous. The lead contained in most of them is probably radiogenic, and its role in the composition is not clear.

Gummite is a convenient name for indeterminate alteration products of uraninite, some of which are non-crystalline with variable water content. Some substances now placed with gummite may prove, upon investigation, to be valid mineral species.

The alteration products of uraninite are all brilliantly colored, mostly in orange and yellow. They possess a perfect cleavage in the basal plane (as here taken) and the acute bisectrix is usually normal to that cleavage. (These features of cleavage and optical orientation are common to most minerals containing considerable amounts of uranium).

5 OXIDES CONTAINING URANIUM (ALSO THORIUM AND ZIRCONIUM)

511	Baddeleyite	ZrO_2
512	URANINITE GROUP	
5121	Uraninite	UO_2
5122	Thorianite	ThO_2
521	Gummite	$UO_3 \cdot nH_2O$
522	Clarkeite	$UO_3 \cdot nH_2O$?
523	Becquerelite	$2UO_3 \cdot 3H_2O$?
524	Schoepite	$4UO_3 \cdot 9H_2O$?
531	Fourmarierite	$PbO \cdot 4UO_3 \cdot 5H_2O$?
532	Curite	$2PbO \cdot 5UO_3 \cdot 4H_2O$?
533	Uranosphaerite	$Bi_2O_3 \cdot 2UO_3 \cdot 3H_2O$?
534	Vandenbrandite	$CuO \cdot UO_3 \cdot 2H_2O$
535	Ianthinite	$2UO_2 \cdot 7H_2O$

Ref.

1. Goldschmidt and Thomassen, *Vidensk. Skr., Mat.-Nat. Kl.*, **2**, 1923.

511   BADDELEYITE [ZrO₂].   *Fletcher* (*Nature*, **46**, 620, 1892; *Min. Mag.*, **10**, 148, 1893).   Brazilite *Hussak* (*Jb. Min.*, **2**, 141, 1892; **1**, 89, 1893; *Min. Mitt.*, **14**, 395, 1895).

C r y s t.   Monoclinic; prismatic — $2/m$.

$a : b : c = 0.9872 : 1 : 1.0194$, $\beta\ 99°07\tfrac{1}{2}'$; $p_0 : q_0 : r_0 = 1.0326 : 1.0065 : 1$

$r_2 : p_2 : q_2 = 0.9935 : 1.0259 : 1$, $\mu\ 80°52\tfrac{1}{2}'$; $p_0'\ 1.0459$, $q_0'\ 1.0194$, $x_0'\ 0.1606$

Forms:[2]

		ϕ	ρ	ϕ_2	$\rho_2 = B$	C	A
c	001	90°00′	9°07$\tfrac{1}{2}$	80°52$\tfrac{1}{2}$′	90°00′	0°00′	80°52$\tfrac{1}{2}$′
b	010	0 00	90 00	......	0 00	90 00	90 00
a	100	90 00	90 00	0 00	90 00	80 52$\tfrac{1}{2}$	0 00
l	120	27 09$\tfrac{1}{2}$	90 00	0 00	27 09$\tfrac{1}{2}$	85 51	62 50$\tfrac{1}{2}$
q	230	34 22$\tfrac{1}{2}$	90 00	0 00	34 22$\tfrac{1}{2}$	84 52	55 37$\tfrac{1}{2}$
m	110	45 44	90 00	0 00	45 44	83 28$\tfrac{1}{2}$	44 16
g	210	64 01	90 00	0 00	64 01	81 48	25 59
d	011	8 57	45 54	80 52$\tfrac{1}{2}$	44 49	45 11	83 35
s	103	90 00	26 59	63 01	90 00	17 51$\tfrac{1}{2}$	63 01
t	102	90 00	34 21	55 39	90 00	25 13$\tfrac{1}{2}$	55 39
r	$\bar{1}$02	−90 00	19 55	109 55	90 00	29 02$\tfrac{1}{2}$	109 55
α	$\bar{1}$01	−90 00	41 31	131 31	90 00	50 38$\tfrac{1}{2}$	131 31
x	112	53 17$\tfrac{1}{2}$	40 27	55 39	67 11	33 30$\tfrac{1}{2}$	58 39$\tfrac{1}{2}$
p	111	49 48$\tfrac{1}{2}$	57 39$\tfrac{1}{2}$	39 39	56 57$\tfrac{1}{2}$	50 55	49 48$\tfrac{1}{2}$
y	$\bar{1}$12	−35 24$\tfrac{1}{2}$	32 01	109 55	64 23$\tfrac{1}{2}$	37 58	107 53$\tfrac{1}{2}$
n	$\bar{1}$11	−40 58$\tfrac{1}{2}$	53 28$\tfrac{1}{2}$	131 31	52 39	59 43$\tfrac{1}{2}$	121 48

Structure cell.[3]   Space group $P2_1/c$; $a_0\ 5.21$, $b_0\ 5.26$, $c_0\ 5.375$; $\beta\ 99°28'$; $a_0 : b_0 : c_0 = 0.991 : 1 : 1.022$; contains Zr_4O_8.

Habit. Crystals usually flattened {100} and short to long prismatic [001]; also tabular {100} and somewhat elongated [010]; rarely equant. {100} and prism faces striated [001]; {100} sometimes also striated [010] or irregularly. Sometimes radially fibrous, with concentric banding in botryoidal masses. Common forms: $a\ b\ c\ m\ d\ r\ n$.

Twinning.[4] Untwinned crystals are rare. (a) On {100}, common; often polysynthetic. (b) On {110},

Balangoda, Ceylon.   common alone or in combination with (a); sometimes polysynthetic. (c) On {201}, rare; sometimes in combination with the preceding laws.

P h y s. Cleavage {001} nearly perfect, {010} and {110} much less so.[5] Brittle. Fracture subconchoidal to uneven. H. 6$\tfrac{1}{2}$. G. 5.4–6.02 (reported range; least in fibrous material); 5.59 (calc.[6]). Luster greasy to vitreous; nearly submetallic in black crystals. Color variable: colorless to yellow, green, reddish or greenish brown, brown, dark brown to iron-black. Streak white to brownish white. In dark-colored specimens transparent only in thin splinters.

O p t.[7] Brown to colorless in transmitted light. Sometimes shows zonal growth-bands (apparently due to Fe_2O_3 or Hf? content). Also commonly exhibits polysynthetic twinning on one or more twin laws. Absorption $X > Y > Z$.

Orientation		n	Pleochroism			
			Ceylon	Brazil[8]	Vesuvius[9]	Bx. neg. (−).
X	$\wedge c = 13°$	2.13 ± 0.01	Yellow	Dark reddish brown	Oil green	$2V$ $30° \pm 1°$.
Y	b	2.19 ± 0.01		Oil green	Reddish brown	$r > v$ rather strong.
Z		2.20 ± 0.01	Brown	Light brown		

C h e m. Zirconium dioxide, ZrO_2. Small amounts of Fe^3 (<1 per cent Fe_2O_3 by weight) and of Hf (up to at least 3 per cent HfO_2[10] by weight) substitute for Zr.

Anal.[11]

	1	2	3	4
CaO	0.06	0.55	....	0.24
Fe_2O_3	0.82	0.41	0.92	0.34
SiO_2	0.19	0.70	0.48	0.45
ZrO_2	98.90	96.52	97.19	97.22
Ign. loss.	0.28	0.39	....	0.67
Rem.	......	0.95	1.26	0.28
Total	100.25	99.52	99.85	99.20
G.	5.72		5.538	

1. Balangoda, Ceylon (crystal).[12] 2. Jacupiranga, Brazil (crystals). Rem. is $(Na,K)_2O$ 0.42, MgO 0.10, Al_2O_3 0.43.[13] 3. Minas Geraes, Brazil (fibrous nodule). Rem. is TiO_2 0.48, Al_2O_3 0.40, MnO trace, H_2O 0.38.[14] 4. Balangoda, Ceylon. Rem. is TiO_2 0.13, $(Y,Ce)_2O_3$ 0.04, MnO 0.04, Al_2O_3 0.07.[15]

Tests. B.B. glows, turns white, and is nearly or quite infusible. Insoluble in hot HCl or HNO_3 and cold dilute HF, but the fine powder is slowly decomposed by hot concentrated H_2SO_4. Slowly decomposed by fusion in $KHSO_4$, but scarcely affected by fusion in NaOH or mixed K_2CO_3 and Na_2CO_3. Becomes colorless when heated upon charcoal.

O c c u r. Found as rounded crystals in gem gravels in Ceylon at Rakwana and Balangoda, associated with zircon, tourmaline, corundum, spinel, ilmenite, geikielite, fergusonite and other rare-earth minerals. Occurs as an accessory mineral in a magnetite-pyroxenite rock (jacupirangite) and in the contact zone of this rock with marble at Jacupiranga, São Paulo, Brazil, associated with ilmenite, zirkelite, apatite, magnetite, perovskite. Also in Brazil as radial fibrous masses and as rolled pebbles in the augite-syenite region of the Serra de Caldas, Minas Geraes; similar material occurs in the diamond sands of the Rio Verdinho, a branch of the Rio Paraná, Matto Grosso. A reported occurrence in a jacupirangite-like rock at Alnö, Sweden, has not been verified.[16] On Mount Somma, Italy, in druses in sanadinite rock associated with fluorite, nepheline, pyrochlore, allanite. As a detrital mineral in gold washings at Nedi, Kilo, Belgian Congo. In the United States found near Bozeman, Montana, in a corundum-syenite. Also reported from the Davis Mountains, Texas.

A r t i f.[17] Crystals apparently identical with baddeleyite have been prepared by fusion of ZrO_2 in borax or salt of phosphorus. On heating, baddeleyite inverts to a tetragonal modification at ca. 1000°, and to a trigonal or pseudohexagonal modification at ca. 1900°; crystals of the tetragonal modification also have been obtained from fusions of ZrO_2 in borax. An isometric modification also has been reported.[18]

N a m e. After Joseph Baddeley, who brought the original specimens from Ceylon. Brazilite from the locality in Brazil (described almost simultaneously with the mineral from Ceylon).

ZIRCONIUM OXIDE. Zirkonoxyd *Hussak* and *Reitinger* (*Zs. Kr.*, **67**, 572, 1902). A radially fibrous botryoidal zirconium dioxide found in Minas Geraes, Brazil, and thought to be possibly polymorphous with baddeleyite. Shown[19] to be identical with baddeleyite.

CALDASITE. *Derby* in *Lee* (*Am. J. Sc.*, **47**, 126, 1919), ZIRKITE[20] and BRAZILITE[20] (= Brazilite *Hussak, Min. Mitt.*, 14, 395 [1895], in part) are names given to zirconium-ore and rock from the Caldas district of Minas Geraes and São Paulo, Brazil, consisting of admixed fibrous baddeleyite, zircon, altered zircon (" orvillite "), and other minerals.

Ref.

1. Unit and orientation of Fletcher (1893). Angles of Zambonini, *Acc. Napoli, Att.*, **15**, 1, 1912.
   Transformation: Zambonini and Hussak (1895) to Fletcher $\frac{1}{2}$0 0 / 0 $\frac{1}{2}$0 / 0 0 1
2. From Goldschmidt (**1**, 137, 1913).
3. Yardley, *Min. Mag.*, **21**, 169 (1920), by x-ray spectrometer and powder methods on material from Ceylon and Brazil; the β angle given apparently is the supplement of the morphological value of Blake and Smith, *Min. Mag.*, **14**, 378 (1907). See also Náray-Szabó, *Zs. Kr.*, **94**, 414 (1936).
4. Hussak (1895).
5. Rogers, *Am. J. Sc.*, **33**, 54 (1912), mentions a cleavage {100} on crystals from Montana; this is possibly a misprint for {001}.
6. The low calculated specific gravity suggests the presence of considerable amounts of Hf in the mineral.
7. Larsen (43, 1921); optical orientation from Fletcher (1893) and Hussak (1895).
8. Hussak (1895).
9. Zambonini (1912).
10. Hevesy and Jantzen, *Zs. anorg. Chem.*, 136, 387, 1924, and Hevesy, *Danske Vidensk. Selsk., Mat.-fys. Medd.*, **6** (1925).
11. The crystals from Rakwana, Ceylon, were shown by Fletcher (1893) to be ZrO_2 with but a trace of Fe_2O_3. For additional analyses of fibrous material (" favas," in part) see Doelter (3 [1], 128, 1926).
12. Blake and Smith (1907).
13. Blomstrand anal. in Hussak (1895).
14. Hussak and Reitinger, *Zs. Kr.*, **37**, 572 (1902).
15. Chernik *Bull. ac. sc. Russie*, 14 [6], 267 (1920).
16. See von Eckermann, *Min. Mag.*, **25**, 413 (1939).
17. For literature see Doelter (1926), Cohn and Tolksdorf, *Zs. phys. Chem.*, **8**, 331 (1930).
18. See Bauer, *Jb. Min., Beil.-Bd.*, **75**, 159 (1939).
19. Yardley (1926).
20. Trade names apparently first used in literature of the Foote Mineral Co., Philadelphia (*Monthly Price List*, September, 1916, and November, 1916; *Mineral Foote-Notes*, March, 1917, and March, 1918).

5121   **U R A N I N I T E** [UO$_2$].   Schwarz Beck-Erz (from Joachimstal) *Brückmann*
(204, 1727).   Beck-Blände = Pseudogalena picea pt. (rest [? all] pitchlike Zinc-
blende) *Wallerius* (249, 1747).   Swart Blende = Pechblende pt. *Cronstedt* (198,
1758).   Pseudogalena nigra compacta, Pechblende *von Born* (133, 1772).   Pechblende,
Eisenpecherz (put under Iron Ores) *Werner* (*Bergm. J.*, 1789).   Uranerz *Klaproth*
(*Ak. Berlin, Mem.*, 160, 1792, for 1786–87; 2, 197, 1797).   Pecherz *Karsten* (56, 1800).
Urane oxydulé *Haüy* (1801).   Pitchblende, Protoxide of Uranium.   Uranatemnite
Chapman (148, 1853).   Uranin *Haidinger* (549, 1845).   Nasturan *von Kobell* (84,
1853).   Pitchblende.   Uranpecherz, Pechuran *Germ.*   Urane oxydulé *Fr.*   Pecurano,
Urano ossidolato *Ital.*   Pezblenda *Span.*

Schweruranerz (from Přibram) *Breithaupt* (903, 1847).   Coracite pt. *Le Conte*
(*Am. J. Sc.*, 3, 117, 173, 1847).   Kristallisirtes Uranpecherz *Scheerer* (*Ann. Phys.*, 77,
570, 1847) = Uranoniobite *Hermann* (*J. pr. Chem.*, 76, 326, 1859).   Cleveite
Nordenskiöld (*Geol. För. Förh.*, 4, 28, 1878).   Bröggerite, Thor-uranin *Blomstrand*
(*Geol. För. Förh.*, 7, 60, 1884).   Nivenite *Hidden* and *Mackintosh* (*Am. J. Sc.*, 38, 481,
1889).   Ulrichite *Kirsch* (*Min. Mitt.*, 38, 227, 1925).

C r y s t.   Isometric; hexoctahedral — 4/m $\bar{3}$ 2/m (?).

Forms:[1]

$$a\{001\}   \qquad   d\{011\}   \qquad   o\{111\}$$

Structure cell.[2]   Isometric (face-centered); a_0 5.47; contains U$_4$O$_8$.

Habit.   Octahedral, cubo-octahedral, cubic or, less commonly, dodecahedral.   Also massive (pitchblende): dense; botryoidal or reniform, with
a banded structure; columnar, or curved lamellar.   In dendrite-like aggregates of small crystals (Grafton Center, New Hampshire).

Twinning.[3]   On {111}, rare.

P h y s.   Fracture uneven to conchoidal.   Brittle.   H. 5–6.   G. 10.95
(artif. UO$_2$[4]); 10.63 (Chihuahua, Mexico[5]): 10.88 (calc. for UO$_2$); 10.36
(calc. for (U,Th)O$_2$, with U : Th = 1 : 1[6]).   The specific gravity decreases
markedly with increasing oxidation of U^4 to U^6.   The specific gravity also
is decreased by the substitution of Th or rare earths for U, but the variations are not clearly shown by the natural material.   Most natural crystals
have G. from 8.0 to 10.0; the colloform varieties (pitchblende) range on the
whole from 6.5 to 8.5.   Luster submetallic to pitchlike or greasy, and dull.
Color steely to velvety black and brownish black; grayish, greenish;
artificial UO$_2$ is greenish brown to brownish black and black.   Streak
brownish black, grayish, olive-green, a little shining.   Transparent in very
thin splinters; the transparency decreases with increasing oxidation of U^4
to U^6 and most natural material is opaque.

O p t.   In transmitted light, greenish, yellowish, or deep brown in
color.   Usually opaque.

In polished section,[7] light gray with a brownish tint.   Isotropic.   May
exhibit dark brown internal reflections.   Reflection percentages: (pitchblende, Joachimstal) green 15, orange 12.5, red 12.5; (thorian crystals,
Norway) green 15.5, orange 14, red 14.

C h e m.[8]   Uranium dioxide, UO$_2$.   The natural material always is
more or less oxidized, and the actual composition lies between UO$_2$ and
U$_3$O$_8$ (U$_{3-4}$O$_8$) with U^4 usually predominant.

The UO_3 content of the mineral is supposedly due to an oxidation process, or auto-oxidation,[10] due to radioactive decay processes which tend to keep the mineral at a slightly higher temperature than its environment. Attempts to use the $UO_2 : UO_3$ ratio for age calculations have led to unsatisfactory results. Pb[11] is always present as the stable end product of the radioactive disintegration of both U and Th. There is no good evidence that any of the Pb reported in analyses is not derived from this disintegration[12] (see also under **Radioactivity**). The rare earths[13] are often reported, in rather small amounts. Th is present in amounts up to 14 per cent in the coarsely crystalline uraninite of pegmatites, but is found only in traces in the finely crystalline variety pitchblende. Although a complete series[14] between UO_2 and ThO_2 (thorianite) has been produced artificially, no natural complete series has been found (see also thorianite). The presence of important amounts of Zr (anal. 2) and Ta[15] needs verification. He, A, N, and other gases are present; He always so, due to its formation by radioactive disintegration processes. A and N have been assumed to be due to absorption from the atmosphere, but the ratio A : N does not always bear out this conclusion. Much of the N reported in the old analyses (prior to the discovery of terrestrial He) is He.

Small amounts of Tl,[16] Mn, Bi, and other elements have been reported, but they are not certainly part of the uraninite composition. These, together with P_2O_5, As_2O_3, SiO_2, alkaline earths, alkalies, Al_2O_3 and Fe_2O_3, are probably due to admixture. The H_2O reported is probably due to alteration (especially in pitchblende).

Anal.[17] The Pb reported as PbO may not be present as the oxide. Many partial analyses giving the Pb/U ratio have been published.

	1	2	3	4	5	6	7
CaO	0.30	0.84	0.18	1.00	0.69	0.09	0.37
MnO	.....	0.16	0.10	0.09	0.002	.....	.....
PbO	0.40	0.70	4.35	6.39	7.02	7.07	9.04
MgO	.....	trace	.....	0.17	0.01	.....	trace
$(Y,Er)_2O_3$	3.41	.....	.....	.....	0.35	0.55	1.11
$(Ce,La)_2O_3$	.....	.....	.....	.....	.....	3.29	.....
La_2O_3	1.02	.....	.....	.....	0.155	.....	0.27
CeO_2	0.71	0.22	.....	.....	0.22	.....	0.18
UO_2	70.09	58.51	72.25	59.30	52.77	.....	46.13
U_3O_8	.....	.....	.....	.....	.....	88.12	.....
UO_3	22.69	25.26	13.27	22.33	37.537	.....	30.63
ThO_2	0.20	.....	7.20	.....	.....	0.16	6.00
ZrO_2	.....	7.59	.....	.....	0.14	.....	0.06
SiO_2	.....	2.79	0.03	0.50	0.095	0.10	0.22
Al_2O_3	0.25	.....	.....	0.20	.....	} 0.49	.....
Fe_2O_3	0.10	.....	0.11	0.21	0.15		0.25
CO_2	.....	.....	.....	.....	0.24	.....	.....
H_2O	[0.41]	1.96	0.68	3.17	0.38	.....	0.74
Insol.	.....	.....	0.04	.....	0.09	0.06	4.42
Rem.	.....	1.79	.....	4.57	0.500	.....	0.19
Total	99.70	99.82	98.21	97.93	100.349	99.93	99.61
G.	10.63	8.068	9.733	6.89	9.660		8.893
$\dfrac{Pb}{(U + 0.36\,Th)}$	0.0046	0.009	0.052	.....	0.084	0.088	0.123

1. Placer de Guadalupe, Chihuahua, Mexico. Rem. is TiO_2 0.06, As_2O_3 0.06. Average of 2 analyses.[18] 2. Black Hawk, Gilpin Co., Colo. (*pitchblende*). Average of two analyses. Rem. is TiO_2 trace, ZnO 0.44, FeO 0.32, alkalies trace, He and other gases 0.02, P_2O_5 0.22, As_2O_5 0.43, chalcopyrite 0.12, pyrite 0.24.[19] 3. Branchville, Conn.[20] 4. Johanngeorgenstadt, Saxony (*pitchblende*). Rem. is Na_2O 0.31, Bi_2O_3 0.75, He and other gases trace, CuO 0.17, P_2O_5 0.06, As_2O_5 2.34, (V_2O_5,MoO_3,WO_3) 0.75, SO_3 0.19.[20] 5. Shinkolobwe, Katanga. Rem. is He 0.159, N_2 0.076, O 0.005, BaO 0.06, alkalies 0.01, MoO_3 0.07, As_2O_3 0.09, P_2O_5 0.03.[21] 6. Morogoro, East Africa. Average of 3 analyses.[22] 7. Gustav's mine, Ånneröd, Norway (*bröggerite*). Rem. is P_2O_5 0.02, He and other gases 0.17. Mean of 2 analyses.[20]

	8	9	10	11	12	13	14
CaO	0.32	0.86	1.01	0.35	0.46	1.72	0.72
MnO	.....	.....	0.03	0.14	0.001	0.13	.....
PbO	10.08	10.92 ˙	10.95	11.69	16.42	16.71	19.50
MgO	.....	0.14	0.08	0.06	0.01	0.06	.....
$(Y,Er)_2O_3$	9.46	9.99	2.14	0.73	1.01	1.19.	} 5.60
$(Ce,La)_2O_3$	.....	2.25	1.88	0.06	....	0.28.	
La_2O_3	2.36	.....	.....	.....	0.80	....	.....
CeO_2	0.34	.....	.....	.....	0.265	....	.....
UO_2	44.17	23.07	39.10	.....	48.87	....	34.49
U_3O_8	.....	.....	.....	86.16	....	64.86	.....
UO_3	20.89	40.60	32.40	.....	28.582	....	36.94
ThO_2	6.69	4.60	10.60	0.10	2.15	13.94	0.15
ZrO_2	0.34	.....	.....	.....	0.22	....	.....
SiO_2	0.46	.....	0.19	0.21	0.055	0.37	.....
Al_2O_3	.....	.....	0.09	} 0.35	....	0.12	} trace
Fe_2O_3	0.14	1.02	0.43		0.30	0.75	
CO_2	.....	.....	.....	.....	....	....	....
H_2O	1.48	4.96	0.70	.....	0.44	not det.	1.40
Insol.	1.47	2.34	0.15	.....	0.15	....	0.53
Rem.	0.08	.....	0.31	.....	0.39	....	0.23
Total	98.28	100.75	100.06	99.85	100.123	100.13	99.56
G.	8.29	7.49	9.062	8.958	9.182	8.968	
$\dfrac{Pb}{(U+0.36\,Th)}$	0.163	0.182	0.157	0.148	0.226	0.261	0.30

8. Baringer Hill, Llano Co., Tex. (*nivenite*). Rem. is He and other gases.[23] 9. Arendal, Norway (*cleveite*). H_2O as ign. loss.[24] 10. Wilberforce, Haliburton Co., Ont. Rem. is He and other gases. H_2O^+ 0.05, H_2O^- 0.65.[25] 11. Lac Pied des Monts, Saguenay district, Quebec.[26] 12. Ingersoll mine, Pennington Co., S. D. Rem. is He 0.08, BaO 0.08, alkalies 0.02, MoO_3 trace, As_2O_3 0.15, P_2O_5 0.06.[21] 13. Winnipeg river area, southeastern Manitoba.[27] 14. Sinyaya pala, Karelia, U.S.S.R. Analysis stated to be mean result of material from this locality. Rem. is Cl.[28]

Var. 1. *Crystallized.* Kristallisirtes Uranpecherz *Scheerer* (*Ann. Phys.*, 77, 570, 1847). Uranoniobite *Hermann* (*J. pr. Chem.*, 76, 326, 1859). Ulrichite *Kirsch* (*Min. Mitt.*, 38, 227, 1925). In crystals, with G. usually ranging between 8.0 and 10.0. The occurrences in pegmatites belong here almost in entirety. Thorium and rare earths are often present. The following sub-varieties are recognized.

Thorian. Bröggerite, Thor-uranin *Blomstrand* (*Geol. För. Förh.*, 7, 60, 1884). Contains Th in substitution for U to at least 13.94 per cent ThO_2 (anal. 13); natural material with Th in excess of this ratio has not been found, but a complete series between U and Th has been obtained artificially. Rare earths and Fe_2O_3[29] are usually present in addition to Th, and the variety is here restricted to material with Th > (Y, Ce, etc.).

Cerian and Yttrian. Cleveite *Nordenskiöld* (*Geol. För. Förh.*, **4**, 28, 1878). Nivenite *Hidden* and *Mackintosh* (*Am. J. Sc.*, **38**, 481, 1889). Contains rare earths in substitution for U. Either the cerium earths or the yttrium earths may predominate, but Y usually is in excess. The range of substitution extends to at least 10 per cent (Y,Ce, etc.)$_2$O$_3$ in analysis 9. In analysis 6, (Ce,La)$_2$O$_3$ predominates over (Y,Er)$_2$O$_3$.

2. *Massive. Colloform.* Pitchblende. Nasturan *von Kobell* (84, 1853). Here belongs the material found in metalliferous veins, with sulfides and arsenides of Fe, Cu, Pb, Co, Ni, Ag, Bi. The specific gravity is relatively low, from 6.5 to 8.5, and Th and the rare earths are generally reported absent (or less than 1 per cent).

Tests. B.B. infusible, or slightly rounded on the edges of thin splinters. Soluble in HF, HNO$_3$, and H$_2$SO$_4$ but only very slowly attacked by HCl. The solubility in acids varies widely, and is greater in varieties containing rare earths. Small amounts of He, N, and other gases usually are disengaged when the mineral is fused with an alkaline carbonate or dissolved in a nonoxidizing inorganic acid.

Occur. Uraninite has four principal modes of occurrence. (1) In granite and syenite pegmatites, associated with zircon, tourmaline, monazite, and carbonaceous material (" thucholite," Canada), mica, feldspar, etc.; often closely associated with minerals containing rare earths and Cb-Ta. The mineral occurs in small distinct crystals or massive, and colloform structure is lacking. The matrix of the uraninite grains may be discolored and radially cracked. Typical localities are Grafton Center, New Hampshire; Villeneuve, Quebec; Cardiff Township, Ontario; southern Norway; Morogoro, East Africa. (2) In high-temperature hydrothermal tin veins. Occurs as colloform crusts (pitchblende), associated with cassiterite, pyrite, chalcopyrite, arsenopyrite, galena, and Co-Ni-Bi-As minerals. Known especially from Cornwall, England. (3) In hydrothermal Co-Ni-Bi-Ag-As veins formed at moderate temperatures. Occurs as colloform masses (pitchblende), associated with pyrite, chalcopyrite, galena, carbonates, barite, fluorite, native bismuth, native silver and other silver minerals, smaltite-chloanthite, niccolite, and other compounds of Co-Ni-As. Notable occurrences of this type are found at Joachimstal, Bohemia; Johanngeorgenstadt and Annaberg, Saxony; Great Bear Lake, Canada. (4) In hydrothermal sulfide veins formed at moderate temperatures, without Co-Ni minerals. Found as colloform crusts, with pyrite, chalcopyrite, sphalerite, galena, etc. Known especially from Gilpin County, Colorado. A partial list of the known localities of uraninite follows.

In Norway found in granite pegmatite at a number of localities in Saetersdalen; *cleveite* from Garta, near Arendal; also well crystallized at Elvestad and Huggenaeskilen and elsewhere on the Ånneröd peninsula (*bröggerite*, pt.). In pegmatite near Chupa, at Chornaya Salma, and on Khito Island in northern Karelia, U.S.S.R., with zircon, monazite, and a carbonaceous material. In Germany found at Johanngeorgenstadt, Schneeberg, and Annaberg in Saxony; in Bohemia, Schlaggenwald, Přibram, in Co-Ni-Bi-Ag veins at Joachimstal,[30] at Freiberg, Saxony, in sulfide and arsenide veins;

in the Riesengebirge, Saxony, in pegmatite at Rabenstein, and in the contact metamorphic magnetite deposit at Schmiedeberg; in Bavaria at Hagendorf in pegmatite, and in the fluorite deposit at Wölsendorf. At Montebras, France, with phosphates and cassiterite in pegmatite. Uraninite was found abundantly at localities in Cornwall, England, in the tin deposits, for the most part in minor veins or shoots cutting the cassiterite veins. At Morogoro in the Uluguru Mountains, East Africa, in pegmatite, and in the Gordonia district, Cape Province, South Africa, in pegmatite. Important deposits of uraninite, largely altered, are found at Kasolo, Shinkolobwe and Kalongwe in the Katanga district of the Belgian Congo;[31] the mineral apparently occurs as replacement lenses and as veins in dolomite schist and slate, associated with the copper ores. The locality at Katanga is noted for the large variety and abundance of secondary uranium minerals derived from the alteration of the uraninite. Found at Kotôge and Masaki in Fukuoka prefecture, Japan, in pegmatite. At Pichhli and Abraki Pahar in the Gaya district, Bengal, India, in pegmatite with zircon, monazite, phosphates, columbite. At Placer de Guadalupe, Chihuahua, Mexico, with gold and pyrite in calcite veins.

In the United States, uraninite occurs sparsely disseminated in granite pegmatite at a number of localities in New England, notably at Grafton Center, New Hampshire, and at Branchville, Haddam Neck, Glastonbury, and Portland, Connecticut. In New York in pegmatite at Bedford, Westchester County, and in the McClear pegmatite near Richville Station, St. Lawrence County. In pegmatite at Spruce Pine and other localities in Mitchell County, North Carolina; also in Yancey County. Uraninite was found abundantly in Gilpin County, Colorado,[32] especially in veins on Quartz Hill, near Central City; the mineral occurred as colloform masses in hydrothermal sulfide veins with pyrite, chalcopyrite, sphalerite, galena, siderite and, rarely, native bismuth. At Baringer Hill, Llano County, Texas (*nivenite*) with gadolinite and other rare-earth and Cb-Ta minerals in granite pegmatite. At Lusk, Wyoming. In pegmatite at the Ingersoll mine, and elsewhere in Pennington County, South Dakota. In Canada,[33] uraninite occurs abundantly at Great Bear Lake, Northwest Territories, in veins with native silver, carbonates, pyrite, chalcopyrite, and a number of Co-Ni-As minerals; also at Hottah Lake, south of Great Bear Lake. In Ontario at Mamainse, Algoma district (*coracite*); in pegmatite with carbonaceous material ("thucholite") and columbate-tantalates in Henvey and in Conger townships, Parry Sound district, and in Butt Township, Nipissing district; found abundantly with calcite, fluorite, and amphibole in pegmatite at Wilberforce in Cardiff Township, Haliburton County. In Quebec, found especially at the Villeneuve mine, Papineau County, in pegmatite; also at the Wallingford mine, Papineau County, as carbonaceous pseudomorphs after uraninite; at Lac Pied des Monts, Saguenay district.

Alter. Uraninite alters easily. Presumably the invariable presence of UO_3 in the composition is due to alteration. Alteration zones[34] are often well marked and these indicate that Th is most easily leached out, and U is less easily leached than Pb. This selective alteration sometimes offers serious difficulties in using the Pb/U ratio for age determinations. The following tabulation indicates the extent of the leaching effect. On a crystal from Wilberforce, Ontario, separated into three zones by filing off equal portions from all faces.[35]

Zone	% Pb	% U	% Th	Pb/U + 0.36Th
Outside	9.15	52.99	5.22	0.1668
Middle	10.06	54.47	15.25	0.1678
Core	11.05	55.50	10.46	0.1864

For a single crystal from Portland, Conn.[36] *using micromethods*

Outer crust	3.36	80.14	2.86	0.041
Outside	3.20	80.20	3.17	0.039
Middle	3.12	78.86	3.26	0.039
Core	3.12	79.00	3.19	0.039

A crystal from Morogoro[37]

Weathered crust	3.42	67.50	<0.06	0.051
Outside	8.34	70.89	0.10	0.118
Core	6.64	73.13	0.20	0.091

Another crystal from Morogoro[37]

Outside	6.12	70.37	......	0.087
Middle	6.17	71.96	......	0.086
Core	7.35	63.59	......	0.099

On a crystal from Auselmyren, Aust-Agder, Norway, a study of successive layers showed that the UO_2 : UO_3 ratio increases inward, as follows.[38]

$$UO_2 : UO_3$$

Outside	1.35
Middle	1.41
Core	1.48

These chemical changes may be accompanied by a change in fracture from uneven to conchoidal and by the assumption of a dull pitchlike luster and color. On further chemical alteration, the mineral affords a wide variety of bright colored, yellow, orange reddish, or green secondary uranium compounds, including hydrated oxides (generally the first formed of the secondary products), silicates, phosphates, sulfates, arsenates, vanadates, carbonates. The formation of these minerals usually involves the complete dissolution and removal of the uraninite with deposition of the secondary compounds after more or less transportation in solution. The name gummite (which see) has been loosely applied to an ill-defined yellow to orange compact and probably inhomogeneous material high in H_2O and UO_3 which commonly forms more or less complete pseudomorphs after uraninite. *Clarkeite* (which see) is a similar material.

   A r t i f.[39] Obtained in crystals by the long-continued fusion of an oxide of uranium in borax, by evaporating a solution of UO_2Cl_2 with NaCl and NH_4Cl to dryness and fusing the residue, and by heating UO_3 to redness in a stream of hydrogen. Mixed crystals with Th are obtained by fusing UO_2 and ThO_2 in borax. Gelatinous hydrous UO_2 is obtained by precipitating uranous salts with alkalies. Experiments in artificial weathering[29] by placing in a closed tube with H_2O at 190° for 10 to 20 hours showed no special leaching of Pb, U, or Fe (on " cleveite " from Norway). A rare-earth uraninite (" bröggerite ") gave a leached crust with only traces of U_3O_8 and ThO_2 remaining.

N a m e. Uraninite in allusion to the composition. Bröggerite after Waldemar Christopher Brögger (1851–1940), Norwegian mineralogist and geologist. Nivenite after William Niven (1850–1937), an American mineral collector and archeologist who was active in developing the pegmatite deposit at Baringer Hill, Texas. Cleveite after the Swedish chemist, P. T. Cleve (1840–1905). Nasturan from ναστός, *compact,* and *uran, uranium,* because a massive uranium mineral. The name pitchblende (pechblende, uranpecherz, *Germ.*) alludes to the pitchlike color and luster of some varieties of the mineral. Coracite probably from κόραξ, *a raven,* in allusion to the color and luster. Ulrichite after the Austrian radiochemist, Carl Ulrich (died 1925).

Radioactivity.[40] Uranium is the parent of two radioactive disintegration series, one leading from the isotope U^{238} (UI) to the isotope Pb^{206} (RaG), the other from U^{235} (AcU) to Pb^{207} (AcD). Thorium also disintegrates, the series here being from Th^{232} (the sole isotope) to Pb^{208} (ThD). The disintegrations are of two kinds: (*a*) where a β-particle (electron) is emitted from the atomic nucleus; (*b*) where an α-particle (ionized He atom) is emitted. The α-process gives rise to the He always found in uraninites. The intermediate products are all short-lived, except Io (half-life 82,250 years) and Ra (half-life 1691 years), both in the $U^{238} \rightarrow Pb^{206}$ series, and Pa in the $U^{235} \rightarrow Pb^{207}$ series. As radioactive disintegration is a nuclear process, proceeding at a fixed and completely unalterable rate, the accumulation of the stable emission product (He) or of the stable end product (Pb) should give an " hourglass " method of determining the time elapsed since the last crystallization of the mineral, provided it was free from such end products at that time, and provided that sufficient time has elapsed for the disintegration series to be in radioactive equilibrium (about 10^6 years). The amount of He generated during geologic time from the amounts of U and Th present in even small crystals of minerals such as uraninite (or even in those carrying only 1 per cent U and Th) is so large, that the resulting partial pressure of He has caused the escape of a considerable percentage of the total formed. In some cases studied 90 per cent of the generated He has been lost. With lead, however, the evidence indicates that in the absence of weathering or other alteration, essentially all the generated Pb remains in the crystal and in the immediate vicinity of the place of its formation.

For approximate calculations, especially for geologically young (Paleozoic or later) minerals, the approximate formula is adequate.

$$\text{Age} = \frac{\text{Pb}}{\text{U} + 0.36\text{Th}} \times 7600 \times 10^6 \text{ years}$$

The factor 0.36 converts the Pb-generating power of Th to its U equivalent. Other factors have been used (0.27 to 0.38), but the most recent work substantiates 0.36. For more accurate work, a logarithmic formula should be used, to allow for the loss of U which has gone to form Pb. A convenient form is

$$\text{Age} = \frac{\log (U + 0.36Th + 1.155Pb) - \log (U + 0.36Th)}{6.6 \times 10^{-5}} \times 10^6 \text{ years}$$

Since the isotopes of U and Th lead to different Pb isotopes, it should be possible, by a determination of the isotopic composition of the Pb in uraninite (or other radioactive mineral) to determine the age independently by the ratios RaG/UI, AcD/AcU, ThD/Th.[41] In general the age derived from the isotope present in the greatest proportion (e.g., RaG/UI for uraninite) gives the most reliable results, largely because the analytical inaccuracies are of lesser importance. Moreover, since UI and AcU, though now present in fixed proportions in all U, have different half-lives, and disintegrate by different paths; the ratio of RaG/AcD is a function of age. Calculations[41] indicate that in many instances ages so figured agree with those obtained by the other ratios. The proportion of AcD to the other Pb isotopes is small, however, so the method is probably not quite as accurate.

In addition to the varying mixture of the three isotopes RaG, AcD, ThD which collectively compose " radiogenic " lead there is also the so-called " common " lead found in ordinary lead minerals of the metalliferous veins, such as galena. This Pb is (so far as is now known) for the most part not the end product of radioactive disintegration. It consists of four isotopes, Pb^{204}, Pb^{206}, Pb^{207}, Pb^{208}, the last three identical with the radiogenic isotopes. The ratio of Pb^{204} to the other isotopes is approximately constant (to about 10 per cent) for all samples of " common " Pb so far examined. Hence, the presence of Pb^{204} in the Pb from a radioactive mineral indicates the presence of " common " Pb. The correction may be

MINERAL	LOCALITY	METHOD	CALCULATED AGE
Pitchblende	Joachimstal[42]	Pb/U, corrected for Pb^{204}	234×10^6 years
"	"	RaG/U^{238}	227
Pitchblende	Katanga[43]	Pb/U, uncorrected	676
"	"	RaG/U^{238}	616
"	"	AcD/RaG	610
Uraninite	Pied des Monts[44]	log formula, uncorrected	956
"	" " "	AcD/RaG	903
"	" " "	RaG/U^{238}	882
"	" " "	log formula, corrected for Pb^{204}	920
Uraninite	Wilberforce[45]	log formula, corrected for " common " Pb	1040
"	"	AcD/RaG	1035
"	"	RaG/U^{238}	1077
Pitchblende	Great Bear Lake[46]	log formula, corrected for " common " Pb	1323
"	" " "	AcD/RaG	1420
"	" " "	RaG/U^{238}	1251

made by subtracting from the mixture of isotopes the amounts corresponding to the ratio of " common " Pb, using Pb^{204} as the index. For some pitchblendes (Joachimstal), the correction is large, for most pegmatite uraninites, it is small.

Some of the better-authenticated age determinations are among those in the table on p. 618.

The results to date indicate a complete agreement, when proper conversion factors are used, between the mean mass number derived from the isotopic proportions, determined with the mass spectrograph,[41] and the chemical atomic weight, for all radiogenic leads.[47] The chemical atomic weight may be used to determine the presence of " common " lead when the amount of impurity is small, and when the Th percentage is low, but for the other cases the method is not so accurate, and is more time consuming.

Ref.

1. {001}, {011}, and {111} are of general occurrence. Parsons, *Univ. Toronto Stud., Geol. Ser.*, **32**, 17 (1932), reported {114} on crystals from Cardiff township, Ont., and Shaub, *Am. Min.*, **23**, 334 (1938), observed {335} on crystals from Grafton Center, New Hampshire.
2. Goldschmidt and Thomassen, *Vidensk. Selsk. Skr. Mat.-nat. Kl.*, 2, 1923, by powder and Laue methods on artificial UO_2 and on natural crystals from southern Norway. UO_2 is isostructural with ThO_2 and CeO_2 and all probably have a fluorite-type structure. Natural uraninite containing much UO_3 through oxidation is apparently structurally identical with UO_2 (noted also by Norton in Alter and Kipp, *Am. J. Sc.*, **32**, 120 [1936]), but on ignition out of contact with oxygen it may recrystallize in part or entirety to U_3O_8, while pure UO_2 remains unchanged. The excess O in the oxidized uraninites may be in solid solution in the structure. Since UO_3 is apparently amorphous the x-ray evidence for excess O in the structure is not conclusive. Pitchblende is structurally identical with uraninite, but has a very small particle size (10^{-4} to 10^{-7} cm.) and somewhat smaller cell dimensions ($a_0 = 5.42 - 5.45$).
3. Observed by Aubel, *C. R.*, **185**, 586 (1927), on crystals from Katanga; Parsons, *Univ. Toronto Stud., Geol. Ser.*, **32**, 17 (1932), on crystals from Cardiff Township, Ontario; Shaub, *Am. Min.*, **25**, 480 (1940), on crystals from St. Lawrence Co., New York.
4. Hillebrand, *U. S. Geol. Sur., Bull.* **113**, 37, 1893, on analyzed artificial crystals.
5. Wells, *Am. Min.*, **15**, 470 (1930).
6. Assuming $a_0 = 5.54$, from $ThO_2 = 5.61$ and $UO_2 = 5.47$ as obtained by Goldschmidt and Thomassen (1923).
7. Schneiderhöhn and Ramdohr (2, 519, 1931).
8. This section was prepared with the aid of Dr. John P. Marble, Washington, D. C.
9. Uraninite was early considered by Blomstrand, *Geol. För. Förh.*, **7**, 60 (1884), Dana (889, 1892) and others to be a uranyl uranate. The mineral was first shown to be essentially UO_2 by Goldschmidt and Thomassen (1923); see also Dunstan and Taylor, *Roy. Soc. London, Proc.*, **76**, 253 (1906). The name *ulrichite* of Kirsch (1925) has been applied to a hypothetical pure UO_2. See also Gleditsch and Bakken, *Arch. Math. Vidensk.*, **41** [5], 1 (1935).
10. See Ellsworth, *Am. J. Sc.*, **9**, 127 (1935); Kirsch and Lane, *Am. Ac. Arts Sc.*, **66**, 357 (1931); Lane, *Am. Min.*, **19**, 1 (1934); Khlopin, *Ac. sc. U.S.S.R., Bull., Mat.-Nat. Cl.*, 489, 1938.
11. On the isotopic constitution of radiogenic lead in uraninite and other minerals see Nier, *Phys. Rev.*, **55**, 150 (1939). On " common " lead see also Nier, *Am. Chem. Soc., J.*, **60**, 1571 (1938).
12. See Hillebrand, *U. S. Geol. Sur., Bull. 113*, 41, 1893.
13. Marble, *Am. Min.*, **24**, 272 (1939), obtained variable small amounts of Ce_2O_3, Y_2O_3, La_2O_3, etc., on two analyses of Great Bear Lake uraninite.
14. See Wells, Fairchild, and Ross, *Am. J. Sc.*, **26**, 45 (1933).
15. Meyer (Inaug. Diss., Berlin, 1916 — Hintze (1 [3A], 4153, 1929) on material from Gilpin County, Colorado.

16. Wleugel, *Zs. Kr.*, **4**, 520 (1880), in pitchblende from Joachimstal.
17. See Doelter (4 [2], 909, 1928) for an extensive tabulation of analyses.   For spectrographic analysis of Katanga uraninite see Hitchen and van Arbel, *C. R.*, **199**, 1133 (1934). For partial analyses giving the Pb/U ratios see, *Nat. Res. Council, Bull. 80*, 1931, and subsequent reports of the Committee on Measurement of Geologic Time, of the National Research Council.
18. Wells, *Am. Min.*, **15**, 470 (1930).
19. Hillebrand, *U. S. Geol. Sur. Bull. 78*, 43, 1891; *ibid., Bull. 220*, 111, 1903.   See also Free, *Phil. Mag.*, **1** [7], 950 (1926).
20. Hillebrand (1891).
21. Davis, *Am. J. Sc.*, **11**, 201 (1926).
22. Hecht anal. in Hecht and Körner, *Monatsh.*, **49**, 438 (1928).
23. Hillebrand, *Am. J. Sc.*, **42**, 390 (1891).
24. Hidden and Macintosh, *Am. J. Sc.*, **38**, 474 (1889), as recalculated by Hillebrand (1891).
25. Ellsworth, *Nat. Res. Council, Ann. Rep.*, App. H, Exhibit A., 1929–30.
26. Ellsworth anal. in Ellsworth and Osborne, *Am. Min.*, **19**, 421 (1934).
27. Ellsworth anal. in DeLury and Ellsworth, *Am. Min.*, **16**, 569 (1931).
28. Nenadkevich, *Ac. sc. U.S.S.R., Bull.*, **20** [6], 767 (1926) — *Min. Abs.*, **3**, 263 (1926).
29. Føyn, *Norsk Geol. Tidsk.*, **17**, 197 (1938).
30. For a description of this occurrence see Doelter (4 [2], 969, 1928).
31. For a description of this occurrence see Thoreau and Terdonck, *Inst. colon. belge, Mem.*, **1** [8], 1933.
32. See Bastin and Hill, *U. S. Geol. Sur., Prof. Pap. 94*, 1917, for a description of this occurrence.
33. For a description of many Canadian occurrences see Ellsworth, *Canada Geol. Sur., Econ. Geol. Ser.*, **11**, 1932; Spence, *Can. Dept. Mines, Mines Br. Rpt. 727–3*, 1932.
34. See the early work of Nordenskiöld, *Geol. För. Förh.*, **4**, 31 (1878); von Foullon, *Geol. Reichsanst., Jb.*, **33**, 1 (1883).   Also Ellsworth, *Am. Min.*, **15**, 455 (1930);   Ross, Henderson, and Posnjak, *Am. Min.*, **16**, 213 (1931); Alter and Kipp, *Am. J. Sc.*, **32**, 120 (1936); Bakken and Gleditsch, *Am. J. Sc.*, **36**, 95 (1938).
35. Alter and Yuill, *Am. Chem. Soc., J.*, **59**, 390 (1937).
36. Hecht, *Zs. anal. Chem.*, **106**, 82 (1936).
37. Hecht, *Ak. Wien, Ber.*, **140** [2A], 599 (1931).
38. Gleditsch and Bakken, *Mikrochim. Acta*, **1**, 83 (1937).
39. Hillebrand, *U. S. Geol. Sur., Bull. 113*, 37, 41, 1893.   Also Mellor (**12**, 39, 1932).
40. Section written by Dr. J. P. Marble.   For more details see Holmes, (*The Age of the Earth*, New York, 1937); also Ellsworth, *Canada Geol. Sur., Econ. Geol. Ser., Bull. 11*, 54, 1932; Føyn (*Über einige Verhältnisse in Uranmineralien*, Oslo, 1938), also Kovarik, *Nat. Res. Council, Bull. 80*, Pt. III, 1931, Holmes, *ibid.*, Pt. IV.
41. See Nier, *Phys. Rev.*, **55**, 150 (1939), and *Am. Chem. Soc., J.*, **60**, 1571 (1938). Also *Nat. Res. Council, Committee on Geologic Time, Reports* for 1940, 1941.
42. Baxter and Kelley, *Am. Chem. Soc., J.*, **60**, 62 (1938).   Nier (1939).
43. Baxter and Alter, *Science*, **77**, 432 (1933); Nier (1939).
44. Muench, *Am. Chem. Soc., J.*, **61**, 2742 (1939); Nier (1939).
45. Wells, *U. S. Geol. Sur., Bull. 878*, 126, 1937; Nier (1939).
46. Marble, *Am. Chem. Soc., J.*, **58**, 434 (1936); Nier (1939).
47. Chemical atomic weights by: Baxter and Bliss, *Am. Chem. Soc., J.*, **52**, 4848 (1930); Baxter, Faull, and Truemmler, *Am. Chem. Soc., J.*, **59**, 702 (1937); Baxter and Alter, *Am. Chem. Soc., J.*, **57**, 467 (1935).

5122   **THORIANITE** [ThO$_2$].   Uraninite *Coomaraswamy* (*Spolia Ceylon.*, 1904 — *Jb. Min.*, I, 165, 1906).   Thorianite *Dunstan* (*Nature*, **69**, 510, 533, 559, 1904); *Dunstan and Jones* (*Roy. Soc. London, Proc.*, **77**, 385, 1906); *Buchner* (*ibid.*, **78**, 385, 1906). α-, β-, and γ-Thorianite *Ogawa* (*Tohoku Imp. Univ., Sc. Rep.*, **1**, 201 (1912) — *Jb. Min.*, II, 12, 1913).

C r y s t.   Isometric;   hexoctahedral — $4/m\,\bar{3}\,2/m$ (?).

Forms:[1]

$$a\{001\}\qquad o\{111\}\qquad m\{113\}$$

Structure cell.[2] Isometric face-centered: a_0 5.61 (artif.), 5.57 (Ceylon, uranoan); contains Th_4O_8.

Habit. In cubic crystals, usually more or less rounded (water-worn).

Twinning. Penetration twins on {111} are very common.[3]

Phys. Cleavage {001}, poor. Fracture uneven to subconchoidal. Brittle. H. $6\frac{1}{2}$. G. 9.7; 9.87 (calc.). The specific gravity and the hardness decrease with increasing alteration. Luster horny to submetallic. Color dark gray to brownish black and black. Streak gray to greenish gray. Transparent in very thin splinters. Isotropic; n variable, averages 2.20±.[4] Radioactive.[5]

Chem. Thorium dioxide, ThO_2. U^4 substitutes for Th to at least U : Th = 1 : 1.1 (anal. 4); a complete series between ThO_2 and UO_2 has been observed in artificial preparations.[6] The U^4 usually is in part or entirety oxidized by secondary processes to U^6. Pb is usually present, in amounts up to ca. 5 weight per cent PbO, and presumably is of radioactive origin. (Ce,La) apparently substitute for Th, to at least 8.0 weight per cent $(Ce,La)_2O_3$ (anal. 2). The role of the Fe_2O_3 and ZrO_2 reported in some analyses is uncertain. He is usually present. The small amount of water reported in most analyses is secondary.

Anal.[7]

	1	2	3	4
CaO	....	....	0.59	0.97
PbO	1.80	2.87	2.29	5.21
$(Ce,La)_2O_3$	....	8.04	1.84	2.49
UO_2	4.73	....	10.32	4.44
U_3O_8	....	12.33	.....	....
UO_3	....	.....	18.88	33.15
ThO_2	93.02	76.22	62.16	38.47
Fe_2O_3	0.29	0.35	1.11	1.57
H_2O	....	....	1.05	4.39
Rem.	....	0.12	0.77	8.70
Total	99.84	99.93	99.01	99.39
G.	9.33	9.5		6.68

1. Betroka, Madagascar.[8] 2. Ceylon. Rem. is insol.[9] 3. Ceylon. Galle district (uranoan). Rem. is insol.[10] 4. Easton, Pa. Rem. is MnO 0.31, MgO 0.53, insol. 7.86.[11]

Var. *Uranoan.* Contains U in substitution for Th.

Tests. Infusible. At high temperatures emits a strong white glow. Insoluble in HCl, but soluble in HNO_3 or H_2SO_4 with evolution of gas, principally He.

Occur. Found originally in Ceylon, chiefly as water-worn crystals associated with zircon, ilmenite, geikielite, thorite, and other heavy minerals in stream gravels; also in pegmatites. Occurs especially in the Galle district, Southern Province (uranoan), in the Balangoda district and near Kondrugala, in Sabaragamuwa Province. In Madagascar at Betroka and with phlogopite, diopside, and spinel at Andolobe, in alluvial deposits. In the black sands of a gold placer on the Boshogoch River, Transbaikalia, Siberia. In the United States at Easton, Pennsylvania (*uranoan*), in serpentine at the contact of limestone with pegmatite.

A l t e r. Alters readily by hydration and oxidation of the uranium, the final product being a gray, yellow, or brown gummite-like substance.[12]

A r t i f.[13] In minute crystals or trellis-like aggregates by long-continued fusion of ThO_2 in borax. Also by heating precipitated hydrous ThO_2, and by ignition of salts of Th with a volatile acid.

N a m e. In allusion to the composition.

Ref.

1. {111} and {113} observed by Lacroix (**1**, 246, 1922) on cubic crystals from Betroka; only {001} has been observed on material from other localities.
2. Goldschmidt and Thomassen, *Vidensk. Selskr., Oslo, Math.-Nat. Kl.*, no. 2, 1923, by powder and Laue methods on natural (Galle, Ceylon) and artificial material.
3. See Lacroix (1922) for figures of twinned crystals from Betroka.
4. Larsen (143, 1921) on material from Ceylon.
5. See Dunstan and Blake, *Roy. Soc. London, Proc.*, **76**, 253 (1905); Strutt, *ibid.*, **76**, 98 (1905), Goldschmidt, *Zs. Kr.*, **45**, 490 (1908).
6. Hillebrand, *U. S. Geol. Sur., Bull. 113*, 41, 1893.
7. For additional analyses see Doelter (3 [1], 222, 1913).
8. Pisani anal. in Lacroix (1922).
9. Dunstan and Blake (1905).
10. Dunstan and Jones (1906).
11. Fairchild anal. in Wells, Fairchild, and Ross, *Am. J. Sc.*, **26**, 45 (1933).
12. See Wells, Fairchild, and Ross (1933) for an analysis of a highly altered thorianite from Easton.
13. Hillebrand (1893), Weiser (**2**, 271, 1935), Goldschmidt and Thomassen (1923).

521 Gummite [$UO_3 \cdot nH_2O$]

The name gummite is here applied as a generic or field term to substances essentially oxides of uranium, usually with Pb, Th, and relatively large amounts of H_2O, whose true identity is unknown. Gummite has the same relation to the well-defined uranium oxides that limonite and wad have to the well-defined iron and manganese oxides. It represents the final stages of oxidation and hydration of uraninite and is, for the most part, a mixture, consisting chiefly, perhaps, of curite.[1] Small percentages of alkalies, alkaline earths, rare earths, Fe_2O_3, Al_2O_3, P_2O_5, and SiO_2 are commonly present in gummite, and appear to be due to subordinate amounts of admixed salts of uranium (uranophane, etc.) or to wholly extraneous gangue material. The physical and chemical properties of gummite as here defined vary widely.

GUMMITE. Feste Uranokker pt. *Werner* (26, 1817); *Hoffmann* (4 [A], 279, 1817). Lichtes Uranpecherz *Freiesleben*. Uranisches Gummi-Erz *Breithaupt* (60, 1830; 218, 1932). Urangummi *Breithaupt* (903, 1847). Phosphor-Gummit *Hermann* (*J. pr. Chem.*, 76, 327, 1859). Gummite *Dana* (179, 1868).

Uranisches Pittin-Erz, Pittinus inferior *Breithaupt* (901, 1847). Coracite pt. *Le Conte* (*Am. J. Sç.*, 3, 117, 173, 1847). Eliasit *Haidinger* (*Geol. Reichsanst., Jb.*, 3 [4], 124, 1852). Pittinit *Hermann* (*J. pr. Chem.*, 76, 322, 1859). Yttrogummite *Nordenskiöld* (*Geol. För. Förh.*, 4, 31, 1878).

Massive, dense. In rounded or flattened masses or crusts, and as pseudomorphs.

P h y s. Fracture conchoidal to uneven. Brittle. H. $2\frac{1}{2}$–5. G. 3.9–6.4. Luster greasy or waxy to vitreous, brilliant to dull; often somewhat resembling gum. Color yellow, orange, reddish yellow to orange-red or hyacinth-red, reddish brown to brownish black, and black.   Streak yellow; also brownish, olive-green.   Transparent in small grains.

O p t.   In transmitted light, orange or yellow in color.   Anisotropic; sometimes very finely divided and seemingly isotropic.   The indices vary widely: n 1.575 (anal. 4, Easton, Pennsylvania[2]), 1.96 (anal. 1, Kambove, Katanga[3]).   Gummite from Spruce Pine, North Carolina[4] (anal. 2), is biaxial negative ($-$), with $2V$ 60° and nX 1.742, nY 1.762, nZ 1.776, and not pleochroic.

C h e m.   No single or definite composition can be attributed to the materials here loosely grouped.   Gummite is essentially composed of an oxide or oxides of uranium, usually with Pb, Th, rare earths (?), and relatively large amounts of H_2O.   Small percentages of alkalies, alkaline earths, Fe_2O_3, Al_2O_3, Mn_2O_3, CuO, Bi_2O_3, P_2O_5, CO_2, and SiO_2 are often present, and appear to be due to admixed salts of uranium or to feldspar or other wholly extraneous material.   The SiO_2 has been regarded as constitutional,[5] but appears to be due to admixed uranophane or other silicate.

Anal.[6]

	1	2	3	4	5
CaO	0.48	0.90	4.54	n.d.	1.37
MgO	0.27	.....	0.85	n.d.	0.12
BaO	.....	2.16		.....	.....
PbO	20.15	5.28	5.04	3.86	14.93
UO_3	73.20	77.99	63.38	.....	60.36
U_3O_8	.....	.....	....	42.70	.....
ThO_2	.....	.....	....	25.06	7.66
SiO_2	0.61	1.97	4.92	.....	3.81
Al_2O_3	.....	0.86	....	n.d.	}0.14
Fe_2O_3	.....	0.29	8.64	n.d.	
H_2O	5.33	8.90	10.24	n.d.	9.42
Rem.	trace	2.51	1.92	11.00	1.75
Total	100.04	100.86	99.53	82.62	99.56
G.					5.273

1. Kambove, Katanga (curite ?).   Rem. is Se trace.[3]   2. Spruce Pine, N. C.   Rem. is insol. 0.08, K_2O 0.86, Na_2O 0.51, ThO_2 and rare earths 1.06.[7]   3. Joachimstal, Bohemia (*eliasite*).   Rem. is Mn_2O_3.[8]   4. Thorian gummite, Easton, Pa.   Rem. is SiO_2 and insol. 5.90, rare earths 5.10.[9]   5. Villeneuve, Quebec (curite ?).   Rem. is (Ce, etc.)$_2O_3$ 0.14, (Y, etc.)$_2O_3$ 1.61, CO_2 small amount undet.[10]

Var. Yttrian.   Yttrogummite *Nordenskiöld* (*Geol. För. Förh.*, **4**, 31, 1878)..   Contains relatively large amounts of the yttrium earths.   Observed as an alteration product of yttrian uraninite.

Thorian.   Contains relatively large amounts of ThO_2 (anal. 4).   Observed as an alteration product of uranoan thorianite.

O c c u r.   Found at many of the known localities of uraninite.   A few localities are listed below.   As an alteration of pitchblende at Joachimstal, Bohemia (*eliasite*, *pittinite*), and at Johanngeorgenstadt and Schneeberg, Saxony.   A yttrian variety (*yttrogummite*) occurs as an alteration of yttrian uraninite in pegmatite near Arendal, southern Norway.   In the Katanga region, Belgian Congo, and in the Gordonia district, Cape Province, South Africa.   In the United States, gummite occurs abundantly as an alteration of uraninite in pegmatite at Spruce Pine and elsewhere in Mitchell County, North Carolina. A thorian variety occurs as an alteration of uranoan thorianite at Easton, Pennsylvania. As an alteration of uraninite in pegmatite at Branchville, Connecticut; Newry, Maine; abundantly at Grafton Center, New Hampshire. In Canada found especially at Villeneuve, Papineau County, Quebec, and as an alteration of pitchblende at Great Bear Lake, Northwest Territories.

A l t e r. Found as an alteration product of, and as more or less complete pseudomorphs after, uraninite (including pitchblende); also observed as an alteration product of uranoan thorianite. The gummite generally forms the orange, reddish, or brownish interior portion of the pseudomorphs after uraninite and grades outwardly into yellow uranophane (see further under uraninite). The gummite that occurs as an alteration of uraninite in pegmatites appears to have been formed by the action of late-stage hydrothermal solutions rather than by weathering processes. Gummite itself alters readily to uranophane.

N a m e. Gummite in allusion to the gumlike appearance of some specimens. Pittinite from πίττα, *pitch*, because it is a black kind of gummite earlier included under the name uranpecherz. Eliasite from the locality in the Elias mine, Joachimstal, Bohemia. Yttrogummite in allusion to the composition.

Ref.

1. See Schoep and de Leenheer, *Bull. soc. belge géol.*, **46**, 309 (1937). The material of anal. 5, from Villeneuve, Quebec, also may be curite.
2. Wells, Fairchild, and Ross, *Am. J. Sc.*, **26**, 45 (1933).
3. Schoep and de Leenheer (1937).
4. Ross, Henderson, and Posnjak, *Am. Min.*, **16**, 213 (1931).
5. von Foullon, *Geol. Reichsanst., Jb.*, **33**, 1 (1883). Gummite had earlier been regarded by Dana (179, 1868), Genth, *Am. Chem. J.*, **1**, 89 (1879), and others as a hydroxide with admixed uranates, silica, etc.
6. For additional analyses see Dana (892, 1892) and Buttgenbach, *Soc. géol. Belgique, Ann.*, **44**, 5X (1922).
7. Henderson anal. in Ross, Henderson, and Posnjak (1931);
8. von Foullon (1883).
9. Fairchild anal. in Wells, Fairchild, and Ross (1933).
10. Ellsworth, *Am. Min.*, **15**, 455 (1930).

522   Clarkeite [$UO_3 \cdot nH_2O$?]. *Ross, Henderson, and Posnjak* (*Am. Min.*, **16**, 213, 1931).

Massive, dense. Fracture conchoidal. H. 4–4½. G. 6.39. Luster slightly waxy. Color dark reddish brown, dark brown. Streak yellowish brown. Transparent in thin grains.

O p t. Orange in transmitted light.

	n	
X	1.997	Bx. neg. (−),
Y	2.098	$2V$ 30°–50°
Z	2.108	$r < v$, weak.

C h e m. Essentially a hydrous or hydrated oxide of uranium, with lead, alkalies, and alkaline earths reported in the analyses.[1] Formula possibly $UO_3 \cdot nH_2O$. Analyses gave:[2]

	1	2
K$_2$O	0.48	1.42
Na$_2$O	3.44	2.61
CaO	2.84	1.10
MgO	0.28	.....
BaO	.....	0.04
PbO	3.71	3.70
Rare earths	2.62	1.12
UO$_3$	81.72	82.76
Fe$_2$O$_3$	0.18	} 0.50
Al$_2$O$_3$	0.92	
SiO$_2$	0.50	0.30
Insol.	0.14	1.20
H$_2$O	3.36	5.22
Total	100.19	99.97

O c c u r. Found as an alteration product of uraninite[3] at Spruce Pine, Mitchell County, North Carolina. Some specimens exhibit a central core of black uraninite, surrounded successively by alteration zones of dark reddish brown clarkeite, orange-red gummite, and bright yellow uranophane.

N a m e. After Frank Wigglesworth Clarke (1847–1931), American mineral chemist, for many years Chief Chemist of the U. S. Geological Survey.

Needs further study.

Ref.

1. Henderson anal. in Ross, Henderson, and Posnjak (1931). Analysis 2 is an average of two; H$_2$O$^-$ 0.64, H$_2$O$^+$ 4.58.

2. Ross, Henderson, and Posnjak (1931) regard the alkalies and alkaline earths as essential, and derive (Na,K,Pb,Ca)O·3UO$_3$·3H$_2$O from anal. 2. Analysis 1 gives different ratios.

3. The relation of clarkeite to the other associated alteration products of uraninite is not clear, and it may be part of a gradational series of alterations of uraninite.

523 **B E C Q U E R E L I T E** [2UO$_3$·3H$_2$O ?]. *Schoep* (*C. R.*, 174, 1240, 1922).

C r y s t. Orthorhombic; dipyramidal — $2/m\ 2/m\ 2/m$.

$a : b : c = 1.1182 : 1 : 1.2100;$[1] $p_0 : q_0 : r_0 = 1.0821 : 1.2100 : 1$

$q_1 : r_1 : p_1 = 1.1182 : 0.9241 : 1;$ $r_2 : p_2 : q_2 = 0.8265 : 0.8943 : 1$

Forms:[2]

		ϕ	$\rho = C$	ϕ_1	$\rho_1 = A$	ϕ_2	$\rho_2 = B$
c	001	.....	0°00'	0°00'	90°00'	90°00'	90°00'
b	010	0°00'	90 00	90 00	90 00	.....	0 00
a	100	90 00	90 00	.....	0 00	0 00	90 00
n	230	30 48	90 00	90 00	59 12	0 00	30 48
M	210	60 47½	90 00	90 00	29 12½	0 00	60 47½
e	011	0 00	50 25½	50 25½	90 00	90 00	39 34½
i	103	90 00	19 50	0 00	70 10	70 10	90 00
f	102	90 00	28 25	0 00	61 35	61 35	90 00
k	305	90 00	32 59½	0 00	57 00½	57 00½	90 00
A	203	90 00	35 48½	0 00	54 11½	54 11½	90 00
j	304	90 00	39 03½	0 00	50 56½	50 56½	90 00
d	101	90 00	47 15½	0 00	42 44½	42 44½	90 00
x	111	41 48½	58 22	50 25½	55 25	42 44½	50 36½
p	211	60 47½	68 02	50 25½	35 57	24 48	63 05½
w	311	69 33½	73 54	50 25½	25 48½	17 07½	70 23½

Structure cell.[3] Space group *Pnma*; a_0 13.93, b_0 12.34, c_0 14.84; $a_0 : b_0 : c_0 = 1.129 : 1 : 1.2026$; contains $U_{26}O_{78} \cdot 39H_2O$ (?).

Habit. Tabular {001} and elongated [010]. {010} striated [100], and {101} striated [010]. Also massive.

Twinning.[4] On {110}, polysynthetic, producing pseudohexagonal aggregates.

Katanga.

Phys. Cleavage {001} perfect, also {101}. H. 2–3. G. 5.2;[5] 5.20 (calc.). Luster adamantine, inclining to greasy. Color amber to brownish yellow. Streak yellow. Transparent.

Opt. Yellow in transmitted light. With increasing temperature $2V$ decreases and the mineral is uniaxial at ca. 100°.[6]

ORIENTATION		n[7]	PLEOCHROISM	
X	c	1.735	Colorless	Bx. neg. (−). 2V 31° (Na)[8]
Y	b	1.820	Light yellow	r > v, marked.[7]
Z	a	1.830	Dark yellow	

Chem. A hydrated oxide of uranium. Formula uncertain, probably $2UO_3 \cdot 3H_2O$.[9] The water is completely lost at ca. 500°.[10] Complete analyses on pure material are lacking.[11]

Occur. Originally found at Kasolo, Katanga, Belgian Congo, with anglesite, soddyite, ianthinite, curite, schoepite, and other secondary uranium minerals, as an alteration product of uraninite. Also found with schoepite as an oxidation product of uraninite at Wölsendorf, Bavaria. A mineral[12] closely related to becquerelite occurs with uranophane, zippeite, and several unidentified uranium minerals as an oxidation product of uraninite at Great Bear Lake, Canada.

Artif. Ill-defined, apparently hydrated, uranium trioxides have been reported[13] but their relation to becquerelite and other natural oxides is unknown.

Name. After A. Henri Becquerel (1852–1908), French physicist, who discovered radioactivity.

Ref.

1. Orientation of Schoep, *Soc. géol. Belgique, Bull.*, **33**, 197 (1923); angles of Palache, *Am. Min.*, **19**, 311 (1934); unit of Billiet and de Jong, *Natuurw. Tijdschr.*, **17**, 157 (1935). Transformation: Schoep to Billiet and de Jong 200/010/002; Palache to Billiet and de Jong 200/010/001.
2. Palache (1934). Rare or uncertain forms:

031	051	405	708	112	632
041	709	506	504	212	421

3. Wolfe (priv. comm., 1941) by Weissenberg method; see also Billiet and de Jong (1935).
4. Schoep (1922); *Bull. soc. min.*, **46**, 9 (1923); **47**, 147 (1924).
5. Billiet and de Jong (1935) by a sedimentation method in water. Schoep, *Ann. mus. Congo belge*, **1** [1], no. 3, 5 (1932) gives 5.68 by the pycnometer method and calculates 5.38 by Gladstone and Dale's law.
6. Schoep (1923).
7. Berman in Palache and Berman, *Am. Min.*, **18**, 20 (1933). Billiet, *Bull. soc. min.*, **49**, 136 (1926), gives $nX = 1.750$, $nY = 1.87$, $nZ = 1.88$.

8. Schoep, *Ann. mus. Congo belge,* **1** [1], no. 2, 13 (1930); given as 30°35'.

9. Indicated by the x-ray study of Billiet and de Jong (1935). Schoep (1932) gives the formula as $4UO_3 \cdot 7H_2O$ and earlier (1922) as $UO_3 \cdot 2H_2O$.

10. For dehydration data see Schoep (1924).

11. Cuvelier in Billiet and de Jong (1935) gives 91.27 per cent UO_3 as the average of two microanalyses. Schoep (1932) gives 9.89 per cent H_2O as the average of three microanalyses. The earlier analyses of Schoep (1922; 1923; 1924) were made on impure material.

12. Palache and Berman (1933) for "mineral X" give $nX = 1.785$, $nY = 1.810$, $nZ = 1.820$ and $a : b : c = 0.490 : 1 : 1.042$. Crystals tabular {001} and elongated [010] with {001}, {010}, {100}, {120}, {111}, {011}, {021}.

13. See Schoep (1923) and Weiser (**2**, 321, 1935).

524   **S C H O E P I T E** [$4UO_3 \cdot 9H_2O$?].   *Walker (Am. Min.,* **8**, 67, 1923).

C r y s t.   Orthorhombic; dipyramidal — $2/m\ 2/m\ 2/m$.

$$a : b : c = 0.8516 : 1 : 0.8745;^1 \qquad p_0 : q_0 : r_0 = 1.0269 : 0.8745 : 1$$

$$q_1 : r_1 : p_1 = 0.8516 : 0.9738 : 1; \qquad r_2 : p_2 : q_2 = 1.1435 : 1.1743 : 1$$

Forms:[2]

		ϕ	ρ	ϕ_1	ρ_1	ϕ_2	ρ_2
c	001	.....	0°00'	0°00'	90°00'	90°00'	90°00'
b	010	0°00'	90 00	90 00	90 00	.....	0 00
a	100	90 00	90 00	.....	0 00	0 00	90 00
M	210	66 56	90 00	90 00	23 04	0 00	66 56
d	011	0 00	41 10	41 10	90 00	90 00	48 50
f	021	0 00	60 14½	60 14½	90 00	90 00	29 45½
q	112	49 35	33 59½	23 37	64 48½	62 49½	68 44½
o	111	49 35	53 27	41 10	52 17½	44 14½	58 36½
p	211	66 56	65 52½	41 10	32 53½	25 57½	69 03

Less common forms:

m	110	h	014	K	012	e	041	t	221	r	213	v	121
g	015	i	027	z	023	x	102	U	122	s	212	w	321

Structure cell.[3]   Orthorhombic; a_0 14.40, b_0 16.89, c_0 14.75; $a_0 : b_0 : c_0 = 0.852 : 1 : 0.873$; contains $U_{32}O_{96} \cdot 72H_2O$ (?).

Habit.   Usually tabular {001}; also equant, or short prismatic [001].

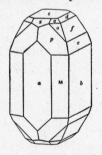
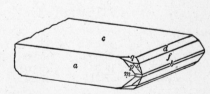

Katanga.

P h y s.   Cleavage {001} perfect. H. 2–3. G. 4.8;[4] 4.83 (calc.). Luster adamantine. Color sulfur- to citron-yellow. Streak yellow. Transparent.

O p t.   Yellow in transmitted light.

ORIENTATION		n^5	PLEOCHROISM	
X	c	1.690 ± 0.003	Colorless	Bx. neg. $(-)$.
Y	b	1.714 ± 0.003	Lemon-yellow	$2V\ 89°.6$
Z	a	1.735 ± 0.003	Lemon-yellow	$r > v$.

C h e m.   A hydrated oxide of uranium.   Formula uncertain, probably $4UO_3 \cdot 9H_2O$.[7]   The water is completely lost at ca. 325°.[8]   Complete analyses of pure material are lacking.[9]

O c c u r.   Found at Kasolo, Katanga, Belgian Congo, as an alteration product of uraninite or ianthinite.   Associated with cobaltian wad, becquerelite, curite, and other secondary uranium minerals.   Also reported at Wölsendorf, Bavaria, upon corroded fluorite with ianthinite and becquerelite.

N a m e.   After Alfred Schoep, Professor of Mineralogy in the University of Ghent.

Ref.

1. Unit of Billiet and de Jong, *Natuurw. Tijdschr.*, **17**, 157 (1935); orientation of Walker (1923); angles mean of those of Walker (1923), Palache, *Am. Min.*, **19**, 310 (1934), Ungemach, *Soc. géol. Belgique, Ann. publ. Congo belge*, **52**, C75 (1929).   Transformation Walker et al. to Billiet and de Jong 200/010/001.
2. See Palache (1934) for resumé of forms.
3. Billiet and de Jong (1935) by rotation method.
4. Billiet and de Jong (1935) by a sedimentation method in water.   Schoep, *Ann. mus. Congo belge*, **1** [1], no. 3, pt. 1, 5 (1932), gives 4.96 by the pycnometer and 4.46 as calculated by Gladstone and Dale's law.
5. Walker (1923).
6. Schoep, *Ann. mus. Congo belge*, **1** [1], no. 2, 18 (1930), measured 89°20′; $2V = 84°32'$ as calculated from the indices.
7. Indicated by the x-ray study of Billiet and de Jong (1935).   See also Schoep (1932), who gives $3UO_3 \cdot 7H_2O$ and earlier (1930) $UO_3 \cdot 2H_2O$.
8. For dehydration data see Schoep, *Bull. soc. min.*, **47**, 147 (1924).
9. Cuvelier in Billiet and de Jong (1935) gives 87.73 per cent UO_3 as an average of four microanalyses.   Schoep (1932) gives 12.10 and 12.55 per cent H_2O by microanalysis, and earlier (1924), *Bull. soc. min.*, **46**, 12, (1923) cites complete analyses of very impure material.

531   **F O U R M A R I E R I T E** $[PbO \cdot 4UO_3 \cdot 5H_2O\ ?]$.   *Buttgenbach (Soc. géol. Belgique, Ann., 47, C41, 1924).*

C r y s t.[1]   Orthorhombic.

$$a : b : c = 1.233 : 1 : 1.089; \qquad p_0 : q_0 : r_0 = 1.132 : 1.089 : 1$$
$$q_1 : r_1 : p_1 = 1.233 : 0.883 : 1; \qquad r_2 : p_2 : q_2 = 0.918 : 0.811 : 1$$

Forms:[2]

	ϕ	$\rho = C$	ϕ_1	$\rho_1 = A$	ϕ_2	$\rho_2 = B$
c	001	.....	0°00′	0°00′	90°00′	90°00′	90°00′
M	101	90°00′	48 33	0 00	41 27	41 27	90 00
o	111	46 07	57 31½	47 26	52 33½	41 27	54 12½

Habit.   Tabular {001} and usually elongated [010].   {001} striated [010].

Katanga.

P h y s.   Cleavage {001} perfect.   H. 3–4.   G. 6.046.   Luster adamantine.   Color red to golden-red; also brown.   Transparent.

O p t.[3] In transmitted light, yellow or reddish yellow in color. Pleochroic in shades of yellow and orange.

ORIENTATION		n	PLEOCHROISM	Bx. neg. (−).
X	c	1.85	Colorless	2V large.
Y	b	1.92	Pale yellow	$r > v$, strong.
Z	a	1.94	Yellow	

C h e m. A hydrated oxide of uranium and lead. Formula uncertain, perhaps $PbO \cdot 4UO_3 \cdot 5H_2O$.[4]

Anal.

	1	2	3
PbO	15.31	12.26	15.83
UO_3	78.51	77.67	77.79
H_2O	6.18	10.07	6.21
Total	100.00	100.00	99.83

1. $PbO \cdot 4UO_3 \cdot 5H_2O$. 2. Katanga. Recalc. average of two analyses after deduction of admixed torbernite and kasolite.[5] 3. Katanga. Analysis recalc. after deduction of 2.07 per cent quartz.[6]

Tests. B.B. blackens but does not fuse. Easily soluble in acids.

O c c u r. A secondary mineral found with torbernite, kasolite, and curite as an alteration product of uraninite at Kasolo, Katanga, Belgian Congo. Found similarly in the fluorite deposit at Wölsendorf, Bavaria, with ianthinite, dewindtite, anglesite.

N a m e. After P. Fourmarier, Professor of Geology at the University of Liége.

Ref.

1. Angles and unit of Buttgenbach (1924) reoriented to bring optical agreement with other uranium oxides. Transformations: Buttgenbach to new orientation: 010/001/100; Palache, *Am. Min.*, **19**, 309 (1934), to new orientation: 010/200/001.
2. Buttgenbach (1924).
3. Larsen and Berman (205, 1934); see also Billiet, *Bull. soc. min.*, **49**, 136 (1926), and Buttgenbach (1924).
4. Schoep, *Bull. soc. min.*, **47**, 157 (1924); the ratio of Pb : U = 10 : 38 for anal. 2.
5. Mélon, *Soc. géol. Belgique, Ann.*, **47**, B200 (1924).
6. Schoep (1924).

532 **C U R I T E** [2PbO·5UO₃·4H₂O ?]. *Schoep (C. R., 173, 1186, 1921).*

C r y s t. Orthorhombic.

$$a : b : c = 0.9595 : 1 : 0.6532;^1 \quad p_0 : q_0 : r_0 = 0.6808 : 0.6532 : 1$$

$$q_1 : r_1 : p_1 = 0.9595 : 1.4689 : 1; \quad r_2 : p_2 : q_2 = 1.5309 : 1.0423 : 1$$

Forms:[2]

		ϕ	$\rho = C$	ϕ_1	$\rho_1 = A$	ϕ_2	$\rho_2 = B$
a	100	90°00′	90°00′	.....	0°00′	0°00′	90°00′
m	110	46 11	90 00	90°00′	43 49	0 00	46 11
o	111	46 11	43 20	33 09	60 19	55 45½	61 38

Katanga.

Structure cell.[3] Space group *Pna* or *Pnam*; a_0 12.52, b_0 12.98, c_0 8.35; $a_0 : b_0 : c_0 = 0.9646 : 1 : 0.6433$; contains $Pb_6U_{15}O_{51}\cdot12H_2O$.

Habit. Crystals prismatic [001] and striated [001]. Usually massive, in aggregates of fine needles or saccharoidal; compact earthy.

Phys. Cleavage {100}.[4] H. 4–5. G. 7.26;[5] 7.12 (calc.). Luster adamantine. Color orange-red. Streak orange. Transparent in thin crystals.

Opt. In transmitted light, yellow to reddish orange in color.

Orientation		n^6	n^7	Pleochroism	
X	b	2.06	....	Pale yellow	Bx. neg. (−).
Y	a	2.11	2.07	Light red-orange	2V large.
Z	c	2.15	2.12	Dark red-orange	$r > v$, strong.

Chem. A hydrated oxide of lead and uranium. Formula uncertain, probably $2PbO\cdot5UO_3\cdot4H_2O$. The water is completely lost at ca. 450°.[8]

Anal.

	1	2	3
PbO	22.90	21.32	21.13
Fe$_2$O$_3$	.....	0.17	0.37
UO$_3$	73.40	74.22	74.28
H$_2$O	3.69	3.51	not det.
Rem.	.....	......	0.14
Total	100.00	99.92	....
G.	7.12	7.192	6.98

1. $2PbO\cdot5UO_3\cdot4H_2O$. 2. Katanga. PbO and UO$_3$ average of two partial analyses, H$_2$O average of three partial analyses.[9] 3. Katanga. Rem. is SiO$_2$ and Te trace.[10]

Tests. B.B. blackens. Easily soluble in acids. Liberates Cl from strong HCl.

Occur. Originally found at Kasolo, Katanga, Belgian Congo, as an oxidation product of uraninite. Associated with torbernite, soddyite, sklodowskite, fourmarierite, and other secondary uranium minerals. A gummite-like mineral found as an alteration product of uraninite at Katanga appears to be identical with curite.[11] A mineral[12] perhaps related to curite occurs with zippeite and becquerelite (?) as an alteration product of uraninite at Great Bear Lake, Canada. A mineral forming a bright red alteration zone around uraninite from Villeneuve, Quebec,[13] also may be curite.

Alter. Found as complete pseudomorphs after uraninite.[14]

Name. After Pierre Curie (1859–1906), French physicist known chiefly for researches on radioactivity carried out jointly with his wife, Marie Sklodowska.

Ref.

1. Palache, *Am. Min.*, **19**, 309 (1934), from measurements of Schoep, and new data.
2. Schoep, *Ann. mus. Congo belge*, **1** [2], Ser. 1, 22 (1930).
3. Shaub (priv. comm., 1941).

4. Berman in Palache (1934); the cleavage is given by Schoep (1930) as {100} or {110}.
5. Shaub (priv. comm., 1941); Schoep (1921) gives 7.192.
6. Larsen and Berman (209, 1934).
7. Billiet, *Bull. soc. min.*, **49**, 136 (1925).
8. For dehydration data see Schoep (1930).
9. Schoep (1921).
10. Hacquaert, *Natuurw. Tijdschr.*, **9**, 34 (1927).
11. Schoep and de Leenheer, *Soc. géol. Belgique, Bull.*, **46**, 309 (1937); analysis cited under gummite.
12. Palache and Berman, *Am. Min.*, **18**, 20 (1933).
13. Ellsworth, *Am. Min.*, **15**, 455 (1930); analysis cited under gummite.
14. See Hacquaert (1927) and Vernadsky and Chamie, *C. R.*, **178**, 1726 (1924).

533   **Uranosphaerite** [$Bi_2O_3 \cdot 2UO_3 \cdot 3H_2O$?]. Uranosphärit *Weisbach* (*Berg.-u.-Hütten. Jb., Sächs. — Jb. Min.*, 315, 1873).

C r y s t. Probably orthorhombic.[1]
Habit. In half-globular aggregated forms, sometimes with a dull or a slightly lustrous surface, sometimes rough and drusy, made up of minute acutely terminated crystals elongated [001]. Structure concentric, also radiated.

P h y s. Cleavage {100}.[2] H. 2–3. G. 6.36. Luster greasy. Color orange-yellow, brick-red. Streak yellow.

O p t.[2]

	ORIENTATION	n	
X	a	1.955 ± 0.01	Bx. pos. (+),
Y	b	1.985 ± 0.01	$2V$ large.
Z	c	2.05 ± 0.01	Dispersion $r < v$, strong.

C h e m. A hydrated oxide (?) of bismuth and uranium, probably $Bi_2O_3 \cdot 2UO_3 \cdot 3H_2O$.
Anal.

	1	2
Bi_2O_3	42.66	44.34
UO_3	52.39	50.88
H_2O	4.95	4.75
Total	100.00	99.97
G.		6.36

1. $Bi_2O_3 \cdot 2UO_3 \cdot 3H_2O$. 2. Schneeberg, Saxony.[3]

Tests. Decrepitates on heating, and falls to pieces to a mass of brown, silky needles.

O c c u r. Found with uranium arsenates, gummite, uranophane (?), and cobaltian wad as an oxidation product of pitchblende in the Walpurgis vein of the Weisser Hirsch mine, near Schneeberg, Saxony.
N a m e. In allusion to the composition and form of aggregation.

Ref.

1. Inferred from the optical properties.
2. Larsen (150, 1921).
3. Winkler, *J. pr. Chem.*, **7**, 5 (1873).

534   **VANDENBRANDITE** [CuO·UO$_3$·2H$_2$O]. *Schoep (Ann. mus. Congo belge,* 1 [1], no. 3, 25, 1932). Uranolepidite *Thoreau (Soc. géol. Belgique, Ann.,* 55, C3, 1933).

C r y s t. Triclinic (?).[1]

Forms:[2]

$$\{001\} \quad \{100\} \quad \{110\} \quad \{1\bar{1}0\}$$

Habit. Small crystals flattened {001}, often in parallel aggregates; sometimes lathlike. Also massive.

P h y s. Cleavage {001} perfect, with a distinct cleavage in the zone [001], and an indistinct cleavage apparently also in that zone.[3] H. 4. G. 5.03.[4] Color dark green to almost black. Streak green. Transparent in small flakes.

O p t. Green in transmitted light. Biaxial, apparently negative (−).[5] Absorption from green to colorless.

	n(KALONGWE)[6]	n(SHINKOLOBWE)[5]	
X	1.77 ± 0.02	1.76±	Dispersion strong.
Y	1.78 ± 0.02		2V large. An optic axis
Z	1.80 ± 0.02	1.80±	is nearly ⊥ {001}.

$Z \wedge$ elong. = 40°±.[5]

C h e m. A hydrated oxide of copper and uranium, CuO·UO$_3$·2H$_2$O. Most of the water is lost at about 320°.[7]

Anal.

	1	2	3
CuO	19.80	18.98	18.86
UO$_3$	71.23	70.40	70.72
SiO$_2$	.....	0.28	.....
H$_2$O	8.97	9.46	10.42
Rem.	.....	0.83	.....
Total	100.00	99.95	100.00
G.		5.03	4.91–4.97

1. CuO·UO$_3$·2H$_2$O. 2. Shinkolobwe, Katanga. Rem. is CaO 0.26, MgO 0.57.[8] 3. Kalongwe, Katanga. Average of several individual determinations of the principal constituents. Recalc. to 100 after deduction of PbO 4.69 as kasolite (3PbO·3UO$_3$·3SiO$_2$·4H$_2$O) and Fe$_2$O$_3$ 1.55, P$_2$O$_5$ 0.21; original total 98.59.[6]

Tests. B.B. fusible at about 1000° to a black mass becoming crystalline on cooling. Soluble with difficulty in cold acids to a yellowish green solution; easily soluble on warming.

O c c u r. A secondary mineral, found at Kalongwe, east of Karungwe, in the Katanga district, Belgian Congo, associated with kasolite, sklodowskite, malachite, goethite, chalcocite, chalcopyrite, and uraninite. Also found at Shinkolobwe in the Katanga district, associated with curite, uranophane, and cobaltian wad.

N a m e. Vandenbrandite after the Belgian geologist who discovered the deposit at Kalongwe, P. Van den Brande. Uranolepidite from λεπίς, *scale,* because a scaly uranium mineral.

Ref.

1. Inferred from the optical properties.
2. Morphological measurements are lacking. The indices are assigned without reference to definite axes or unit.
3. Schoep (1932) on crystals from Kalongwe. Thoreau (1933) describes three cleavages in material from Shinkolobwe: a perfect cleavage parallel to the flattening of the laths, a distinct cleavage parallel to the elongation of the laths and normal to the first cleavage, and an indistinct cleavage whose trace on the flattening is oblique to the direction of elongation.
4. Thoreau (1933) by pycnometer on material from Shinkolobwe. Schoep (1932) gives 4.91–4.97 for material from Kalongwe.
5. Thoreau (1933).
6. Schoep (1932).
7. For dehydration data see Schoep (1932).
8. Boubnoff anal. in Thoreau (1933).

535   **I A N T H I N I T E** [$2UO_2 \cdot 7H_2O$?].   *Schoep* (*Natuurw. Tijdschr.*, 7, 97, 1926).

C r y s t. Orthorhombic.

$a : b : c = 0.9996 : 1 : 1.2964;$[1] $p_0 : q_0 : r_0 = 1.2969 : 1.2964 : 1$

$q_1 : r_1 : p_1 = 0.9996 : 0.7711 : 1;$ $r_2 : p_2 : q_2 = 0.7714 : 1.0004 : 1$

Forms:[2]

		ϕ	$\rho = C$	ϕ_1	$\rho_1 = A$	ϕ_2	$\rho_2 = B$
c	001	.....	0°00′	0°00′	90°00′	90°00′	90°00′
f	230	33°42′	90 00	90 00	56 18	0 00	33 42
d	011	0 00	52 21½	52 21½	90 00	90 00	37 38½
M	203	90 00	40 15	0 00	49 45	49 45	90 00
$g]$	201	90 00	68 55	0 00	21 05	21 05	90 00

Habit. Tiny rectangular plates {001} elongated [010]. Also prismatic [010], or thick tabular {001}.

P h y s. Cleavage {001} perfect. H. 2–3. Luster submetallic. Color violet-black (alters on the edges to yellow). Streak brown-violet. Transparent.

O p t. In transmitted light, dark violet in color.

Katanga.

ORIENTATION		n^3	PLEOCHROISM	
X	c	1.674 ± 0.003	Colorless	
Y	b	1.90 ± 0.02	Violet	Bx. neg. (−).
Z	a	1.92 ± 0.02	Dark violet	

C h e m. A hydrated oxide or hydroxide of uranium. Formula uncertain, perhaps $2UO_2 \cdot 7H_2O$.[4] A microanalysis[5] gave U_3O_8 [82.90], Fe_2O_3 1.25, ign. loss 15.85, total 100.00.

O c c u r. Found as an alteration product of uraninite at Shinkolobwe-Kasolo, Katanga, Belgian Congo, associated with schoepite and becquerelite. At Wölsendorf, Bavaria,[6] with kasolite, parsonsite, dewindtite, fourmarierite, becquerelite, and schoepite.

A l t e r. Alters readily to schoepite, becquerelite, and an unidentified yellow material.

N a m e. From ἰάνθινος, *violet colored.*

Ref.

1. Angles of Schoep (1926); orientation of Palache, *Am. Min.*, **19**, 309 (1934); unit chosen to conform to that of schoepite and becquerelite.   Transformation: Schoep to new 0$\frac{2}{3}$0/001/100; Palache (1934) to new 200/010/001.
2. Schoep (1926).
3. Billiet, *Bull. soc. min.*, **49**, 136 (1926).
4. Schoep, *Soc. géol. Belgique, Ann.*, **49**, B310 (1927).
5. Schoep (1926); see also Schoep (1927).
6. Schoep and Scholz, *Soc. géol. Belgique, Bull.*, **41**, 71 (1931).

6 HYDROXIDES AND OXIDES CONTAINING HYDROXYL

The hydroxides are, for the most part, layered-lattice structures. Brucite consists of double (OH) sheets parallel to the basal plane, with Mg between the sheets. Since only weak bonds hold the (OH) sheets together the perfect cleavage is explained by the structure.[1] The same kind of structure, with some modifications, is found in gibbsite and in lepidocrocite. Members of the hydrotalcite group and of the dimorphous sjogrenite group probably also have a brucite-like structure, as indicated by their physical and chemical similarity to the other hydroxides.

61 AX_2 TYPE

611	BRUCITE GROUP	
6111	Brucite	$Mg(OH)_2$
6112	Pyrochroite	$Mn(OH)_2$
6113	Portlandite	$Ca(OH)_2$
612	LEPIDOCROCITE GROUP	
6121	Lepidocrocite	$FeO(OH)$
6122	Boehmite	$AlO(OH)$
613	Manganite	$MnO(OH)$
614	Stainierite	$CoO(OH)$?
615	HYDROTALCITE GROUP	
6151	Hydrotalcite	$Mg_6Al_2(OH)_{16} \cdot CO_3 \cdot 4H_2O$
6152	Stichtite	$Mg_6Cr_2(OH)_{16} \cdot CO_3 \cdot 4H_2O$
6153	Pyroaurite	$Mg_6Fe_2(OH)_{16} \cdot CO_3 \cdot 4H_2O$
616	SJOGRENITE GROUP	
6161	Manasseite	$Mg_6Al_2(OH)_{16} \cdot CO_3 \cdot 4H_2O$
6162	Sjogrenite	$Mg_6Fe_2(OH)_{16} \cdot CO_3 \cdot 4H_2O$
6163	Barbertonite	$Mg_6Cr_2(OH)_{16} \cdot CO_3 \cdot 4H_2O$
617	Brugnatellite	$Mg_6Fe(OH)_{13} \cdot CO_3 \cdot 4H_2O$
618	Psilomelane	$BaMn^2Mn_3^4O_{16}(OH)_4$

62 AX_3 TYPE

621	Sassolite	$B(OH)_3$
622	Gibbsite	$Al(OH)_3$
623	Bauxite	
624	Hydrocalumite	$Ca_4Al_2(OH)_{14} \cdot 6H_2O$

Ref.

1. Bragg (107, 1937).

BRUCITE GROUP

HEXAGONAL — P; SCALENOHEDRAL — $\bar{3}\,2/m$

		c	a_0	c_0	G
Brucite	$Mg(OH)_2$	1.5208	3.125Å	4.75Å	2.39
Pyrochroite	$Mn(OH)_2$	1.401	3.34	4.68	3.25
Portlandite	$Ca(OH)_2$	1.365	3.585	4.895	2.23

The members of this group possess a layered-lattice structure, and this is reflected in the platy habit of their crystals and in the perfect cleavage {0001} parallel to the layers. The minerals are flexible and soft $(2-2\frac{1}{2})$. Limited isomorphism is found between Mg and Mn. The small number of available analyses, however, influences the record of compositional variation in the species.

The minerals of the group are formed at comparatively low temperatures (less than 200°) in hydrothermal veins.

6111   B R U C I T E [$Mg(OH)_2$]. Native Magnesia (from New Jersey) *Bruce* (*Am. Min. J.*, **1**, 26, 1814). Hydrate of Magnesia *Aikin* (236, 1815), *Cleaveland* (429, 1822), *Hall* (28, 1824), *Robinson* (166, 1825). Brucite, ou Hydrate de magnésie *Beudant* (838, 1824). Talk-Hydrat, Magnesia-Hydrat *Germ.* Monoklinoëdrisches Magnesiahydrat oder Texalith (from Texas, Penn.) *Hermann* (*J. pr. Chem.*, **82**, 368, 1861). Amianthus (from Hoboken, New Jersey) *Pierce* (*Am. J. Sc.*, **1**, 54, 1818) = Amianthoid Magnesite, Nemalite *Nuttall* (*Am. J. Sc.*, 4, 18, 1821) = Brucite (Talk-Hydrat, " hierher zu gehoren scheint ") *Leonhard* (245, 1826), *Whitney* (*J. Soc. Nat. Hist. Boston*, 36, 1849). Manganbrucit *Igelström* (*Ak. Stockholm Öfv.*, **39**, 83, 1882). Manganobrucite. Ferrobrucite.

C r y s t.   Hexagonal — P; scalenohedral — $\bar{3}\,2/m$.

$$a : c = 1 : 1.5208;^1 \qquad p_0 : r_0 = 1.7561 : 1$$

Forms:[2]

		ϕ	ρ	M	A_2
c	0001	....	0°00'	90°00'	90°00'
m	$11\bar{2}0$	0°00'	90 00	90 00	60 00
z	$01\bar{1}3$	$-30\ 00$	$30\ 20\frac{1}{2}$	104 38	64 03
e	$01\bar{1}2$	$-30\ 00$	41 17	109 16	55 09
r	$10\bar{1}1$	30 00	$60\ 20\frac{1}{2}$	64 30	90 00
h	$07\bar{7}5$	$-30\ 00$	67 52	$117\ 35\frac{1}{2}$	$36\ 39\frac{1}{2}$
t	$04\bar{4}1$	$-30\ 00$	81 54	119 40	$30\ 58\frac{1}{2}$

Structure cell.[3]   Space group $C\bar{3}m$; a_0 3.125 ± 0.005, c_0 4.75 ± 0.005; $a_0 : c_0 = 1 : 1.520$; contains $Mg(OH)_2$ in hexagonal unit.

Habit.   Crystals usually broad tabular {0001} often subparallel aggregates of plates; a manganoan variety is sometimes acicular [0001]. Also commonly foliated massive; fibrous, with fibers separable and elastic; rarely fine granular.

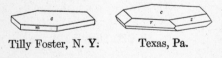

Tilly Foster, N. Y.   Texas, Pa.

Oriented growths.   Observed enclosing pyroaurite, with brucite {0001} [$10\bar{1}0$] ‖ pyroaurite {0001}[$10\bar{1}0$].[4]

P h y s. Cleavage {0001} perfect. Foliae separable and flexible. Sectile. H. $2\frac{1}{2}$. G. 2.39 ± 0.01; 2.40 (calc.). Luster on cleavages pearly, elsewhere waxy to vitreous. Color white, inclining to pale green, gray, or blue; in manganoan varieties honey-yellow to brownish red and deep brown (by alteration?). Streak white. Transparent. Exhibits percussion and pressure figures on {0001}.[5] Pyroelectric, on cooling — the extremities of [0001] negative, and the lateral edges positive.[6] The thermal expansion[7] is 4.47 ± 0.20 × 10^5 ⊥ {0001}, 1.10 ± 0.15 × 10^5 ⊥ {10$\bar{1}$0}.

O p t. Colorless in transmitted light. Often exhibits optical anomalies[8] due to mechanical deformation or aggregation of crystals; at times biaxial with small $2V$ due to the anomalies. Abnormal interference colors, due to marked change of birefringence with wavelength, are often observed.

O	E	
1.559	1.580[8]	Uniaxial pos. (+).
1.59	1.60	Anal. 5, manganoan.

C h e m. Magnesium hydroxide, $Mg(OH)_2$. Mn substitutes for Mg up to at least Mg : Mn = 5 : 1 (anal. 5). Fe^2 is often present in substitution for Mg, usually in amounts of only a few per cent but sometimes as high as Mg : Fe = 25 : 2 (anal. 3). Zn also occurs in small amounts in substitution for Mg (anal. 5). The CO_2 sometimes reported is probably due to admixed hydromagnesite or other impurity. Nearly all the H_2O is lost at 410°.[9]

Anal.[10]

	1	2	3	4	5
MgO	69.12	67.34	60.33	57.81	51.46
FeO	.....	.....	9.57	.....	.....
ZnO	.....	.....	.....	.....	3.67
MnO	.....	0.89	.....	14.16	18.11
H₂O	30.88	31.52	28.60	28.00	26.76
Rem.	.....	0.39	1.95	.....	.....
Total	100.00	100.14	100.45	99.97	100.00
G.	2.40	2.385			

1. $Mg(OH)_2$. 2. Wood's mine, Texas, Pa. Rem. is SiO_2.[11] 3. Ferroan brucite, fibrous. Asbestos, Quebec. Rem. is Fe_2O_3.[12] 4. Manganoan brucite. Small amounts of SiO_2 and $CaCO_3$ have been deducted. Jacobsberg, Sweden.[13] 5. Manganoan and zincian brucite. Franklin, N. J. Recalc. after deduction of about 3 per cent $CaCO_3$.[14]

Var. Ordinary. In crystals, plates or foliated masses. White to pale greenish in color.

Fibrous. Nemalite *Nuttall* (*Am. J. Sc.*, **4**, 18, 1821). In fibers or laths, usually elongated [10$\bar{1}$0] but sometimes [11$\bar{2}$0].[15] Some fibrous brucite is reported to be highly ferroan, but this may be owing to admixed magnetite.

Ferroan. Ferrobrucite. Contains a considerable amount of Fe^2 in substitution for Mg (anal. 3). Turns brown on exposure.

Manganoan. Manganbrucite *Igelström* (*Ak. Stockholm, Öfv.*, **39**, 83, 1882). Manganobrucite. Contains a considerable amount of Mn^2 in substitution for Mg (anal. 4, 5).

Tests. B.B. infusible, glows brightly, and the ignited material reacts alkaline. In C.T. becomes opaque and friable, sometimes turning gray to brown; the manganoan variety becomes dark brown. Easily soluble in acids.

O c c u r. Brucite occurs typically as a low-temperature hydrothermal vein mineral in serpentine and chloritic or dolomitic schists; also in crystalline limestones as an alteration product of periclase. Associated with calcite, aragonite, hydromagnesite, artinite, brugnatellite, talc, magnesite, deweylite. At Kraubat, Styria, with serpentine, magnesite, and hydromagnesite. In the Tirol in the Pfitschthal, and in the Fleimsthal at Canzocoli near Predazzo as an alteration of a periclase marble. At Teulada, Sardinia, Italy. In periclase-bearing limestone blocks thrown out by Vesuvius. At Swinna Ness, Unst, Shetland Islands, Scotland, with hydromagnesite in serpentine. In Sweden at Philipstad as an alteration of periclase in limestone, and similarly at Nordmark and Jakobsberg (*manganbrucite*); also at Långban. In the Urals in the region of Slatoust, in part well crystallized.

In the United States originally found at Hoboken, New Jersey, with hydromagnesite, artinite, dolomite, in serpentine, in part fibrous (the original *nemalite*). In Pennsylvania at Texas, Lancaster County, at Wood's mine and Low's mine, in fine crystals and broad plates up to 19 cm. across; near Reading and Sinking Spring, Berks County, with aragonite and serpentine in dolomite. Finely crystallized at the Tilly Foster mine, Brewster, Putnam County, New York. In a large deposit in the Lodi district, Nevada, with hydromagnesite. At Crestmore, Riverside County, California, as an alteration of periclase in marble. Fibrous brucite with fibers over 20 in. in length occurs with chrysotile and serpentine at Asbestos, Quebec.[16]

A l t e r. Often observed as an alteration product of periclase, and sometimes composes brucite-calcite rocks (pencatite, predazzite) often with hydromagnesite and serpentine, by the hydration of periclase marbles. Also observed as pseudomorphs after dolomite. Alters readily to hydromagnesite; less often to brugnatellite, serpentine, and deweylite. Ignited brucite ("metabrucite")[17] consists of an aggregate of periclase crystallites oriented with periclase $\{111\}[110] \parallel \{0001\}[10\bar{1}0]$ of the original brucite.[18]

A r t i f.[19] By heating to 200° mixed solutions of $MgCl_2$ and excess KOH; the crystals of brucite separate on cooling. Observed in crystals as a deposit in a steam boiler using waters containing $MgCl_2$. Also by reaction of NaOH solutions upon MgO at elevated temperatures.

N a m e. After Archibald Bruce (1777–1818), an early American mineralogist, who first described the species. *Nemalite* (more correctly *nematolite*) is from νῆμα, *thread*, in allusion to the fibrous structure.

Ref.

1. On crystals from Texas, Pa., by Hessenberg, in Dana (252, 1892).
2. In Dana (252, 1892).
3. Space group and structure by Aminoff, *Geol. För. Förh.*, **41**, 405 (1919); *Zs. Kr.*, **56**, 506 (1921). Cell dimensions by Garrido, *Zs. Kr.*, **95**, 189 (1936), on unanalyzed

brucite from Texas, Pa. A manganoan brucite (10.46 per cent MnO) from Långban, Sweden, gave Aminoff (1919) a_0 = 3.13, c_0 = 4.75.

4. Meixner, *Cbl. Min.*, 5, 1938, from Kraubat, Styria.
5. Mügge, *Jb. Min.*, I, 57, 1884; I, 110, 1898.
6. Hankel, *Ann. Phys.*, 6, 53 (1879).
7. Megaw, *Roy. Soc. London, Proc.*, 142A, 198 (1933).
8. Bauer, *Jb. Min., Beil.-Bd.*, 2, 70 (1883).
9. Kurnakov and Černych (1926), Clarke and Schneider, *Zs. Kr.*, 18, 417 (1890).
10. For many additional analyses see Hintze (1 [2A], 2086, 1910); also Kurnakov and Černych, *Mem. soc. russe min.*, 55, 74 (1926) — *Jb. Min.*, I, 313, 1927; Fenoglio, *Soc. geol. ital. Boll.*, 46, 13 (1927).
11. Kurnakov and Černych (1926).
12. Gonyer anal. in Berman, *Am. Min.*, 17, 313 (1932).
13. Igelström, *Ak. Stockholm, Handl.*, 187, 1858 — *Am. J. Sc.*, 31, 358 (1861).
14. Bauer anal. in Bauer and Berman, *Am. Min.*, 15, 346 (1930).
15. Michel-Lévy and Lacroix (162, 1888); Berman, *Am. Min.*, (1932); Garrido, *Zs. Kr.*, 95, 189 (1936); de Jong, *Bull. Inst. Geol. Yugoslav.*, 6, 241 (1938) — *Min. Abs.*, 7, 360 (1939).
16. Berman (1932).
17. Rinne, *Fortsch. Min.*, 3, 160 (1913). Büssem and Koberich, *Zs. phys. Chem.*, 17, 310 (1932).
18. Garrido, *C. R.*, 203, 94 (1936); *Zs. Kr.*, 95, 189 (1936). West, *Am. Min.*, 17, 316 (1932), found periclase [110] ‖ brucite [10$\bar{1}$0] in fibrous material from Quebec. See also Rinne, *Zs. deutsche geol. Ges.*, 43, 234 (1891).
19. Literature in Mellor (4, 290, 1923).

6112   **P Y R O C H R O I T E** [Mn(OH)$_2$]. *Igelström* (*Ann. Phys.*, 122, 181, 1864; *Ak. Stockholm, Öfv.*, 21, 205, 1864). Eisenpyrochroite *Flink* (*Geol. För. Förh.*, 41, 433, 1919).

Wiserit (not wiserine = xenotime) *Haidinger* (493, 1845).

C r y s t. Hexagonal — *P*; scalenohedral — $\bar{3}\,2/m$.

$$a : c = 1 : 1.3999;^1 \qquad p_0 : r_0 = 1.6154 : 1$$

Forms:[2]

		ϕ	ρ	M	A_2
c	0001	.....	0°00′	90°00′	90°00′
m	10$\bar{1}$0	30°00′	90 00	60 00	90 00
a	11$\bar{2}$0	0 00	90 00	90 00	60 00
p	10$\bar{1}$4	30 00	22 00$\frac{1}{2}$	79 12	90 00
o	10$\bar{1}$2	30 00	38 57	71 41	90 00
q	30$\bar{3}$4	30 00	50 29	67 18$\frac{1}{2}$	90 00
r	10$\bar{1}$1	30 00	58 15$\frac{1}{2}$	64 50	90 00
s	30$\bar{3}$2	30 00	67 35$\frac{1}{2}$	62 28	90 00
t	90$\bar{9}$4	30 00	74 37$\frac{1}{2}$	61 10$\frac{1}{2}$	90 00
x	71$\bar{8}$6	23 25	63 49	69 06$\frac{1}{2}$	84 05$\frac{1}{2}$

Structure cell.[3] Space group $C\bar{3}m$; a_0 3.34, c_0 4.68; $a_0 : c_0 = 1 : 1.401$; contains Mn(OH)$_2$.

Habit. Crystals tabular {0001}; also less commonly rhombohedral with large {10$\bar{1}$2} or {10$\bar{1}$1}; rarely prismatic [0001] with {11$\bar{2}$0} and {0001} developed. Usually in foliated masses, and as thin veinlets.

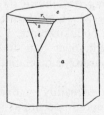

Franklin, N. J.

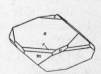

Långban.

Phys. Cleavage {0001} perfect. Thin flakes flexible. H. $2\frac{1}{2}$. G. 3.25 ± 0.02; 3.25 (calc.). Luster pearly on the cleavages. When fresh, colorless to pale greenish or bluish, but on exposure soon becoming bronze-brown and then black. Transparent in thin pieces, becoming opaque with increasing alteration, and flesh-red or amethystine color by transmitted light. Percussion figure[4] on {0001} with rays ‖ [10$\bar{1}$0]. **Opt.** In transmitted light, colorless to brown (when altered). Some times abnormally biaxial with small $2V$. Uniaxial negative ($-$).

	n_{red}	DICHROISM	
O	1.723	Brown	Absorption $O > E$, strong in brown.
E	1.681	Lighter brown	

In polished section[5] strongly reflecting in the black altered material.
Chem. Manganese hydroxide, $Mn(OH)_2$. Mg substitutes for Mn up to at least Mn : Mg = 5 : 1 (anal. 4). Small amounts of Zn (anal. 4) and perhaps Fe also substitute for Mn.[6]
Anal.[7]

	1	2	3	4
MnO	79.65	77.3	76.56	66.98
MgO	.....	1.7	2.39	6.56
CaO	.....	trace	0.29	0.32
FeO	.....	0.4	0.47	1.39
ZnO	.....	....	.....	3.08
CO₂	.....	....	1.99	0.37
H₂O	20.35	20.9	18.57	20.57
Rem.	.....	....	.....	0.89
Total	100.00	100.3	100.27	100.16
G.	3.25	3.24		

1. $Mn(OH)_2$. 2. Långban, Sweden.[8] 3. Moss mine, Nordmark, Sweden.[9] 4. Franklin, N. J. Rem. is MnO_2 0.89.[10]

Tests. In C.T. a small piece becomes verdigris green at the surface, then dirty green, and finally brownish black. Easily soluble in dilute HCl to a clear colorless solution.

Occur. Essentially a low-temperature hydrothermal mineral. Found associated with hausmannite, rhodochrosite, calcite, dolomite. Originally from Persberg, Philipstad, Sweden; also from Långban, from the Moss mine at Nordmarken, and with barite and polyarsenite at the Sjö mine, Örebro. Reported from Gonzen, near Sarganz, St. Gall, Switzerland (*wiserite*). In minute black tablets in druses in limonite near Prijedor, Bosnia, Yugoslavia. In the United States found in secondary, hydrothermal, veinlets cutting franklinite ore at Franklin and Sterling Hill, New Jersey, associated with rhodochrosite, gageite, acicular willemite, chlorophoenicite, calcite, hodgkinsonite. Found in a boulder of manganese ore in Alum Rock Park, near San José, Santa Clara County, California,[11] associated with tephroite, hausmannite, ganophyllite, rhodochrosite, barite, and psilomelane.

Alter. Changes readily, on oxidation, to a manganic compound; also to manganite. Mooreite occurs as a product of reworking of pyrochroite at Sterling Hill, New Jersey.

A r t i f.[12] Obtained in crystals by reaction in water solution of $MnCl_2$ and KOH in absence of oxygen.

N a m e. From $\pi\hat{v}\rho$, *fire*, and $\chi\rho o\iota\alpha$, *color*, because of the change of color upon ignition.

Ref.

1. Flink, *Ak. Stockholm, Handl.*, **12** [2], no. 2, 2 (1886).
2. Flink, *Bull. Geol. Inst. Upsala*, **5**, 1900; *Ark. Kemi*, **3** [35], 106 (1910); Palache (50, 1935).
3. Aminoff, *Geol. För. Förh.*, **41**, 407 (1919), on crystals from Långban.
4. Sjögren, *Geol. För. Förh.*, **27**, 37 (1905).
5. Orcel and Pavlovitch, *Bull. soc. min.*, **54**, 157 (1931).
6. An iron-rich (presumably ferroan) variety is mentioned by Flink, *Geol. För. Förh.*, **41**, 433 (1919), as occurring at Långban, Sweden, but no analysis is given.
7. For additional analyses see Hintze (**1** [2A], 2091, 1910) and Palache (1935).
8. Mauzelius anal. in Sjögren (1905).
9. Stahre anal. in Nordenskiöld, *Geol. För. Förh.*, **4**, 163 (1878).
10. Gage anal. in Palache (1935).
11. Rogers, *Am. J. Sc.*, **48**, 443 (1919).
12. de Schulten, *Bull. soc. min.*, **10**, 326 (1887); Grigoriev, *Mem. soc. russe min.*, **63**, 67 (1934) — *Min. Abs.*, **7**, 140 (1938).

BACKSTROMITE. Pseudopyrochroite *Aminoff* (*Geol. För. Förh.*, **40**, 427, 1918). Bäckströmite *Aminoff* (*Geol. För. Förh.*, **41**, 473, 1919). Baeckstroemite.

A name given to a hypothetical orthorhombic modification of $Mn(OH)_2$ dimorphous with pyrochroite. Found as pseudomorphs consisting largely of manganite and believed to have been derived from pyrochroite pseudomorphous after the original, supposititious backstromite. In black to brown prismatic, orthorhombic crystals,[1] with traces of cleavage {010}. Analyses correspond to a mixture of manganite and pyrochroite. Sometimes as oriented growths with pyrochroite, with backstromite {010}[100] || pyrochroite {0001}[10$\bar{1}$0]

Found at Långban, Sweden, associated with calcite, barite, fluorite, manganite, pyrochroite. Named after Professor Helge Bäckström, of the University of Stockholm.

An artificial orthorhombic modification of $Mn(OH)_2$ has been reported.[2]

Ref.

1. Aminoff (1919) gives a detailed morphological description, with $a : b : c = 0.7393 : 1 : 0.6918$. The possible crystal structure of backstromite has been discussed by Buerger, *Am. Min.*, **22**, 48 (1937).
2. Grigoriev, *Mem. soc. russe min.*, **63**, 67 (1934) — *Min. Abs.*, **7**, 140 (1938).

6113 **P O R T L A N D I T E** [Ca(OH)₂]. *Tilley* (*Min. Mag.*, **23**, 419, 1933).

C r y s t. Hexagonal — P; scalenohedral — $\bar{3}\,2/m$.[1]

Structure cell. Space group $C\bar{3}m$;[1] $a_0\ 3.585 \pm 0.001$, $c_0\ 4.895 \pm 0.003$;[2] $a_0 : c_0 = 1 : 1.365$; contains $Ca(OH)_2$.

Habit. As minute hexagonal plates. Artificial crystals[3] are tabular {0001}, with {10$\bar{1}$0} as linear faces.

P h y s. Cleavage {0001} perfect. Flexible. Sectile. H. 2. G. 2.230 ± 0.003;[4] 2.24 (calc.). Luster on cleavage surfaces pearly. Colorless. Transparent. Thermal expansion coefficient[5] ⊥ {0001} = $(3.34 \pm 0.20) \times 10^5$, and ⊥ {10$\bar{1}$0} = $(0.98 \pm 0.08) \times 10^5$.

O p t.[6] In transmitted light, colorless. Uniaxial negative $(-)$. $O = 1.574$, $E = 1.547$.

C h e m.   Calcium hydroxide.   CaO 75.64, H_2O 24.31, total 100.00. Analyses of natural material are lacking.

Tests.   Soluble in water to an alkaline solution.   Easily soluble in dilute HCl.

O c c u r.   Found intimately associated with afwillite and calcite in the larnite-spurrite contact rocks at Scawt Hill, county Antrim, Ireland, and ultimately derived by the alteration of the calcium silicates.   Reported as a yellow powder in fumaroles on Vesuvius.[7]

A l t e r.   Alters to $CaCO_3$ on exposure to moist air or to water containing CO_2.

A r t i f.[3]   In good crystals by slow interdiffusion of $CaCl_2$ and NaOH solutions; also by reaction of KOH solutions on $CaCO_3$.   Found in portland cement.

N a m e.   Proposed in view of the occurrence of $Ca(OH)_2$ as a common product of hydration of portland cement.

Ref.

1. Cell type, crystal class and space group by analogy with brucite. See Tilley (1933).
2. Megaw in Tilley (1933) on artificial crystals; imperfect natural crystals gave a_0 3.64 ± 0.10, c_0 4.85 ± 0.10.
3. See Ashton and Wilson, *Am. J. Sc.*, **13**, 209 (1927).
4. Merwin in Ashton and Wilson (1927) on artificial material; the natural material has G. 2.23.
5. Megaw, *Roy. Soc. London, Proc.*, **142A**, 198 (1933).
6. Indices from Merwin in Ashton and Wilson (1927).
7. Minguzzi, *Per. Min.*, **8**, 5 (1937).

LEPIDOCROCITE GROUP

		a_0	b_0	c_0	$a : b : c$
Lepidocrocite	FeO(OH)	3.87	12.51	3.06	0.309 : 1 : 0.245
Boehmite	AlO(OH)	3.78	11.8	2.85	0.320 : 1 : 0.242
Manganite	MnO(OH)	8.86	5.24	5.70	1.691 : 1 : 1.088
					$\beta = 90°$

The members of the group differ from goethite and diaspore in the nature of the H-O bond.[1]   In this group the hydrogen is probably held as hydroxyl (OH).   The sheet structure gives rise to the excellent cleavage.

Little miscibility between Fe and Al is found in the group, and intermediate minerals are not known.

Manganite is not closely related structurally to the other two minerals of the group, but it is included here because of chemical similarities.

Ref.

1. See Bragg (112, 1937).

6121   **L E P I D O C R O C I T E** [FeO(OH)].   Göthit (from Eiserfeld near Siegen) *Lenz* (46, 1806); in *Moll* (*Efem. Berg.- Hütt.*, 4, 505 (1808)); in *Ullmann* (304, 1814). Pyrrhosiderite *Ullmann* (144, 148, 299, 304, 316, 1814 (but given many years before to his class); earlier in *Hausmann* (268, 1813)).   Rubinglimmer *Hausmann* (268,

1813). Lepidokrokit (= Schuppig-fasriger Brauneisenstein from Hollerter Zug) *Ullmann* (148, 316, 1814; earlier in *Hausmann* (269, 1813)). γ-$Fe_2O_3\cdot H_2O$.
Hydrogöthit *Zemyatchensky* (*Soc. nat. St. Pétersbourg, Trav.,* **20**, 1889 — *Zs. Kr.,* **20**, 185, 1892).

C r y s t. Orthorhombic; dipyramidal — $2/m\,2/m\,2/m$?.[1]

$$a : b : c = 0.309 : 1 : 0.245;^2 \qquad p_0 : q_0 : r_0 = 0.793 : 0.245 : 1$$

$$q_1 : r_1 : p_1 = 0.309 : 1.26 : 1; \qquad r_2 : p_2 : q_2 = 4.08 : 3.24 : 1$$

Forms: [3]

		ϕ	$\rho = C$	ϕ_1	$\rho_1 = A$	ϕ_2	$\rho_2 = B$
c	001	.....	0°00′	0°00′	90°00′	90°00′	90°00′
b	010	0°00′	90 00	90 00	90 00	.....	0 00
a	100	90 00	90 00	.....	0 00	0 00	90 00
w	031	0 00	36 19	36 19	90 00	90 00	53 41
d	201	90 00	57 46	0 00	32 14	32 14	90 00
t	131	47 10	47 14	36 19	57 25½	51 35½	60 03½

Structure cell.[4] Space group *Amam*; a_0 3.87, b_0 12.51, c_0 3.06; a_0 : $b_0 : c_0 = 0.309 : 1 : 0.245$; contains $Fe_4O_4(OH)_4$.

Habit. As scales flattened {010} and slightly elongated [100]. {010} sometimes striated [100]. Usually as isolated crystals attached by an edge to the matrix, or aggregated into palmate or plumose groups; most crystals have a rounded indistinct [010] zone; also as loose rosettes; massive, bladed to fibrous or micaceous. The fibrous varieties are elongated [100].

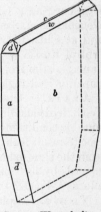

P h y s. Cleavage {010} perfect, {100} less perfect, {001} good. Brittle. H. 5. G. 4.09 ± 0.04;[5] 3.96 (calc.). Luster submetallic. Color ruby-red to reddish brown. Streak dull orange. Transparent.

O p t.[6] In transmitted light reddish, orange-red, yellowish according to thickness of section. Biaxial, negative (−), $2V = 83°$. Strongly pleochroic, with absorption $X < Y < Z$. Dispersion slight.

Siegen, Westphalia.

ORIENTATION		n	ABSORPTION (Thick Grains)	ABSORPTION (Thin Grains)
X	b	1.94	Clear yellow	Nearly colorless
Y	c	2.20	Dark red-orange	Orange to yellow
Z	a	2.51	Darker red-orange	Orange to yellow

In polished section[7] gray-white in color with strong anisotropism and strong pleochroism. Reflection percentages: green 20.5, orange 17, red 16.

C h e m. A monobasic ferric oxide, $FeO(OH)$, dimorphous with goethite. The CO_2 found in some analyses is probably due to admixed siderite. The Mn^3 commonly reported possibly may be in substitution for Fe^3. The small amounts of SiO_2 reported in most analyses are doubtless due to impurities.

Anal.[8]

	1	2	3	4	5	6
Fe_2O_3	89.86	88.91	88.11	89.90	85.80	82.67
Mn_2O_3	.....	.....	.....	.....	trace	1.24
SiO_2	.....	0.22	.....	.....	0.91	0.92
H_2O	10.14	10.93	11.97	10.77	11.02	11.68
Rem.	.....	.....	.....	.....	2.37	3.27
Total	100.00	100.06	100.08	100.67	100.10	99.78
G.	3.96				3.854	3.841

1. FeO(OH). 2. Herdorf, Siegen. Average of two closely agreeing analyses.[9]
3, 4. Eleonore mine, Dünsberg.[10] 5. Easton, Pa. Rem. is $FeCO_3$ calculated from CO_2
determination.[5] 6. Easton, Pa. Rem. is MgO 0.12, Al_2O_3 0.24, and $FeCO_3$ calculated
from the CO_2 determination.[5]

O c c u r. The occurrence and association of lepidocrocite are the same
as that of goethite, and the two species often occur together, with crystals
of the former often resting on goethite crusts. The following localities are
among those known certainly to afford lepidocrocite. In Germany well
crystallized in the Eisenzeche mine at Eiserfeld, Siegen; also in the neighborhood of Herdorf, and at Rossbach and Müsen; at the Eleonore mine at
Dünsberg near Giessen, Hesse-Nassau; at the Frankenholz mine, near
Neuenkirchen, Saar. In France at Rancié en Sem, near Vicdessos, l'Ariège,
and at Chizeuil, Saône-et-Loire. Near Trosna and at other localities in
central Russia (*hydrogoethite*). In the United States at Easton, Pennsylvania; at the Iron Mountain mine, Shasta County, California; in the Lake
Superior iron region.

A r t i f.[11] Obtained by the oxidation of freshly prepared hydrous
Fe_3O_4, hydrous $3Fe_2O_3 \cdot 2FeO$, Fe_2S_3, and FeS. Also by the oxidation under
suitable conditions of ferrous compounds. Mixtures of goethite and lepidocrocite result from the slow oxidation of ferrous bicarbonate in the air, and
from the slow oxidation of $FeCl_2$ at 40–50°. As pseudomorphs after FeOCl
crystals by heating these in water. Thermal dehydration of lepidocrocite
affords γ-Fe_2O_3[12] (maghemite).

N a m e. Lepidocrocite from λεπίs, *scale*, and κροκη, *thread*, in allusion
to the occasional palmate or plumose mode of aggregation. Pyrrhosiderite
from πυρρós, *fire-red*, and σίδηρos, *iron*, in allusion to the color. The name
goethite properly belongs to the species here described, since the name was
originally given by Lenz to the material from Eiserfeld now known to be
lepidocrocite.[13] Goethite, however, is in general use to designate the compound $HFeO_2$, of which the crystals from Cornwall show the characteristic properties, and it seems best not to restore its actual meaning.

HYDROGOETHITE. *Zemyatchensky* (*Soc. nat. St. Pétersbourg, Trav.*, **20** 1889 —
Zs. Kr., **20**, 185, 1892). Hydrogöthite.

A supposed hydrous ferric oxide, $3Fe_2O_3 \cdot 4H_2O$, from Dankow and Trosna in Government of Tula, central Russia. Optically identical with lepidocrocite,[14] and apparently
differs from that species only in containing adsorbed or capillary water above the
formula FeO(OH).

Ref.

1. The morphological evidence (Berman and Wolfe, priv. comm., 1940) points to a possible hemimorphism with the c-axis as hemimorphic axis; most crystals have a distinctly different development at the two ends of the axis. However, the structural work of Ewing, *J. Chem. Phys.*, **3**, 421 (1935) and Goldzstaub, *Bull. soc. min.*, **58**, 6 (1935), does not indicate a symmetry other than holohedral. See also Peacock, *Roy. Soc. Canada, Trans.*, [3] sec. 4, **36**, 107 (1942).

2. Unit, orientation, and ratio of Ewing (1935) by x-ray method.

3. Forms, on Siegen crystals, by Berman and Wolfe (priv. comm., 1940). Cesáro and Abraham, *Ac. Belgique, Bull.*, 178, 1903, and Posnjak and Merwin, *Am. J. Sc.*, **47** 322 (1919), found in addition: {104}, {102}, {203} and {301}. Rose (71, 1852) measured lepidocrocite crystals and found $x\{102\}$ and $f\{120\}$. The a-axis of Rose is our c-axis, with b of Rose our b. Transformations: Cesáro and Abraham to new elements $003/0\frac{2}{5}0/100$; Posnjak and Merwin to new elements $00\frac{1}{2}/010/\frac{1}{2}00$. The crystals described by Himmel and Schroeder, *Zbl. Min.*, [A], 97, 1939, from Neuenkirchen, are apparently not lepidocrocite.

4. Ewing (1935) on crystals from Eiserfeld.

5. Posnjak and Merwin (1919).

6. Posnjak and Merwin (1919); see also Larsen and Berman (144, 1934), who give also $X = c$ and $Y = a$, $2V = 90°$ (in the new orientation).

7. Schneiderhöhn and Ramdohr (2, 564, 1931).

8. Additional analyses of material from localities known to afford lepidocrocite are cited in the literature, but there is no certainty that these actually refer to that species.

9. Schwiersch, *Chem. Erde*, **8**, 276 (1933).

10. Willmann, *Cbl. Min.*, 676, 1921.

11. See Weiser (2, 40, 1935) and Posnjak and Merwin (1919).

12. See Schwiersch (1933), Goldzstaub, *C. R.*, **193**, 533 (1931), Posnjak and Merwin (1919), Goldzstaub (1935).

13. The separate identity of lepidocrocite, long considered the same as goethite, was first established by Lacroix (3, 360, 1901) on the basis of optical dissimilarity, and later confirmed in a more extensive study by Posnjak and Merwin (1919); the x-ray study of Böhm (1925) still further confirmed the separate identity of the two minerals.

14. Cf. Samojloff, *Zs. Kr.*, **34**, 701 (1901), **35**, 272 (1901); and Posnjak and Merwin (1919).

6122   **B O E H M I T E** [AlO(OH)].   Bauxit *Böhm* (*Zs. anorg. Chem.*, **149**, 203, 1925). Boehmite *de Lapparent* (*C. R.*, **184**, 1661, 1927).   Böhmit *Germ.* γ-$Al_2O_3 \cdot H_2O$.

Bauxite pt. *Berthier* (*Ann. mines*, **6**, 531, 1821); *Dufrénoy* (**2**, 347, 1844; **3**, 799, 1847); *Deville* (*Ann. chim. phys.*, **61**, 309, 1861).

C r y s t.   Orthorhombic; dipyramidal — $2/m\ 2/m\ 2/m$?.[1]

$$a : b : c = 0.320 : 1 : 0.242$$

Forms: [2]

$$c\{001\},\quad n\{120\}$$

Structure cell.[3]   Space group $Amam$; a_0 3.78, b_0 11.8, c_0 2.85; $a_0 : b_0 : c_0 = 0.320 : 1 : 0.242$; contains $Al_4O_4(OH)_4$.

Habit.   In microscopic lenticular crystals tabular {001}.   Usually disseminated or in pisolitic aggregates.

P h y s.   Cleavage {010}.   G. 3.01–3.06[4] (artif.); 3.11 (calc.).   Optical properties uncertain[5] but probably biaxial negative $(-)$, $Y = c$, $Z = b$, mean refractive index about 1.64.

C h e m.   A basic oxide of aluminum, AlO(OH), dimorphous with diaspore. Al_2O_3 84.97, H_2O 15.03, total 100.00.   Analyses of pure natural material are lacking.[6]

O c c u r.   Widely distributed in bauxite, and at times forms the principal constituent of the rock. Demonstrated localities include Gánt and Baratka, Hungary; Stangenrod, Harz, Germany; Monte Maggiore, Italy; Ayrshire, Scotland. In France at Recoux, Var, and Pereille and Cardarcet, l'Ariège. In the United States in the Linwood-Barton district, Georgia.

A r t i f.[7]   Obtained as an intermediate product in the dehydration of gibbsite; by heating precipitated hydrous aluminum oxide or gibbsite under pressure; as relatively good crystals by heating $Al(NO_3)_3$ solutions made acid with HNO_3 at 320–360° and 200–300 atmospheres pressure. Boehmite affords γ-Al_2O_3 on heating.

N a m e.   After J. Böhm, a German chemist who first recognized the substance.

Ref.

1. Goldzstaub, *Bull. soc. min.*, **59**, 348 (1936), as derived from the x-ray study which showed boehmite to be isostructural with lepidocrocite. See also Böhm, *Zs. anorg. Chem.*, **149**, 203 (1925).
2. Forms found by de Lapparent, *Bull. soc. min.*, **53**, 262 (1930), who erroneously gives {110} as the index of the prism form *n*.
3. Goldzstaub (1936).   Space group inferred from isostructural relation with lepidocrocite.
4. Fricke and Severin, *Zs. anorg. Chem.*, **205**, 287 (1932), and van Nieuwenburg and Pieters, *Rec. trav. chim. Pays-Bas*, **48**, 32 (1929), who give the higher value.
5. de Lapparent (1930) gives a birefringence of 0.020 with $Y = c, Z = b$. Schwiersch, *Chem. Erde*, **8**, 252 (1933), gives α and β 1.632, γ 1.639.   van Nieuwenburg and Pieters (1929) give a mean refractive index of 1.645. Achenbach, *Chem. Erde*, **6**, 307 (1931) gives 1.624 ± 0.003 for the refractive index at room temperature.
6. The composition of the artificial material has been established by direct analysis and by dehydration studies; see Edwards and Tosterud, *J. Phys. Chem.*, **37**, 483 (1933), Weiser and Milligan, *J. Phys. Chem.*, **38**, 1175 (1934), Fricke and Severin (1932).   The identity of the artificial and natural materials was shown by Hocart and de Lapparent, *C. R.*, **189**, 995 (1929), de Lapparent (1930) and others.
7. Literature in Weiser (**2**, 92, 1935); see also Lehl, *J. Phys. Chem.*, **40**, 47 (1936), Ewell and Insley, *J. Res. Nat. Bur. Standards*, **15**, 173 (1935).

613   M A N G A N I T E [MnO(OH)].   Manganaise cristallisé *de Lisle* (330, 1772; **3**, 101, 1783).   Manganèse oxydé metalloïde *Haüy* (**4**, 1801).   Grau-Braunsteinerz pt. *Werner* (1789); *Karsten* (1800).   Graumanganerz pt. *Karsten* (1808). Glanzmanganerz *Breithaupt* (240, 1823).   Grau-Braunstein pt. *Hausmann* (288, 1813; 390, 1847).   Gray Oxide of Manganese pt.   Prismatoidisches Mangan-Erz *Mohs* (488, 1824).   Manganite *Haidinger* (*Roy. Soc. Edinburgh, Trans.*, **11**, 122, 1827). Acerdèse *Beudant* (**2**, 678, 1832).   Newkirkite *Thomson* (**1**, 509, 1836).   Braunmanganerz *Quenstedt* (531, 1855).   Sphenomanganite *Flink* (*Geol. För. Förh.*, **41**, 329, 1919).

C r y s t.   Monoclinic;   prismatic — $2/m$ (pseudo-orthorhombic).[1]

$a : b : c = 0.8441 : 1 : 0.5448$,[2] $\beta\ 90°00'$; $p_0 : q_0 : r_0 = 0.6454 : 0.5448 : 1$

$q_1 : r_1 : p_1 = 0.8441 : 1.5494 : 1$; $\mu\ 90°00'$ $r_2 : p_2 : q_2 = 1.8355 : 1.1847 : 1$

Forms: [3]

		ϕ	$\rho = C$	ϕ_1	$\rho_1 = A$	ϕ_2	$\rho_2 = B$
c	001	.....	0°00′	0°00′	90°00′	90°00′	90°00′
b	010	0°00′	90 00	90 00	90 00	.....	0 00
y	130	21 33	90 00	90 00	68 27	0 00	21 33
t	250	25 21½	90 00	90 00	64 38½	0 00	25 21½
l	120	30 38½	90 00	90 00	59 21½	0 00	30 38½
k	230	38 18	90 00	90 00	51 42	0 00	38 18
m	110	49 50	90 00	90 00	40 10	0 00	49 50
i	430	57 40	90 00	90 00	32 20	0 00	57 40
d	210	67 07	90 00	90 00	22 53	0 00	67 07
h	410	78 05	90 00	90 00	11 55	0 00	78 05
e	011	0 00	28 35	28 35	90 00	90 00	61 25
f	021	0 00	47 27½	47 27½	90 00	90 00	42 32½
u	101	90 00	32 50½	0 00	57 09½	57 09½	90 00
p	111	49 50	40 11	28 35	60 27½	57 09½	65 24½
v	221	49 50	59 22½	47 27½	48 53	37 46	56 17
x	365	30 38½	37 14	33 10½	72 02½	68 50	58 38
χ	414	78 05	33 24½	7 45½	57 24	57 09½	83 28½
g	313	74 17	33 50½	10 17½	57 35	57 09½	81 19½
s	212	67 07	35 01	15 14½	58 05½	57 09½	77 06½
n	121	30 38½	51 42½	47 27½	66 25½	57 09½	47 31½

Structure cell. [4] Space group $B2_1/d$; a_0 8.86, b_0 5.24, c_0 5.70; $\beta = 90°$; $a_0/2 : b_0 : c_0/2 = 0.8454 : 1 : 0.5439$; contains $Mn_8O_8(OH)_8$ in given unit cell.

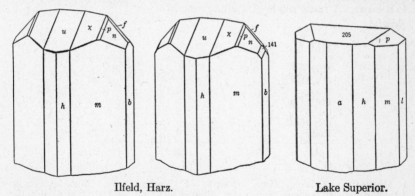

Ilfeld, Harz.   Lake Superior.

Habit. Crystals striated and short to long prismatic [001]. Often terminated by {001} alone, by {001} with macrodomes, or by a series of macropyramids; sometimes highly modified. Prismatic faces deeply striated [001], and terminal {h0l} or {hkl} faces striated ‖ to their mutual intersections. Crystals often grouped in bundles, or markedly composite subparallel [001]. seldom granular; stalactitic.

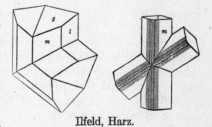

Ilfeld, Harz.

Also columnar to coarse fibrous;

Twinning. (*a*) Twin plane {011}, both as contact and penetration twins; often repeated and with composition face either parallel or inclined, analogous to rutile. (*b*) Twin plane {100}, lamellar,[5] assuming a monoclinic symmetry for the mineral.

P h y s. Cleavage {010} very perfect, {110} and {001} less perfect. Fracture uneven. Brittle. H. 4. G. 4.33 ± 0.01; 4.38 (calc.). Luster submetallic. Color dark steel-gray to iron-black. Streak reddish brown, sometimes nearly black. Transparent only in thin splinters. Translation gliding[6] with T{010}, t[001].

O p t.[7] In transmitted light, red-brown in color. Faintly pleochroic with absorption X and $Y < Z$. Manganite has been stated[6] to show inclined extinction with $Z \wedge c = 4° \pm$.

	ORIENTATION	n_{Li}	PLEOCHROISM	
X	a	2.25 ± 0.02	Reddish brown	Bx. pos. (+). 2V
Y	b	2.25 ± 0.02		small. Dispersion
Z	c	2.53 ± 0.02	Red-brown	$r > v$, very strong.

In polished section[8] gray-white with a brownish tint. Anisotropic, with weak pleochroism, and frequently exhibits blood-red internal reflections. Reflection percentages: ‖ [100], green 16.5, orange 12, red 12.5; ‖ [001], green 19, orange 16, red 15.5.

C h e m. A basic oxide of manganese, $MnO(OH)$.

Anal.[9]

	1	2	3
MnO	80.66	79.55	79.60
O	9.12	9.27	8.76
H_2O	10.22	10.32	10.16
$(Fe,Al)_2O_3$	....	0.30	0.35
BaO	....	0.15	....
PbO, CuO	....	0.10	0.10
CaO	....	0.10	trace
$(Na,K)_2O$	....	0.22	....
Rem.	....	0.28	1.23
Total	100.00	100.29	100.20
G.	4.38	4.34–4.39	4.29

1. $MnO(OH)$. 2. Ilfeld, Harz. Average of three analyses. Rem. is gangue.[10] 3. Långban, Sweden (sphenomanganite). Rem. is SiO_2 0.11, MgO 0.87, Sb_2O_3 0.25.[11]

Tests. B.B. infusible. Soluble in concentrated HCl with evolution of Cl.

O c c u r. Occurs as a low-temperature hydrothermal vein mineral associated with barite, calcite, siderite, braunite, hausmannite (Ilfeld, Harz). Commonly as replacement or other deposits formed by meteoric waters, associated with pyrolusite, goethite, psilomelane, barite, limonite; generally occurs in deposits of pyrolusite or psilomelane. In residual clays, and rarely as a hot-spring deposit.

Found abundantly and in fine crystals at Ilfeld, Harz, Germany, in veins in porphyrite with barite and calcite; also at Ilmenau, Thuringia, in part as pseudomorphs after calcite scalenohedra; in the neighborhood of Siegen,

Westphalia; at Horhausen, Rhineland. At Macskamezö, Transylvania. In France at several localities in the valleys of Lauron and d'Aure, Hautes-Pyrénées, and at Las Cabesses and Rancié, Ariège. In Cornwall, England, in the Botallack mine, St. Just; also at Egremont, Cumberland, at Exeter, Devonshire, and from Granam, near Towie, Aberdeen, Scotland. In Sweden at Långban (*sphenomanganite* pt.) and at Bölet, near Undenäs. In the Changpin district, north of Peiping, China.

Found in the United States at the Jackson mine, Negaunee, Michigan, and elsewhere in the Lake Superior iron district. Well crystallized at Powells Fort, near Woodstock, Shenandoah County, Virginia, in large part altered to pyrolusite. In the Cartersville district, Bartow County, Georgia. Has been noted at Sterling Hill, New Jersey, with garnet in the zinc ore. Numerous small deposits of manganite admixed with pyrolusite and psilomelane occur in California, notably in the Livermore-Tesla district in Alameda County. In the Lake Valley district, Sierra County, New Mexico. In Canada manganite occurs at Cheverie, Walton, and elsewhere in Hants County, Nova Scotia.

Alter. Very commonly alters to pyrolusite; also to psilomelane, braunite, hausmannite. Pseudomorphs of manganite after calcite are frequent, and the mineral has been observed as an alteration product of pyrochroite and rhodochrosite.

Artif. Obtained in crystals[12] by heating $MnCl_2$ and CaO to redness in an oxidizing atmosphere over a long period. When heated[13] in oxygen or air, manganite is converted to MnO_2 (pyrolusite), and in nitrogen to Mn_2O_3 (hausmannite).

Name. In allusion to the composition. Acerdèse, from ἀκερδής, *nonprofitable*, was given because the material is of little value for bleaching purposes.

SPHENOMANGANITE *Flink* (*Geol. För. Förh.*, **41**, 329, 1919).
A name given to designate material from Långban, Sweden, with a sphenoidal habit[14] but otherwise like manganite. Presumably identical with manganite.[15]

Ref.

1. Buerger, *Zs. Kr.*, **95**, 163 (1936) has presented x-ray and polished section evidence showing that manganite is monoclinic. Earlier suggestions of low symmetry by Mügge, *Cbl. Min.*, 1, 1922, and possible sphenoidal symmetry by Flink (see sphenomanganite, *Geol. För. Förh.*, **41**, 329 [1919]), and others have not been generally recognized. An effort to find morphological and microscopic evidence of lower symmetry and twinning on {100} (as proposed by Buerger) has led to negative results, after an examination of many crystals (priv. comm., Palache and Berman, November, 1940); therefore the conventional orthorhombic interpretation has been retained for the angle table.
2. Elements of Haidinger, *Edinburgh J. Sc.*, **4**, 41 (1826) — Dana (249, 1892) modified. The x-ray unit of Buerger (1936) has doubled a and c values. However, with the latter unit, considerably more complexity is introduced into the form series, and the common forms are not unit forms. Since the habit is orthorhombic, orthorhombic elements and angles are given.
3. Goldschmidt, **5**, 191 (1918); also Palache (priv. comm., 1940). Since it has not been found possible to distinguish positive and negative forms ($\beta = 90°$), no effort to separate them has here been made.

Rare or uncertain forms:

100	940	1·0·15	177	525
150	520	1·0·10	133	323
270	830	2·0·15	3·11·7	232
590	310	105	17·30·30	141
350	610	103	32·60·45	493
560	10·1·0	205	647	521
12·13·0	12·1·0	17·0·20	20·1·20	541
10·9·0	16·1·0	201	10·1·10	721
650	30·1·0	601	616	10·5·1
320	1·0·20	443	515	

4. Buerger (1936) by Weissenberg method on crystals from Ilfeld; see earlier Garrido, *Bull. soc. min.*, **58**, 224 (1935), Ferrari and Scherillo, *Zs. Kr.*, **78**, 496 (1931), de Jong, *Natuurw. Tijdschr.*, **12**, 69 (1930). On the structural relation to marcasite see Buerger, *Am. Min.*, **22**, 48 (1937).
5. Buerger (1936).
6. Mügge (1922).
7. Larsen (104, 1921).
8. Schneiderhöhn and Ramdohr, (**2**, 555, 1931).
9. For additional analyses see Doelter (3 [2], 846, 1926).
10. Gorgeu, *Bull. soc. chim.*, **9**, 650 (1893) — *Zs. Kr.*, **25**, 313 (1895).
11. Flink, *Geol. För. Förh.*, **41**, 329 (1919).
12. Kuhlmann, *C. R.*, **52**, 1283 (1861), and Des Cloizeaux, *C. R.*, **52**, 1323 (1861).
13. Pavlovitch, *C. R.*, **200**, 71 (1935).
14. See also for merohedral manganite Haidinger, *Edinburgh, J. Sc.*, **4**, 41 (1826), Koechlin, *Min. Mitt.*, **9**, 24 (1887), Busz, *Zs. Kr.*, **15**, 624 (1889), Watson and Wherry, *Washington Ac. Sc., J.*, **8**, 550 (1918).
15. The apparently merohedral development of some forms is anomalous, since x-ray study shows manganite to be holohedral.

614   **STAINIERITE** [CoO(OH)]. *Schoep* and *Cuvelier* (*Soc. géol. Belgique, Bull.*, **39**, 74, 1929).

Botryoidal and mammillary crusts, internally layered and microcrystalline or as radial needle-like crystals. Cross section of needles hexagonal or pseudohexagonal. Apparently not isostructural with goethite.[1] Sometimes apparently twinned with twin plane parallel to elongation.

Phys. Cleavage normal to elongation, with an inclined cleavage (developed in grinding). Fracture of aggregates uneven to conchoidal. H. 4–5. G. 4.13–4.47. Luster dull to metallic. Color black, steel-gray. Streak black. Opaque. Nonmagnetic.

In polished section[2] gray-white in color and strongly anisotropic with strong pleochroism and deep cobalt-blue to purple internal reflections (very fine-grained material appears isotropic).

Chem. A hydrous oxide of cobalt, probably $Co_2O_3 \cdot H_2O$ or possibly CoO(OH). Adsorbed and capillary water is usually present in excess of the formula,[3] and small amounts of Cu apparently substitute for Co (with Cu : Co = 1 : 24 in anal. 3).

Anal.[3]

	1	2	3	4
Co_2O_3	90.20	68.72	84.60	83.54
CuO	.....	2.68	3.46	0.92
Fe_2O_3	.....	9.45	.....	0.63
Al_2O_3	.....	6.87	.....	.....
H_2O	9.80	10.15	11.15	11.97
Rem.	.....	2.67	.....	2.54
Total	100.00	100.54	99.21	99.60

1. $Co_2O_3 \cdot H_2O$. 2. Mindigi, Belgian Congo. Rem. is SiO_2.[4] · 3. Mindigi, Belgian Congo.[5] 4. Kadjilangwe, Belgian Congo. Rem. is insol. 1.66, CaO 0.88.[6]

Tests. Soluble in HCl to a green solution with liberation of Cl.

Occur. A secondary mineral formed by the oxidation of cobaltiferous carbonates and other cobalt minerals. Associated with malachite, hematite, cobaltian wad, and various ill-defined hydrous cobalt oxides (mindigite, etc.).[7] Found at Mindigi, Luishia, and Kadjilangwe (Luambo) in the Katanga district, Belgian Congo. Occurs abundantly in the Goodsprings district, Nevada.[9]

Artif. Hydrous cobaltic oxide is formed by the oxidation of cobaltous salts in acidic or alkaline solution. A number of definite hydrates have been reported,[10] but the existence of only $Co_2O_3 \cdot H_2O$ can be regarded as certain. Sols and gels of hydrous cobaltic oxide, as well as of hydrous cobaltic-cobaltous oxide and cobaltous hydroxide, are well known.[11]

Name. After Professor Xavier Stainier, of the University of Ghent.

Ref.

1. de Jong, *Natuurw. Tijdschr.*, **12**, 69 (1930), from x-ray powder study; see also Cooke and Doan, *Am. Min.*, **20**, 274 (1935), for x-ray measurements of the Nevada occurrence. Spacings (in Ångstroms) derived from x-ray powder pictures of the Nevada material are (with intensities in brackets):

5.02(2)	2.48(1)	1.84(3)	1.45(4)	1.21(1)
4.55(5)	2.36(5)	1.60(1)	1.38(3)	1.20(1)
2.61(1)	2.03(2)	1.53(2)	1.23(2)	1.13(1)

2. Schoep and Cuvelier (1929), de Leenheer, *Zbl. Min.*, 281, 1938, Cooke and Doan (1935); see also under heterogenite in Schneiderhöhn and Ramdohr (**2**, 558, 1931).
3. For dehydration data see de Leenheer (1938).
4. Cuvelier in Schoep and Cuvelier (1929).
5. de Leenheer, *Natuurw. Tijdschr.*, **17**, 44, 148 (1935).
6. de Leenheer (1938).
7. For description of the paragenesis in the Katanga occurrences see de Leenheer (1935, 1938). An additional analysis mentioned in Schneiderhöhn and Ramdohr (1931) is said to approach the formula $Co_2O_3 \cdot 2H_2O$.
9. Hewett, *U. S. Geol. Sur., Prof. Pap.* **162**, 84, 1931, and Cooke and Doan (1935).
10. Mellor (**14**, 589, 1935).
11. Weiser (**2**, 160, 166, 1935).

The following ill-defined minerals are colloidal materials possibly differing from stainierite and each other only in particle size, content of adsorbed and capillary water, and the presence of admixed impurities. With increasing admixture of manganese oxide the materials grade to the substances listed under cobaltian wad (*asbolite*).

WINKLERITE. *Breithaupt (Jb. Min.*, 816, 1872).

In bluish to violet-black masses with conchoidal fracture and dark brown streak. H. 3. G. 3.43, 3.72. Analyses[1] of material admixed with an arsenate of Cu and Ca indicate a hydrous cobalt and nickel oxide. Found as an alteration product of erythrite with malachite and halloysite (?) at Oria near Almeria, in the Sierra Alhamilla, Spain. Named after Dr. Clemens A. Winkler (1838–1904), Professor of Chemistry at the Mining Academy, Freiberg.

HEUBACHITE.   *Sandberger (Ak. München., Ber.,* 238, 1876; 413, 1885).
In thin sootlike incrustations, and in dendritic or small spherical aggregates.   H. $2\frac{1}{2}$.
G. 3.75.   Color deep black.   Streak submetallic.   Analysis[1] indicates a hydrous cobalt
and nickel oxide with Fe_2O_3.   Occurs as a secondary product coating barite at the St.
Anton mine in the Heubachthal, near Wittichen, Baden, and at the Eberhard mine near
Alpirsbach, Württemberg.   Reported from Copiapó, Chile.

TRANSVAALITE.   *McGhie* and *Clark (Eng. Min., J.,* 50, 96, 1890).
An oxidation product of smaltite (?) occurring in black nodular masses.   H. 4.
G. 3.846.   The analysis[1] suggests a hydrous cobalt oxide admixed with an arsenate
(erythrite ?) and other impurities.   Found at a mine about 30 miles north of Middeburg,
Transvaal, South Africa.

SCHULZENITE.   *Martens (Act. soc. sc. Chile,* 5, 87, 1895; *Bull. soc. min.,* 19,
211, 1896).
A massive material with conchoidal fracture and black color and streak.   H. $3\frac{1}{2}$.
G. 3.39.   The analysis[2] suggests a hydrous oxide of Co^3, Co^2, and Cu^2.   Supposed to
have come from northern Chile.   Named after J. Schulze, in whose mineral collection
the specimen was contained.

HETEROGENITE.   *Frenzel (J. pr. Chem.,* 5, 404, 1872).   Lubumbashite (*local
name at Katanga*).
In globules or reniform masses.   Fracture conchoidal or dense.   H. 3–4.   G. 3.44.
Luster dull to vitreous.   Color black or reddish to blackish brown.   Streak dark brown.
Analyses[3] suggest a hydrous cobaltic and cobaltous oxide.   Found as an alteration product of smaltite with pharmacosiderite and calcite at Schneeberg, Saxony.   A similar
mineral containing some CuO occurs at Katanga.[4]   Reported from New Caledonia.

MINDIGITE.   *de Leenheer (Natuurw. Tijdschr.,* 16, 237, 1934; *Ann. Serv.
Mines, Com. Spec. Katanga,* 6, 35, 1936).
As glassy botryoidal crusts with conchoidal fracture.   Does not give an x-ray diffrac-
tion pattern.   H. $3\frac{1}{2}$.   G. 3.07.   Color pitch-black.   Streak brownish black.   In
polished section strongly anisotropic.[5]   Essentially a hydrous cobalt oxide, with CuO.
Analyses gave:

	Co_2O_3	CuO	H_2O	Insol.	Total
1	76.05	9.22	14.79	....	100.06
2	77.05	7.34	14.74	0.66	99.79

Found at Mindigi, Katanga, Belgian Congo.   Similar materials containing small
amounts of manganese oxide have been found[6] at Kambove and Tuashi at Katanga (see
also under asbolite).

TRIEUITE.   *de Leenheer (Natuurw. Tijdschr.,* 17, 91, 1935).
Massive, with conchoidal fracture and vitreous luster.   Does not give an x-ray diffraction pattern.   H. $3\frac{1}{2}$.   G. 3.13.   Color black.   In transmitted light isotropic with
$n = 1.85$.   In polished section isotropic with cobalt-blue to violet internal reflections;
not pleochroic.   A hydrous cobalt oxide with admixed or constitutional CuO.   Analysis[7] gave: Co_2O_3 53.58, CuO 22.63, SiO_2 1.50, H_2O 20.16, CO_2 1.36, total 99.23.   Found
at the Star of the Congo mine, Katanga, Belgian Congo.   Named after R. du Trieu de
Terdonck, chief geologist of the Union Minière du Haut Katanga.

BOODTITE.   *de Leenheer (Natuurw. Tijdschr.,* 18, 77, 1936).
A friable gray-black material with a bronzy luster.   H. 3.   G. 3.1–3.4.   Essentially
hydrous cobalt oxide, with minor CuO and Fe_2O_3, admixed[5] with talc, kaolin, and
quartz.   Found in the Star of the Congo mine, Katanga, Belgian Congo.   Named after
Anselm Boetius de Boodt (1550–1634), Belgian physician and author of a well-known
work on gems.

Ref.

1. See Dana (259, 260, 1892).
2. See Dana (61, 1899).
3. See Hintze (1 [2A], 2096, 1910).
4. Schoep, *Bull. soc. chim. Belg.,* 30, 207 (1921).

5. de Leenheer, *Zbl. Min.*, 341, 1938.
6. de Leenheer, *Natuurw. Tijdschr.*, **18**, 77 (1936).
7. Cuvelier in de Leenheer, *Natuurw. Tijdschr.*, **17**, 91 (1935); an earlier analysis of rather similar material by Schoep (1921) was ascribed to heterogenite.

HYDROTALCITE AND SJOGRENITE GROUPS

CELL CONTENTS (HEX. COORD.)

Hydrotalcite Group (Rhombohedral)

		a_0	c_0
Hydrotalcite	$Mg_{18}Al_6(OH)_{48}(CO_3)_3 \cdot 12H_2O$	6.13	46.15
Stichtite	$Mg_{18}Cr_6(OH)_{48}(CO_3)_3 \cdot 12H_2O$	6.18	46.38
Pyroaurite	$Mg_{18}Fe_6(OH)_{48}(CO_3)_3 \cdot 12H_2O$	6.19	46.54

Sjogrenite Group (Hexagonal)

Manasseite	$Mg_6Al_2(OH)_{16}CO_3 \cdot 4H_2O$	6.12	15.34
Barbertonite	$Mg_6Cr_2(OH)_{16}CO_3 \cdot 4H_2O$	6.17	15.52
Sjogrenite	$Mg_6Fe_2(OH)_{16}CO_3 \cdot 4H_2O$	6.20	15.57

These minerals comprise two isostructural groups, hexagonal — R and hexagonal — P, that stand in polymorphous relation to each other.[1] The general formula for the two groups is $Mg_6R_2^3(OH)_{16}CO_3 \cdot 4H_2O$, where R^3 = Al, Cr, or Fe. This formula requires a doubling of both a_0 and c_0 for the rhombohedral group and a doubling of a_0 for the hexagonal group, over the observed cell dimensions, in order to give rational cell contents. The explanation of this discrepancy is not apparent.[2]

The species of both groups have a perfect cleavage {0001}, are soft (H. $1\frac{1}{2}$–$2\frac{1}{2}$), of low specific gravity (G. $\sim$ 2) and form plates {0001} or contorted fibro-lamellar aggregates. The indices of refraction and the cell volumes decrease in the order Fe-Cr-Al. Structurally, the members of both groups appear to be layer-lattices based on a stacking of hydroxide layers along [0001] as in brucite. All the minerals occur as very low-temperature hydrothermal products, usually in serpentine or other highly magnesian rocks, and the hexagonal and rhombohedral analogues often are found intimately admixed.

Ref.

1. Frondel, *Am. Min.*, **26**, 295 (1941).
2. See Frondel (1941) and Aminoff and Broomé, *Ak. Stockholm, Handl.*, **9**, no. 5, 23 (1930).

6151 HYDROTALCITE [$Mg_6Al_2(OH)_{16} \cdot CO_3 \cdot 4H_2O$]. Hydrotalkit (?) *Hostetter (J. pr. Chem.*, **27**, 376, 1842). Hydrotalcite *Frondel (Am. Min.*, **26**, 295, 1941).
  Voelknerite (?) *Hermann (Ac. sc. St. Pétersbourg*, **5**, 127, 1846; *J. pr. Chem.*, **40**, 11, 1847; **46**, 257, 1849). Houghite *Shepard (Am. J. Sc.*, **12**, 210, 1851).

C r y s t. Hexagonal — R.[1]

Structure cell.[1] Rhombohedral. a_0 6.13, c_0 46.15; $a_0 : c_0 = 1 : 7.528$; contains $Mg_{18}Al_6(OH)_{48}(CO_3)_3 \cdot 12H_2O$.

Habit. Massive, with a foliated or contorted lamellar structure on {0001}; also lamellar-fibrous or in indistinct plates {0001}.

P h y s. Cleavage {0001} perfect.[2] Laminae flexible but not elastic; crushes to a talclike powder. Feel greasy. H. 2. G. 2.06 ± 0.03;[3] 2.00 (calc.). Luster pearly to waxy. Color white, sometimes with a brownish tint. Streak white. Transparent.

O p t.[1] In transmitted light colorless. Uniaxial negative $(-)$. Sometimes biaxial due to strain with small variable $2V$. Nonpleochroic.

$$n$$

O	1.511 ± 0.003
E	1.495 ± 0.003

C h e m. A hydrated carbonate-hydroxide of magnesium and aluminum, $Mg_6Al_2(OH)_{16}CO_3 \cdot 4H_2O$,[4] polymorphous[1] with manasseite. Small amounts of Fe^3 apparently can substitute for Al. None of the available analyses is known certainly to have been made on material free from admixture with manasseite.

Anal.[5]

	1	2	3
MgO	40.05	39.72	39.52
Al$_2$O$_3$	16.87	15.32	14.42
Fe$_2$O$_3$	.....	1.89	2.44
H$_2$O	35.80	35.46	36.28
CO$_2$	7.28	7.60	7.33
Rem.	.....	0.72	0.56
Total	100.00	100.71	100.55

1. $Mg_6Al_2(OH)_{16}CO_3 \cdot 4H_2O$. 2. Kongsberg, Norway. Mixture of hydrotalcite and manasseite. Rem. is SiO$_2$ 0.44, FeO 0.28.[6] 3. Snarum, Norway. Probably a mixture of hydrotalcite and manasseite. Rem. is insol.[7]

Tests. B.B. glows and exfoliates slightly but does not fuse. Easily soluble with effervescence in dilute HCl.

O c c u r. Originally described from Snarum, Norway, where it occurs intimately admixed with manasseite as foliated masses in yellowish green serpentine; found similarly at Nordmark, Norway. A mineral apparently either hydrotalcite or manasseite occur in the Urals implanted on talc schist at Schischimsk in the Slatoust district (*voelknerite*), and with brucite, pyroaurite, antigorite, and calcite in an asbestos mine at Bashenowo. In the United States hydrotalcite has been found as an alteration product of spinel at Somerville (*houghite*), St. Lawrence County, and at Amity, Orange County, New York; hydrotalcite or manasseite also occurs in New York at Rossie, St. Lawrence County, at Antwerp and Oxbow, Jefferson County, and in New Jersey at Vernon, Sussex County.

A l t e r. Observed as an alteration product of spinel.

N a m e. Hydrotalcite from its resemblance to talc in its physical properties and its high water content. Houghite after Franklin B. Hough of Somerville, New York. Voelknerite after Captain Völkner, Director of the Kussinsk (Russia) smelter.

HOUGHITE. *Shepard* (*Am. J. Sc.*, **12**, 210, 1851).

Identical[1] with hydrotalcite. Found as pseudomorphs after spinel, and probably also scapolite, in crystalline limestone at Somerville, St. Lawrence County, and other localities in northern New York State.

Ref.

1. Frondel (1941).

2. Hermann (1847) mentions an indistinct cleavage or parting inclined to {0001} on material from Slatoust not known definitely to be hydrotalcite or manasseite.

3. Range of best values (on material not known to be free from admixed manasseite).
4. The formula given is analogous to the formulas of other members of the group. Admixture with the polymorphous manasseite is common and thus no change in composition is found on analysis. The material from Somerville, N. Y., is shown, by x-ray examination (Frondel, 1941) to be essentially pure hydrotalcite, but no good analysis is available.
5. For additional analyses see Doelter (3 [2], 295, 1926), Manasse, *Att. soc. tosc., Proc., Verb.*, 24, 92 (1915), Foshag, *U. S. Nat. Mus., Proc.*, 58, 147 (1920), Kurnakov and Černych, *Cbl. Min.*, 353, 1928.
6. Foshag (1920).
7. Manasse (1915).

6152　**S T I C H T I T E** [$Mg_6Cr_2(OH)_{16}\cdot CO_3\cdot 4H_2O$].　Stichtite pt. *Petterd* (167, 1910). Stichtite *Frondel* (*Am. Min.*, 26, 295, 1941).
　　Chrom-brugnatellite *Hezner* (*Cbl. Min.*, 569, 1912).

C r y s t.　Hexagonal — R.[1]

Structure cell.[1]　Rhombohedral.　a_0 6.18, c_0 46.38; $a_0 : c_0 = 1 : 7.505$; contains $Mg_{18}Cr_6(OH)_{48}(CO_3)_3\cdot 12H_2O$.

Habit.　Massive, in matted or contorted aggregates of plates or fibers, and as cross-fiber veinlets; in micaceous scales.

P h y s.　Cleavage {0001}, perfect.　Laminae flexible but not elastic; crushes to a talclike powder.　Feel greasy.　H. $1\frac{1}{2}$–2.　G. 2.16;[2] 2.11 (calc.).　Luster waxlike to greasy, faintly pearly.　Color intense lilac to rose-pink.　Streak very pale lilac to white.　Transparent.

O p t.[1]　In transmitted light, delicate rose-pink to lilac in color.　Uniaxial negative (−).　Sometimes biaxial due to strain with small variable $2V$.　Elongation usually positive.　Weakly pleochroic.

	n	PLEOCHROISM
O	1.545 ± 0.003	Dark rose-pink to lilac
E	1.518 ± 0.003	Light rose-pink to lilac

C h e m.　A hydrated carbonate-hydroxide of magnesium and chromium, $Mg_6Cr_2(OH)_{16}CO_3\cdot 4H_2O$,[3] polymorphous[1] with barbertonite.　Considerable amounts of Fe[3] and Al apparently can substitute for Cr.　Analyses of material known definitely to be free from admixture with barbertonite are lacking.

Anal.

	1	2	3	4	5
MgO	36.98	36.0	37.12	36.59	36.70
FeO	.....	....	1.10	0.28	0.85
Fe_2O_3	.....	9.0	.....	4.04	10.60
Al_2O_3	.....	....	.....	2.24	0.90
Cr_2O_3	23.24	11.5	20.44	14.08	8.90
CO_2	6.73	7.2	10.45	6.94	6.90
H_2O	33.05	36.1	27.26	33.01	30.45
SiO_2	.....	....	3.87	2.09	4.50
Rem.	.....	....	.....	trace	0.15
Total	100.00	99.8	100.24	99.27	99.80
G.	2.11	2.12	2.16		

1. $Mg_6Cr_2(OH)_{16}CO_3\cdot 4H_2O$. 2. Dundas, Tasmania. Contains chromite and probably barbertonite.[4] 3. Dundas, Tasmania (*Chrom-brugnatellite*). Contains chromite, serpentine and probably barbertonite. H_2O^+ 26.31, H_2O^- 0.95.[5] 4. Dundas, Tasmania. Probably contains serpentine and barbertonite. Rem. is CaO.[6] 5. Barberton, Transvaal. Contains chromite, serpentine and probably barbertonite. Rem. is NiO 0.10, Na_2O 0.05. K_2O trace.[7]

Tests. B.B. glows brightly, turns light gray or brownish and becomes magnetic but does not fuse. Easily soluble with effervescence in dilute HCl, affording a bright green solution.

O c c u r. Found as blebs or veinlets in serpentine rock, closely associated with chromite, barbertonite, antigorite. Originally found at Dundas, Tasmania. At Kaapsche Hoop, Barberton district, Transvaal. In Canada at the Megantic mine, Black Lake, Quebec.

A l t e r. Observed as an alteration product of chromite.

N a m e. After Robert Sticht, formerly General Manager of the Mount Lyell Mining and Railway Co., Tasmania.

CHROM-BRUGNATELLITE. *Hezner* (*Cbl. Min.*, 569, 1912).
A name given to the stichtite from Dundas, Tasmania, through lack of knowledge of the original description. Identical with stichtite.[8]

Ref.

1. Frondel (1941), from x-ray data.
2. Best value of Poitevin and Graham, *Geol. Sur. Canada, Mus. Bull.*, **27**, 29 (1918), on material from Black Lake shown by Frondel to be free from admixed barbertonite.
3. The formula is probably correct despite the fact that no analysis of homogeneous material is available (see anal.). Other members of the group clearly have an analogous formula.
4. Wesley anal. in Petterd (167, 1910).
5. Hezner, *Cbl. Min.*, 569, 1912.
6. Foshag, *U. S. Nat. Mus., Proc.*, **58**, 147 (1920).
7. McCrae and Weall anal. in Hall, *Geol. Soc. South Africa, Trans.*, **24**, 182 (1922).
8. Himmelbauer, *Min. Mitt.*, **32**, 135 (1913).

6153   P Y R O A U R I T E [$Mg_6Fe_2(OH)_{16} \cdot CO_3 \cdot 4H_2O$]. Pyroaurit (?) *Igelström* (*Ak. Stockholm, Öfv.*, **22**, 608, 1865). Pyroaurite pt. *Aminoff* and *Broomé* (*Ak. Stockholm, Handl.*, **9** [3], no. 5, 23, 1930). Pyroaurite *Frondel* (*Am. Min.*, **26**, 295, 1941).

C r y s t. Hexagonal — R.[1]
Structure cell.[2] Rhombohedral. a_0 6.19, c_0 46.54; $a_0 : c_0 = 1 : 7.519$; contains $Mg_{18}Fe_6(OH)_{48}(CO_3)_3 \cdot 12H_2O$.
Habit. Tabular {0001} with the lateral faces striated and indistinct; also thick tabular {0001} with {01$\bar{1}$5} alone or with {20$\bar{2}$5}.
P h y s. Cleavage {0001} perfect. Laminae flexible but not elastic; crushes to a talclike powder. H. 2½. G. 2.12 ± 0.02; 2.12 (calc.). Luster waxy to vitreous, pearly. Color yellowish or brownish white; also green, colorless. Transparent.
O p t.[2] In transmitted light colorless. Uniaxial negative (−). Pleochroic. Sometimes biaxial due to strain with small variable $2V$.

	n	PLEOCHROISM
O	1.564 ± 0.003	Pale yellowish, brownish, reddish
E	1.543 ± 0.003	Colorless

C h e m. A hydrated carbonate-hydroxide of magnesium and ferric iron, $Mg_6Fe_2(OH)_{16}CO_3 \cdot 4H_2O$, polymorphous[2] with sjogrenite. Mn^2 and Al apparently can substitute for Mg and Fe^3, respectively. Only one (anal. 5) of the many reported analyses[3] is known certainly to have been made on a sample free from admixture with sjogrenite.

Anal.

	1	2	3	4	5	6
MgO	36.55	35.44	35.60	33.92	35.84	34.8
Al_2O_3	.....	0.11	.....	7.24	.....	....
Fe_2O_3	24.13	23.19	23.73	17.18	23.37	22.0
MnO	.....	0.28	.....	.....	0.01	4.5
CO_2	6.65	7.01	6.49	6.31	7.30	....
H_2O	32.67	33.62	33.12	34.52	33.63	36.1
Rem.	.....	0.51	0.67	.....	.....	0.5
Total	100.00	100.16	99.61	99.17	100.15	97.9
G.	2.12	2.10				2.07

1. $Mg_6Fe_2(OH)_{16}CO_3 \cdot 4H_2O$. 2. Långban, Sweden. A mixture of pyroaurite and sjogrenite. Rem. is FeO 0.10, SiO_2 0.41.[4] 3. Långban, Sweden. Probably a mixture of pyroaurite and sjogrenite. Rem. is Mn_2O_3 0.28, insol. 0.39.[5] 4. Bashenowo, Urals. Material either pyroaurite, sjogrenite or a mixture of both. Possibly contains admixed hydrotalcite or gibbsite.[6] 5. Rutherglen, Ontario. Pure pyroaurite.[7] 6. Nordmark, Sweden. Material probably either pyroaurite or sjogrenite. Rem. is insol. Analysis on 0.0205 gm. No test made for CO_2.[8]

Tests. B.B. infusible, glows, exfoliates somewhat, turns golden yellow to reddish brown and becomes magnetic. Easily soluble with effervescence in HCl.

Occur. Originally found at Långban, Sweden, intergrown with calcite as a low-temperature hydrothermal vein mineral. The material from this locality was later shown[9] to be an intimate mixture of pyroaurite and sjogrenite; the two minerals often occur together in parallel growths. Also found at Kraubat, Styria, associated with brucite, aragonite, calcite, hydromagnesite, artinite, magnesite in serpentine. With brugnatellite, artinite, hydromagnesite in the Val Malenco, Lombardy, and the Val Ramazzo, Liguria, Italy. In serpentine at Mediakamen and Belikamen, Servia. In the United States as a coating upon serpentine at Blue Mont, Maryland. In cavities in a dolomite rock at Rutherglen, Ontario.

Minerals apparently identical with either pyroaurite or sjogrenite have been described from the Moss mine, Nordmark, Sweden[10] (anal. 6), and from Bashenowo, Urals.[11]

Alter. Observed as an alteration product of brucite.

Name. Pyroaurite in allusion to the golden yellow color assumed on heating at relatively low temperatures.

Ref.

1. Aminoff and Broomé (1930) by Laue and powder x-ray study and Frondel (1941) by Weissenberg method. The forms {0221} and {1011} reported by Flink, *Bull. Geol. Inst. Upsala*, 5, 87 (1901), on rough crystals from Långban correspond approximately to {0115} and {2025} in the structural cell of Frondel (1941).

2. Frondel (1941).

3. See Doelter (4 [3], 1016, 1931); Manasse, *Att. soc. tosc.*, *Proc.*, 24, 92 (1915); Kurnakov and Černych, *Cbl. Min.*, 353, 1928.

4. Johansson anal. in Aminoff and Broomé (1930).

5. Manasse (1915).

6. Černych anal. in Kurnakov and Černych (1928).

7. Ellsworth, *Univ. Toronto Stud.*, *Geol. Ser.*, 42, 33 (1939).

8. Mauzelius anal. in Sjögren, *Bull. Geol. Inst. Upsala*, **2**, 59 (1894); the analysis is close to the formula $(Mg,Mn)_6Fe_2(OH)_{18}\cdot 6H_2O$, analogous to that of igelstromite.
9. Aminoff and Broomé (1930) and Frondel (1941).
10. Sjögren (1894).
11. Kurnakov and Černych (1928).

IGELSTROMITE.   *Heddle (Min. Mag.*, **2**, 107, 1878; **1**, 111, 1910).

A silvery white mineral with pearly luster found in thin veins in serpentine on the Island of Haaf Grunay, Shetland Islands, Scotland.   Analyses gave:

	1	2	3
Fe_2O_3	22.13	22.45	23.63
MgO	37.80	37.57	36.85
CO_2	1.02	1.03	.....
H_2O	39.27	39.51	40.02
Total	100.22	100.56	100.50

Originally considered to be a variety of pyroaurite, but differs from pyroaurite (and sjogrenite) in the near absence of CO_2. The formula (anal. 3) is close to $Mg_6Fe_2(OH)_{18}\cdot 6H_2O$. On ignition turns chocolate-brown and becomes magnetic. Named after L. J. Igelström (1822–97), Swedish mineralogist.

6161   M A N A S S E I T E $[Mg_6Al_2(OH)_{16}\cdot CO_3\cdot 4H_2O]$.   *Frondel (Am. Min.*, **26**, 295, 1941).   Hydrotalcite pt.

C r y s t.   Hexagonal — *P*.
Structure cell.   Hexagonal. a_0 6.12, c_0 15.34; $a_0 : c_0 = 1 : 2.507$; contains $Mg_6Al_2(OH)_{16}CO_3\cdot 4H_2O$.
Habit.   Massive, with a foliated or contorted structure; lamellar on {0001}.
P h y s.   Cleavage {0001} perfect.   Laminae flexible but not elastic; crushes to a talclike powder.   Feel greasy.   H. 2.   G. 2.05 ± 0.05; 2.00 (calc.).   Luster waxy, pearly.   Color white; also bluish, grayish, or brownish white.   Transparent.
O p t.   In transmitted light colorless.   Uniaxial negative (−).   Sometimes biaxial due to strain, with small and variable $2V$.

	n
O	1.524 ± 0.003
E	1.510 ± 0.003

C h e m.   A hydrated carbonate-hydroxide of magnesium and aluminum, $Mg_6Al_2(OH)_{16}CO_3\cdot 4H_2O$, polymorphous with hydrotalcite.
Anal.[1]

	1	2
MgO	40.05	39.38
Al_2O_3	16.87	16.59
Fe_2O_3	.....	0.21
CO_2	7.28	7.48
H_2O	35.80	36.34
Total	100.00	100.00
G.	2.00	2.05

1. $Mg_6Al_2(OH)_{16}CO_3\cdot 4H_2O$.   2. Snarum, Norway.   Contains a few per cent of hydrotalcite.   Analysis recalc. after deduction of SiO_2 0.35 and gibbsite 6.38.[2]

O c c u r. Found intimately associated with hydrotalcite in serpentine at Snarum and Nordmark, Norway. At Amity, Orange County, New York, with hydrotalcite, dolomite, and serpentine. Possibly also at other localities earlier referred to hydrotalcite (which see).

N a m e. After Ernesto Manasse (1875–1922), formerly Professor of Mineralogy at the University of Florence.

Ref.

1. See under hydrotalcite for analyses of mixtures containing manasseite.
2. Gonyer anal. in Frondel (1941).

6162 **B A R B E R T O N I T E** [$Mg_6Cr_2(OH)_{16}\cdot CO_3\cdot 4H_2O$]. *Frondel (Am. Min.,* **26,** 295, 1941). Stichtite pt.

C r y s t. Hexagonal — *P.*

Structure cell. Hexagonal. a_0 6.17, c_0 15.52; $a_0 : c_0 = 1 : 2.515$; contains $Mg_6Cr_2(OH)_{16}CO_3\cdot 4H_2O$.

Habit. Massive, in matted or contorted masses of fibers or plates flattened {0001}; also as cross-fiber veinlets.

P h y s. Cleavage {0001} perfect. Laminae flexible but not elastic; crushes to a talclike powder. Feel greasy. H. $1\frac{1}{2}$–2. G. 2.10 ± 0.05; 2.11 (calc.). Luster waxy to pearly. Color intense lilac to rose-pink. Streak very pale lilac to white. Transparent.

O p t. In transmitted light rose-pink to lilac in color. Uniaxial negative (−). Sometimes biaxial due to strain with small variable $2V$. Weakly pleochroic. Elongation usually positive (+).

	n	PLEOCHROISM
O	1.557 ± 0.003	Dark rose-pink to lilac
E	1.529 ± 0.003	Light rose-pink to lilac

C h e m. A hydrated carbonate-hydroxide of magnesium and chromium, $Mg_6Cr_2(OH)_{16}CO_3\cdot 4H_2O$, polymorphous with stichtite. Analyses of material known certainly to be free from admixture with stichtite[1] are lacking (see analyses under stichtite).

O c c u r. Found intimately associated with stichtite, chromite and antigorite as veinlets and small masses in serpentine rock at Dundas, Tasmania, and Kaapsche Hoop, Barberton district, Transvaal. A mineral probably identical with barbertonite occurs with chromite and antigorite in serpentine at Cunningsburgh,[2] Scotland.

N a m e. From the occurrence in the Barberton district, Transvaal.

Ref.

1. An analysis by Dixon in Read and Dixon, *Min. Mag.,* **23,** 309 (1933), of material from Cunningsburgh, Scotland, possibly may represent barbertonite only.
2. Read and Dixon (1933).

6163 **S J O G R E N I T E** [$Mg_6Fe_2(OH)_{16}\cdot CO_3\cdot 4H_2O$]. Pyroaurite pt. *Aminoff* and *Broomé (Ak. Stockholm, Handl.,* **9,** 3, no. 5, 23, 1930). Sjogrenite *Frondel (Am. Min.,* **26,** 295, 1941).

C r y s t. Hexagonal — $P.^1$

Structure cell.[2] Hexagonal. a_0 6.20, c_0 15.57; $a_0 : c_0 = 1 : 2.511$; cell contents $Mg_6Fe_2(OH)_{16}CO_3 \cdot 4H_2O$.

Habit. Thin plates {0001}, with a hexagonal outline and with striated and indistinct lateral faces.

P h y s. Cleavage {0001} perfect. Thin plates flexible but not elastic; crushes to a talclike powder. H. $2\frac{1}{2}$. G. 2.11 ± 0.03;[2] 2.11 (calc.). Luster waxy to vitreous, pearly on cleavages. Color yellowish or brownish white. Transparent.

O p t.[2] In transmitted light, colorless. Uniaxial negative $(-)$. Pleochroic.

	n	PLEOCHROISM
O	1.573 ± 0.003	Pale yellow to brownish
E	1.550 ± 0.003	Colorless

C h e m. A hydrated carbonate-hydroxide of magnesium and ferric iron, $Mg_6Fe_2(OH)_{16}CO_3 \cdot 4H_2O$, polymorphous with pyroaurite. Analyses of material known certainly to be free from admixture with pyroaurite are lacking (see analyses under pyroaurite).

Tests. B.B. infusible, exfoliates somewhat, turns golden brown to yellow-brown and becomes magnetic. Easily soluble with effervescence in dilute acids.

O c c u r. Known only from Långban, Sweden, where it occurs associated with calcite and pyroaurite as a low-temperature hydrothermal product. The mineral frequently occurs as parallel growths upon crystals of pyroaurite.

N a m e. After Hjalmar Sjögren (1856–1922), Swedish mineralogist and formerly Professor of Mineralogy at the University of Stockholm.

Ref.

1. Aminoff and Broomé (1930), by Laue and powder x-ray study.
2. Frondel (1941).

617   B R U G N A T E L L I T E [$Mg_6Fe(OH)_{13}CO_3 \cdot 4H_2O$]. *Artini* (*Acc. Linc., Att.*, **18**, 5, 3, 1909).

C r y s t. Hexagonal — P.[1]

Structure cell.[2] Hexagonal. a_0 5.47, c_0 15.97; $a_0 : c_0$ 1 : 2.92; contains $Mg_6Fe(OH)_{13}CO_3 \cdot 4H_2O$.

Habit. Massive, in lamellar or foliated masses of small flakes flattened {0001}. The flakes sometimes have a three- or six-sided outline with striations intersecting at 60°.

P h y s. Cleavage {0001}, perfect. Crushes to a talclike powder. H. about 2. G. 2.14;[3] 2.21 (calc.). Luster pearly. Color flesh-pink to yellowish or brownish white. Streak white. Transparent.

O p t. In transmitted light colorless to pink. Uniaxial negative $(-)$. Pleochroic.

	n^4	PLEOCHROISM
O	1.540 ± 0.003	Yellowish red
E	1.510 ± 0.003	Colorless

C h e m. A hydrated carbonate-hydroxide of magnesium and ferric iron, $Mg_6Fe(OH)_{13}CO_3 \cdot 4H_2O$. Small amounts of Mn^2 substitute for Mg. Approximately $4H_2O$ is lost at $150°$.[5]

Anal.

	1	2	3	4	5
MgO	43.63	39.13	40.36	42.79	43.08
MnO	.....	1.77	1.98	1.80	1.92
Fe₂O₃	14.39	16.12	14.65	13.20	12.98
CO₂	7.93	8.00	8.04	7.78	7.45
H₂O	34.05	32.42	33.50	33.77	33.25
Rem.	.....	2.18	1.15	1.03	1.05
Total	100.00	99.62	99.68	100.37	99.73

1. $Mg_6Fe(OH)_{13}CO_3 \cdot 4H_2O$. 2. Monte Ramazzo, Liguria, Italy. Rem. is CaO 1.19 (present as calcite), insol. 0.99.[6] 3. Viu, Val di Lanzo, Piedmont, Italy. Rem. is insol. 1.15.[7] 4. Val Malenco, Lombardy, Italy. Rem. is insol.[8] 5. Cogne, Val d'Aosta, Piedmont, Italy. Rem. is insol.[2]

Tests. B.B. turns golden yellow and becomes magnetic but does not fuse. Easily soluble with effervescence in dilute HCl.

O c c u r. Found as crusts and coatings along cracks in serpentine rock, associated with artinite, hydromagnesite, pyroaurite, magnesite, chrysotile, aragonite, brucite. Originally found in Italy at Ciappanico in the Val Malenco, Lombardy; later found at Viu in the Val di Lanzo, Piedmont; as an alteration product of brucite at Monte Ramazzo, Liguria; at Cogne in the Val d'Aosta, Piedmont.

Said to occur at Iron Hill, Gunnison County, Colorado.

N a m e. After Luigi Brugnatelli (1859–1928), formerly Professor of Mineralogy in the University of Pavia.

Ref.

1. From x-ray Laue study of Fenoglio, *Per. Min.*, **9**, 1 (1938), who gives the crystal class as $3m$, 32, or $\bar{3}\, 2/m$.
2. Fenoglio (1938).
3. Fenoglio (1938) by heavy liquid; Larsen (194, 1921) gives 2.07.
4. Larsen (54, 1921) on material from Monte Ramazzo; values for O as low as 1.533 have been reported (see Frondel, *Am. Min.*, **26**, 295 [1941]).
5. For dehydration data see Artini, *Acc. Linc., Att.*, **31**, 491 (1922).
6. Artini (1922).
7. Fenoglio, *Soc. geol. ital., Boll.*, **46**, 13 (1927).
8. Artini (1909).

EISENBRUCITE. *Sandberger (Jb. Min.*, II, 288, 1880). Ferropyroaurite *Meixner* (*Cbl. Min.*, 363, 1937).

Described as a highly ferroan brucite (with 18.73 per cent FeO). Found in serpentine at Siebenlehn, near Freiberg, Saxony. The physical properties and analyses[1] indicate that it is a mixture, probably largely of pyroaurite[2] with perhaps hydromagnesite, chrysotile, or brucite.

Ref.

1. See Dana (253, 1892) and Kurnakov and Černych, *Mem. soc. russe min.*, **55**, 74 (1926) — *Jb. Min.*, I, 313, 1927.
2. Gaubert, *Bull. soc. min.*, **48**, 216 (1925). Meixner (1937) considers the material to be the ferroan analogue of pyroaurite, with the formula $5Mg(OH)_2 \cdot MgCO_3 \cdot 2Fe(OH)_2 \cdot 4H_2O$.

621   S A S S O L I T E [B(OH)$_3$].   Sale sedativo naturale *Höfer* (Sopre Sal. Sed. nat. Tosc., Firenze, 1778); *Mascagni* (*Mem. soc. ital.*, **8**, 487, 1779).   Native Sedative Salt.   Acidum boracis, *vulgo* Sal sedativum *Bergmann* (1782).   Native Boracic Acid *Kirwan* (1796).   Sassolin *Karsten* (40, 75, 1800).   Acide boracique *Fr.*   Boric Acid.

Borate de Fer *Beudant* (**2**, 250, 1832); *d' Halloy* (1833).   Lagonite *Huot* (**1**, 290, 1841).   Sideroborine *Huot* (**1**, 273, 1841).   Lagunit *Kenngott.*

C r y s t.   Triclinic; pinacoidal — $\bar{1}$.

$a : b : c = 0.9990 : 1 : 0.9228;$ $\alpha\ 92°30',$ $\beta\ 101°11\frac{1}{2}',$ $\gamma\ 119°51'$[1]

$p_0 : q_0 : r_0 = 1.0640 : 1.0438 : 1;$ $\lambda\ 80°30',$ $\mu\ 75°36',$ $\nu\ 58°54'$

$p_0'1.0996,$ $q_0'1.0787;$ $x_0'0.1973,$ $y_0'0.1714$

Forms: [2]

		ϕ	ρ	A	B	C
c	001	49°09′	14°37′	75°36′	80°30′	.....
b	010	0 00	90 00	58 54	.....	80°30′
a	100	58 54	90 00	.....	58 54	75 36
M	1$\bar{1}$0	118 28$\frac{1}{2}$	90 00	59 34$\frac{1}{2}$	118 28$\frac{1}{2}$	84 53$\frac{1}{2}$
v	011	8 58	51 41	59 40	39 11$\frac{1}{2}$	41 18$\frac{1}{2}$
u	0$\bar{1}$1	167 44	42 52$\frac{1}{2}$	102 41$\frac{1}{2}$	131 40$\frac{1}{2}$	51 10$\frac{1}{2}$
y	102	55 43$\frac{1}{2}$	38 57$\frac{1}{2}$	51 07	69 15$\frac{1}{2}$	24 29
x	$\bar{1}$02	−112 22$\frac{1}{2}$	16 28$\frac{1}{2}$	106 17	96 12	30 41
s	1$\bar{1}$1	106 35$\frac{1}{2}$	49 55$\frac{1}{2}$	59 00	102 37	43 22$\frac{1}{2}$
r	$\bar{1}$11	−47 30	45 16$\frac{1}{2}$	101 34$\frac{1}{2}$	61 19	48 41

Structure cell. [3]   Space group $P\bar{1}$; a_0 7.04, b_0 7.04, c_0 6.56; $\alpha\ 92°30'$, $\beta\ 101°10'$, $\gamma\ 120°$; $a_0 : b_0 : c_0 = 1 : 1 : 0.932$; cell contents $H_{12}B_4O_{12}$.

Habit.   Crystals tabular {001}, and pseudohexagonal in development; rarely needle-like [001].   Usually small scales; sometimes grouped in stalactitic forms.   As coatings.

Twinning. [4]   Common, with twin axis [001].

P h y s.   Cleavage {001}, perfect, micaceous.   Crystals flexible.   Feel smooth and unctuous.   H. 1.   G. 1.48 ± 0.02; 1.48 (calc.).   Luster pearly.   Color white to gray, sometimes tinted yellow or brown by included sulfur or limonite.   Transparent.   Taste acidulous, and slightly saline and bitter.

O p t. [5]   In transmitted light, colorless.   Biaxial negative (−).   Dispersion imperceptible.

	n	
X	1.340 ± 0.005	2V very small, and unchanged by
Y	1.456 ± 0.003	heating to 75°. X nearly ⊥ {001}.
Z	1.459 ± 0.003	Axial plane nearly parallel b and ⊥ {001}.

C h e m.   Boric acid, B(OH)$_3$.   B$_2$O$_3$ 56.39, H$_2$O 43.61, total 100.00. No modern analyses are available.

Tests. [6]   B.B. fuses easily to a clear glass.   Soluble in water and in alcohol.

Occur. Long known to occur in the waters of the Tuscan lagoons, and recognized in the solid state by Mascagni in 1779 on the rims of the hot spring at Sasso, 8 km. from Castelnuovo; localities and establishments for extracting the substance include Lardarello (earlier called Monte Cerboli or Mons Cerberi), Castelnuovo, Monte Rotondo, Serrazzano, Lago, Lustignano, and Travale. The hot vapors of the lagoons consist largely of boric acid. The compound is collected by passing the vapors through water and evaporating the solution by means of the steam from the springs. The substance also exists in other natural waters, as at Wiesbaden and Aachen in Germany, and in Lake County, California. Found abundantly as a sublimation product in the crater of Vulcano, in the Lipari Islands, and also on Vesuvius. In the Solfatara at Pozzuoli, with realgar. Reported in the borax deposits of the Puga Valley, in Ladak, Tibet.

Artif.[7] Formed as crystals by adding HCl or H_2SO_4 to a concentrated water solution of borax or other borate.

Name. From the locality, Sasso, Tuscany, at which it was first found.

LAGONITE. Borate de Fer *Beudant* (**2**, 250, 1832), *d'Halloy* (1833). Lagonite *Huot* (**1**, 290, 1841). Sideroborine *Huot* (**1**, 273, 1841). Lagunit *Kenngott*.
A yellow earthy mineral found as an incrustation at the Tuscan lagoons and described as a ferric borate. Stated[8] to be a mixture of limonite and sassolite.

Ref.

1. Angles of Haushofer, *Zs. Kr.*, **9**, 77 (1884) on artificial crystals; unit and orientation of Zachariasen, *Zs. Kr.*, **88**, 150 (1934), by x-ray methods. Transformations: Dana (255, 1892) to Zachariasen $\frac{1}{2}\frac{1}{2}0/100/001$. Haushofer to Zachariasen $\frac{1}{2}\frac{1}{2}0/010/001$.
2. Brooke and Miller (282, 1852).
3. Zachariasen (1934) on artificial crystals.
4. See Brooke and Miller (282, 1852), Des Cloizeaux (**2**, 2, 1874). Tazaki, *J. Sc. Hirosima Univ.*, [A], 9(1), 21, 1939, in Donnay and Taylor, *Nat. canadien*, **67**, 145 (1940), has proposed twin axes [230], [4$\overline{1}$0], and [010]; Donnay and Taylor have discussed the theoretical probabilities of these various twin laws.
5. Larsen (130, 1921); see also Hintze (**1** [2A], 1941, 1910).
6. Some specimens react for S and NH_3 due to characteristic admixed impurities.
7. For an account of the preparation of boric acid from pandermite, boracite, native borax (tincal) and other source materials see Mellor (**5**, 49, 1924).
8. D'Achiardi, *Per. Min.*, 3, 9, 36 (1932).

622 **GIBBSITE** [$Al(OH)_3$]. Wavellite (from Richmond) *Dewey* (*Am. J. Sc.*, **2**, 249, 1820). (Not the wavellite of Babington in *Davy*, *Phil. Trans.*, 162, 1805.) Gibbsite *Torrey* (*N. Y. Med. Phys. J.*, **1**, no. 1, 68, April, 1822). Hydrargillite (Gibbsite of Torrey) *Cleaveland* (224, 782, 1822). Hydrargillite *Rose* (*Ann. Phys.*, **48**, 564, 1839). Gibbsitogelit *Tučan* (*Cbl. Min.*, 768, 1913). γ-$Al(OH)_3$.
Beauxite (= Bauxite) pt. *Dufrénoy* (**2**, 347, 1844; **3**, 799, 1847); *Berthier* (*Ann. mines*, **6**, 531, 1821).

Cryst. Monoclinic;[1] prismatic — $2/m$.

$a : b : c = 1.7089 : 1 : 1.9184$; $\beta\ 94°31'$;[2] $p_0 : q_0 : r_0 = 1.1226 : 1.9124 : 1$
$r_2 : p_2 : q_2 = 0.5229 : 0.5870 : 1$; $\mu\ 85°29'$; $p_0'\ 1.1271$, $q_0'\ 1.9184$, $x_0'\ 0.0790$

Forms:

		ϕ	ρ	ϕ_2	$\rho_2 = B$	C	A
c	001	90°00′	4°31′	85°29′	90°00′	0°00′	85°29′
b	010	0 00	90 00	.....	0 00	90 00	90 00
a	100	90 00	90 00	0 00	90 00	85 29	.....
m	110	30 25	90 00	0 00	30 25	87 43	59 35
n	870	33 51½	90 00	0 00	33 51½	87 29	56 08½
μ	210	49 34½	90 00	0 00	49 34½	86 34	40 25½
l	410	66 56	90 00	0 00	66 56	85 50½	23 04
t	920	69 16	90 00	0 00	69 16	85 46½	20 44
d	$\overline{1}$01	−90 00	46 19	136 19	90 00	50 50	136 19
s	$\overline{3}$12	−59 13	61 55	148 09½	63 09½	65 49½	139 17
u	$\overline{6}$23	−59 31½	68 22	155 17½	61 52	72 16½	143 14½

Structure cell.[3] Space group $P2_1/n$; $a_0 = 8.624$, $b_0 = 5.060$, $c_0 = 9.700$, $\beta = 85°26′$; $a_0 : b_0 : c_0 = 1.7043 : 1 : 1.9168$; contains $Al_8(OH)_{24}$.

Habit. Crystals tabular {001}, with {100} and {110} usually well developed and giving a hexagonal aspect. Occasionally in lamellar-radiate spheroidal concretions. Also stalactitic, or small mammillary and incrusting, with a smooth surface, and often a faint fibrous structure within; compact earthy; as enamel- or hyalite-like coatings.

Twinning.[4] (a) About [130] as twin axis, very common (the forms {001} and {00$\overline{1}$} are in parallel position and [010] zone axis coincides with [$\overline{1}$10] zone axis). (b) On {001}, common; usually this twin law is combined with one of the other laws. (c) On {100}, not common; (001 ∧ $\overline{0}$01 = 9°02′). (d) On {110}, rare; (001 ∧ $\overline{0}$01 = 4°34′).

Phys. Cleavage {001} perfect. Tough. H. 2½–3½. G. 2.40 ± 0.02 (crystals), 2.3–2.4 (massive); 2.44 (calc.). Luster on cleavage surfaces pearly, of other surfaces vitreous. Color white, grayish, greenish, or reddish white; also reddish yellow when impure. Transparent. A strong argillaceous odor when breathed on. Percussion figure on {001} with rays ⊥ to {100} and {110}; pressure figure on {001} with separations ∥ {100}.[5] Thermal expansion[6] ⊥ {010} = (1.09 ± 0.08) × 10⁵, ⊥ {001} = (1.54 ± 0.10) × 10⁵, ⊥ {100} = (1.31 ± 0.07) × 10⁵, ⊥ {10$\overline{1}$} = (3.90 ± 0.20) × 10⁵, ⊥ {101} = (−0.56 ± 0.07) × 10⁵.

Opt.[7]

	ORIENTATION	n[9]	
X	b	1.568	Bx. pos. (+). 2V = 0° ±.
Y	Y ∧ c = 69°	1.568 } ± 0.001	2V = 0° for blue at 26½° C.[8]
Z	Z ∧ c = −21°[10]	1.587	dispersion varies.

Above 56½° C, $Y = b$ and $Z \wedge c = -45½°$ (for red) on material from the Urals.[8] When fibrous, the elongation is either (+) or (−), and has inclined extinction.[11]

Chem. Aluminum hydroxide, $Al(OH)_3$. The small amounts of Fe_2O_3 and SiO_2 reported in many analyses are probably due to impurities. The P_2O_5 of some analyses (anal. 6) presumably represents admixed or adsorbed phosphates.

Anal.[12]

	1	2	3	4	5	6
CaO	.....	0.17	0.20	.....	.....	.....
MgO	.....	trace	0.03	.....	.....	0.10
Al_2O_3	65.35	64.92	62.80	64.20	63.59	64.24
Fe_2O_3	.....	trace	0.44	.....	.....	trace
SiO_2	.....	1.03	2.78	0.39	2.01	1.33
H_2O	34.65	34.12	33.74	35.13	34.75	33.76
Rem.	.....	.....	0.04	.....	.....	0.57
Total	100.00	100.24	100.03	99.72	100.35	100.00
G.	2.44	2.37	2.42	2.40	2.35	

1. $Al(OH)_3$. 2. Klein-Tresny, Moravia.[13] 3. Kodikanal, Madras, India. Rem. is TiO_2.[14] 4. Talevadi, Bombay, India.[15] 5. Bhekowli, Satara district, India.[16] 6. Richmond, Mass. Rem. is P_2O_5.[17]

Tests. In C.T. becomes white and opaque and yields water. B.B. infusible, whitens, gives off light and becomes very hard. Slowly soluble in concentrated H_2SO_4 and readily soluble in hot alkalies.

Occur. The typical occurrence is as a secondary product resulting from the alteration of aluminous minerals. It occurs under the same conditions as bauxite and is present in the characteristic bauxite deposits and in the laterites, at times as the chief mineral of such occurrences. Also as a low-temperature hydrothermal mineral in veins or cavities in alkalic or other igneous rocks.

Crystallized gibbsite occurs near Slatoust in the Schischimsk Mountains, Urals, in cavities in talc schists associated with serpentine and magnetite; the larger crystals are several inches long. In crystals filling cavities in natrolite on the islands of Eikaholm and Lille-Arö in the Langesund fiord, Norway. As an alteration of corundum in the mountains of Gümedagh (Messogis) east of Ephesus, Asia Minor. In bauxite at Vogelsberg, Hesse, Germany, and in the French and Hungarian bauxite deposits; the bauxite of the Gold Coast also contains gibbsite. With bassanite at Vesuvius, Italy. In laterite and bauxite at a number of localities in India, as at Kodikanal, Madras, and at Talevadi, Belgaum district, Bombay. Found in the laterites of Seychelles Island, Indian Ocean, and in Madagascar. At Dundas, Tasmania, as white coatings upon limonite and psilomelane. Long known from the neighborhood of Ouro Preto (Villa Rica) in Minas Geraes, Brazil, and in the bauxite deposits of British and French Guiana.

The original locality of gibbsite was in the United States at Richmond, Berkshire County, Massachusetts, where it occurred as radial fibrous stalactites and crusts in a limonite deposit. Also at Unionville, Chester County, Pennsylvania, with corundum; at the Clove limonite mine, Unionvale, Dutchess County, New York; abundant in the bauxite deposits of Arkansas; an impure variety with chalcoalumite and malachite at Bisbee, Arizona.

Alter. Gibbsite has often been observed as an alteration crust upon or as complete pseudomorphs after corundum; also as an alteration product of feldspars and other aluminous silicates, and of chalcaluminite. The gibbsite in some bauxite deposits probably has at least in part been formed at the expense of boehmite.

A r t i f.[18]   May be obtained artificially by hydrolyzing or passing CO_2 into alkali aluminate solutions. May also be prepared as spherulitic growths by leaching $CaO + Al_2O_3$ fusions above 50°. A dimorphous form, the so-called bayerite,[19] or α-$Al(OH)_3$, not found in nature, is produced by relatively rapid precipitation from cool or less strongly alkaline solutions and from acid solutions, but this product, on aging, inverts to gibbsite.[20] On heating, gibbsite changes to boehmite, and at higher temperatures, to γ-Al_2O_3.

N a m e.   Gibbsite after Colonel George Gibbs (1777–1834), the original owner of the Gibbs mineral collection acquired by Yale College early in the nineteenth century. Hydrargillite from ὕδωρ, *water*, and ἄργιλλος, *white clay*.

Gibbsite is here preferred as the species name because the name hydrargillite has had an unfortunate history. The Devonshire mineral first designated hydrargillite[21] was shown to be an aluminum phosphate[22] which had previously been named wavellite.[23] The aluminum hydroxide found at Richmond, Massachusetts, was named gibbsite in 1822. In 1839 the name hydrargillite was again revived[24] as a designation for crystallized aluminum hydroxide from Slatoust, supposedly different from gibbsite. This was shown to be in error, but the name has persisted as a designation for the crystallized occurrences. In view of the confusion in the literature concerning the name, it is better dropped.

Ref.

1. First shown to be monoclinic by Des Cloizeaux (648, 715, 1867) by optical means.
2. Brögger, *Zs. Kr.*, **16**, 16 (1890). Uncertain forms: {520}, {310}, {$\bar{2}$11}.
3. Megaw, *Zs. Kr.*, **87**, 185 (1934), by Weissenberg method on material from Langesund Fiord, Norway, with analysis of the structure; see also Pauling, *Proc. Nat. Ac. Sc.*, **16**, 123 (1930).
4. Brögger, *Zs. Kr.*, **16**, 24 (1890) with his fifth law (no. 1 in text, above) as modified by Johnsen, *Cbl. Min.*, 407, 1907. Another possible (but improbable) twin law given is ($\bar{3}$·1·54).
5. Mügge, *Jb. Min.*, I, 56, 1884, and Brögger (1890).
6. Megaw, *Roy. Soc. London, Proc.*, **142A**, 198 (1933).
7. A general lack of agreement in the literature concerning certain of the optical properties is to be noted. The extinction angles given by Des Cloizeaux (1867) are not in agreement with the angles given by Brögger (1890); the refractive indices of Brögger (1890) are not close to those given by Larsen (78, 1921) for a number of different localities, and by Polyanin, *Uchenye Zapiski Kazan State Univ.*, **98** [5–6], 153 (1938) — *Min. Abs.*, **7**, 440 (1940). The artificial material examined by Achenbach, *Chem. Erde*, **6**, 307 (1931) has $\alpha = \beta = 1.577$, $\gamma = 1.595$.
8. Des Cloizeaux (1867).
9. Larsen (1921) as an average of closely agreeing determinations.
10. Brögger (1890).
11. Larsen (78, 1921); Michel-Lévy and Lacroix (226, 1888; *Zs. Kr.*, **18**, 324, 1891).
12. Additional analyses in Hintze (1 [2A], 1944, 1910).
13. Kovar, *Ak. Wiss. Bohm., Abh.*, **28** (1899) — *Zs. Kr.*, **34**, 705 (1901).
14. Warth, *Min. Mag.*, **13**, 172 (1902).
15. Rama Rau anal. in Fermor, *Rec. Geol. Sur. India*, **34**, 167 (1906).
16. Brown anal. in Fermor (1906).
17. Smith and Brush, *Am. J. Sc.*, **16**, 51 (1853).

18. See Doelter (**3** [2], 475, 1926) and Weiser (**2**, 90, 1935); also Schwiersch, *Chem. Erde*, **8**, 252 (1933); Noll, *Jb. Min., Beil.-Bd.*, **70**, 65 (1935); Hüttig and Kostelitz, *Zs. anorg. Chem.*, **187**, 1 (1930); Lehl, *J. phys. Chem.*, **40**, 47 (1936).
19. See particularly Weiser (1935).
20. The aging of colloidal hydrous aluminum oxide apparently proceeds through the sequence boehmite → bayerite → gibbsite.
21. Davy, *Roy. Soc. London, Phil. Trans.*, 162, 1805.
22. Fuchs, *Schweigger's J.*, **18**, 288 (1816); **24**, 121 (1818).
23. Babington, *Roy. Soc. London, Phil. Trans.*, 162, 1805.
24. Rose, *Ann. Phys.*, **48**, 564 (1839).

ZIRLITE. *Pichler* (*Jb. Min.*, **57**, 1871; **51**, 1875).
A hydrous aluminum oxide found as yellowish white vitreous crusts in a sandy marl near Zirl, Tirol, and Nassereit. Easily soluble in acids.
Probably gibbsite.

SCHANYAVSKITE. *Nikolajewsky* (*Ac. sc. St. Pétersbourgh, Bull.*, **715**, 1912 — *Chem. Zbl.*, II, 630, 1912). Schaniawskite. Schanjawskite.
A transparent glassy material found with allophane-like minerals in crevices in dolomite near Moscow, Russia. Given the formula $Al_2O_3 \cdot 4H_2O$ from the analysis; Al_2O_3 53.63, CaO 2.28, MgO 0.35, SiO_2 1.33, H_2O 40.95, total 98.44. Named after A. L. Schanyavsky of the University of Moscow.
Apparently a hardened gel, $AlO(OH) \cdot nH_2O$. Probably identical with gibbsite.

623 **Bauxite.** Alumine hydratée de Beaux *Berthier* (*Ann. mines*, **6**, 531, 1821). Beauxite *Dufrénoy* (**2**, 347, 1844; **3**, 799, 1847). Bauxite *Deville* (*Ann. chim. phys.*, **61**, 309, 1861). Wocheinite *Flechner* (*Zs. deutsche geol. Ges.*, **18**, 181, 1866; *Geol. Reichsanst., Jb.*, 1866). Cliachite *Adam* (73, 1869). Kliachite, Kljakite.
The name bauxite was originally applied to a supposed species with the composition $Al_2O_3 \cdot 2H_2O$ found at Baux (or Beaux) near St. Reny, Bouches-du-Rhône, France. This material is a mixture of a number of different minerals composing a rock mass, and the original analysis[1] approached only by chance the ratio cited. The supposed compound $Al_2O_3 \cdot 2H_2O$ has not been found either as a natural or as an artificial product.
Bauxite properly is used as a generic term for rocks rich in hydrous aluminum oxides. The principal constituents are gibbsite, boehmite, and diaspore, any of which may at times be dominant. Bauxite grades with increasing content of hydrous iron oxides into laterite.
The ill-defined, very fine-grained and frequently gel-like hydrous aluminum oxides in bauxite and laterite have received various names, including cliachite, bauxitite,[2] sporogelite,[3] diasporogelite,[4] and alumogel.[5] Hematogelite[6] has been used to designate the colloidal ferric oxide often present.

Ref.

1. Berthier (1821).
2. Doelter and Dittler, *Cbl. Min.*, 104, 1912.
3. Kišpatič, *Jb. Min., Beil.-Bd.*, **34**, 513 (1912).
4. Tučan, *Cbl. Min.*, 68, 1913.
5. Pauls, *Zs. pr. Geol.*, **21**, 545 (1913).
6. Tučan, *Cbl. Min.*, 68, 1913.

624 **H Y D R O C A L U M I T E** [$Ca_4Al_2(OH)_{14} \cdot 6H_2O$]. *Tilley* (*Min. Mag.*, **23**, 607, 1934).

C r y s t . Monoclinic, pseudohexagonal; sphenoidal — 2.[1]
Structure cell. Space group $P2_1$; a_0 9.6, b_0 11.4, c_0 16.84, β 69°; $a_0 : b_0 : c_0 = 0.842 : 1 : 1.477$; contains $Ca_{16}Al_8(OH)_{56} \cdot 24H_2O$.
Habit. Massive.
P h y s . Cleavage {001} perfect, with a poor cleavage inclined at about 60° to {100}. H. 3. G. 2.15; 2.15 (calc.). Luster vitreous; on

cleavage surfaces inclining to pearly. Colorless to light green. Transparent. Strongly pyroelectric.

O p t. In transmitted light, colorless. On heating, $2V$ diminishes until at 90–95° the mineral becomes sensibly uniaxial.

	ORIENTATION	n	
X	$\wedge c < 3°$	1.535	Bx. neg. (−).
Y	b	1.553	$2V = 24° \pm 2°$.
Z		1.557	

C h e m. A hydrated hydroxide of Ca and Al, $Ca_4Al_2(OH)_{14} \cdot 6H_2O$. (The observed water content is closer to $5H_2O$, possibly because of the loss by dehydration at normal conditions.)

Anal.

	1	2	3
CaO	41.33	40.0	41.5
Al_2O_3	18.82	18.1	18.8
H_2O	39.85	}40.3	38.5
CO_2	.....		1.8
Total	100.00	98.4	100.6
G.	2.15	2.15	

1. $Ca_4Al_2(OH)_{14} \cdot 5H_2O$.   2, 3. Scawt Hill.[2]

Tests. In C.T. decrepitates and loses water. Soluble in weak HCl.

O c c u r. Found with afwillite, portlandite, ettringite in vugs in a larnite rock in the contact zone at Scawt Hill, county Antrim, Ireland.

A r t i f. A number of artificial compounds close to hydrocalumite have been found[3] in the system $CaO-Al_2O_3-H_2O$.

N a m e. In allusion to the composition.

Ref.

1. Crystal class from x-ray structural data of Megaw in Tilley (1934).
2. Hey anal. in Tilley (1934).
3. See Mylius, *Acta Ac. Aboensis, Math. Phys.*, **7**, no. 3 (1933) and Assarsson, *Zs. anorg. Chem.*, **191**, 333 (1930); **200**, 391 (1931); **205**, 338 (1932).

618   **P S I L O M E L A N E** [$BaMn^2Mn_8^4O_{16}(OH)_4$]. Derb Brunsten pt. *Wallerius* (268, 1747). Magnesia indurata pt. *Cronstedt* (106, 1758). Schwarz Braunsteinerz pt. *Werner (Bergm. J.*, 386, 1789). Verhärtetes Schwarz Braunsteinerz pt. *Emmerling; Karsten* (54, 1800). Verhärtetes Schwarz-Manganerz pt. *Karsten* (72, 1808). Schwarz-Eisenstein pt. *Werner, von Leonhard, et al.* Black Hematite, Black Iron Ore, Compact Black Manganese Ore pt. Hartmanganerz pt. Psilomelane *Haidinger (Roy. Soc. Edinburgh, Trans.*, **11**, 129, 1827). Leptonemerz, Leptonematite (?) *Breithaupt.* (Not leptonematite *Adam* [75, 1869] = braunite.) Schwarzer Glaskopf pt.*Germ.* Psilomelanite *Egleston (U.S. Nat. Mus.Bull. 33*, 137, 1887). χ-psilomelane *Fermor (Rec. Geol. Sur. India*, **48**, 120, 1917). Manganomelane pt. *Klockmann* (422, 1922).
    Romanechite *Lacroix* (4, 6, 1910).

C r y s t.[1] Orthorhombic.
Structure cell.[2] Orthorhombic; a_0 9.1, b_0 13.7, c_0 2.86; $a_0 : b_0 : c_0 =$ 0.66 : 1 : 0.209; contains $H_4BaMnMn_8O_{20}$ or $BaMn^2Mn_8^4O_{16}(OH)_4$.

Habit. Found only massive, as botryoidal, reniform, or mammillary crusts, and stalactitic; also earthy and pulverulent.

P h y s. H. 5–6, decreasing in the earthy varieties. G. 4.71 ± 0.01;[2] 4.42 (calc.). Luster submetallic; dull. Color iron-black, passing into dark steel-gray. Streak brownish black to black, shining. Opaque.

In polished section[3] much of the material previously placed under psilomelane is seen to consist of mixtures of several different minerals, including pyrolusite.

C h e m. A basic oxide of barium, bivalent and quadrivalent manganese; probably $BaMnMn_8O_{16}(OH)_4$.[2] Ba and Mn^2 approximate to 1 : 1 in the analyses cited. Small amounts of Cu, Co, Ni, Mg, Ca, W, and alkalies are often present as adsorbed or admixed impurities or possibly in substitution for (Ba,Mn). Most analyses[4] of so-called psilomelane apparently refer to mixtures with pyrolusite or other materials and are of interest only from a technical standpoint. In, Ga, Tl, Rb have been found on spectroscopic examination.

Anal.

	1	2	3	4	5	6	7	8	9	10
Li₂O	.....			....	....	....	....	....	0.0016	....
Na₂O	.....	trace	trace	....	0.02	.....	0.1	0.15	1.30	0.42
K₂O	.....			0.42	0.08	.....		0.20	0.60	0.11
CaO	.....	0.19	0.26	0.66	.....	.....	0.4	0.08	1.55	0.05
MgO	.....	0.15	0.13	0.13	0.30	.....	0.2	0.25	0.33	trace
BaO	16.04	17.46	17.48	12.38	15.73	16.36	16.8	15.08	16.03	14.40
CuO	.....	0.48	0.31	0.38	trace	.....	....	0.08	0.046	0.25
CoO	.....	0.90	1.00	0.48	.....	.....	....	0.25	....	....
MnO	7.42	7.09	7.12	7.90	10.70	10.18	8.5	7.63	6.14	6.70
MnO₂	72.77	66.62	66.73	70.38	68.00	66.98	69.2	70.78	67.69	59.65
SiO₂	.....	0.52	0.51	0.09	0.59	0.26	....	0.05	0.34	0.90
Al₂O₃	.....	0.37	0.35	0.73	....	.....	....	0.30	0.25	0.55
Fe₂O₃	.....	0.15	0.20	0.18	0.30	.....	....	0.21	0.05	3.27
WO₃	.....	0.89	0.68	....	0.28	.....	....	0.30	0.16	....
H₂O⁺	3.77	4.38	4.41	4.18	3.82	6.22	4.8	3.30	4.68	3.78
H₂O⁻	.....	0.48	0.50	1.88	0.48			0.45		0.49
Rem.	.....	trace	trace	0.03	trace	.....	....	1.36	1.01	8.72
Total	100.00	99.68	99.68	99.82	100.30	100.00	100.0	100.17	100.17	99.29
G.		4.71			4.697			4.54		4.21

1. $H_4BaMnMn_8O_{20}$. 2. Schneeberg, Saxony.[7] 3. Eibenstock, Saxony. Rem. is NiO trace.[7] 4. Restormel mine, Lostwithiel, Cornwall. Rem. is NiO 0.03.[7] 5. Schneeberg, Saxony. Rem. is NiO trace.[8] 6. Schneeberg, Saxony.[9] 7. Romanèche, France. Rem. is $(Na,K)_2O$ 0.1.[10] 8. Tekrasai, Bengal, India. Rem. is PbO 0.08, NiO 0.20, ZnO 0.30, P_2O_5 0.74, S 0.04, Cl trace.[11] 9. Romanèche, France (romanechite). Rem. is SrO 0.03, PbO 0.094, ZnO 0.035, TiO_2 0.01, As_2O_5 0.82, P_2O_5 0.015.[12] 10. Tucson, Ariz. Rem. is insol. 8.35, TiO_2 trace, P_2O_5 0.05, PbO 0.32.[19]

Tests. Infusible, or slightly rounded on thinnest splinters. Loses O on ignition. Soluble in HCl with evolution of Cl. Ignited material often gives an alkaline solution on extraction with water.

O c c u r.[6] Psilomelane is a secondary mineral formed under surface conditions of temperature and pressure, and found associated with pyrolusite, goethite, limonite, hausmannite, chalcophanite, braunite. A common weathering product of manganous carbonates or silicates, and may form large residual deposits or impregnations.   Abundant in concretionary forms in beds in lake and swamp deposits and clays.   Replacement deposits in calcareous or dolomitic rocks formed by meteoric waters are often of large extent, and the mineral sometimes occurs in small amounts as a hypogene hydrothermal product.   Mn and Fe commonly are separately removed and concentrated during weathering.[13]   Colloidal processes play a major role in the transportation and deposition of psilomelane.[14]

Psilomelane as here defined probably occurs at only a small proportion of the many previously reported localities,[15] since the name was formerly extended to hard hydrous manganese oxides in general, often with little or no Ba.   The true identity of much of this material is still unknown (see wad), but in part it doubtless is admixed pyrolusite and psilomelane.

Originally described from Schneeberg, Saxony, as botryoidal crusts (*leptonematite*, pt.); also at Eibenstock in vein gossan.   Abundantly in the Elgersburg-Öhrenstock manganese district in Thuringia, Germany, associated with pyrolusite as weathering products of manganese veins.   In France at Romanèche, Saône-et-Loire (*romanechite*), as botryoidal and pulverulent masses associated with barite, calcite, fluorite, goethite.   A lithian psilomelane occurs at Salm Chateau, near Ottrez, Belgium.   Botryoidal and pulverulent psilomelane occurs at Lead Geo, west of Holy Head, on the Orkney Islands, Scotland.   In Sweden at Skidberg, Leksandtal.   At Tekrasai, Singhbhum district, and elsewhere in the Central Provinces, India.   In the United States at Austinville, Wythe County, Virginia, and at Tucson, Arizona.

A l t e r .   Psilomelane has been described as an alteration product of, or as a pseudomorph after, a large number of minerals.   Here may be mentioned manganite, rhodochrosite, calcite, fluorite, barite, manganoan siderite, pharmacosiderite, rhodonite, franklinite, huebnerite.   The true identity of the alteration product in most instances is uncertain (see further under wad).

A r t i f .   Numerous attempts have been made to prepare[16] the various oxides of manganese containing Ba, Pb, alkalies, etc., but a compound of the constitution here accepted for the species has not yet been made.

N a m e .   From ψιλός, *smooth, bald, naked,* and μέλας, *black,* in allusion to the form of aggregation.   Romanechite from the locality at Romanèche, France.

ROMANECHITE.   *Lacroix* (4, 6, 1910).
A name given to a supposed variety of psilomelane found as radial fibrous botryoidal crusts at Romanèche, Saône-et-Loir, France.   The analyses[17] and x-ray pattern[20] are identical with psilomelane.   In part a mixture,[18] probably with pyrolusite.

Ref.

1. Polished section study (see Schneiderhöhn and Ramdohr [2, 515, 1931]) and x-ray examination by Vaux, *Min. Mag.,* **24**, 521 (1937), and Ramsdell, *Am. Min.,* **17**, 143 (1932), have shown that most of the material referred in the past to psilomelane is a mixture, often with pyrolusite.   The chemical and x-ray study of Vaux (1937) of the

original psilomelane from Schneeberg, Saxony, indicates that the name properly belongs to an orthorhombic species with the composition $H_4BaMnMn_8O_{20}$. The status and relations to true psilomelane of the many psilomelane-like minerals described in the literature still remain to be determined; the latter are here described under the general term *wad*.

2. Vaux (1937).

3. See Schneiderhöhn and Ramdohr (1931), Orcel and Pavlovitch, *Bull. soc. min.*, 54, 108 (1932).

4. For additional analyses see Hintze (1 [3A], 3601, 1929). Commercial analyses of manganese ores are widely scattered through the literature; see Harder, *U. S. Geol. Sur., Bull. 427*, 1910, Hall, *Geol. Soc. South Africa, Trans.*, 29, 17 (1927).

5. Hartley and Ramage, *J. Chem. Soc. London*, 71, 533 (1897).

6. For discussions of the occurrence and origin of psilomelane and psilomelane-like minerals (see also wad) see Krusch, *Zs. pr. Geol.*, 15, 129 (1907), Harder (1910), Lindgren (1933).

7. Bennett anal. in Vaux (1937).

8. Hallowell anal. in Vaux (1937).

9. Turner, *Roy. Soc. Edinburgh, Trans.*, 11, 172 (1831).

10. Gorgeu, *Bull. soc. min.*, 13, 21 (1890).

11. Pattinson anal. in Fermor, *Mem. Geol. Sur. India*, 37, 100 (1909).

12. Zambonini and Caglioti, *C. R.*, 192, 750 (1931).

13. See Vogt, *Zs. pr. Geol.*, 14, 223 (1906); Sullivan, *Am. Inst. Min. Eng., Trans.*, 803, 1910.

14. See Beyschlag, *Zs. pr. Geol.*, 27, 1 (1919); Cornu and Leitmeier, *Koll.-Zs.*, 4, 285, 295 (1909).

15. For a lengthy list of occurrences of psilomelane-like materials see Hintze (1 [3A], 3597, 1929).

16. Literature in Hintze (1929).

17. See anal. 9, and Lacroix (4, 8, 1910) for additional analyses.

18. See Fairbanks, *Am. Min.*, 8, 211 (1923).

19. Milton anal. in Wells, *U. S. Geol. Sur., Bull. 878*, 92, 1937.

20. Vaux (1937) and Frondel (priv. comm., 1940) by powder method.

MULTIPLE OXIDES

The multiple oxides here are arranged primarily according to the $A +$ $B : O$ ratio, and secondarily according to the $A : B$ ratio. They bear somewhat the same relation chemically to the simple oxides, that the sulfosalts bear to the sulfides. The multiple oxides have two nonequivalent metal atoms, but the strength of bonding between them and oxygen is of the same order, and therefore no discrete molecular groups are found in the structure. These minerals therefore represent the so-called isodesmic compounds,[1] as do also the simple oxides.

Many of the minerals grouped here have previously been placed in the oxides; others have been called manganates, aluminates, ferrates, columbates, tantalates, zirconates, and titanates.[2] The present classification has certain advantages in that these essentially similar minerals are placed together and near the simple oxides with which they have many properties in common.

The outstanding group in the multiple oxides is the spinel group, which shows a remarkable chemical variation. The A atoms are in four coordination forming a tetrahedron of oxygens, and the B atoms are in six coordination with octahedra of oxygen about them. The oxygens are essentially in cubic close-packing.[1]

The perovskite structure is simple with the A atoms in 12 coordination, and the B atoms in 6 coordination.[1] Other minerals of this class are more complex in structure, and many of the rarer minerals here found have not yet been studied.

The multiple oxides containing Cb, Ta, and Ti have special characteristics, and they are most conveniently separated from the other multiple oxides. They are, therefore, to be found in the section immediately after this.

7 MULTIPLE OXIDES

71 ABX_2 TYPE

711	Delafossite	$CuFeO_2$

712	GOETHITE GROUP	
7121	Diaspore	$HAlO_2$
7122	Goethite	$HFeO_2$

713	Limonite	

72 AB_2X_4 TYPE

721	SPINEL GROUP	
	Spinel series	
7211	Spinel	$MgAl_2O_4$
7212	Hercynite	$FeAl_2O_4$
7213	Gahnite	$ZnAl_2O_4$
7214	Galaxite	$MnAl_2O_4$
	Magnetite series	
7215	Magnesioferrite	$MgFe_2O_4$
7216	Magnetite	$FeFe_2O_4$
7217	Franklinite	$ZnFe_2O_4$
7218	Jacobsite	$MnFe_2O_4$
7219	Trevorite	$NiFe_2O_4$
721·10	Maghemite	Fe_2O_3
	Chromite series	
721·11	Magnesiochromite	$MgCr_2O_4$
721·12	Chromite	$FeCr_2O_4$

722	HAUSMANNITE GROUP	
7221	Hausmannite	$MnMn_2O_4$
7222	Hetaerolite	$ZnMn_2O_4$
7223	Hydrohetaerolite	$Zn_2Mn_4O_8 \cdot H_2O$

723	Chrysoberyl	$BeAl_2O_4$

724	Crednerite	$CuMn_2O_4$

73 AB_4X_7 TYPE

7311	Hoegbomite	$Mg(Al,Fe,Ti)_4O_7$
7312	Sapphirine	$(Mg,Fe)_{15}(Al,Fe)_{34}Si_7O_{80}$
732	Plumboferrite	$PbFe_4O_7$

733	Magnetoplumbite	$Pb(Fe,Mn)_6O_{10}$?

734	Hematophanite	$Pb(Cl,OH)_2 \cdot 4PbO \cdot 2Fe_2O_3$?

74 ABX_3 TYPE

741	Quenselite	$PbMnO_2(OH)$

7421	Perovskite	$CaTiO_3$

	(See also ilmenite series)	
7422	Uhligite	

75 A_2BX_5 TYPE

751	Pseudobrookite	Fe_2TiO_5

76 AB_2X_5 TYPE

761	Chalcophanite	$ZnMn_2O_5 \cdot 2H_2O$?
762	Zirkelite	$(Ca,Fe,Th,U)_2(Ti,Zr)_2O_5$

77 AB_3X_7 TYPE

7711	Coronadite	$MnPbMn_6O_{14}$
7712	Hollandite	$MnBaMn_6O_{14}$
7713	Cesarolite	$PbMn_3O_7 \cdot H_2O$

Ref.

1. See Evans (203, 1939).
2. Dana (1892).

711   DELAFOSSITE [$CuFeO_2$].   *Friedel* (*C. R.*, 77, 211, 1873).

C r y s t.   Hexagonal — R; scalenohedral — $\bar{3}\,2/m$.[1]

$$a : c = 1 : 1.945;^2 \qquad p_0 : r_0 = 2.246 : 1$$

Forms:[3]

		ϕ	ρ	M	A_2
c	0001	111	.....	0°00′	90°00′	90°00′
m	$10\bar{1}0$	$2\bar{1}\bar{1}$	30°00′	90 00	60 00	90 00
r	$10\bar{1}1$	100	30 00	66 00	62 49½	90 00

Structure cell.[4] Space group $R\bar{3}m$; a_{rh} 5.96, α 29°26′; a_0 3.02, c_0 17.10; $a_0 : c_0 = 1 : 5.66$; contains $CuFeO_2$ in the rhombohedral unit.

Habit. Crystals tabular {0001} to equant, with {0001} and {$10\bar{1}1$} as dominant forms. As botryoidal crusts.

Twinning. Contact twins on {0001} have been observed.[3]

P h y s. Cleavage {$10\bar{1}0$} imperfect.[5] Brittle. H. 5½.[6] G. 5.41;[7] 5.52 (calc. for artificial material). Luster metallic. Color and streak black. Opaque. Weakly magnetic. In polished section[8] rose brown-white in color, with strong anisotropism. Pleochroism distinct: O light golden brown, E darker rose-brown.

C h e m. Copper iron oxide, $CuFeO_2$.

Anal.

	1	2	3	4
Cu	41.99	42.14	41.32	40.68
Fe	36.88	33.56	37.26	37.91
O	21.13	[19.74]	[21.21]	[21.41]
Rem.	.....	3.52	0.21	......
Total	100.00	98.96	100.00	100.00
G.	5.52	5.07		

1. $CuFeO_2$. 2. Ekaterinburg, Siberia. Rem. is Al_2O_3 3.52.[9] 3. Bisbee, Ariz. Rem. is insol. 0.21 (hematite). Average of two analyses.[10] 4. Salmon, Id. Recalc. to elements from oxide values. Original analyses recalc. to 100.00 after deduction of insol. 30.94 and sol. SiO_2 0.70.[11]

Tests. Easily fusible. Becomes magnetic on heating. Readily soluble in HCl and H_2SO_4, but insoluble in HNO_3.

O c c u r. Originally found on clay from the region of Ekaterinburg, Siberia. Reported as a secondary mineral from the Copreasa mine, Sonoripa district, Sonora, Mexico; from the Cartagenera mine, near Pedroso, Sevilla, Spain; from Pfaffenreuth, Oberpfalz, Germany. In the United States in large amounts at Bisbee, Arizona, as crystals and as botryoidal crusts with hematite, cuprite, native copper and tenorite; in spherulitic aggregates in clay at Kimberley, Nevada. At Eureka, Nevada, as botryoidal crusts with limonite and malachite.[12] At the Pope-Shenon copper mine, near Salmon, Idaho, as a primary mineral associated with biotite, magnetite, and quartz.

N a m e. After the French mineralogist, G. Delafosse (1796–1878).

Ref.

1. Crystal class from Rogers, *Am. J. Sc.*, **35**, 290 (1913), on crystals from Bisbee. Soller and Thompson, *Am. Phys. Soc.*, *Bull.*, **10**, 17 (1935) give the same crystal class for artificial $CuFeO_2$.
2. The ratio of Rogers (1913) is admittedly on poor material. The x-ray study of artificial material leads to a c-axis ratio wherein c of Rogers is tripled. This would make the terminal forms of Rogers incompatible with the rhombohedral rule of indices $(h + i + l = 3n)$.
3. Rogers (1913). Uncertain forms: $\{10\bar{1}4\}$, $\{01\bar{1}2\}$.
4. Soller and Thompson (1935) on artificial material. The natural material was shown to be identical with the artificial material by Pabst, *Am. Min.*, **23**, 175 (1938).
5. Rogers (1913). Friedel (1873) described the mineral as occurring in small plates and cleaving into thin opaque laminae.
6. Rogers (1913). Friedel (1873) gave $2\frac{1}{2}$.
7. Frondel (priv. comm., 1939) on 8-mg. aggregate of crystals from Bisbee; massive botryoidal material gave 5.07. Friedel (1873) gave 5.07.
8. Ramdohr, *Zbl. Min.*, 296, 1937.
9. Friedel (1873).
10. Bohart anal. in Rogers (1913).
11. Schaller anal. in Ross, *U. S. Geol. Sur.*, *Bull. 774*, 23, 1925.
12. New locality (Frondel, priv. comm., 1939); identified by x-ray powder pattern.

GOETHITE GROUP

ORTHORHOMBIC DIPYRAMIDAL — $2/m\,2/m\,2/m$

		$a : b : c$	a_0	b_0	c_0
Diaspore	$HAlO_2$	0.4689 : 1 : 0.3019	4.40	9.39	2.84
Goethite	$HFeO_2$	0.4593 : 1 : 0.3034	4.64	10.00	3.03

Diaspore and goethite differ from the corresponding hydroxyl minerals, boehmite and lepidocrocite, in not having (OH) groups and in that the H acts as a cation in two-fold coordination between oxygen.[1] The minerals of this group are harder than the corresponding minerals of the lepidocrocite group. They are, on the whole, better crystallized.

Ref.

1. See Bragg (111, 1937).

7121   **D I A S P O R E** [$HAlO_2$]. *Haüy* (4, 1801). Blättricher Hydrargillite *Hausmann* (442, 1813). Empholite *Igelström* (*Bull. soc. min.*, **6**, 40, 1883; *Nordenskiöld, Geol. För. Förh.*, 9, 30, 1887). Diasporogelite pt. *Tučan* (*Cbl. Min.*, 768, 1913). Mangandiaspore *Chudoba* (*Cbl. Min.*, 11, 1929).

C r y s t. Orthorhombic; dipyramidal — $2/m\,2/m\,2/m$.

$a : b : c = 0.4689 : 1 : 0.3019;$[1] $p_0 : q_0 : r_0 = 0.6438 : 0.3019 : 1$

$q_1 : r_1 : p_1 = 0.4689 : 1.5532 : 1;$ $r_2 : p_2 : q_2 = 3.3124 : 2.1327 : 1$

Forms:[2]

		ϕ	$\rho = C$	ϕ_1	$\rho_1 = A$	ϕ_2	$\rho_2 = B$
b	010	0°00′	90°00′	90°00′	90°00′	....	0°00′
l	140	28 04	90 00	90 00	61 56	0°00′	28 04
k	130	35 24½	90 00	90 00	54 35½	0 00	35 24½
m	110	64 52½	90 00	90 00	25 07½	0 00	64 52½
e	021	0 00	31 07½	31 07½	90 00	90 00	58 52½
s	111	64 52½	35 25	16 48	58 21	57 13½	75 45½
p	121	46 50½	41 26	31 07¼	61 08½	57 13½	63 05

Less common:

c	001	z	160	Z	230	W	103	i	502	u	384	o	191
a	100	ϕ	3·10·0	f	011	w	101	t	221	d	4·10·5	β	7·18·6
n	1·10·0	y	120	μ	094	α	706	x	163	g	7·16·8	G	27·4·11
D	180	X	7·12·0	δ	061	γ	201	v	142	q	131	r	512

Structure cell.[3] Space group $Pbnm$; a_0 4.40, b_0 9.39, c_0 2.84; $a_0 : b_0 : c_0 = 0.468 : 1 : 0.302$; contains $H_4Al_4O_8$.

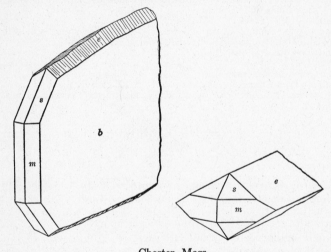

Chester, Mass.

Habit. Crystals commonly thin platy {010} and elongated [001]; sometimes acicular [001]; rarely tabular {100}. Faces in zone [010] striated [010]; in zone [001] striated [001]; and in zone [0$\bar{1}$2] striated [0$\bar{1}$2]. Also foliated massive and in thin scales; sometimes stalactitic. Disseminated.

Twinning.[4] Uncommon, on {061}, or on {021} (from France) with a reentrant of about 60°± to produce pseudohexagonal aggregates (as in chrysoberyl) normal to the pseudohexagonal axis a[100].

Phys. Cleavage {010} perfect, {110} less so, {100} in traces. Fracture conchoidal. Very brittle. H. 6½–7. G. 3.3–3.5; 3.44 ± 0.02 (crystals); 3.37 (calc.). Luster brilliant; pearly on cleavage faces, elsewhere vitreous. Color white, grayish white, colorless; also greenish gray, hair-brown, yellowish, lilac, pink; sometimes violet-blue in one direction, reddish plum in another and pale asparagus-green in the third;[5] rose-red to dark red in the manganoan variety (anal. 4). Transparent.

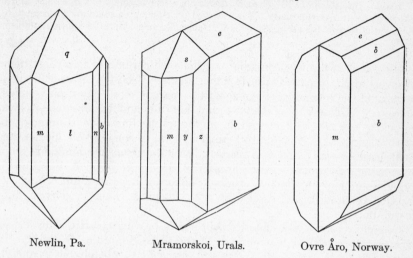

| Newlin, Pa. | Mramorskoi, Urals. | Ovre Åro, Norway. |

O p t.[6] In transmitted light colorless or faintly tinted. Pleochroic,[5] with absorption $X < Y < Z$.

	ORIENTATION	n_{Na}	
X	c	1.702	Bx. pos. (+).
Y	b	1.722	$2V84$–$85°$.
Z	a	1.750	$r < v$, weak.

C h e m.[7] Hydrogen aluminum oxide, $HAlO_2$ [or $AlO(OH)$] (dimorphous with boehmite). Mn^3 substitutes for Al in small amounts (anal. 4); Fe^3 also substitutes for Al, to about Fe : Al = 1 : 19 (anal. 6). SiO_2 and occasionally P_2O_5 are reported in analyses and are due to admixture.

Anal.[8]

	1	2	3	4	5	6
Al_2O_3	84.98	84.44	84.23	78.58	83.0	77.95
Fe_2O_3	.....	0.18	.....	1.96	3.0	6.60
Mn_2O_3	.....	.....	.....	4.32	....	.....
CaO	.....	.....	0.10	trace	....	.....
SiO_2	.....	0.42	1.37	0.11	....	.....
H_2O	15.02	14.99	14.67	14.65	14.8	15.00
Rem.	.....	trace	.....	......	....	0.45
Total	100.00	100.03	100.37	99.62	100.8	100.00
G.	3.37			3.328	3.39	3.40

1. $HAlO_2$. 2. Kossoibrod, Ural Mts. Rem. is TiO_2.[9] 3. Shŏkŏzan, Japan.[10] 4. Manganian. Postmasburg, South Africa.[11] 5. Chester, Mass. Fe_2O_3 includes some TiO_2.[12] 6. Ural Mts. Rem. is P_2O_5.[13]

Var. Ferrian. Contains Fe^3 up to at least Fe : Al = 1 : 19 (anal. 6). Color often brown.

Manganian. Mangandiaspore *Chudoba* (*Cbl. Min.*, 11, 1929). Contains Mn^3 up to at least Mn : Al = 1 : 29 (anal. 4). Color rose-red to deep red.

Tests. Infusible in C.T. Decrepitates strongly, separating into white scales and at a high temperature yields water. The variety from Schemnitz is said not to decrepitate. Some varieties react for Fe^3 or Mn^3. Not attacked by acids, but after ignition soluble in H_2SO_4.

O c c u r. Diaspore commonly occurs with corundum as a constituent of emery rock, in part as crusts lining crevices (Chester, Massachusetts); associated with margarite, magnetite, margarodite, chloritoid, spinel, chlorite. Widespread in bauxite and laterite, and in aluminous clays. Found associated with corundum in crystalline limestone (Campolongo, Switzerland), as a later hydrothermal mineral in some alkalic pegmatites (southern Norway), and as a recrystallization product of aluminous xenoliths in igneous rocks. Also formed by the hydrothermal alteration of other aluminous minerals or rocks (Shŏkŏzan, Japan; Dilln, Hungary; Rosita, Colorado) and associated with kaolinite, alunite, pyrophyllite, corundum.

Originally found with chloritoid in emery-bearing chlorite schists near Mramorskoi, south of Kossoibrod, in the Ural Mountains, U.S.S.R. In Sweden at the Hörrsjöberg, Wermland (*empholite*) embedded in pyrophyllite and damourite with tourmaline, rutile, and kyanite. Found sparingly in the nepheline-syenite pegmatites of southern Norway, sometimes as an inclusion in zeolitic alteration products of nepheline; found similarly in the Julianehaab district, Greenland. At Dilln, near Schemnitz,. Hungary as good crystals in a kaolinized rock (called dillnite), and as a principal constituent of the bauxite deposits at Gánt. With garnet at Jordansmühl, Silesia, Germany. In Switzerland at Campolongo, Tessin, in cavities in crystalline limestone with corundum, tourmaline, pyrite, calcite. Diaspore, with boehmite and gibbsite, is a common constituent of French bauxites and others.[14] Found with emery in the mountains of Gümedagh, east of Ephesus, Asia Minor, and on the islands of Naxos, Nikaria, and Samos, Greece. Found in Japan at Shŏkŏzan, Bungo Province, with alunite, pyrophyllite, and kaolinite as a hydrothermal alteration of porphyrite. Diaspore occurs as an important constituent of aluminous shales and granulites in the Gamagara sedimentary series in the Waterberg system, South Africa; also in the Postmasburg district, Griqualand-West (*mangandiaspore*) with a manganian mica. Observed with spinel and clinochlore as a product of contact metamorphism of greenstones at Kenidjack and Botallack, Cornwall. In laterite in Tonkin, China, and on the island of Yap.

In the United States a notable occurrence in emery at Chester, Massachusetts, as large plates and crystals and as drusy crusts along fractures. At Trumbull, Connecticut, with topaz and margarodite. With corundum and margarite at Newlin, near Unionville, Chester County, Pennsylvania. In cavities in massive corundum at the Culsagee mine, near Franklin,

Macon County, North Carolina. On Mount Robinson, in the Rosita Hills, Custer County, Colorado, with alunite in an altered rock. Found near Laws at White Mountain, California, with andalusite, corundum, pyrophyllite, alunite, lazulite in quartz-mica schist. Widespread in the bauxites and aluminous clays of Arkansas, Missouri, and elsewhere in the United States.

Alter. Diaspore has been reported[15] as an alteration product of corundum, and kaolin pseudomorphs after diaspore have been reported.

Artif. Has been reported[16] formed in crystals by heating hydrous aluminum oxide in a NaOH solution under pressure, and in other ways, but the true nature of the product is doubtful and it may have been boehmite or gibbsite. On thermal dehydration[17] diaspore affords α-Al_2O_3 (corundum); the corundum is oriented to the original diaspore with corundum [111], [110], [11$\bar{2}$] ‖ diaspore [100], [010], [001].

Name. From διασπείρειν, *to scatter*, alluding to the usual decrepitation before the blowpipe. Haüy states that the species was first made known by Le Lièvre, who found a specimen in a mineral dealer's in Paris and had given it to Vauqueline for analysis. The locality is supposed to have been the Ural Mountains.

Ref.

1. Unit and angles of Koksharov (**3**, 169, 1858) to conform with the x-ray unit of Ewing, *J. Chem. Phys.*, **3**, 203 (1935); orientation of Dana (246, 1892). Transformations:

Koksharov to new elements	001/010/100
Dana to new elements	100/020/001

In this orientation the a[100] axis is the pseudohexagonal axis conforming with the corresponding c[001] pseudohexagonal axis of chrysoberyl. For the structural relations between these two minerals see Bragg (111, 1937).
2. Goldschmidt (**3**, 54, 1916); Waterkamp, *Cbl. Min.*, 522, 1916; Yoshiki, *Ac. Imp. Japan, Proc.*, **9** [3], 109 (1933).
3. Ewing (1935); also space group and structure earlier determined by Takané, *Ac. Imp. Japan, Proc.*, **9**, 113 (1933) and Deflandre, *Bull. soc. min.*, **55**, 140 (1932).
4. de Lapparent, *Bull. soc. min.*, **53**, 255 (1930).
5. Haidinger, *Ann. Phys.*, **61**, 309 (1844).
6. Michel-Lévy and Lacroix (178, 1888); *C. R.*, **106**, 777 (1888); very similar values for the indices and axial angle are given by Yoshiki (1933) and Des Cloizeaux (565, 1867), and for the manganian material of anal. 4 by Chudoba, *Cbl. Min.*, 11, 1929.
7. The role of the hydrogen in diaspore is uncertain, and has variously been taken as a separate cation or as OH; see Bragg (111, 1937) for a general discussion.
8. For additional analyses see Hintze (**1** [2A], 1976, 1970).
9. Schwiersch, *Chem. Erde*, **8**, 259 (1933), average of two.
10. Yoshiki (1933).
11. Chudoba (1929).
12. Jackson, *Am. J. Sc.*, **42**, 108 (1866.)
13. Hermann, *J. pr. Chem.*, **106**, 70 (1869).
14. de Lapparent (1930).
15. Genth, *Am. Phil. Soc., Proc.*, **13**, 372 (1873).
16. See Doelter (**3** [2], 468, 1926) and Weiser and Milligan, *J. phys. Chem.*, **36**, 3010 (1932); **38**, 1175 (1934).
17. Deflandre, *Bull. soc. min.*, **55**, 140 (1932).

KAYSERITE.   *Walther* (*Zs. deutsche geol. Ges.*, **73**, 316, 1921). Tanatarite *Petrushkevich* (*Bull. Geol. Min. Circle, Ekaterinoslav. Min. Inst.*, **2**, 17, 1926; *Tanatar*, *ibid.*, **9**, 1927).

Monoclinic.[1] In micaceous flakes, with a perfect cleavage parallel to the flattening. Brittle. H. $5\frac{1}{2}$–$6\frac{1}{2}$. G. 3.385 (Kairakty, Russia). Colorless to white.

O p t. Material from Cerro Redondo, Uruguay, shows inclined extinction on the flat face up to 46° against the traces of a second cleavage intersecting the flakes. Dispersion $r < v$. $2V$ very large. X 1.68, Z 1.74. Material from Kairakty, Russia, is optically positive (+), with $2V$ 83–84°, and elongation negative (−). Axial plane parallel perfect cleavage. Shows inclined extinction up to 30° in sections $\perp$ to Bx_a against the traces of the perfect cleavage. X 1.70, Z 1.75.

C h e m. The analyses, cited below, are fairly close to the formula $Al_2O_3 \cdot H_2O$.

	Al_2O_3	Fe_2O_3	MgO	CaO	SiO_2	H_2O	Total
1	74.25	1.44	1.72	3.09	3.72	15.02	99.24
2	81.24	1.01	0.34	....	3.13	14.75	100.47

1. Kairakty, Russia (tanatarite).[2]   2. Cerro Redondo, Uruguay (kayserite).[3]

O c c u r. Found in microscopic veinlets as an alteration product of corundum at Cerro Redondo, Minas, Uruguay (*kayserite*). In crevices in chromite associated with chromian tourmaline, uvarovite and fuchsite at Kairakty, Government of Kustanaisky, Central Asia, U.S.S.R.

N a m e. Kayserite after Emanuel Kayser of Marburg, Germany. Tanatarite after Professor Joseph Tanatar of the Ekaterinoslav Mining Institute.

Stated to be a monoclinic modification of $Al_2O_3 \cdot H_2O$, trimorphous with diaspore and boehmite. Most of the optical properties are very close to diaspore, and conclusive evidence of species validity is lacking.

Ref.

1. Inferred from the optical data. The probable identity of kayserite and tanatarite has been pointed out by Foshag, *Am. Min.*, **13**, 493 (1928), and Walther in Brauns, *Jb. Min.*, I, 84, 1928.
2. Petruschkevich (1926).
3. Walther (1921).

MINASITE.   *Farrington* (*Geol. Soc. Am. Bull.*, **23**, 728, 1912; *Am. J. Sc.*, **41**, 355, 1916).

A name proposed and later abandoned for a supposed hydrous aluminum oxide found as a pebble in diamond washings in Minas Geraes, Brazil.

7122   **G O E T H I T E** [$HFeO_2$]. Eisenglimmer pt. (from Siegen) *Becher* (*Min. Beschr. Oranien-Nass. Lande*, 401, 1789). Kryst. fasriger Brauneisenstein *Mohs* (**3**, 403, 1804). Haarförmige Brauneisenstein *Hausman* (270, 1813) = Nadeleisenerz *Breithaupt* (1823). Brown Iron-stone pt., Brown Iron-ore pt., Brown Hematite pt. of *Jameson, Phillips*. Sammteisenerz, Sammetblende pt. = Przibramit in *Glocker* (549, 1831). Hierro pardo *Span.* Göthite. α-$Fe_2O_3 \cdot H_2O$.

Chileit *Breithaupt* (*J. pr. Chem.*, **19**, 103, 1840). Onegit (from Lake Onega) *Andre* [of Brünn] (Tageblatt, no. 18, 1802); *Moll* (**2**, 109, 112, 1806) = Ore of Titanium *various authors* for 25 years = Fullonite = Goethite *later authors*.

Xanthosiderite *Schmid* (*Ann. Phys.*, **84**, 495, 1851). Gelbeisenstein *Hausmann* (279, 1813). Mesabite *Winchell* (*Am. Inst. Mining Eng., Trans.*, **21**, 661, 1893). Ehrenwerthite *Cornu* (*Zs. pr. Geol.*, **17**, 82, 1909). Limonite (including Brauner Glaskopf, Bog Ore, and other synonyms) *of older writers in large part*.

C r y s t. Orthorhombic; dipyramidal — $2/m\,2/m\,2/m$.

$a : b : c = 0.4593 : 1 : 0.3034;$[1] $\quad p_0 : q_0 : r_0 = 0.6606 : 0.3034 : 1$

$q_1 : r_1 : p_1 = 0.4593 : 1.5138 : 1;$ $\quad r_2 : p_2 : q_2 = 3.2960 : 2.1773 : 1$

Forms:[2]

		ϕ	$\rho = C$	ϕ_1	$\rho_1 = A$	ϕ_2	$\rho_2 = B$
b	010	0°00′	90°00′	90°00′	90°00′	.....	0°00′
a	100	90 00	90 00	.....	0 00	0°00′	90 00
y	120	47 26	90 00	90 00	42 34	0 00	47 26
m	110	65 20	90 00	90 00	24 40	0 00	65 20
e	021	0 00	31 15	31 15	90 00	90 00	58 45
u	101	90 00	33 27	0 00	56 33	56 33	90 00
s	111	65 20	36 01	16 52½	57 42	56 33	75 47½
p	121	47 26	41 53½	31 15	60 32½	56 33	63 09

Less common:

c	001	n	160	L	7·10·0	d	041	α	104	N 401	ϕ 38·16·27
D	180	l	140	o	340	i	051	β	102	A 151	ρ 321
k	3·20·0	x	230	ν	560	f	081	γ	301	w 423	

Structure cell.[3] Space group $Pbnm$; $a_0\,4.64$, $b_0\,10.0$, $c_0\,3.03$; $a_0 : b_0 : c_0 = 0.464 : 1 : 0.303$; contains $H_4Fe_4O_8$.

Habit. Prismatic [001] and striated [001]; also flattened into tablets or scales on {010}; as velvety aggregates of capillary crystals, grading into acicular [001] and long prismatic forms often radially grouped. Usually massive, as reniform, botryoidal or stalactitic masses with an internal concentric or radial fibrous structure. The fibers are elongated [001], and a color banding in shades of brown or yellow is often developed ⊥ to the direction of the fibers. Also bladed or columnar; compact, with a flat conchoidal fracture; ocherous or earthy and often impure from the presence of clay, sand, etc. In compact or fibrous concretionary nodules (brown clay ironstone| pt.; Adlerstein, Klappenstein, pt., *Germ.*), sometimes pisolitic, as an aggregation of pealike concretions (Bohnerz, *Germ.*; *bean ore*), or oolitic. The so-called bog ore is generally loose and porous in texture.

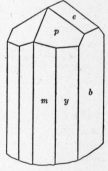

P h y s. Cleavage {010} perfect, {100} less so. Fracture uneven. Brittle. H. 5–5½. G. 3.3–4.3 (massive material), 4.28 ± 0.01[4] (crystals); 4.17 (calc.). Luster of crystals imperfect adamantine-metallic, sometimes dull; fibrous varieties often silky. Color of crystals blackish brown; massive varieties yellowish or reddish brown, and when earthy brownish yellow, ocher-yellow. Streak brownish yellow, orange yellow, ocher-yellow. Transparent in thin splinters.

O p t.[5] Biaxial negative (−), $2V$ small to medium; uniaxial negative (−) for wavelengths 610–620 mμ; $r > v$ strong. Also optic angle changes with temperature: uniaxial at 59° for 578 mμ. Absorption $Z > Y > X$ in yellow (for white light). Absorption increases rapidly below 550 mμ.

ORIENTATION

	n_{Na}	Red	Yellow	PLEOCHROISM
X	2.260	b	b	Clear yellow
Y	2.393	a	c	Brownish yellow
Z	2.398	c	a	Orange-yellow

Shows characteristic green interference colors on {010}.

Fibrous varieties show anomalous optical effects[6] due to impurities as thin films between the fibers, and also because of random and subparallel orientations about a common axis (the c[001] axis).

In polished section[7] gray in color with strong anisotropism and slight pleochroism. Massive material exhibits a flamboyant granular and sometimes banded structure. Reflection percentages: green 17.5, orange 14, red 13.

C h e m. Hydrogen iron oxide, $HFeO_2$, of same composition as lepidocrocite. Mn is often present, in amounts up to 5 per cent Mn_2O_3 by weight, and may be in substitution for Fe. The small amounts of SiO_2 reported in most analyses are probably due to admixture. The massive varieties often contain adsorbed or capillary H_2O in amounts up to several per cent.

Anal.[8]

	1	2	3	4	5
Fe_2O_3	89.86	89.65	89.03	88.24	88.65
SiO_2	.....	0.36	0.70	1.07	1.25
H_2O	10.14	10.19	10.22	10.54	9.97
Total	100.00	100.20	99.95	99.85	99.87
G.	4.17	4.264	4.250	4.172	

1. $HFeO_2$. 2. Florissant, Colo.[6] 3. Cornwall, England.[6] 4. Diamond Hill, R. I. (fibrous).[6] 5. Friedrichroda, Thuringia. With CaO trace. Average of two analyses.[9]

Tests. Heated in C.T. loses water and is converted to α-Fe_2O_3 (hematite). Fusible with difficulty. Most varieties give a reaction for Mn. Soluble in HCl.

O c c u r. One of the commonest of minerals and, after hematite, the commonest of the ferric oxides. The species includes most of the material formerly classed under limonite. Typically formed under oxidizing conditions at ordinary temperatures and pressures as a weathering product of ferriferous minerals, especially siderite, pyrite, magnetite, and glauconite. Also as a direct inorganic or biogenic precipitate from marine or meteoric waters, and widespread as a deposit in bogs and springs. Rarely and in small amounts as a low-temperature hydrothermal vein product, and then usually associated with amethystine quartz and calcite. Goethite, with limonite, forms the weathered capping or gossan of sulfide veins; residual deposits of igneous and other rocks containing ferrous-iron minerals are widely distributed in countries of warm climate where rock decay has progressed without interruption for a long time (laterites). Associated with hematite, psilomelane, pyrolusite, manganite, calcite, quartz, lepidocrocite, clay minerals, and limonite; rarely with zeolites.

Deposits of goethite are very widespread, although usually small, and the mineral constitutes an important ore of iron. Only a very few localities will be mentioned here.[10] Found at numerous localities in Nassau, Westphalia, and the Rhine Provinces, Germany, especially at Siegen (does not include the rubinglimmer = lepidocrocite, found at Siegen), Eiserfeld, Herdorf, Hörhausen, and Oberstein; in Bohemia as velvety coatings (*przibramite, sammetblende*) and fine crystals at Přibram; in Carinthia at Leoben and Wölch as velvety coatings and massive. Goethite is the principal constituent of the valuable minette ores of Alsace-Lorraine. In France with lepidocrocite at Chizeuil, Saône-et-Loire, and Rancié, l'Ariège. Well-crystallized material has been found in Cornwall, England, at the Restormel mine, Lostwithiel, the Botallack mine, St. Just, and in the neighborhood of Redruth. Early found as crusts and as acicular crystals in amethyst on an island in Lake Onega, Russia (*onegite, fullonite*); widespread in residual iron ore deposits in central Russia. Found in Chile at San Antonio and elsewhere in Coquimbo Province, in part as pseudomorphs after pyrite (*chileite*). Large deposits of goethite, limonite, and hematite occur in Cuba as residual mantles resulting from the weathering of serpentine in the Mayari and Moa districts, Oriente Province, and the San Felipe district, Camaguey Province.

In the United States[11] goethite is common in the Lake Superior hematite deposits, and has been obtained in notable specimens at the Jackson mine, Negaunee, and the Superior mine, near Marquette, in Michigan; the mineral occurs in part well crystallized but mostly in botryoidal, stalactitic, or earthy forms. Well-crystallized goethite occurs with smoky quartz, microcline, and siderite in pockets in pegmatites in the Pikes Peak granite in the region of Pikes Peak and Florissant, Colorado, and in part forms pseudomorphs after large crystals of siderite. Remarkable pseudomorphs of goethite after pyrite have been found at Pelican Point, Great Salt Lake, Utah. Large deposits formed by the weathering of glauconitic sediments occur in the coastal plain region of east Texas. Residual brown iron ores also are abundant in the Appalachian region, mainly in Alabama, Georgia, Virginia, and Tennessee.

Alter. Pseudomorphs have been observed of hematite after goethite,[12] and of goethite after siderite, pyrite, barite, calcite. The very common pseudomorphs of so-called limonite after pyrite probably consist for the most part of goethite, although this has been proved in only a few instances. Most of the limonite pseudomorphs are probably goethite (see under limonite).

Artif.[13] Obtained by oxidation of solutions of ferrous compounds, by slow hydrolysis of most ferric salts, and by the aging of sols and gels of hydrous basic ferric oxide. Highly hydrous material is obtained by oxidation of ferrous bicarbonate solutions and by the slow oxidation of ferrous chloride at room temperature; these preparations largely lose their nonessential water at temperatures below 100°. Also by digesting hydrous ferric oxide in alkaline solution at 150° in an autoclave. Crystals have been prepared by heating $FeCl_2$ solutions under pressure. On thermal dehydration[14] goethite gives pseudomorphs consisting of small crystals of hematite arranged[15] in parallel position, together with others in twin position with {111} as twin plane; the axes [100], [010], [001] of goethite correspond to [111], [1$\bar{1}$0], [11$\bar{2}$] of hematite.

N a m e. After the poet and philosopher Goethe (1749–1832). The name properly belongs to γ-FeO(OH), lepidocrocite, as noted under that species, but is here retained because of long-established usage. The name onegite has priority, but was given without proper description and the true nature of the material long remained unknown.

XANTHOSIDERITE. Gelbeisenstein *Hausmann* (279, 1813). Xanthosiderit *Schmid* (*Ann. Phys.*, **84**, 495, 1851). Yellow Ocher pt. Bog Ore pt.

In fine needles or fibers, stellate, and concentric; as an ocher. Luster silky or greasy; also earthy. Color in needles golden yellowish, brown to brownish red; as an ocher, yellow of different shades, more or less brown, sometimes reddish. Streak ocher-yellow. Ascribed the formula $Fe_2O_3 \cdot 2H_2O$. Analyses[16] of material referred to xanthosiderite vary widely. Originally found in Germany at Ilmenau as silky needles, and later reported from many other localities. Named from ξανθός, *golden yellow*, and σίδηρος, *iron*, in allusion to the color.

Identical with goethite.[17] Contains adsorbed and capillary water, $HFeO_2 \cdot nH_2O$.

EHRENWERTHITE. *Cornu* (*Zs. pr. Geol.*, **17**, 82, 1909).

A name needlessly given to designate the colloidal varieties of goethite. Named after Professor Joseph von Ehrenwerth of Leoben, Styria.

Ref.

1. Angles of Miller (273, 1852); orientation of Dana (247, 1892); unit of Goldzstaub, *Bull. soc. min.*, **58**, 6 (1935), derived from x-ray cell. Transformations: Miller to new elements 010/200/001; Dana to new elements 100/020/001. See also Peacock, *Roy. Soc. Canada, Trans.*, [3], Sec. 4, **36**, 107 (1942).

2. Goldschmidt (4, 72, 1918); Jahn, *Mitt. d. Vögtländ. Ges. Naturforsch.*, [5],10, 1929.

3. Goldzstaub (1935), *C. R.*, **195**, 964 (1932), *ibid.*, **193**, 533 (1931), on crystals from Cornwall. See also Böhm, *Zs. Kr.*, **68**, 567 (1928).

4. Posnjak and Merwin, *Am. J. Sc.*, **47**, 311 (1919), by pycnometer; values between 4.23 and 4.27 were obtained on single Cornish crystals (Frondel, priv. comm., 1940) on the microbalance; the value 4.37 given by Yorke, *Phil. Mag.*, **27**, 264 (1845) is too high.

5. Posnjak and Merwin (1919) indicate that the mineral is optically negative for all wavelengths; Mügge, *Jb. Min.*, **1**, 62 (1916), however, states that it is positive for yellow at temperatures below 59°. The latter has measured the axial angle for different temperatures. Change in optical orientation with wavelength reported by Pelikan, *Min. Mitt.*, **1**, 2 (1895) and by Posnjak and Merwin (1919). See also Schwierisch, *Chem. Erde*, **8**, 252 (1933) — p. 298; also Nuffield and Peacock, *Univ. Toronto, Geol. Ser.*, **47**, 53 (1942).

6. Posnjak and Merwin (1919).

7. Schneiderhöhn and Ramdohr (**2**, 561, 1931).

8. For additional analyses see Doelter (3 [2], 669, 1923).

9. Schwiersch, *Chem. Erde*, **8**, 271 (1933), average of two.

10. For additional localities see under goethite and limonite in Hintze (1 [2A], 1991, 2008, 1910).

11. Many additional occurrences of goethite and so-called brown iron ores are listed by Schrader, Stone, and Sanford, *U. S. Geol. Sur. Bull. 624*, 1917; see also Lindgren (293, 1928).

12. Spencer, *Min. Mag.*, **18**, 339 (1919).

13. See Weiser (**2**, 39, 1935); Baudisch and Welo, *Chem. Rev.*, **15**, 45 (1934); Posnjak and Merwin, *J. Am. Chem. Soc.*, **44**, 1965 (1922); Doelter (3 [2], 678, 1926).

14. See Schwiersch (1933); Posnjak and Merwin (1919); Kurnakov and Rode, *Zs. anorg. Chem.*, **169**, 57 (1928).
15. Goldzstaub (1931); see also Böhm (1928).
16. See Danà (174, 1868), Leitmeier and Goldschlag, *Cbl. Min.*, 473, 1917.
17. Posnjak and Merwin (1919) from optical and dehydration studies, with analysis, and x-ray study of Böhm (1928). The optical data of Larsen (80, 1921) also are close to goethite.

713   **LIMONITE.** The name limonite formerly was given to a hydrous iron oxide with the supposed formula $2Fe_2O_3 \cdot 3H_2O$.[1] No compound of this formula has been found in artificial systems,[2] and investigations[3] by x-ray and other methods have shown that most of the natural material classed as limonite actually is cryptocrystalline goethite with adsorbed or capillary water. Limonite may conveniently be retained as a field or generic term to refer to natural hydrous iron oxides whose real identity is unknown. Such material is typically vitreous and isotropic, gives few, faint and diffuse x-ray diffraction effects, and has a variable and indefinite water content. The substances here included under the name appear for the most part to represent hardened gel masses of hydrous basic ferric oxide, $FeO(OH) \cdot nH_2O$ or $HFeO_2 \cdot nH_2O$, equivalent respectively to lepidocrocite or goethite, and, in less part, hydrous ferric oxide, $Fe_2O_3 \cdot nH_2O$, equivalent to hematite. The physical and chemical properties of limonite are here defined vary widely.

Limonite. Σχιστὸς λίθος (from Iberia) *Dioscorides.* Schistus, Haematites *Pliny* (**36**, 37, 38). Haematites pt., Blodsten pt. (rest red hematite) *Wallerius* (260, 1747); *Cronstedt* (178, 1758). Glaskopf pt. *Wallerius* (336, 1750). Hématite pt. *Wallerius* (469, 1753). Braun-Eisenstein (incl. Eisenrahm, Brauner Glaskopf) pt. *Werner* (*Bergm. J.*, 383, 1789). Brauneisenstein pt. (rest goethite) *Hausmann* (268, 1813). Braun-Eisenstein, Stilpnosiderit *Ullmann* (146, 305, 148, 313, 1814). Brown Iron Stone pt., Brown Hematite, Brown Ocher *Jameson* (253, 261, 1816). Limonite pt. (rest goethite, Bog Ore) *Beudant* (**2**, 702, 1832). (Not Limonite *Hausmann* (1813) = Bog Ore only.) Eisenoxyd-Hydrat pt. *Leonhard* (342, 1821). Pecheisenerz pt. (= Eisenpecherz pt.) *Breithaupt* (94, 97, 236, 238, 1823). Hyposiderite *Breithaupt* (**3**, 894, 1847). Ferrite *Vogelsang* (*Zs. deutsche geol. Ges.*, **24**, 529, 1872). Glanzeisenstein *Bauer* (567, 1904). Brun, Gul Jernmalm, Myrmalm, Sjömalm *Swed.* Hierro arcilloso, globoso, palustre, etc., *Span.* Brauner Glaskopf, Bohnerz, pt. *Germ.* Limonitogelite *Tučan* (*Cbl. Min.*, 768, 1913).

Ωχρα, yellow-ocher, *Theophrastus* ? Sil *Pliny* (**33**, 56, 38). Ochra nativa, *Germ.* Berggeel, *Agricola* (466, 1546). Ochra native, Sil, Berggelb, Ockergelb *Gessner* (8, 1565). Ochriger Brauneisenstein *Werner*, *Karsten.* Brown-Ocher pt., Yellow-Ocher pt.

Minera Ferri subaquosa, Minera Ferri lacustris, var. palustris, Sjömalm, Myrmalm *Wallerius* (263, 1747). Mine de fer limoneuse *Wallerius* (1753). Ferrum limosum, etc. *Wallerius* (**2**, 256, 1775). Raseneisenstein (incl. Morasterz, Sumpferz, Wiesenerz) pt. *Werner* (*Bergm. J.*, 383, 1789). Marsh Ore, Bog Ore, Meadow Ore pt. *Kirwan, Jameson,* etc. Limonit (= Raseneisenstein or Bog Ore) *Hausmann* (283, 1813). (Not Limonite of *Beudant,* which included all hydrous oxides of iron.) Limnit *Glocker* (62, 1847).

In stalactitic, botryoidal, or mammillary forms and as varnish-like coatings; pitchlike; earthy or loose and porous; flocculent; ocherous. Usually without internal structure and vitreous; the material with a fibrous or subfibrous internal structure and yellowish brown streak formerly placed with limonite appears in general to be *goethite*.

Phys. Fracture conchoidal, subconchoidal to uneven, and earthy. Extremely brittle in vitreous forms. H. variable, mostly $4-5\frac{1}{2}$. G. 2.7–4.3. Luster vitreous to dull. Color various shades of brown, commonly dark brown to brownish black, and when earthy dull brown, brownish yellow, ocher-yellow; also reddish brown to reddish black and orange-brown ($Fe_2O_3 \cdot nH_2O$?). Streak yellowish brown to reddish. Stalactitic and botryoidal forms occasionally have an iridescent tarnish in shades of green and rose. Transparent in thin fragments.

O p t.[4] In transmitted light, yellow, yellow brown, brown, reddish brown, red. Isotropic; sometimes with indefinite anomalous birefringence up to ca. 0.04 and at a maximum for rays vibrating $\perp$ to the surface of crusts or stalactites. Index variable, usually about 2.00–2.10. The grains often absorb the index liquid and the apparent index increases on standing. Some red isotropic or birefringent material has n 2.2–2.4 ($Fe_2O_3 \cdot nH_2O$?).

C h e m. No single or definite composition can be attributed to the materials here loosely grouped. Probably largely hydrous basic ferric oxide, $HFeO_2 \cdot nH_2O$; also hydrous ferric oxide, $Fe_2O_3 \cdot nH_2O$, and possibly other, unrecognized, hydrous iron oxides. Often admixed with colloidal silica,[5] sand, clay minerals, manganese oxides, jarosite, phosphates, humic acids. Analyses[6] are chiefly of technical interest.

O c c u r. Limonite always is a secondary material formed under oxidizing conditions at ordinary temperatures and pressures. It may be formed in place by the direct oxidation of some other iron mineral, or be formed as an inorganic or biogenic precipitate in bog, lacustrine, or marine deposits. Frequently observed as a spring deposit. The material, in part goethite, constitutes the weathered capping or gossan of many metallic veins, and occurs in residual deposits upon rocks containing ferrous-iron minerals. Limonite always occurs intimately associated with goethite, and often is found associated with hematite and secondary manganese ores. The principal mineral of most occurrences formerly listed under limonite[7] is now known to be goethite. It is not practicable to attempt any separation of the localities on a mineralogical basis.

A l t e r. Limonite has been reported as an alteration product of, or as pseudomorphs after, a large number of minerals. The true identity of the hydrous iron oxide composing the alteration usually has not been shown, but can be presumed to be goethite in most instances. Very frequently as pseudomorphs after pyrite, siderite, and marcasite; also after ankerite, amphibole, barite, biotite, chalcopyrite, calcite, cuprite, cerussite, dolomite, dufrenite, fluorite, fayalite, gypsum, hematite, magnetite, olivine, pyroxene, pyrrhotite, scorodite, sphalerite; less commonly after beryl, beraunite, copiapite, chlorite, cacoxenite, cronstedtite, garnet, galena, ludwigite, pharmacosiderite, pyromorphite, pyroaurite, vivianite, wolframite. Observed as the petrifying material of wood and leaves.

N a m e. Limonite from λειμών, *meadow*, in allusion to the characteristic occurrence in bogs. Stilpnosiderite, from στιλπνός, *shining*.

The following ill-defined materials conform to the name limonite as defined above.

LIMNITE. Quellerz *Hermann* (*J. pr. Chem.*, **27**, 53, 1842). Limnite *Dana* (178, 1868). Raseneisenerz, Sumpferz, Wiesenerz *Germ.* For the most part bog ore, recent in origin and containing organic acids with phosphates, admixed sand, etc.

The composition $Fe_2O_3\cdot 3H_2O$ has been attributed to this material, but the water is no doubt in large part adsorbed or mechanically enclosed.[8]

KALIPHITE. *Ivanov* (*J. pr. Chem.*, **33**, 87, 1844). A dark brown fibrous material, apparently a mixture of a hydrous iron oxide with manganese oxides and zinc silicate.

HYPOXANTHITE. *Rowney* (*Edinburgh New Phil. J.*, **2**, 308, 1855). Sienna Earth. A brownish yellow clayey ocher.

MELANOSIDERITE. *Cooke* (*Am. Ac. Arts Sc.*, *Proc.*, **10**, 451, 1875). In banded black vitreous masses with reddish internal reflections. Streak brownish to brick-red. Fracture subconchoidal. Very brittle. H. $4\frac{1}{2}$. G. 3.39. In transmitted light isotropic, with n_{Na} variable.[9] Analysis gave:[10] Fe_2O_3 75.13, Al_2O_3 4.34, SiO_2 7.42, H_2O + 100° 7.68, H_2O − 100° 6.17, total 100.74. Gelatinizes in HCl. From Mineral Hill, Delaware County, Pennsylvania. Named from $\mu\epsilon\lambda\alpha\varsigma$ and $\sigma\iota\delta\eta\rho\sigma\varsigma$, in allusion to the color and composition. Originally regarded as a hydrated basic ferric silicate, but no doubt a mixture of a hydrous oxide of iron with colloidal silica or a silicate.[11]

AVASITE. *Krenner* (*Földt. Közl.*, **2**, 105, 1881 — *Zs. Kr.*, **8**, 537, 1883). Found as black vitreous masses with conchoidal fracture in a limonite deposit in the Avasthal, Szathmár, Hungary. H. $3\frac{1}{2}$. G. 3.33. In thin splinters, reddish. Composition given as $5Fe_2O_3\cdot 2SiO_2\cdot 9H_2O$. Acetic acid dissolves the iron oxide and leaves the silica as glassy particles. Probably a mixture of a hydrous iron oxide with silica.

ESMERALDAITE. *Eakle* (*Univ. California, Dept. Geol. Bull.*, **2**, 320, 1901). Occurs as vitreous black, pod-shaped masses in a limonitic rock in Esmeralda County, Nevada. Very brittle. H. $2\frac{1}{2}$. G. 2.578. Streak yellow-brown. In transmitted light deep red and isotropic; n_{Na} variable, 1.725–1.735, and increasing on standing in the liquid.[9] Analysis gave:[12] Fe_2O_3 56.14, Al_2O_3 5.77, CaO 3.35, P_2O_5 4.49, organic 1.37, SiO_2 2.05, H_2O + 110° 15.94, H_2O − 110° 10.24, total 99.35. Assigned the formula $Fe_2O_3\cdot 4H_2O$, on the unjustifiable assumption that the water all belongs to the ferric oxide and that the other constituents are impurities. A mixture, probably largely of a hydrous iron oxide.

Ref.

1. For a history of the name and of the various interpretations of the constitution see Hintze (**1** [2A], 2008, 1910) and Doelter (**3** [2], 667, 680, 1926).
2. See Welo and Baudisch, *Chem. Rev.*, **15**, 45 (1934); Weiser (**2**, 39, 1935); Posnjak and Merwin, *Am. J. Sc.*, **47**, 311 (1919); *Am. Chem. Soc. J.*, **44**, 1965 (1922); Böhm, *Zs. anorg. Chem.*, **149**, 212 (1925).
3. For x-ray studies see Böhm, *Zs. Kr.*, **68**, 567 (1928), Posnjak and Merwin (1922); for optical studies see Posnjak and Merwin (1919), (1922); Gaubert, *C. R.*, **181**, 869 (1925); Pelikan, *Min. Mitt.*, **14**, 5 (1895); Cesáro and Abraham, *Ac. sc. belge, Bull.*, **178**, 1903; for dehydration studies see Posnjak and Merwin (1919); Kurnakov and Rode, *Zs. anorg. Chem.*, **169**, 57 (1928); Schwiersch, *Chem. Erde*, **8**, 252 (1933).
4. Posnjak and Merwin (1919), (1922).
5. See Doelter (1926).
6. Many analyses are cited by Doelter (1926); also Wells, *U. S. Geol. Sur., Bull. 878*, 92, 1937.
7. See Hintze (1910) for a long list of occurrences; also under brown iron ore in Schrader, Stone, and Sanford, *U. S. Geol. Sur., Bull. 624*, 1917, for occurrences in the United States.
8. See also Rammelsberg (187, 1865), Doelter (1926), Hintze (1910).
9. Frondel (priv. comm., 1940).
10. Melville anal. in Cooke (1875), average of three; additional analyses in Genth (216, 1876).
11. See also Genth (1876).
12. Schaller anal. in Eakle, *Univ. California, Dept. Geol. Bull.*, **2**, 320, 1901, average of several.

SPINEL GROUP — AB_2X_4

The spinel group, as here divided, consists of three series, and each of the series contains a number of well-defined species as follows.

SPINEL SERIES		MAGNETITE SERIES	CHROMITE SERIES
	Al	Fe	Cr
Mg	Spinel	Magnesioferrite	Magnesiochromite
Fe	Hercynite	Magnetite	Chromite
Zn	Gahnite	Franklinite	Artificial
Mn	Galaxite	Jacobsite	Artificial
Ni	Artificial	Trevorite	Artificial

In the natural compounds the pure end components are rarely found; the species are designated by the predominant divalent and trivalent atoms, and the varieties by the next most dominant constituent. Thus, in the formula AB_2X_4, a mineral with dominant Zn and Fe^3 is called franklinite, and if Mn^2 is the next most dominant constituent, the varietal name is manganoan franklinite. In addition to the natural spinels a considerable number of artificial spinels have been described,[1] where $A =$ Co, Cd, Cu and $B =$ Co, Ti, Sn, V, Ga, In, Mn. One of the further complexities of composition in the artificial spinels is a tendency for substitution of A atoms for part of the B atoms of the formula, i.e., the formula may be written $BABX_4$ (as in the compounds $GaMgGaO_4$, etc.).[2] Another chemical feature of interest is the ability of artificial Mg, Al spinel to contain considerable excess of Al_2O_3 without impairment of the spinel structure.[3] Magnetite, in the same way, may contain considerable quantities of excess Fe_2O_3, as shown in artificial preparations.[4] The three series in the spinels are based on the trivalent elements. Under natural conditions of occurrence there is more or less complete miscibility within each series, whereas there is comparatively little miscibility between the series. The presence of ilmenite in magnetite, presumably as an exsolution product, indicates that Ti is not held to any considerable extent in solid solution at normal temperatures. Likewise the presence of hercynite as an exsolution product in natural magnetite indicates a limited miscibility of Al and Fe^3. The presence of hausmannite inclusions in jacobsite suggests a limited Fe^3-Mn^3 substitution.[5]

The A and B atoms are in four and six coordination, respectively, in the structure,[6] with $A_8B_{16}O_{32}$ in the unit cell. However, γ-Al_2O_3 and maghemite (γ-Fe_2O_3) have 32 oxygens in the unit cell but a deficiency of the cations, and consequently, vacant positions in the structure.[7] The lattice dimensions increase in the order Zn, Mg, Fe, Mn, and Al, Cr, Fe^3 (with the exception $ZnFe_2O_4$)[8] and this is, in general, the order of increase of the ionic radii. The Al spinels are harder, of lower specific gravity, and lower refractive index than the Fe and Cr spinels. Likewise they are more transparent to light.

All the spinel minerals occur predominantly in high-temperature deposits and close to the magmatic source. The Cr spinels occur principally in the basic igneous rocks such as peridotite. The Al and Fe spinels are found in both basic and acidic igneous rocks, and the Al spinels, especially those high in Mg, also are widespread as recrystallization products in limestone.

Ref.

1. See, for example, Mellor (**5**, 295, 1924; **11**, 201, 1931; **13**, 731, 914, 1934). Also Clark, Ally, and Badger, *Am. J. Sc.*, **22**, 539 (1931).
2. Barth and Posnjak, *Washington Ac. Sc., J.*, **21**, 225 (1931); *Zs. Kr.*, **82**, 325 (1932).
3. Rinne, *Jb. Min., Beil.-Bd.*, **58**, 43 (1928).
4. Greig, Posnjak, Merwin, and Sosman, *Am. J. Sc.*, **30**, 239 (1935).
5. Johansson, *Zs. Kr.*, **68**, 107 (1928).
6. In Bragg (97, 1937); also Evans (206, 1939).
7. See further in Verwey, *Zs. Kr.*, **91**, 65 (1935).
8. Clark, Ally, and Badger (1931).

Spinel Series

7211　**S P I N E L** [MgAl₂O₄].　''Ανθραξ pt., ''Ανθρακα περι Μίλητον *Theophrastus.*
Carbunculus pt., Lychnis pt. (rest ruby sapphire), *Pliny* (37, 25, 29). Spinella, Carbunculus pt., Rubinus pt., Carbunculus ruber parvus, = *Germ.* Spinel, Ballagius (a pallido colore videtur appellasse), = *Germ.* Ballas, Lychnis, = *Germ.* Gelblichter Rubin, *Agricola* (293, 1546, 463, 1546). Rubin orientales octaedrici, seu octohedris comprehensi, quae modo triangula sunt, modo trapezia, aliquando hedrae oblongae angulos solidos occupant, etc., *Cappeler* (*Prodrom.*, 1723). Rubinus pt. (Spinell, Ballas, Rubicelle) *Wallerius* (115, 1747). Rubis spinelle octaëdre (Spinelle, Balais) *de Lisle* (**2**, 224, 1783) (by de Lisle first made distinct in species from Ruby Sapphire). Ceylanite *Delametherie* (*J. phys.*, **42**, 23, 1793). Zeylanit *Karsten* (**28**, 72, 1800). Zeilanite. Pleonaste *Haüy* (1801). Ceylonit *Rammelsberg.* Candite (from Candy, Ceylon) *Bournon.* Chlorospinel *Rose* (*Ann. Phys.*, **50**, 652, 1840). Gahnit *B. de Marni* (1833). Picotite *Charpentier* (*J. mines*, **32**, 321, 1812; *Ann. phys.*, 47, 205, 1814). Chromceylonite *Dana* (221, 1892). Magnochromite *Bock* (Inaug. Diss. Breslau, 1868), *Websky* (*Zs. deutsche geol. Ges.*, **25**, 394, 1873); Alumisches Eisenerz *Breithaupt* (234, 1832). Magnesiochromite pt. *Dana* (228, 1892). Talkspinell *Hintze* (**1** [4], 3, 1921). Mitchellite *Pratt* (*Am. J. Sc.*, **7**, 281, 1899). Ruby Spinel. Spinel-ruby. Iron-magnesia spinel. Magnesia-iron spinel. Magnesia spinel. Spinelle *Fr.* Spinell *Germ.* Espinella *Span.* Chrome-spinel pt. Ferropicotite *Lacroix* (**4**, 306, 1910; *Bull. soc. min.*, **41**, 195, 1918). Gahnospinel *Anderson* and *Payne* (*Min. Mag.*, **24**, 547, 1937). Alkali-spinel *von Eckermann* (*Geol. För. Förh.*, **44**, 757, 1922).

7212　**H E R C Y N I T E** [FeAl₂O₄]. Chrysomelane *Müller.* Hercynit *Zippe* (1839). Hercinit *bad orthogr.* Iron Spinel pt. Chromohercynite *Lacroix* (*Bull. soc. min.*, **43**, 69, 1920). Chromhercynite. Picotite pt. Chromceylonite pt. Ceylonite pt. Ironmagnesia Spinel pt.

7213　**G A H N I T E** [ZnAl₂O₄]. Zinc Spinel. Automolite (from Fahlun) *Ekeberg* (**1**, 84, 1806). Gahnit *von Moll* (*Efem.*, **3**, 78, 1807). Spinelle Zincifère *Haüy* (67,99, 1809). Dysluite (from Sterling, New Jersey) *Keating* (*Ac. Sc. Philadelphia, J.*, **2**, 287, 1821); *Shepard* (**1**, 158, 1832; **2**, 176, 1835); *Thomson* (**1**, 220, 1836). Kreittonite *von Kobell* (*J. pr. Chem.*, **44**, 99, 1848). Spinellus superius *Breithaupt* (623, 1847).

7214　**G A L A X I T E** [MnAl₂O₄]. Manganspinel *Krenner* (*Zs. Kr.*, **43**, 471, 1907). Galaxite *Ross* and *Kerr* (*Am. Min.*, **17**, 15, 1932).

C r y s t.　Isometric; hexoctahedral — 4/m 3̄ 2/m.

Forms:[1]

　　a{001}　　*d*{011}　　*o*{111}　　*m*{113}　　*n*{112}　　*q*{133}　　*p*{122}

Structure cell.[2]　Space group *Fd3m*.　Cell dimensions on pure artificial compounds:[3]

		a_0
Spinel	MgAl₂O₄	8.086 ± 0.003
Hercynite	FeAl₂O₄	8.119 ± 0.002
Gahnite	ZnAl₂O₄	8.062 ± 0.001
Galaxite	MnAl₂O₄	8.271 ± 0.002

Contains $A_8B_{16}O_{32}$ in unit.

Habit. Usually octahedral; less often modified by $a\{010\}$ or $d\{011\}$; rarely dodecahedral or cubic. Hercynite and galaxite have not been found as crystals. Also massive, coarse granular to compact and as irregular or rounded embedded grains.

Twinning. Common on $\{111\}$, the *spinel law*, with twinned aggregates often flattened parallel $\{111\}$, the composition plane. Sometimes as sixlings by repeated twinning. Etch figures on spinel have been described.[4]

P h y s. Separation plane $\{111\}$ indistinct, and probably parting rather than cleavage. Fracture conchoidal; sometimes uneven to splintery. Brittle. H. $7\frac{1}{2}$–8.[5]　G. for the pure artificial compounds:

		Calculated
Spinel	$MgAl_2O_4$	3.55
Hercynite	$FeAl_2O_4$	4.39
Gahnite	$ZnAl_2O_4$	4.62
Galaxite	$MnAl_2O_4$	4.03

Actual measured specific gravities lie between the calculated values, and are proportional to the elements present (see under analyses). The specific gravity increases with Fe and Zn content in the series. Luster vitreous, splendent to nearly dull. Color variable: red (ruby-spinel gem) to blue, green, brown to nearly colorless; gahnite is usually dark blue-green, sometimes yellow or brown; hercynite and galaxite are black. Streak: spinel, white; gahnite, gray; hercynite, dark grayish green to dark green; galaxite red-brown. The Mg rich members of the series are quite transparent; they become less so as other elements such as Mn, Fe^2, Zn, and Fe^3 enter into the composition. Melting point $2135° \pm 20°$[6] (spinel).

O p t. Isotropic. Shows a weak anomalous birefringence rarely.[7] Also anomalous pleochroism is found in some blue zincian spinels.[8]　Refractive indices:

	n	Analysis Number
Spinel	1.720 ± 0.005	Ordinary range
Spinel (artif.)	1.719 Na	Pure[9]
Spinel (Sweden)	1.720	Anal. 5[10], contains alkalies
Spinel (Ceylon)	1.747 Na	Anal. 4, zincian[11]
Spinel (Peekskill)	1.775 ± 0.005[12]	Anal. 7, ferroan
Hercynite ? (Poughkeepsie)	1.800 ± 0.005[12]	
Gahnite (Mineral Hill)	1.790 ± 0.002	Anal. 13[13]
Gahnite (artif.)	1.805[14]	
Galaxite (Galax)	1.923	Anal. 23[15]

In the spinel series a linear variation of refractive index with the Mg/Zn ratio has been shown[11] and presumably a similar relation between the other members holds.[16]

C h e m. Oxides with the general formula AB_2O_4, where A is Mg, Fe^2, Zn, and less often Mn^2, in all proportions. Smaller amounts of alkalies (anal. 5) and Co (anal. 13) are sometimes reported, and Si, although frequently given, may be due to impurity in the analyzed sample.[17]　Ga has been found spectroscopically in some gahnites.[18]　B of the formula is predominantly Al in the spinel series, although Fe^3, Cr, Mn^3, V, and Ti often substitute for the Al in considerable part (see the magnetite and chromite series). The ratio A/B in the formula is nearly always a close approximation to 1 : 2 in natural spinels,[19] and most deviations can be ascribed to impurities in the analyzed sample. Wide variations, however, are found in the Mg/Al ratio of artificial spinels;[20] the magnetite series may also show a similar variation (see under magnetite and maghemite).

Anal.[21]

	1	2	3	4	5	6	7	8
MgO	26.50	25.92	25.19	16.78	24.76	17.20	13.36	27.49
FeO	0.69	0.62	.....	1.93	9.62	13.60	21.78	.....
MnO	.....	0.18	0.07	.....	.....	.....	.....	.....
ZnO	.....	.....	1.62	18.21	.....	.....	.....	.....
Al$_2$O$_3$	70.41	66.25	67.84	63.21	57.80	59.06	64.86	57.34
Fe$_2$O$_3$	.....	5.32	4.12	.....	3.04	10.72	.....	14.77
Cr$_2$O$_3$	1.44	.....	.....	.....	.....	trace	.....	.....
SiO$_2$	.....	0.28	0.91	.....	0.94	.....	.....	.....
Rem.	1.75	1.70	0.36	.....	3.53	.....	.....	0.62
Total	100.79	100.27	100.11	100.13	99.69	100.58	100.00	100.22
G.			3.623	3.97	3.683			

1. Spinel. Ceylon. Rem. is Na$_2$O 1.11, K$_2$O 0.64. Average of two analyses.[22] 2. Spinel. Monte Somma. Rem. is CaO 1.69, CoO 0.003, NiO 0.007, CuO 0.004, SnO trace, Sb$_2$O$_3$ trace.[23] 3. Spinel. Adamello, Trentino. Rem. is Na$_2$O 0.22, TiO$_2$ 0.14.[24] 4. Spinel, zincian (*gahnospinel*). Ceylon. Average of two microanalyses on 10-mg. samples.[25] 5. Spinel, alkali. Mansjö Mt., Sweden. Rem. is Na$_2$O 1.38, K$_2$O 1.31, CaO 0.84.[26] 6. Spinel, ferriferroan. Velay, France.[27] 7. Spinel, ferroan. Peekskill, N. Y.[28] 8. Spinel, ferrian. Slatoust, Urals. Rem. is CuO 0.62.[29]

	9	10	11	12	13	14	15	16
MgO	13.65	16.98	.....	0.13	0.42	2.38	2.64	10.33
FeO	17.45	12.87	1.72	.....	4.86	8.54	14.79	4.56
MnO	0.26	.....	0.50	1.13	0.26	0.10	.....	.....
ZnO	.....	.....	41.66	39.62	34.48	31.38	27.44	23.77
Al$_2$O$_3$	42.09	42.91	53.73	49.78	54.50	57.70	48.40	60.76
Fe$_2$O$_3$	3.80	0.85	2.53	8.58	.....	.....	7.47	0.58
Cr$_2$O$_3$	22.76	26.59	.....	.....	.....	0.09	.....	.....
SiO$_2$	.....	.....	0.70	0.57	1.50	.....	.....	.....
Rem.	trace	.....	.....	.....	3.12	0.01	.....	.....
Total	100.01	100.20	100.84	99.81	99.14	100.20	100.74	100.00
G.	4.12	4.004	4.57	4.89–4.91		4.38		
n			1.818			1.782		

9. Spinel, chromian, Namban, Western Australia. Rem. is NiO trace.[30] 10. Spinel, chromian. Drahonín, Moravia.[31] 11. Gahnite. Greenbushes, Western Australia.[32] 12. Gahnite, ferrian. Franklin, N. J. Mean of 2 analyses.[33] 13. Gahnite, cobaltian. Carroll Co., Md. Rem. is insol. 1.50, CuO 0.14, CoO 1.48.[34] 14. Gahnite, ferroan. Gillingara, Western Australia. Rem. is NiO 0.01.[35] 15. Gahnite, ferriferroan (*kreittonite*). Bodenmais, Bavaria.[36] 16. Gahnite, magnesian. Cotopaxi mine, Chaffee Co., Colo.[37]

	17	18	19	20	21	22	23
MgO	.....	2.92	10.02	9.37	10.3	5.33	1.50
FeO	.....	35.67	24.53	24.00	24.9	27.00	16.36
MnO	7.60	.....	.....	0.15	....	1.10	34.03
ZnO	16.80	.....	.....	.....	....	.....	trace
Al$_2$O$_3$	30.49	61.17	53.52	60.84	56.0	27.12	45.71
Fe$_2$O$_3$	41.93	.....	10.35	4.26	....	0.61	.....
Cr$_2$O$_3$	.....	.....	.....	....	8.0	38.64	.....
SiO$_2$	2.96	.....	0.92	0.77	2.0	0.28	0.96
Rem.	0.40	.....	0.67	1.00	....	0.25	trace
Total	100.18	99.76	100.01	100.39	101.2	100.33	98.56
G.	4.551				4.08	4.415	4.234
n							1.923

⟡

17. Gahnite, ferrian (*dysluite*). Sterling Hill, N. J. Rem. is H_2O 0.40.[38] 18. Hercynite. Ronsberg, Bohemia.[39] 19. Hercynite, magnesian. Whittles, Pittsylvania Co., Va. Rem. is TiO_2 0.67.[40] 20. Hercynite, magnesian. Island of Mull, Scotland. Rem. is CaO 0.36, H_2O 0.14, TiO_2 0.50.[41] 21. Hercynite, chromian. Lake Lherz, Dept. l'Ariège, France.[42] 22. Hercynite, chromian (*chromohercynite*). Between Farafangana and Vangaindrano, Madagascar. Rem. is H_2O 0.25.[43] 23. Galaxite. Galax, N. C. Total Fe reported as FeO, with TiO_2 and CaO trace.[44]

Var.

SPINEL

1. *Ordinary.* Essentially Mg, Al spinel with these elements predominant.

Gem varieties: Ruby-spinel or Spinel-ruby.[45] Balas Ruby (rose-red). Rubicelle (yellow or orange-red). Almandine, Almandine-spinel (violet). (Not almandine = garnet.) Also blue, blue-green, sapphire blue, lavender, indigo, violet, mauve to nearly colorless. Essentially pure Mg, Al spinel, with some blue gems containing Zn in small amounts.[46]

2. *Ferroan.* Ceylonite, Ceylanite *Delametherie* (*J. phys.*, **42**, 23, 1793). Pleonaste *Haüy.* Picotite pt. *Charpentier* (*J. mines*, **32**, 321, 1812; *Ann. Phys.*, **47**, 205, 1814). Iron-magnesia Spinel, pt. Ferropicotite *Lacroix* (**4**, 306, 1910; *Bull. soc. min.*, **41**, 195, 1918). With Fe^2 next most abundant after Mg.

3. *Zincian.* Gahnospinel *Anderson* and *Payne* (*Min. Mag.*, **24**, 547, 1937). Contains Zn in substitution for Mg (anal. 4) and probably grades to gahnite.[47]

4. *Ferrian.* Chlorospinel *Rose* (*Ann. Phys.*, **50**, 652, 1840). With Fe^3 next most abundant after Al (anal. 6, 8).

5. *Chromian.* Picotite proper *Charpentier* (*J. mines*, **32**, 321, 1812; *Ann. Phys.*, **47**, 205, 1814). Chrome-Spinel. Magnochromite *Bock* (Inaug. Diss., Breslau, 1868), *Websky* (*Zs. deutsche geol. Ges.*, **25**, 394, 1873); Alumisches Eisenerz *Breithaupt* (234, 1832). Chromceylonite *Dana* (221, 1892). Magnesiochromite pt. *Dana* (228, 1892). Mitchellite *Pratt* (*Am. J. Sc.*, **7**, 281, 1899). Contains a large proportion of Cr in substitution for Al (anal. 9, 10).

HERCYNITE

1. *Ordinary.* Essentially Fe^2, Al spinel with these elements predominant.

2. *Magnesian.* Picotite pt. Ceylonite pt. Pleonaste pt. Iron-magnesia spinel pt. Contains Mg in considerable amounts in substitution for Fe^2 (anal. 19, 20) and grades presumably to ferroan spinel.

3. *Ferrian.* A partial series between Al and Fe^3 is probably formed (anal. 19). See also under aluminian magnetite.

4. *Chromian.* Chromohercynite *Lacroix* (*Bull. soc. min.*, **43**, 69, 1920). Cr probably forms a complete series with Al (anal. 22 has Al : Cr = 1 : 1).

GAHNITE

1. *Ordinary.* Essentially Zn, Al spinel.
2. *Magnesian.* Zinc spinel pt. Presumably forms a series to zincian spinel (see anal. 16).
3. *Ferroan.* Kreittonite pt. *von Kobell* (*J. pr. Chem.*, **44**, 99, 1848). The Zn : Fe ratio goes to 1.64 : 1 (anal. 15).
4. *Ferrian.* Kreittonite pt. Dysluite *Keating* (*Ac. Sc. Philadelphia, J.*, **2**, 287, 1821); *Shepard* (**1**, 158, 1832; **2**, 176, 1835); *Thomson* (**1**, 220, 1836). Contains Fe^3 in substitution for Al (anal. 12, 15, 17) but some of the analyses are probably on impure material.

GALAXITE

1. *Ordinary.* Essentially Mn, Al spinel. No pure material has been found in nature.
2. *Ferroan.* The only available analysis of this species is a ferroan galaxite (anal. 23).

Tests. Infusible. On heating, the red spinels often become brown or black and opaque; on cooling, these first become green, then colorless, and finally resume the original red color. Hercynite becomes brick-red in O.F. Soluble with difficulty in concentrated H_2SO_4. Decomposed by fusion with $KHSO_4$.

Occur. The members of the spinel series are essentially high-temperature minerals. They are found chiefly as (*a*) accessories in igneous rocks (mostly basic), (*b*) in aluminum-rich xenoliths in igneous rocks, (*c*) in metamorphosed highly aluminous schists, (*d*) in contact metamorphic limestone deposits,[48] (*e*) in granite pegmatites (gahnite), (*f*) sometimes in ore veins of higher temperatures of formation, (*g*) in placers derived from the above sources. Examples are given below of the most notable occurrences, but many more less-important localities have been reported in the literature.

Spinel occurs in Sweden at Kafveltorp at Nya-Kopparberg with chondrodite, galena, sphalerite, chalcopyrite, pyrite, diopside, in a high-temperature replacement deposit; in crystalline limestone at Åker (blue) and Tunaberg; in the Mansjö Mountains, Helsingland (*alkali spinel*). In Finland in crystalline limestone at Pargas with chondrodite. A ferrian variety (*chlorospinel*) at Slatoust in the Urals, Russia, in a talc schist with magnetite, garnet, vesuvianite. In Germany with forsterite in metamorphic limestone near Passau, and similarly in the Spessart and with wollastonite near Auerbach; with garnet in schist inclusions in granite porphyry at Schenkenzell in the Black Forest as a recrystallization product; in phonolite of the Olbrück in the Eifel and in the crystalline schists and sanidinite bombs of the Laacher See region; in the Tirol abundantly on Monzoni in the contact zone. In Italy with mica and vesuvianite in ejected blocks on Mount Somma, and similarly in Latium; with sillimanite, andalusite and cordierite in andesite on the Lipari Islands. With forsterite, chondrodite, scapolite, etc., in crystalline limestone at Mercus and Arignac, north of

Tarascon, on the borders of l'Ariège, France; in basaltic tuffs and sands at Velay and various other localities in the Plateau Central (ferroan; *ferropicotite*). In Ceylon found abundantly associated with phlogopite, corundum (including gem varieties), zircon, etc., in contact metamorphosed limestone, in pegmatites, and in residual or detrital deposits derived therefrom, in a number of districts; the mineral often is of gem quality. Similarly found in Burma. In the Vizagapatam district, Madras, India, with sapphirine in the contact zone of an ultrabasic igneous rock with aluminous sediments. Found in Madagascar at Andrahomana in pegmatite with andalusite and grandidierite as a product of assimilation of aluminous xenoliths; in schist with phlogopite and diopside south of Betroka; in basaltic tuffs in the regions of Antsirane and Ankalampo. In the United States found abundantly, associated with phlogopite, graphite, corundum, tremolite, augite, norbergite, scapolite, magnesian tourmaline, rutile, etc., in a belt of pre-Cambrian crystalline limestone which extends some 30 miles from Amity, New York, to Andover, New Jersey. Some of the many localities within this region[49] include Edenville, Amity, Warwick, and Mounts Adam and Eve in New York and Vernon, Newton, Sparta, Hamburg, Franklin, and Sterling Hill in New Jersey. Found similarly in New York in Grenville marble at numerous localities in St. Lawrence and Jefferson counties; also with magnetite at Monroe, Orange County, and in fine-grained aggregates with corundum, magnetite, hematite (emery-rock) at Peekskill, Westchester County, at the contact of schist with basic igneous rocks.[50] In Massachusetts in crystalline limestone at Bolton, Boxborough, Chelmsford, and Littleton, and embedded in slate near Springfield; in emery near Chester in Hampden County. With corundum at the Culsagee mine, near Franklin, Macon County, North Carolina, and similarly at Dudleyville, Alabama. Near Whittles, Virginia (in emery). In Canada black spinel is found in crystalline limestone with phlogopite, apatite, etc., at Burgess and Wakefield, Ontario; with clintonite at Daillebout, Joliette County.

Hercynite was originally from Natschetin and Hoslau near Ronsberg at the eastern foot of the Bohmerwald, Bohemia; also with sillimanite, garnet, andalusite scattered through the granulites of Saxony; with corundum in schist inclusions in granite porphyry near Schenkenzell in the Black Forest. In Switzerland with corundum and sillimanite in gabbro at Le Prese, Veltlin. As pebbles in diamond placers in Bahia, Brazil. From near Erode, district of Coimbatore, Madras, India. In cassiterite placers near Moorina, Tasmania. A chromian variety (*chromohercynite*) from the region between Farafagana and Vangaindrano, Madagascar. In the emery deposit at Peekskill, Westchester County, New York, and in Virginia with hoegbomite in emery near Whittles, Pittsylvania County. The spinel often observed as an exsolution growth in magnetite has been ascribed to hercynite, but the exact identity of this material is uncertain.

Gahnite occurs in the crystalline schists; in granite pegmatites; in contact metamorphosed limestone; in high-temperature replacement ore deposits in schists or quartzose rocks (Fahlun and Riddarhyttan, Sweden); in pyritic zones in schists which may also contain arsenopyrite and cobaltite. The most abundant occurrences are at Fahlun, Sweden, and in the high-temperature metamorphic zinc deposits at Franklin and Sterling Hill, New Jersey. Some of the more important or typical occurrences follow. In Germany at Silberberg, near Bodenmais (*kreittonite*), and at Querbach in the Riesengebirge, Silesia. In contact metamorphosed limestone at Tiriolo, Calabria, Italy, with vesuvianite. In Sweden at several of the mines at Fahlun (*automolite*) and at Riddarhyttan and other localities. In granite pegmatite at Träskböle, Perniö parish, Finland. Reported in rounded crystals or fragments in the diamond placers of Minas Geraes, Brazil. In Western Australia in mica schist at Gillingarra and with stauro-lite and sillimanite in quartzite at Goyamin Pool, both in South West Division, and as a detrital mineral with tantalite at Wodgina and Green-bushes. In the Nellore district, Madras, India. In pegmatite at Ambato-fotsikely, Madagascar. In the United States gahnite is found at Franklin and Sterling Hill, New Jersey (*dysluite*), in the crystalline limestone wall rock adjacent to the ore body and occasionally in the ore itself. Octahe-dral crystals 5 in. on an edge associated with jeffersonite have been found. Found in granite pegmatites at Topsham, Maine; Haddam, Connecticut; Deake mine and Chalk Mountain mine, Mitchell County, North Carolina; near Lima P. O., Middletown Township, Delaware County, Pennsylvania. A deep blue cobaltian variety from old copper mines in Carroll County, Maryland. At Rowe, Massachusetts, in a pyritic lens in gneiss and schist with chalcopyrite, rutile, ilmenite, apatite, epidote. As a detrital mineral with rhodolite (garnet) and corundum in Mason Branch, near Franklin, Macon County, North Carolina; at Ore Knob. At the Canton mine, Cherokee County, Georgia. In Colorado at the Cotopaxi mine, Chaffee County, in crystals superficially altered to chlorite.

Galaxite occurs in a vein with alleghanyite, calcite, spessartite, rhodonite, tephroite at Bald Knob near the town of Galax, Alleghany County, North Carolina.

Alter. The members of the spinel series are, in general, relatively resistant to ordinary chemical attack. Spinel alters to talc, mica, serpen-tine, hydrotalcite and, less commonly, to corundum[51] or augite. The inte-rior and sometimes the edges and corners of the serpentine and hydrotalcite pseudomorphs may remain unaltered. The name *houghite* was early given[52] to a supposed species later shown to be hydrotalcite derived from the altera-tion of spinel. Pseudomorphs have been found of spinel after corundum, forsterite, clinochlore, and the mineral has repeatedly been observed as an alteration product of sillimanite. Gahnite has been found outwardly altered to sphalerite, chlorite and muscovite. Corundum occurs as partial or complete pseudomorphs after hercynite.

Artif. The members of the spinel series are easily prepared artifi-cially by sintering or fusing the mixed oxides (more readily in the presence of mineralizers such as boric oxide, borates, lead oxide, HCl or H_2O vapor, or chlorides), by decomposing the vapors of the mixed chlorides or fluorides, and in a wide variety of other ways.[53]   Mg-Al-spinel of gem quality is made artificially by the Verneuil and other processes;[54] the material is pigmented by the addition of small amounts of metallic oxides.

Some of the spinels have been formed accidentally in metallurgical processes, or otherwise.   Gahnite has been observed on the walls of zinc muffles and in slags.[55]

N a m e.   The origin of the name spinel is unknown.   The name *Spinellus* appears in the *Lapidum Gemmarum* of Boetius de Boot (1647). Rubicelle and Balas-ruby are jeweler's terms of uncertain origin; balas-ruby possibly from Balakhsh, the name of a district in Ceylon where precious spinel was found.   *Picotite* is named after Picot de la Peyrous (1744–1818), Professor of Natural History at Toulouse and Inspector of Mines, who described the rock, lherzolite, in which picotite was originally found. *Chlorospinel* in allusion to the grass green color of the mineral.   *Pleonaste*, from πλεόνασμος, *excess*, was so named by Haüy because forms other than the octahedron occurred thereon.   *Ceylonite* from the locality in Ceylon. *Gahnite* after the Swedish chemist, J. G. Gahn (1745–1818).   *Automolite* from αὐτόμολος, *a deserter*, alluding to the occurrence of zinc in what was thought to be an unexpected place.   *Kreittonite* from κρείττων, *stronger*, because heavier than some other spinels.   *Dysluite* from δυσ-, *difficult*, and λύω, *dissolve*, alluding to difficulties encountered in making a solution of the mineral.   *Galaxite* from a plant, *Galax*, abundant in the region in which the mineral was discovered.   *Hercynite* is from the Latin name of the Bohemian Forest, *Silva Hercynia*, where the mineral was first found.   *Mitchellite* after Elisha Mitchell (1793–1857), Professor of Mineralogy and Geology in the University of North Carolina.

Ref.

1. Goldschmidt (8, 70, 1922) and (for gahnite) Brush, *Am. J. Sc.*, **1**, 28 (1871). The form p{122} is not reported on gahnite.   Rare and doubtful forms: for spinel — {013}, {116}, {223}, {177}, {133}, {233}, {677}, {135}; for gahnite {118}, {114}.
2. Earliest structure study by Bragg, *Phil. Mag.*, **30**, 305 (1915), and also by Nishikawa, *Tokyo Math. Phys. Soc., Proc.*, **8**, 199, 1915.   See Barth and Posnjak, *Washington Ac. Sc., J.*, **21**, 225 (1931); *Zs. Kr.*, **82**, 325 (1932), and Machatschki, *Zs. Kr.*, **80**, 416 (1931) — **82**, 348 (1932) on different elements in similar structural position.
3. Clark, Ally, and Badger, *Am. J. Sc.*, **22**, 539 (1931).
4. Becke, *Min. Mitt.*, **7**, 200 (1885).
5. See Holmquist on hardness measured by ease of polish, *Geol. För. Förh.*, **42**, 393 (1920); **44**, 485 (1922).
6. Merwin and Rankin, *Am. Chem. Soc., J.*, **38**, 368 (1916).
7. Rinne, *Jb. Min., Beil.-Bd.*, **58**, 43 (1928), has shown that the artificial spinels with a large excess of Al_2O_3 have an anomalous birefringence as large as 0.003, and exhibit a gridlike, or other regular pattern.
8. Anderson and Payne, *Min. Mag.*, **24**, 547 (1937).
9. Rinne (1928), gives $n = 1.71889$.
10. von Eckermann, *Geol. För. Förh.*, **44**, 201 (1922).
11. Anderson and Payne (1937) give $n = 1.7465$.
12. In Larsen (84, 1921).
13. Shannon, *Am. Min.*, **8**, 147 (1923).
14. In Larsen and Berman (58, 1934).
15. Ross and Kerr, *Am. Min.*, **17**, 15 (1932).

16. Rinne (1928) has shown that the artificial spinels show a small change in refractive index with the variation in the MgO/Al_2O_3 ratio, as follows: $MgO/Al_2O_3 = 1$, $n_{Na} = 1.719$; $MgO/Al_2O_3 = 1/5$, $n_{Na} = 1.729$.

17. Merwin and Rankin, *Am. J. Sc.*, **45**, 301 (1918) have found small amounts of Si in artificial spinel.

18. Papish and Stilson, *Am. Min.*, **15**, 521 (1930).

19. A recent analysis of a gahnite, for example, as given by Palache (priv. comm., 1941) deviates markedly from the usual ratio.

20. Rinne (1928) shows a variation of Mg : Al from 1 : 1 to 1 : 126. The end component of such a series may be the artificial γ-Al_2O_3 which has the spinel structure. See also Hägg and Söderholm, *Zs. phys. Chem.*, **29**, 88 (1935), and Merwin and Rankin (1916). A small variation in cell edge with the Al content is shown (for Mg : Al = 1 : 1, $a_0 = 8.056$, for Mg : Al = 1 : 125, $a_0 = 7.987$).

21. Analyses chosen are (*a*) recent good analyses, (*b*) those which demonstrate the variation in the series, (*c*) those which refer to type material. Many analyses are widely scattered in the literature but these do not materially add to the variation in composition here shown. See Hintze (**1** [4a], 1921); Doelter (**3** [2], 515, 1924) — (**4** [2], 718, 1927).

22. Pfeil, *Cbl. Min.*, 146, 1902.

23. Zambonini and Carobbi, *Ac. Sc. Napoli, Boll.*, **41** (1930) — *Fortschr. Min.*, **20**, 69 (1936).

24. Bendig anal. in Gottfried, *Geol. Bundsanst. Wien, Vh.*, **182**, 1928.

25. Hey anal. in Anderson and Payne (1937).

26. Hoglund anal. in von Eckermann (1922).

27. Pisani anal. in Lacroix, *Bull. soc. min.*, **41**, 186 (1918).

28. Rogers, *Ann. New York Ac. Sc.*, **21**, 69 (1911).

29. Rose, *Ann. Phys.*, **50**, 652 (1840).

30. Simpson, *Min. Mag.*, **19**, 99 (1920).

31. Kokta, *Spisy vyd. priro. fak. Masarykovy Univ.*, no. 201, 1935 — *Min. Abs.*, **6**, 155 (1935).

32. Bowley anal. in Simpson, *Roy. Soc. Western Australia, J.*, **17**, 137 (1931).

33. Adams anal. in Brush (1871).

34. Shannon (1923).

35. Simpson, *Roy. Soc. Western Australia, J.*, **16**, 25 (1930).

36. Krauss in Oebbeke, *Mitt. Min.-Geol. Inst. Erlangen* — *Jb. Min.*, **17**, 1891.

37. Keller anal. in Genth, *Am. Phil. Soc., Proc.*, **20**, 391 (1882).

38. Thomson (**1**, 221, 1836).

39. Quadrat, *Ann. Chem., Pharm.*, **55**, 367 (1845).

40. Steiger anal. in Watson, *Am. Min.*, **10**, 7 (1925).

41. Radley anal. in Thomas, *Geol. Soc. London, Q. J.*, **78**, 229 (1922).

42. Damour, *Soc. Geol. France Bull.*, **19**, 413 (1862).

43. Raoult anal. in Lacroix, *Bull. soc. min.*, **43**, 69 (1920).

44. Shannon anal. in Ross and Kerr (1932).

45. For a discussion of Cr in red spinels see Schlossmacher, *Zs. Kr.*, **72**, 468 (1930); **76**, 370 (1931); Weigel and Habich, *Jb. Min., Beil.-Bd.*, **57**, 1 (1928); Weigel and Ufer, *ibid.*, 397; Wild and Klemm, *Cbl. Min.*, 29, 1926; Klemm, *ibid.*, 267, 1927; Vogel, *Jb. Min., Beil.-Bd.*, **68**, 401 (1934). For variation in color with temperature see Weigel, *Jb. Min., Beil.-Bd.*, **48**, 274 (1923).

46. On Fe^2 in blue spinels see Anderson and Payne (1937).

47. Material with less than ca. 17 per cent ZnO has not been analyzed, but the existence of zincian material in this range is indicated by the observations of Anderson and Payne (1937); see also anal. 3.

48. For a discussion of the occurrence of spinel in metamorphic rocks see Tilley, *Geol. Mag.*, **40**, 101 (1923).

49. See Spencer *et al.*, *U. S. Geol. Sur., Folio 161*, 1908; Palache (1935); Shepard, *Am. J. Sc.*, **21**, 321 (1832).

50. Butler, *Am. Min.*, **21**, 537 (1936).

51. Ferrier and Graham, *Trans. Royal Soc. Canada*, **22** [3], 31 (1928); Roth (229, 1879).

52. See Dana (256, 1892).

53. Literature in Mellor (**13**, 914, 1934; **11**, 201, 1931; **5**, 295, 1924; **13**, 731, 1934). For a list of all the spinels formed artificially see under spinel group discussion.

54. For a description of artificial gem spinels see Rinne (1928).

55. Faber, *Chem. Erde*, **10**, 105 (1935).

Magnetite Series

7215   M A G N E S I O F E R R I T E [MgFe₂O₄]. Magnoferrit *Rammelsberg (Ann. Phys.*, **107**, 451, 1859). Magneferrit *Kenngott (Ueb.*, 98, 1859; 96, 1860). Magnesioferrite *Dana* (226, 1892).

7216   M A G N E T I T E [FeFe₂O₄]. 'Ηράκλεια λίθος (from Heraclea, in Lydia) *Greek.* [Λίθος] σιδηρονάγουσα *Theophrastus.* (Not μαγνῆτις λίθος = talc *Theophrastus.*) Μαγνῆς λίθος *Dioscorides* (5, 147). Magnes, Sideritis, Heraclion *Pliny* (36, 25); Id., *Germ.* Siegelstein *Agricola* (243, 466). (1) Minera ferri nigricans, magneti amica. (2) Magnet, (3) Jern Sand *Wallerius* (256, 262, 1746). Minera Ferri attractoria, Magnet *Cronstedt* (184, 1758). Magnetischer Eisenstein (including Eisenstein) *Werner.* Fer oxydulé *Haüy.* Magnetite *Haidinger* (551, 1845.) Ferroferrit *Hintze* (**1** [4A], 34, 1921). Silfbergit (Not silfbergite = Fe-Mn amphibole.) *Niggli* (*Zs. Kr.*, **60**, 337, 1924). Vanado-magnetite *Heron* (*Geol. Sur. India, Rec.*, **71**, 44, 1936); *Tipper* (*Bull. Imp. Inst. London*, **34**, 451, 1936). Coulsonite *Dunn* (*Geol. Sur. India, Mem.*, **49**, 21, 1937); *Dunn* and *Dey* (*Trans. Mining Geol. Inst. India*, **31**, 131, 1937). Manganmagnetite *Dana* (225, 1892). Talk-eisenerz *Breithaupt* (*Schweigger's J.*, **68**, 287, 1833). Magnetic Iron Ore; Octahedral Iron Ore; Oxidulated Iron. Magneteisenstein, Magneteisenerz, Eisenoxydoxydul, *Germ.* Magnetjernmalm, Svartmalm, *Swed.* Fer oxydulé, Fer oxydé magnétique, Aimant, *Fr.* Ferro ossidolato, Ferro magnetico, Calamita, *Ital.* Hierro magnético *Span.* Eisenmulm. Eisenmohr. Lodestone.

Muschketowite pt. *Federov* and *Nikitin* (*Ann. geol. min. Russie*, **3**, 87, 99, 1899). Mouchketovite. Dimagnetite *Shepard* (*Am. J. Sc.*, **13**, 392, 1852).

7217   F R A N K L I N I T E [ZnFe₂O₄]. Francklinite *Berthier* (*Ann. mines*, **4**, 489, 1819). Zinkoferrit *Hintze* (**1** [4A], 66, 1921). Magnofranklinite *Koenig*? in *Canfield* (*Geol. Sur., New Jersey, Final Rep.*, **2** [1], 14, 1892).

7218   J A C O B S I T E [MnFe₂O₄]. Damour (*C. R.*, **69**, 168, 1869). Jakobsite. Manganomagnetit *Flink* (*Ak. Stockholm, Bh.*, **12** [2], 2, 20, 1886). Manganoferrit *Hintze* (**1** [4A], 65, 1921). Vredenbergite pt. *Fermor* (*Geol. Sur. India, Rec.*, **37**, 199, 1909).

7219   T R E V O R I T E [NiFe₂O₄]. *Crosse* (*J. Chem. Met. Min. Soc., South Africa*, **21**, 126, 1921 — *Am. Min.*, **8**, 37, 1923); *Walker* (*Univ. Toronto Stud., Geol. Ser.*, **16**, 53, 1923). Nickelmagnetite *Doelter* (3[2], 666, 1926).

C r y s t.   Isometric; hexoctahedral — $4/m\,\bar{3}\,2/m$.

Forms:[1]

	a 001	*d* 011	*o* 111	*η* 015	*f* 013	*e* 012	*m* 113	*n* 112	*q* 133	*p* 122	*v* 135
Magnesioferrite			x								
Magnetite	x	x	x			x	x	x	x	x	x
Franklinite	x	x	x	x	x		x	x			x
Jacobsite		x	x								
Trevorite			x								

Structure cell.[2]   Space group *Fd3m.* Cell dimensions (artif. compounds):[3]

		a_0
Magnesioferrite	(MgFe₂O₄)	8.366 ± 0.001
Magnetite	(FeFe₂O₄)	8.374 ± 0.003
Franklinite	(ZnFe₂O₄)	8.403 ± 0.004
Jacobsite	(MnFe₂O₄)	8.457 ± 0.002
Trevorite	(NiFe₂O₄)	8.41

Cell contents $A_8 B_{16} X_{32}$.

Habit. Usually octahedral, sometimes dodecahedral (magnetite)[4] with striae on {011} ∥ [0$\bar{1}$1]; less often with modifying {001} or {*hhl*}; skeletonized crystals of magnetite of microscopic size are sometimes found in igneous rocks. Magnesioferrite, jacobsite, and trevorite are rarely found as crystals. Massive, granular, coarse or fine.

Twinning. Common on {111}, with same face as composition face. Twins flattened ∥ {111} (the typical spinel twin) or as lamellar twins,[5] producing striae on {111}. Twin gliding (magnetite), with K_1{111}, K_2{11$\bar{1}$}.[6]

Etching and *oriented growths.* Characteristic etch patterns are shown by magnetite[7] and franklinite.[8] Oriented growths between magnetite and the following minerals have been noted: hematite overgrowths;[9] hematite inclusions;[10] ilmenite inclusions;[11] hercynite (?) inclusions;[12] rutile overgrowths;[9] chlorite overgrowth;[9] pyrophanite inclusions;[10] magnetite upon hematite;[9] magnetite inclusions in muscovite;[13] magnetite inclusions in hematite;[14] magnetite inclusions in ilmenite;[15] magnetite upon olivine.[16] Also hematite upon magnesioferrite.[9]

P h y s. Cleavage {111} reported but this is probably a parting. Parting on {111} especially good in magnetite[17] and less so in franklinite. {001}, {011}, {138} also reported as parting planes in magnetite.[17] A parting at {3·50·60}, approximately, reported for jacobsite.[18] H. $5\frac{1}{2}$-$6\frac{1}{2}$ (5 given for trevorite). Specific gravities:

	OBSERVED	CALCULATED[19]	
Magnesioferrite	4.56–4.65	4.51	
Magnetite	5.175	5.20	
Franklinite	5.07–5.22	5.32	
Jacobsite	4.76	5.03	(anal. 22)
Trevorite	5.164	5.20	

Luster metallic to semimetallic, splendent to nearly dull. Color black to brownish black. Streak black (magnetite, magnesioferrite), to reddish brown (franklinite), to brown (jacobsite, trevorite). Transmit light in only the thinnest splinters; the high Mg and Al varieties being less opaque than the Fe and Mn members. M.P. ca. 1591° (magnetite).[20] Magnetic:[21] magnetite, magnesioferrite, and trevorite strongly so; jacobsite and franklinite weakly magnetic. For magnetite, I 250, H 50 along *a*-axis, with H the intensity of magnetic field, I the intensity of magnetization. Some magnetites have a polarity (lodestone). Magnetite is a good conductor of electricity.

O p t. Only thin splinters transmit light, and then feebly. Isotropic.

	n	
Magnesioferrite	2.38±	Artificial[22]
Magnetite	2.42	589.6(Na)[23]
Franklinite	2.36±	nLi[24]
Jacobsite	2.3±	Sweden[25]
Trevorite	2.3 ?	Transvaal[25]

In polished section isotropic; reflection percentages and color:[26]

	COLOR	INTERNAL REFLECTION	REFLECTION PERCENTAGE		
			Green	Orange	Red
Magnetite	Gray, with brownish tint	None	21	21	21
Franklinite	White	Red	16.5	14.5	14
Jacobsite	Gray-white with olive tint	Brown	19.5	17	16

Twin lamellae and zonal growths are sometimes shown by magnetite in polished section. Regular patterns of oriented inclusions of ilmenite, hercynite, hematite, and pyrophanite are often observed under the microscope. The oxidation of magnetite along specific directions also produces a regularity of pattern.

C h e m. Oxides of the general formula AB_2O_4, where A is Mg, Fe,[2] Zn, Mn, and less often Ni. B is essentially Fe^3, with Al, Cr, Mn^3, and V substituting for the Fe^3 in comparatively small amounts (see under varieties) in this series. The natural spinels do not commonly show wide variations in the B part of the formula. The ratio $A : B$ in the formula is uniformly $1 : 2$ with the exceptions noted for magnetite and maghemite (which see).[10] Oriented inclusions of ilmenite in magnetite are generally attributed to exsolution of the former from a higher-temperature homogeneous magnetite containing considerable Ti.[27] The presence of oriented hercynite as a probable exsolution product suggests that Al can replace Fe^3 to only a limited extent in this series, at low temperatures. Mn^3 may replace Fe^3 at higher temperatures in jacobsite, as shown by the probable exsolution of hausmannite in an iron spinel[49] (see also vredenbergite).

Anal.[28]

	1	2	3	4	5	6	7	8
MgO	.....	trace	.....	.....	.....	trace	3.24	4.98
FeO	31.03	30.78	30.94	29.32	26.93	25.66	22.70	20.50
MnO	.....	.....	trace	trace	3.80	8.20	8.46	1.50
ZnO	.....	.....	.....	.....	.....	.....	.....	.....
Al2O3	.....	0.21	.....	.....	.....	.....	0.62	.....
Fe2O3	68.97	68.85	69.05	68.92	69.32	61.71	59.71	69.70
Cr2O3	.....	.....	.....	trace	.....	1.42	.....	.....
Mn2O3	.....	.....	.....	.....	.....	.....	.....	3.32
TiO2	.....	trace	.....	trace	.....	2.35	5.32	.....
SiO2	.....	0.27	.....	.....	.....	0.59	0.16	.....
Rem.	.....	trace	.....	1.76	.....	0.02	.....	.....
Total	100.00	100.11	99.99	100.00	100.05	99.95	100.21	100.00
G.					5.064		4.913	4.67

1. $FeFe_2O_4$. 2. Magnetite. Lover's Pit, Mineville, N. Y. Rem. is CaO trace.[29] 3. Magnetite. Mesabi Range, Minn.[30] 4. Magnetite, nickeloan. Pregrattan, Tirol. Rem. is NiO 1.76. Recalc. after deduction of insol. 0.28.[31] 5. Magnetite, manganoan. Vester Silfberg, Sweden.[32] 6. Magnetite, chromian, and manganoan. Siberia. Rem. is ign. loss 0.02.[33] 7. Magnetite, manganoan, and titanian. St. Joseph du Lac, Quebec.[34] 8. Magnetite, manganian. New Zealand. Recalc. after deduction of SiO_2 2.38 as serpentine.[35]

	9	10	11	12	13	14	15	16
MgO	5.15	0.70	5.83	6.74	20.16	12.58	9.47	.....
FeO	26.69	40.10	26.58	18.72	.....	.....	16.82	15.65
MnO	.....	0.42	.....	3.40	.....	.....	2.10	9.53
ZnO	.....	.....	.....	.....	.....	.....	.....	6.78
Al_2O_3	5.64	1.74	15.14	6.57	.....	.....	10.37	0.65
Fe_2O_3	54.97	23.98	46.95	61.95	79.84	86.96	59.01	67.42
Cr_2O_3	.....	.....	.....	.....	.....	.....	.....	.....
Mn_2O_3	.....	.....	.....	.....	.....	.....	.....	.....
TiO_2	7.57	32.20	5.01	1.31	.....	.....	2.40	.....
SiO_2	0.14	0.10	0.13	1.10	.....	.....	.....	0.08
Rem.	0.10	.....	0.11	.....	.....	.....	.....	.....
Total	100.26	99.24	99.75	99.79	100.00	99.54	100.17	100.11
G.			4.725				4.558	

9. Magnetite, titanian. Norway. Rem. is CaO 0.10.[29] 10. Magnetite, titanian (?). Near Vaskapu, Hungary.[36] 11. Magnetite, aluminian. Magnet Cove, Ark. Rem. is CaO 0.11.[29] 12. Magnetite, magnesian, and aluminian. Schelingen, Kaiserstuhl, Germany. Average of two analyses.[37] 13. $MgFe_2O_4$. 14. Magnesioferrite. Vesuvius. Contains some admixed hematite.[38] 15. Magnesioferrite, ferroan. Magnet Cove, Ark.[34] 16. Franklinite. Sterling Hill, N. J. Average of four analyses of strongly magnetic material.[39]

	17	18	19	20	21	22	23	24
MgO	.....	0.34	.....	.....	.....	9.26	0.24	.....
FeO	.....	.....	.....	.....	.....	2.57	1.96	.....
MnO	16.37	9.96	10.46	.....	30.76	13.94	.....	.....
NiO	.....	.....	.....	.....	.....	.....	29.71	31.87
ZnO	15.91	20.77	23.11	23.30	.....	.....	.....	.....
Al_2O_3	.....	.....	.....	.....	.....	.....	.....	.....
Fe_2O_3	56.57	66.58	63.40	65.05	69.24	73.96	66.24	68.13
Cr_2O_3	.....	.....	.....	.....	.....	.....	.....	.....
Mn_2O_3	10.52	.....	4.44	14.77	.....	.....	.....	.....
TiO_2	.....	.....	.....	.....	.....	0.09	.....	.....
SiO_2	.....	0.72	0.17	0.30	.....	.....	1.40	.....
Rem.	.....	1.14	.....	.....	.....	.....	0.36	.....
Total	99.37	99.51	101.58	103.42	100.00	99.82	99.91	100.00
G.	5.187	5.09	.....	.....	.....	4.76	5.165	.....

17. Franklinite. Franklin, N. J.[40] 18. Franklinite. N. J. Rem. is H_2O 0.71, CaO 0.43. State of oxidation of the Fe and Mn not known.[41] 19. Franklinite. Franklin, N. J. Average of two analyses of feebly magnetic material.[39] 20. Franklinite. N. J.[42] 21. $MnFe_2O_4$. 22. Jacobsite. Jacobsberg, Sweden.[43] 23. Trevorite. Transvaal. Rem. is H_2O 0.36.[44] 24. $NiFe_2O_4$.

Var.

MAGNESIOFERRITE

1. *Ordinary*. Essentially Mg, Fe^3 spinel, with these elements predominant.

2. *Ferroan*. A ratio of Fe : Mg = 1 : 1 (anal. 15) is reported.

MAGNETITE

1. *Ordinary*. With Fe^2 and Fe^3 predominant. Ocherous varieties. Eisenmulm *Germ.*, black earthy magnetite.

2. *Magnesian*. Magnesioferrite pt. *Dana* (226, 1892). Contains Mg (anal. 12).

3. *Manganoan.* Manganmagnetite *Dana* (225, 1892). Silfbergite *Niggli* (*Zs. Kr.*, **60**, 337, 1924). Contains Mn^2 substituting for Fe^2 (anal. 5, 6, 7).

4. *Nickelian.* Contains Ni substituting for Fe^2 (anal. 4). Usually only in minor amounts.

5. *Aluminian.* Contains as much as 15 per cent Al (anal. 11), but usually the amounts are small in magnetite.[45]

6. *Chromian.* Containing Cr in substitution for Fe^3 in generally small amounts (anal. 6). Where more is reported the evidence for homogeneity is lacking.[46]

7. *Titanian.* Titanomagnetite. Titaniferous magnetite. May contain as much as 7.5 per cent TiO_2, substituting perhaps for both Fe^2 and Fe^3. Most analyses of supposedly high titanium magnetite were obviously made on inhomogeneous samples containing what may be exsolved ilmenite.[27]

8. *Vanadian.* Vanado-magnetite *Heron* (*Geol. Sur. India, Rec.*, **71**, 44, 1936); *Tipper* (*Bull. Imp. Inst., London*, **34**, 451, 1936). Coulsonite *Dunn* (*Geol. Sur. India, Mem.*, **49**, 21, 1937), *Dunn* and *Dey* (*Mining Geol. Inst. India, Trans.*, **31**, 131, 1937). As high as 4.84 per cent V reported (from India), and small amounts are frequently present.[47]

FRANKLINITE

1. *Ordinary.* Dominantly Zn, Fe^3 members, but no franklinites with only these constituents have been reported (anal. 18).

2. *Manganoan.* With Mn^2 next most abundant after Zn and Fe^3 (anal. 19).

3. *Manganian.* With substitution of Mn^3 for Fe^3 of the ordinary variety (anal. 17).

4. *Ferroan.* With Fe^2 substituting for the Zn.

JACOBSITE

1. *Ordinary.* Dominantly Mn^2, Fe^3 member, but the only analyses available show considerable Mg and Fe^2 (anal. 22).

2. *Magnesian.* In which the Mg is next most dominant after the Mn^2.

Tests. Infusible. Magnetite is fusible with difficulty in thin splinters. In O.F. magnetite and franklinite lose their magnetism. Difficultly soluble in HCl (franklinite and jacobsite dissolve in HCl, sometimes with evolution of Cl). Decomposed by fusion with $KHSO_4$.

O c c u r. Magnetite is one of the most abundant and widespread of oxides. It is found under diverse geological conditions and in some deposits in sufficient abundance to constitute an important iron ore. The following are the principal types of occurrence: (*a*) as a magmatic segregation deposit (Kiruna), with apatite and pyroxene; (*b*) as an accessory mineral in igneous rocks, rather widespread but in minor amounts;[52] (*c*) in metamorphic deposits such as in limestones associated with garnet, diopside, olivine, pyrite, hematite, and chalcopyrite (Iron Springs, Utah); in chlorite schists, with pyrite (Chester, Vermont) as single well-formed octahedral crystals; (d) replacement deposits derived from pegmatitic solutions (New Jersey Highlands) and associated with biotite, amphiboles, epidote, and alkali feldspars; as an accessory in granite pegmatites, as individual striated crystals; (e) in sulfide vein deposits of relatively high temperatures;[50] (f) as a product of fumarolic activity (Valley of Ten Thousand Smokes);[51] (g) as a detrital mineral in marine or fluviatile deposits; (h) rarely as an oxidation product in the zone of weathering; (i) in stony meteorites and as a black crust on meteoritic irons.

Only those localities of magnetite noteworthy because of commercial importance or because of exceptional specimens can be mentioned here. In Sweden large deposits of magnetite occur at a number of places, notably at Kiruna and nearby Gellivare and at Långban, Norberg, Persberg, Toberg, Dannemora; well-crystallized material has been obtained at Nordmark, Vermland, and at Gammalkroppa in Kroppu parish. A manganian variety at Vester Silfberg, in Dalecarlia, Sweden. In Norway in the pegmatites of the Fredriksvärn and Langesund fiord regions, and in schist in the vicinity of Arendal, and in northern Norway in the Varanger district. In the U.S.S.R. large deposits of magnetite are being exploited in the Urals at Magnetigora, at various localities in the Slatoust district, at Blagodat and elsewhere. In Germany a great many occurrences have been described, most of them only of mineralogical interest: as a druse mineral with tridymite in andesite in the Siebengebirge; as an associate of perovskite in crystalline limestone in the Kaiserstuhl, Baden; as crusts with pyrrhotite around native iron inclusions in the basalt of Bühl, near Cassel; in deposits of the contact metamorphic type at Bergiesshübel in Saxony and Schmiedeberg in Silesia; in cubic crystals in serpentine at Gulsen near Kraubat in Styria, and in limestone at Wildenau near Schwarzenberg, Saxony. In the Tirol in large octahedra in chlorite schist at Greiner and elsewhere in the Zillerthal; at Scalotta near Predazzo large well-developed crystals in a contact zone. In large deposits of the contact metamorphic type in the Banat, in southeastern Hungary, notably at Oravicza, Moravicza, Vaskö, and Dognácska. In Italy fine specimens come from Traversella, Piedmont, from a contact of limestone and diorite; in fumaroles on Vesuvius. Found in Switzerland in notable specimens on Lercheltini Alp and elsewhere in the Binnental and from the vicinity of Zermatt and Viesch in Ober-Wallis. Large deposits of magnetite are found in South Africa in the Bushveld Complex and elsewhere. In Mexico in the Cerro del Mercado, Durango, with hematite and apatite. A vanadian magnetite (*coulsonite*) occurs at Bihar, India, as veins and lenses in gabbro, with hematite, ilmenite, rutile, goethite, and lepidocrocite.

In the United States numerous deposits of magnetite of magmatic or late magmatic affiliations are found in the eastern part of the Adirondack region of New York, notably in the Mineville district near Port Henry and at Lyon Mountain. Similar deposits are found in the Highlands of New Jersey. A notable occurrence with chondrodite, clinochlore, dolomite, serpentine, enstatite at Tilly Foster, Putnam County, New York, and a nearby similar occurrence at Mahopac. In North Carolina in a large deposit at Cranberry. At Magnet Cove, Arkansas. Commercial deposits of the contact metamorphic types are found at many places in the western United States, among which are Fierro, New Mexico, the Iron Springs district in southern Utah, the Calumet deposit, Chaffee County, Colorado, and Heroult, Shasta County, California. At Cornwall and elsewhere in Pennsylvania and in Virginia where Triassic diabase has intruded Paleozoic calcareous shale. Deposits of magnetite in gneiss formed by regional metamorphism of iron-rich sediments occur in the Llano region, Texas, and contact metamorphism of the hematite ores of the Lake Superior region have locally given rise to deposits containing magnetite and grünerite. Magnetite with a radiating columnar structure and a mammillary surface occurs in a vein in peridotite in the Sudbury district, Ontario. Lodestone is widely distributed in small amounts and usually occurs in the outcrops of the magnetite deposits.

Franklinite is the dominant mineral of the great zinc deposits at Franklin and Sterling Hill, New Jersey,[53] where it forms thick beds in crystalline limestone free from any other mineral or admixed with various amounts of zincite, willemite, rhodonite, and tephroite. Usually in rounded octahedral crystals or in granular masses; occasionally in sharp crystals, sometimes highly modified, in recrystallized portions of the ore body or in secondary veinlets. Octahedrons up to 7 in. on an edge have been found. The mineral has been said to occur at Altenberg, near Aix-la-Chapelle, Germany, in amorphous masses, and at a few other localities, but verification is lacking.

Magnesioferrite is found chiefly in fumaroles, where it appears to have formed by the reaction at high temperatures of steam and ferric chloride vapors with MgO or other magnesian material.[54] Noted in Italy at Vesuvius, especially in the lavas of 1855; also on Etna, Sicily; at Stromboli and Vulcano in the Lipari Islands. In France on Puy de la Tache, Mont Dore, Puy-de-Dôme. Usually intergrown with or incrusted by hematite. Also at Magnet Cove, Arkansas.

Jacobsite was originally from Jacobsberg, Vermland, Sweden, where it occurs in crystalline limestone with white mica and native copper; also in Sweden at Långban with tephroite and calcite, in the Sjö and the Glakärn mines, Örebro, and at Vester Silfberg, Dalecarlia. In gneiss at Debarstica, near Tatar-Pazardžik, Bulgaria. Reported from manganese deposits at Maczkamezö, Hungary, and in the Vizagapatam district, India.

Trevorite is a nickel ore found massive or as imperfect crystals embedded in a green talc rock on the farm Bon Accord, near Sheba Siding, in the Transvaal, South Africa.

A l t e r.   Magnetite alters to limonite and also to hematite (see martite) and maghemite. Alterations or pseudomorphs after magnetite have also been found of pyrite, cassiterite, various chlorites, anatase, talc, dolomite, chalcopyrite, siderite, and serpentine; alteration of titanian magnetite may produce rutile, anatase, sphene. Magnetite has been found as an alteration of or pseudomorph after siderite, pyrite, various amphiboles and pyroxenes, mica, chondrodite, dolomite, garnet, pyrrhotite, hauerite, marcasite (?), perovskite, brookite, sphene. More or less coarsely fibrous pseudomorphs of magnetite after chrysotile or picrolite have been found at a number of localities.[55] Pseudomorphs of magnetite after hematite are common[56] (in part called *eisenmohr* or *muschketowite*). *Dimagnetite*,[57] a supposed species from Monroe, Orange County, New York, appears to be a pseudomorph of magnetite after ilvaite. Franklinite alters to chalcophanite, apparently through the intermediate stage of hydrohetaerolite and limonite, and also alters to wad.

A r t i f. Magnetite is often observed as a furnace product, in slags, and in sintered hematite ores.[58] The so-called hammer-, smithy-, or iron-scale of the blacksmiths and roll-scale of milled iron is largely magnetite. Bricks, vitreous clay ware, and porcelain acquire a permanent magnetization parallel to the earth's magnetic field because of the formation of magnetite during the firing.

Magnetite has been prepared artificially at ordinary temperatures as a gel or precipitate by the oxidation in alkaline solutions of $Fe(OH)_2$ and by the precipitation by alkalies of mixed solutions of ferric and ferrous salts;[59] other modes of preparation of magnetite include the oxidation of iron at high temperatures in air or steam, by passing steam over $FeCl_2$ at dull red heat, by heating $FeCO_3$ in steam, nitrogen, or carbon dioxide at dull red heat, and by heating Fe_2O_3 in hydrogen containing water vapor.

Magnesioferrite has been found in sintered magnesite of furnace linings and other refractories.

N a m e. *Magnetite* from the locality *Magnesia*, bordering on Macedonia. Pliny favors Nicander's derivation from *Magnes*, who first discovered it, as the fable runs, by finding, on taking his herds to pasture, that the nails of his shoes and the iron ferrule of his staff adhered to the ground. *Coulsonite* after Dr. Arthur Lennox Coulson of the Geological Survey of India. *Trevorite* after Major T. G. Trevor, Mining Inspector for the Pretoria district, Transvaal, South Africa, where the mineral was discovered. *Magnesioferrite* is the preferred form of the name magnoferrite, given in allusion to the magnesian nature of the material. *Jacobsite* from the original locality at Jakobsberg, Sweden. *Silfbergite* from the locality at Vester Silfberg, Sweden. *Franklinite* after the locality at Franklin, New Jersey, and also in honor of Benjamin Franklin after whom the place was named.

NICKEL OXIDE. *Blake (Proc. California Ac. Sc.,* 5, 200, 1874).

Yellow scales found in magnetite sand in placers in the Fraser River, British Columbia. Yellow; magnetic. Presumed from a bulk analysis of the sand to have the composition Ni_3O_4.

Ref.

1. Magnetite forms from Goldschmidt (5, 176, 1918) and Starraba (*Geogr. Catania*, 18, 1922 — *Min. Abs.*, 2, 191, 1923). Rare or doubtful forms:

0·1·15	059	9·9·92	115	335	377	5·7·21	7·9·11
0·9·46	0·7·11	1·1·10	114	223	355	134	4·5·6
015	035	117	227	155	1·9·13	123	9·11·13
013	079	116	225	144	179	234	
025	1·1·16	9·9·55	449	255	168	345	

Franklinite forms from Palache (45, 1935). Rare and uncertain: {133}, {122}.
Jacobsite forms from Johansson, *Zs. Kr.*, 68, 107 (1928). Rare and uncertain: {1·1·15}, {115}, {5·5·14}, {225}, {335}, {166}, {566}, {178}, {146}, {237}, {357}.
2. The structure of magnetite was early determined by Bragg, *Nature*, 95, 561 (1915); *Phil. Mag.*, 30, 305 (1915).
3. Clark, Ally, and Badger, *Am. J. Sc.*, 22, 539 (1931). Also Holgersson, *Lunds Univ. Årskrift*, 23 [9], 1927 — *Strukturber.*, 1, 416 (1931), for Ni and Zn members. Johansson (1928) reports a space group symmetry $F4_13$ on a supposed jacobsite of gyroidal symmetry. The identity of the material is uncertain.
4. See Chudoba and Schilly, *Jb. Min.*, *Beil.-Bd.*, 68, 241 (1934).
5. Kemp, *Am. J. Sc.*, 40, 62 (1890); Cathrein, *Zs. Kr.*, 12, 47 (1886); Mügge, *Jb. Min.*, 244, 1889.
6. Grühn, *Jb. Min.*, 99, 1918.
7. Becke, *Min. Mitt.*, 7, 200 (1885); Brugnatelli, *Zs. Kr.*, 14, 243 (1888); Mielke, *Ak. Leipzig, Ber.*, 74, 319 (1922); Mügge, *Jb. Min.*, *Beil.-Bd.*, 32, 491 (1911).
8. Mügge (1911) and Becke (1885).
9. Mügge, *Jb. Min.*, *Beil.-Bd.*, 16, 335 (1905) gives:

Magnetite $\{111\}[110] = \{100\}$ [001] rutile
Magnetite $\{111\}[110] = \{0001\}[10\bar{1}0]$ chlorite
Magnetite $\{111\}[110] = \{0001\}[10\bar{1}0]$ hematite
Magnesioferrite $\{111\}[110] = \{0001\}[10\bar{1}0]$ hematite

10. Greig, Posnjak, Merwin, and Sosman, *Am. J. Sc.*, 30, 239 (1935), as an exsolution product.
11. Exsolved (?) ilmenite in magnetite, with magnetite $\{111\}[\bar{1}\bar{1}1] = (0001)[\bar{1}2\bar{1}0]$ ilmenite.
12. Schneiderhöhn and Ramdohr (2, 581, 1931) give:

Magnetite $\{111\}$ $= (001)$ pyrophanite
Magnetite $\{001\}[001]$? $= \{001\}$? [001] ? hercynite

13. Frondel and Ashby, *Am. Min.*, 22, 104 (1937), give a number of positions of orientation of the magnetite inclusions.
14. Magnetite $\{111\}[110] = \{0001\}[10\bar{1}0]$ hematite.
15. Magnetite $\{111\}[110] = \{0001\}[10\bar{1}0]$ ilmenite.
16. Starrabba, *Geogr. Catania*, 18, 1922 — *Zs. Kr.*, 60, 343 (1924), gives several positions of oriented overgrowths of magnetite on olivine.
17. The parting is usually attributed to twinning, but Greig, Merwin, and Posnjak, *Am. Min.*, 21, 504 (1936), show that it may be a consequence of mechanical deformation or thermal contraction. Lehmann, *Zs. Kr.*, 11, 610 (1886), states that contraction cracks on {001} and {011} are formed by quenching.
18. Flink, *Ak. Stockholm, Bh.*, 12 [2], 20 (1886).
19. The calculations are for the corresponding pure artificial compounds. For franklinite the value of $ZnFe_2O_4$ is used.
20. Greig, Posnjak, Merwin, and Sosman (1935).
21. *International Critical Tables*.
22. Merwin and Roberts, *Am. J. Sc.*, 21, 145 (1931).
23. Loria and Zahrzewski, *Ak. Krakau*, 1910 — Hintze (1 [4A], 39, 1921).
24. Larsen (76, 1921).
25. Larsen and Berman (246, 1934).
26. Schneiderhöhn and Ramdohr (2, 578, 596, 599, 600, 1931); also for jacobsite Orcel and Pavlovitch, *Bull. soc. min.*, 54, 108 (1932).

27. See Ramdohr, *Ak. Berlin, Abh.*, **14** (1939); *Jb. Min., Beil.-Bd.*, **54**, 320 (1926). Jouravsky, *C. R.*, **202**, 1689 (1936); Greig, *Econ. Geol.*, **27**, 25 (1932); Bruhns, *Jb. Min.*, **2**, 1899; Kamiyama, *Japanese J. Geol. Geogr., Abs.*, **7**, 1 (1930) — *Min. Abs.*, **5**, 35 (1932). The presence of ilmenite inclusions is not definite proof of exsolution or of a high Ti iron spinel.

28. Other analyses in Doelter (**3** [2], 639, 1924, 655, 656, 658, 666, 1925). The accurate determination of Fe^2 in the presence of both Mn^2 and Mn^3 and the separation of the latter two in the analyses are impossible by known analytical procedures.

29. Keyes anal. in Newhouse and Glass, *Econ. Geol.*, **31**, 704 (1936).

30. Ellestad anal. in Gruner, *Econ. Geol.*, **29**, 757 (1934).

31. Petersen, *Jb. Min.*, 837, 1867.

32. Weibull, *Min. Mitt.*, **7**, 109, 1886.

33. Chernik, *Ac. sc. St. Pétersbourg, Bull.*, **2**, 75 (1908) — *Zs. Kr.*, **50**, 66 (1911).

34. Harrington, *Min. Mag.*, **14**, 373 (1907).

35. Chester, *Min. Mag.*, **8**, 125 (1889).

36. Szentpétery, *Acta chem. min. physica*, **6**, 55 (1937); **7**, 54 (1938).

37. Hugel (Inaug. Diss., Freiburg, 1912 — *Zs. Kr.*, **60**, 334 [1924]).

38. Rammelsberg (133, 1875).

39. Seyms, *Am. J. Sc.*, **12**, 210 (1876).

40. Stone, *Sch. Mines Q.*, **8**, 148 (1887).

41. Schaller anal. in Palache, *Am. J. Sc.*, **29**, 177 (1910).

42. Brush, *Am. J. Sc.*, **29**, 177 (1910).

43. Johansson (1928).

44. Todd anal. in Walker, *Univ. Toronto Stud., Geol. Ser.*, 53, 1923.

45. Most analyses giving appreciable Al are not on material of demonstrated homogeneity. See Schneiderhöhn and Ramdohr (1931) and others on the presence of hercynite inclusions in magnetite.

46. Cathrein, *Zs. Kr.*, **8**, 323 (1883); **12**, 37 (1886).

47. Pope, *Trans. Am. Inst. Min. Eng.*, **29**, 372 (1899).

48. Whether the iron present is reported as divalent or trivalent is a matter of choice; the state of oxidation of the manganese is also not known. Under these circumstances the varietal designations are somewhat dependent on the way the analysis has been reported.

49. Johansson (1928); Deb, *C. R.*, **209**, 518 (1939).

50. See a recent work of Schwartz and Ronbeck, *Econ. Geol.*, **35**, 585 (1940).

51. Zies, *Nat. Geog. Soc., Tech. Pap., Katmai Ser.*, **1** [4], (1929).

52. Newhouse, *Geol. Soc. Am., Bull.*, **47**, 1 (1936).

53. Palache (1935).

54. Draper, *Am. J. Sc.*, **30**, 106 (1935).

55. Sandberger, *Jb. Min.*, 175, 1867; Miers, *Min. Mag.*, **11**, 271 (1897); Perry, *Am. J. Sc.*, **20**, 177 (1930).

56. For instance, see Kemp, *Sch. Mines Q.*, **14**, 52 (1892); Ross, *U. S. Geol. Sur., Bull. 763*, 66, 1925, Smitheringale, *Econ. Geol.*, **23**, 203 (1928); Hickok, *ibid.*, **28**, 218 (1933).

57. See Dana (151, 1868).

58. Schwartz, *Econ. Geol.*, **24**, 592 (1929).

59. See Weiser (**2**, 88, 1935).

VREDENBERGITE. *Fermor (Geol. Sur. India, Rec.*, **37**, 199, 1909).

Originally described as $Mn_3^2Mn_6^3Fe_4^3O_{18}$, isometric or tetragonal, from the Nágpur district, India, but subsequently shown[1] to be a mixture of jacobsite with enclosed needles of hausmannite. DEVADITE *Fermor, Nat. Inst. Sc. India, Proc.*, **4**, 253 (1938), and GARIVIDITE *Fermor (ibid.)* are names proposed for oxides of Mn and Fe believed to represent the primary, homogeneous minerals of vredenbergite intergrowths from Devada and Garividi in the Vizagapatam district, Madras, India.

Ref.

1. Schneiderhöhn and Ramdohr (**2**, 602, 1931); Orcel and Pavlovitch, *Bull. soc. min.*, **54**, 166 (1932); Dunn, *Nat. Inst. Sc. India, Proc.*, **1**, 103 (1936). Fermor (1938) believes these may be unmixed from an original homogeneous material.

721·10　**Maghemite** [Fe_2O_3].　Ferromagnetic ferric oxide *Sosman* and *Posnjak* (*Washington Ac. Sc., J.*, **15**, 329, 1925).　Maghemite *Wagner* (*Econ. Geol.*, **22**, 845, 1927).　(Not the maghemite = impure ilmenite, hematite, limonite, etc., of *Walker, Univ. Toronto Stud., Geol. Ser.*, **29**, 17 [1930].)　Oxymagnite *Winchell* (*Am. Min.*, **16**, 270, 1931).　Sosmanit *Schneiderhöhn* and *Ramdohr* (**2**, 537, 1931).　$\gamma\text{-}Fe_2O_3$.

C r y s t.　Isometric, related to magnetite and the spinel group.[1] Massive.　a_0 8.31 ± (nearly the same as magnetite); contains $Fe_{21\frac{1}{3}}O_{32}$ in the unit cell.[2]

P h y s.　H. 5.　Color brown.[3]　Streak brown.　By transmitted light, brown to yellow and isotropic, with refractive index higher than that of goethite.[1]　In polished section white to grayish blue in color and isotropic. Highly magnetic (about the same as magnetite).[4]

C h e m.　Presumably Fe_2O_3, but may contain minor amounts of H_2O, TiO_2, MgO, etc.[5]

Anal.

	1	2
FeO	8.67	2.40
Fe_2O_3	89.15	85.3
TiO_2	1.37	.....
H_2O	.....	3.1
Rem.	1.19	4.30
Total	100.38	95.1

1. Alameda Co., Calif.　Rem. is SiO_2 1.15, Al_2O_3 0.04, MgO and CaO trace.　Mixture of maghemite and magnetite.[6]　2. Iron Mt., Shasta Co., Calif.　Rem. is insol. 1.80, volatiles 2.5, CaO present.[7]

O c c u r.　Forms presumably by slow oxidation at low temperatures in a gossan, and may be derived from magnetite or from lepidocrocite.[8] The brown alteration product of many magnetites, especially on specimens found near the surface, is apparently maghemite.[9]　Found originally in gossan at Iron Mountain, Shasta County, California; also in Alameda County.　From the Windpass mine, British Columbia.　Said to occur in the Bushveld igneous complex of South Africa.　In lava at Mount Elgon, British East Africa, and in weathered shonkinite at Katzenbuckel, Baden. Reported[12] from Durant, Oklahoma, as rounded ocherous masses of a red-brown color and strongly polar.　The oxidation of meteoric iron has been said to produce ferromagnetic iron oxide, but the magnetism may be due to admixed magnetite or trevorite.[12]　Other localities have been reported.

A l t e r.　Maghemite is principally an alteration product derived from magnetite, or by dehydration from lepidocrocite.

A r t i f.[10]　Easily produced by the oxidation of precipitated magnetite at low temperatures.　May also be prepared by the dehydration of lepidocrocite (but not goethite) below 750°; when heated above this the change is to hematite.　The natural magnetites yield maghemite when oxidized under moderate heat but some of the natural impure magnetites will yield a magnetic oxide at 1000°.[11]

N a m e.　From the first syllables of *mag*netite and *hem*atite, in allusion to the magnetism and composition.

Ref.

1. Sosman and Posnjak, *Washington Ac. Sc., J.*, **15**, 329 (1925).
2. Formula suggested by the structure proposed by Verwey, *Zs. Kr.*, **91**, 66 (1935), who shows that the earlier work of Thewlis, *Phil. Mag.*, **12**, 1089 (1931), does not adequately explain the facts, since a cell content of $Fe_{24}O_{36}$ requires a specific gravity of 5.33 (hematite and magnetite are both lower) and this is unlikely because maghemite is a less stable form than hematite; also the conclusion of Thewlis is not in conformity with the relations between the α- and γ-Al_2O_3, a parallel system. The structure of Verwey yields a specific gravity of 4.74 and is identical with the magnetite structure except that one Fe in nine is missing, thus yielding the cell contents here given. The cell dimensions cited are those of Buerger in Newhouse and Glass, *Econ. Geol.*, **31**, 699 (1936).
3. Helbroun and Wilson, *Phys. Soc. London, Proc.*, **41**, 100 (1928), found that some of their artificial magnetic oxide preparations were red.
4. For measurements of the magnetic susceptibilities of some maghemite and magnetite samples see Newhouse and Glass (1936).
5. Only partial analyses of the natural magnetic oxide are available (see Hintze [308, 1936]) and these are not conclusive. Helbroun and Wilson (1928) found that some of their most highly magnetic ferric oxides, prepared from magnetites and lepidocrocite, contained impurities of Mg and Mn, and these may have been present as magnetic ferrites of the spinel type.
6. Keyes anal. in Newhouse and Glass (1936).
7. Hostetter anal. in Sosman and Posnjak (1925).
8. Sosman and Posnjak (1925), verified by Helbroun and Wilson (1928).
9. Newhouse, *Econ. Geol.*, **24**, 62 (1929).
10. See Sosman and Posnjak (1925); Helbroun and Wilson (1928); Welo and Baudisch, *Phil. Mag.*, **50**, 339 (1925); Baudisch and Welo, *Chem. Rev.*, **15**, 45 (1934).
11. Helbroun and Wilson (1928) infer that the magnetic oxide produced at high temperatures from magnetite is a ferrite, and therefore not the same as maghemite.
12. Shannon, *U. S. Nat. Mus., Proc.*, **72**, 1 (1927).

Chromite Series

721·11 **MAGNESIOCHROMITE** [$MgCr_2O_4$]. Chrompicotite *Petersen (J. pr. Chem.*, **106**, 137, 1869). Magnesiochromite pt. *Dana* (228, 1892). Chrome-Spinel pt. Picrochromite *Simpson (Min. Mag.*, **19**, 99, 1920). Magnochromite *Fisher (Am. Min.*, **14**, 355, 1929). Ferrichromspinel *Betekhtin (Ann. Inst. Mines, Leningrad*, **8**, 38, 1934).

721·12 **CHROMITE** [$FeCr_2O_4$]. Fer chromaté aluminé (from Var, France) *Vauqueline (Bull. soc. philom.*, **55**, 57, 1800). Eisenchrom (from Ural) *Meder (Crell's Ann.*, **1**, 500, 1798); *Karsten* (**56**, 79, 1800; 74, 1808). Fer chromaté *Haüy* (**4**, 1801). Chromate of Iron, Chromic Iron. Ferrochromate. Chrome-spinel pt. Chromsaures Eisen, Chromeisenstein *Germ.* Eisenchrome *Beudant* (1832). Siderochrome *Huot* (**1**, 287, 1841). Chromoferrite *Chapman* (1843). Chromit *Haidinger* (550, 1845). Chrompicotite *Lacroix* (**4**, 311, 1910). Ferrochromit *Hintze* (1 [4A], 70, 1921). Chromjernmalm *Swed.* Fer chromé, Fer chromaté *Fr.* Siderocromo, Cromite, Cromoferrite, Ferro cromato *Ital.* Hierro cromado *Span.* Beresofite (not beresovite = syn. crocoite) *Simpson (Min. Mag.*, **19**, 99, 1920); Beresofskite *Simpson* (**8**, 1932). Alumochromite, Magnoferrichromite, Ferrichrompicotite *Betekhtin* (1934). Irite pt. *Hermann (J. pr. Chem.*, **23**, 276, 1841).

Cryst. Isometric; hexoctahedral — $4/m\,\bar{3}\,2/m$.

Forms:[1] (Chromite)

a	001	o	111	f	013	m	113	ρ	144	p	**122**
d	011	η	015	e	012	n	112	q	133		

Crystals of magnesiochromite not reported.

Structure cell.[2] Space group $Fd3m$. Magnesiochromite (artif.) a_0 8.305 ± 0.001, chromite (artif.) a_0 8.344 ± 0.003; contains $(Mg,Fe)_8Cr_{16}O_{32}$ in unit cell.

Habit. Crystals not common; octahedral, sometimes modified by {001}. Commonly massive; fine granular to compact.

Phys. Cleavage none.[3] Fracture uneven. Brittle. H. $5\frac{1}{2}$ (chromite). G. magnesiochromite 4.2 ± 0.1, 4.43 (calc.); chromite 4.5–4.8,[4] 5.09 (calc. for pure $FeCr_2O_4$). Metallic luster. Color black. Streak brown (chromite). Transmits light in thin splinters only. Sometimes feebly magnetic.

Opt. In transmitted light, brown to brownish black in thin splinters, and often shows black anastomosing cracks. Isotropic. Refractive indices: for chromite 2.08 (Nottingham, Pennsylvania, Cr_2O_3 51.21 per cent);[5] 2.16 (North Carolina).[5] In polished section[6] chromite is isotropic, gray-white with brownish tint in color, and with brownish red internal reflections. Reflection percentage: green 15, orange and red 12.5.

Chem. Chromite, essentially $FeCr_2O_4$, apparently always has some Mg substituting for Fe, and thus grades to magnesiochromite $MgCr_2O_4$, and probably can form a complete series to that substance. Mn^2 and Zn are rare constituents (anal. 3 and 5). Fe^3 and Al substitute for the Cr, the latter substitution commonly accompanied by a high Mg content (anal. 4, 5). Fe^3 does not commonly substitute for Cr to any considerable extent, although a ratio of Fe : Cr = 0.56 : 1 is reported (anal. 3), but this may be due to admixed magnetite or to oxidation of Fe^2. A supposed titanian chromite[7] is probably a mixture of chromite and rutile. Magnesiochromite contains notable amounts of Fe^2 and Al and therefore grades to spinel and chromite.

Anal.[8] Only a small number of the many chromite analyses are given here, but these show the range of composition on material of probable homogeneity.

	1	2	3	4	5	6	7	8	9
MgO	.....	0.40	2.70	4.00	14.83	20.55	16.65	14.77	20.96
FeO	32.09	33.00	25.08	27.60	11.35	12.98	8.51	19.04	.....
MnO	.....	.....	.....	.....	0.14	.....	0.23	0.58	.....
Al$_2$O$_3$	.....	.....	0.37	12.38	14.03	20.06	21.70	24.58	.....
Fe$_2$O$_3$	.....	.....	25.65	.....	3.79	.....	6.93	.....	.....
Cr$_2$O$_3$	67.91	65.49	43.46	56.70	55.51	46.87	44.56	41.23	79.04
SiO$_2$	.....	0.50	.....	.....	0.24	.....	0.88	.....	.....
Rem.	.....	.....	2.74	trace	0.37	.....	0.89	.....	.....
Total	100.00	99.39	100.00	100.68	100.26	100.46	100.35	100.20	100.00
G.		4.5					4.25	4.21	

1. $FeCr_2O_4$. 2. Chromite. Admire meteorite.[9] 3. Chromite, zincian, and ferrian. Ramberget, Norway. Rem. is ZnO 2.74. Total Fe as Fe_2O_3 recalc. to fit spinel formula, after deduction of 4.3 per cent olivine.[10] 4. Chromite, aluminian. Allegan meteorite. Rem. is TiO$_2$ trace.[9] 5. Magnesiochromite. Caribou pit, Coleraine Township, Q. Rem. is TiO$_2$ 0.17, CaO 0.11, H$_2$O+ 0.07, H$_2$O− 0.02.[11] 6. Magnesiochromite Lützelberg, Kaiserstuhl, Germany.[12] 7. Magnesiochromite, ferrian. Mont Djeti, Togo, Africa. Rem. is CaO 0.78, H$_2$O 0.02, ign. loss 0.09.[13] 8. Magnesiochromite, aluminian. Tampadel, Silesia.[14] 9. $MgCr_2O_4$.

MAGNESIOCHROMITE

1. *Ordinary.* Dominantly $MgCr_2O_4$ but always with a considerable amount of Fe^2 substituting for Mg.

2. *Ferroan.* Chromepicotite pt. Chrome-spinel pt. $(Mg,Fe)Cr_2O_4$. Contains Fe^2 as the next most dominant constituent after Mg and Cr (anal. 8) and grades to chromite.

3. *Aluminian.* Contains Al substituting for the Cr; usually accompanied by an increase in the Mg content.

4. *Ferrian.* Contains Fe^3 substituting for Cr.

CHROMITE

Var.

1. *Ordinary.* Dominantly $FeCr_2O_4$. Most chromite, however, contains some Mg and Al.

2. *Magnesian.* Magnesiochromite pt., *Dana* (228, 1892). Chrome Spinel pt. Beresofite *Simpson* (*Min. Mag.*, **19**, 99, 1920). With Mg the next most important constituent after Fe^2; grades into magnesiochromite, with which chromite presumably forms a complete series.

3. *Aluminian.* Contains Al in substitution for the Cr (anal. 4).

Tests: In R.F. chromite is slightly rounded on the edges of thin splinters, and becomes magnetic. Insoluble in acids. Decomposed by fusion in $KHSO_4$.

Occur. Most peridotites and related rocks, as well as derived serpentines, contain chromite as an accessory mineral. At times the mineral is sufficiently abundant in these rocks, or as a magmatic segregation from them, to constitute a profitable source of the ore. Commercial amounts of chromite are sometimes found in heavy stream sands in serpentine areas. Meteorites frequently contain crystals and nodules of chromite. Olivine, pyroxene, chromian spinel, chromian idocrase, uvarovite, chromian chlorites, magnetite, pyrrhotite, and niccolite are minerals frequently associated with chromite. Only the more important deposits are mentioned here.

In Asia Minor near Antioch, Smyrna, and Brussa. Large deposits in Southern Rhodesia, notably in the Selukwe district where the mineral occurs in talcose, chloritic, and serpentine schists representing metamorphosed peridotites, and in the serpentine of the Great Dike. In New Caledonia, Cuba, India, and the Philippines. Originally from Gassin, Department Var, France. At Ramberget, near the island of Hestmandö, Norway (*zincian*). Small deposits have been worked at Uskub and other localities in Yugoslavia; at Ferndinandovo in the Rhodope foothills, Bulgaria; in the Urals associated with platinum; in New South Wales in the Pine Mountain district. In the United States chromite has been mined in Maryland in the Bare Hills near Baltimore and elsewhere; in Pennsylvania, notably at Wood's mine, near Texas, Lancaster County, and at Unionville, Chester County; in California in Shasta and Siskiyou counties and in the Great Serpentine Dike in Eldorado and Placer counties; also in Oregon, Wyoming, North Carolina. In Canada in the serpentine areas of Quebec. Common in meteorites.

Magnesiochromite has the same type of occurrence and association as chromite. In Germany in serpentine in the Schwarzenberg, near Tampadel, Silesia; at Lützelberg, in the Kaiserstuhl, Baden. From Ferdinandovo, Bulgaria; a ferrian variety on Mount Djeti, Togo. In dunite on Dun Mountain, New Zealand (*chrompicotite*). In New Caledonia. In Canada in veins or dikes in volcanic rocks on Scottie Creek, Lillooet district, British Columbia, and from Coleraine Township and elsewhere in Quebec.

A l t e r. To limonite, and more rarely to stichtite. Also reported as a pseudomorph after garnet.

A r t i f. Prepared by fusing the mixed oxides.

N a m e. *Chromite* was named in allusion to the composition. *Beresofite* from the locality at Beresof in the Urals. *Magnesiochromite* is the preferred form of the name magnochromite, given in allusion to the magnesian nature of the material. *Picrochromite* also alludes to the magnesian composition.

CHROMITITE. *Jovitchitch (Ak. Wiss. Wien, Ber.*, 117, 813, 1908; *Bull. soc. min.*, **35**, 511, 1912).

Found as small octahedral crystals in mica schist and stream sands at Zeljin Mountain, in the Kapaonik Mountains, Yugoslavia. G. 3.1. Analysis gave: total Fe as Fe_2O_3 30.59, Al_2O_3 6.23, Cr_2O_3 59.68, CaO 1.25, MgO 3.89, total 101.64. Assigned the formula $FeCrO_3$, but probably a mixture of chromite with magnetite or hematite.

Ref.

1. Goldschmidt (**2**, 153, 1913). Rare and uncertain forms: {255}, {477}.
2. Clark, Ally, and Badger, *Am. J. Sc.*, **22**, 539 (1931), on artificial material.
3. An indistinct cleavage on {111} sometimes given for the spinel minerals, but this is probably a parting plane.
4. The low specific gravities given for natural chromites are due to substitution of more or less Mg and Fe^3 for the Fe^2 and Cr, respectively, in the pure compound.
5. Larsen (57, 1921).
6. Schneiderhöhn and Ramdohr (**2**, 596, 1931).
7. Knop, *Zs. Kr.*, **20**, 299 (1892), in Doelter (4 [2], 686, 1927).
8. A large number of analyses can be found in Doelter (4 [2], 681, 1927).
9. Tassin, *U. S. Nat. Mus., Proc.*, **34**, 685 (1908).
10. Donath, *Am. Min.*, **16**, 484 (1931).
11. Ellestad anal. in Parsons, *Univ. Toronto Stud., Geol. Ser.*, **42**, 75 (1939).
12. Knop, *Jb. Min.*, 697, 1877.
13. Raoult anal. in Arsandaux, *Bull. soc. min.*, **48**, 70 (1925).
14. Lazczynski anal. in Traube, *Zs. deutsche geol. Ges.*, **46**, 58 (1894).

7221 H A U S M A N N I T E [$MnMn_2O_4$]. Schwarz Braunsteinerz pt. *Werner* (*Bergm. J.*, 386, 1789). Schwarz Manganerz pt., Verhärtetes Schwarzbraunsteinerz pt. *Karsten* (72, 100, 1808). Black Manganese. Blättricher Schwarz-Braunstein *Hausmann* (293, 1813). Manganèse oxydé hydraté, Manganèse oxydé noir brunâtre *Haüy* (1822). Pyramidal Manganese Ore *Haidinger* (**2**, 416, 1824). Schwarzmanganerz, Gewässertes Manganhyperoxydul *Leonhard* (760, 1826). Hausmannite *Haidinger (Roy. Soc. Edinburgh, Trans.*, **11**, 127, 1827). Glanzbraunstein *Hausmann* (405, 1847). L'oxyde rouge de manganèse *Fr.* Scharfmanganerz *Germ.*

Cryst. Tetragonal; ditetragonal dipyramidal — $4/m\,2/m\,2/m$.

$a : c = 1 : 1.6364;$[1] $p_0 : r_0 = 1.6364 : 1$

Forms:[2]

		ϕ	ρ	A	$\bar{M}$
c	001	.....	$0°00'$	$90°00'$	$90°00'$
a	010	$0°00'$	90 00	90 00	45 00
m	110	45 00	90 00	45 00	90 00
i	019	0 00	$10\,18\frac{1}{2}$	90 00	82 44
s	013	0 00	$28\,36\frac{1}{2}$	90 00	$70\,12\frac{1}{2}$
σ	012	0 00	$39\,17\frac{1}{2}$	90 00	63 24
v	035	0 00	$44\,28\frac{1}{2}$	90 00	60 18
u	023	0 00	$47\,29\frac{1}{2}$	90 00	58 35
p	011	0 00	58 34	90 00	$52\,53\frac{1}{2}$
n	021	0 00	$73\,00\frac{1}{2}$	90 00	47 27
e	112	45 00	49 10	$57\,39\frac{1}{2}$	90 00
x	169	$9\,27\frac{1}{2}$	47 53	82 59	$64\,28\frac{1}{2}$
h	136	18 26	$40\,46\frac{1}{2}$	78 05	73 01
r	123	26 34	50 39	69 46	$75\,50\frac{1}{2}$
t	358	30 58	$50\,01\frac{1}{2}$	66 47	$64\,26\frac{1}{2}$
k	121	26 34	74 43	$79\,17\frac{1}{2}$	$72\,14\frac{1}{2}$

Structure cell.[3] Space group $I4/amd$; a_0 5.75, c_0 9.42; $a_0 : c_0 = 1 : 1.638$; cell contents $Mn_4Mn_8O_{16}$.

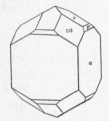 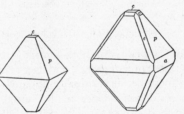

Långban, Sweden.   Jacobsberg, Norway.   Ilfeld, Harz.

Habit. Pseudo-octahedral {011}; {013} usually smooth and bright, {011} often dull and striated parallel [100]. Also granular massive, coherent.

Twinning. Twin plane {112}, often repeated as fivelings; also lamellar.[9]

Phys. Cleavage {001} nearly perfect, {112} and {011} indistinct. Fracture uneven. Brittle. H. $5\frac{1}{2}$. G. $4.84 \pm 0.01;$[4] 4.84 (calc.). Luster submetallic. Color brownish black. Streak chestnut-brown. Transparent in extremely thin splinters. Twin gliding,[5] with $K_1\{112\}$, $K_2\{\bar{1}12\}$. Specific magnetic susceptibility:[6] $K = 6.10^{-6}$.

Opt. In transmitted light, deep reddish brown in color and non-pleochroic.

$$nLi^7 \qquad nLi^8 \text{ (Anal. 3)}$$

$$
\begin{array}{lll}
O & 2.46 \pm 0.02 & 2.45 \pm 0.02 \\
E & 2.15 \pm 0.02 & 2.15 \pm 0.02
\end{array}
\qquad \text{Uniaxial neg. } (-).
$$

In polished section[9] gray-white in color with distinct anisotropism and with deep blood-red to reddish brown internal reflections. Often exhibits a lamellar twinning on {112}. Weakly pleochroic with O light and E dark gray white. Reflection percentages: green 20, orange 16.5, red 13.

Chem. An oxide of manganese, $MnMn_2O_4$. Zn substitutes for Mn^2, with Zn : Mn = 1 : 11 in anal. 5. No complete series to hetaerolite has been found, although the latter is of the same structure.[10] Fe substitutes[11] for Mn to about Fe : Mn = 1 : 23 (anal. 6).

Anal.[12]

	1	2	3	4	5	6
MnO	93.01	92.48	91.38	92.10	83.40	86.52
O	6.99	7.10	7.78	6.93	7.05	6.52
ZnO	.....	.....	.....	.....	8.60	}0.55
BaO	.....	0.14	0.26	0.11	.....	
CaO	.....	.....	trace	.....	0.10	0.43
MgO	.....	.....	trace	.....	trace	1.00
Fe₂O₃	.....	.....	.....	.....	0.30	4.30
H₂O	.....	.....	0.62	0.73	0.05	.....
Rem.	.....	0.17	.....	0.15	0.70	0.57
Total	100.00	99.89	100.04	100.02	100.20	99.89
G.	4.84	4.856	4.836	4.83		

1. Mn_3O_4. 2. Ilmenau, Thuringia. Rem. is SiO_2.[13] 3. Batesville, Ark.[14] 4. Ilfeld, Harz. Rem. is insol.[15] 5. Ilmenau, Thuringia. Rem. is $(K,Na)_2O$ 0.40, SiO_2 0.30, and traces of CO_2, SO_3, P_2O_5.[16] 6. Långban, Sweden. Rem. is CO_2 0.37, richterite 0.20.[17]

Tests. Infusible. Soluble in hot HCl with evolution of Cl.

Occur. Occurs typically in high-temperature hydrothermal veins; also as a contact metamorphic mineral, and as a recrystallization product in metamorphosed sedimentary or residual manganese ores. Probably widespread in manganese deposits formed by circulating meteoric waters (Batesville) and in residual ores. Associated with braunite, magnetite, hematite, barite, psilomelane, pyrolusite, wad.

Only a few of the known localities can be mentioned. In Germany a notable occurrence at Öhrenstock in the neighborhood of Ilmenau, Thuringia; at Ilfeld in the Harz; near Greimerath, Rhine Province. In the lower Averser valley, Graubünden, Switzerland. In Italy in the Aosta valley, Torino, and as coatings on sodalite crystals in cavities of the lava of 1631 on Vesuvius. In the neighborhood of Jakobeny, Bukovina, Bulgaria. At Granau, Aberdeenshire, Scotland, and at Whitehaven, Cumberland, England. Hausmannite occurs at Jacobsberg, Sweden, with garnet, magnetite, hematite, manganophyllite, and jacobsite in granular limestone; abundantly and in fine crystals at Långban; also at the Moss mine and at the Harstig and Pajsberg mines in Vermland; with braunite at the Sjö mine, Örebro. Reported from localities in the Central Provinces, India. In fine crystals at Miguel Burnier, Minas Geraes, Brazil.

Found in the United States in the Batesville district, Arkansas, with pyrolusite and psilomelane; in California in the Prefumo Canyon district, San Luis Obispo County, near Meadow Valley, Plumas County, and with pyrochroite and tephroite in a boulder in Alum Rock Park, Santa Clara County; at Lake Crescent and Humptulups, Washington; reported from Franklin, New Jersey.

A l t e r. Reported as pseudomorphs after calcite and manganite, and observed altered to wad.

A r t i f.[17] Readily obtained as crystals by heating MnO or precipitated Mn_3O_4 in air with a mineralizer and by decomposing $MnCl_2$ in an oxidizing atmosphere; also formed by strongly heating the higher oxides of manganese.[18]

N a m e. After J. F. L. Hausmann (1782–1859), Professor of Mineralogy at the University of Göttingen.

Ref.

1. Orientation and unit of Miller (257, 1852); the angles are the weighted mean of those of Flink, *Ak. Stockholm, Bh.*, **12** [7], 40 (1888); **16** [4], (1891), and Koechlin, *Min. Mitt.*, **27**, 262 (1908). Miller's elements conform to the smallest structural cell of Aminoff, *Zs. Kr.*, **64**, 475 (1936); the elements of Flink, Koechlin, and others conform to the doubled cell, which is face centered. Transformation: Flink to Miller $\frac{1}{2}\frac{1}{2}0/\frac{1}{2}\frac{1}{2}0/001$.
2. Goldschmidt (4, 120, 1918). Uncertain forms: {0·5·11}, {113}.
3. Aminoff (1936).
4. From values 4.836 of Miser and Fairchild, *Washington Ac. Sc., J.*, **10**, 1 (1920), 4.83 of Krüll, *Chem. Erde*, **7**, 473 (1932), 4.856 of Rammelsberg, *Ann. Phys.*, **124**, 521 (1865) and 4.83 of Frondel (priv. comm., 1940) on a Långban crystal by the microbalance.
5. Mügge, *Cbl. Min.*, 73, 1916.
6. Feytis, *C. R.*, **152**, 708 (1911).
7. Larsen (83, 1921) on material from Plumas Co., Calif.
8. Larsen in Miser and Fairchild (1920) on material from Batesville, Ark.
9. Schneiderhöhn and Ramdohr (2, 575, 1931) and Orcel and Pavlovitch, *Bull. soc. min.*, **54**, 108 (1932).
10. Frondel (priv. comm., 1940) from x-ray powder study.
11. Verwey and van Bruggen, *Zs. Kr.*, **92**, 136 (1935), find by x-ray studies that there is a wide range of solid solution of Fe^3 in Mn_3O_4 with a concomitant development of a defect lattice, that is, vacant positions in the lattice; with increasing substitution of Fe the axial ratio decreases until at Mn : Fe = 60 : 40 the structure becomes isometric and of the spinel type.
12. For additional analyses see Hintze (1 [3A], 3584 (1929), and Miser and Fairchild (1920).
13. Rammelsberg (144, 1875).
14. Miser and Fairchild (1920).
15. Krüll (1932).
16. Gorgeu, *Bull. soc. min.*, **16**, 133 (1893).
17. Gorgeu, *Bull. soc. min.*, **29**, 1109 (1903).
18. See Krüll (1932); Mellor (14, 231, 1932) and Pavlovitch, *C. R.*, **200**, 71 (1935).

7222 **H E T A E R O L I T E** [$ZnMn_2O_4$]. *Moore* (*Am. J. Sc.*, **14**, 423, 1877); *Palache* (*Am. Min.*, **13**, 297, 1928; *U. S. Geol. Sur., Prof. Pap. 180*, 48, 1935). (Not Hetaerolite of *Ford* and *Bradley, Am. J. Sc.*, **35**, 600 [1913] = Hydrohetaerolite.) Zinc hausmannite.

C r y s t. Tetragonal; ditetragonal dipyramidal — $4/m\,2/m\,2/m$.[1]

$\qquad a : c = 1 : 1.5952$;[2] $p_0 : r_0 = 1.5952$

Forms:

		ϕ	$\rho = C$	A	$\overline{M}$
c	001	.....	0°00′	90°00′	90°00′
p	011	0°00′	57 55	90 00	53 11½
e	112	45 00	48 26½	58 03½	90 00

Structure cell.[3] Space group $I4/amd$; a_0 5.74, c_0 9.15; $a_0 : c_0 = 1$:
1.594; contains $Zn_4Mn_8O_{16}$.

Franklin, N. J.

Habit. Octahedral, at times with small basal truncations. Also massive.

Twinning. Twin plane {112}, as fivelings. Some individuals of the twinned group may be smaller or lacking.

P h y s. Cleavage {001} indistinct.[4] Fracture uneven. Brittle. H. 6. G. 5.18;[5] 5.23 (calc.). Luster submetallic, shining. Color black. Streak dark brown. Transparent in very thin splinters.

O p t. In transmitted light, deep reddish brown in color. Absorption $E > O$, faint, in red-brown. Indices:

$$
\begin{array}{lll}
n^6 & n^7 & \\
O = 2.34 \pm 0.02 & 2.35 & \text{Uniaxial neg. } (-). \\
E = 2.14 \pm 0.02 & 2.10 &
\end{array}
$$

C h e m. An oxide of zinc and manganese, $ZnMn_2O_4$. A small amount of Mn^2 substitutes for Zn in the reported analysis.

Anal.

	1	2
ZnO	34.02	32.46
MnO	.....	1.86
Mn_2O_3	65.98	64.21
Rem.	.....	1.10
Total	100.00	99.63
G.		4.85

1. $ZnMn_2O_4$. 2. Sterling Hill, N. J. Rem. is MgO 0.49, Fe_2O_3 0.24, SiO_2 0.18, H_2O 0.19.[8]

Tests. B.B. infusible.

O c c u r. Found at Sterling Hill, New Jersey, as drusy crystals with franklinite, and also massive with chalcophanite. At Franklin, New Jersey, with jeffersonite, hodgkinsonite, willemite, and calcite in hydrothermal veinlets cutting the massive ore.

A r t i f.[9] Obtained in crystals by fusion of the sulfates of manganese, zinc, and sodium. The Mg and Cd analogues also are known.

N a m e. The name hetaerolite was first given by Moore, in 1877, to a mineral found associated with chalcophanite at Sterling Hill, New Jersey. Moore considered the mineral to be anhydrous and to be the zinc analogue of hausmannite. A later analysis[10] of a fibrous secondary mineral from Sterling Hill apparently identical with the original material of Moore indicated the presence of a significant amount of water. This mineral, together with the material of Moore and with a similar hydrous mineral from

Leadville, Colorado,[11] was separated by Palache[12] under the name hydro-hetaerolite (which see) and the name hetaerolite was retained, in the sense originally intended by Moore, for the anhydrous analogue of hausmannite here described. The original material of Moore, however, was later shown[13] to be identical with hetaerolite as here defined. The name hetaerolite is from ἑταῖρος, *companion*, in allusion to the association with chalco-phanite on some specimens.

Ref.

1. Crystal class from x-ray Weissenberg study of Frondel and Heinrich, *Am. Min.*, **27**, 48 (1942).
2. Palache (1928) on material from Franklin, N. J., in the orientation and unit of the structural cell.
3. Frondel and Heinrich (1942) by x-ray Weissenberg study of measured crystals of Palache (1928).
4. Frondel and Heinrich (1942) note two additional cleavages, probably on {112} and {011}.
5. Frondel and Heinrich (1942) by microbalance.
6. Larsen (84, 1921) on material from Franklin.
7. Berman in Palache (1928) on material from Sterling Hill.
8. Bauer anal. in Palache (1928).
9. Gorgeu, *Bull. soc. chim. franc.*, **10**, 653 (1873).
10. Schaller anal. in Palache, *Am. J. Sc.*, **29**, 177 (1910).
11. Described by Ford and Bradley, *Am. J. Sc.*, **35**, 600 (1913) under the name hetaerolite.
12. Palache (1910).
13. Frondel and Heinrich (1942).

7223 **Hydrohetaerolite** [$Zn_2Mn_4O_8 \cdot H_2O$]. Hetaerolite *Ford* and *Bradley* (*Am. J. Sc.*, **35**, 600, 1913). (Not the hetaerolite of *Moore, Am. J. Sc.*, **14**, 423 [1877] ?.) Wolftonite *Butler* (*Econ. Geol.*, **8**, 8, 1913). Hydrohetaerolite *Palache* (*Am. Min.*, **13**, 297, 1928; *U. S. Geol. Sur., Prof. Pap. 180*, 53, 1935).

Apparently tetragonal.[1] Massive, in fibrous crusts with a botryoidal surface. The fibers are elongated [011]?

P h y s. Cleavable parallel to the elongation of the fibers. H. 5–6. G. 4.6? (Leadville[2]). Luster submetallic. Color dark brown to brownish black. Streak dark brown. Transparent in very thin splinters.

O p t.[3] In transmitted light, dark brown in color.

$$n$$
$$O = 2.26 \pm 0.02 \qquad \text{Uniaxial neg. } (-)$$
$$E = 2.10 \pm 0.02 \qquad \text{Elongation pos. } (+)$$

C h e m. An oxide of zinc and manganese of uncertain formula, per-haps $Zn_2Mn_4O_8 \cdot H_2O$. The Si reported in the analyses has been ascribed to admixture, but may be present in substitution for Mn^3.

Anal.

	1	2	3	4
ZnO	32.78	33.43	37.56	37.66
Fe₂O₃	.....	0.77	.....	0.67
Mn₂O₃	63.59	60.44	56.00	54.63
H₂O	3.63	3.89	4.36	3.78
SiO₂	.....	1.71	2.69	2.91
Total	100.00	100.24	100.61	99.65
G.		4.85	4.6	

1. $Zn_2Mn_4O_8 \cdot H_2O$. 2. Sterling Hill, N. J. $H_2O^+ 1.42$, $H_2O^- 2.47$.[4] 3. Wolftone mine, Leadville, Colo. Average of two analyses.[5] 4. Leadville, Colo.[6]

Tests. B.B. infusible. In C.T. yields water but not oxygen. Easily soluble in HCl, giving off chlorine.

O c c u r. Found at the Wolftone mine, Leadville, Colorado, associated with chalcophanite, hemimorphite, and smithsonite in oxidized ore. Reported from Sterling Hill, New Jersey, with chalcophanite.

N a m e. Because the composition is that of hetaerolite plus water. For a history of the usage of the name hydrohetaerolite see under hetaerolite.

Evidence of species validity is lacking.

Ref.

1. Indicated by the x-ray powder and Weissenberg fiber study of Frondel and Heinrich, *Am. Min.*, **27**, 48 (1942), but rigorous proof of the symmetry is lacking. Cell dimensions, a_0 5.71, c_0 9.04; space group (partial) $I4/a \; d$; cell contents $Zn_4Mn_8O_{16} \cdot 2H_2O$ (?); calc. G. 5.51.
2. Ford and Bradley (1913); this value is probably very low.
3. Larsen (84, 1921) on material from Leadville. The indices given by Palache (1935) for hydrohetaerolite from Sterling Hill refer instead to hetaerolite. Orcel and Pavlovitch, *Bull. soc. min.*, **54**, 108 (1932), describe the properties in polished section of a mineral from Sterling Hill probably identical with hydrohetaerolite.
4. Schaller anal. in Palache (1910).
5. Bradley anal. in Ford and Bradley (1913).
6. Palmer anal. in Wells, *U. S. Geol. Sur., Bull. 878*, 91, 1937.

723   **C H R Y S O B E R Y L** [BeAl$_2$O$_4$]. (Not Chrysoberyl [= var. Beryl] of the Ancients.) Krisoberil *Werner* (*Bergm. J.*, 373, 387, 1789; 84, 1790). Chrysoberyll *Karsten, Lenz*, etc. Cymophane *Haüy* (*J. mines*, 4, 5, 1798). Alexandrite *Nordenskiöld* (*Russ. Ges. Min. Schr.*, 1842). Alaunerde + Kieselerde *Klaproth* (1, 97, 1795); *Arfvedson* (*Ak. Stockholm, Handl.*, 1822). Aluminate of Glucina, mainly, *Seybert* (*Am. J. Sc.*, **8**, 105, 1824); *Bergemann* (*De Chrys.*, Göttingen, 1826).

C r y s t. Orthorhombic; dipyramidal — $2/m \; 2/m \; 2/m$.

$$a : b : c = 0.5823 : 1 : 0.4707;^1 \qquad p_0 : q_0 : r_0 = 0.8083 : 0.4707 : 1$$

$$q_1 : r_1 : p_1 = 0.5823 : 1.0371 : 1; \qquad r_2 : p_2 : q_2 = 2.1245 : 1.7173 : 1$$

Forms:[2]

		ϕ	$\rho = C$	ϕ_1	$\rho_1 = A$	ϕ_2	$\rho_2 = B$
c	001	.....	0°00′	0°00′	90°00′	90°00′	90°00′
b	010	0°00′	90 00	90 00	90 00	.....	0 00
m	110	59 47½	90 00	90 00	30 12½	0 00	59 47½
M	011	0 00	25 12½	25 12½	90 00	90 00	64 47½
s	021	0 00	43 16½	43 16½	90 00	90 00	46 43½
r	031	0 00	54 41½	54 41½	90 00	90 00	35 18½
x	101	90 00	38 57	0 00	51 03	51 03	90 00
o	111	59 47½	43 05	25 12½	53 49	51 03	69 53½
n	121	40 39	51 08	43 16½	59 31	51 03	53 47½

Less common: $a\{100\}$, $k\{120\}$, $u\{032\}$, $v\{112\}$, $w\{221\}$.

Structure cell.[3] Space group *Pmnb*; a_0 5.47, b_0 9.39, c_0 4.42 (all $\pm$ 1 per cent); $a_0 : b_0 : c_0 = 0.583 : 1 : 0.471$; contains Be$_4Al_8O_{16}$.

Habit. Simple crystals usually tabular $\{001\}$; occasionally short prismatic [100] or, less often, [001]. Striated on $\{001\}$ $\|$ [100]. Twinned crystals are generally flattened $\perp$ to the composition plane, and have a feather-like striation on {001}; or sometimes form six-rayed spokelike aggregates.

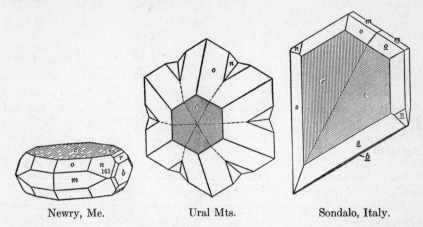

| Newry, Me. | Ural Mts. | Sondalo, Italy. |

Twinning.[4] Common, with twin plane {130}. Both contact and penetration twins, often repeated and forming pseudohexagonal crystals as viewed along [001], with or without reentrant angles.

P h y s. Cleavage {110} quite distinct,[5] {010} imperfect, {001} poor. Fracture uneven to conchoidal. Brittle. H. $8\frac{1}{2}$. G. 3.75 ± 0.10; 3.69 (calc.). Luster vitreous. Color asparagus-green, grass-green, emerald-green, greenish white, and yellowish green; greenish brown; yellow; sometimes raspberry- or columbine-red by transmitted light (*alexandrite*). Streak colorless. Transparent. Sometimes a bluish opalescence or chatoyancy (*cymophane*), notably on {010}; also asteriated or with a cat's eye effect. Electrical conductivity increases with temperature.[6]

O p t.[7] In transmitted light colorless to pale shades of green, yellow, or red.

	ORIENTATION	n	PLEOCHROISM	
X	c	1.746	Columbine-red	Bx. pos. (+).
Y	b	1.748	Orange-yellow	$r > v$.
Z	a	1.756	Emerald-green	$2V$ 70° ±.

The refractive indices vary, apparently with the Fe content, even in the same crystal. At an elevated temperature $Y = a$. The dispersion of the indices is $n_{Tl} - n_{Li} = 0.008 ± 0.001$.

C h e m. An oxide of beryllium and aluminum, $BeAl_2O_4$. Fe^3 is usually present (in amounts up to 6 per cent by weight Fe_2O_3; anal. 2), presumably in substitution for Al but possibly due to oxidation of Fe^2. Small amounts of Cr have been reported in the variety alexandrite. The Fe^2 reported in anal. 3 presumably is in substitution for Be. Ti has been reported in a few old analyses (anal. 4), but may be due to mechanically included (or exsolved) rutile. Sc has been found spectrographically in crystals from Madagascar.[17]

Anal.

	1	2	3	4	5	6
BeO	19.71	17.78	19.15	16.87	18.56	18.80
FeO	.....	.....	3.60	.....	.....	.....
Al₂O₃	80.29	76.76	76.34	74.85	76.40	74.86
Fe₂O₃	.....	6.07	.....	4.06	1.30	3.91
TiO₂	.....	.....	0.55	2.97	0.22	0.19
Rem.	.....	.....	0.30	0.55	3.12	1.88
Total	100.00	100.61	99.94	99.30	99.60	99.64
G.	3.69	3.52	3.648			

1. BeAl₂O₄. 2. Rivière du Poste, Quebec.⁹ 3. Golden, Colo. Rem. is ign. loss 0.30.¹⁰ 4. Brazil. Rem. is ign. loss 0.55. Recalc. after deduction of 5.13 per cent SiO₂.¹¹ 5. Bershea Su, Gold Coast. Colorless crystal. Rem. is SiO₂ 2.24, MgO 0.40, CaO 0.48.¹² 6. Bershea Su, Gold Coast. Yellow green crystal. Rem. is SiO₂ 1.12, MgO 0.76.¹²

Var. *Ordinary.* Color pale green, yellowish green, and translucent *en masse.* Sometimes clear yellow and transparent and then used as a gem.

Alexandrite. Color emerald-green, but columbine-red by transmitted light and usually also by artificial light. The colors¹³ are possibly due to Cr and Fe. A gem variety.

Cat's Eye. *Asteriated.* Cymophane. Color greenish, yellowish. Exhibits a fine chatoyant effect, due to oriented needle-like inclusions or hollow canals in parallel position. A gem variety.

Tests. B.B. unaltered. Not attacked by acids, but decomposed by fusion with KOH or KHSO₄. Fuses with great difficulty in borax or salt of phosphorus.

O c c u r. Found in granite pegmatite and aplite; also in mica schists and, rarely, in dolomitic marble. Often found as a detrital mineral, with diamond, corundum, garnet, cassiterite. Found in pegmatite with almandite, spinel and beryl at Schinderhübel, near Marschendorf, Moravia, Germany. In the Ural Mountains¹⁴ with phenakite and beryl in mica schist on the Takowaja River, about 90 km. northeasterly from Ekaterinburg (*alexandrite*); also in the Orenburg district, southern Urals, as yellow and yellow-green crystals with euclase in placers. In dolomite with corundum at Campolungo, near St. Gotthard, Switzerland. In pegmatite in the neighborhood of Sondalo, Veltlin, Italy, and similarly at Olgiasca, Lake Como. In aplite near Helsinki, Finland, and found in pegmatite at several localities in Saetersdalen, Norway. In the Mourne Mountains, Ireland. Found in diamond sands from near Sombula, south of Gwelo, Southern Rhodesia; also from Katanga, Belgian Congo, and from Bershea Su on the Gold Coast. Gem crystals occur in pegmatite at Miakanjovato and elsewhere in Madagascar. Found abundantly in Ceylon in the gem gravels, including both the cat's eye and alexandrite varieties; also rarely at Mogok, Upper Burma. With cassiterite in placers at Takajama, Mino Province, Japan. In Western Australia at Dowerin. In Brazil near Collintina, Espirito Santo, as trillings forming hexagonal aggregates sometimes quite perfect and more than 4 cm. on a side.

In the United States chrysoberyl occurs in pegmatites at a number of localities in Maine, including Hartford, Stoneham, Norway, Canton, Peru, Stowe, Mechanics Falls in Minot Township, Buckfield, Greenwood, Topsham. Early recognized[15] at Haddam, Connecticut, in pegmatite with columbite, tourmaline, gahnite, beryl. Near Orange Summit, New Hampshire. At Greenfield, near Saratoga, New York, in pegmatite with garnet, tourmaline, apatite. Found in schist in a building excavation on Washington Heights, Manhattan Island, New York City. In rough twinned crystals ranging up to 14 by 12 by 2.5 cm. in size in pegmatite near Golden, Colorado. In Canada in pegmatite on Rivière du Poste, Muskinonge County, Quebec.

A r t i f.[16] Easily obtained from fusion of Al_2O_3, BeO, H_3BO_3 and $CaCO_3$ as large crystals, which may be variously tinted by impurities; also by the reaction of AlF_3, BeF_2, and B_2O_3 at white heat, and by fusion of BeO and Al_2O_3 with alkali sulfates or nepheline.

N a m e. *Chrysoberyl* from χρυσός, *golden*, and βήρυλλος, *beryl*, in allusion to the color. *Cymophane*, from κῦμα, *wave*, and φαίνεσθαι, *appear*, alludes to a peculiar opalescence the crystals sometimes exhibit. *Alexandrite* is named after a former Czar of Russia, Alexander II.

Ref.

1. Unit and orientation of Des Cloizeaux, *Ann. chim. phys.*, [3], **13** (1845); angles of Melczer, *Zs. Kr.*, **33**, 246 (1900). Transformation Dana (1892) to Des Cloizeaux 001/010/100.

2. Forms from Goldschmidt (**2**, 154, 1913) and Adams and Graham, *Roy. Soc. Canada, Trans.*, [3] sec. 4, **20**, 113 (1926). Rare or uncertain forms:

130	025	054	092	201	122	10·1·10	131
017	012	075	051	115	233	515	151
016	035	094	061	113	243	313	161
015	034	052	071	20·20·11	253	323	8·10·7
014	045	072	0·10·1	331	354	656	241
013	076	041	302	772	4·10·5	232	311
							9·18·1

3. Bragg and Brown, *Zs. Kr.*, **63**, 122 (1926). The a_0 and c_0 of these authors have been interchanged to conform with the morphological orientation. They point out the close similarity of the structures of chrysoberyl and chrysolite, with the Al and Be of the former in the equivalent positions of Mg and Si of the latter. However, no isomorphous intermediate compounds are known. The structure and axial ratio of diaspore are likewise similar to those of chrysoberyl. See Bragg (111, 1937).

4. See Brauns, *Cbl. Min.*, 357, 1929; Hessenberg, *Jb. Min.*, 871, 1862; Himmel and Schroeder, *Cbl. Min.*, 257, 1933; Cathrein, *Zs. Kr.*, **6**, 257 (1881); Liffa, *Zs. Kr.*, **36**, 614 (1902).

5. Dana (230, 1892); some observers give a good cleavage {010} and lacking on {110}; see Palache, *Am. Min.*, **9**, 217 (1924).

6. Doelter, *Ak. Wien, Ber.*, **109**, 49 (1910).

7. The optical properties given by Des Cloizeaux (**1**, 59, 1857; **2**, 28, 1859); *Ann. mines*, 14, 364 (1859), and by Melczer, *Zs. Kr.*, **33**, 240 (1900), are unfortunately not tied to material of a specific composition, and therefore are of little use as precise data. The values here given are averages. Des Cloizeaux finds a change in optical orientation with temperature increase, and $r < v$.

8. For older analyses see Doelter (**3** [2], 513, 1926).

9. Evans, *Am. J. Sc.*, **19**, 316 (1905).

10. Schoder anal. in Waldschmidt and Gaines, *Am. Min.*, **24**, 267 (1939).

11. Bergemann anal. in Rammelsberg (129, 1875).

12. Junner, *Rep. Geol. Sur. Gold Coast*, 14, 1933.
13. For spectroscopic study of alexandrite see Wild and Klemm, *Cbl. Min.*, 31, 1926; 20, 1932. The absorption spectrum has been studied by Hlawatsch, *Min. Mitt.*, 22, 500 (1903).
14. See Fersmann (74, 1929) for a complete description of the locality.
15. Discovered in 1810 by Archibald Bruce and mistaken for corundum; later shown to be chrysoberyl by Haüy.
16. For literature see Doelter (1926).
17. Lacroix, *C. R.*, 171, 421, 1920.

724   **C R E D N E R I T E** [$CuMn_2O_4$]. Kupferhaltige Manganerz *Credner* (*Jb. Min.*, 5, 1847). Mangankupferoxyd *Hausmann* (1582, 1847). Mangankupfererz, Crednerit *Rammelsberg* (*Ann. Phys.*, 74, 559, 1849).

C r y s t. Monoclinic?; possibly pseudohexagonal by twinning.

Habit. In thin six-sided plates, in radiating, hemispherical or spherulitic groupings. Also as earthy coatings.

Twinning. A three-fold set of striae intersecting on the plate at about 60° perhaps represent twin lamellae.[1] Polysynthetic twinning has been noted in some polished sections.[2]

P h y s. Perfect cleavage in the plane of the plate, and less perfect along the striae and inclined about 76° to the plate.[1] H. 4. G. 5.01 ± 0.02.[3] Luster bright metallic. Color iron-black. Streak sooty black, with brownish tint. Opaque. In polished section[2] anisotropic; in some sections shows fine polysynthetic twin lamellae.

C h e m. An oxide of copper and manganese, $CuMn_2O_4$.[4] The small amounts of BaO, CaO, and H_2O reported in early analyses are probably due to impurities.

Anal.[5]

	1	2	3
CuO	33.51	40.65	34.68
MnO	59.75	52.55	58.62
O	6.74	5.78	6.70
Rem.	.....	1.48	.....
Total	100.00	100.46	100.00
G.		4.96–4.98	5.03

1. $CuMn_2O_4$. 2. Friedrichroda. Rem. is BaO 1.48.[6] 3. Higher Pitts, Somerset. Analysis recalc. after deduction of 6.10 malachite and 1.05 cerussite.[1]

Tests. B.B. fusible only on thin edges. Soluble in HCl with evolution of Cl. Insoluble in HNO_3.

O c c u r. A secondary mineral found at Friedrichroda in Thuringia, Germany, intergrown with psilomelane and hausmannite, and with malachite, volborthite, barite, calcite, and wad. Also at Higher Pitts, Mendip Hills, Somerset, England, with cerussite, hydrocerussite, and malachite; usually on the outside of nodules of lead ore between the cerussite and the enclosing wad. Said to occur massive near Calistoga, Napa County, California.

A l t e r. Along cleavage cracks to malachite.

N a m e. After C. F. Credner (1809–76), mining geologist and mineralogist.

Ref.

1. Spencer and Mountain, *Min. Mag.*, **20**, 87 (1923).
2. Orcel and Pavlovitch, *Bull. soc. min.*, **54**, 108 (1932).
3. Includes value 5.03 (Higher Pitts) of Spencer and Mountain (1923), the highest value (5.07) of Credner (1847) and the values 4.959 and 4.977 of Rammelsberg (1849).
4. Spencer and Mountain (1923).
5. For additional analyses see Spencer and Mountain (1923).
6. Rammelsberg (1849).

7311   H O E G B O M I T E   [Mg(Al,Fe,Ti)$_4$O$_7$?].   Högbomit *Gavelin* (*Bull. Geol. Inst. Upsala*, **15**, 289, 1916).

C r y s t.   Hexagonal $- R.$[1]

$$a : c = 1 : 3.11;^2 \qquad p_0 : r_0 = 3.59 : 1$$

Forms:

		ϕ	ρ	A_1	A_2
c	0001	.....	0°00′	90°00′	90°00′
r	10Ī1	30°00′	74 26	33 27½	90 00

Habit.   Crystals rare; thick to thin tabular {0001}. Usually as microscopic embedded grains.

Twinning.   (*a*) On {0001}, sometimes repeated.   (*b*) Probably on a rhombohedron.

P h y s.   Cleavage {0001} imperfect; also an indistinct cleavage (parting ?) parallel to a rhombohedron. Fracture conchoidal. Brittle. H. 6½. G. 3.81±.[3] Luster metallic adamantine. Color black. Streak gray. Transparent only in thin splinters. Weakly magnetic.

O p t.[4]   In transmitted light, brown in color with distinct pleochroism. Uniaxial negative ($-$). O 1.853, dark golden brown; E 1.803, light golden brown.

In polished section[5] gray in color with distinct anisotropism and weak pleochroism; sometimes exhibits a lamellar twinning on {0001} or on a rhombohedron.

C h e m.   An oxide of Mg, Al, Fe^3, and Ti. The formula is uncertain, possibly Mg(Al,Fe^3,Ti)$_4$O$_7$.

Anal.

	1	2
MgO	14.98	15.44
MnO	.....	0.14
Fe$_2$O$_3$	14.84	17.41
Cr$_2$O$_3$	.....	0.29
Al$_2$O$_3$	56.82	61.19
TiO$_2$	13.36	5.53
Total	100.00	100.00

1. Mg(Al,Fe^3,Ti)$_4$O$_7$, with Al:Fe:Ti = 6 : 1 : 1.   2. Routevare, Sweden. Analysis recalculated after deduction of 15.3 per cent ferroan spinel and 7.1 per cent ilmenite.

O c c u r.   Originally found in the Routevare district, Lapland, in magnetite ore, associated with corundum, ferroan spinel, gibbsite, pyrrhotite, and ilmenite. In a corundum-rich magnetite ore at Rödstand, Söndmöre, western Norway. In the United States near Whittles, Pittsylvania County, Virginia, with hercynite, magnetite, and corundum (emery rock), and similarly in the emery deposits near Peekskill, Westchester County, New York.

N a m e. After Professor Arvid Gustaf Högbom of the University of Upsala.

Ref.

1. Symmetry class not known.
2. The rhombohedron given by Gavelin (1916) is here taken as the unit, because the assignment by Gavelin of $\{02\bar{2}1\}$ to the only terminal form is not justified.
3. Calculated from the specific gravity of an analyzed mixture of hoegbomite, spinel, and ilmenite.
4. Ross in Watson, *Am. Min.*, **10**, 1 (1925) gives: O 1.848, dark brown; E 1.817, light golden brown to nearly colorless, for unanalyzed material from Virginia.
5. Schneiderhöhn and Ramdohr (**2**, 537, 1931).

7312   S A P P H I R I N E $[(Mg,Fe)_{15}(Al,Fe)_{34}Si_7O_{80}]$. Sapphirin *Giesecke* (Stromeyer, *Göttingen gel. Anz.* 1994, 1819; *Untersuch. Misch. Mineralk.*, **1**, 391 [1821]). Sapphirine. Sapphirin pt. [rest blue spinel] *Hausmann* (427, 1847).   Saphirine.

C r y s t.   Monoclinic; prismatic — $2/m$.

$a : b : c = 0.69 : 1 : 0.70,\ \beta = 111°27';^1\ p_0 : q_0 : r_0 = 1.01 : 0.65 : 1$

$r_2 : p_2 : q_2 = 1.53 : 1.56 : 1,\ \mu = 68°33';\ p_0' = 1.09,\ q_0' = 0.70,\ x_0' = 0.39$

Forms:[2]

		ϕ	ρ	ϕ_2	$\rho_2 = B$	C	A
c	001	90°00'	21°27'	68°33'	90°00'	. . . .	68°33'
b	010	0 00	90 00	. . . . .	0 00	90°00'	90 00
a	100	90 00	90 00	0 00	90 00	68 33	. . . .
m	110	57 17	90 00	0 00	57 17	72 05	32 43
f	011	29 18	38 45	68 33	56 55	33 05	72 09
q	021	15 41	55 29	68 33	37 30	52 30	77 08
e	101	90 00	55 57	34 03	90 00	34 30	34 03
d	$\bar{1}01$	90 00	35 00	125 00	90 00	56 27	125 00
u	$\bar{1}31$	−18 26	65 41	125 00	30 10	73 52	106 45

Structure cell.[3] a_0 9.70, b_0 14.55, c_0 10.05; $a_0 : b_0 : c_0 = 0.667 : 1 : 0.691$.

Habit.   Tabular $\{010\}$, sometimes also slightly elongated $[001]$. Usually in disseminated grains, or aggregations of grains.

P h y s.   Cleavage $\{100\}$, $\{001\}$, and $\{010\}$, indistinct.[4]   Fracture subconchoidal to uneven. H. $7\frac{1}{2}$, decreasing with alteration. G. 3.4–3.5, 3.486 (Fiskernaes[5]). Luster vitreous. Color pale blue, bluish or greenish gray; also green. Transparent.

O p t.[6]   In transmitted light, pale blue in color. Broad polysynthetic twinning on one or possibly two laws is sometimes observed.[7]

	n^8	n_{Na}^9	n_{red}^{10}
Orient.	(Transvaal, anal. 3)	(Quebec, anal. 6)	(Fiskernaes, anal. 1)
X	1.714	1.729	1.7055
$Y = b$	1.719		1.7088
Z	1.720		1.7112

Pleochroism: X pinkish buff, yellowish, pale smoky brown, colorless; Y sky blue, sapphire blue, greenish blue; Z dark sky blue, dark sapphire blue. Bx. neg. $(-)$. Dispersion inclined, $r < v$, distinct. $Z \wedge c = 6°$ in the obtuse axial angle. $2V = 50\frac{1}{2}°$. Absorption $X < Y < Z$.

Chem. An oxide of magnesium, aluminum, and silicon. Fe^2 substitutes for Mg to about Mg : Fe $= 3 : 1$ in anal. 6, and Fe^3 substitutes in small amounts for Al. The analyses also clearly show a complex substitution involving Al and (Si,Mg), and the formula may be represented as $Mg_{15-x}Al_{34}Al_{2x}Si_{7-x}O_{80}$ where x ranges between 0 and 1 in the listed analyses. Small amounts of B have been reported.[11]

Anal.[12]

	1	2	3	4	5	6
MgO	19.78	21.42	15.22	16.23	17.13	15.28
FeO	0.65	0.78	3.09	4.31	7.65	9.08
Fe$_2$O$_3$	0.93	1.42	1.69	.....	.....	.....
Al$_2$O$_3$	65.29	60.46	62.38	61.69	60.49	62.98
SiO$_2$	12.83	15.08	12.95	15.19	14.56	13.44
H$_2$O$^+$	.....	0.01	4.80	1.60	.....	.....
H$_2$O$^-$	.....	0.05	0.05	0.19	.....	.....
Rem.	0.31	1.17	0.10	0.86	0.56	.....
Total	99.79	100.39	100.28	100.07	100.39	100.78
G.	3.486		3.398	3.31	3.542	3.54

1. Fiskernaes, Greenland. Rem. is ign. loss.[13] 2. Itrongay, Madagascar. Rem. is Na$_2$O trace, K$_2$O trace, CaO 0.42, B$_2$O$_3$ 0.75.[14] 3. Transvaal. Rem. is MnO trace, Na$_2$O trace, K$_2$O 0.10.[15] 4. Val Codera, Italy. Average of 2. Rem. is CaO 0.49, MnO 0.12, TiO$_2$ 0.25.[16] 5. Vizagapatam district, India. Rem. is ign. loss.[17] 6. St. Urbain, Quebec.[9]

Var. *Ferroan.* Contains Fe^2 in substitution for Mg to at least Mg : Fe $= 3 : 1$ (anal. 6). Material with Mg : Fe $= 0.44 : 1$ has been reported[18] but is not well validated. The blue color of the mineral deepens with increase in tenor of Fe^2.

Tests. B.B. alone and with borax infusible. Insoluble in HF and other acids. Slowly decomposed by fusion in Na$_2$CO$_3$ or KHSO$_4$.

Occur. A high-temperature metamorphic mineral, found associated with spinel, corundum, calcic plagioclase, biotite, sillimanite, cordierite, anthophyllite, kornerupine, and hypersthene in rocks relatively high in Al and Mg and low in Si. Sapphirine probably also occurs as a primary magmatic product in subsilicic rocks (Quebec).

Originally found with anthophyllite at Fiskernaes on the west coast of Greenland. With hypersthene in enclosures of biotite-schist in pegmatite near Marignisandougou, Guinea. In Madagascar near Itrongay, and with sillimanite, cordierite, almandite and corundum in highly aluminous paragneisses at Sakena. With corundum and biotite in a coarse granitic rock in the northern Transvaal. At the Alpe Brasciadega, Val Codera, Prov. Sondrio, Italy. In a contact metamorphosed rock in the Vizagapatam district, India, with hercynite and hypersthene. In the United States in sillimanite-cordierite schist in the Peekskill emery district, New York. At St. Urbain, Quebec, as a primary constituent (?) in an ilmenite and rutile differentiate from anorthosite.

Alter. Sapphirine alters easily by hydration, and ultimately may break down to a mixture of biotite and corundum or to a talclike substance.

A r t i f.[19] Efforts to synthesize sapphirine from fusion have been unsuccessful. Sapphirine melts incongruently at 1500° to spinel, sillimanite and a siliceous glass.

N a m e. In allusion to the sapphire-like color.

Ref.

1. Lacroix (5, 73, 1913) on Madagascar crystals as recalculated by Mountain, *Min. Mag.*, **25**, 277 (1939), with *c* halved as indicated by the x-ray rotation data of Gossner and Mussgnug, *Jb. Min.*, **58**, 233 (1928). The angles of the prism zone conform to those observed earlier by Ussing, *Zs. Kr.*, **15**, 600 (1889), on Greenland crystals, but none of the measured angles of Mountain (1939) correspond to the angle given by Ussing for (010) ∧ (011) and the exact correlation of the two orientations remains obscure. Transformation, Lacroix to x-ray : 100/010/00½.
2. Mountain (1939). Rare: {270}, {111}, {121}, {141}.
3. Gossner and Mussgnug (1928) by rotation method.
4. All the cleavages have not been noted by all observers. {001} and {100} noted by Mountain (1939) and {010} established by Cornelius and Dittler, *Jb. Min.*, **59**, 27 (1929); the {010} cleavage possibly may be a parting due to twinning.
5. Ussing (1889) by suspension in a heavy solution.
6. The optical properties as given by different observers are not entirely in agreement; the data here given are largely those of Mountain (1939).
7. Cornelius and Dittler (1929) on material from Val Codera, Italy, and Berman (priv. comm., 1941) on material from Fiskernaes.
8. Mountain (1939).
9. Warren, *Am. J. Sc.*, **33**, 263 (1912).
10. Ussing (1889), average of two prism determinations.
11. Lacroix and de Gramont, *Bull. soc. min.*, **44**, 67 (1921), in material from Madagascar and Greenland.
12. For additional analyses see Doelter (2 [2], 628, 1915).
13. Ussing (1889).
14. Raoult anal. in Lacroix and de Gramont (1921).
15. Mountain (1939).
16. Cornelius and Dittler (1929).
17. Walker and Collins, *Rec. Geol. Sur. India*, **36**, pt. 1,1 (1907).
18. Middlemiss, *Rec. Geol. Sur. India*, **31**, 38 (1904), from Vizagapatam, India.
19. Dittler, *Zs. anorg. Chem.*, **174**, 342 (1928).

732   **P L U M B O F E R R I T E** [$PbFe_4O_7$].   *Igelström (Ak. Stockholm Öfv.*, **38** [8], 27, 1881).

C r y s t. Hexagonal — *R*; trigonal trapezohedral — 3 2.

$$a : c = 1 : 3.9720; \qquad p_0 : r_0 = 4.5865 : 1$$

Forms:[1]

		φ	ρ	M	A_2
c	0001	.....	0°00′	90°00′	90°00′
m	10$\bar{1}$0	30°00′	90 00	60 00	90 00
a	11$\bar{2}$0	0 00	90 00	90 00	60 00
n	10$\bar{1}$6	30 00	37 23½	72 19½	90 00
p	10$\bar{1}$2	30 00	66 26½	62 43½	90 00
r	10$\bar{1}$1	30 00	77 42	60 45	90 00
s	40$\bar{4}$1	30 00	86 53	60 03	90 00
e	11$\bar{2}$2	0 00	75 52	90 00	60 59½
f	11$\bar{2}$1	0 00	82 49½	90 00	60 15½
h	5·5·$\overline{10}$·3	0 00	85 41	90 00	60 05½
i	22$\bar{4}$1	0 00	86 23	90 00	60 04

Less common:

d	52$\bar{7}$0	l	10$\bar{1}$8	q	2023	t	41$\bar{5}$9	v	51$\bar{6}$8	x	8·5·$\bar{13}$·9
k	10$\bar{1}$9	o	10$\bar{1}$3	g	5·5·$\overline{10}$·4	u	5·2·$\bar{7}$·12	w	8·3·$\bar{11}$·13	y	31$\bar{4}$3
										z	21$\bar{3}$2

Structure cell.[1] Space group possibly $C3_12$; a_0 11.86, c_0 47.14; a_0 : $c_0 = 1 : 3.9747$; contains $Pb_{42}Fe_{168} O_{294}$ in the hexagonal unit.

Habit. Crystals thick tabular {0001}. Commonly in cleavable masses.

Phys. Cleavage {0001}. H. 5. G. 6.07; 5.94 (calc. for anal. 3), 6.55 (calc. for pure $PbFe_4O_7$). Color nearly black. Streak red.

Chem. Lead iron oxide, or lead ferrate, $PbFe_4O_7$, with minor amounts of Mn, Ca, Fe^2, Mg.

Anal.[2]

	1	2	3
PbO	41.14	32.65	33.03
Fe_2O_3	58.86	63.53	63.01
FeO	.....	0.70	0.78
MnO	.....	1.55	1.41
CaO	.....	0.39	0.40
MgO	.....	0.88	0.34
Rem.	.....	0.30	0.78
Total	100.00	100.00	99.75
G.	6.55	5.98–6.02	6.07

1. $PbFe_4O_7$. 2. Jakobsberg, Sweden. Rem. is H_2O 0.30. Average of two analyses after deducting small amounts of impurities and recalculating.[3] 3. Jakobsberg, Sweden. Rem. is K_2O 0.13, Na_2O 0.17, Sb_2O_3 0.25, TiO_2 0.08, insol. 0.15.[1]

Tests. Easily soluble in HCl with evolution of Cl and a residue of lead chloride.

Occur. In Sweden at the Jakobsberg manganese mine, Nordmark, Vermland, associated with jacobsite, andradite, and copper in narrow veins in granular limestone; also from the Sjö mine in Örebro.

Name. From the composition.

Ref.

1. Johansson, *Zs. Kr.*, **68**, 87 (1928). Rare forms:

54$\bar{9}$0	4·1·$\bar{5}$·24	9·7·$\overline{16}$·21	32$\bar{5}$5	53$\bar{8}$5	6·4·$\overline{10}$·3
1·0·$\bar{1}$·13	10·7·$\overline{17}$·56	9·5·$\overline{14}$·22	11·4·$\overline{15}$·16	32$\bar{5}$3	43$\bar{7}$2
1·0·$\bar{1}$·10	3·1·$\bar{4}$·14	32$\bar{5}$7	53$\bar{8}$8	41$\bar{5}$3	7·3·$\overline{10}$·3
10$\bar{1}$7	6·5·$\overline{11}$·24	8·3·$\overline{11}$·14	21$\bar{3}$3	6·5·$\overline{11}$·5	61$\bar{7}$2
10$\bar{1}$4	9·7·$\overline{16}$·35	9·5·$\overline{14}$·17	8·5·$\overline{13}$·12	10·4·$\overline{14}$·7	72$\bar{9}$2
40$\bar{4}$3	3·2·$\bar{5}$·11	8·1·$\bar{9}$·12	71$\bar{8}$8	31$\bar{4}$2	7·5·$\overline{12}$·2
11$\bar{2}$8	11·4·$\overline{15}$·28	42$\bar{6}$7	81$\bar{9}$9	9·8·$\overline{17}$·7	7·3·$\overline{10}$·1
11$\bar{2}$4	5·1·$\bar{6}$·12	7·2·$\bar{9}$·11	10·7·$\overline{17}$·14	71$\bar{8}$4	
22$\bar{4}$7	5·4·$\bar{9}$·15	41$\bar{5}$6	52$\bar{7}$6	10·7·$\overline{17}$·7	
22$\bar{4}$3	10·7·$\overline{17}$·28	7·3·$\overline{10}$·11	9·5·$\overline{14}$·11	9·7·$\overline{16}$·6	
10·7·$\overline{17}$·98	5·3·$\bar{8}$·13	51$\bar{6}$7	61$\bar{7}$6	7·4·$\overline{11}$·4	
2·1·$\bar{3}$·14	7·1·$\bar{8}$·15	9·1·$\overline{10}$·12	9·5·$\overline{14}$·10	10·4·$\overline{14}$·5	

The above list of forms from Johansson gives them only in the plus-right dodecant, and many of the forms do not obey the rhombohedral rule of indices $(h + i + l = 3n)$. The form list as given is therefore not adequate.

2. Older analyses presumably on impure material by Igelström, *Geol. För. Förh.*, **16**, 594 (1894).

3. Mauzelius anal. in Aminoff *Geol. För. Förh.*, **47**, 266 (1925).

733　　MAGNETOPLUMBITE [(Pb,Mn^2,Mn^3)(Fe^3,Mn^3,Ti)$_6$O$_{10}$?].　*Amin-off* (*Geol. För. Förh.*, **47**, 283, 1925).

C r y s t.　Hexagonal;　dihexagonal dipyramidal — $6/m\,2/m\,2/m$.

$$a : c = 1 : 3.912;　　p_0 : r_0 = 4.5169 : 1$$

Forms:

	ϕ	ρ
r　$10\bar{1}1$	$30°00'$	$77°31'$

Habit.　Steep pyramidal, doubly terminated.

Structure cell.　Space group $C6/mcc$ or $C6/mcm$;　a_0 6.06,　c_0 23.69; $a_0 : c_0 = 1 : 3.909$;　contains (Pb,Mn^2,Mn^3)$_4$(Fe^3,Mn^3,Ti)$_{24}$O$_{40}$.[2]

P h y s.　Cleavage {0001} perfect.　H. 6.　G. 5.517.　Color gray-black. Streak dark brown.　Strongly magnetic.

C h e m.　An oxide of manganese, lead, titanium, and ferric iron, essentially (Pb,Mn^2,Mn^3)(Fe^3,Mn^3,Ti)$_6$O$_{10}$.[2]　The composition, however, is not well established.

Anal.[3]

PbO	MnO	Al$_2$O$_3$	Fe$_2$O$_3$	Mn$_2$O$_3$	TiO$_2$	Rem.	Total
20.02	3.73	1.86	52.22	17.27	4.14	0.76	100.0

1. Långban.　Rem. is CaO 0.28, MgO 0.15, Cr$_2$O$_3$ 0.25, H$_2$O 0.08.

Tests.　Slowly soluble in HCl with slight evolution of Cl.

O c c u r.　Found as distinct crystals associated principally with manganophyllite and kentrolite at Långban, Vermland, Sweden.

N a m e.　Indicates the magnetic properties and lead content of the mineral.

Ref.

1. Aminoff (1925).　Adelsköld, *Ark. Kemi*, **12** [29] (1938), gives $C6/mmc$ as the space group of an artificial material supposedly the same as magnetoplumbite.
2. Using Aminoff's x-ray data and the corrected analysis of Blix, *Geol. För. Förh.*, **59** 300 (1937).　Previous formulas are not close to the analytical results.　The supposed composition PbFe$_{12}$O$_{19}$, by analogy with so-called β-alumina, proposed by Adelsköld (1938) is not indicated by analysis.
3. The original analysis, by Almström in Aminoff (1925), failed to indicate the trivalent nature of most of the manganese.　Cited analysis by Blix (1937).

734　　HEMATOPHANITE [Pb(Cl,OH)$_2$·4PbO·2Fe$_2$O$_3$?].　Hämatophanit *Johansson* (*Zs. Kr.*, **68**, 102, 1928).

C r y s t.[1]　Tetragonal;　dipyramidal ditetragonal — $4/m\,2/m\,2/m$.

Structure cell.[2]　Space group probably $P\bar{4}2m$, $P4mm$, $P42$, or $P4/mmm$;　a_0 7.801,　c_0 15.23;　$a_0 : c_0 = 1 : 1.952$;　contains Pb$_{15}$Fe$_{12}$(Cl,OH)$_6$O$_{30}$ (?).

Habit.[3]　Thin tablets {001}, in part in lamellar aggregates.

P h y s.　Cleavage {001} very good;　also a parting (?) inclined to {001}.　H. 2–3.　G. 7.70.　Luster submetallic.　Color deep red-brown. Streak yellowish red.　Transparent in very thin flakes.

O p t.　In transmitted light, blood-red in color.　Uniaxial negative (−).　Birefringence low.

C h e m. An oxide of lead and ferric iron containing Cl. Formula uncertain, perhaps $Pb(Cl,OH)_2 \cdot 4PbO \cdot 2Fe_2O_3$.[3] Analysis gave (average of two): Na_2O 0.38, K_2O 0.17, CaO 0.26, MgO 0.06, MnO 0.29, FeO 0.22, PbO 73.26, Fe_2O_3 22.01, $FeTiO_3$ 0.20, Cl_2 2.17, H_2O, 0.73, insoluble 0.42, total (less $O = Cl_2 = 0.49$) 99.68.

Tests. Easily soluble in dilute HCl or HNO_3.

O c c u r. Found with plumboferrite, jacobsite, andradite, native copper, cuprite and cerussite in calcite at Jacobsberg, near Finnmossen, Wermland, Sweden.

N a m e. Presumably in allusion to the blood-red color in transmitted light.

Ref.

1. Symmetry established by x-ray Laue study, Johansson (1928). Morphological data are lacking.
2. From rotation and powder x-ray measurements of Johansson (1928).
3. Johansson (1928).

741 **Q U E N S E L I T E** [$PbMnO_2(OH)$]. *Flink* (*Geol. För. Förh.*, 47, 377, 1925).

C r y s t. Monoclinic; prismatic — $2/m$.

$a : b : c = 0.9828 : 1 : 1.6869$, $\beta\ 93°29'$;[1] $p_0 : q_0 : r_0 = 1.7164 : 1.6838 : 1$

$r_2 : p_2 : q_2 = 0.5939 : 1.0194 : 1$, $\mu\ 86°31'$; $p_0'1.7196$, $q_0'1.6869$, $x_0'0.0609$

Forms:

		ϕ	ρ	ϕ_2	ρ_2	C	A
c	001	90°00′	3°29′	86°31′	90°00′	.....	86°31′
b	010	0 00	90 00	....	0 00	90°00′	90 00
a	100	90 00	90 00	0 00	90 00	86 31	.....
m	110	45 33	90 00	0 00	45 33	87 31	44 27
e	011	2 04	59 21½	86 31	30 42½	59 17½	88 43½
d	3̄01	−90 00	78 54	168 54	90 00	82 23	168 54
p	111	46 33	67 49	29 19½	50 26½	65 24½	47 46

Habit. Tabular {010}; also slightly elongated [001] or [100]. Striated on {011} ‖ [100].

P h y s. Cleavage {001} perfect, almost micaceous. Thin laminae flexible. H. 2½. G. 6.84.[2] Luster metallic to adamantine. Color pitch-black. Streak dark brown-gray. Opaque. In polished section[3] strongly anisotropic.

O p t.[4] Deep brown in transmitted light. $X = b = 2.30\pm$; Y near c. Biaxial positive $(+)$?, absorption $Z > X$.

C h e m. An oxide of lead and manganese, $Pb_2Mn_2O_5 \cdot H_2O$ or $PbMnO_2(OH)$.

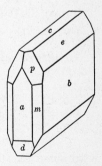

Långban, Sweden.

Anal.

	PbO	MnO	H_2O	O	Rem.	Total
1	71.74	22.79	2.89	2.58	....	100.00
2	70.21	23.44	3.05	2.40	0.90	100.00

1. $Pb_2Mn_2O_5 \cdot H_2O$.   2. Långban. Recalc. after deduction of 1.46 per cent $CaCO_3$ and 0.28 per cent Fe_2O_3. Rem. is MgO 0.30, CaO 0.15, Na_2O 0.28, K_2O 0.17^5.

Tests. Infusible at red heat. Soluble in dilute acids, including acetic, with evolution of Cl.

O c c u r. Found at Långban, Sweden, in the "Amerika" stope, associated with calcite and barite in crevices cutting hausmannite, hematite, braunite ore.

N a m e. After Professor Percy Dudgeon Quensel (1881–) of the University of Stockholm.

Ref.

1. Flink (1925) modified by LaForge (priv. comm.). Wolfe (priv. comm., 1940) measured crystals from a specimen identified by Flink and obtained $a : b : c = 1.2659 : 1 : 0.9416$, $\beta = 102°06'$. The measurements, however, were no better than those of Flink and sufficient material for a thorough study was not available. The relation of Wolfe's axes to Flink's are approximately $102/030/\overline{3}00$.
2. Calculated from the value (6.775) for the analyzed mixture with calcite and magnetite — Ahlström in Flink (1925).
3. Orcel and Pavlovitch, *Bull. soc. min.*, **54**, 155 (1931).
4. Berman (priv. comm., 1940) on material identified by Flink.
5. Ahlström anal. in Flink (1925).

7421   **P E R O V S K I T E** [$CaTiO_3$]. Perowskit *Rose* (*Ann. Phys.*, **48**, 558, 1839; **2**, 128, 1842). Perofskite. Dysanalyte *Knop* (*Zs. Kr.*, **1**, 284, 1877), [in part perovskite of earlier writers]. Metaperovskite *Fedorov* (*Zs. Kr.*, **20**, 74, 1892). Knopite *Holmquist* (*Geol. För. Förh.*, **15**, 588, 1893; **16**, 73, 1894). Loparite *Fersmann* (*C. r. ac. sc. Russie*, 59, 1922; *Trans. Northern Sc. Econ. Exped.*, **16**, 17, 68, 1923); *Kouznetzov* (*Bull. comité géol.*, 44, 663, 1925).

C r y s t. Pseudoisometric; possibly monoclinic.[1]

Forms:[2] (in the isometric orientation)

a 001 d 011 o 111 g 023 δ 034 ζ 045 m 113 p 122 T 249

Structure cell. a_0 (for a pseudoisometric unit).

	a_0
Perovskite (Urals[3])	7.645 ± 0.015
Perovskite (Zermatt[4])	7.590
Columbian perovskite (Magnet Cove[4])	7.652
Columbian perovskite (Kaiserstuhl[3])	7.677 ± 0.018
Columbian perovskite (Kola[5])	7.71 ± 0.02

Contains $(Ca,Na,Ce)_8(Ti,Cb)_8O_{24}$.

Habit. Crystals usually cubic and sometimes highly modified, but the planes often irregularly distributed. Cubic faces striated parallel [001] and apparently penetration twins (as if of pyritohedral individuals); also striated ∥ [110]. Sometimes {001} less developed with {113} and {449} prominent. Also (especially in cerian and columbian varieties) as cubo-octahedra or octahedra. Rarely in reniform masses showing small cubes on the surface, or massive granular.

Twinning.[6] On {111} as: (*a*) penetration twins[6] (especially in the Ce or Cb varieties); (*b*) lamellar twinning of very complex nature.[7]

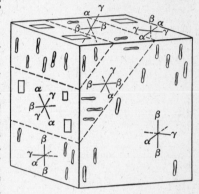

P h y s. Cleavage {001} imperfect. Fracture uneven to subconchoidal. Brittle. H. 5½. G. 4.01 ± 0.04, 4.04 (calc. for artif. $CaTiO_3$[8]); the specific gravity increases in the cerian and columbian varieties (see analyses). Luster adamantine to metallic-adamantine and metallic in black material; sometimes dull. Color black, grayish black, brownish black, reddish brown to shades of yellow; the columbian varieties are black. Streak colorless, grayish. Dark-colored material transparent only in thin splinters.

O p t.[9] In transmitted light colorless to dark brown. Either isotropic[10] (commonly in the cerian and columbian varieties) or weakly birefringent.[11] Biaxial positive (+), $2V = 90° ±$,[12] $r > v$; $Y = c$, $X = a$ (for the orthorhombic interpretation);[13] or $Y = b$, $Z \wedge c$ (or a) $= 45°$ (in the monoclinic interpretation).[14] Twin lamellae parallel to {001} (in the orthorhombic orientation) show extinction at 45° to the lamination. Pleochroism weak with $Z > X$. In polished section[15] dark bluish gray with brown internal reflections; not noticeably anisotropic.

	n	LOCALITY
Perovskite	2.34	Iron Hill, Colo.[16]
Cerian perovskite	2.37	Kola Peninsula (anal. 5[17])
Cerian perovskite	2.30	Alnö, Sweden[18]
Columbian perovskite	2.33 ± 0.02	Magnet Cove, Ark.[18]

C h e m. Essentially calcium titanium oxide, $CaTiO_3$. Cb substitutes for Ti up to Cb : Ti = 2 : 5 (anal. 12). Ta has been reported in material from Magnet Cove, Arkansas (anal. 10), but this observation has not been verified.[19] Rare earths, chiefly Ce, substitute for Ca up to Ce : Ca = 4 : 7 (anal. 8); a high rare-earth content also has been reported (anal. 7) in material from Siberia not shown certainly to be perovskite. Fe^2, to Fe : Ca = 1 : 5 (anal. 9), and (Na,K), to (Na,K) : Ca = 1 : 1 (anal. 8), also substitute for Ca. Small amounts of Sr and V have been reported.[19]

Anal.[20]

	1	2	3	4	5	6
Na_2O	.....	.....	.....	.....	.....	0.79
K_2O	.....	.....	.....	.....	.....	0.38
CaO	41.24	40.69	40.29	38.35	37.52	33.32
MgO	.....	trace	.....	.....	0.14	.....
FeO	.....	.....	0.86	2.07	0.70	4.19
$(Y,Er)_2O_3$	.....	.....	.....	.....	}2.23	.....
$(Ce,La)_2O_3$	.....	.....	.....	.....		6.81
SiO_2	.....	.....	.....	.....	0.96	.....
TiO_2	58.76	58.67	58.63	58.66	56.35	54.12
Cb_2O_5	.....	.....	.....	.....	.....	.....
Ta_2O_5	.....	.....	.....	.....	.....	.....
H_2O	.....	.....	.....	.....	0.73	0.21
Rem.	.....	.....	.....	.....	1.04	.....
Total	100.00	99.36	99.78	99.08	99.67	99.82
G.	4.04		3.98			4.21

1. $CaTiO_3$.   2. Emerese, Val d'Aosta, Italy.[21]   3. St. Ambrogio, Piedmont, Italy.[22] 4. Oberwiesenthal, Saxony.[23]   5. Cerian perovskite.   Afrikanda station, Kola Peninsula.   Rem. is Al_2O_3 0.24, Fe_2O_3 0.78, MnO 0.02, H_2O^+ 0.57, H_2O^- 0.16.[24]   6. Cerian perovskite (*knopite*).   Norrvik, Alnö region, Sweden.[25]

	7	8	9	10	11	12
Na_2O	not det.	8.60	4.37	.....	trace	1.72
K_2O	not det.	0.43	.....	.....	.....	0.44
CaO	11.00	5.08	25.60	33.22	21.69	23.51
MgO	0.24	.....	.....	0.74	trace	.....
FeO	1.70	.....	9.22	.....	1.81	5.69
$(Y,Er)_2O_3$	4.43	1.54	.....	5.42	.....	.....
$(Ce,La)_2O_3$	32.75	33.17	2.80	0.10	8.80	3.08
SiO_2	trace	0.47	2.21	0.08	trace	0.33
TiO_2	47.59	50.24	50.93	44.12	39.90	38.70
Cb_2O_5	.....	not det.	4.86	4.38	22.32	25.99
Ta_2O_5	.....	.....	.....	5.08	trace	.....
H_2O	.....	.....	.....	.....	.....	.....
Rem.	1.07	0.04	0.23	6.39	4.93	0.82
Total	98.78	99.57	100.22	99.53	99.45	100.28
G.	4.122	4.88	4.21	4.18	4.13	4.26

7. Cerian perovskite (?) Siberia.   Rem. is MnO 0.84, ign. loss 0.23.[26]   8. Cerian, alkalian, and columbian perovskite (*loparite*).   Chibina tundra, Kola Peninsula. $(Ce,La)_2O_3$ includes Ce_2O_3 18.99 and $(Di,La)_2O_3$ 14.18.[27]   Contains a large but undetermined amount of Cb[28].   Rem. is ZrO_2.   9. Columbian perovskite (*dysanalyte*).   Vogtsburg, Kaiserstuhl, Germany.   Rem. is MnO 0.23.[29]   10. Columbian perovskite.   Magnet Cove, Ark.   Rem. is Fe_3O_4 0.73, Fe_2O_3 5.66.[30]   11. Columbian perovskite.   Uva Province, Ceylon.   Rem. is MnO 0.17, Fe_2O_3 4.76. $(Ce,La)_2O_3$ contains Ce 60 per cent, La 25 per cent, Di 10 per cent.[31]   12. Columbian perovskite.   Vogtsburg, Kaiserstuhl, Germany.   Rem. is Al_2O_3 0.82.[32]

Var. Ordinary. Essentially $CaTiO_3$. Color yellow to brownish black.

Columbian. Dysanalyte Knop (*Zs. Kr.*, **1**, 284, 1877). Loparite *Fersmann* (*C.r. ac. sc. Russie*, **59**, 1922; *Trans. Northern Sc. Econ. Exped.*, **16**, 17, 68, 1923); *Kouznetzov* (*Bull. comité géol.*, **44**, 663, 1925). Contains Cb in substitution for Ti to at least Cb : Ti = 2 : 5 (anal. 12). Dysanalyte has been shown to be a variety of perovskite.[33] Material from the Chibina tundra, Kola (*loparite*, anal. 8) with a relatively high specific gravity of

4.88^{34} may have a Cb content in excess of this ratio.[35] Alkalies, rare earths, and Fe^2 are usually present in addition to Cb. Color black. Habit frequently cubo-octahedral or octahedral.

Cerian. Knopite *Holmquist* (*Geol. För. Förh.*, **15**, 588, 1893; **16**, 73, 1894). Contains rare earths, largely Ce, in substitution for Ca to at least Ce : Ca = 4 : 7 (anal. 8). Alkalies and Fe^2 are also present. Color black. Habit cubic or cubo-octahedral. Knopite has been shown to be of the same structure as perovskite.[36]

Tests. B.B. infusible. Decomposed by hot concentrated H_2SO_4 and by HF.

O c c u r. Perovskite occurs both as an accessory mineral of the magmatic stage and as a late stage deuteric mineral in basic igneous rocks, especially those containing melilite, nepheline, or leucite (Eifel). Also in basic pegmatites associated with such rocks, and in metamorphosed limestones at the contact with alkalic or basic intrusives (Magnet Cove). Also found in chlorite or talc schists (Urals). A few of the many known localities are listed below.

Originally found in fine crystals in chlorite schist in the Slatoust district, Urals. In crystals and reniform masses in talc schist by the Findelen glacier near Zermatt, Switzerland, and in chlorite schist on the Wildkreuzjoch, Pfitsch, in the Tirolian Alps. A columbian variety (*dysanalyte*) occurs in contact metamorphosed limestone at Vogtsburg and Schelingen in the Kaiserstuhl, Baden, Germany, and perovskite occurs as an accessory mineral in the alkalic-basic intrusives of this district. In the nepheline- and leucite-bearing basaltic lavas of the Eifel and Laacher See districts in Rhenish Prussia. In nepheline rocks at Oberwiesenthal, Saxony. Found in Italy in the Val Malenco, at Emerese in the Val d'Aosta, and at St. Ambrogio, Susa, in Piedmont. In ejected blocks of limestone on Mount Somma, Vesuvius. Reported in magnetite-rich igneous rocks at Catalão, Goyaz, and near Bagagem, Minas Geraes, in Brazil. Cerian perovskite (*knopite*) occurs in contact metamorphosed limestone on the island of Alnö, Sweden, and nearby at Norrvik and Kringelfjärd on the mainland. A cerian variety also occurs in pegmatite segregations in a pyroxenite near Afrikanda station on the Kola Peninsula, Russia, and a columbian and rare-earth variety (*loparite*) is found with eudialyte, aegirite, sphene in pegmatites of the contact zone of the nephelinitic intrusive of the Chibina tundra, Kola.

In the United States a columbian variety occurs in limestone metamorphosed at the contact with alkalic rocks at Magnet Cove, Arkansas. Perovskite occurs as an accessory mineral in peridotite at Syracuse, New York, and Elliot County, Kentucky. In nepheline-syenite pegmatite in the Bearpaw Mountains, Montana. Found abundantly as a magmatic accessory mineral and as a late-stage deuteric product in melilite rocks in the Iron Hill district, Gunnison County, Colorado.[37] A cerian variety occurs in a basic pegmatite at Moose Creek, near Leanchoil, British Columbia.

A l t e r. Observed as an alteration product of sphene and ilmenite. Pseudomorphs of magnetite and of ilmenite after perovskite have been found; also reported in part or entirety altered to a fine grained yellow to brown mixture largely composed of anatase.

A r t i f. Cubic and octahedral crystals of $CaTiO_3$ identical in optical and other characters with natural perovskite are obtained by heating the constituents with a flux.[38] Also observed in the systems $CaO-TiO_2-SiO_2$-Al_2O_3 and $CaO-TiO_2-SiO_2$,[39] and in Ti-rich ultra-basic slags.[40] Artificial $NaCbO_3$ ($a_0 = 7.78$) is isostructural with $CaTiO_3$.

N a m e. Perovskite after Count L. A. Perovski of St. Petersburg. Knopite after A. Knop (1828–1893), German mineralogist who discovered the columbian pervoskite (dysanalyte). Dysanalyte from δυσανάλυτος, *hard to undo*, in allusion to the difficulty of analysis. Loparite from the Russian name for the Lapp inhabitants of the Kola Peninsula.

Ref.

1. Morphologically perovskite conforms to isometric symmetry, but the crystals consist internally of regularly intergrown optically biaxial lamellae. The true symmetry of the lamellae has been the subject of much investigation. For general surveys of this work see especially Ben Saude, Preiss. *Göttingen*, 1882; Holmquist, *Bull. Geol. Inst. Upsala*, **3**, 181 (1897); Bowman (*Min. Mag.* **15**, 156, 1908); Zedlitz, *Jb. Min., Beil.-Bd.*, **75**, 245 (1939). The optical characters (see further the references under 9) and the symmetry of the etch figures (see Baumhauer, *Zs. Kr.*, **4**, 187 [1880], Ben Saude [1882], and Bowman [1908]) have been variously interpreted as indicating orthorhombic or monoclinic symmetry. Baumhauer (1880) and Bowman (1908) accepted the symmetry as orthorhombic with $a : b : c = 1 : 1 : 0.7071$. Böggild, *Zs. Kr.*, **50**, 408 (1912), gave $a : b : c = 0.9881 : 1 : 1.4078$. However, the x-ray Laue study of Zedlitz (1939) indicates that the true symmetry probably is monoclinic. The x-ray powder data of Barth, *Norsk Geol. Tidsskr.*, **8**, 201 (1925), Levi and Natta, *Acc. Linc., Att.*, **2** [6], 39 (1925), Zedlitz (1939), is consistent with a (pseudo-) isometric cell with a_0 about 7.6 Å. If the monoclinic interpretation of Zedlitz (1939) is valid the {001} of Bowman (1908) must be the {010} of a monoclinic orientation. Transformations: Böggild to isometric orientation $1\bar{1}0/110/001$; Des Cloizeaux to isometric $\frac{1}{2}\frac{1}{2}0/\frac{1}{2}\frac{1}{2}0/001$.
2. Goldschmidt (**5**, 32, 1918; **6**, 131, 1920); Gennaro, *Acc. Torino, Att.*, **66**, 433 (1931). Rare or uncertain:

0·1·14	029	012	1·1·10	112	3·4·10
019	0·3·10	059	115	223	3·4·6
015	0·2·5	0·8·11	449	238	234

Also some vicinal faces.
3. Zedlitz (1939).
4. Barth (1925). The columbian perovskite may be truly isometric. See also Zedlitz (1939) on this point.
5. Gaertner, *Jb. Min., Beil.-Bd.*, **61**, 1 (1930).
6. Kouznetzov (1925) and Holmquist, *Geol. För. Förh.*, **16**, 73, 1894.
7. Interpreted as a mimetic intergrowth of individuals of orthorhombic or lower symmetry, by Des Cloizeaux, *Jb. Min.*, **43**, 372 (1878), Baumhauer (1880), Tschermak, *Min. Mitt.*, **5**, 194 (1882), among others. Considered to be due to inversion by Ben Saude (1882), Klein, *Jb. Min.*, **1**, 248 (1884), and others. Efforts to revert perovskite to an isometric form at elevated temperatures were, however, not successful. See Brauns (349, 1891), Ben Saude (1882), Mügge, *Cbl. Min.*, 36, 1908. For a discussion of the geometrical (and optical) relations of the lamellae, see Bowman (1908) and Böggild (1912).
8. From a_0 7.629 of Zedlitz (1939).
9. Bowman (1908) has studied the anisotropic lamellae optically and by etching. See also Soellner, *Cbl. Min.*, 310 (1912); Des Cloizeaux (**2**, 214, 1893), *Bull. soc. min.*, **16**, 218 (1893); Ben Saude (1882); Klein (1884); Baumhauer (1880); Bøggild (1912); Holmquist (1897). There is no complete consistency in the optical data.

10. In Larsen (71, 1921).

11. Bowman (1908), however, gives a birefringence of 0.017, not in agreement with most observations.

12. Sometimes given as optically negative, and with small axial angle. See also Des Cloizeaux (594, 1867) for changes in axial angle due to heating.

13. Bowman (1908).

14. In conformity with the symmetry revealed by etching and by the position of the optical indicatrix. See Bowman (1908).

15. Ramdohr, *Zbl. Min.*, 300, 1937.

16. Larsen and Hunter, *Washington Ac. Sc., J.*, 4, 473 (1914).

17. Kupletsky, *Ac. sc. U.S.S.R., Bull.*, 109, 1936.

18. Larsen (96, 71, 1921).

19. Barth (1925), by x-ray spectrographic study. Hevesy, Alexander, and Würstlin, *Zs. anorg. Chem.*, 181, 95 (1929), found small amounts of Cb and Ta in perovskite.

20. For additional analyses see Dana (722, 724, 1892); Holmquist, *Geol. För. Förh.*, 16, 73 (1894); Meigen and Hügel, *Zs. anorg. Chem.*, 82, 242 (1913); Ellsworth and Walker, *Geol. Sur. Canada, Summ. Rep. 230A*, 1926; Burova in Kupletsky, *Int. Geol. Cong. XVII Session, Kola Guide*, 48, 1937.

21. Millosevich, *Acc. Linc., Rend.*, 10 [1], 209 (1901).

22. Boeris, *Acc. Linc., Rend.*, 9 [1], 52 (1900).

23. Sauer, *Zs. deutsche geol. Ges.*, 37, 448 (1885).

24. Egorov anal. in Kupletsky (1936).

25. Holmquist (1894).

26. Chernik, *Ac. sc. St. Pétersbourg, Bull.*, 2, 75 (1908) — *Zs. Kr.*, 50, 66 (1912).

27. Knipowicz anal. in Kouznetzov (1925).

28. Reported by Gaertner (1930), by x-ray spectrographic study.

29. Hauser, *Zs. anorg. Chem.*, 60, 237 (1908).

30. Mar, *Am. J. Sc.*, 40, 403 (1890).

31. Chernik, *Ac. sc. St. Pétersbourg, Bull.*, 1913–1914 — *Jb. Min.*, I, 36, 1915.

32. Meigen and Hügel, *Zs. anorg. Chem.*, 82, 242 (1913).

33. Barth (1925), by x-ray study; also Zedlitz, *Fortschr. Min.*, 20, 1 (1936), *Jb. Min., Beil.-Bd.*, 75, 245 (1939).

34. Frondel (priv. comm., 1941) on single crystals by the microbalance; Kouznetzov (1925) gives 4.78.

35. An x-ray study by Gaertner (1930) has shown the identity of structure with perovskite; the close relation to perovskite was earlier recognized by Kouznetzov (1925)

36. From x-ray study of Frondel (priv. comm., 1941); the close relation to perovskite was earlier recognized by Holmquist (1894) and others.

37. Larsen and Goranson, *Am. Min.*, 17, 343 (1932); Larsen and Hunter (1914).

38. See Hintze (2 [2], 1648, 1897) and Zedlitz (1939).

39. Nisioka, *Sc. Rep. Tôhoku Univ.*, 24 [1], 707 (1935), Iwasé and Fukusima, *Bull. Chem. Soc. Japan*, 7, 91 (1932).

40. Carstens, *Zs. Kr.*, 77, 504 (1931).

7422 **Uhligite.** Hauser (*Zs. anorg. Chem.*, 63, 340, 1909). (Not uhligite *Cornu*, *Zs. chem. ind. Koll.*, 4, 17 [1909].)

Pseudoisometric.

Habit. Octahedral with modifying {001}. {111} striated parallel [011]. Twinned on {111}.

Structure cell.[1] a_0 (for a pseudoisometric cell) = 7.639 ± 0.003.

P h y s. Cleavage {001}, imperfect. Fracture conchoidal. H. $5\frac{1}{2}$. G. 4.15 ± 0.1. Luster metallic. Color black. Streak gray to brownish gray. Transparent in thin splinters with a yellowish brown to dark brown color. Exhibits an internal structure of biaxial lamellae, similar to those in perovskite.

C h e m. Essentially an oxide of titanium and calcium, with zirconium and aluminum apparently substituting for titanium. The analysis is close to $Ca_3(Ti,Al,Zr)_9O_{20}$, with Ti : Al : Zr about 61 : 21 : 18. X-ray study,[2] however, indicates that the mineral is structurally identical with perovskite (ABO_3). Analysis gave: CaO 19.00, Fe_2O_3 trace, Al_2O_3 10.50, TiO_2 48.25, ZrO_2 21.95, Cb_2O_5 trace, total 99.70.

O c c u r. Found in nepheline-syenite on the shore of Lake Magadi, Tanganyika, East Africa.

N a m e. After J. Uhlig, leader of the expedition on which the material was collected.

Possibly a variety of perovskite.

Ref.

1. Zedlitz, *Jb. Min., Beil.-Bd.*, **75**, 245 (1939); *Fortschr. Min.*, **20**, 66 (1936), on type material.
2. Zedlitz (1939). The original analysis presumably is in error.

751   **P S E U D O B R O O K I T E** [Fe_2TiO_5].   *Koch* (*Min. Mitt.*, **1**, 77, 344, 1878).

C r y s t. Orthorhombic; dipyramidal — $2/m \, 2/m \, 2/m$.

$a : b : c = 0.9777 : 1 : 0.3727$;[1] $p_0 : q_0 : r_0 = 0.3812 : 0.3727 : 1$

$q_1 : r_1 : p_1 = 0.9777 : 2.6233 : 1$; $r_2 : p_2 : q_2 = 2.6831 : 1.0228 : 1$

Forms:[2]

		ϕ	$\rho = C$	ϕ_1	$\rho_1 = A$	ϕ_2	$\rho_2 = B$
b	010	0°00′	90°00′	90°00′	90°00′	.....	0°00′
a	100	90 00	90 00	.....	0 00	0°00′	90 00
m	110	45 39	90 00	90 00	44 21	0 00	45 39
μ	210	63 57	90 00	90 00	26 03	0 00	63 57
y	031	0 00	48 11½	48 11½	90 00	90 00	41 48½
e	101	90 00	20 52	0 00	69 08	69 08	90 00
l	301	90 00	48 50	0 00	41 10	41 10	90 00
q	111	45 39	28 04	20 26½	70 20½	69 08	70 48
s	121	27 05	39 56	36 42	73 00½	69 08	55 08½
p	131	18 49½	49 45	48 11½	75 44½	69 08	43 44½

Less common forms:

$n\{120\}$ $h\{340\}$ $x\{021\}$ $r\{212\}$ $w\{252\}$ $v\{141\}$ $t\{412\}$

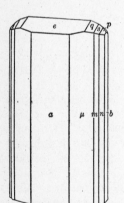

Thomas Mts., Utah.   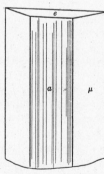 Havredal, Norway.

Structure cell.[3] Space group *Bbmm*; a_0 9.79, b_0 9.93, c_0 3.725; $a_0 : b_0 : c_0 = 0.986 : 1 : 0.375$; contains $Fe_8Ti_4O_{20}$.

Habit. Usually tabular {100} and elongated [001]; sometimes long prismatic or needle-like [001]. {100} and {hk0} striated [001].

Twinning. Reported on various {hk0} planes, but these are doubtful.[4]

Oriented Growths. Pseudobrookite crystals containing oriented inclusions of rutile have been found,[5] but the positions of orientation are not known. Also, pseudobrookite oriented upon hematite[6] and magnetite,[7] as follows:

Pseudobrookite $\{121\}[2\bar{1}0]$ ‖ hematite $\{0001\}[\bar{1}100]$

Pseudobrookite $\{100\}[001]$ ‖ magnetite $\{111\}[110]$

Phys. Cleavage $\{010\}$ distinct[8]. Fracture uneven to subconchoidal. H. 6. G. 4.39 (Havredal[9]), 4.33 (Thomas Range[10]); 4.39 (calc.). Luster metallic adamantine, inclining to greasy on fracture surfaces. Co'or dark reddish brown to brownish black and black. Streak reddish brown or ocher-yellow. Transparent in very thin splinters.

Opt. In transmitted light, yellowish or reddish brown in color. The crystals often are filled with inclusions.

ORIENTATION		n_{Li}^{11}	n^{12}	
X	b	2.38 ± 0.02	$2.347\pm$	Bx. pos. (+). $2V = 50°\pm$.[11] $r < v$.[13]
Y	c	2.39		Absorption in brown, $X < Y > Z$.
Z	a	2.42 ± 0.02	$2.375\pm$	

Chem. An oxide of titanium and ferric iron, Fe_2TiO_5.[14] The analyses usually show a considerable excess of TiO_2 over this formula, apparently due to admixed rutile. The MgO and SiO_2 reported in some analyses also appear to be due to admixture.

Anal.[15]

	1	2	3	4
Fe_2O_3	66.65	57.65	60.57	66.42
TiO_2	33.35	42.35	38.12	33.59
MgO	.....	.....	1.26	.....
Total	100.00	100.00	99.95	100.01
G.	4.39			4.63 ± 0.17

1. Fe_2TiO_5. 2. Aranyer Berg, Transylvania. Recalc. after deduction of SiO_2 1.29, MgO 1.00.[16] 3. Thomas Range, Utah.[17] 4. Artificial Fe_2TiO_5. Average of two analyses.[18]

Tests. B.B. infusible or nearly so. More or less decomposed by HF and by hot HCl or H_2SO_4. Soluble when heated in a closed tube with H_2SO_4 mixed with HF or HCl. Decomposed by fusion with $KHSO_4$.

Occur. Pseudobrookite commonly occurs as a pneumatolytic or fumarolic product in volcanic igneous rocks and as a reaction product of xenoliths in such rocks. Usually associated with hypersthene, tridymite, hematite, magnetite, mica, sanidine, apatite, rutile. Most of the known localities are listed below.

Originally found at Aranyer Berg near Piski, Transylvania, with tridymite, hypersthene (szaboite), and garnet in and near cavities in andesite, and as a recrystallization product of xenoliths in the magma. In Germany found as a product of fumarolic action on basalt at Hessenbrücker Hammer, west of Laubach, Hesse; in altered shonkinite in the Katzenbuckel, Odenwald, Baden, and as a reaction product of granitic xenoliths in the volcanic rocks of the Laacher See, Rhineland. Found upon the lava of 1872 at

Vesuvius, associated with hematite, sellaite (?), magnetite.   In France in cavities in andesite and trachyte at Riveau Grande, Mont-Dore, Puy-de-Dôme, associated with tridymite, hypersthene, sanidine; also in altered basalt at Royal, Puy-de-Dôme.   At Jumilla, Spain, with apatite in an altered igneous rock (jumillite).   At Havredal, Bamle, Norway, embedded in wagnerite altered to apatite; also associated with ilmenite, quartz, feldspar.   In the Haûran Mountains southeast of Damascus, Syria, in altered basalt.   On the Islands Fayal and San Miguel in the Azores, with hypersthene in trachyte.   In altered rhombenporphyry on Kilimanjaro, East Africa, and as a pneumatolytic product in basalt on the Island of Réunion, Indian Ocean.   Found in andesite at Miravalles, Costa Rica.

In the United States pseudobrookite occurs with hypersthene and apatite in cavities in a basalt on Red Cone, Crater Lake, Oregon.   At several localities in the Thomas Range, Utah, in lithophysae in rhyolite associated with topaz, bixbyite, beryl (rose-colored), hematite, ilmenite; the crystals here are lathlike and sometimes several centimeters long.

A r t i f.   Observed as a sublimation product in a sulfate roasting oven.[18]

N a m e.   From $\psi\epsilon\upsilon\delta\acute{\eta}s$, *false*, and *brookite*, because not brookite although thought at the time to be similar to it.

Ref.

1. Orientation of Koch, *Min. Mitt.*, **1**, 77, 331 (1878); angles of Palache, *Am. Min.*, **19**, 14 (1934); unit of Pauling, *Zs. Kr.*, **73**, 97 (1930).
2. Palache (1934); *Am. Min.*, **20**, 660 (1935).
3. Pauling, *Zs. Kr.*, **73**, 97 (1930), by the oscillation and Laue methods on crystals from Aranyer Berg, with analysis of the structure.
4. For a statistical study of regularly intergrown pseudobrookite crystals see Balogh *Vh. u. Mitt. Siebenbürg. Ver. Naturw. Hermannstadt*, **77**, I, 64 (1927); also Ramdohr, *Notizbl. Ver. Erdkunde, Hess. Geol. Landesanst.*, **5**, 191 (1923). For a structural inter-pretation of the supposed twins on {230} see Gliszczynski and Stoicovici, *Zbl. Min.*, 343, 1937. The twinning on {210}, {230}, {570}, and other {hk0} planes needs verifi-cation.
5. Pauling (1930).
6. Palache (1935); in this orientation pseudobrookite {011} is practically parallel with hematite {11$\bar{2}$3}.
7. Ramdohr (1923).
8. A cleavage {0kl} was reported by Tornebohm cited in Rosenbusch (1 [2], 281, 1927) on crystals from Behring Island not certainly identified as pseudobrookite.
9. Cederström, *Zs. Kr.*, **17**, 133 (1889); other values include 4.56–4.70 of Doss, *ibid.*, **20**, 569 (1892) on artificial crystals, and the values 4.98 of Koch (1878) and 4.60 of Mark and Rosbaud, *Jb. Min., Beil.-Bd.*, **54**, 127 (1926) on crystals from Aranyer Berg.
10. Frondel (priv. comm., 1941) by the microbalance on single crystals.
11. Larsen (123, 239, 1921) on crystals from Aranyer Berg.
12. Ramdohr (1923) on crystals from Hessenbrücker Hammer.
13. Lattermann, *Min. Mitt.*, **9**, 47 (1887).
14. This formula is indicated by the x-ray structural study of Pauling (1930), and by the analyses of Doss (1892) on pure artificial material and of Gonyer in Palache (1935) on relatively pure natural material from the Thomas Range, Utah. The formula $Fe_4Ti_3O_{12}$ has been proposed by Cederström (1889), Frenzel, *Min. Mitt.*, **14**, 126 (1894), and others, but the observations of Pauling (1930) indicate that the higher TiO_2 content is due to admixed rutile.
15. For additional analyses see Hintze (499, 1937).
16. Traube anal. in Frenzel, *Min. Mitt.*, **14**, 126 (1894).
17. Gonyer anal. in Palache (1935).
18. Doss (1892).

761   **C H A L C O P H A N I T E** $[(Zn,Mn,Fe)Mn_2O_5 \cdot 2H_2O\ ?]$.   *Moore* (*Am. Chem.*, **6**, 1, 1875). Hydrofranklinite *Roepper* (in Dana, 61, 1882).

C r y s t. Hexagonal — R ?.[1]

$$a : c = 1 : 3.5267; \qquad p_0 : r_0 = 4.0713 : 1$$

Forms:[2]

$$c(0001) \qquad r(10\bar{1}1); \qquad c \wedge r = 76°12'$$

Habit. Minute crystals tabular $\{0001\}$, or with $\{0001\}$ and $\{10\bar{1}1\}$ equally developed giving an octahedral habit. Commonly in drusy botryoidal or stalactitic crusts, the tabular crystals arranged on edge. Also massive; dense, granular, or platy fibrous.

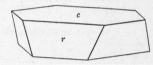

Franklin, N. J.

P h y s. Cleavage $\{0001\}$ perfect. Thin plates flexible. H. $2\frac{1}{2}$. G. 4.00 ± 0.10. Luster metallic. Color bluish to iron-black. Streak chocolate-brown, dull. Transparent in very thin splinters.

O p t. In transmitted light[3] deep red-brown to nearly opaque. Strongly pleochroic. Uniaxial negative ($-$).

	n	PLEOCHROISM
O	Much above 2.72	Nearly opaque
E	Near 2.72	Deep red

In polished section[4] white in color with extremely high anisotropism and very strong pleochroism. Exhibits deep red internal reflections.

C h e m. An oxide of zinc and manganese, $(Zn,Mn,Fe)Mn_2O_5 \cdot 2H_2O$. Mn^2 substitutes for Zn to about $Mn : Zn = 10 : 27$ in anal. 2, and Fe^2 substitutes for Zn to about $Fe : Zn = 10 : 16$ in anal. 4.

Anal.

	1	2	3	4
ZnO	27.94	21.70	20.80	18.25
MnO	.....	6.58	4.41	.....
FeO	.....	.....	.....	10.00
MnO₂	59.69	59.94	61.57	58.48
Fe₂O₃	.....	0.25	.....	.....
H₂O	12.37	11.58	12.66	11.85
Insol.	.....	.....	.....	0.25
Total	100.00	100.05	99.44	98.83
G.		3.903		4.012

1. $ZnMn_2O_5 \cdot 2H_2O$. 2. Sterling Hill, N. J. Average of two analyses. Crystals.[5] 3. Sterling Hill, N. J. Stalactitic masses. Average of two analyses. Recalc. after deduction of 1.27 per cent limonite.[5] 4. Sterling Hill, N. J. (*hydrofranklinite*).[6]

Tests. In C. T. yields water and oxygen, exfoliates slowly, and changes to a golden brown color. B.B. becomes yellowish bronze to copper-red in color, and fuses slightly on the edges. Soluble in HCl with evolution of chlorine.

O c c u r. A secondary mineral, found associated with hydrous oxides of manganese and iron. The mineral was originally found in the Passaic mine at Sterling Hill, New Jersey, as botryoidal and stalactitic crusts lining cavities in a mass of residual debris made of fragments of quartz and other rocks and of more or less decomposed franklinite, willemite, and zincite. Also found[7] in the Wolftone mine, Leadville, Colorado, as drusy crusts associated with limonite, smithsonite, and hemimorphite. Reported from Dundas, Tasmania, and Palestine, and said[8] to be a minor constituent of much so-called psilomelane and pyrolusite.

N a m e. From χαλκός, *brass*, and φαίνεσθαι, *to appear*, in allusion to the change of color on ignition.

Ref.

1. The crystals are trigonal in development, but the lattice mode is undeterminable with the data at hand. Elements of Moore (1875).
2. Moore (1875); see also Penfield and Kreider, *Am. J. Sc.*, **48**, 141 (1894).
3. Larsen (56, 1921) on material from Sterling Hill, New Jersey, and Leadville, Colorado.
4. Orcel and Pavlovitch, *Bull. soc. min.*, **54**, 108 (1932), and Ramdohr, *Zbl. Min.*, **134**, 1938.
5. Moore (1875).
6. Penfield and Kreider (1894).
7. Ford, *Am. J. Sc.*, **38**, 502 (1914).
8. Ramdohr (1938).

762   **Zirkelite** [$(Ca,Fe,Th,U)_2(Ti,Zr)_2O_5$?].   *Hussak* (*Min. Mitt.*, **14**, 408, 1894). Zirkelite *Hussak* and *Prior* (*Min. Mag.*, **11**, 86, 1895).   (Apparently not the Zirkelite of *Blake* and *Smith*, *Min. Mag.*, **16**, 309 [1913].)

Isometric,[1] in flattened octahedra.   Twinning on $\{111\}$ is very common, both polysynthetic and as complicated fourlings.

P h y s. Fracture conchoidal. Brittle. H. $5\frac{1}{2}$. G. 4.741.[2] Luster resinous. Color black. Transparent in very thin splinters, with a dark brown or reddish brown color. $n\ 2.19 \pm 0.01$.[3]

C h e m. Essentially an oxide of zirconium, titanium, calcium, ferrous iron, thorium, uranium, and rare earths. The formula is approximately $A_2B_2O_5$ with A = Ca, Fe, Th, U, Ce; B = Ti, Zr. Ca : Fe : Ce about $19 : 11 : 2$, and Zr : Ti about $43 : 19$. Analysis gave:[4] CaO 10.79, MgO 0.22, FeO 7.72, Ce_2O_3 2.52, Y_2O_3 (?) 0.21, UO_2 1.40, ThO_2 7.31, ZrO_2 52.89, TiO_2 14.95, ign. loss 1.02, total 99.03.

Tests. B.B. fusible on the edges of thin splinters. Decomposed by HF and by fusion in $KHSO_4$.

O c c u r. Found at Jacupiranga, São Paulo, Brazil, with perovskite and baddeleyite in a magnetite-pyroxenite (jacupirangite).

N a m e. After Ferdinand Zirkel (1838–1912), German petrographer, and formerly Professor of Mineralogy at the University of Leipzig.

Ref.

1. The relation of the mineral here described to the so-called zirkelite from Ceylon of Blake and Smith (1913) is not clear, but the composition of the two minerals appears to be different. A reexamination by Blake and Smith (1913) of some of the original material of Hussak and Prior (1895) suggests that the symmetry of the Brazilian mineral possibly is hexagonal or rhombohedral.
2. Prior, *Min. Mag.*, **11**, 180 (1896); an earlier determination by Hussak and Prior (1895) gave 4.706.
3. Larsen (160, 1921).
4. Prior (1896); an approximate analysis was given earlier by Hussak and Prior (1895).

UNNAMED MINERAL.   *Chernik (Gorny J.,* **12**, 740, 1927 — *Jb. Min.,* I, 355, 1928).

An ill-defined black cleavable material from Putelitschorr, Chibina tundra, Kola Peninsula, Russia. Luster submetallic, on the cleavage adamantine. Very difficultly fusible. Analysis gave: Na_2O 2.21, K_2O 1.44, CaO 16.48, FeO 4.32, MoO_3 2.90, ZrO_2 1.61, WO_3 24.55, TiO_2 24.37, Ta_2O_5 20.47, ign. loss 0.74, total 99.09. The Ta_2O_5 contains Cb, with Ta : Cb = 6 : 1.

UNNAMED MINERAL.   Zirkelite *Blake* and *Smith (Min. Mag.,* **16**, 309, 1913). (Apparently not Zirkelite of *Hussak* and *Prior, Min. Mag.,* **11**, 86 [1895].)

Cryst.[1]   Hexagonal — *P.*

$$a : c = 1 : 1.165;   p_0 : r_0 = 1.345 : 1$$

Forms:[1]

		ϕ	$\rho = C$	M	A_2
c	0001	′.....	0°00′	90°00′	90°00′
m	10$\bar{1}$0	30°00′	90 00	60 00	90 00
d	10$\bar{1}$2	30 00	33 55	73 48	90 00
e	20$\bar{2}$3	30 00	41 52½	70 30	90 00
r	10$\bar{1}$1	30 00	53 22	66 20½	90 00
s	20$\bar{2}$1	30 00	69 36½	62 03	90 00

Habit.   Crystals tabular {0001}, or prismatic [0001].   {20$\bar{2}$1} striated parallel edge with {0001}.

Twinning.   On {10$\bar{1}$1}.

Phys.   Cleavage {0001} indistinct.[2]   Fracture subconchoidal.   H. $5\frac{1}{2}$–6. G. 4.3–5.2, decreasing with the content of Th and U (see analyses).   Luster submetallic to resinous.   Color black or brownish black.   Streak chocolate-brown; darker in the uranium-rich varieties.   In very thin splinters transparent and reddish brown in color.   Metamict.   Isotropic.

Chem.   Probably an oxide with the general formula $(A,B)_4O_7$; with *A* : *B* from 1 : 3 to 3 : 8 (anal. 1 and 2); *A* = Ca, Mg, rare earths, Fe, U, Th?; *B* = Zr, Ti, Th?.   The water present may be due to alteration.   Hf substitutes for Zr to about 1.2 per cent HfO_2 by weight.[3]   He and N have been reported.

Anal.[4]

	1	2	3	4	5
CaO	6.87	6.78	8.55	9.35	8.18
MgO	2.34	3.04	1.33	1.08	1.96
FeO	4.07	4.42	4.72	4.65	3.73
(Ce, etc.)$_2O_3$	2.68	1.40	}0.32	}0.83	.....
(Y, etc.)$_2O_3$	1.08	0.40			.....
U_3O_8	1.06	0.65	4.66	2.08	14.31
ThO_2	20.44	18.78	8.33	8.51	0.23
ZrO_2	30.73	32.56	34.19	32.64	35.27
TiO_2	29.50	30.95	36.26	36.06	34.87
H_2O	0.46	1.05	1.70	1.74	1.68
Rem.	0.41	.....	......	2.26	0.44
Total	99.64	100.03	100.06	99.20	100.67
G.	5.0–5.1	4.72	4.47	4.32	4.40

1. Bambarabotuwa district, Ceylon.   Rem. is MnO 0.03, PbO 0.38.[5]   2. Bambarabotuwa.[5]   3. Southern Sabaragamuwa Province, Ceylon.[5]   4. Southern Sabaragamuwa.   Rem. is Al_2O_3 2.26.[5]   5. Southern Sabaragamuwa.   Rem. is PbO 0.44.[5]

Var.   *Uranian.*   Contains U in appreciable amounts (anal. 5).

Tests. Decomposed by HF. The fine powder is slowly attacked by HCl. Decomposed by fusion in $KHSO_4$.

O c c u r. Found in alluvial deposits in Ceylon at Walaweduwa, and in the upper part of the stream Alupola, in the Bambarabotuwa district of Sabaragamuwa Province (the thorium-rich material of anal. 1, 2). Also from not specifically designated localities in southern Sabaragamuwa Province (the uranium-rich material of anal. 3–5). Associated with zircon, corundum, spinel, tourmaline, and several rare-earth minerals.

Ref.

1. Blake and Smith (1913) accept the identity of the mineral here described with the apparently isometric zirkelite of Hussak and Prior (1895) from Brazil, and draw attention to the very marked pseudoisometric character of the Ceylon crystals. It is impossible, however, to reconcile the composition of the two minerals. Chernik, *Ac. sc. St. Pétersbourg, Bull.*, 163, 1914 — *Jb. Min.*, II, 30, 1915, has described, with an analysis, a mineral from Sabaragamuwa Province somewhat similar to that here described. The morphological data cited refer to material from southern Sabaragamuwa Province (anal. 3–5); morphological measurements are lacking for the thorium-rich material from the Bambarabotuwa district.
2. Observed on the thorium-rich crystals (anal. 1, 2) from the Bambarabotuwa district.
3. Hevesy and Jantzen, *Zs. anorg. Chem.*, **136**, 387 (1934), on material apparently from Ceylon.
4. A partial analysis also is given by Blake and Smith (1913).
5. Blake anal. in Blake and Smith (1913).

7711 C O R O N A D I T E [$MnPbMn_6O_{14}$]. *Lindgren* and *Hillebrand* (*Am. J. Sc.*, 18, 448, 1904; *U.S.Geol.Sur.,Bull. 262*, 42, 1905; *Zs. Kr.*, 43, 380, 1907).

C r y s t. Tetragonal or pseudotetragonal, and isostructural with hollandite.[1]

Structure cell.[1] A pseudotetragonal (?) cell has a_0 6.95, c_0 5.72; $a_0 : c_0 = 1 : 0.823$; contains $MnPbMn_6O_{14}$.

Habit. Massive; in botryoidal crusts with a fibrous structure.

P h y s. H. $4\frac{1}{2}$–5. G. 5.44 (Morocco).[2] Luster dull to submetallic. Color dark gray to black. Streak brownish black. Opaque. In polished section[3] almost galena-white in color and strongly anisotropic; in part isotropic.

C h e m. An oxide of lead and manganese, $MnPbMn_6O_{14}$.[4] The water reported in the analyses is probably nonessential.

Anal.

	1	2	3
PbO	27.37	28.66	28.68
CuO	....	0.05	0.14
MnO	8.69	7.12	8.02
MnO₂	63.94	60.80	59.60
Al₂O₃	....	0.68	0.10
Fe₂O₃	....	1.10	0.60
H₂O⁺	....	1.11	1.80
Rem.	....	0.48	0.87
Total	100.00	100.00	99.81
G.		5.246	5.505

1. $MnPbMn_6O_{14}$. 2. Coronado vein, Clifton-Morenci, Ariz. Rem. is ZnO 0.11, MoO_3 0.37. Recalc. after deduction of 7.22 per cent insol. and 0.45 alkalies, CaO, MgO and loss. Al_2O_3 contains V.[5] 3. Bou Tazoult, Morocco. Rem. is BaO 0.23, CaO 0.05, P_2O_5 0.03, As_2O_5 0.04, V_2O_5 0.20, SO_3 0.02, CO_2 0.04, SiO_2 0.26.[6]

O c c u r. Found in the oxidized zone of the Coronado vein, in the Clifton-Morenci district, Arizona. Also found in the upper levels of a manganese deposit at Bou Tazoult, Imini, Morocco.

N a m e. After Francisco Vasquez de Coronado (ca. 1500–54), a Spanish explorer of the American southwest.

Ref.

1. Frondel and Heinrich, *Am. Min.*, **27**, 48 (1942), by x-ray powder study of type material.
2. Frondel and Heinrich (priv. comm., 1942) by microbalance on type material. Orcel (1932) gives 5.505.
3. Orcel (1932) and Lindgren, *Am. Min.*, **18**, 548 (1933).
4. Frondel and Heinrich (1942).
5. Hillebrand anal. in Lindgren and Hillebrand (1904).
6. Campredon anal. in Orcel, *C. R.*, **194**, 1956 (1932).

7712 **H O L L A N D I T E** [MnBaMn$_6$O$_{14}$]. *Fermor (Trans. Min. Geol. Inst. India,* 1, 76, 1906; *Geol. Sur. India, Rec.*, **36**, 295, 1908; *Geol. Sur. India, Mem.*, **37**, 87, 1909; *Geol. Sur. India, Rec.*, **48**, 103, 1917).

C r y s t. Tetragonal or pseudotetragonal and isostructural with coronadite.[1]

Structure cell.[2] A pseudotetragonal (?) cell has a_0 6.94, c_0 5.71; $a_0 : c_0 = 1 : 0.823$; contains MnBaMn$_6$O$_{14}$ (?).

Habit. Short prismatic, terminated by a flat pyramid. Also massive; fibrous.

Twinning. Twins have been reported.[3]

P h y s. Cleavage prismatic, distinct. The crystals readily break parallel [001] into striated chips or fibers. Brittle. H. 6 on crystal faces, less on fracture surfaces. G. 4.95. Luster metallic shining. Color silvery gray to grayish black and black. Streak black. In polished section[4] white in color with strong anisotropism and weak pleochroism. Reflection percentages: green 28.5, orange 22.5, red 22.5.

C h e m. An oxide of barium and manganese, probably MnBaMn$_6$O$_{14}$.[5] The reported analysis shows an excess of trivalent metals, including Fe^3, and a deficiency of divalent Mn over this ratio.

Anal.[6]

	1	2
BaO	20.56	17.59
MnO	9.51	5.12
MnO$_2$	69.93	65.63
Fe$_2$O$_3$	.....	10.56
Al$_2$O$_3$	.....	0.94
Total	100.00	99.84
G.		4.95

1. MnBaMn$_6$O$_{14}$. 2. Kájlidongri, India.[7]

O c c u r. Found originally at Kájlidongri, Jhabua State, central India, as rough crystals in quartz veins traversing the manganese ore body. Said to occur at Sitapár and elsewhere in the Chhindwára district; in the Nágpur and Báághát districts; at Banswara, Rajputana. Reported from Ambatomiady, Madagascar.

N a m e.   After Dr. T. H. Holland (1868–), Director of the Geological Survey of India.

Ref.

1. Fermor (1917) measured rough crystals from Kájlidongri and considered them to be tetragonal dipyramidal with $a : c = 1 : 0.2035$. Two terminal forms, $\{111\}$ with ρ $16°03\frac{1}{2}'$ and $\{331\}$ with ρ $40°48\frac{1}{2}'$, and 57 forms, mostly with very complex indices, in the prism zone were reported. X-ray powder study by Frondel and Heinrich, *Am. Min.*, 27, 48 (1942), indicates that the true symmetry probably is less than tetragonal.
2. Frondel and Heinrich (1942), by x-ray powder method on material from Kájlidongri.
3. Fermor (1917) reports twins on $\{1 \cdot 10 \cdot 1\}$ on hollandite (?) from Banswara.
4. Schneiderhöhn and Ramdohr (2, 514, 1931), Orcel and Pavlovitch, *Bull. soc. min.*, 54, 134 (1931).
5. Inferred from the isostructural relation to coronadite shown by the x-ray powder study of Frondel and Heinrich (1942).
6. An additional analysis of a mineral ascribed to hollandite from Bálághát, India, is given by Fermor (1909); the analysis differs widely in ratio from that cited.
7. Winch anal. in Fermor (1909).

772   Cesarolite [$PbMn_3O_7 \cdot H_2O$].   *Buttgenbach* and *Gillet* (*Soc. géol. Belgique, Ann.*, 43, 239, 1920).

In friable masses resembling coke, and in botryoidal crusts. H. $4\frac{1}{2}$. G. 5.29. Luster dull to submetallic. Color steel-gray. In polished section[1] crusts are inwardly isotropic and outwardly composed of anisotropic spherules.

C h e m.   A hydrous oxide of Pb^2 and Mn^4. The formula is uncertain, perhaps $PbMn_3O_7 \cdot H_2O$. Analysis gave Pb 36.29, MnO 42.65, O 13.26, Fe 0.49, Al 0.79, other metals 0.36, Na_2O 0.18, H_2O 3.30, insoluble 0.75, total 98.07.

Tests.   Infusible.   Soluble in HCl with evolution of Cl.

O c c u r.   Found in cavities in galena at Sidi-amor-ben-Salem, Tunis.
N a m e.   After Giuseppe R. P. Cesáro (1849–1939), Professor of Mineralogy and Crystallography at the University of Liége.
Needs further study.

Ref.

1: Orcel and Pavlovitch, *Bull. soc. min.*, 54, 108 (1932).

8 MULTIPLE OXIDES CONTAINING COLUMBIUM, TANTALUM, AND TITANIUM

The minerals here listed have generally been called columbates, tantalates, and titanates.[1] However, recent crystallochemical work[2] indicates that they, as well as other oxygen compounds containing more than one metallic element, are best considered as multiple oxides, of the so-called isodesmic[2] type. Early crystallographic work[3] has demonstrated the similarity of the crystals of these compounds with certain simple (isodesmic) oxides. Structural similarities have been noted[4] between the two types.

The chemical constitution of most of the minerals containing Cb, Ta, or Ti as a major constituent can be expressed[5] by the formula $A_m B_n O_{2(m+n)}$, where $m : n$ is between 1 : 1 and 1 : 2, and A = rare earths, U, Ca, Th, Fe^2, Na, Mn, Zr; B = Cb, Ta, Ti, Sn, W?, Zr?, Fe^3.

The role of Zr is uncertain, and often the role of Fe is indeterminate because the state of oxidation cannot be deduced from analysis[6] in the presence of U. The role of water in these minerals is not known, but it is generally considered the result of alteration, because the most highly altered material invariably shows the most water in analysis.

The crystallography of these multiple oxides is only imperfectly known because they are nearly all noncrystalline pseudomorphs of the original minerals, that is, they are *metamict*.[7] The crystals are usually rough and of such size that only contact measurements can be made. When they are heated they revert, presumably, to the original structure[7] (emitting a glow, due to the crystallization), but the crystalline units are tiny and not oriented with respect to the original external faces. The change in structure after the ignition can readily be detected under the microscope or by x-ray powder diffraction pictures. Most of the crystallographic measurements, except on a few species such as columbite and tapiolite (which are not metamict) are to be considered inaccurate and inconclusive. They show that the minerals are often pseudotetragonal and, by manipulating the axial ratios, can be made to agree fairly well with each other. The following table of transformations demonstrates the relationships derived.

The transformations are to tapiolite, the tetragonal member of these oxides.

	To Tapiolite	Transformed Elements 1.000 : 1 : 1.939 (tapiolite)
Euxenite	002/200/0$\frac{3}{2}$0	0.931 : 1 : 1.980
Priorite	200/010/00$\bar{3}$	0.949 : 1 : 2.002
Eschynite	200/010/003	0.973 : 1 : 2.021
Samarskite	100/001/010	1.054 : 1 : 1.932

Also, the relation between the axial ratios of columbite and euxenite is close.

	a		b		c
Columbite	0.4023	:	1	:	0.3580
Euxenite	0.3789	:	1	:	0.3527

Certain strong similarities in the x-ray powder pictures of the ignited samples indicate that most of these multiple oxides containing the rare earths, Cb, Ta, and Ti have similar structures.[8]

The classification here is strictly on chemical grounds, that is, according to the $A + B : O$ ratio and after that according to the $A : B$ ratio, mainly because crystallographic criteria are inconclusive. For this reason many names heretofore considered as designating good species have been introduced into the synonymy of better-known minerals. An aid to classification has been x-ray powder pictures.[8] Many species of doubtful value appear among these minerals, and it is better that they be not given full status.

81 ABX_4 TYPE

		A	B
811	Pyrochlore-microlite		·
	Series $A_2B_2O_6(O,OH,F)$		
8111	Pyrochlore	} Na, Ca, K, Mg, Fe, Mn, Ce,	Cb, Ta, Ti, Sn ?, Fe^3, W
8112	Microlite	} La, Di, Er, Y, Th, Zr, U	Ta, Cb, Ti, Sn ?, Fe^3, W
812	Scheteligite ?		
813	Fergusonite Series ABO_4		
8131	Fergusonite	} Y, Er, (Ce,La,Di),Fe^2	Cb, Ta, Ti, Sn, W
8132	Formanite	} U, Zr, Th, Ca	Ta, Cb, Ti, Sn, W
814	Yttrotantalite	ABO_4 ? Fe^2, Y, U, Ca, Mn, Ce, Th	Cb, Ta, Ti, Zr, Sn
815	Polymignite	ABO_4 Ca, Fe^2, (Y,Er,Ce), Zr, Th	Cb, Ti, Ta, Fe^3
816	Ishikawaite	ABO_4 U, Fe^2, (Y,Er,Ce)	Cb, Ta
817	Loranskite	Y, Ce, Ca, Zr (?)	Ta, Zr (?)
818	Stibiotantalite Series ABO_4		
8181	Stibiotantalite	Sb, Bi	Ta, Cb
8182	Stibiocolumbite	Sb, Bi	Cb, Ta
819	Bismutotantalite	Bi	Ta, Cb
81·10	Simpsonite	? ABO_4 Al	Ta

82 $A_mB_nX_p$ TYPE

$m : n$ from 2 : 3 to 3 : 5

821	Arizonite	Fe	Ti
822	Kalkowskite	Fe	Ti
823	Oliveiraite	Zr	Ti
824	Brannerite	U, Ca, Fe, Y, Th	Ti

83 AB_2X_6 TYPE

		A	B
831	Tapiolite Series AB_2O_6		
8311	Tapiolite	Fe, Mn	Ta, Cb
8312	Mossite	Fe, Mn	Cb, Ta
832	Columbite-tantalite Series		
8321	Columbite	Fe, Mn, Sn ?	Cb, Ta, W
8322	Tantalite	Fe, Mn	Ta, Cb
833	Euxenite-polycrase Series		
8331	Euxenite	Y, Ca, Ce, U, Th	Cb, Ta, Ti
8332	Polycrase	Y, Ca, Ce, U, Th	Ti, Cb, Ta, Fe³
	Eschwegeite		
834	Yttrocrasite		
835	Eschynite-priorite Series		
8351	Eschynite	Ce, Ca, Fe², Th	Ti, Cb, Ta
8352	Priorite	Y, Er, Ca, Fe, Th	Ti, Cb, Ta
8361	Samarskite	Y, Er, Ce, La, U, Ca, Fe, Pb, Th	Cb, Ta, Ti, Sn, W, Zr (?)
8362	" Samarskite "		
837	Thoreaulite $SnTa_2O_7$	Sn	Ta

84 $A_mB_nX_p$ TYPE

where $m : n \gtreqless 1 : 3$

841	Betafite Series	U, Ca, Th, Pb, Ce, Y	Ti, Cb, Ta, Fe, Al ?
841	Betafite		
842	Djalmaite		
843	Ampangabeite	Y, Er, U, Ca, Th	Cb, Ta, Fe³ Ti
844	Delorenzite		

Ref.

1. Dana (1892) and others.
2. For a general reference see Evans (203, 1939).
3. Brögger (1897) and Schaller, *U. S. Geol. Sur., Bull. 509*, 9, 1912, have shown the crystallographic relations of AX_2 and ABX_4 minerals (tapiolite and rutile, etc.).
4. Goldschmidt, *Vidensk. Skr., Mat.-Nat. Kl.*, no. 1, 17, 1926, has shown the structural relationship between tapiolite and rutile. Sturdivant, *Zs. Kr.*, **75**, 88 (1930), has related the structure of columbite and brookite.
5. Berman and Frondel (priv. comm., 1941). See also Machatschki, *Chem. Erde*, **7**, 56 (1932); *Zs. Kr.*, **72**, 291 (1929).
6. Wells, *J. Am. Chem. Soc.*, **50**, 1017 (1928).
7. See Brögger, *Zs. Kr.*, **25**, 427 (1896). Also Mügge, *Cbl. Min.*, 721, 753, 1922; Goldschmidt, *Vidensk. Skr., Mat.-Nat. Kl.*, 1, no. 5, 51, 1924.
8. Berman and Frondel (priv. comm., 1941).

Pyrochlore-Microlite Series

$$A_2B_2O_6(O,OH,F)$$

Pyrochlore is predominantly $NaCaCb_2O_6F$ and microlite is $(Na,Ca)_2$-$Ta_2O_6(O,OH,F)$. The composition, however, varies widely, with

A = Na, Ca, K, Mg, Fe², Mn², Sb³, Pb?, Ce, La, Di, Er, Y, Th, Zr, U
B = Cb, Ta, Ti, Sn?, Fe³, W?

and many supposed independent species are apparently varieties belonging in this series.

Some of the members of the series are nearly always altered and some are metamict. After ignition they yield the x-ray diffraction picture typical of microlite and pyrochlore.

8111　**P Y R O C H L O R E** [NaCaCb$_2$O$_6$F]. Pyrochlor (from Frederiksvärn) *Wöhler* (*Ann. Phys.*, **7**, 417, 1826). Hydrochlor, Fluochlor *Hermann* (*J. pr. Chém.*, **50**, 186, 187, 1850). Niobpyrochlor *Machatschki* (*Chem. Erde*, **7**, 56, 1932).

Pyrrhit *Rose* (*Ann. Phys.*, **48**, 562, 1840; Reis. Urals, **2**, 1842). Koppit *Knop* (*Jb. Min.*, **67**, 1875). Hatchettolite *Smith* (*Am. J. Sc.*, **13**, 365, 1877), *Allen* (*Am. J. Sc.*, **14**, 128, 1877). Azor-pyrrhit *Hubbard* (*Verh. natur-hist. Ver. preuss. Rheinland, Sitzber.*, **43**, 217, 1886). Uranpyrochlor *Holmquist* (*Geol. Inst. Upsala, Bull.*, **3**, 181, 1896). Chalcolamprite *Flink* (*Medd. Grønland*, **14**, 234 (1898); **24**, 160, 1901). Endeiolite *Flink* (*Medd. Grønland*, **24**, 166, 1901). Marignacite *Weidman* and *Lenher* (*Am. J. Sc.*, **23**, 287, 1907). Ellsworthite *Walker* and *Parsons* (*Univ. Toronto Stud., Geol. Ser.*, **13**, 1923).

8112　**M I C R O L I T E** [(Na,Ca)$_2$Ta$_2$O$_6$(O,OH,F)]. *Shepard* (*Am. J. Sc.*, **27**, 361, 1835; **32**, 338, 1837; **43**, 116, 1842). Pyrochlore *Hayes* (*Am. J. Sc.*, **43**, 33, 1842; **46**, 158, 1844). Haddamite *Shepard* (*Am. J. Sc.*, **50**, 93, 1870). Tantalpyrochlor *Machatschki* (*Chem. Erde*, **7**, 56, 1932).

Neotantalite *Termier* (*Bull. soc. min.*, **25**, 34, 1902). Niobtantalpyrochlor *Machatschki* (*Chem. Erde*, **7**, 56, 1932). Metasimpsonite *Simpson* (*Dept. Mines Western Australia, Rep. 1937*, 88, 1938).

C r y s t.　Isometric; hexoctahedral — $4/m\,\bar{3}\,2/m$.[1]

Forms:[2]

	a	d	o	m	n	p
	001	011	111	113	112	122
Pyrochlore	x	x	x	x	x	
Microlite	x	x	x	x	x	x
Ellsworthite[3]	x	x	x	x		

Structure cell.　Space group $Fd3m$.
Cell dimensions:[4]

	a_0	Anal.	Ref.
Pyrochlore (aver. of 4)	10.35		4
Microlite (Donkerhuk)	10.37 − 10.40	16	5
Microlite (Topsham)	10.39 + 0.01	18	6
Koppite (Kaiserstuhl)	10.37 + 0.01	6	7

Contains essentially Na$_8$Ca$_8$(Cb,Ta)$_{16}$O$_{48}$(OH,F)$_8$. The natural material is usually metamict and gives only a faint diffraction picture; on ignition, however, the crystallinity is restored.[8]

Habit.　Octahedral, often with subordinate {011}, {113} or {001}. Some crystals of microlite are as large as 6 cm. (Amelia) despite the name of the mineral; also in irregular masses or embedded grains.

Twinning.[9]　Spinel-law twins, twin plane {111}, have been observed but are rare.

P h y s.　Cleavage (or parting?) octahedral, sometimes distinct (particularly in thin section) but usually not distinguishable. Fracture subconchoidal to uneven or splintery. Brittle. H. 5–5$\frac{1}{2}$, but lower in altered material. G. 4.2–6.4, increasing with Ta content (see analyses); hydration or other alteration induces a marked decrease in specific gravity. Ignition of the sample increases the specific gravity; the following are representative values.[10]

	LOCALITY	ANAL.	G.
Pyrochlore	Alnö	2	4.45
Uranian (hatchettolite)	North Carolina	11	4.77 − 4.90
Microlite	Topsham	18	6.42 ± 0.04
Titanian pyrochlore	Urals	5	4.35
Pyrochlore	Calculated for $a_0 = 10.35$	1	4.33
Microlite	Calculated for $a_0 = 10.40$	20	6.33

Luster vitreous or resinous, the latter on fracture surfaces. Color of pyrochlore brown to black, often brown in yellowish, reddish, or blackish shades; color of microlite pale yellow to brown, sometimes hyacinth-red, olive-buff or green. Streak of pyrochlore light brown, yellowish brown; of microlite pale yellowish or brownish. The dark-colored varieties transmit light only in thin splinters.

Opt. Isotropic, but may show weak anomalous birefringence in the nonmetamict material. Colorless, or pale yellow, brown, etc., in material with a deep body color; sometimes cloudy. May show a zonal structure in shades of brown or yellow. n apparently decreases with increasing alteration by hydration. On ignition n increases to 2.0–2.2.[11] Microlite from Topsham (anal. 18) gives $n = 2.023 \pm 0.003$. Other values[12] on unanalyzed material range from 1.93 to 2.02. Other members of the series lie between the microlite values. Pyrrhite has $n = 2.16$[12] and koppite has $n = 2.12$ to 2.18.[12]

Chem. A complex oxide containing essentially calcium, sodium, columbium, and tantalum, with hydroxyl and fluorine. The formula can be written $A_2B_2O_6(O,OH,F)$,[13] with A = Na, Ca, K, Mg, Fe^2, Mn^2, Sb^3, Pb?,

$$Ce, La, Di, Er, Y, Th, Zr, U$$
$$B = Cb, Ta, Ti, Sn?, Fe^3?, W?$$

in the approximate order of importance. Pyrochlore is essentially $NaCaCb_2O_6F$, and microlite is $(Na,Ca)_2Ta_2O_6(O,OH,F)$.

The observed maximum percentages of the various oxides reported are:

	PER CENT	REF.		PER CENT	REF.
Na_2O	6.3	14	ThO_2	7.6?	19
K_2O	4.2	15	UO_2	11.4	Anal. 9
CaO	18.1	Anal. 2	UO_3	15.5	Anal. 11
MgO	1.6	16	ZrO_2	5.7	Anal. 3
FeO	10.0	17	TiO_2	13.5	17
MnO	7.7	18	SnO_2	4.0	20
$(Ce,La,Di)_2O_3$	13.3	Anal. 8	Fe_2O_3	9.7	Anal. 6
$(Y,Er)_2O_3$	5.1	Anal. 8	WO_3	0.3	Anal. 15

Cb and Ta apparently vary continuously throughout the series, but most analyses are close to one end or the other end. The rare-earth elements appear for the most part at the Cb end of the series. SiO_2 is reported in small amounts; Pb occurs with uranian members. Hf has been reported in pyrochlore.[21]

Anal.[22]

	1	2	3	4	5	6	7
Na₂O	8.52	4.99	3.99	5.31	3.35	2.89	.....
K₂O	.....	0.60	0.38	.....	0.87	1.64	.....
CaO	15.41	18.13	9.08	10.93	14.05	15.88	13.62
MnO	.....	.....	0.44	.....	.....	0.01	0.22
FeO	.....	1.14	.....	5.53	2.52	.....	.....
MgO	.....	.....	.....	.....	trace	0.27	.....
Y₂O₃	.....	.....	.....	.....	}0.56	.....	.....
Er₂O₃	.....	.....	.....	.....		.....	.....
Ce₂O₃	.....	4.36	}3.41	5.50	2.16	8.15	.....
Di₂O₃	.....	.....		.....	1.94	.....	.....
La₂O₃	.....	.....		.....	1.23	1.68	.....
UO₂	.....	.....	.....	.....	.....	.....	8.42
UO₃	.....	.....	.....	.....	.....	.....	10.68
ZrO₂	.....	4.90	5.71	.....	.....	0.61	.....
SnO₂	.....	.....	.....	.....	.....	.....	0.25
ThO₂	.....	.....	.....	4.96	4.28	.....	.....
SiO₂	.....	.....	10.86	.....	.....	.....	2.68
Fe₂O₃	.....	1.87	.....	.....	.....	9.73	3.80
TiO₂	.....	.....	0.52	5.38	8.32	0.75	9.79
Cb₂O₅	73.05	63.64	59.65	58.27	56.01	56.43	34.27
Ta₂O₅	.....	.....	.....	.....	.....	0.15	4.27
F	5.22	4.31	5.06	3.75	2.77	1.53	0.49
H₂O	.....	0.47	1.79	.....	.....	1.09	11.42
Rem.	.....	.....	.....	1.53	2.63	.....	0.41
Total	102.20	102.54	102.76	101.16	100.69	100.81	100.32
−O = F	2.20	1.81	2.13	1.60	1.16	0.65	0.21
Total	100.00	100.73	100.63	99.56	99.53	100.16	100.11
G.		4.446	3.77	4.220	4.354		3.758

1. NaCaCb₂O₆F. 2. Pyrochlore, Alnö.[23] 3. Chalcolamprite, Narsarsuk.[24] SiO₂ probably due to admixture. 4. Pyrochlore, Brevik. Rem. is loss on ign. FeO contains UO₂.[25] 5. Pyrochlore, Urals. Rem. is UOₓ 2.63, GeO₂ trace, ZrO₂ trace.[26] 6. Koppite, Kaiserstuhl.[27] 7. Ellsworthite, Hybla, Ont. (chocolate-brown). Rem. is PbO 0.41.[28]

	8	9	10	11	12	13	14
Na₂O	2.52	.....	3.15	1.37	2.35	}3.68	}2.50
K₂O	0.57	.....	.....	trace	.....		
CaO	4.10	13.25	6.00	8.87	10.62	13.84	.....
MnO	trace	0.51	trace	.....	.....	.....	2.85
FeO	0.02	.....	6.32	2.19	.....	8.25	4.57
MgO	0.16	0.36	trace	0.15	trace	1.14	trace
Y₂O₃	5.07	}0.62	.....	.....	}0.46	.....	.....
Er₂O₃	trace		.....	.....		.....	.....
Ce₂O₃	13.33	}0.12	12.34	.....	5.90	2.06	.....
Di₂O₃	trace		0.63	.....	.....	.....	.....
La₂O₃	trace		0.71	.....	.....	.....	.....
UO₂	.....	11.40	8.33	.....	.....	.....	.....
UO₃	.....	4.41	.....	15.50	.....	.....	trace
ZrO₂	.....	4.12	.....	.....	4.65	0.12	.....
SnO₂	trace	1.44	.....	0.30	.....	.....	0.43
ThO₂	0.20	0.52	trace	.....	trace	.....	.....
SiO₂	3.10	1.57	.....	.....	.....	1.51	1.32
Fe₂O₃	0.50	3.46	0.26	.....	.....	.....	.....
TiO₂	2.88	11.37	4.20	1.61	9.11	1.61	.....
Cb₂O₅	55.22	31.33	26.22	34.24	30.70	(26) }62.77 (37)	22.00
Ta₂O₅	5.86	10.29	27.39	29.83	33.03		57.70
F	.....	.....	1.90	.....	2.17	.....	.....
H₂O	6.40	4.29	1.45	4.49	1.37	5.02	6.30
Rem.	.....	0.54	.....	.....	.....	.....	1.57
Total	99.93	99.60	98.90	98.55	100.36	100.00	99.24
−O = F	.....	.....	0.80	.....	0.91	.....	.....
Total			98.10		99.45		
G.	4.13	4.509	4.21	4.77–4.90	4.955		5.193

8. Marignacite, Wis. Rem. is WO_3 trace, Al_2O_3 trace, H_2O includes H_2O+ 110 5.95 and H_2O- 110 0.45.[29] 9. Hatchettolite, Hybla, Ontario (black). Rem. is PbO 0.54.[28] 10. Pyrochlore, Tschoroch, Caucasus.[30] 11. Hatchettolite, N. C. With PbO trace, SnO_2 contains WO_3.[31] 12. Pyrochlore, Sundsvall, Sweden.[32] 13. Microlite, Söve, Norway. Includes Fe_2O_3 with FeO.[33] 14. Neotantalite, France. Rem. is Al_2O_3 1.43, CuO 0.14.[34]

	15	16	17	18	19	20
Na_2O	2.86	0.72	3.26	3.37	1.18	5.76
K_2O	0.29	0.21	0.64	0.41	0.15	.....
CaO	11.80	6.79	10.48	15.03	12.78	10.43
MnO	.....	0.51	.....	.....	0.11	.....
FeO	.....	....	2.77	.....	0.47	.....
MgO	1.01	0.27	0.34	0.07	.....	.....
Y_2O_3	0.23	1.07		0.35	.....	.....
Ce_2O_3	0.17	0.55		0.26	.....	.....
Di_2O_3	.....	....	0.50	.....	.....	.....
La_2O_3	.....	....		.....	.....	.....
UO_2	.....	4.03	4.21	.....	.....	.....
UO_3	1.59	....	.....	0.77	.....	.....
ZrO_2	1.05	0.30	.....	.....	.....	.....
SnO_2	.....	0.38	.....	1.61	0.37	.....
ThO_2	.....	0.26	.....	.....	.....	.....
SiO_2	.....	0.13	.....	.....	0.40	.....
Fe_2O_3	0.29	0.92	.....	.....	0.72	.....
TiO_2	.....	1.07	1.58	.....	0.51	.....
Cb_2O_5	7.74	2.65	.....	3.56	3.64	.....
Ta_2O_5	68.43	72.38	73.72	74.27	77.00	82.14
F	2.85	....	.....	.....	1.09	.....
H_2O	1.17	5.94	2.72	0.27	2.00	1.67
Rem.	0.77	1.53	.....	0.17	0.55	.....
Total	100.25	99.71	100.22	100.14	100.97	100.00
$-O = F$	1.20				0.46	
Total	99.05				100.51	
G.	5.656	5.06	5.93	6.42	5.77	

15. Microlite, Amelia Court House. Rem. is BeO 0.34, WO_3 0.30, Al_2O_3 0.13.[35]
16. Microlite, Donkerhuk. Rem. is CuO 0.05, SrO 0.70, Bi_2O_3 0.42, PbO 0.36.[36]
17. Microlite, Landås. Contains a very small amount of Cb in the Ta_2O_5. H_2O includes H_2O- 110 2.33 and H_2O+ 110 0.39.[37] 18. Microlite, Topsham. Rem. is WO_3 0.17.[38] 19. Microlite, Wodgina. Rem. is Al_2O_3 0.55.[39] 20. $NaCaTa_2O_6(OH)$.

Var. *Ordinary.* Essentially sodium, calcium, columbium, and tantalum, with subordinate amounts of other elements.

Uranian. Hatchettolite Smith (*Am. J. Sc.*, **13**, 365, 1877), Allen (*Am. J. Sc.*, **14**, 128, 1877). Uranpyrochlor Holmquist (*Bull. Geol. Inst. Upsala*, **3**, 181, 1896). Ellsworthite *Walker* and *Parsons* (*Univ. Toronto Stud., Geol. Ser.*, **13**, 1923). Contains U in considerable amounts (anal. 7, 9, 10, 11).

Titanian. Ti is found in amounts up to 13.5 per cent TiO_2 (anal. 9, 12) in substitution for Cb-Ta.

Cerian. Contains Ce (including Di and La) in considerable amounts (anal. 6, 8, 10) in substitution for Ca, Na.

Ferroan. Contains Fe^2 in amounts up to 10.0 per cent FeO (see also anal. 10).

Ferrian. Contains Fe^3 in amounts up to 9.7 per cent Fe_2O_3 (anal. 6), presumably in substitution for Cb, Ta in part.

Tests. B.B. infusible; some varieties may fuse with difficulty to a slaggy or enamel-like dark mass. May turn yellowish green or otherwise change color on ignition. Fine powder insoluble or soluble with difficulty in HCl; slowly decomposed by concentrated H_2SO_4 and readily by fusion in $KHSO_4$. The metamict material often recalesces on heating.

O c c u r. Pyrochlore typically occurs in pegmatites derived from alkalic rocks and is then associated with zircon, apatite, aegirite and a number of uncommon Zr, Ti, Cb, Ta, and rare-earth minerals. Also as an accessory mineral in nepheline syenites and various alkalic dike rocks, in limestones metamorphosed at the contact with alkalic intrusives (*koppite*, pt.), in extrusive, alkalic rocks (*pyrrhite*, pt.), and in greisen.

Found in Norway at Fredricksvärn and Laurvik in nepheline syenite pegmatite with zircon, polymignite, cerian apatite, black hornblende; also on the island Lövö, opposite Brevik, with magnetite, zircon, and thorite, and on Stokö, Little Arö and other points in the Langesund fiord[40] in alkalic pegmatites; in the ijolite-melteigite rocks and the metamorphosed limestones of the Fen region. In Sweden in the Alnö region in limestone altered by contact with nepheline syenite intrusives, with perovskite, zircon, knopite, apatite, olivine, and magnetite, and in syenite. Near Schelingen and elsewhere in the Kaiserstuhl, Baden, Germany, (*koppite*) in contact-metamorphosed limestone with apatite, forsterite, and magnesioferrite. From the Laacher See, in sanidine bombs and in the pegmatite inclusions in leucite tuff. At San Piero, Elba (*pyrrhite*) with red tourmaline and lepidolite; at Monte Somma (*pyrrhite*). At Miask, Ilmen Mountains, in nepheline syenite with eschynite, zircon, principally; also at Alabashka near Mursinsk (*pyrrhite*) in feldspar cavities, with topaz; as a minor accessory mineral in dike rocks in the Mariupol district, Ukraine; in the Chibine tundra, Kola Peninsula, U.S.S.R. In France at Brocq en Menet, Cantal, in inclusions of sodalite syenite in phonolite. In the Azores, at San Miguel, as orange-red octahedra (*pyrrhite*). In Greenland in augite syenite at Ivigtut, and in the Julianehaab district. In greisen at Kiambi, Belgian Congo. In aegirite nepheline syenite on the Island of Los, French Guiana, with villiaumite, astrophyllite, fluorite, catapleite, and lavenite.

Pyrochlore has been reported from several localities in the United States: in granite pegmatite at Newry, Maine; in syenite from Pikes Peak, Colorado; from San Diego County, California; from near Wausau, Wisconsin (*marignacite*) with acmite, lepidomelane, rutile, fluorite, and several zirconium minerals in a pegmatite in an area of alkalic rocks, and elsewhere. The uranian variety, *hatchettolite*, occurs with samarskite (and in part grown in parallel position upon it[41]) in the pegmatites of Mitchell County, North Carolina; reported from Pala, California, as inclusions in quartz and in tourmaline crystals, and from west of Mount Bity, Madagascar;[42] from Hybla, Monteagle Township, Hastings County, Ontario, in black or amber masses with cyrtolite, garnet, and columbite in microcline pegmatite;[43] also (*ellsworthite*) from Monteagle Township as chocolate-brown and amber-yellow masses in salmon-colored calcite with zircon, sphene, and smoky quartz.

Microlite typically occurs in the albitized parts of granite pegmatites. Tantalite and columbite are frequent associates. Found in Norway with tantalite and albite at Låndas and elsewhere in the Iveland district, Satesdal, in limestone at Söve, Telemark, with euxenite at Kragerö, and with yttrotantalite at Hattevik, near Moss. In Sweden at Varuträsk in pegmatite with stibiotantalite as alteration products of the so-called stibiomicrolite, and in pegmatite at Üto and Bohuslän. In Finland at Skogböle with ixiolite. In France found with cassiterite in sands obtained by washing of the kaolin of Colettes and Echassières, Allier (*neotantalite*); and from Coudier à Larmont, St. Sylvestre, and La Chèze, Haute Vienne, Plateau Central. At Donkerhuk, South-West Africa, with tantalite and albite in granite pegmatite; in Rhodesia near Odzi Siding with tantalite and lepidolite in greisen, and with tantalite in pegmatite in the Victoria tin field, Ndanga district. In Greenland at Narsarsuk and Igaliko. Reported from Ampasibitika, Antandranokomby, and elsewhere in Madagascar, from São Paulo and Ouro Preto, Brazil. In Western Australia, intergrown with tapiolite as stream pebbles from Strelley, as stream pebbles from Wodgina, at Greens Well, and in the cassiterite placers at Greenbushes with tantalite and columbite.

In the United States microlite was found at Chesterfield, Massachusetts, as minute octahedrons (possibly pyrochlore[44]) in albite with red and green tourmaline, spodumene, columbite, and cassiterite; similarly at Branchville, Connecticut. Also in Connecticut in the granite pegmatites at Haddam, Haddam Neck, Middletown, and Portland, associated with columbite, albite, and the other pegmatite minerals. At the pegmatites in the vicinity of Amelia Court House, Virginia, in octahedrons up to 6.5 cm. on an edge and in masses, one of which weighed 8 lb., in albite or smoky quartz associated principally with spessartite, columbite, fluorite, monazite, and beryl. In Maine at Topsham with albite, topaz, tourmaline, lepidolite, and rarely stibiotantalite; in pegmatite, at Newry with albite, columbite and tourmaline, and similarly at nearby Black Mountain, Rumford. At Embudo, New Mexico, as glassy yellow crystals with lepidolite and spodumene, and near Ohio City, Colorado. In California near Hemet, Riverside County, with lepidolite and quartz, and from San Diego County.

Alter. Readily altered by hydration, often with partial removal of Na and Ca. This change may be accompanied by a loss of crystallinity[45] which, however, may be restored by heating to redness. The alteration is accompanied by a decrease in G and often by a change in color. Microlite has been observed as an alteration product of tapiolite and of the so-called stibiomicrolite.

Artif.[46] The compounds $NaCaCb_2O_6F$ and $NaCaTa_2O_6F$ have been synthesized by fusion of CaO, NaF and $(Ta,Cb)_2O_5$, and have been shown by x-ray study to be identical with pyrochlore-microlite; cerian and uranian varieties have also been prepared. The artificial compounds $Ca_2Cb_2O_7$ and $Ca_2Ta_2O_7$ are known and are dimorphous (orthorhombic and isometric (?)).

Name. Pyrochlore from πῦρ, *fire*, and χλωρός, *green*, because the mineral turns green (but not always) on ignition. Microlite from μικρός, *small*, in allusion to the minute size of the crystals from the original locality (Chesterfield, Massachusetts).

The following are very likely members of the pyrochlore-microlite series, or varieties, and are so considered here. They are to be discredited as species.

PYRRHITE. Pyrrhit *Rose* (**2**, 1842; *Ann. Phys.*, **48**, 562, 1840). Azorpyrrhit *Hubbard* (*Vh. naturhist. Ver. preuss. Rheinland, Sitzber.*, **43**, 217, 1886).

In octahedrons, usually a millimeter or less in size. Color orange-yellow to orangered. G. 4.13 (Laacher See[47]). Isotropic. n 2.16 ± 0.02 (Azores). Pyrrhite from the Azores and the Laacher See was shown[48] by x-ray study to belong in the pyrochloremicrolite series. Complete analyses are lacking.[49] Named from πυρρός, *reddish*.

KOPPITE. *Knop* (*Jb. Min.*, 67, 1875).

In small octahedrons sometimes with {011}. Spinel twins have been observed. Color dark red-brown to cherry-red. Luster adamantine. Essentially a columbate of Ca, Ce, Fe, Na, and K (anal. 6). Isotropic. n 2.15 ± 0.03. Named after Hermann Kopp (1817–1892), formerly Professor of Chemistry at Heidelberg. Shown to belong in the pyrochlore-microlite series.[50]

HATCHETTOLITE. *Smith* (*Am. J. Sc.*, **13**, 365, 1877), *Allen* (*ibid.*, **14**, 128, 1877). Uranpyrochlor *Holmquist* (*Bull. Geol. Inst. Upsala*, **3**, 181, 1896).

In octahedrons with subordinate {001} and {113}, also massive. Fracture subconchoidal. Brittle. H. 4 (Hybla[51]), 5 (North Carolina). G. 4.509 (Hybla[51]), 4.77–4.90 (North Carolina). Luster resinous. Color black to yellowish brown or amber. Transparent. Isotropic. n 1.98 ± (North Carolina[12]). Composition essentially that of a uranian pyrochlore (anal. 9, 11).[52] For localities see under pyrochlore. Named after the English chemist, Charles Hatchett (1765–1847), who first discovered the element columbium. Doubtless a uranian pyrochlore.[53]

CHALCOLAMPRITE. *Flink* (*Medd. Grønland*, **14**, 234, 1898; **24**, 160, 1901).

In small octahedrons, often hollow or cracked and containing needles of aegirite in the openings. Not metamict. No cleavage. Fracture subconchoidal or splintery. Brittle. H. 5½. G. 3.77. Luster on fracture surfaces greasy; the crystal faces have a copper-red to green metallic iridescence. Color dark grayish brown inclining to red. Streak ash-gray. Transparent in thin splinters. Isotropic. n variable, averaging about 1.87.[12] Close to pyrochlore in composition[54], but containing about 10 per cent SiO_2 (anal. 3) Named from χαλκός, *copper*, and λαμπρός, *brilliant*, in allusion to the coppery iridescence of the crystal faces. Probably identical with pyrochlore.[55]

ENDEIOLITE. *Flink* (*Medd. Grønland*, **24**, 166, 1901).

In octahedrons, often twinned on the spinel law. Fracture subconchoidal to splintery. Said to be of a somewhat doughy consistency, and that impressions may be made on it by the point of a needle. H. 4½. G. 3.44 Luster on fresh fractures greasy, but vitreous to metallic on crystal faces. Color dark chocolate-brown. Powder yellowish gray. Transparent in very thin splinters. Isotropic. Similar in composition[56] to chalcolamprite, but differing in that OH is largely substituted for F. Found at Narsarsuk, Greenland, implanted on aegirite and associated with elpidite, leucosphenite, epididymite, zinnwaldite, and other uncommon minerals in a microcline aegirite pegmatite in syenite. Named from ἔνδεια, *want*, and λίθος, *stone*, in allusion to the fact that the analysis showed a considerable loss. Probably an altered pyrochlore.

MARIGNACITE. *Weidman* and *Lenher* (*Am. J. Sc.*, **23**, 287, 1907). In octahedrons. Brittle. Fracture conchoidal. H. 5–5½. G. 4.13. Not metamict. Luster resinous on fracture surfaces. Color light to dark brown. Streak light brown to yellowish brown. Transparent. Exhibits anomalous birefringence. Composition essentially that of pyrochlore (anal. 8). For locality see under pyrochlore. Named after the French chemist, Galisard de Marignac (1817–1894). Apparently an altered pyrochlore.

ELLSWORTHITE. *Walker* and *Parsons* (*Univ. Toronto Stud., Geol. Ser.*, **13**, 1923). Massive. Metamict. Fracture subconchoidal to uneven. Brittle. H. 4–4½. G. 3.608 (amber yellow), 3.758 (chocolate-brown). Luster adamantine. Color amber-yellow in one variety and dark chocolate-brown in another (less altered). Isotropic. n 1.89±. Composition close to pyrochlore (anal. 7),[58] but relatively high in U and H_2O and low in alkalies. For localities see under pyrochlore. Named after H. V. Ellsworth (1889–   ) of the Canadian Geological Survey. Apparently an altered uranian variety, allied to hatchettolite, in the pyrochlore-microlite series.[59]

NEOTANTALITE. *Termier* (*Bull. soc. min.*, **25**, 34, 1902). In octahedrons, sometimes with small {011}. H. 5–6. Luster nearly adamantine. Color yellow. Transparent. Isotropic. n 1.96±.[12] Contains scales of hematite. Close to tantalite in composition (anal. 14), but apparently an altered microlite.[60] For locality see under microlite.

METASIMPSONITE. *Simpson* (*Dept. Mines Western Australia, Rep. 1937*, 88, 1938); *Taylor* (*Roy. Soc. Western Australia, J.*, **25**, 93, 1939). An alteration product of simpsonite, later identified with microlite.

Ref.

1. Crystal class from x-ray structural study of Gaertner, *Jb. Min., Beil.-Bd.*, **61**, 1 (1930) on pyrochlore.
2. In Dana (726, 727, 728, 1892).
3. Ellsworth, *Am. Min.*, **12**, 49 (1927) on crystals from Cardiff Township. The composition, however, indicates that these may not belong in this series.
4. Cell dimensions for many members of the series have been published, but, in general, these are not tied to specific analyzed samples. This is particularly regrettable, because microlite and pyrochlore are known to be variable in composition even from the same locality. The values for pyrochlore by Gaertner (1930) are on unanalyzed samples (ignited), and they are generally smaller than the microlite values. The artificial pyrochlore gives, according to Gaertner, $a_0 = 10.378$ (which is very close to the best microlite values). See also Bjørlykke, *Norsk Geol. Tidskr.*, **14**, 145 (1934); Rosén and Westgren, *Geol. För. Förh.*, **60**, 226 (1938); Machatschki, *Chem. Erde*, **7**, 64 (1932); *Cbl. Min.*, 33, 1932.
5. Reuning, *Chem. Erde*, **8**, 207 (1933).
6. Shaub in Palache and Gonyer, *Am. Min.*, **25**, 411 (1940).
7. Brandenberger, *Zs. Kr.*, **76**, 322 (1931).
8. For thermal study of pyrochlore see Liebisch, *Ak. Berlin, Ber.*, **20**, 350 (1910).
9. Flink, *Medd. Grønland*, **14**, 234 (1898); **24**, 166 (1901), on endeiolite and microlite from Greenland; also in koppite from the Kaiserstuhl; see Osann (132, 1927).
10. Other specific gravity values on unanalyzed material are: by Draisin (priv. comm., 1940), microlite, Newry 5.85; microlite, Amelia Court House, 6.05; microlite, Embudo, 5.99. Glass, *Am. Min.*, **20**, 752 (1935), obtained 5.9–6.0, 5.49–5.74 on amber and olive microlite respectively, from Amelia Court House.
11. Larsen and Berman (60, 61, 1934).
12. Larsen (1921) gives a number of values for unanalyzed samples. See also Glass, *Am. Min.*, **20**, 752 (1935), for refractive indices of Amelia Court House specimens. Also Kreutz, *Ak. Wiss., Krakau*, **54**, 227 (1915) — *Jb. Min.*, 134, 1918, gives prism measurements ($n = 2.012$) on Miask pyrochlore.
13. After Machatschki (1932) and Rosén and Westgren (1938).
14. In pyrochlore; see Holmquist, *Bull. Geol. Inst. Upsala*, **3**, 253 (1896).
15. In koppite; see Knop, *Jb. Min.*, **67**, 1875.
16. In koppite; see Bailey, *J. Chem. Soc. London*, **49**, 153 (1886).
17. Pyrochlore, Fredricksvärn. See Rammelsberg, *Ak. Berlin, Ber.*, **183**, 1871. An older anal. by Hayes, *Am. J. Sc.*, **46**, 158 (1844), gave $TiO_2 = 20.0$ per cent.

18. In microlite, Üto. See Nordenskiöld, *Geol. För. Förh.*, **3**, 282 (1872).
19. In pyrochlore from Miask. Rammelsberg (1871).
20. In microlite, Greenland. See Nordenskiöld, *Geol. För. Förh.*, **16**, 336 (1894).
21. Hevesy and Jantzen, *Zs. anorg. Chem.*, **136**, 387 (1924).
22. For additional analyses see Hintze (534, 1938), Doelter (3 [1], 95, 251, 1918) and Wells, *U. S. Geol. Sur., Bull. 878*, 114, 1937.
23. Holmquist, *Geol. För. Förh.*, **15**, 588 (1893).
24. Mauzelius anal. in Flink (1901).
25. Rammelsberg, *Ak. Wiss. Berlin, Monatsber.*, 198, 1871.
26. von Chroustchoff, *Russ. Min. Ges., Vh.*, **31**, 415 (1894).
27. Jakob anal. in Brandenberger (1931). See also Knop, *Jb. Min.*, **67**, 1875, and Bailey, *J. Chem. Soc. London*, **49**, 153 (1886), for additional analyses.
28. Todd anal. in Walker and Parsons, *Univ. Toronto Stud., Geol. Ser.*, 21, 1923; a second analysis is given of lighter colored material.
29. Weidman and Lenher, *Am. J. Sc.*, **23**, 287 (1907).
30. Chernik, *Ann. geol. min. Russ.*, **5**, 196 (1902).
31. Allen, *Am. J. Sc.*, **14**, 128 (1877); see also Smith, *Am. J. Sc.*, **13**, 365 (1877), for additional analyses.
32. Chernik, *J. phys. Chem. Russ.*, **36**, 457 (1904).
33. Rødland anal. in Brögger, *Vidensk. Selsk., Oslo, Mat.-Nat. Kl.*, 1920, no. 9 (1921)— *Min. Abs.*, **2**, 166 (1923).
34. Pisani anal. in Termier, *Bull. soc. min.*, **25**, 34 (1902).
35. Dunnington, *Am. Chem. J.*, **3**, 130 (1881).
36. Klüss anal. in Reuning, *Chem. Erde*, **8**, 186 (1933), who cites an additional analysis.
37. Bjørlykke anal., *Norsk Geol. Tidskr.*, **14**, 145 (1934).
38. Gonyer in Palache and Gonyer (1940).
39. Simpson, *Roy. Soc. Western Australia, J.*, **15**, 99 (1929).
40. Brögger, *Zs. Kr.*, **16**, 509 (1890).
41. Dana (727, 1892).
42. Lacroix, *Bull. soc. min.*, **31**, 246 (1908); **34**, 64 (1911), with partial analysis.
43. Walker and Parsons (1923).
44. See Hintze (532, 533, 1938).
45. For a discussion of the metamict columbates and tantalates see Goldschmidt, *Vidensk. Selsk., Oslo, Mat.-Nat. Kl.*, I, no. 5, 51, 1924.
46. Rosén and Westgren (1938); Gaertner (1930); Holmquist (1896); Joly, *Ann. sc. école norm. sup.*, 6, 125 (1877).
47. Brauns (99, 1922).
48. Machatschki, *Chem. Erde*, **7**, 64 (1932); *Cbl. Min.*, 33, 1932, by rotation method with a_0 10.39 ± 0.02 (Azores), a_0 10.41 ± 0.02 (Laacher See). See Hintze (539, 1938) for a discussion of the history and characters of pyrrhite.
49. Brauns (98, 1922) cites a partial analysis, and qualitative chemical tests have also been reported in Dana (728, 1892).
50. Brandenberger (1931), with a_0 10.37 ± 0.01 on material from the Kaiserstuhl. See also Machatschki (1932). Earlier investigators variously classed koppite as a distinct species or as pyrochlore; see Hintze (1 [4A], 402, 1923).
51. Walker and Parsons (1923).
52. See discussion of constitution in Machatschki (1932).
53. Machatschki (1932). The material had earlier been considered to be a somewhat altered pyrochlore by Allen (1877) and others.
54. Recognized by Flink (1901). The composition has also been discussed by Gossner, *Jb. Min., Beil.-Bd.*, **52**, 269 (1925).
55. The x-ray powder pattern appears to be identical with that of pyrochlore (Frondel, priv. comm., 1940). The crystals are stated by Flink (1901) to contain a large number of microscopic inclusions to which the Si content may be owing.
56. For analysis see Flink (1901), with 11.48 per cent SiO_2 by difference (by analogy with chalcolamprite).
57. Machatschki (1932), who considers the mineral to contain quartz as an impurity (microscopic inclusions of quartz and feldspar were mentioned by Weidman and Lenher (1907)) and that Na and Ca have been leached from the Cb-O framework and replaced by water.
58. See recalculation of this analysis in Bjørlykke (1934). The high water content is no doubt due to alteration. The SiO_2 may be due to impurities.
59. Bjørlykke (1934) found the x-ray powder pattern of the (ignited) dark massive

material from Hybla to be that of pyrochlore, with a_0 10.281 ± 0.009. The crystallized material from Cardiff Township, Ontario, described by Ellsworth, *Am. Min.*, **12**, 49 (1927), has not been shown to be identical with pyrochlore and possibly may belong with betafite or elsewhere.

60. Machatschki (1932). The x-ray powder pattern does not appear to differ from that of microlite (Frondel, priv. comm., 1939).

812   **Scheteligite** [(Ca,Y,Sb,Mn)$_2$(Ti,Ta,Cb)$_2$(O,OH)$_7$]. *Bjørlykke (Norsk Geol. Tidskr.*, **17**, 47, 1937).

In rough orthorhombic (?) crystals. Metamict. Fracture conchoidal. H. $5\frac{1}{2}$. G. 4.74. Color black, brilliant. Streak pale yellow to grayish. In thin splinters transparent and reddish brown in color. Isotropic.

C h e m. An oxide (or columbate-tantalate-titanate) with the possible formula A_2B_2(O,OH)$_7$, where A = Ca, Y, Sb, Bi, Mn, Fe and B = Ti, Ta, Cb, W. Analysis gave: CaO 10.73, FeO 1.88, MnO 6.19, Y$_2$O$_3$ 6.00, Sb$_2$O$_3$ 7.77, Bi$_2$O$_3$ 2.54, WO$_3$ 5., TiO$_2$ 18.73, Cb$_2$O$_5$ 8.65, Ta$_2$O$_5$ 20., loss on ignition 2.00, SiO$_2$ 6.00 (from which is calculated 9.70 per cent microcline), total 99.14.

Tests. Insoluble in strong acids, except HF.

O c c u r. In pegmatite at Torvelona, Iveland, Norway, associated with plagioclase, tourmaline, native bismuth, euxenite, thortveitite, monazite, alvite, beryl, garnet, magnetite.

N a m e. After Professor Jacob Schetelig (1875–1935), Norwegian mineralogist and formerly director of the Mineralogical Museum in Oslo.

STIBIOMICROLITE. *Quensel* and *Berggren (Geol. För. Förh.*, **60**, 216, 1938). A hypothetical mineral inferred from its disintegration products, stibiotantalite, microlite, and native antimony.[1] From Varuträsk, Sweden.

Ref.

1. Rosén and Westgren, *Geol. För. Förh.*, **60**, 232 (1938), have examined the components by x-ray methods. Bulk analyses of the mixture are given by Berggren, *Geol. För. Förh.*, **63**, 52 (1941); **60**, 216 (1938).

Fergusonite Series

8131   **F E R G U S O N I T E** [(Y,Er,Ce,Fe)(Cb,Ta,Ti)O$_4$]. *Haidinger (Roy. Soc. Edinburgh, Trans.*, **10**, 274, 1826). Tyrite *Forbes (Edinburgh New Phil. J.*, **1**, 67, 1855; *Phil. Mag.*, **13**, 91, 1857). Bragite *Forbes* and *Dahll (Nyt Mag.*, **8**, 227, 1855). Yttrotantalite pt. (gray, brown, yellow).

Rutherfordite *Shepard (Am. J. Sc.*, **12**, 209, 1851; **14**, 344, 1852; **20**, 57, 1880). Adelpholite, Adelfolit *N. Nordenskiöld* (1855; *Jb. Min.*, 313, 1858), *A. E. Nordenskiöld (Ak. Stockholm, Öfv.*, **20**, 452, 1863; *Ann. Phys.*, **122**, 615, 1864). Kochelite *Websky (Zs. deutsche geol. Ges.*, **20**, 250, 1868). Arrhenite *Nordenskiöld; Engstrom* (Inaug. Diss., Upsala, 1877 — Dana [745, 1892]). Sipylite *Mallet (Am. J. Sc.*, **14**, 397, 1877; **22**, 52, 1881). Mono-, Di-, and Trihydrated Fergusonite *Hidden* and *Mackintosh (Am. J. Sc.*, **38**, 482, 1889). Risörite *Hauser (Ber.*, **40**, 3118, 1907; *Zs. anorg. Chem.*, **60**, 230, 1908).

8132   **F O R M A N I T E** [(U,Zr,Th,Ca)(Ta,Cb,Ti)O$_4$]. *Berman* and *Frondel* (priv. comm., March, 1941). Fergusonite *Simpson (Australasian Assoc. Adv. Sc.*, **12**, 310, 1909).

C r y s t.   Tetragonal; dipyramidal — $4/m$.

$$a : c = 1 : 1.464;^1 \qquad p_0 : r_0 = 1.464 : 1$$

Forms:[2]

		ϕ	ρ	A	$\overline{M}$
c	001	....	0°00′	90°00′	90°00′
g	230	33°41½′	90 00	56 18½	78 41½
s	111	45 00	64 13	50 27	90 00
x	131	18 26	77 48½	71 59½	64 04½
z	231	33 41½	79 16½	56 58½	78 52½

Structure cell.[3]   Space group uncertain: $P4/m$, $P4_2/m$, $P4/n$, or $P4_2/n$.   Cell dimensions:

		a_0	c_0	$a_0 : c_0$	
Fergusonite	Högtveit	7.74	11.31	1 : 1.461	
Fergusonite	Gryting	7.78	11.41	1 : 1.466	Anal. 7 ("risorite")
YCbO$_4$	Artif.	7.76	11.32	1 : 1.458	
YTaO$_4$	Artif.	7.75	11.41	1 : 1.472	

Contains $(Y,Er)_8(Cb,Ta,Ti)_8O_{32}$.   The mineral as found is metamict, but crystallizes on ignition.[4]

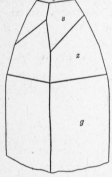

Fergusonite. Southern Norway.

Habit.   Prismatic [001] to pyramidal, sometimes with {001} prominent and often showing the hemihedral form {231}; occasionally long prismatic [001]. Also in irregular masses and grains.

P h y s.   Cleavage {111} in traces.[5]   Fracture subconchoidal.   Brittle.   H. $5\frac{1}{2}$–$6\frac{1}{2}$.   G. 5.6–5.8, decreasing markedly with hydration and increasing with Ta content; 5.38 (calc. for YCbO$_4$[6]), 7.03 (calc. for YTaO$_4$[6]); 4.68 (Risör); 4.72 (calc. Risör).   The specific gravity increases on ignition.   Luster externally dull, on the fracture brilliantly vitreous and submetallic.   Color externally gray, yellow, brown, or dark brown due to alteration; on fracture surfaces brownish black, velvety black.   Streak brown; yellowbrown, greenish gray.   Transparent in thin splinters.

O p t.   In transmitted light, light brown to dark brown in color and sometimes cloudy.   The metamict material is isotropic.   On ignition it becomes anisotropic but in such fine grain as to permit measurement only of the mean index of refraction.[7]   Large ignited grains, however, may exhibit birefringence possibly due to strain.[7]   Refractive indices:

	METAMICT	IGNITED (Mean Index)
Baringer Hill[9]	2.19 ± 0.02	.....
Boksput, Africa[10]	2.05	.....
Risör[11]	2.08	2.07
No locality[11]	2.115	2.070
No locality[11]	2.175	2.142
Risör[11]	2.08	2.08
Virginia[11]	2.06	2.06

Anisotropic crystals with an isotropic (metamict) shell have been found at Hundholmen, Norway.[12] Uniaxial, negative $(-)$, with strong birefringence and weak pleochroism, $O > E$.

C h e m. Essentially an oxide (or columbate-tantalate) of yttrium, erbium, columbium, and tantalum, with the type formula ABO_4.[13]

A = Y, Er, Ce, La, Di, U^4, Zr, Th, Ca, Fe^2.

B = Cb, Ta, Ti, Sn, W.

· A complete series apparently exists between the predominantly columbium *fergusonite* and the almost pure tantalum member, *formanite*. Water is reported in nearly all analyses, but is undoubtedly due to alteration.[14]

The following approximate limits of substitution are found, in the most reliable analyses.

A-Atoms	Maximum Weight Per Cent of Oxide	Anal.	B-Atoms	Maximum Weight Per Cent of Oxide	Anal.
Y	40.?	2	Cb	47.	8
Er	14.?	6	Ta	55.5	12
Ce, La, Di	9.35	5	Ti	6.0	7
Fe^2	2.04	5	Sn	0.98	9
U^4	8.16	6	W	0.8	
Zr	2.09	5			
Th	4.85	10			
Ca	4.17	11			

Small amounts of F, N, He, and Ra have been reported.[15]

Anal.

	1	2	3	4	5	6
CaO	.....	1.40	1.16	2.74	2.61	1.93
MnO	.....	.....	.....	.....	trace	.....
MgO	.....	0.58	trace	.....	0.05	0.28
FeO	.....	.....	.....	.....	2.04	.....
Y_2O_3	45.93	}40.39	}37.64	}31.36	}27.94	22.68
Er_2O_3	.....					13.95
Ce_2O_3	.....		1.26	.....	1.37	3.33
La_2O_3	.....	} 0.89	1.99	.....	3.92	.....
Di_2O_3	.....		.....	.....	4.06	.....
UO_2	.....	3.18	0.85	3.93	.....	8.16
UO_3	.....	.....	0.85	3.12	.....	.....
ThO_2	.....	.....	2.91	0.83	.....	.....
ZrO_2	.....	.....	.....	.....	2.09	.....
SnO_2	.....	0.35	.....	.....	0.08	0.83
Al_2O_3	.....	1.35	0.20	0.85	.....	.....
Fe_2O_3	.....	0.66	3.97	3.75	.....	.....
TiO_2	.....	1.15	1.65			
Cb_2O_5	54.07	}44.97	}43.77	42.79	46.66	43.36
Ta_2O_5	.....			.....	2.00	2.04
H_2O	.....	3.92	.....	8.19	3.19	4.18
Rem.	.....	1.14	4.92	2.44	4.47	.....
Total	100.00	99.98	100.32	100.00	100.48	100.74
G.	5.38	5.30		4.36–4.48	4.89	5.267

1. $Y_2Cb_2O_8$. 2. Fergusonite. Hakatamura, Japan. Rem. is SiO_2 0.79, CO_2 0.35.[17] 3. Fergusonite. Naegi, Japan. Rem. is SiO_2 2.83, ign. loss 2.09 (H_2O − 110 0.24, H_2O + 110 1.85).[18] 4. Fergusonite. Baringer Hill, Tex. Rem. is PbO 1.94, F 0.50.[19] 5. Sipylite. Amherst Co., Va. Rem. is Na_2O 0.16, K_2O 0.06, Li_2O trace, BeO 0.62, WO_3 0.16, UO 3.47, F trace, $(Y,Er)_2O_3$ given in original as Y_2O_3 ca. 1.0 and Er_2O ca. 26.94.[20] 6. Bragite. Helle, Arendal, Norway.[21]

	7	8	9	10	11	12	13
CaO	1.93	1.96	1.23	2.10	4.17	2.18	.....
MnO	.....	0.13	0.15	.....	.....	0.87	.....
MgO	.....	0.05	0.05	.....	.....	.....	.....
FeO	2.61	0.71	0.78	.....	0.72	trace	.....
Y_2O_3	}36.28	}36.47	}35.03	}27.54	24.45	23.00	33.83
Er_2O_3					8.26	8.38	
Ce_2O_3	}		0.72	}	.....	}	.....
La_2O_3	} 2.88	} 4.16	} 2.25	} 4.06	.....	} 0.94	.....
Di_2O_3	}				.....		.....
UO_2	0.10	.....	4.68	2.12	2.13	.....	.....
UO_3	.....	3.32	.....	.....	.....	1.18	.....
ThO_2	trace	.....	2.51	4.85	.....	1.02	.....
ZrO_2	.....	.....	trace	0.89	.....	.....	.....
SnO_2	0.01	trace	0.98	0.26	.....	.....	.....
Al_2O_3	0.81	trace	.....	.....	.....	.....	.....
Fe_2O_3	1.20	.....	.....	0.72	.....	.....	.....
TiO_2	6.00	.....	.....	0.26	.....	2.20	.....
Cb_2O_5	36.21	47.12	39.30	34.79	28.14	2.15	.....
Ta_2O_5	4.00	5.10	6.25	17.03	27.04	55.51	66.17
H_2O	7.11	.....	4.00	.....	5.12	.....	.....
Rem.	1.33	.....	1.84	5.26	.....	3.36	.....
Total	100.47	99.02	99.77	99.88	100.03	100.79	100.00
G.	4.179	5.78	4.97	4.98	4.774	6.236	7.03

7. Risörite. Risör, Norway. Rem. is N and He 0.90, CO_2 0.23, PbO 0.20.[22]   8. Fergusonite, Blum mine, Ilmen Mts. With K_2O, Na_2O, SiO_2, and WO_3 trace.[23]   9. Fergusonite. Berg, near Råde, Norway. Rem. is SiO_2 1.44, BeO 0.40.[24]   10. Fergusonite. Near Ambatofotsikely, Madagascar. Rem. is ign. loss 5.26.[25]   11. " Yellow yttrotantalite. " Ytterby, Sweden.[23] 12. Formanite. Cooglegong, Western Australia. Rem. is ign. loss 3.36.[26]   13. $Y_2Ta_2O_8$.

Tests. Infusible. On ignition most varieties afford water (and He,N), and the powder acquires a greenish or light brownish tint. May recalesce on heating, and apparently most markedly in material with a relatively high G. and low water content. Partly decomposed by H_2SO_4 or HCl, with separation of $(Cb,Ta)_2O_5$. Completely decomposed by strong HF and by fusion in $KHSO_4$.

Var. Titanian. Risörite *Hauser (Ber.,* **40**, 3118, 1907; *Zs. anorg. Chem.,* **60**, 230, 1908). Contains Ti in substitution for Cb-Ta in relatively large amounts (6 per cent in anal. 7). Risörite was originally thought to be a distinct species, but has since been shown[27] to be a titanian fergusonite.

Uranian. U is usually present, in substitution for Y-Er, in amounts ranging up to 8 per cent UO_2 (anal. 6).

Erbian. Er is usually present in substitution for Y, in amounts up to at least Y : Er = 2.8 : 1 (anal. 6). The supposed erbium columbate, *sipylite,* is identical with fergusonite and contains largely Y instead of Er.[28]

Occur. Fergusonite occurs in granite pegmatites, particularly those rich in rare earths, columbium, tantalum, and beryllium, and is associated with zircon, biotite, magnetite, monazite, gadolinite, thalenite, orthite, euxenite, and other rare-earth minerals.

All the known localities are not mentioned here. Originally brought by Giesecke in 1806 from Kikertaursuk (Kangek) in the Julianehaab district in Greenland, where it was found embedded in quartz. In granite pegmatites at many localities in the Iveland district of southern Norway with gadolinite, thalenite and many other rare species; *tyrite* was found with euxenite at Hampemyr on the island of Tromö, at Helle on the mainland, and at Näskul, about 10 miles east of Arendal; *bragite* was from Helle, Narestö, Alve, and Askerö. Also in Norway from Berg, near Råde, from near Moss on the island Dillingö in Vansjö, at several localities near Arendal on the Ånneröd peninsula; from Hundholmen in northern Norway in pegmatite with allanite, yttrofluorite, xenotime, gadolinite, and microcline, and at a number of other localities.[29] *Risörite* is from a pegmatite in Gryting, Gjerrestad parish, near Risör, Norway. Found with samarskite, ilmenorutile, and ilmenite in the Blum mine, Ilmen Mountains, U.S.S.R. In Sweden at Ytterby (*arrhenite, pt.; yellow yttrotantalite, pt.*) in pegmatite with xenotime, cyrtolite and biotite, and at Kårarfvet near Fahlun (*brown and gray yttrotantalite, pt.*). With columbite in pegmatite at Laurinmaki, in Tammela, Finland (*adelpholite*). With ilmenite in pegmatite in the Kochelwiese, near Schreiberhau, Silesia (*kochelite*), and in pegmatite with magnetite and zircon near Königshain, near Gorlitz, Silesia.

In gem gravels at Rakwana and elsewhere in Ceylon. In Africa reported from placers in the Ambabaan district, Swaziland, with monazite, cassiterite, and euxenite (?), from Morogoro, East Africa, from Fort Victoria, Southern Rhodesia, and from Onseepkans, Kenhardt, and Boksput, Gordonia, in Cape Province. In Japan with allanite in pegmatite at Hakatamura and at Hagata, both in Iyo Province, and in river sand near Takayama and Naegi, in Mino Province. In Madagascar in pegmatite at a number of localities, associated with euxenite, betafite, and biotite; south of Lake Itasy; at Fiadanana; west of Ambatovohangy; at Ranomafana; southwest of Ambatofotsikely. Formanite is abundant in Western Australia at Cooglegong, in placers with cassiterite, monazite, euxenite, and gadolinite.

In the United States fergusonite occurs in North Carolina as pebbles in gold placers at Brindletown, Burke County (*rutherfordite, pt.*) with monazite, samarskite, anatase, and other heavy detrital minerals; with allanite and cyrtolite in pegmatites near Spruce Pine, Mitchell County, and in placers near Golden P. O., Rutherford County. In South Carolina found loose in the soil with zircon near Storeville, Anderson County. At Amelia Court House, Virginia, in pegmatite with allanite, and on the northwest slope of Little Friar Mountain, Amherst County, Virginia (*sipylite*) with allanite, zircon, and magnetite. Found abundantly in the pegmatite at Baringer Hill, Llano County, Texas, associated with gadolinite, biotite, microline, quartz, fluorite, and a variety of rare-earth minerals; sometimes in crystals up to 8 in. long and 1 in. thick; usually immediately associated with cyrtolite, uraninite, mackintoshite, thorogummite, and gadolinite, and sometimes enclosed in the latter mineral. Parallel growths of uraninite upon fergusonite have been noted from this locality.[30] In Massachusetts at Rockport, Cape Ann, with cyrtolite and microcline in pegmatite. Reported from Torrington, Connecticut, in quartz.

Alter. Alters readily by hydration, without loss of external form. The change is accompanied by a decrease in specific gravity, by a change in color, and by the loss of crystallinity (which may be restored by heating to redness).[31]

A r t i f.[32]   The compounds $YTaO_4$ and $YCbO_4$ have been produced by fusion of Y_2O_3 and Ta_2O_5 or Cb_2O_5, and have been shown by x-ray study to be identical with fergusonite.

N a m e.   Fergusonite after the Scotch physician, Robert Ferguson (1799–1865).   Risörite from the town, Risör, near which it was found. Sipylite from Sipylus, one of the children of Niobe, in allusion to the names niobium and tantalum.   Formanite after Francis Gloster Forman, government geologist of Western Australia.

RUTHERFORDITE.   *Shepard* (*Am. J. Sc.*, **12**, 209, 1851; **14**, 344, 1852; **20**, 57, 1880).   Adelpholite, Adelfolit *N. Nordenskiöld* (1855; *Jb. Min.*, 313, 1858); *A. E. Nordenskiöld* (*Ak. Stockholm, Öfv.*, **20**, 452, 1863; *Ann. Phys.*, **122**, 615, 1864). Kochelite *Websky* (*Zs. deutsche Geol. Ges.*, **20**, 250, 1868).   Arrhenite *Nordenskiöld; Engstrom* (Inaug. Diss. Upsala, 1877 — Dana [745, 1892]), Mono-, Di-, and Trihydrated Fergusonite *Hidden* and *Mackintosh* (*Am. J. Sc.*, **38**, 482, 1889). Names given to various materials[33] which are doubtless altered fergusonite.

SIPYLITE.   *Mallet* (*Am. J. Sc.*, **14**, 397, 1877; **22**, 52, 1881).

A supposed columbate of erbium in irregular masses and tetragonal octahedra from Little Friar Mountain, Amherst County, Virginia (anal. 5).   Shown[28] to contain largely Y instead of Er and to be identical with fergusonite.

RISÖRITE.   *Hauser* (*Ber.*, **40**, 3118, 1907; *Zs. anorg. Chem.*, **60**, 230, 1908). Shown[27] to be a titanian variety of fergusonite (cf. anal. 7).   From a pegmatite at Gryting, near Risör, Norway.

Ref.

1. Crystal class from Haidinger, *Roy. Soc. Edinburgh, Trans.*, **10**, 272 (1826), on crystals from Greenland.   Rammelsberg, *Ber.*, **5**, 17 (1872), and Prior, *Min. Mag.*, **13**, 219 (1903), have pointed out a morphological resemblance to scheelite, but Barth, *Norsk Geol. Tidskr.*, **9**, 23 (1926), has shown that the crystal structures of these minerals are different.

2. In Goldschmidt (4, 1, 1918).

3. Barth (1926) by the powder method on fergusonite from Högtveit, Norway, and from Gryting, Norway (risörite).

4. See Goldschmidt, *Vidensk. Selskr., Mat.-Nat. Kl.*, I, no. 5, 51, 1924, for a discussion of the metamict columbates and tantalates.   See also Barth and Berman, *Chem. Erde*, **5**, 37 (1930).   The material from Hundholmen, Norway, is said not to be metamict.

5. Kôzu and Masuda, *Sc. Rep. Tôhoku Univ.*, ser. III, **3**, 1 (1926), also report a prominent cleavage {001}.

6. From cell dimensions of the artificial material given by Barth (1926).

7. Barth (1926).

8. Prior, *Min. Mag.*, **10**, 234 (1893), and Brögger, *Vidensk. Selskr., Mat.-Nat. Kl.*, no. 6, 33, 1906.

9. Larsen (74, 1921).

10. Mountain, *Rec. Albany Museum, Grahamstown*, **4**, 122 (1931) — *Min. Abs.*, **4**, 475 (1931).

11. Barth and Berman (1930).

12. Vogt, *Cbl. Min.*, 373, 1911.

13. See Machatschki, *Zs. Kr.*, **72**, 291 (1929), for a discussion of the crystal chemistry of fergusonite.

14. Hidden and Mackintosh, *Am. J. Sc.*, **38**, 482 (1889), erroneously considered the water to be constitutional and postulated the existence of mono-, di-, and trihydrates. The work of Barth (1926) on artificial material disproved the hydrate theory.

15. See Hintze (1 [4A], 279, 1922); Sasaki, *Bull. Chem. Soc. Japan*, **1**, 253 (1926); and Okada, *J. Geol. Soc. Tokyo*, **35**, 336 (1928).

16. For additional analyses see Hintze (1922).   Hess and Wells, *Am. J. Sc.*, **19**, 17 (1930), give a further analysis (2) of a mineral from Petaca, New Mexico, referred to samarskite but which may be related to fergusonite.   See p. 800.

17. Kimura anal. in Sato, *J. Faculty Sc. Univ. Tokyo*, II, **1**, 49 (1925) — *Min. Abs.*, **3**, 268 (1927).
18. Shibata and Kimura, *J. Chem. Soc. Japan*, **42**, 1 (1921) — *Min. Abs.*, **2**, 36 (1923).
19. Hidden and Mackintosh, *Am. J. Sc.*, **38**, 482 (1889).
20. Mallet, *Am. J. Sc.*, **14**, 397 (1877).
21. Rammelsberg, *Ak. Berlin, Sitzber.*, 406, 1871.
22. Hauser, *Zs. anorg. Chem.*, **60**, 230 (1908).
23. Chernik, *Bull. ac. sc. russe*, **15**, 419 (1921) — *Min. Abs.*, **2**, 405 (1924).
24. Blomstrand anal. in Brögger, *Zs. Kr.*, **45**, 83 (1908).
25. Pisani anal. in Lacroix, *Bull. soc. min.*, **38**, 130 (1915).
26. Simpson, *Proc. Australasian Assoc. Adv. Sc.*, **12**, 310 (1909).
27. Barth, *Norsk Geol. Tidskr.*, **9**, 37 (1926); Machatschki, *Zs. Kr.*, **72**, 291 (1929).
28. Goldschmidt, *Videnskr. Selskr., Mat.-Nat. Kl.*, I, no. 5, 51 (1924); see also Delafontaine, *C. R.*, **87**, 933 (1878).
29. For Norwegian localities see Björlykke, *Norsk Geol. Tidskr.*, **14**, 211 (1935), and Hintze (1922).
30. Hidden, *Am. J. Sc.*, **19**, 430 (1905).
31. See Barth (1926), who found that metamict fergusonite recrystallizes on heating to an aggregate of randomly oriented crystallites.
32. Barth (1926).
33. See Dana (730, 731, 745, 1892) for analyses and description.

814 **Yttrotantalite** [(Fe,Y,U,Ca,etc.)(Cb,Ta,Zr,Sn)O₄]. Yttrotantal *Ekeberg* (*Ak. Stockholm*, **23**, 80, 1802). Tantal oxidé yttrifère *Haüy* (1822). Yttroilmenite *Hermann* (*J. pr. Chem.*, **38**, 119, 1846). Schwarzer Yttrotantalite.

C r y s t. Orthorhombic.

$$a : b : c = 0.54 : 1 : 1.13;^1 \qquad p_0 : q_0 : r_0 = 2.09 : 1.13 : 1$$
$$q_1 : r_1 : p_1 = 0.54 : 0.48 : 1; \qquad r_2 : p_2 : q_2 = 0.88 : 1.85 : 1$$

Forms:[2]

		ϕ	$\rho = C$	ϕ_1	$\rho_1 = A$	ϕ_2	$\rho_2 = B$
c	001	.....	0°00′	0°00′	90°00′	90°00′	90°00′
b	010	0°00′	90 00	90 00	90 00	.....	0 00
q	150	20 19	90 00	90 00	69 41	0 00	20 19
p	120	42 48	90 00	90 00	47 12	0 00	42 48
m	110	61 38	90 00	90 00	28 22	0 00	61 38
o	210	74 53	90 00	90 00	15 07	0 00	74 53
β	011	0 00	48 30	48 30	90 00	90 00	41 30
s	201	90 00	76 34	0 00	13 26	13 26	90 00

Habit. Prismatic [001] with {110} and {010} prominent; also tabular {010}.

P h y s. Cleavage {010} indistinct. Fracture small conchoidal. H. 5–5½. G. 5.7 ± 0.2. Luster submetallic to vitreous and greasy. Color black, brown.[3] Streak gray. Transmits light in thin splinters. Isotropic (metamict), becomes crystalline on heating. In section red-brown and isotropic $n = 2.15 \pm 0.02.^4$

C h e m. Essentially iron, yttrium, uranium, columbium, and tantalum oxide (or columbate-tantalate) with the formula $A_6B_7O_{25}$ (close to ABO_4) with

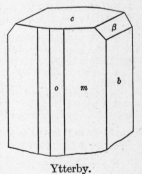

Ytterby.

$$A = Fe^2, Y, U, Ca, Mn, Ce, Th$$
$$B = Cb, Ta, Ti, Zr, Sn$$

The ratios of the principal constituents are: $Fe : Y : U = 9 : 8 : 1$ and $Cb : Ta = 1 : 1$ approx. (for the Berg and Hattevik analyses).

Anal.

	1	2
CaO	1.28	2.42
MgO	0.15	0.15
FeO	7.48	7.61
MnO	1.85	1.01
PbO	....	0.30
Y_2O_3	12.48	12.52
Er_2O_3	3.58	3.54
Ce_2O_3	0.42	0.51
La_2O_3	1.71	0.41
UO_2	3.85	4.48
SnO_2	1.20	2.96
ThO_2	0.67	0.81
TiO_2	1.67	2.63
ZrO_2	0.57	0.46
WO_3	0.66	2.02
Cb_2O_5	20.38	17.75
Ta_2O_5	39.53	37.26
H_2O	0.51	1.16
Rem.	1.88	2.10
Total	99.87	100.10
G.	5.92	5.85

1. Yttrotantalite. Berg, Norway. Rem. is Na_2O 0.57, BeO 0.35, SiO_2 0.96.[5]
2. Yttrotantalite. Hattevik, Norway. Rem. is Na_2O 0.81, K_2O 0.10, BeO 0.58, SiO_2 0.61.[5]

Tests. Infusible. In C.T. yields water (on altered material ?), turns yellow. On intense ignition becomes white. Not decomposed by acids. Decomposed on fusion with potassium bisulphate.

Occur. In Norway in pegmatites at Hattevik, east of Dillingö, and near Berg (or Elvestad) in Råde. In Sweden at Ytterby (in part fergusonite); with albite, garnet, and altered topaz at Finbo and Brodbo, near Fahlun, Sweden. The reported occurrence in Ceylon is probably not yttrotantalite.[6]

Ref.
1. Based on poor measurements, with a contact goniometer, on crystals from Ytterby, by Nordenskiöld, *Ak. Stockholm, Öfv.*, **17**, 28 (1860). Brögger (153, 1906) on crystals from Hattevik obtained approximate measurements close to samarskite values. He gives an axial ratio of $a : b : c = 0.5566 : 1 : 0.5173$, in close agreement with samarskite.
2. Nordenskiöld (1860) in Dana (738, 1892). See also Brögger (1906).
3. The supposed yellow yttrotantalite from Ytterby and Kararfvet are fergusonite. See Rammelsberg, *Ak. Berlin, Ber.*, 406, 1871.
4. Larsen (158, 1921); the locality is given as Dillingö, Moss, Sweden, but it is assumed that this must refer to the Norwegian locality.
5. Blomstrand anal. in Brögger (1906).
6. Chernik, *Ac. sc. St. Pétersbourg, Bull.*, 1913 — *Jb. Min.*, I, 39, 1915. The analysis is closer to hjelmite, which see.

815   **P O L Y M I G N Y T E** [(Ca, Fe^2, Y, etc., Zr,Th)(Cb,Ti,Ta)O_4]. Polymignit Berzelius (*Ak. Stockholm, Handl.*, 338, 1824).

Cryst. Orthorhombic; dipyramidal — $2/m\ 2/m\ 2/m$.[1]

$a : b : c = 0.7121 : 1 : 0.5121$;[2] $p_0 : q_0 : r_0 = 0.7191 : 0.5121 : 1$

$q_1 : r_1 : p_1 = 0.7121 : 1.3905 : 1$; $r_2 : p_2 : q_2 = 1.9527 : 1.4043 : 1$

Forms:[3]

		ϕ	$\rho = C$	ϕ_1	$\rho_1 = A$	ϕ_2	$\rho_2 = B$
c	001	.....	0°00′	0°00′	90°00′	90°00′	90°00′
b	010	0°00′	90 00	90 00	90 00	.....	0 00
a	100	90 00	90 00	.....	0 00	0 00	90 00
t	140	19 20½	90 00	90 00	70 39½	0 00	19 20½
s	120	35 04½	90 00	90 00	54 55½	0 00	35 04½
m	110	54 32½	90 00	90 00	35 17½	0 00	54 32½
l	210	70 24	90 00	90 00	19 36	0 00	70 24
p	111	54 32½	41 26½	27 07	57 22½	54 16½	67 25½
q	232	43 07	46 27½	37 32	60 18	54 16½	58 03
r	131	25 05	59 29	56 56½	68 35	54 16½	38 43½

Habit. Prismatic [001], striated [001]; also somewhat flattened {100}.

Phys. Cleavage {100} and {010} in traces (?). Fracture conchoidal. H. 6½. G. 4.77–4.85. Luster sub-metallic to metallic, brilliant. Color black. Streak dark brown. Transparent in very thin splinters.

Opt. In transmitted light, reddish brown and isotropic (metamict). $n = 2.22 \pm 0.01$ (Fredricksvärn).[4]

Chem. An oxide (or columbate-titanate-zirconate) of uncertain formula, possibly ABO_4:[5] with A = Ca, Fe^2, (Y,Er,Ce), Zr, Th; B = Cb, Ti, Ta, Fe^3. Hafnium has been reported[6] (0.9 per cent HfO_2 in Fredricksvärn

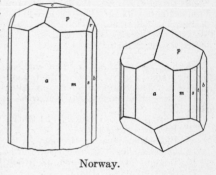

Norway.

material). The small amount of water is presumably due to alteration (metamict).

Anal.

	1	2	3
CaO	4.2	6.98	5.31
MgO	trace	0.16	0.42
FeO	.....	2.08	0.77
MnO	2.7	1.32	0.73
$(Y,Er)_2O_3$	11.5	2.26	21.56
Ce_2O_3	} 5.0	5.91	5.17
$(La,Di)_2O_3$		5.13	.....
ZrO_2	14.4	29.71	14.50
ThO_2	.....	3.92	.....
SnO_2	trace	0.15	trace
Fe_2O_3	12.2	7.66	.....
TiO_2	}	18.90	1.26
Cb_2O_5	}46.3	11.99	6.37
Ta_2O_5	}	1.35	42.17
Rem.	.....	2.67	1.47
Total	96.3	100.19	99.73
G.	4.806	4.77–4.85	6.337

1. Polymignyte. Fredricksvärn. SiO_2, K_2O trace.[7] 2. Polymignyte. Fredricksvärn. Rem. is SiO_2 0.45, Al_2O_3 0.19, PbO 0.39, Na_2O 0.59, K_2O 0.77, H_2O 0.28.[8] 3. Polymignyte? Siberia. Rem. is Na_2O 1.47; SiO_2, Al_2O_3, H_2O trace.[9]

Tests. B.B. infusible and unchanged in color.   Fine powder more or less decomposed by H_2SO_4, and completely by HF or fused $KHSO_4$.

Occur. Originally from Fredricksvärn, Norway, where it was found in pegmatite with soda-orthoclase, barkevikite, magnetite, nephelite, zircon and pyrochlore; also in augite-syenite (laurvikite); found similarly associated at the island of Svenör.   Reported from Siberia with magnetite and knopite in syenite (anal. 3); from Nuk, Christianshaab district, Greenland, in granite pegmatite (euxenite?[10]), and in several unconfirmed localities in Moravia.[11]   Said to occur at Beverly, Massachusetts.

Name. From πολύς, *many*, and μιγνύναι, *mix*, in allusion to the complex composition.

Ref.

1. Inferred from the figure given by Haidinger, *Edinburgh J. Sc.*, 3, 1825, and reproduced in Goldschmidt (6, 97, 1920, Fig. 2).
2. Brögger, *Zs. Kr.*, **16**, 387 (1890), on crystals from Fredericksvärn, corresponding to material of anal. 2.   The crystals do not justify a ratio much beyond the second place of decimals (Berman, 1941).   X-ray powder pictures of the ignited Fredericksvärn material are the same as yttrotantalite, from Ytterby.
3. Brögger (1890).
4. Larsen (122, 1921).
5. The various analyses do not yield similar formulas.   Anal. 1 gives ABO_4 approximately; anal. 2 gives $A_8B_9O_{37}$; anal. 3 gives $A_3B_3O_{11}$ (with Zr in the B part of the formula (?).   The composition is approximately $CaY_2ZrCb_2O_{11}$ (Berman, priv. comm., 1941).   See also Gossner, *Jb. Min., Beil.-Bd.*, **53**, 265 (1925), and Groth and Mieleitner (118, 1921).
6. von Hevesy and Jantzen, *Zs. anorg. Chem.*, **133**, 113 (1924).
7. Berzelius (1824).
8. Blomstrand anal. in Brögger, *Zs. Kr.*, **16**, 387 (1890).
9. Chernik, *Ac. sc. St. Pétersbourg, Bull.*, **2**, 75 (1908) — *Jb. Min.*, I, 189, 1910.
10. Bøggild, *Medd. Grønland*, **32**, 513 (1905).
11. See Hintze (492, 1937).

816   **Ishikawaite** [(U,Fe,Y, etc.) (Cb,TaO₄)].   *Kimura (J. Geol. Soc., Tokyo*, **29**, 316, 1922).   *Shibata* and *Kimura (J. Chem. Soc., Japan*, **43**, 301, 648, 1922).

The tabular crystals {100} are supposedly orthorhombic, with the forms:

$c\{001\}$ $b\{010\}$ $a\{100\}$ $n\{140\}$ $m\{110\}$ $h\{320\}$ $g\{210\}$

and an axial ratio $a : b : c = 0.9451 : 1 : 1.1472$.[1]   Fracture conchoidal. H. 5–6. G. 6.2–6.4. Luster waxy. Color black. Streak dark brown. Opaque.

The mineral is essentially a uranium, iron, rare earth, and columbium oxide (or columbate), with the formula $(U,Fe^2,Y, etc.)(Cb,Ta)O_4$.[2]   The composition is analogous with some of the early reported samarskites. Found with samarskite in pegmatite in the Ishikawa district, Iwaki Province, Japan.

Analysis gave: CaO 0.86, MgO 1.07, FeO 11.78, MnO 0.40, $(Y,Er,Ce,La,Di)_2O_3$ 8.40, UO_2 21.88, SnO_2 1.20, TiO_2 0.21, Al_2O_3 0.87, Cb_2O_5 36.80, Ta_2O_5 15.00, H_2O 0.89, SiO_2 0.30, total 99.66. G. 6.3.

Ref.

1. See Ōhashi, *J. Geol. Soc., Tokyo*, **31**, 166 (1924) — *Min. Abs.*, **2**, 380 (1925), for an alternate orientation yielding $\frac{1}{2}b : a : c = 0.529 : 1 : 1.213$, in supposed conformity with yttrotantalite and samarskite.
2. Berman and Frondel (priv. comm., 1941).   The ratio is Fe : Y : U = 21 : 6 : 8.

817   **Loranskite** [(Y,Ce,Ca,Zr (?))(Ta,Zr ?)O₄ ?].   *Melnikow* (*Zs. Kr.*, **31**, 505, 1899).

In crystals resembling samarskite.[1] Fracture conchoidal. Brittle. H. 5. G. 4.6; 4.16.[2] Luster submetallic. Color black. Streak greenish gray. In thin splinters, transparent, and greenish yellow.

Chem. An oxide (or tantalate-zirconate ?) with a possible formula $(Y,Ce,Ca)_4Zr_3Ta_4O_{22}$ based on an incomplete analysis, as follows: CaO 3.3, Fe_2O_3 (?) 4.0, $(Y,Er)_2O_3$ 10.0, $(Ce,La)_2O_3$ 3.0, ZrO_2 20.0, Ta_2O_5 47.0, ign. loss 8.15, total 95.45. G. 4.16. Said to contain some TiO_2 and MnO.[2]

Tests. Incompletely decomposed by acids and by fusion in alkalies; completely decomposed by fusion in KHF_2 and, with difficulty, in $KHSO_4$.

Occur. In pegmatite at Impilahti (Imbilax) on Lake Ladoga near Pitkäranta, Finland. Associated with wiikite.

Name. After A. M. Loranski, formerly Inspector of the Mining Institute, St. Petersburg.

An ill-defined material of uncertain affiliations, possibly related to polymignyte.

Ref.

1. Borgström, *Geol. För. Förh.*, **32**, 3, 1531 (1910), described supposed loranskite from the region of Impilahti, and gave a figure and ratio based on contact measurements ($a : b : c = 0.5317 : 1 : 0.5046$). Forms: {100}, {010}, {110}, {201}. There is no certainty that this material is the same as the original material of Melnikow. Borgström considers that loranskite and wiikite belong to the same group.
2. Nikolajew, *Russ. Ges. Min., Vh.*, **35** [2], 11 (1897).

Stibiotantalite Series

8181   **STIBIOTANTALITE** [SbTaO₄]. *Goyder* (*Proc. Chem. Soc. London*, **9**, 184, 1892; *J. Chem. Soc. London*, **63**, 1076, 1893).
8182   **STIBIOCOLUMBITE** [SbCbO₄]. *Schaller* (priv. contr. in Dana 74, 1915).

Cryst. Orthorhombic; pyramidal — $m\,m\,2$.[1]

$a : b : c = 0.4169 : 1 : 0.4696$;[2] $p_0 : q_0 : r_0 = 1.1264 : 0.4696 : 1$

$q_1 : r_1 : p_1 = 0.4169 : 0.8878 : 1$; $r_2 : p_2 : q_2 = 2.1295 : 2.3986 : 1$

Forms:[3]

		ϕ	$\rho = C$	ϕ_1	$\rho_1 = A$	ϕ_2	$\rho_2 = B$
b'	010	0°00′	90°00′	90°00′	90°00′	.....	0°00′
$'b$	0$\bar{1}$0	180 00	90 00	−90 00	90 00	.....	180 00
n'	130	38 38½	90 00	90 00	51 21½	0°00′	38 38½
m'	110	67 22	90 00	90 00	22 38	0 00	67 22
$'m$	1$\bar{1}$0	112 38	90 00	−90 00	22 38	0 00	112 38
n'	012	0 00	13 13	13 13	90 00	90 00	76 47
$'\eta$	0$\bar{1}$2	180 00	13 13	−13 13	90 00	90 00	103 13
δ	101	90 00	48 24	0 00	41 36	41 36	90 00
w'	111	67 22	50 40	25 09½	44 26½	41 36	72 41

Less common:

c	001	β'	170	e'	011	$'h$?	0$\bar{3}$2	$'w$?	1$\bar{1}$1	$'x$	1$\bar{3}$3	ϵ	171
α'	190	γ'	150	h'	032	l'	021	x'	133	y'	132		

Structure cell.[4] Space group Pna, a_0 4.916, b_0 5.542, c_0 11.78; $a_0 : c_0 : b_0 = 0.4173 : 1 : 0.4705$. (In the morphological orientation the space group is Pcn.) Contains $Sb_4(Ta,Cb)_4O_{16}$.

Habit. Prismatic [001]. {010} and {110} striated ∥ [001]. The crystals often show no morphological evidence of hemimorphism.

Twinning.[5] Polysynthetic, with twin axis [001] and composition plane {010}; also with the individuals irregularly intergrown.

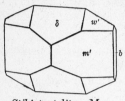

Stibiotantalite. Mesa Grande, Calif.

P h y s. Cleavage {010} distinct, and {100} indistinct.[5] Fracture subconchoidal to granular. Brittle. H. $5\frac{1}{2}$. G. 7.34 (for Ta : Cb = 19 : 1; anal. 2) to 5.98 (for Ta : Cb = 1 : 4.8; anal. 6), decreasing with Cb content; 7.53 (calc. for $SbTaO_4$[7]), 5.68 (calc. for $SbCbO_4$[7]). Luster resinous to adamantine. Color dark brown to light yellowish brown; also reddish yellow, reddish brown, greenish yellow. Streak pale yellow to yellow-brown. Transparent. Exhibits marked pyroelectricity.[5]

O p t.[8] In transmitted light pale yellow-brown to brown in color. Crystals sometimes are roughly zoned in yellow and brown. Biaxial

	Orientation	Crystal 1			Crystal 2		
		n_{Li}	n_{Na}	n_{Tl}	n_{Li}	n_{Na}	n_{Tl}
X	a	2.3470	2.3742	2.4014	2.3686	2.3977	2.4261
Y	b	2.3750	2.4039	2.4342	2.3876	2.4190	2.4508
Z	c	2.4275	2.4568	2.4876	2.4280	2.4588	2.4903
	2V (calc.)	73°40′	75°5′	77°38′	70°0′	73°25′	77°50′

Crystal 1: G. 6.818, Ta_2O_5 39 per cent and Cb_2O_5 17.5 per cent (est.)
Crystal 2: G. 6.299, Ta_2O_5 22.5 per cent and Cb_2O_5 30 per cent (est.)

positive (+). $r < v$, strong. With increase in Cb, the refractive indices and dispersion increase, the birefringence decreases and 2V decreases (except for Tl light).

C h e m. Presumably an oxide of antimony and tantalum-columbium, $Sb(Ta,Cb)O_4$. A complete series probably exists between Ta and Cb. Bi substitutes for Sb in small amounts.

Anal.

	1	2	3	4	5	6
Sb_2O_3	39.76	40.64	40.95	44.26	49.28	52.31
Bi_2O_3	.....	0.30	0.60	0.33	0.53	.....
Ta_2O_5	60.24	57.29	41.92	33.86	13.00	.....
Cb_2O_5	.....	1.79	16.19	21.47	37.30	47.69
Total	100.00	100.02	99.66	99.92	100.11	100.00
G.	7.53	7.345	6.80	6.72	5.98	5.68

1. $SbTaO_4$. 2. Greenbushes. Total given as 100.12 in original.[9] 3. Mesa Grande. Average of three analyses.[10] 4, 5. Mesa Grande. Average of two analyses.[11] 6. $SbCbO_4$.

Tests. F. 4. Readily soluble in HF, but not appreciably attacked by HCl, HNO_3, or boiling concentrated H_2SO_4.

O c c u r. Originally found in abundance as pebbles in the cassiterite placers of Greenbushes, near Bridgetown, Wodgina district, Western Australia (*stibiotantalite*). The pebbles often contain a core of tantalite, and the mineral, in part, fills veinlets or occupies small cavities in masses of tantalite. In fine crystals at Mesa Grande, San Diego County, California, (in part, stibiocolumbite) in pegmatite with pink beryl, lepidolite, pink tourmaline and, rarely, cassiterite. At Topsham, Maine, in pegmatite as tiny crystals (probably *stibiotantalite*) deposited with albite upon microlite. With microlite and native antimony in pegmatite at Varuträsk, Sweden, as alteration products of the so-called stibiomicrolite (*stibiotantalite*).

N a m e. In allusion to the composition.

Ref.
1. Symmetry first established by Penfield and Ford, *Am. J. Sc.*, **22**, 61 (1906).
2. Angles of Penfield and Ford (1906), unit of Ungemach, *Bull. soc. min.*, **32**, 92 (1909), on crystals from Mesa Grande; orientation of Palache, *Am. Min.*, **25**, 411 (1940). The original orientation and unit of Penfield and Ford (1906) was chosen in an attempt to show its supposed relationship to columbite. Ungemach (1909) placed the polar axis vertical and chose the proper unit; Palache made the principal zone [001] with the polar axis [010], the orientation here chosen. Transformations:

Penfield and Ford to Palache $0\frac{1}{12}0/\frac{1}{4}00/00\frac{1}{4}$
Ungemach to Palache $100/001/010$
Penfield and Ford to Ungemach $0\frac{1}{12}0/00\frac{1}{9}/\frac{1}{4}00$

3. Forms of Ungemach (1909), corrected by Palache (1940).
4. Dihlström, *Zs. anorg. Chem.*, **239**, 57 (1938), by Laue and rotation methods on unanalyzed material from Mesa Grande.
5. Penfield and Ford (1906).
6. Simpson, *Australasian Ac. Sc., Rep.*, **11**, 455 (1907), cites values ranging between 6.41 and 7.50.
7. For cell dimensions given by Dihlström (1938) without consideration of the probable variation in the series Ta-Cb.
8. Penfield and Ford (1906) by prism method on crystals from Mesa Grande.
9. Simpson, *Roy. Soc. Western Australia, J.*, **22**, 1 (1936).
10. Foote and Langley, *Am. J. Sc.*, **30**, 399 (1910).
11. Ford, *Am. J. Sc.*, **32**, 288 (1911).

819   **B I S M U T O T A N T A L I T E**   [Bi(Ta,Cb)O_4].   *Wayland* and *Spencer* (*Min. Mag.*, **22**, 185, 1929).

C r y s t. Orthorhombic.[1]

$a : b : c = 0.4266 : 1 : 0.4848;$[2] $p_0 : q_0 : r_0 = 1.1363 : 0.4848 : 1$

$q_1 : r_1 : p_1 = 0.4266 : 0.8800 : 1;$ $r_2 : p_2 : q_2 = 2.0580 : 2.3439 : 1$

Forms:

		ϕ	$\rho = C$	ϕ_1	$\rho_1 = A$	ϕ_2	$\rho_2 = B$
b	010	$0°00'$	$90°00'$	$90°00'$	$90°00'$	....	$0°00$
g	130	38 00	90 00	90 00	52 00	$0°00'$	38 00
m	110	$66\ 53\frac{1}{2}$	90 00	90 00	$23\ 06\frac{1}{2}$	0 00	$66\ 53\frac{1}{2}$
k	011	0 00	25 52	25 52	90 00	90 00	64 08
δ	101	90 00	48 39	0 00	41 21	41 21	90 00
w	111	$66\ 53\frac{1}{2}$	$51\ 00\frac{1}{2}$	25 52	44 22	41 21	$72\ 14\frac{1}{2}$
x	431	$72\ 15\frac{1}{2}$	78 10	$55\ 29\frac{1}{2}$	$21\ 13\frac{1}{2}$	$12\ 24\frac{1}{2}$	$72\ 38\frac{1}{2}$

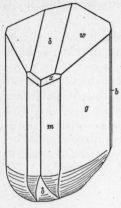

Uganda.

Habit. Stout prismatic [001]; the crystals often are misshapen or irregular.

P h y s. Cleavage none. Parting probably on {101} and {$\bar{1}$01} good, on {010}, less so. Fracture subconchoidal. H. 5. G. 8.26.[3] Luster submetallic. Color pitch-black; sometimes superficially altered to a dull pinkish yellow material. Streak black. Transparent in very thin splinters. Not pyroelectric.

O p t. In transmitted light smoke-gray to colorless. Fragments give parallel extinction and are biaxial. n very high. Birefringence about 0.1 to 0.15.

C h e m. An oxide of bismuth and tantalum, $Bi(Ta,Cb)O_4$. Cb substitutes in small amounts for Ta.

Anal.

	1	2	3	4
Bi_2O_3	51.33	52.56	49.86	50.46
Ta_2O_5	48.67	40.12	41.15	31.14
Cb_2O_5	.....	6.63	6.46	14.76
MnO	.....	0.12	0.12	.....
Rem.	.....	0.48	1.35	3.52
Total	100.00	99.91	98.94	99.88
G.		8.44	8.03	

1. $BiTaO_4$. 2. Uganda. Rem. is $(Al,Fe)_2O_3$ 0.11, SnO_2 and Sb_2O_3 0.04, ign. loss 0.33 and trace of ZrO_2 and TiO_2. No rare earths or U_3O_8.[4] 3. Uganda. Rem. is $(Al,Fe)_2O_3$ 0.30, ign. loss 1.04.[4] 4. Uganda. Rem. is SiO_2 2.16, Mn_3O_4 and Fe_2O_3 1.36. Cb and Ta separated by SeOCl method.[5]

Tests. Insoluble in acids, including HF.

O c c u r. Found in pegmatite with black tourmaline, small amounts of cassiterite and large buff-colored plates of muscovite at Gamba Hill (32°10′ E, 0°30′ N) in southwestern Uganda, Africa.

A l t e r. Superficially coated and veined by a pinkish yellow material, that is largely isotropic, but with some admixed birefringent material, and is apparently a hydrated oxide of tantalum and bismuth.[6]

N a m e. In allusion to the composition.

Ref.

1. Although the crystals do not show pyroelectric activity, the symmetry class is probably pyramidal, in conformity with stibiotantalite. X-ray powder pictures of the two minerals are very similar (Frondel, priv. comm., 1941).
2. Angles of Wayland and Spencer (1929), orientation and unit of Palache, *Am. Min.*, **25**, 411 (1940), as adopted for stibiotantalite. Transformation, Wayland and Spencer to Palache 0$\frac{1}{10}$0/100/00$\frac{1}{3}$.
3. Wayland and Spencer (1929) give 8.15; two fragments (received from the British Museum) gave 8.26 with the microbalance.
4. Wynn anal. in Wayland and Spencer (1929).
5. Commercial anal. in Wayland and Spencer (1929).
6. See anals. by Hey in Wayland and Spencer (1929).

81·10 **SIMPSONITE** [Al₂Ta₂O₈]. *Bowley (Roy. Soc. Western Australia, J.,* **25**, 89, 1938–39).

C r y s t. Hexagonal; hexagonal dipyramidal — $6/m$?.

Forms:

$$\{0001\}, \quad \{10\bar{1}0\}$$

Structure cell.[1] Shows hexagonal dipyramidal $(6/m)$ symmetry; a_0 6.2, c_0 4.5; $a_0 : c_0 = 1 : 0.73$; contains Al₂Ta₂O₈?.

Habit. Tabular to short prismatic [0001].

P h y s. G. 5.92–6.27; 5.99 (calc.). Colorless; the crystals are externally altered and dull, cream-colored. Transparent. Uniaxial positive (+). n 2.06 and birefringence about 0.1.

C h e m. Essentially an oxide of aluminum and tantalum (or a tantalate), Al₂Ta₂O₈, with some Ca, Na, Fe, Sn, and water, the latter possibly due to alteration. It is not certain what part of the analyses are due to impurities.

Anal.

	1	2	3
Na₂O	.....	1.16	0.68
K₂O	.....	0.24	0.42
CaO	.....	3.40	3.19
MnO	.....	0.08	0.04
FeO	.....	0.16	0.44
PbO	.....	0.42	.....
SnO₂	.....	2.00	1.19
SiO₂	.....	1.78	2.34
Al₂O₃	18.75	16.75	18.64
Fe₂O₃	.....	0.14	0.48
Cb₂O₅	.....	0.33	0.32
Ta₂O₅	81.25	72.31	71.48
H₂O + 110°	.....	1.35	1.39
H₂O − 110°	.....	0.20	0.03
F	.....	0.21	0.38
Total	100.00	100.53	101.02
G.	5.99	6.525	6.27

1. Al₂Ta₂O₈.   2. Western Australia.[2]   3. Western Australia.[3]

Tests. Insoluble in HCl and H₂SO₄, but decomposed by fusion in alkali hydroxides or carbonates and KHSO₄.

O c c u r. Found as incomplete and partially altered crystals in a quartz-biotite-pegmatite at Tabba Tabba, Western Australia.

A l t e r. Surficially altered to and veined by a colorless isotropic material and a white opaque granular material, with some muscovite and quartz.

N a m e. After Dr. E. S. Simpson (1875–1939), formerly government mineralogist and analyst of Western Australia.

Ref.

1. Taylor, *Roy. Soc. Western Australia, J.,* **25**, 93 (1938–39) by Laue method.
2. Murray anal. in Bowley (1938–39).
3. Grace anal. in Bowley. Also partial analyses given.

CALCIOSAMARSKITE. *Ellsworth (Am. Min., 13, 63, 66, 1928).*
Massive, or in rough square prisms (Parry Sound). Cleavage none. Fracture irregular to subconchoidal. H. $6\frac{1}{2}$. G. 4.48 (Parry Sound), 4.74 (Hybla). Black, with a brown-gray powder. Luster submetallic. Brownish and isotropic (metamict) in transmitted light. n 2.015[1] (Hybla), 2.095 (Parry Sound).

A supposed calcian samarskite, but the x-ray diffraction pattern of ignited material is different from typical samarskite.[2] The analyses 1 and 2 yield:[3]

Hybla   (Ca,Y, etc., U,Th)$_3$(Cb,Ta,Fe,Ti,Sn)$_5$O$_{15}$
and Parry Sound (Ca,Y, etc., U,Th,Zr)$_3$(Cb,Ta,Fe^3,Ti)$_5$O$_{16}$.
with Ca : Y : U + Th = 9 : 4 : 5; Cb + Ta : Fe : Ti + Sn = 7 : 2 : 1 (Hybla)
    Ca : Y : U + Th + Zr = 3 : 3 : 2; Cb + Ta : Fe : Ti = 20 : 2 : 1 (Parry Sound).

Anal.

	1	2
CaO	7.56	4.76
PbO	0.44	0.38
(Y,Er)$_2$O$_3$	11.38	10.71
(Ce,La,Di)$_2$O$_3$	1.68	4.04
UO$_2$	9.00	.....
UO$_3$	1.67	.....
U$_3$O$_8$	.....	13.38
ThO$_2$	3.34	2.16
ZrO$_2$	0.02	0.24
SnO$_2$	1.49	0.48
TiO$_2$	2.50	1.43
Fe$_2$O$_3$	7.67	3.01
Cb$_2$O$_5$	43.32	43.50
Ta$_2$O$_5$	2.54	4.86
SiO$_2$	2.39	1.92
H$_2$O	3.64	6.44
Rem.	0.69	1.51
Total	99.33	98.82
G.	4.738	4.485

1. Calciosamarskite, Hybla, Ont. Atomic weight of (Y,Er) = 101.5 (average). Rem. is FeO 0.21, MnO 0.04, Al$_2$O$_3$ 0.16, BeO 0.26, MgO 0.02; H$_2$O includes $-110°$ 0.40. Pb/U + 0.38 Th = 0.04.[4] 2. Calciosamarskite. Parry Sound, Ont. Rem. is MgO 0.14, MnO 0.23, Al$_2$O$_3$ 0.65, BeO 0.49, C present. UO$_2$, UO$_3$, FeO not determinable because of presence of carbon. H$_2$O includes 0.68 at $-110°$.[5]

Found at Hybla, Ontario, at the Woodcox mine, associated with columbite and cyrtolite in the pegmatite, at Parry Sound, Ontario, as rough square prisms up to a $\frac{1}{2}$ in. in diameter associated with a carbonaceous pseudomorph after uraninite (thucholite) and cyrtolite, in feldspar.

Ref.

1. Larsen and Berman, (61, 62, 1934).
2. Berman (priv. comm., 1941). The Hybla material gives a pattern similar to that of yttrotantalite.
3. Berman (priv. comm., 1941).
4. Ellsworth, *Am. Min.*, 13, 63 (1928).
5. Ellsworth, *Am. Min.*, 13, 66 (1928).

NOHLITE. *Nordenskiöld (Geol. För. Förh., 1, 7, 1872).*
Massive. Fracture uneven. Brittle. H. $4\frac{1}{2}$–5. G. 5.04. Luster vitreous. Blackbrown. Streak brown. Analysis gave: CaO 4.67, MgO + MnO 0.28, FeO 8.09, CuO 0.11, (Y,Er)$_2$O$_3$ 14.36, Ce$_2$O$_3$ 0.25, UO$_3$ 14.43, ZrO$_2$ 2.96, Cb$_2$O$_5$ 50.43, H$_2$O 4.62. Total 100.20. The analysis yields a formula: (Ca,Mg,Fe^2, Y, etc., U)$_2$(Cb,Zr,Fe^3)$_3$O$_{10}$.[1] Found in a feldspar quarry at Nohl, near Kongelf, Sweden; one piece of 297 grams at this locality was apparently a part of a mass twenty times as great.

Ref.

1. Berman and Frondel (priv. comm., 1941). If all the Fe is bivalent the formula is approximately ABO_4.

BETAFITE ?. *Pisani* (in *Lacroix* [1, 384, 1922]) from Ambatolampikely, Madagascar, yielded a formula $A_2B_3O_{10}$ with A = Ca : U = 2 : 1; B = Cb : Ti : Fe^3 = 6 : 5 : 1. Analysis gave: CaO 11.61, MnO 0.25, $(Ce,La)_2O_3$ 1.20, UO_3 28.60, ThO_2 1.25, Al_2O_3 0.50, Fe_2O_3 1.38, TiO_2 17.30, Cb_2O_5 32.10, Ta_2O_5 trace, H_2O 5.20, total 99.39. G. 4.475.

The composition does not resemble that of betafite. The mineral is inadequately described and its authenticity is open to doubt.

821   **Arizonite** [$Fe_2Ti_3O_9$]. *Palmer (Am. J. Sc.*, **28**, 353, 1909).

Massive and as indistinct crystals. Possibly monoclinic.[1]

P h y s. Fracture subconchoidal. Brittle. H. $5\frac{1}{2}$. G. 4.25. Luster submetallic to metallic. Color dark steel gray on fresh fractures. Streak brown. Transparent in very thin splinters. Not magnetic.

O p t.[2] In transmitted light deep red in color. n_{Li} 2.62±. Biref. moderate. Pleochroism very weak, in red, with absorption, $Z > X$.

C h e m. A titanate of iron, $Fe_2Ti_3O_9$. Analysis gave:

	Fe_2O_3	FeO	TiO_2	H_2O 110−	H_2O 110+	Rem.	Total
1	39.99	....	60.01	....	....	....	100.00
2	38.38	0.70	58.27	0.18	1.02	1.58	100.12

1. $Fe_2Ti_3O_9$. 2. Arizona. Rem. is TiO_2 0.56 (anatase), SiO_2 1.02.

Tests. Partially decomposed by HCl, and completely by hot concentrated H_2SO_4.

O c c u r. Found with gadolinite in pegmatite about 25 miles southeast of Hackberry, Mohave County, Arizona.

A l t e r. To anatase, the material becoming almost entirely changed to a meshwork of fine anatase aggregates and then dull in luster and brownish yellow in color.

A r t i f. $Fe_2O_3.3TiO_2$ has been reported[3] formed by ignition of the mixed oxides in the proper ratio.

N a m e. After the locality, Arizona.

Needs further study.

Ref.

1. Wright in Palmer (1909) describes approximate measurements with the contact goniometer which suggest monoclinic symmetry. $a : b : c$ = 1.88 : 1 : 2.37; β 125°; observed faces {001}, {00$\bar{1}$}, {$\bar{1}$0$\bar{1}$}, {110}, {$\bar{1}$12}.
2. Wright in Palmer (1909); Larsen (41, 1921).
3. Muthmann, Weiss, and Heramhof, *Ann. chim.*, **355**, 161 (1907), but not verified by Pesce, *Gazz. chim. ital.*, **61**, 109 (1931).

822   **Kalkowskite** [$Fe_2Ti_3O_9$?]. Kalkowskyn *Rimann (Cbl. Min.*, 18, 1925).

In thin irregularly bounded plates showing a fibrous structure in transmitted light.

P h y s. Fracture conchoidal. H. $3\frac{1}{2}$. G. 4.01 ± 0.03. Luster submetallic, inclining to waxy or horny. Color light brown, dark brown, black. Streak reddish brown. Transparent in thin splinters.

O p t. In transmitted light, reddish brown in color. Elongation of fibers positive (+). Birefringence low. Not pleochroic. $n > 1.769$.

C h e m. Essentially an oxide of titanium and ferric iron. Small amounts of rare earths, Ca, Al, and Si are present, probably due to admixture; also (Cb,Ta). The formula is uncertain, perhaps $Fe_2Ti_3O_9$.[1] The small amount of water present may be due to alteration. Analysis gave:[2] K_2O [0.67], CaO 1.64, MgO 0.48, $(Ce,La)_2O_3$ 2.66, SiO_2 5.63, Al_2O_3 2.21, Fe_2O_3 28.66, TiO_2 54.62, $(Cb,Ta)_2O_5$ 1.67, P_2O_5 0.28, H_2O 3.27, total 101.79.

Tests. Partially decomposed by HCl.

O c c u r. Found in the Serro do Itacolumy, Minas Geraes, Brazil, in a fine-grained schistose muscovite layer in quartzite. Associated with zircon, monazite, almandite.

N a m e. After Professor E. L. Kalkowsky (1851–1938) of the University of Dresden.

Needs further study.

Ref.

1. Rimann (1925) gives $(Fe,Ce)_2O_3 \cdot 4(Ti,Si)_2$. Foshag, *Am. Min.*, **10**, 135 (1925), notes that if the SiO_2 is excluded the ratios are close to those of arizonite, $Fe_2Ti_3O_9(?)$.
2. Fisher anal. in Rimann (1925).

823   **Oliveiraite** $[Zr_3Ti_2O_{10} \cdot 2H_2O]$. *Lee* (*Rev. soc. Brazil, Sc. no.*, **1**, 31, 1917, *Am. J. Sc.*, **47**, 129, 1919).

Massive. No cleavage. In transmitted light, yellowish green. Metamict. Isotropic; in places anisotropic with multiple twinning and a radial fibrous structure.

C h e m. An oxide of titanium and zirconium, possibly $Zr_3Ti_2O_{10} \cdot 2H_2O$. The water content may be due to alteration. Analysis gave: ZrO_2 63.36, TiO_2 29.92, H_2O 6.48, total 99.76.

O c c u r. Found near Pomba, Minas Geraes, Brazil, apparently formed by the alteration of euxenite.

N a m e. After Francisco de Paula Oliveira of the Geological Survey of Brazil.

Needs verification.

824   **Brannerite** $[(U,Ca,Fe,Y,Th)_3Ti_5O_{16}$?]. *Hess* and *Wells* (*Franklin Institute, J.*, **189**, 225, 779, 1920).

As rounded detrital pebbles and prismatic crystals.

P h y s. Fracture conchoidal. H. $4\frac{1}{2}$. G. 4.5–5.43. Color black. Externally brownish yellow due to alteration. Streak dark greenish brown. Transparent in very thin splinters. Radioactive.

O p t. In transmitted light, yellowish green in color. Metamict. Isotropic. Indices:[1] n_{Li} 2.26 ± 0.02, n_{Na} 2.30 ± 0.02.

C h e m. Essentially an oxide of titanium, uranium, and calcium, with minor yttrium, thorium, and ferrous iron. The formula is uncertain, possibly $A_3B_5O_{16}$ with A = U, Ca, Fe, Y, Th; B = Ti. Analysis (on material with G. 5.42) gave: CaO 2.9, BaO 0.3, SrO 0.1, PbO 0.2, FeO 2.9, $(Yt,Er)_2O_3$ 3.9, UO_2 10.3, UO_3 33.5, ThO_2 4.1, ZrO_2 0.2, SiO_2 0.6, TiO_2 39.0, CO_2 0.2, H_2O 2.0, total 100.2. The state of oxidation of the Fe and U is uncertain. The water content probably is due to alteration. Contains He.

Tests. Decomposed by hot concentrated H_2SO_4 or by fusion with $KHSO_4$.

Occur. Found as detrital crystals and grains in a gold placer near the head of Kelly Gulch in western Custer County, Idaho.
Name. After J. C. Branner (1850–1922), American geologist.

Ref.
1. Larsen in Hess and Wells (1920).

Tapiolite Series

8311 **TAPIOLITE** [$FeTa_2O_6$]. Tapiolit *Nordenskiöld* (*Ak. Stockholm, Öfv.*, **20**, 445, 1863). Tantalite (from Sukula) *Arppe* (*Act. Soc. Fenn.*, **6**, 590, 1861).
Skogbölite *Nordenskiöld* (30, 1855). Tantalite mit zimmtbraunem Pulver *Berzelius*. Tammela-tantalit *Nordenskiöld* (*Act. Soc. Fenn.*, **1**, 119, read April 25, 1832; *Ann. Phys.*, **50**, 656, 1840).
8312 **MOSSITE** [$Fe(Cb,Ta)_2O_6$]. *Brögger* (*Vidensk. Selskr. Oslo, Mat.-Nat. Kl.*, **7**, 3, 1897). Manganomossite *Simpson* (*Rep. Dept. Mines, Western Australia*, 120, 1923).

Cryst. Tetragonal; ditetragonal dipyramidal — $4/m \, 2/m \, 2/m$.[1]

$$a : c = 1 : 1.9392;^2 \qquad p_0 : r_0 = 1.9392 : 1$$

Forms:[3]

		ϕ	ρ	A	$\bar{M}$
c	001	.....	0°00′	90°00′	90°00′
a	010	0°00′	90 00	90 00	45 00
m	110	45 00	90 00	45 00	90 00
n	230	33 41½	90 00	56 18½	78 41½
e	013	0 00	32 52½	90 00	67 25½
s	011	0 00	62 43½	90 00	51 04
p	113	45 00	42 26	61 30	90 00

Structure cell.[4] Space group $P4/mnm$; cell dimensions:

	a_0	c_0	$a_0 : c_0$
Tapiolite (Greenbushes, Western Australia)	4.745	9.21	1 : 1.941
Mossite (Norway)	4.711	9.12	1 : 1.936

Contains $(Fe,Mn)_2(Ta,Cb)_4O_{12}$.
Habit. Short prismatic [001] or equant, with {001}, {100}, {110}, {113} usually well developed. The untwinned crystals often appear monoclinic or orthorhombic due to distortion.
Twinning.[5] (*a*) On {013}, very common; the twins are distorted by

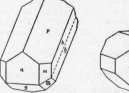

Moss, Norway.   Topsham, Me.

Tapiolite

elongation on [0$\bar{3}$1] (parallel to an edge of an adjacent pair of 113 faces) and simulate orthorhombic symmetry. (*b*) On {101}, rare.[6] (*c*) On {1·0·18} ?, rare.[6]

P h y s. Cleavage none. Fracture uneven to subconchoidal. H. 6–6$\frac{1}{2}$. G. 7.90 ± 0.05; 8.17 (calc. for tapiolite, FeTa$_2$O$_6$), 6.93 (calc. for Norwegian material with supposed Cb : Ta = 1 : 1, on basis of cell dimensions[7]). An increase in the Cb content decreases the specific gravity sharply. Luster subadamantine to submetallic, sometimes brilliant. Color pure black, sometimes superficially brownish black. Streak cinnamon brown to brownish black. Transparent in extremely thin splinters.

O p t.[8] In transmitted light, yellowish to reddish brown and very strongly pleochroic.

	n_{Li}	PLEOCHROISM	
O	2.27 ± 0.01	Pale yellowish or reddish brown	Uniaxial pos. (+).
E	2.42 ± 0.05	Nearly opaque	

In polished section exhibits twin lamellae on {013}.[9]

C h e m. Essentially an oxide (or tantalate) of iron and tantalum, FeTa$_2$O$_6$, with Mn and Cb substituting for the Fe and Ta respectively, in some amount. It has not been shown, however, that the natural tetragonal series extends to a high Cb content (the orthorhombic columbite-tantalite series is complete[10]). The name *mossite* refers to the possible high Cb end of the series.

Anal.

	1	2	3	4	5	6	7	8	9	10
CaO	.....	0.15	1.96	.....	.....	.....	....	.....	.....	.....
MgO		.....	0.10	.....	.....	.....	0.15	.....	.....	.....
FeO	13.99	13.41	10.69	14.68	15.60	14.84	13.68	14.47	16.62	4.64
MnO	.....	0.96	1.49	1.10	...	0.42	0.88	0.81	.....	12.02
SnO$_2$	.....	1.26	0.34	.....	0.59	0.32	0.53	0.48	0.18	.....
TiO$_2$	.....	.....	0.18	.....	....	1.38	trace	.....	.....	3.92
Cb$_2$O$_5$	.....	.....	1.37	2.50	3.90	5.18	9.19	11.22	}82.92	34.64
Ta$_2$O$_5$	86.01	84.44	82.55	77.36	78.58	77.23	75.16	73.91		44.53
Rem.	.....	0.14	1.14	.....	1.29	.....	0.07	.....	.....	0.26
Total	100.00	100.36	99.82	95.64	99.96	[99.37]	99.66	[100.89]	99.72	100.01
G.	8.17	7.85	7.45		7.22	7.190 ?	7.762	7.946	6.45	6.21

1. FeTa$_2$O$_6$. 2. Skogbölite. Skogböle, Finland. Rem. is CuO.[11] 3. Tapiolite. Tabba Tabba North, Western Australia. Rem. is H$_2$O + 105 0.31, Fe$_2$O$_3$ 0.83.[12] 4. Tapiolite. Punia, Belgian Congo.[13] 5. Tapiolite. Near Custer City, Custer Co., S. D. SnO$_2$ contains WO$_3$. Rem. is insol. 1.29.[14] The low G. indicates a large content of Cb$_2$O$_5$. 6. Tapiolite. Minnehaha Gulch, Custer Co., S. D.[15] 7. Tapiolite. Rosendal, Kimito, Finland. Rem. is (Y,Ce)$_2$O$_3$ 0.07.[16] 8. Tapiolite. Sukula, Finland.[17] 9. Mossite. Råde, near Moss, Norway. Contains Ta$_2$O$_5$ ca. 52, Cb$_2$O$_5$ ca. 31.[18] 10. Manganoan mossite (?). Yinnietharra, Western Australia. Rem. is H$_2$O +. Possibly manganoan columbite.[19]

Var. Manganoan. Manganomossite *Simpson* (*Rep. Dept. Mines, Western Australia*, 120, 1923). Material from Yinnietharra, Western Australia, has Mn : Fe about 3 : 1 (anal. 10); however, this mineral has not been shown with certainty to belong in the tapiolite-mossite series.

Tests. B.B. infusible. Differs from most tantalite in giving no or a weak Mn reaction. Decomposed by fusion in $KHSO_4$.

Occur. Tapiolite occurs in granite pegmatites, and as a detrital mineral in areas of granite pegmatites.

Mossite is known only from Berg (?), in Råde parish, near Moss, Norway; reported also (*manganoan*) from Yinnietharra, Western Australia, in tin placers (but it is not certain that this belongs to the species). Tapiolite occurs in pegmatite with tourmaline, beryl, albite, muscovite, tantalite, spodumene, triplite, triphylite at a number of localities in Tammela and Kimito parishes, Finland, notably Skogböle (*skogbölite*) and Rosendal in Kimito, and Sukula and Härkäsaari in Tammela; the mineral was recognized as early as 1746. Reported from Chanteloube, Haute-Vienne, France. In Western Australia in placers with cassiterite and columbite-tantalite and in pegmatites in the Tabba Tabba and Greens Wells districts in the Pilbara goldfield. In the United States at Topsham, Sagadahoc County, and Paris, Oxford County, in Maine; at several localities in Minnehaha Gulch, near Custer City, Custer County, South Dakota.

Name. Tapiolite is named from an ancient Finnish divinity. Mossite from the locality near Moss, Norway.

SKOGBÖLITE. *Nordenskiöld* (30, 1855). Tantalit mit zimmtbraunem Pulver *Berzelius*. Tammela-tantalit *Nordenskiöld* (*Act. Soc. Fenn.*, 1, 119, read April 25, 1832; *Ann. Phys.*, 50, 656, 1840).

An iron tantalate, $FeTa_2O_6$ (anal. 1), from Härkäsaari in Tammela and Skogböle in Kimito, Finland. In supposed prismatic orthorhombic crystals, later shown[20] to be distorted twinned crystals of tapiolite.

Ref.

1. The crystallographic relation of tapiolite to cassiterite, rutile and other oxides of the AX_2 type has been discussed by Schaller, *U. S. Geol. Sur., Bull. 509*, 9 (1912), and Brögger (1897). V. M. Goldschmidt, *Vidensk. Selskr., Oslo, Mat.-Nat. Kl.*, 1, 17 (1926), has shown the structural similarity of tapiolite and rutile.

2. Angles of Nordenskiöld (in Dana [738, 1892]), unit of Goldschmidt (1926). Transformation: Nordenskiöld to Goldschmidt 100/010/003. Brögger (1897) gives for mossite, from Moss, Norway, $a : c = 1 : 0.6438$.

3. In Goldschmidt (8, 113, 1922); also Buttgenbach, *Inst. roy. colon. Belge, Bull.*, 4, 215 (1933). Rare or uncertain: {015}, {029}, {023}, {1·1·12}, {116}, {139}, {2·3·10}, {289}. Other forms reported for skogbölite not here recorded.

Brögger (1897) has shown that the crystals of skogbölite (supposedly orthorhombic) of Nordenskiöld (1855) are identical with tapiolite. Transformation skogbölite Nordenskiöld to new ratio of tapiolite: 01⅖/⅘00/033.

4. Goldschmidt (1926) on original mossite (anal. 9) from Råde, Norway, and on tapiolite from Greenbushes, Western Australia.

5. For a description of the twinning see Simpson, *Min. Mag.*, 18, 107 (1917), and Brögger (1897).

6. Simpson (1917).

7. The specific gravities of the higher Cb members, as given with the analyses, are inconsistent. The relation may be the same as in the columbite-tantalite series (which see). The data on the supposedly high Cb member, mossite, are apparently not too accurate since the G. determined (6.45) differs materially from the value calculated from the molecular weight and unit cell (6.93). The chemical composition of mossite is known only approximately.

8. Larsen (141, 1921) on material from Haut-Vienne, France, G. 7.4.

9. Pehrman in Schneiderhöhn and Ramdohr (2, 606, 1931).

10. See columbite-tantalite series, under analyses.

11. Nordenskiöld, *Ann. Phys.*, 101, 629 (1857).

12. Simpson, *Min. Mag.*, **18**, 107 (1917).
13. Sporck anal. in Buttgenbach, *Inst. roy. colon. Belge, Bull.*, **4**, 211 (1933).
14. Headden, *Colorado Sc. Soc., Proc.*, **8**, 177 (1906).
15. Headden, *Am. J. Sc.*, **3**, 293 (1922); also another analysis of material from a different locality that may be tapiolite. The given specific gravity is low for this composition.
16. Pehrman, *Acta Ac. Aboensis, Math. Physica*, **6**, 1 (1932) — *Min. Abs.*, **5**, 383 (1933).
17. Rammelsberg, *Ak. Wiss. Berlin, Monatsber.*, 181, 1872.
18. Thesen anal. in Brögger, *Vidensk. Selskr., Oslo, Mat.-Nat. Kl.*, **6**, 50 (1906).
19. Simpson, *Rep. Dept. Mines, Western Australia*, 120, 1923.
20. Brögger (1897); the x-ray powder pattern of the Skogböle skogbölite is identical with that of tapiolite (Frondel, priv. comm., 1940).

IXIOLITE. *Nordenskiöld (Ann. Phys.*, **101**, 632, 1857). Kimito-tantalite *Nordenskiöld.* Ixionolite *Wiik.* Kassiterotantal *Hausmann.* Cassiterotantalite.

Orthorhombic ?,[1] in rectangular prisms with {100}, {001}, {010}. Sometimes twins on {103}. Fracture uneven to subconchoidal. Brittle. H. 6–6½. G. 7.0–7.3. Luster submetalic. Color blackish gray to steel gray.

C h e m. An oxide of iron, manganese, columbium, and tantalum, or a tantalate $(Fe,Mn)(Cb,Ta)_2O_6$. Sn is reported in small amounts.

Anal.[2]

	1	2	3
CaO	.....	.....	0.42
MgO	.....	.....	0.37
FeO	9.19	}14.83	1.34
MnO	5.97		10.87
SnO₂	1.70	2.94	8.92
Cb₂O₅	19.24	12.26	7.63
Ta₂O₅	63.58	69.97	70.49
Ign. loss	0.23	.....	0.18
Total	99.91	100.00	100.22
G.	7.232	7.272	7.36

1. Skogböle, Finland.[3] 2. Skogböle, Finland. Cb_2O_5 contains ca. 1 per cent TiO_2.[3] 3. Wodgina, Western Australia.[4]

Found with tapiolite (skogbölite) in pegmatite at Skogböle in Kimito, Finland. Reported from Wodgina, Western Australia, in pegmatite with albite and muscovite. Reported[5] from the Ilmen Mountains, Russia.

Named from Ixion, a mythological character related to Tantalus.

Probably identical with tapiolite.

Ref.

1. The supposed orthorhombic elements of Nordenskiöld, *Ann. Phys.*, **101**, 632 (1857), are: $a : b : c = 0.5508 : 1 : 1.2460$. This ratio can be considered as derived from a distorted twin of tapiolite, according to the transformation: ixiolite to tapiolite $010/\overline{3}0\frac{1}{2}/\frac{3}{2}0\frac{3}{2}$. The twin plane then becomes {011}. See also Dana (736, 1892); Brögger, *Vidensk. Selskr., Oslo, Mat.-Nat. Kl.*, **7**, 12 (1897); Simpson, *Min. Mag.*, **18**, 107 (1917); Schaller, *U. S. Geol. Sur., Bull. 509*, 9, 1912. An x-ray powder pattern of unauthenticated ixiolite from the type locality was found similar to that of tapiolite (Frondel, priv. comm., 1941).
2. An early analysis by Nordenskiöld (1857) showed 12.79 per cent SnO_2, but the material was not of proven homogeneity.
3. Rammelsberg, *Ak. Berlin, Ber.*, 163, 167, 1871.
4. Simpson, *Rep. Australasian Assoc. Adv. Sc.*, **12**, 314 (1910); massive material, not shown to be distinct from tantalite or tapiolite or to be homogeneous, and therefore of doubtful value.
5. Vernadsky and Fersman, *Ac. sc. St. Pétersbourgh, Bull.*, **4**, 511 (1910).

ADELPHOLITE. Adelfolit *Nordenskiöld* (1855; *Jb. Min.*, 313, 1858; *Nordenskiöld, Ak. Stockholm, Öfv.*, **20**, 452, 1863; *Ann. Phys.*, **122**, 615, 1864).

A substance found in apparently tetragonal prismatic crystals embedded in feldspar at Laurinmaki, Tammela, Finland. No cleavage. Fracture conchoidal. H. 3½–4½.

G. 3.8. Luster greasy. Color yellowish brown to brown and black. Streak white or yellowish white. Transparent in thin splinters.

In composition apparently a columbate of Fe and Mn, containing 41.8 per cent $(Cb,Ta)_2O_5(?)$, 9.7 per cent H_2O, and a small amount of SnO_2 and SiO_2.

Possibly an altered mossite; a poorly defined substance.

HJELMITE. *Nordenskiöld (Ak. Stockholm, Öfv.*, 17, 34, 1860; *Ann. Phys.*, 111, 279, 286, 1860; *J. pr. Chem.*, 81, 202, 1760). Hielmite.

C r y s t. Orthorhombic?.

$a : b : c = 0.4645 : 1 : 1.0264;^1$ $p_0 : q_0 : r_0 = 2.2097 : 1.0264 : 1$

$q_1 : r_1 : p_1 = 0.4645 : 0.4526 : 1;$ $r_2 : p_2 : q_2 = 0.9743 : 2.1529 : 1$

Forms:

		ϕ	$\rho = C$	ϕ_1	$\rho_1 = A$	ϕ_2	$\rho_2 = B$
p	230	55°08′	90°00′	90°00′	34°52′	0°00′	55°08′
m	110	65 05	90 00	90 00	24 55	0 00	65 05
r	101	90 00	65 39	0 00	24 21	24 21	90 00
q	201	90 00	77 15	0 00	12 45	12 45	90 00

Habit. Crystals usually rough and indistinct; also massive, in rounded or prismatic aggregates.

P h y s. No apparent cleavage. Fracture granular. H. 5. G. 5.2–5.8. Luster metallic. Color black to iron black. Streak grayish black, sometimes with a brownish green tint. Transparent in very thin splinters.

O p t.[2] In transmitted light, dark yellowish brown to opaque. Anisotropic, but sometimes altered externally or along fractures to an isotropic material. Optically positive $(+)$, and nearly or quite uniaxial.

	n_{LI}	PLEOCHROISM
X	2.30 ± 0.02	Yellowish brown
Z	2.40 ± 0.04	Nearly opaque

C h e m. An oxide or columbate-tantalate containing Y, Fe^2, U^4, Sn, Mn, Ca, Cb, Ta. The formula is close to AB_2O_6 (or $A_2B_3O_{10}$), with $A = Y$, Fe^2, U^4, Mn, Ca; $B = Cb$, Ta, Sn, W. The water is presumably due to alteration. Helium has been reported.[3]

Anal.[4]

	1	2
CaO	4.26	4.05
MgO	0.26	0.45
FeO	8.06	2.41
MnO	3.32	5.68
Y_2O_3	5.19	1.81
Ce_2O_3	1.07	0.48
UO_2	4.87	4.51
SnO_2	6.56	4.60
Cb_2O_5	}62.42	16.35
Ta_2O_5		54.52
WO_3	.....	0.28
H_2O	3.26	4.57
Rem.	0.10	.....
Total	99.37	99.71
G.	5.82	5.655

1. Kårarfvet, Sweden. Rem. is CuO 0.10; SnO_2 contains WO_3.[5] 2. Kårarfvet, Sweden.[6]

Tests.   In C.T. decrepitates and yields H_2O.   Infusible, and turns brown in O.F.

O c c u r.   From the Kårarfvet mine, near Fahlun, Sweden, with garnet, altered topaz, gadolinite, orthoclase, albite, or oligoclase and asphaltum in pegmatite.   Reported at Stripåsen (= microlite?), between Krylbo and Norberg, Sweden, with allanite, tantalite and albite in pegmatite.[7]
A l t e r.   By hydration to an isotropic (metamict) mass.
N a m e.   After the Swedish chemist, P. J. Hjelm (1746–1813).
A doubtful species, possibly related to tapiolite (or samarskite).

Ref.

1. Weibull, *Geol. För. Förh.*, **2**, 371 (1887), on rough crystals of poor quality.   The a-axis is a pseudotetragonal axis; the mineral may be tetragonal, and thus related to tapiolite.
2. Larsen (85, 1921).
3. Ramsay, Collie, and Travers, *J. Chem. Soc. London*, **67**, 684 (1894).   For Pb/U ratio see Boltwood, *Am. J. Sc.*, **23**, 80 (1907).
4. For additional analyses see Dana (741, 1892).
5. Nordenskiöld (1860).
6. Rammelsberg (3, 926, 1870).
7. The x-ray powder picture of material labeled from Stripåsen is similar to microlite (Berman, 1941).

Columbite-Tantalite Series

8321   **COLUMBITE** [(Fe,Mn)(Cb,Ta)$_2$O$_6$].   Ore of Columbium (from Connecticut) *Hatchett* (*Roy. Soc. London, Phil. Trans.*, 1802).   Columbite *Jameson* (**2**, 582, 1805).   Hemiprismatisches Tantalerz *Mohs*.   Tantalite de Bavière (Bodenmais).   Columbate of Iron.   Columbeisen *Germ*.   Baierine *Beudant* (**2**, 655, 1832).   Torrelite *Thomson* (*Rec. Gen. Sc.*, **4**, 408, 1836).   Niobite *Haidinger* (549, 1845).   Greenlandite *Breithaupt* (*B.H. Ztg.*, **17**, 61, 1858).   Dianite *von Kobell* (*Ak. München, Ber.*, March 10, 1860).   Manganocolumbite.   Ferrocolumbite.
   Mangantantalite *Nordenskiöld* (*Geol. För. Förh.*, **3**, 284, 1877).   Mengite *Rose* (**2**, 83 (1842) = Ilmenite *Brooke* (*Phil. Mag.*, **10**, 187, 1831)).   Hermannolite *Shepard* (*Am. J. Sc.*, **50**, 90, 1870; **11**, 140, 1876).   Ferro-ilmenite *Hermann* (*J. pr. Chem.*, **2**, 118, 1870).   Toddite *Ellsworth* (*Am. Min.*, **11**, 332, 1926).
8322   **TANTALITE** [(Fe,Mn)(Ta,Cb)$_2$O$_6$].   Tantalit *Ekeberg* (*Ak. Stockholm, Handl.*, **23**, 80, 1802).   Tantale oxidé ferro-manganésifère pt. *Haüy*.   Tantalite de Limoges.   Prismatisches Tantalerz *Mohs*.   Ferrotantalite *Thomson* (*Rec. Gen. Sc.*, **4**, 416, 1836).   Siderotantal *Hausmann* (**2**, 960, 1847).   Ildefonsit *Haidinger* (548, 1845) = Harttantalerz *Breithaupt* (230, 1832; 874, 1847).   Manganotantalite *Arzruni* (*Russ. Ges. Min., Vh.*, **23**, 181, 1887).   Ferrotantalite.

C r y s t.   Orthorhombic;[1] dipyramidal — $2/m\ 2/m\ 2/m$.

$a : b : c = 0.4023 : 1 : 0.3580;$[2] $p_0 : q_0 : r_0 = 0.8899 : 0.3580 : 1$

$q_1 : r_1 : p_1 = 0.4023 : 1.1237 : 1;$ $r_2 : p_2 : q_2 = 2.7933 : 2.4858 : 1$

Forms: [3]

		ϕ	$\rho = C$	ϕ_1	$\rho_1 = A$	ϕ_2	$\rho_2 = B$
c	001	.....	0°00′	0°00′	90°00′	90°00′	90°00′
b	010	0°00′	90 00	90 00	90 00	.....	0 00
a	100	90 00	90 00	.....	0 00	0 00	90 00
z	150	26 26	90 00	90 00	63 34	0 00	26 26
g	130	39 38½	90 00	90 00	50 21½	0 00	39 38½
m	110	68 05	90 00	90 00	21 55	0 00	68 05
k	011	0 00	19 42	19 42	90 00	90 00	70 18
e	201	90 00	60 40	0 00	29 20	29 20	90 00
u	111	68 05	43 48½	19 42	50 02½	48 20	75 01½
s	221	68 05	62 28	35 36	34 38½	29 20	70 42½
β	121	51 11	48 48	35 36	54 06½	48 20	61 51½
o	131	39 38½	54 21½	47 02½	58 46	48 20	31 56
n	211	78 37½	61 09	19 42	30 49½	29 20	80 03

Less common forms:

$d\{170\}$ $y\{160\}$ $l\{012\}$ $f\{032\}$ $h\{021\}$ $i\{101\}$ $\pi\{231\}$ $t\{241\}$

Structure cell.[4] Space group *Pbcn* (in our orientation *Pcan*); a_0 5.082, b_0 14.238, c_0 5.730; $c_0 : b_0 : a_0 = 0.4024 : 1 : 0.3569$; contains $(Fe,Mn)_4(Cb,Ta)_8O_{24}$.

Habit.[5] Short prismatic [001] or, less frequently, [100] or [010]; also

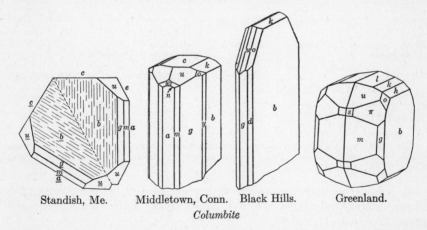

Standish, Me.   Middletown, Conn.   Black Hills.   Greenland.

Columbite

equant. Often rectangular prisms with the pinacoids prominent; sometimes thin tabular {010} (Etta Mine, South Dakota) or thick tabular {100}; less often pyramidal, and then with {111} dominant. In large groups of parallel or subparallel crystals; also massive.

Twinning. (a) Twin plane {201}, common.[6] Usually contact twins, heart-shaped and showing a delicate feather-like striation on {010}; also penetration twins. Sometimes repeated, giving pseudohexagonal trillings. (b) Twin plane

Tantalite.
Paris, Me.

{203}, rare.[7]   Heart-shaped contact twins striated on {010}; sometimes repeated, giving pseudohexagonal trillings.   (c) Twin plane {501}, rare.[8] (d) Twin plane {1·15·0}, rare.[8]

P h y s.   Cleavage {010} distinct, {100} less so.   Fracture subconchoidal to uneven.   Brittle.   H. 6 (columbite), 6–6$\frac{1}{2}$ (tantalite), with H. [010] > H. [001] on {100}.[9]   G. 5.20 ± 0.05 (columbite) to 7.95 ± 0.05 (tantalite) increasing linearly with an increase in the Ta_2O_5 content (5.20 + 0.03 × %Ta_2O_5 = G. ± 0.05 for any intermediate member of the series[10]). The Fe : Mn ratio does not materially affect the specific gravity.   G. (calc. for Fe : Mn = 1 : 1 and 17 per cent Ta_2O_5 in unit cell) 5.48.   Color iron-black to brownish black, with reddish brown internal reflections (especially in the manganoan varieties).   Frequently tarnished iridescent. Streak dark red to black.   Transparent in thin splinters.   Paramagnetic.[11] Translation (?) gliding with T{100}, and t[001] and [010].[9]

O p t.   In transmitted light, red, reddish yellow, reddish brown (the manganoan variety transmitting more light).   Some varieties strongly pleochroic in brown and red-brown, with $Z > X$.   With an increase in Ta_2O_5 the refractive index decreases and the birefringence increases.   The orientation is apparently uniform with $X = a$, $Y = b$, $Z = c$.

	1	2	3	4	5
nX	....	....	2.26 ± 0.02	....	2.19 ± 0.01
nY	2.45 ca.	2.40 ± 0.03	2.32 ± 0.02	2.30–2.40	2.25 ± 0.01
nZ	....		2.43 ± 0.02		2.34 ± 0.01
Biref.	Strong	Extreme	0.17		0.15
Absorption	....	Strong	Red-brown	Red-brown	Strong
		$Z > X$	$Z > X$	$Z > X$	
$2V$	....	Bx. (−) ?	$2V$ large (+)	....	$2V$ large (+)
					$r < v$,
					moderate
G	5.48	....	....	7.30	6.5
Estimated Ta_2O_5	9.3	....	....	70.0	43.3

1. Columbite.   Cañon City, Colo.   2. Ferroan columbite.   Haddam, Conn.   3. Tantalite.   S. D.   4. Tantalite.   Ala.   5. Manganoan ? tantalite.   Amelia Court House, Va.

In polished section[13] gray-white with brownish tint, with red or reddish brown internal reflections.   Weakly anisotropic.   Reflection percentages: green 15, orange 17, red 14.

C h e m.   An oxide of iron, manganese, columbium, and tantalum, or a columbate-tantalate, $(Fe,Mn)(Cb,Ta)_2O_6$, with complete gradation in the components.   Small amounts of Sn substitute for (Fe,Mn) and are usually reported in analyses, as is W, the latter substituting for (Cb,Ta).   The elements Ti,[15] (Y,Ce), Mg,[16] U (in toddite) have been reported in substantial amounts, but have been ascribed to impurities.   Spectrographic analyses of a number of columbites have been made.[17]   He and N have been detected in small amounts.[18]

Anal.

	1	2	3	4	5	6	7	8
MnO	10.49	3.28	5.97	14.79	8.79	12.45	16.25	4.31
FeO	10.63	17.33	15.04	5.45	11.38	8.07	1.89	13.32
SnO$_2$	.....	0.73	0.67	} 0.88	0.45	0.11	0.32	} 0.38
WO$_3$	.....	0.13	.....		.....	0.45	.....	
Cb$_2$O$_5$	78.88	77.97	72.37	68.00	63.77	56.48	47.22	34.60
Ta$_2$O$_5$	.....	.....	5.26	9.88	11.33	22.12	34.27	46.02
Rem.	.....	0.48	0.58	0.53	3.92	0.15	.....	1.52
Total	100.00	99.92	99.89	99.53	99.64	99.83	99.95	100.15
G.		5.395	5.32	5.201	5.273	5.661	6.170	6.444

1. (Fe,Mn)Cb$_2$O$_6$, with Fe : Mn = 1 : 1.   2. Ferroan columbite, Greenland. Rem. is ZrO$_2$ 0.13, MgO 0.23, CaO trace, PbO 0.12.[20] 3. Columbite. Ånneröd, Norway. Rem. is CaO 0.58.[21] 4. Columbite. Old Mike mine, Custer Co., S. D. Rem. is TiO$_2$ 0.53.[22] 5. Columbite. Ambatofotsikely, Madagascar. Rem. is U$_3$O$_8$ 2.02, SiO$_2$ 0.40, TiO$_2$ 1.50, Al$_2$O$_3$ trace.[23] 6. Columbite. Near Cañon City, Colo. Rem. is ign. loss 0.15.[24] 7. Manganoan columbite. Elk Creek, Pennington Co., S. D.[25] 8. Ferroan columbite. Harney City, Pennington Co., S. D. Rem. is TiO$_2$ 1.52.[22]

	9	10	11	12	13	14	15	16
MnO	12.49	4.16	5.66	14.15	1.20	13.88	1.19	6.90
FeO	4.22	12.64	11.91	1.63	14.30	1.17	13.28	6.98
SnO$_2$	.....	.....	} 0.44	} 0.48	0.82	} 0.67	} 0.10	.....
WO$_3$	.....	.....			.....			.....
Cb$_2$O$_5$	31.30	31.27	27.22	15.11	13.14	4.47	1.97	.....
Ta$_2$O$_5$	51.99	51.93	53.47	68.65	70.53	79.81	83.57	86.12
Rem.	.....	.....	1.30	0.55	.....	0.33	.....	.....
Total	100.00	100.00	100.00	100.57	99.99	100.33	100.11	100.00
G.			6.725	7.03	7.277	7.301	7.975	

9. (Fe,Mn)(Cb,Ta)$_2$O$_6$ with Fe : Mn = 1 : 3 and Cb : Ta = 1 : 1.   10. (Fe,Mn)(Cb,Ta)$_2$O$_6$ with Fe : Mn = 3 : 1 and Cb : Ta = 1 : 1.   11. Tantalite. Tin Mountain, Custer Co., S. D. Rem. is TiO$_2$ 1.30. Recalc. after deduction of CaO 0.48.[22] 12. Manganoan tantalite. Wodgina district, Western Australia. Rem. is TiO$_2$ 0.40, H$_2$O 0.07, NiO trace, CaO trace, MgO 0.15.[26] 13. Ferroan tantalite. Rosendal, Kimito parish, Finland.[27] 14. Manganoan tantalite. Sanarka, Russia. Rem. is CaO 0.17, ign. loss 0.16.[28] 15. Ferroan tantalite. Old Mike mine, Custer Co., S. D. With TiO$_2$ trace.[22] 16. (Fe,Mn)Ta$_2$O$_6$, with Fe : Mn = 1 : 1.

Var.

A. Columbite   with Cb > Ta.

Ferroan. Ferrocolumbite. With Fe : Mn > 3 : 1 as here considered.

Manganoan. Manganocolumbite. With Mn : Fe > 3 : 1.

Tungstenian? Possibly WO$_3$ may enter to the extent of 13 per cent (Iveland).[14]

B. Tantalite   with Ta > Cb.

Ferroan. Ferrotantalite. With Fe : Mn > 3 : 1.

Manganoan. Manganotantalite. With Mn : Fe > 3 : 1.

Tests. B.B. unaltered. Fine powder more or less completely decomposed by fusion in borax, salt of phosphorus, potash, or potassium bisulfate; partially decomposed by evaporation with concentrated H$_2$SO$_4$.

O c c u r. Minerals of the columbite-tantalite series are the most abundant and widespread of the natural columbates and tantalates. Tantalite is the principal ore of tantalum. Found in granite pegmatites, particularly those with a well-marked albite and Li silicate and Li-Mn-Fe phosphate phase. Associated with albite, microcline, beryl, lepidolite, muscovite, black and colored (Li) tourmaline, spodumene, lithiophilite-triphylite, amblygonite, triplite, samarskite, apatite, microlite, and, very frequently, cassiterite; also, less commonly, with pollucite, petalite, gadolinite, fluorite, topaz, wolframite, phenakite. Found as detrital minerals, sometimes in important amounts, in areas of granitic rocks and pegmatites. Marked variation in the ratio of Cb to Ta and in Fe to Mn is often found in material from a single locality and even in a single specimen or crystal. Oriented growths have been noted of columbite upon samarskite and of euxenite and ampangabeite upon columbite.

Only a few of the known localities can be mentioned here.[29] In Norway columbite is found with samarskite and monazite in granite pegmatites at many localities in the region between the Kristiania fiord and the east coast of Vandsjö. In Sweden tantalite occurs at Finbö and Broddbö, both near Fahlun, at Varuträsk (columbite, tantalite), and at Utö (*mangantantalite*). Columbite (also *mengite*) occurs in Russia in the region of Miask in the Ilmen Mountains with samarskite, zircon, topaz, and other pegmatite minerals, and as a detrital mineral (*columbite, manganoan tantalite*) in the gold placers of the Sanarka region, Orenburg, southern Urals. At a number of localities in Bengal, India (*columbite*). In Germany an early recognized occurrence (1812) at Rabenstein, near Zwiesel, Bavaria (sometimes given' as Bodenmais); also at Hagendorf near Pleystein and other localities in the Oberpfalz, with triplite, triphylite. In Italy, at Craveggia, Val Vigezzo, Piedmont, columbite occurs with tourmaline, spessartite, and beryl. Tantalite and columbite occur in France in pegmatites in the neighborhood of Chanteloube, near Limoges, Haute-Vienne. Columbite has been found at several localities in Japan, notably Makabe, Hitachi Province, and Ishikawayama, Iwaki Province, in Yamanō. Tantalite and columbite together with ferroan and manganoan varieties occur in important amounts in pegmatites and as detrital minerals in the Wodgina, Cooglegong, Bellinger, Greenbushes, and other districts in Western Australia. At several localities in the Belgian Congo, and in the tin fields of Namaqualand, Cape Province, and Erongo, South-West Africa.

Columbite is a common mineral in the potash-rich pegmatites of Madagascar, with beryl, monazite, muscovite, zircon, ampangabeite as associated minerals: in very large crystals at Ambatofotsikely and Ampangabe, at Morafeno, Samiresy, Befanamo in the region of Ankazobe, and elsewhere. In Greenland columbite occurs (also *greenlandite*) in the cryolite deposit at Ivigtut in the Fredrikshaab district. In South America columbite has been found with beryl and triplite near San Roque, Sierra de Cordoba, Argentina; as a detrital mineral in diamond sands near Lençoes and at other localities in Bahia, Brazil.

Columbite and tantalite are widely distributed in the United States. Found in small amounts in many of the pegmatites of New England. In

Maine columbite occurs at Greenwood, Mount Mica, Stoneham, Auburn, Standish, a manganoan tantalite at Mount Apatite, a manganoan columbite at Black Mountain, Rumford, tantalite at Paris. In New Hampshire at Plymouth and Acworth. In Massachusetts with cassiterite at Beverly, near Northfield, and at Chesterfield. The original specimen of columbite was found prior to 1734 in the neighborhood of New London, Connecticut; the exact locality is unknown.[30] Also in Connecticut at Haddam (also *hermannolite* and *ferroilmenite*) and Haddam Neck, Portland, Middletown and Branchville (*manganoan columbite*). In New York with chrysoberyl at Greenfield, Saratoga County (*columbite*). From Mineral Hill and Boothwyn (*columbite*), Delaware County, and elsewhere in Pennsylvania. Tantalite has been found in Coosa County, Alabama. In North Carolina, columbite-tantalite occurs in Alexander County and with samarskite at several localities in Mitchell and Yancey counties; near Storeville, Anderson County, South Carolina. In Virginia in the pegmatites in the neighborhood of Amelia Court House (*columbite-tantalite, manganoan tantalite*). In California columbite-tantalite has been found in San Diego County at the Victor mine, Rincon, near Ramona, in the Chihuahua Valley and manganoan tantalite near Pala. In Idaho in placers and pegmatites in Boise County. In the Bridger Mountains, Wyoming (*tantalite, columbite*). Columbite has been found in Colorado at several places in the Pikes Peak region, on Turkey Creek, near Morrison, Jefferson County, and at other localities. In South Dakota[31] columbite occurred abundantly in the Etta, Bob Ingersoll, Peerless, and other mines near Keystone, Pennington County; a single group of large flattened crystals at the Ingersoll mine weighed about 2000 lb. Columbite and tantalite have also been obtained in considerable amounts in placers and pegmatites in the Tinton area, Lawrence County, in the Old Mike and other mines north of Custer, Custer County, and in pegmatites near Hill City, Oreville, and elsewhere in Pennington County, all in South Dakota.

In Canada columbite-tantalite have been found at a number of localities, including the Woodcox mine, Monteagle Township, in Lyndoch Township, Renfrew County, and in Dill Township, Sudbury District (*toddite*), in Ontario; from Pointe du Bois, Manitoba, and near New Ross Corner, Nova Scotia.

N a m e.[32] Tantalite from the mythical *Tantalus*, in allusion to the difficulties encountered in making a solution in acids of the mineral preparatory to analysis. Columbite from Columbia, a name of America, whence the original specimen was obtained and in which specimen the element columbium was first recognized in 1802 by Hatchett. The synonym *niobite* derives from the later name for the metal, niobium.

TODDITE. *Ellsworth* (*Am. Min.*, **11**, 332, 1926).

Found as small masses associated with columbite and garnet in pegmatite in Dill Township, Sudbury district, Ontario. Fracture subconchoidal. Very brittle. H. 6½. G. 5.041. Luster submetallic, brilliant. Color pitch-black. Streak brownish gray. In very thin splinters transparent and dark brown in color. Isotropic. Analysis gave:

CaO 2.02, MnO 2.62, FeO 4.38, MgO 0.22, BeO 0.47, PbO 0.44, Fe_2O_3 4.68, $(Y,Er)_2O_3$ 3.42, $(Ce,La)_2O_3$ 0.76, UO_2 8.71, UO_3 2.37, Cb_2O_5 53.73, Ta_2O_5 8.97, H_2O (+) 3.59, H_2O (−) 0.35, ZrO_2 0.06, TiO_2 0.85, ThO_2 0.47, SnO_2 0.53, SiO_2 1.77, total 100.41.

Although this material has been considered to be a uranian-columbite, the extremely low specific gravity, the absence of cleavage and the relatively large content of rare earths, Ca, Fe^3, and water render such an interpretation improbable. Evidence of admixture has been found in some specimens,[33] and the material may be a mixture of columbite and some other mineral, possibly euxenite.

Ref.

1. Brögger, *Vidensk. Selskr., Oslo, Mat.-Nat. Kl.*, **6**, 71, 1906, noted the crystallographic resemblance to brookite, and also to other minerals such as wolframite, olivine, pucherite, and valentinite. Sturdivant, *Zs. Kr.*, **75**, 88 (1930), has noted the structural resemblance to brookite.

2. Values of Dana (731, 1892), orientation of Schrauf, *Ak. Wien, Ber.*, **44** [1], 445 (1861), unit of Breithaupt, *B. H. Ztg.*, **17**, 61 (1858), the latter conforming with the x-ray unit of Sturdivant (1930). Transformation: Dana to Schrauf $0\frac{1}{3}0/100/00\frac{1}{3}$. Transformations to others in Taylor, *Am. Min.*, **25**, 123 (1940). The ratio of columbite is very close to that of tantalite, and a separate set of values is not needed. See Dana.

3. In Goldschmidt (**2**, 180, 1913); also Bonshtedt (in *Min. Abs.*, **3**, 146 [1926]). Rare or uncertain forms:

190	012	083	041	302	1·15·9	163	141	411
140	085	031	102	991	133	162	161	

4. Sturdivant, *Zs. Kr.*, **75**, 88 (1930), by Laue and oscillation methods on crystals from Norway, with G. = 5.71, hence ca. 17 per cent Ta_2O_5.

5. For a detailed description of various habits see Schrauf (1861), Brögger (1906), and Lacroix (**2**, 366, 1922).

6. First recognized by Rose, *Ann. Phys.*, **64**, 171, 336 (1845), on crystals from Rabenstein. See also Brögger (1906).

7. Dana (732, 1892). See also Ungemach, *Bull. soc. min.*, **39**, 27 (1916).

8. Brögger (1906).

9. Mügge, *Jb. Min.*, I, 147, 1898.

10. Conversely the percentage of Ta_2O_5 may be estimated to within a few per cent by this relation: per cent $Ta_2O_5 = (G. − 5.20)/0.03$ (Berman, 1941). For many specific gravity determinations see Dana (733, 1892); Headden, *Am. J. Sc.*, **41**, 89 (1891), on Black Hills specimens; Marignac, *Bibl. Univ.*, **25**, 25 (1866); Mügge, *Cbl. Min.*, 417, 1924; Simpson, *Roy. Soc. Western Australia, J.*, **23**, 17 (1937). All the values are not consistent and the relation given above is therefore only an approximation.

11. Schrauf (1861).

12. Larsen (59, 1921).

13. Schneiderhöhn and Ramdohr (**2**, 604, 1931).

14. Bjørlyyke *Norsk Geol. Tidsk.*, **14**, 271 (1935), reports 13 per cent of WO_3 (estimated from x-ray spectrograph) in a columbite from Iveland. The analysis, however, is not consistent, and some doubt must be cast on it.

15. Weiss and Landecker, *Zs. anorg. Chem.*, **64**, 96 (1909).

16. Koenig, *Ac. Sc. Philadelphia, Proc.*, **39**, 1876, from Coosa, Alabama; see also Kenngott, *Jb. Min.*, 168, 1877, and Smith, *Am. J. Sc.*, **15**, 203 (1878).

17. Bjørlyyke (1935). Sc has been reported in spectrographic work on columbite. See Hintze (**1** [4A], 442, 1923).

18. Hintze (1923).

19. For additional analyses see Dana (733, 1892), Hintze (1923) and for more recent analyses: Quensel and Berggren, *Geol. För. Förh.*, **60**, 223 (1938); Simpson, *Roy. Soc. Western Australia, J.*, **18**, 61 (1932); Buttgenbach, *Bull. Inst. roy. colon. Belge*, **4**, 209 (1933); Shibata and Kimura, *J. Chem. Soc. Japan*, **42**, 1 (1921) — *Min. Abs.*, **2**, 36, 381 (1925); Walker, *Univ. Toronto Studies, Geol. Ser.*, **30**, 10 (1931); Clarke in Wells, *U. S. Geol. Sur., Bull. 878*, 113, 1937; Iimori and Hata, *Sc. Papers Inst. Phys. Chem. Res. Tokyo*, **34**, 1010 (1938) — *Min. Abs.*, **7**, 358 (1939). Analyses of massive material referred to columbite-tantalite may possibly belong to tapiolite-mossite.

20. Blomstrand, *J. pr. Chem.*, **99**, 41 (1866).

21. Blomstrand in Brögger, *Vidensk. Selskr., Oslo, Mat.-Nat. Kl.*, **6**, 64 (1906).
22. Headden, *Am. J. Sc.*, **3**, 298 (1922).
23. Duparc, Sabot, and Wunder, *Bull. soc. min.*, **36**, 5 (1913).
24. Headden, *Colorado Sc. Soc., Proc.*, **8**, 57 (1905).
25. Headden, *Am. J. Sc.*, **41**, 101 (1891).
26. Simpson in Maitland, *Geol. Survey Western Australia, Bull.*, **23**, 65 (1906) — *Zs. Kr.*, **45**, 314 (1908).
27. Rammelsberg, *Ak. Berlin, Ber.*, 164, 1872.
28. Blomstrand anal. in Arzruni, *Russ. Min. Ges., Vh.*, **23**, 181 (1883).
29. For additional localities see Hintze (1923).
30. The specimen referred to was presented by John Winthrop (?–1747), of a Puritan family famous in the early development of New England, to the Royal Society of London in 1734. Originally the specimen may have belonged to John Winthrop, Jr. (1606–1676), first Governor of Connecticut and grandfather of John Winthrop, who possessed a collection of natural curiosities and was active in the early iron mining industry of Connecticut. The specimen was incorporated into the collection of Sir Hans Sloane (1660–1753), at that time President of the Royal Society, and passed in 1753 into the British Museum, then founded. The original specimen is still preserved (B.M. 60309). A picture is given in the *Exotic Mineralogy* (1811–1820, **1**, 11, Plate 6) of Sowerby. The exact locality at which the mineral was found is uncertain. The catalogue of Sloane gave the locality as Nautneauge. This name (also Neatneague, Namueg, Naumeag), according to a letter from J. Hammond Trumbull to Professor G. J. Brush of Yale University (July 16, 1882), " . . . originally given to the plantation at New London, may have extended — as were the bounds of the plantation — east of the Thames, to the Mystic, including what is now Groton. I conjectured that the columbite was found near Winthrop's mill a short distance above the head of Mystic, and there used to be a local tradition to that effect; though it had no definite value." It has also been surmised by Mitchell, *Med. Repos.*, **8**, that the specimen was found at New London in a spring of water near the home of Governor Winthrop, but no locality has since been detected at that place. Haddam, Middletown, and other known localities of columbite in the region of New London have also been suggested as the place of discovery.
31. Hess, *U. S. Geol. Sur., Bull. 380*, 131, 1908.
32. For a history of the metals Cb and Ta and of the nomenclature of the columbite-tantalite minerals see Dana (735, 1892) and Hintze (1923).
33. Berman (priv. comm., 1940).

CALCIOTANTALITE. *Simpson (Australasian Assoc. Adv. Sc., Rep.*, **11**, 452, 1907). Found as pebbles in a cassiterite placer at Greens Well, Wodgina district, Western Australia. Only an analysis is given of the material:

MnO	FeO	MgO	CaO	TiO$_2$	SnO$_2$	Cb$_2$O$_5$	Ta$_2$O$_5$	Ign.	Total	G.
1.39	8.42	0.62	7.78	0.54	0.72	6.44	73.82	trace	99.73	6.04

Possibly a mixture of microlite and tantalite.[1]

Ref.

1. Simpson (1907) says pebbles associated with these were mixtures of microlite and tantalite, and that the material here described only " appeared homogeneous."

Euxenite-Polycrase Series

8331 **E U X E N I T E** [(Y,Ca,Ce,U,Th)(Cb,Ta,Ti)$_2$O$_6$]. *Scheerer, Ann. Phys.* (**50**, 149, 1840; **72**, 566, 1847). Lyndochite *Ellsworth* (*Am. Min.*, **12**, 212, 1927). Tanteuxenite *Simpson* (*Roy. Soc. Western Australia, J.*, **14**, 45, 1928).
8332 **P O L Y C R A S E** [(Y,Ca,Ce,U,Th)(Ti,Cb,Ta)$_2$O$_6$]. *Scheerer* (*Ann. Phys.*, **62**, 430, 1844).

C r y s t. Orthorhombic; dipyramidal — $2/m\ 2/m\ 2/m$.[1]

$$a : b : c = 0.3789 : 1 : 0.3527;[2] \qquad p_0 : q_0 : r_0 = 0.9309 : 0.3527 : 1$$

$$q_1 : r_1 : p_1 = 0.3789 : 1.0743 : 1; \qquad r_2 : p_2 : q_2 = 2.8353 : 2.6395 : 1$$

Forms:[3]

		ϕ	$\rho = C$	ϕ_1	$\rho_1 = A$	ϕ_2	$\rho_2 = B$
c	001	....	0°00′	0°00′	90°00′	90°00′	90°00′
b	010	0°00′	90 00	90 00	90 00	....	0 00
a	100	90 00	90 00	....	0 00	0 00	90 00
m	110	69 15	90 00	90 00	20 45	0 00	69 15
w	011	0 00	19 25½	19 25½	90 00	90 00	70 34½
d	101	90 00	42 57	0 00	47 03	47 03	90 00
e	201	90 00	61 45½	0 00	28 14½	28 14½	90 00
p	111	69 15	44 52	19 25½	48 43½	47 03	75 31½
q	121	52 50½	49 26	35 12½	52 44½	47 03	62 41½
γ	131	41 20½	54 38½	46 37	57 24½	47 03	52 14½

Habit. Stout prismatic [001], sometimes flattened {010} (polycrase). The faces on polycrase and, to a less extent, euxenite are striated parallel to their intersection with {010}. Often in parallel or subparallel and slightly radial aggregates of crystals. Also massive. Commonest forms: $b\ d\ m\ p\ a$.

Twinning. (a) Common on {201}; the twins are flattened {010} and striated [001]; (b) Possibly on {101}, rare;[4] (c) possibly on {013}.[4]

Phys. Fracture subconchoidal to conchoidal. H. 5½–6½. G. 5.00 ± 0.10 (for Cb : Ta > 2 : 1, and apparently not varying markedly with varying ratio of (Cb + Ta) : Ti); 5.3–5.9 (for Cb : Ta < 1 : 1); the G. decreases with alteration and increases after ignition. Luster often brilliant, submetallic, or somewhat greasy or vitreous. Color black, sometimes with a greenish or brownish tint. Streak yellowish, grayish, or reddish brown. Transparent in thin splinters. Metamict.

Euxenite.
Madagascar.

Opt.[5] In transmitted light, brown, yellow-brown, or reddish brown. Isotropic (metamict). The refractive index increases after ignition.

	n	
Euxenite	2.24 ± 0.02	(Hitterö)
Euxenite	2.195	(no locality; 2.23 after ignition)
Euxenite	2.06	(no locality; 2.22 after ignition)
Polycrase	2.248	(Santa Clara, Brazil[6])

Chem. An oxide, or titanate-columbate, of the type AB_2O_6,[7] with A = Y, Ce, Ca, U, Th; B = Ti, Cb, Ta, Fe³. The predominant constituents are Y, Ca, Ti, Cb, and Ta. The high Ti end of the series is called polycrase, and the high Cb + Ta member is euxenite. The normal member of the series has Cb > Ta, although tantalian varieties are not uncommon. The ratios Ti : Cb + Ta lie between 2 : 3 (anal. 1) and 3 : 1 (anal. 13). Some reported analyses[8] contain up to 9 per cent Al_2O_3 and as much as 21 per cent SiO_2, but these constituents have not been shown to be present in considerable amount in homogeneous samples. Members of the series are radioactive;[9] they contain He and N.[10] Rare earth elements,[11] Hf,[12] Ge,[13] and Sc[14] have been noted in members of the series.

Anal.[15]

	1	2	3	4	5	6	7
CaO	4.86	2.22	0.97	1.92	1.08	2.03	0.85
MgO	0.13	.....	....	0.03	0.06	0.07	0.08
MnO	0.59	0.35	0.28	0.28	0.16	0.19	.....
PbO	0.37	trace	1.71	1.35	0.63	1.01	0.43
FeO	0.77	.....	....	.....	1.13	0.14	1.37
Al_2O_3	0.13	.....	0.31	0.26	trace	0.45	trace
(Ce, etc.)$_2O_3$	4.34	7.22	9.54	0.44	2.20	0.87	2.45
$(Y,Er)_2O_3$	18.22	17.48	16.36	24.31	27.73	24.95	27.32
UO_2	0.67	.....	....	8.61	5.83	7.25	5.64
UO_3	0.04	3.35	4.16	0.20	.....	1.51	.....
U_3O_8	.....	.....	....	.....	.....	.....	
ThO_2	4.95	trace	2.86	3.94	3.58	2.64	4.60
SnO_2	0.12	0.14	0.44	0.07	0.18	0.14	0.11
SiO_2	0.07	0.90	0.13	0.09	0.17	1.08	.....
Fe_2O_3	1.32	1.18	1.53	2.07	.....	2.16	
TiO_2	16.39	14.17	21.05	22.96	25.68	25.04	24.43
Cb_2O_5	41.43	3.83	15.27	28.62	27.64	22.28	29.00
Ta_2O_5	3.84	47.31	22.95	2.65	1.27	5.32	1.01
H_2O	1.96	.....	....	2.23	2.55	2.37	.....
Rem	0.04	2.40	2.28	0.26	0.27	0.05	2.87
Total	100.24	100.55	99.84	100.29	100.16	99.55	100.16
G.	4.909	5.77	5.55	5.002		4.983	

1. "Lyndochite." Lyndoch Township, Renfrew Co., Ont. Al_2O_3 contains BeO. Rem. is ZrO_2 0.04. $H_2O - 110°$ 0.06, $H_2O + 110°$ 1.90. Pb/U + 0.38Th = 0.15.[16] 2. "Tanteuxenite." Cooglegong, Western Australia. Rem. is ign. loss 2.40, Na_2O trace.[17] 3. "Tanteuxenite." Woodstock, Western Australia. (Ce, etc.)$_2O_3$ contains (La,Di)$_2O_3$ 0.14. Rem. is ign. loss 2.24, Bi_2O_3 0.04.[18] 4. Euxenite. Sabine Township, Nipissing district, Ont. Al_2O_3 contains BeO. Rem. is ZrO_2 0.05, Na_2O 0.17, K_2O 0.04. $H_2O - 110°$ 0.08, $H_2O + 110°$ 2.15. Pb/U + 0.38Th = 0.144.[19] 5. Euxenite. Alve, Arendal, Norway. $(Y,Er)_2O_3$ contains ca. 12.22 per cent Er_2O_3. Rem. is ZrO_2 trace, Na_2O 0.18, K_2O 0.09.[20] 6. Euxenite. Maberly, Ont. Rem. is BeO 0.05, $H_2O - 110°$ 0.08, $H_2O + 110°$ 2.29. Pb/U + 0.38Th = 0.11.[21] 7. Euxenite. Hitterö. Rem. is ign. loss 2.87 and WO_3 trace.[22]

	8	9	10	11	12	13
CaO	0.09	.....	0.66	2.94	.....	1.02
MgO	0.12	.....	0.14	trace	.....	0.35
MnO	trace	.....	....	.....	.....	0.34
PbO	0.20	.....	0.46	0.86	0.64	.....
FeO	0.51	2.87	4.94	.....	.....	trace
Al_2O_3	.....	.....	.....	0.30	0.44	0.76
(Ce, etc.)$_2O_3$	0.62	.....	2.58	} 14.48	} 29.28	3.55
$(Y,Er)_2O_3$	25.64	27.55	25.42	.....	.....	25.03
UO_2	.....	.....	5.49	9.96	.....	
UO_3	.....	13.77	....	.....	.....	6.69
U_3O_8	10.50	.....	....	.....	6.48	
ThO_2	1.34	.....	3.80	1.06	5.22	1.76
SnO_2	.....	.....	0.13	.....	trace	.....
SiO_2	0.74	.....	....	1.10	.....	
Fe_2O_3	2.63	.....	....	6.76	0.78	.....
TiO_2	27.70	29.31	31.45	25.68	34.41	30.43
Cb_2O_5	12.73	19.48	} 20.72	7.49	20.31	4.35
Ta_2O_5	13.89	.....		16.07	.....	23.10
H_2O	.....	5.18	....	.....	2.04	.....
Rem.	3.00	.....	3.97	12.56	.....	2.82
Total	99.71	98.16	99.76	99.26	99.60	100.20
G.	4.99	4.72–4.78				5.37

8. Polycrase. Maberly, Ont. Rem. is ign. loss 3.00.[23] 9. Polycrase. Henderson Co., N. C. TiO_2 contains some Cb_2O_5.[24] 10. Polycrase. Slättåkra, Sweden. Rem. is WO_3 0.09, ign. loss 3.88.[25] 11. Polycrase? Ramskjaer, Norway. Rem. is ign. loss 12.56.[26] 12. Polycrase. Santa Clara, Brazil. Cb_2O_5 contains some Ta_2O_5. Pb/U + $0.36Th = 0.0826$.[27] 13. Tantalian polycrase. Cooglegong, Western Australia. $(Ce,$ etc.$)_2O_3$ contains 1.73 $(La,Di)_2O_3$. $(Y,Er)_2O_3$ contains 9.27 Er_2O_3. Rem. is ign. loss 2.82.[28]

Var. *Tantalian.* Tanteuxenite *Simpson (Roy. Soc. Western Australia, J.,* **14**, 45, 1928). Tantalian euxenite. Tantalian polycrase. Ta has been found to substitute for Cb to Cb : Ta = 1 : 7.4 in euxenite (anal. 2) and to Cb : Ta = 1 : 3.2 in polycrase (anal. 13).

Tests. B.B. infusible and often becomes lighter colored. Glows markedly on heating.[29] More or less completely decomposed by hot concentrated HCl, HF, or H_2SO_4 and by fusion in $KHSO_4$.

Occur. Found in granite pegmatites, sometimes in large amounts, associated with biotite, muscovite, ilmenite, monazite, xenotime, zircon, beryl, magnetite, garnet, allanite, gadolinite, blomstrandine; also less frequently, thorite, uraninite, betafite, and columbite. Also as a detrital mineral in areas of granitic rocks. Discolorations and radial fractures are frequently noted in the matrix of crystals or masses of euxenite-polycrase and other metamict or highly radioactive minerals. Oriented growths have been noted of polycrase upon priorite and of euxenite upon columbite.

Only a few of the many known occurrences can be listed here.[30] Euxenite and polycrase are known from a hundred or more localities in Norway alone. Euxenite was originally from Jölster, Sönd Fiord, western Norway (possibly blomstrandine); polycrase was originally from Rasvåg, on the island of Hitterö. Also in Norway at the islands Kragerö and Hvaler south of Fredrikstad, and at Alve on Tromö, Helle, Mörefjaer and numerous other localities along the coast between Tvedstrand and Arendal; at Svinör, Hitterö and other localities in the neighborhood of Lindesnes in southwestern Norway; widespread in pegmatites in Iveland[31] and Evje parishes in Satersdal. In Finland at Huntila, near Pitkäranta. In Sweden at Slättåkra in Alsheda parish, Lön Jonköping (polycrase). In Greenland at Karrakungak, at Puisortok on the eastern coast, and at Nuk in the Christianshaab district.

Found at many localities in Madagascar[32] in the potash-rich pegmatites, associated with monazite, beryl, columbite, magnetite, betafite, etc., and rarely, scapolite, chrysoberyl, bismuth. The crystals often are deeply altered. At Ankazobê near Ambohitantely, on Mount Vohambohitra, at Ranomafana, at Samiresy and Ambatofotsikely, and at numerous other places. At Kivu in the Belgian Congo; and in Namaqualand, Cape Province. As detrital masses at Cooglegong and Woodstock in Western Australia (tantalian euxenite). In Brazil at Pomba, Santa Clara, and Esperito Santo in Minas Geraes. Euxenite is an abundant mineral in some Canadian pegmatites.[33] In Ontario in Sabine and Mattawan townships, Nipissing district; in Lyndoch Township, Renfrew County (*lyndochite*); reported also from other places.

Polycrase has been found in the United States near Marietta, Greenville County, South Carolina, on the Davis farm, near Zirconia, Henderson County, North Carolina, and at Baringer Hill, Llano County, Texas; the mineral has also been reported from placers near Pioneerville, Boise County, Idaho. Euxenite occurs at Morton, Delaware County, Pennsylvania. In Canada polycrase has been found in Ontario in Calvin Township, Nipissing District, in South Sherbrooke Township, Lanark County, and elsewhere.

Alter. Euxenite-polycrase is ordinarily metamict,[34] in common with most rare-earth oxides of Cb, Ta, and Ti, and becomes crystalline only on ignition. Often superficially altered to a yellowish material relatively high in water; the alteration has been said to be accompanied by enrichment in SiO_2[35] and by a decrease in rare earths, U^6 (from U^4) and Ti.[36] Altered crystals are usually minutely fractured. Oliveiraite has been reported as an alteration product of euxenite.

Name. Euxenite from εὔξενος, *friendly to strangers, hospitable*, in allusion to the rare elements that it contains. Polycrase from πολύς, *many*, and κρᾶσις, *mixture*. Lyndochite from the locality in Lyndoch Township, Ontario.

LYNDOCHITE. *Ellsworth* (*Am. Min.*, **12**, 212, 1927).

In crystals closely similar in form and angles to euxenite.[37] Fracture conchoidal. H. 6½. G. 4.909. Black, with pale yellow powder and vitreous luster. Isotropic. The analyzed material contains a small amount of admixed columbite (anal. 1). Found in pegmatite with microcline, beryl, columbite, garnet, magnetite, fluorite, zircon in Lyndoch Township, Renfrew County, Ontario, Canada.

A variety of euxenite-polycrase relatively high in Ca and Th and low in U.

TANTEUXENITE. *Simpson* (*Roy. Soc. Western Australia, J.*, **14**, 45, 1928).

Found as indistinct tabular orthorhombic crystals in tin placers in the Pilbara gold field, Western Australia. Fracture subconchoidal. H. 5–6. G. 5.4–5.9. Luster resinous with brownish black color. In transmitted light amber-yellow and isotropic. In composition (see anal. 2, 3)[38] essentially a variety of euxenite with Ta substituting in large amount for Cb. A tantalian polycrase (anal. 13) has also been found at this locality.

Ref.

1. Brögger, *Vidensk. Skr., Mat.-Nat. Kl.*, **6**, 82 (1906). The morphological similarity of euxenite and polycrase was first recognized by Scheerer (1847) and the chemical relationship by Brögger (1906). The polar nature of [001] reported by Hidden and Mackintosh, *Am. J. Sc.*, **41**, 423 (1891), is not verified by the observations of Brögger (1906) and others.
2. Brögger (1906).
3. Brögger (1906) and Lacroix (**1**, 387, 1922).
4. Hidden and Mackintosh (1891).
5. Larsen (**73**, 1921), Larsen and Berman (**62, 63, 64**, 1934). The data for polycrase in Larsen (**122**, 1921) where $n = 1.70$ must refer to another mineral.
6. Hess and Henderson, *J. Franklin Institute*, **200**, 235 (1925).
7. Machatschki, *Zs. Kr.*, **72**, 291 (1929). The constitution of euxenite-polycrase has earlier been discussed by Prior in Doelter (**3** [1], 104, 1918) and others. See group discussion for further data on relation to other minerals of similar composition.
8. See Hintze (470, 1936; anal. 4, 8, 14, 18, 25, 26, 40).
9. See Lacroix (**2**, 131, 1922), Miguet (*Le radioact. et les prin. corps. radio.*, Paris, 119, 1917), Betim, *C. R.*, **161**, 179 (1915) and Lange, *Naturwiss.*, **82**, 3 (1910).
10. Lange (1910) and others.

792 MULTIPLE OXIDES CONTAINING CB, TA, AND TI

11. Hauser and Wirth, *Ber.*, **42**, 4443 (1909); Lange (1910); Rowland in Hidden and Mackintosh (1891); Bjørlykke, *Norsk Geol. Tidsk.*, **14**, 265 (1935).
12. Hevesey and Jantzen, *Zs. anorg. Chem.*, **133**, 113 (1924).
13. Lincio, *Cbl. Min.*, 143, 1904.
14. Rowland in Hidden and Mackintosh (1891).
15. For additional analyses see Hintze (470, 1936). A few of the reported analyses of euxenite-polycrase probably refer to priorite (or to some other mineral). The determinations of Cb, Ta, and Ti in many of the recent analyses and in all of the older ones are probably in considerable error in this series as well as in other Cb-Ta-Ti minerals.
16. Ellsworth, *Am. Min.*, **12**, 215 (1927).
17. Simpson, *Roy. Soc. Western Australia, J.*, **14**, 45 (1928).
18. Murray anal. in Simpson (1928).
19. Ellsworth, *Am. Min.*, **13**, 486 (1928).
20. Blomstrand anal. in Brögger (1906).
21. Ellsworth, *Am. Min.*, **12**, 366 (1927).
22. Hauser and Wirth, *Ber.*, **42**, 4443 (1909).
23. Miller and Knight, *Am. J. Sc.*, **44**, 243 (1917).
24. Hidden and Mackintosh, *Am. J. Sc.*, **41**, 424 (1891).
25. Hauser and Wirth (1909).
26. Bjørlykke, *Norsk Geol. Tidskr.*, **12**, 79 (1931).
27. Henderson anal. (total wrong in original) in Hess and Henderson, *J. Franklin Inst.*, **200**, 235 (1925).
28. Simpson, *Proc. Australasian Assoc. Adv. Sc.*, **12**, 313 (1909).
29. See Liebisch, *Ak. Berlin, Ber.*, I, no. 20, 350, 1910, for thermal behavior.
30. See also Hintze (480, 1936).
31. See Bjørlykke, *Norsk Geol. Tidskr.*, **14**, 211 (1935).
32. See Lacroix (**1**, 386, 1922).
33. See Ellsworth, *Canada Dept. Mines, Econ. Geol. Ser., Bull.*, **11**, 1932.
34. See Goldschmidt, *Vidensk. Skr., Mat.-Nat. Kl.*, **5**, 1924; Gossner, *Jb. Min., Beil.-Bd.*, **52**, 265 (1925); and Mügge, *Cbl. Min.*, 721, 753, 1922; also Liebisch (1910) and Rimann, *Zbl. Min.*, 19, 1925.
35. Ellsworth, *Am. Min.*, **12**, 329 (1926).
36. Lee, *Rev. soc. Brasil. sc.*, **1**, 37 (1917); see also Grossmann, *C. R.*, **159**, 777 (1914).
37. The forms {100}, {010}, {110}, {310} or {410}, {201}, and {111} were identified by contact measurements.
38. Additional analysis in Simpson (1928).

KHLOPINITE. Starik (*Problems Soviet Geol.*, **3**, 70, 1933); Starik and Segel (*Trudui Central Geochem. Lab.*, Leningrad and Moscow, for 1931, 43, 1932); Schubnikova and Yuferov (*Rep. on New Minerals*, Leningrad, 104, 1934). Chlopinite. Hlopinite.

Black. G. 5.24. Isotropic, with $n > 1.768$. Contains essentially Cb, Ta, Ti, Y, U^4, and Fe^3. Formula[1] perhaps $(Y,U^4,Th)_3(Cb,Ta,Ti,Fe)_7O_{20}$. Contains 1.15 cc. He per gram.[2] Analysis gave: CaO 0.96, FeO 1.83, Fe_2O_3 8.16, Y_2O_3 17.65, UO_2 8.12, ThO_2 2.22, TiO_2 10.01, Cb_2O_5 39.92, Ta_2O_5 7.37, H_2O 2.94, rem. 1.46, total 100.64. Rem. is $(Na,K)_2O$ 0.24, BeO 0.03, SiO_2 0.61, MnO 0.26, PbO 0.19, MgO 0.13.

Easily fusible. Decomposed with difficulty by H_2SO_4. Found with monazite and feldspar at Khilok, Transbaikalia, Siberia. Named after the Russian chemist, V. G. Khlopin.

A doubtful species.

Ref.

1. This is close to the euxenite-polycrase series in composition and may be closely related to that series.
2. Starik, *Rep. XVI Int. Geol. Cong.*, **1**, 217 (1936), who also gives data on the leaching of Ra from khlopinite and on the geological age.

ESCHWEGITE. Guimarães (*Bol. Inst. Brasil. Sc.*, **2**, 1, 1926).
Found as pebbles in the upper Rio Doce, Minas Geraes, Brazil. Fracture conchoidal. H. 5½. G. 5.87. Color dark reddish gray. In thin splinters transparent and dark red. Isotropic (metamict) with n between 2.15 and 2.20. An oxide (or columbate-tantalate)

essentially of Y, Ti, Cb, and Ta, with the possible formula AB_2O_6, with A = (Y,Er), U, Th; B = Cb, Ta, Ti, Fe^3. Analysis: $(Y,Er)_2O_3$ 27.28, UO_2 1.96, ThO_2 0.57, Fe_2O_3 2.05, TiO_2 18.75, Cb_2O_5 25.17, Ta_2O_5 21.58, H_2O 3.09, total 100.45.

Named after Baron W. L. von Eschwege (1777–1855).

Probably a member of the euxenite series, but imperfectly known.

834 **Yttrocrasite** $[(Y,Th,U,Ca)_2(Ti,Fe^3,W)_4O_{11}$?]. *Hidden* and *Warren* (*Am. J. Sc.*, **22**, 515, 1906; *Zs. Kr.*, **43**, 18, 1906).

C r y s t. Apparently orthorhombic. A rough crystal exhibited the three pinacoids, a prism and an orthodome.[1]

P h y s. Fracture uneven and small conchoidal. H. $5\frac{1}{2}$–6. G. 4.80. Luster bright pitchy to resinous. Color black. Coated by a dull brown alteration product. Transparent in thin splinters. Radioactive.

O p t. In transmitted light, rich amber to light yellow in color. In part metamict and isotropic, in part weakly anisotropic. n ranges from 2.12 to 2.15.[2]

C h e m. Essentially an oxide of the rare earths and titanium (or a titanate) with the general formula[3] $A_2B_4O_{11}$, where A = Y, Th, U, Ca; B = Ti, Fe^3, W. Analysis gave: CaO 1.83, MnO 0.13, PbO 0.48, MgO trace, $(Yt,Er)_2O_3$ 25.67, $(Ce,La)_2O_3$ 2.92, UO_2 1.98, UO_3 0.64, WO_3 1.87, ThO_2 8.75, SiO_2 trace, Fe_2O_3 1.44, TiO_2 49.72, Cb_2O_5 present, Ta_2O_5 trace, CO_2 0.68, H_2O 4.36, H_2O − 0.10, total 100.57.

Tests. B.B. infusible, turns grayish and cracks open to a slight extent. Fine powder soluble (with slight effervescence) when boiled in H_2SO_4, affording an opalescent pale yellowish green solution. Easily decomposed by HF.

O c c u r. Found in granite pegmatite in Burnet County, Texas, about three miles east of the Baringer Hill pegmatite in Llano County.

N a m e. Apparently from *yttro* and κρᾶσις, *mixture*, because a compound of yttrium with many other elements.

Ref.

1. The crystal is stated to resemble the figure of yttrotantalite given in Dana (738, 1892).

2. Larsen (158, 1921).

3. An alternate formula, including the water, might be $YTi_2O_5(OH)$. See also Hidden and Warren (1906) and Zambonini, *Zs. Kr.*, **45**, 76 (1908), who derive very complex formulas.

Eschynite-Priorite Series

8351 **E S C H Y N I T E** $[(Ce,Ca,Fe^2,Th)(Ti,Cb)_2O_6]$. Aeschynit *Berzelius* (*Jahresber. Chem. Min.*, **9**, 195, 1828). Dystomes Melan-Erz *Mohs* (459, 1839). Äschynit. Aeschynite.

8352 **P R I O R I T E** $[(Y,Er,Ca,Fe^2,Th)(Ti,Cb)_2O_6]$. *Brögger* (*Zs. Kr.*, **3**, 481, 1879). *Prior* (*Min. Mag.*, **12**, 96, 1899). Priorite *Brögger* (*Vidensk. Skr., Mat.-Nat. Kl.*, **6**, 98, 1906). Blomstrandin *Brögger* (*Vidensk. Skr., Mat.-Nat. Kl.*, **6**, 98, 1906). Blomstrandinite.

C r y s t.[1] Orthorhombic; dipyramidal — $2/m\ 2/m\ 2/m$.[2]

ESCHYNITE

$a : b : c = 0.4867 : 1 : 0.6737;$[3] $p_0 : q_0 : r_0 = 1.3842 : 0.6737 : 1$

$q_1 : r_1 : p_1 = 0.4867 : 0.7224 : 1;$ $r_2 : p_2 : q_2 = 1.4843 : 2.0547 : 1$

Forms:[4]

		ϕ	$\rho = C$	ϕ_1	$\rho_1 = A$	ϕ_2	$\rho_2 = B$
c	001	....	0°00'	0°00'	90°00'	90°00'	90°00'
b	010	0°00'	90 00	90 00	90 00	....	0 00
n	130	34 24½	90 00	90 00	55 35½	0 00	34 24½
r	120	45 46½	90 00	90 00	44 13½	0 00	45 46½
m	110	64 03	90 00	90 00	25 57	0 00	64 03
x	021	0 00	53 25	53 25	90 00	90 00	36 35
d	101	90 00	54 09½	0 00	35 50½	35 50½	90 00
p	111	64 03	56 59½	33 58	41 03½	35 50½	68 28

PRIORITE

$$a : b : c = 0.4746 : 1 : 0.6673;^{[5]} \quad p_0 : q_0 : r_0 = 1.4060 : 0.6673 : 1$$
$$q_1 : r_1 : p_1 = 0.4746 : 0.7112 : 1; \quad r_2 : p_2 : q_2 = 1.4986 : 2.1070 : 1$$

Forms:[6]

		ϕ	$\rho = C$	ϕ_1	$\rho_1 = A$	ϕ_2	$\rho_2 = B$
c	001	....	0°00'	0°00'	90°00'	90°00'	90°00'
b	010	0°00'	90 00	90 00	90 00	....	0 00
a	100	90 00	90 00	....	0 00	0 00	90 00
t	140	27 46½	90 00	90 00	62 13½	0 00	27 46½
n	130	35 05	90 00	90 00	54 55	0 00	35 05
r	120	46 29½	90 00	90 00	43 30½	0 00	46 29½
m	110	64 36½	90 00	90 00	25 23½	0 00	64 36½
u	023	0 00	23 59	23 59	90 00	90 00	66 01
v	045	0 00	28 19	28 19	90 00	90 00	61 41
x	021	0 00	53 09½	53 09½	90 00	90 00	36 50½
d	101	90 00	54 34½	0 00	35 25½	35 25½	90 00
p	111	64 36½	57 16½	33 56½	40 32	35 25½	68 51½
z	658	68 25	48 35½	22 38½	45 52	43 29	73 59
π	121	46 29½	62 43	53 09½	49 52	35 25½	52 16½

Habit. Prismatic to short prismatic [001]; sometimes tabular {010}, and striated [100] on {010}; less often prismatic [100] (priorite). Commonest forms: $b\,c\,m\,n\,x$ (x prominent on eschynite). Crystals sometimes large. Also massive.

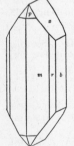

Eschynite.
Miask.

Phys. Cleavage {100} in traces?.[7] Fracture conchoidal. Brittle. H. 5–6. G. 5.19 ± 0.05 (eschynite); 4.95 ± 0.10 (priorite). Luster submetallic to resinous to waxy, sometimes brilliant or dulled (by alteration ?). Color black to various shades of brown and yellow. Streak almost black, to brown (eschynite) and reddish yellow (priorite).

Opt. Isotropic (metamict) and transmits light in only the thinnest splinters. Reddish brown to light brown. Becomes anisotropic on ignition, and the refractive index increases somewhat.[8] $n = 2.26 \pm 0.01$ (for eschynite),[9] increasing to 2.285 on ignition; for priorite, $n = 2.142 \pm 0.01$, after ignition $n = 2.24$.

Chem. Members of the series are of the type AB_2O_6,[10] with A = Ce, Ca, Fe[2], Th and B = Ti, Cb predominantly in eschynite, and similarly in priorite except that Y, Er substitute for Ce in the former. Ti : Cb > 1 in all reported analyses, with a reported maximum of Ti : Cb = 3.6 : 1 (anal. 11). The rare-earth elements are dominant in the A part of the formula, and Th is, in general, more abundant in the eschynite portion of the series. Minor constituents, which, in some instances are due to admixture, are, for A: Mn, Pb, U, Sn, Zr; for B: Ta, Al, Si. The water reported in most analyses is presumably due to alteration. He, N, and Ra have been found in the species.[11]

Anal.[12]

	1	2	3	4	5	6
CaO	2.52	2.50	2.75	2.34	4.12	2.71
MnO	.....	.....	.....	0.03	0.19	.....
PbO	.....	.....	.....	.....	.....	.....
MgO	.....	.....	.....	0.01	0.22	.....
FeO	4.28	3.34	3.17	2.20	5.63	3.48
$(Y,Er)_2O_3$	4.53	3.10	1.12	0.98	17.11	17.46
Ce_2O_3	19.50	}19.41	18.49	15.50	4.32	3.89
$(La,Di)_2O_3$	.....		5.60	11.00	.....	.....
UO_2	.....	.....	.....	.....	0.49	.....
U_3O_8	.....	.....	.....	.....	.....	.....
SnO_2	trace	.....	0.18	0.15	0.29	.....
ThO_2	15.42	17.55	15.75	11.27	0.61	17.04
ZrO_2	.....	.....	.....	.....	.....	.....
SiO_2	.....	.....	.....	.....	2.12	trace
Al_2O_3	.....	.....	.....	.....	.....	trace
TiO_2	22.60	21.20	21.81	23.88	21.89	22.21
Cb_2O_5	23.85	32.51	29.64	}30.93	36.68	32.35
Ta_2O_5	6.97	.....	.....		.....	.....
H_2O	.....	.....	.....	.....	3.69	.....
Rem.	.....	.....	1.07	0.98	2.14	.....
Total	99.67	99.61	99.58	99.27	99.50	99.14
G.		5.168	5.230	5.34	4.996	4.681

1. Eschynite. Hitterö. Al_2O_3 and SiO_2, trace.[13] 2. Eschynite. Miask.[14] 3. Eschynite. Miask. Rem. is ignition loss.[15] 4. Eschynite. Urals. Rem. is ignition loss 0.98; F, PbO, Al_2O_3, and SiO_2 trace.[16] 5. Priorite. Embabaan Dist., Swaziland. Aver. of two partial analyses. Rem. is UO_3 2.14.[17] 6. Priorite. Urals.[18]

	7	8	9	10	11
CaO	1.94	1.80	2.06	1.02	1.04
MnO	.....	0.30	0.32	0.27	0.16
PbO	0.42	0.84	0.15	0.06	0.35
MgO	0.23	0.15	0.06	0.04	0.28
FeO	2.61	1.43	1.73	1.48	1.73
$(Y,Er)_2O_3$	21.21	25.62	28.72	28.76	26.66
Ce_2O_3	3.71	}2.48	}1.72	}1.97	}4.69
$(La,Di)_2O_3$	.....				
UO_2	1.75	5.35	.....	4.01	3.24
U_3O_8	.....	.....	3.98	.....	.....
SnO_2	trace	0.18	0.06	0.12	0.20
ThO_2	2.48	4.28	7.58	7.69	7.93
ZrO_2	2.62	1.33	.....	trace	0.50
SiO_2	0.71	0.40	0.21	0.38	.....
Al_2O_3	0.78	.....	trace	.....	1.36
TiO_2	21.95	27.39	32.75	32.91	34.07
Cb_2O_5	35.51	23.35	18.13	17.99	15.08
Ta_2O_5	.....	1.15	0.62	0.89	1.30
H_2O	.....	2.56	1.07	1.88	0.96
Rem.	3.77	1.17	0.19	0.41	.....
Total	99.69	99.78	99.35	99.88	99.55
G.		4.91	4.88	4.82–4.93	

7. Priorite. Frikstad, Norway.[19] 8. Priorite. Arendal. Rem. is ZnO 0.09, Na_2O 0.90, K_2O 0.18.[20] 9. Priorite. Slutsch River, Wolhynia. Rem. is Na_2O 0.10, K_2O 0.09.[20] 10. Priorite. Urstad, Hitterö. Rem. is Na_2O 0.22, K_2O 0.19.[21] 11. Priorite. Miask. WO_3 trace.[22]

Tests. Eschynite: B.B. swells and turns to rusty brown. Does not glow on ignition. Fine powder partially decomposed by H_2SO_4, completely by HF and in a fusion with $KHSO_4$. Priorite: Infusible. Fine powder more or less completely decomposed by hot HCl or H_2SO_4.

O c c u r. Eschynite is found in nepheline syenite and in the nepheline-free miascite, with feldspar, zircon, and samarskite, at Miask, in the Ilmen Mountains. Priorite occurs in granite pegmatites, with euxenite, zircon, monazite, xenotime, allanite, and other rare-earth minerals (Norway).

Eschynite was originally found at Miask, Ilmen Mountains, Russia. Also reported from the gold sands of the Orenberg district, southern Urals. From Hitterö, Norway. Reported in granite pegmatite at Döbschütz, near Görlitz, Silesia.

Priorite was found originally at Urstad on the island of Hitterö in southwest Norway, and later at another locality on the island; other Norwegian localities are: Eitland in Vance parish, Lister; Satersdalen in Evje parish, Lundekleven; abundantly at Kåbuland, Iveland parish; near Arendal, Mörefjär and Saltero; at Frikstad. At Miask, in the Ilmen Mountains, both priorite and eschynite; on the Slutsch River, between Rogatschew and Baranowka, Wolhynia. As detrital crystals in tin placers in the Embabaan district, Swaziland, Africa. From Madagascar[23] in pegmatite at Tongafeno, at Ambohitromby near Ambatofotsy, at Ambedabao, and at other localities.

N a m e. Eschynite from αίσχύνη, shame, in allusion to the inability of chemical science, at the time of its discovery, to separate some of its constituents. Priorite, after G. T. Prior (1862–1936), Keeper of Minerals in the British Museum. Blomstrandine after G. W. Blomstrand (1826–97), Professor of Chemistry at the University of Lund.

Ref.

1. Elements and angles are given for both eschynite and priorite because the given values are sufficiently different, and they may be indicative of the chemical difference between the two members of the series.
2. See the published figures in Koksharov (**3**, 384, 1858), and others.
3. Koksharov (1858).
4. In Goldschmidt (**1**, 2, 1913).
5. Brögger on priorite from Hitterö, *Vidensk. Skr., Mat.-Nat. Kl.*, **6**, 98 (1906).
6. Brögger (1906) and Lacroix (**3**, 305, 1923).
7. Given for eschynite.
8. Larsen and Berman (65, 1934).
9. Larsen (72, 1921). The Hitterö specimen referred to by Larsen may be priorite. The value given in this text refers to eschynite from the Ilmen Mts.
10. Machatschki, *Chem. Erde*, **7**, 72 (1932).
11. In Hintze (3, 1936).
12. Older analyses in Dana (522, 1868). See also Chernik, *Ac. sc. St. Pétersbourg, Bull.*, **2**, 389 (1904) — *Jb. Min.*, 190 (1910); Starynkevitch-Borneman, *C. R., ac. sc. U.S.S.R.*, 144, 1925 — *Jb. Min.*, II, 148, 1927.
13. Chernik, *Ac. sc. St. Pétersbourg, Bull.*, **2**, 389 (1904) — *Jb. Min.*, I, 190, 1910.
14. Rammelsberg, *Zs. deutsche geol. Ges.*, **29**, 815 (1877).
15. Marignac, *Bibl. Univ.*, **29**, 282 (1867).
16. Chernik, *J. Russ. Phys.-Chem. Ges., Abt.*, 61, 735 — *Jb. Min.*, I, 243, 1930.
17. Prior (1899).
18. Chernik, *Ac. sc. St. Pétersbourg, Bull.*, 949, 1912 — *Jb. Min.*, II, 210, 1914.
19. Hauser and Herzfeld in Schetelig, *Vidensk. Skr., Mat.-Nat. Kl.*, **1**, 147 (1922).

20. Chernik, *Bull. ac. sc. russ.*, 495, 1922 — *Jb. Min.*, **I**, 126, 1926.
21. Blomstrand anal. in Brögger (1906).
22. Hauser and Herzfeld, *Cbl. Min.*, 756, 1910.
23. Lacroix (**1**, 392, 1922; **3**, 305, 1923).

8361 **SAMARSKITE** [(Y,Er,Ce,U,Ca,Fe,Pb,Th)(Cb,Ta,Ti,Sn)$_2O_6$]. Urano-tantal *Rose* (*Ann. Phys.*, **48**, 555, 1839). Samarskit (Uranniobit) *Rose* (*Ann. Phys.*, **71**, 157, 1847). Yttroilmenit *Hermann* (*J. pr. Chem.*, **42**, 129, 1847; **44**, 216, 1848). Eytlandite *Adam* (31, 1869). Ännerödite, Aanerödite, pt. *Brögger* (*Geol. För. Förh.*, **5**, 354, 1881).

C r y s t. Orthorhombic.

$$a : b : c = 0.5456 : 1 : 0.5177;^1 \qquad p_0 : q_0 : r_0 = 0.9489 : 0.5177 : 1$$

$$q_1 : r_1 : p_1 = 0.5456 : 1.054 : 1; \qquad r_2 : p_2 : q_2 = 1.932 : 1.833 : 1$$

Forms:[2]

		ϕ	$\rho = C$	ϕ_1	$\rho_1 = A$	ϕ_2	$\rho_2 = B$
c	001	.....	0°00′	0°00′	90°00′	90°00′	90°00′
b	010	0°00′	90 00	90 00	90 00	.....	0 00
a	100	90 00	90 00	.....	0 00	0 00	90 00
l	130	19 21½	90 00	90 00	70 38½	0 00	19 21½
h	120	42 30	90 00	90 00	47 30	0 00	42 30
m	110	61 23	90 00	90 00	28 37	0 00	61 23
e	101	90 00	43 30	0 00	46 30	46 30	90 00
x	201	90 00	62 13	0 00	27 47	27 47	90 00
p	111	61 23	47 13½	27 22	49 53	46 30	69 25
z	121	42 30	54 33	46 00	56 36½	46 30	53 05½
v	131	50 42	67 49	57 13½	44 13½	27 47	54 05½

Habit. Prismatic [001] (with rectangular cross section); less often tabular {100} or {010}; sometimes elongated [010], with prominent {101}. Crystals rough. Often massive (and then not easily identified as samarskite).

P h y s. Cleavage {010} indistinct (?). Fracture con-choidal to small conchoidal. Brittle. H. 5–6. G. 5.69 (probably best value), the low values (as low as 4.1) are due, no doubt, to alteration; high titanian varieties may reach 6.2 (anal. 8). The specific gravity is said to decrease on ignition.[3] Luster on the fracture vitreous to resinous, sometimes submetallic, and splendent; the crystals often are externally dull. Color velvet black, sometimes with a brownish tint; externally often brown or yellowish brown due to alteration. Streak dark reddish brown to black; also gray, yellow-brown, etc., on altered material. Transparent in thin splinters.

Southern Nor-way.

O p t. In transmitted light, light brown to dark brown in color. Ordi-narily metamict and isotropic. Anisotropic samarskite has been reported, but without verification.[4] Refractive index variable, with $n = 2.20 \pm 0.05$ reported[5] on unanalyzed material.

C h e m.[6] An oxide (or columbate-tantalate) principally of the rare earths, calcium, iron, uranium and thorium, with columbium, tantalum, and titanium. The formula is probably AB_2O_6 with A = Y, Er, Ce, La, U, Ca, Fe^2, Pb, Th; B = Cb, Ta, Ti, Sn, W, Zr (?). Water is usually reported in analyses, but it is believed present as a result of alteration. SiO_2 is often reported in analyses, but is probably due to admixture, or alteration. Ra, N, and He have been reported.[7]

Anal.

	1	2	3	4	5	6	7	8	9
CaO	0.55	0.51	4.30	2.43	3.79	0.33	0.37	0.27	0.94
MgO	.....	0.41	0.13	.....	0.19	0.02	0.09	.....	trace
FeO	10.75	11.15	4.40	5.40	4.08	2.11	.....	0.32	7.36
MnO	0.78	0.69	0.86	.....	0.79	1.75	0.79	0.78	trace
PbO	.....	0.15	0.77	.....	0.98	0.338	0.51	0.72	.....
Y_2O_3	14.49	7.83	}9.07	}9.50	}8.33	}12.47		6.41	6.65
Er_2O_3	.....	13.37						10.71	2.72
Ce_2O_3	.....	0.25				0.53	}14.10	0.54	3.82
La_2O_3	.....	0.37	}0.89	}4.05	}1.90	}1.55		}1.80	1.07
Di_2O_3	4.17	1.56							0.74
UO_2	.....	.....	9.66	8.70	10.82	7.85	.....	4.02	4.35
UO_3	12.55	11.23	6.78	.....	5.38	.....	17.20	.....	.....
SnO_2	0.08	0.79	0.57	.....	0.15	.....	.....	0.95	trace
ThO_2	.....	1.73	2.51	1.05	2.59	3.47	3.03	3.64	4.23
TiO_2	.....	0.68	.....	1.42	......	1.40	.....	.....	0.60
ZrO_2	.....	1.03	0.62	.....	0.79	.....	.....	2.29	2.17
Fe_2O_3	.....	2.13	.....	.....	......	9.82	10.18	8.77	.....
Al_2O_3	.....	0.19	0.36	0.80	0.45	.....	.....	.....	0.80
WO_3	.....	1.41	.....	.....	......	.....	.....	2.25	1.90
Cb_2O_5	37.51	32.02	38.83	43.60	46.44	42.00	}51.38	27.77	33.80
Ta_2O_5	18.20	11.18	10.70	11.15	1.81	14.73		27.03	26.88
H_2O	1.12	1.22	6.54	11.14	7.61	0.65	1.55	1.58	0.22
Rem.	.....	0.85	3.34	.....	4.11	0.49	0.09	0.46	0.73
Total	100.20	100.75	100.33	99.24	100.21	99.508	99.29	100.31	98.98
G.						5.696	5.68	6.18	

1. Samarskite. Mitchell Co., N. C. Average of 2 analyses, one partial.[9] 2. Samarskite. Miask. Rem. is Na_2O 0.28, K_2O 0.21, ZnO 0.17, SiO_2 0.12, G_2O_2 (?) 0.07.[10] 3. Samarskite. Odegardsletten, Norway. Rem. is Na_2O 0.76, K_2O 0.08, BeO 0.30, BaO 0.38, SiO_2 1.82.[11] 4. Samarskite. Antanamalaza, Madagascar.[12] 5. Samarskite. Aslaktaket, Norway.[13] 6. Samarskite. Glastonbury, Conn. Rem. is SiO_2 0.03, undetermined 0.46. Pb/U + 0.36Th = 0.039, yielding an age of 292 million years.[14] 7. Samarskite. Topsham, Me. Rem. is insol. 0.09. TiO_2 included in the $(Cb,Ta_2)O_5$.[15] 8. Samarskite. Devil's Head Mt., Colo. Rem. is ZnO 0.05, K_2O 0.17, $(Na,Li)_2O$ 0.24. ZrO_2 includes some TiO_2.[16] 9. Samarskite. Tschoroch River, Caucasus. Rem. is $(Na,K)_2O$ 0.48, BeO 0.25.[17]

Tests. In the C.T. decrepitates, glows, cracks open, turns black (sometimes greenish or yellowish) and decreases in specific gravity. B.B. fuses on edges to a black glass. Decomposed by fusion with $KHSO_4$. Finely powdered samarskite is more or less decomposed by hot concentrated H_2SO_4, HCl or HNO_3.

Occur. Samarskite is found in granite pegmatites, often in close association with columbite. Other associates are monazite, magnetite, zircon, beryl, biotite, uraninite, muscovite, eschynite, albite, topaz, and garnet. Oriented growths of columbite upon samarskite, with the crystal axes of the two minerals parallel, are frequently found,[18] and oriented growths of uranian microlite upon samarskite have been noted.[19]

Samarskite originally was from near Miask, in the southern Ural Mountains, with columbite, eschynite, monazite, and garnet in pegmatite; also in the U.S.S.R. as detrital grains in monazite sands of the Batum region. In Norway at Ånneröd, near Moss, with beryl, topaz, monazite, etc., and parallel overgrowths of columbite (*ännerödite*) in pegmatite; also at a number of localities in the granite pegmatite region of southern Norway,[20] and especially in the Iveland district, Satersdalen. In Sweden at the Nothamns mine, Väddön (*hydrosamarskite*). With cyrtolite, garnet and muscovite in pegmatite near Gridalur, Nellore district, Madras, India. In the neighborhood of Kotei, Borneo. In Madagascar with almandite and magnetite in pegmatite near Antanamalaza. At Kivu, in the Belgian Congo. From Ishikawa, Iwaki Province, Japan. From Divino de Ubá, Minas Geraes, Brazil, in pegmatite with monazite, muscovite and parallel overgrowths of columbite.

In the United States, samarskite was found at Wiseman's mica mine, Greasy Creek Township, Mitchell County, North Carolina (*rogersite*, in part), with columbite, uranian microlite, and muscovite; reported from Spruce Pine, from near Asheville, and from other localities in North Carolina. In pegmatite near Jones Falls, Baltimore, Maryland. At the Spinelli quarry, South Glastonbury, and from Pelton's quarry, Portland, both in Connecticut. With monazite in the pegmatite at Topsham, Maine. In Colorado from near Ohio City, Gunnison County, with columbite, albite, topaz, and beryl in a lepidolite-rich pegmatite, and with cyrtolite at Devil's Head, Douglas County. Reported in the heavy concentrates of a gold placer deposit near Idaho City, Boise County, Idaho. From Nuevo, California. In Canada reported from the Maisonneuve mine, Berthier County, Quebec, with black tourmaline, garnet, beryl, and fergusonite (?).

Alter. Samarskite alters readily by hydration. The crystals also are often surficially bounded by a yellow or brown alteration shell, and complete pseudomorphs are sometimes found. Some of this material is relatively high in rare earths.

Name. Samarskite after Colonel von Samarski of Russia.

Ref.

1. Dana, *Am. J. Sc.*, **11**, 202 (1876). The measurements are not much better than a degree, more or less.
2. Goldschmidt (**8**, 6, 1922).
3. See Hintze (**1** [4A], 413, 1923).
4. Van Aubel, *Ann. soc. géol. Belgique*, **58**, *Annexe Publ., Congo Belge*, Fasc. I, C, 38, 1935 — *Jb. Min.*, I, 145, 1936, on material from Kivu, Belgian Congo.
5. Larsen (129, 158, 1921).
6. The difficulties of assigning a formula to this species are due principally to the uncertainties in the role of iron. The ferric iron undoubtedly substitutes for part of the Cb and Ta, while ferrous iron probably substitutes for the elements in the A part of the formula. Most early analyses assign the extra oxygen to uranium and report the Fe as of low valence. The best modern analyses, however (see anal. 6 and 7), report most of the Fe as Fe_2O_3. The analysis of Glastonbury samarskite by Wells (*Rep. Comm. Geol. Time*, 60, 1937) yields a formula $(Y, \text{etc.}, Ca, Fe^2, Mn, U, Th)_2 (Cb, Ta, Fe, Ti)_5 O_{14}$. An x-ray powder picture of an ignited sample of the analyzed material gives the same result as typical samarskite, similarly ignited, from North Carolina and Miask, the original localities for the mineral. For a further discussion of the formula and composition of samarskite see Machatschki, *Chem. Erde*, **7**, 72 (1932), who gives $A_3B_4O_{14}$, also Hess and Wells, *Am. J. Sc.*, **19**, 17 (1930); Brögger, *Vidensk. Selskr.*, Oslo, *Mat.-Nat. Kl.*, **6**, 142, 154 (1906).

7. See Hintze (1923), and also, for Ra content, Okada, *J. Geol. Soc. Tokyo*, **35**, 336 (1928) — *Min. Abs.*, **5**, 332 (1933).

8. Material from North Carolina, Miask, Glastonbury, and Topsham (represented by anal. 1, 2, 6, 7) give identical x-ray diffraction patterns, when ignited. The other cited analyses are recent and sufficiently like the authenticated analyses to be considered here as samarskite. Other recent so-called samarskites cannot be correlated with those here given, or have been shown to be different in some important respect. See further under the related species immediately following samarskite. Additional analyses of supposed samarskites may be found in Hintze (1923), Ellsworth, *Am. Min.*, **13**, 66 (1928); Fenner, *Am. J. Sc.*, **16**, 382 (1928) (gives U, Th, Pb only).

9. Allen, *Am. J. Sc.*, **14**, 131 (1877).

10. Chroustschoff anal., *Russ. min. Ges.*, *Vh.*, **31**, 412 (1894).

11. Blomstrand in Brögger (1906). See also Goldschmidt, *Zs. Kr.*, **44**, 493 (1908), on radioactivity of this material.

12. Pisani anal. in Lacroix, *C. R.*, **152**, 559 (1911).

13. Blomstrand in Brögger (1906).

14. Wells anal. (*Rep. Comm. Geol. Time*, 76, 1935).

15. Gonyer anal. (*Rep. Comm. Geol. Time*, 60, 1937).

16. Hillebrand anal., *Colorado Sc. Soc., Proc.*, **3**, 38 (1888).

17. Chernik, *J. Phys. Chem. russe*, **34**, 684 (1902).

18. Brögger (1906), and Schetelig, *Vidensk. Selskr.*, *Oslo*, *Mat.-Nat. Kl.*, **1** (1922).

19. Dana (727, 1892).

20. See Brögger (1906) and Bjørlykke, *Norsk Geol. Tidskr.*, **14**, 211 (1935).

8362   " Samarskite."   *Hess* and *Wells* (*Am. J. Sc.*, **19**, 17, 1930).

A supposed samarskite from Petaca, New Mexico, yielding the formula[1] (Ca,Pb,Y,U) $(Cb,Ta,Ti,Fe^3)_2O_6$ with Ca + Pb : Y, etc. : U = 2 : 3 : 1 approx. and Cb + Ta : Ti : Fe^3 = 14 : 2 : 3. This corresponds to the typical samarskite formula, and the physical properties are much like that mineral, but an x-ray picture of the ignited material does not fit the typical samarskites.[1]

Analysis is as follows: CaO 4.22, MnO 0.89, PbO 0.43, ZnO 0.04, $(Y,Er)_2O_3$ 17.64, Ce_2O_3 0.31, $(La,Di)_2O_3$ trace, UO_2 4.85, UO_3 7.67, SnO_2 0.02, ThO_2 1.58, TiO_2 4.29, Fe_2O_3 5.85, Cb_2O_5 41.39, Ta_2O_5 7.27, loss on ignition 2.06, Bi_2O_3 0.02, undetermined 0.27; total 98.80.   G. 5.67.   Pb/U + 0.38Th = 0.038.

Ref.

1. Berman and Frondel (priv. comm., 1941). X-ray powder pictures of ignited samples of the Petaca material show that the highly radioactive portion is similar to yttrotantalite and the weakly radioactive part is much like fergusonite.

The following minerals are either altered samarskites, or poorly defined materials perhaps related to samarskite:

VIETINGHOFITE.   *v.* Lomonosov and Damour (*Ac. sc. St. Pétersbourg, Bull.*, **23**, 463, 1877).

A supposed ferroan samarskite of uncertain composition (anal. 1) yielding only approximately ABO_4, with A largely Fe^2, Y, U; B = Cb, Ti. Of doubtful validity.

ROGERSITE.   *Smith* (*Am. J. Sc.*, **13**, 367, 1877).

Probably an altered samarskite, from Mitchell County, North Carolina. Of little validity.

PLUMBONIOBITE.   *Hauser* and *Finckh* (*Ber.*, **42**, 2270, 1909; **43**, 417, 1910).

A supposed columbate essentially of Y, U, Pb and Fe (anal. 2). Metamict. In irregularly developed crystals, partly altered to secondary uranium minerals, from pegmatite at Morogoro, Uluguru Mountains, Tanganyika, Africa. Perhaps a plumbian variety of samarskite.

HYDROSAMARSKITE.   *Nordenskiöld* (*Ak. Stockholm, Bihang.*, **17** [2], no. 1, 8, 1891). An altered samarskite.

Anal.

	1	2
CaO	.....	3.05
MgO	0.83	.....
FeO	23.00	5.70
MnO	2.67	0.11
PbO	.....	7.62
Y_2O_3	6.57	}14.26
Er_2O_3	.....	
Ce_2O_3	⎫	.....
La_2O_3	} 1.57	.....
Di_2O_3	⎭	.....
UO_2	.....	13.72
U_2O_3	8.85	.....
ThO_2	.....	0.06
TiO_2	1.84	1.20
ZrO_2	0.96	trace
Al_2O_3	.....	0.28
WO_3	.....	0.15
Cb_2O_5	51.00	46.15
Ta_2O_5	.....	1.18
H_2O	.....	6.38
Rem.	1.80	0.41
Total	99.09	100.27
G.	5.53	4.80

1. Vietinghofite. Rem. is loss on ign.   2. Plumboniobite. Rem. is loss on ign.

WIIKITE. *Ramsay* and *Zilliacus (Finsk. Vet.-Soc. Förh., Öfv.*, **39**, 58, 1897); *Borgström (Geol. För. Förh.*, **32**, 1531, 1910). Alpha-wiikite, Beta-wiikite *Ant-Wuorinen (Comm. géol. Finlande, Bull.*, **19**, no. 115, 213, 1936).

A name[1] applied to ill-defined mixtures and alteration products of minerals high in Cb, Ta, Ti, Si, Y, from pegmatites in Impilahti parish on Lake Ladoga, Finland. Associated with allanite and monazite. Supposedly different types, representing various stages of alteration or kinds of admixture, have been described.[2] Color and luster variable: yellow or brown and waxy, black and metallic or asphaltic, etc. H. $4\frac{1}{2}$–6. G. 3.6–5.1. The principal components appear to be a black orthorhombic mineral resembling samarskite,[3] and a brown isometric betafite-like mineral;[4] allanite may also be admixed.

The analyses[5] vary widely. Some of the analyses suggest a Ti-rich samarskite or a euxenite-like mineral. The radioactivity,[6] rare-earth[7] and scandium[8] content of the mixtures called wiikite have been investigated. Named after F. J. Wiik (1839–1909), Finnish geologist.

NUOLAITE. *Lokka (Comm. géol. Finlande, Bull.*, **13**, no. 82, 21, 1928). Gamma-wiikite *Ant-Wuorinen (Comm. géol. Finlande, Bull.*, **19**, no. 115, 213, 1936).

A name applied to a mixture largely of a nearly colorless and a black opaque substance. Forms veinlets in feldspar at Nuolainniemi, Lake Ladoga, Finland. Seven analyses give, roughly, CaO 2, MgO 1, FeO 3, Fe_2O_3 3–8, Ce_2O_3 2, Y_2O_3 7, ThO_2 2–4, SiO_2 3, TiO_2 7, Cb_2O_5 39, Ta_2O_5 23, H_2O 3. The black component is possibly related to or altered from samarskite.

Ref.

1. See Lokka, *Comm. géol. Finlande, Bull.*, **13**, no. 82 (1928) for the history of this material.
2. See Borgström (1910); Orlow, *Cbl. Min.*, 257, 1922; Lokka (1928); and Ant-Wuorinen (1936).
3. Morphological data based on contact measurements are given by Borgström (1910), with $a : b : c = 0.5317 : 1 : 0.5046$, and by Lokka (1928), with $a : b : c = 0.536 : 1 : 0.528$. Forms: {100}, {010}, {110}, {210}, {101}, {201}, {212}.
4. Bjørlyyke, *Norsk Geol. Tidskr.*, **12**, 87 (1931) by x-ray study.

5. Summarized in Lokka (1928), with later analyses in Ant-Wuorinen (1936).
6. Lokka (1928).
7. Sahama and Väkätalo, *C. r. soc. géol. Finlande,* no. 13, 1939.
8. Orlow (1922).

837   **T H O R E A U L I T E** [SnTa$_2$O$_7$]. *Buttgenbach* (*Soc. géol. belgique, Bull.,* **56**, 327, 1933).

C r y s t. Monoclinic?.[1]
Habit. Rough crystals, prismatic [001].
Twinning. Lamellar twins, with composition face {010}.
P h y s. Cleavage {100} perfect, {011} imperfect. H. 6. G. 7.6–7.9.
Luster resinous to adamantine. Color brown. Streak yellow with green-ish tint. Transparent in thin splinters.
O p t.[3] In transmitted light yellow. Biaxial positive (+), 2V 25°,
Y = b, Z ∧ c = 27°. Mean index 2.38±. Birefringence on {100}
cleavages 0.039.
C h e m. An oxide of tin and tantalum, SnTa$_2$O$_7$.
Anal.

	1	2
SnO$_2$	22.41	21.88
Ta$_2$O$_5$	77.59	72.83
SiO$_2$	.....	1.85
Al$_2$O$_3$	.....	1.02
Fe$_2$O$_3$	.....	0.50
CaO	.....	1.28
Total	100.00	99.36
G.		7.6–7.9

1. SnTa$_2$O$_7$.   2. Katanga.   With trace of Cb$_2$O$_5$, Sb$_2$O$_3$, MnO, and MgO.[2]

O c c u r. With cassiterite in pegmatite at Monono, Katanga, Belgian Congo.
N a m e. After Professor J. Thoreau, University of Liége.

Ref.

1. Buttgenbach (1933) and Mélon, *Ac. roy. Belgique, Cl. Sc., Bull.,* 473, 1935. Inferred from optical properties.
2. Mélon (1935). Also an approx. analysis and a spectrographic examination (with Sb, Pb, Ti, Zn, Ni, Tl and Mg) in Buttgenbach (1933).
3. Mélon (1935).

Betafite Series

$$AB_3X_9 \cdot nH_2O?$$

The chief characteristics of the series are as follows.
1. Isometric crystals (metamict).
2. Predominantly uranium, titanium, and columbium oxides with

$$A = \text{U, Ca, Th, Pb, Ce, Y}$$
$$B = \text{Ti, Cb, Ta, Fe, Al}$$

arranged in their relative order of abundance. The role of water, other than some basic water in the X part of the formula, is not well understood. The specific gravities given refer, for the most part, to the metamict mineral.

Considerable uncertainty exists about the relations of the minerals here grouped together and their relationship to the pyrochlore-microlite series.

841   **BETAFITE** [(U,Ca)(Cb,Ta,Ti)$_3$O$_9$·nH$_2$O]. *Lacroix (Bull. soc. min.,* **35,** 84, 233, 1912; **37,** 101, 1914; *C. R.,* **154,** 1040, 1912).

Samiresite *Lacroix (Bull. soc. min.,* **35,** 84, 1912; *C. R.,* **154,** 1040, 1912). Blomstrandite *Lindstrom (Geol. För. Förh.,* **2,** 162, 1874). (Not the blomstrandine, blomstrandinite of *Brögger, Vidensk. Selskr., Oslo, Mat.-Nat. Kl.,* **6,** 98 [1906].) Mendelejevite *Vernadsky (Ac. sc. St. Pétersbourg,* **8** [2], 1368, 1914; *C. R.,* **176,** 993, 1923). Mendelyeevite. Mendeleyevite. Titanian betafite. Unnamed *Bjørlykke (Norsk Geol. Tidskr.,* **12,** 73, 1931).

C r y s t.   Isometric; possibly hexoctahedral — $4/m\,\bar{3}\,2/m$.

Forms:

	a	d	o	g	m	r
	001	011	111	023	113	233
Betafite[1]	x	x	x	x	x	x
Titanian[2]		x	x			
Blomstrandite[3]	x	x	x		x	
Samiresite[4]	x	x	x		x	
Mendeleyevite[5]	x	x				

Structure cell.[6]   Cubic.   Cell dimensions not well established.   Metamict, but recrystallizes on ignition.

Habit.   Usually octahedral, often modified by {011}; rarely with more complex modifications (as in betafite).   Sometimes flattened on {011} or {001} (betafite), or elongated [001] or [111].

P h y s.   Fracture conchoidal.   Brittle.   H. 4–5$\frac{1}{2}$ (blomstrandite is said to be 5$\frac{1}{2}$).   G. 3.7–5 (samiresite, containing lead, has the higher value. The water content, probably due to alteration, gives abnormally low specific gravities for this type of compound.)   Luster waxy to vitreous to semi-metallic.   Color greenish brown (betafite) to yellow (samiresite) to black (titanian variety).   Transmits light in thin fragments.   Metamict.

O p t.[7]   In transmitted light nearly colorless and isotropic. $n =$ 1.915 ± 0.02 (Antaifasy), 1.925 ± 0.01 (Betafo), 1.92–1.96 (samiresite).

C h e m.[8]   Essentially an oxide, or columbate-tantalate, of uranium, calcium, columbium, tantalum, and titanium, (U,Ca)(Cb,Ta,Ti)$_3$O$_9$·nH$_2$O. The agreement with the formula is not good and the chemistry of betafite needs further investigation.   Minor amounts of Pb (in samiresite), Th, Fe^3, Sn, Fe^2, rare earths, are reported.   The role of water, always reported, is not understood, but it is probably due to alteration.   Strongly radioactive.

Anal.[9]

	1	2	3	4	5	6	7	8
CaO	....	3.93	3.45	3.12	4.00	8.96	7.02	6.62
MnO	....	0.15	....	....	0.50	....	....	....
PbO	7.35	0.10	trace	trace	....	1.70	1.42	0.33
MgO	....	0.13	0.40	trace	0.20	trace	trace	trace
FeO	1.06	1.20	....	....	1.35	....	....	
$(Y,Er)_2O_3$	....	3.11	0.90		0.30	....	} 3.30	} 5.96
$(Ce,La)_2O_3$	0.20	1.61	0.60	1.00	2.50	....		
UO_2	21.20							9.64
UO_3	....	26.37	26.60	27.15	18.10	15.52	20.20	....
SnO_2	0.10	0.37	0.30	0.37	0.30	....	....	....
ThO_2	....	1.30	1.30	1.12	....	....	0.04	0.12
SiO_2	....	0.59	....	....	....	0.62	0.64	0.42
Al_2O_3	0.74	0.24	2.10	1.50	....	0.98	0.36	1.20
Fe_2O_3	....	2.25	2.87	0.50	....	5.52	6.96	6.24
TiO_2	6.70	16.51	18.30	16.20	10.80	35.05	34.22	32.27
Cb_2O_5	45.80	37.36	34.80	34.80	23.30	8.51	10.11	11.95
Ta_2O_5	3.70	1.46	trace	1.00	28.50	12.85	7.61	11.75
H_2O	12.45	2.47	7.60	12.50	9.60	9.63	7.45	13.59
Rem.	0.30	....	....	0.38	0.40	....	....	....
Total	99.60	99.15	99.22	99.64	99.85	99.34	99.33	100.19
G.		4.83–4.93	4.17	3.75	4.74	3.93–3.98	4.31–4.34	

1. Samiresite. Samiresy. Rem. is K_2O 0.30, ign. 12.45.[10] 2. Betafite. Sludianka.[11] 3. Betafite. Ambolatara.[12] 4. Betafite. Ambalahazo. Rem. is K_2O 0.38.[12] 5. Blomstrandite (?). Tongafeno. Rem. is Bi_2O_3.[12] 6. Titanian betafite. Tangen, Norway. Black, with vitreous luster.[13] 7. Tangen, Norway. Black with dull luster. (H_2O given as 7.00 per cent).[13] 8. Tangen, Norway. Yellow-brown, with vitreous luster.[13]

Var. Ordinary. Calcium and uranium, with predominant columbium and subordinate titanium and tantalum.

Plumbian. Samiresite. With Pb : U = 3 : 8 (anal. 1).

Titanian. With Ti : Cb + Ta : Fe^3 = 9 : 3 : 1 (anal. 6).

Tests. Fuses with difficulty to a black slag. More or less decomposed by acids.

Occur. Found typically with other rare-earth minerals in granite pegmatites. Associated minerals are euxenite, fergusonite, allanite, altered zircon, and beryl (Madagascar). Parallel inclusions of magnetite in betafite have been noted. Occurs in Madagascar as large crystals (some groups up to 6 kg.) at Ambatolampikely, and as crystals (up to 7 cm. in diameter) at Sama and Andibakely; also at Ambolotara west of Betafo; at Antanifotsy, 2 km. east of Ampangabe; at numerous localities in the region between Antanifotsy and Marafeno. At Samiresy, southeast of Antsirabe (*samiresite*) with native bismuth and pyromorphite; at Tongafeno as large crystals (*blomstrandite*?) with beryl, columbite and zircon. In Siberia at Sludianka, on Lake Baikal (*mendelejevite*) in a pegmatite with titanite, garnet, zircon, magnetite, and pyroxene. In Norway a titanian variety is found in the pegmatite at Hogsjaaen, near Tangen; also at Evje, Landsnerk, and Ljosland in Satersdalen.

Alter. Most crystals are superficially or entirely altered to a yellow material of high water content and diminished radioactivity.

N a m e. Betafite from Betafo in Madagascar. Samiresite is likewise named after Samiresy in Madagascar. Mendelejevite (or mendelyeevite) is after the Russian chemist Dmitri Ivanovitch Mendelyeev (1834–1907). Blomstrandite is after C. W. Blomstrand (1826–97), Professor of Chemistry at the University of Lund.

Ref.

1. Lacroix (1, 379, 1922).
2. Bjørlykke, *Norsk Geol. Tidskr.*, **12**, 73 (1931).
3. Lacroix (1, 383, 1922) on crystals from Madagascar (see anal. 5) presumed to be the same as the original massive material from Sweden.
4. Lacroix, *Bull. soc. min.*, **35**, 84 (1912).
5. Vernadsky, *Ac. sc. St. Pétersbourg, Bull.*, **8** [2], 1368 (1914).
6. Reuning, *Chem. Erde*, **7**, 186 (1933), obtained 11.04 Å. on ignited material, not shown to be betafite, from Ambatofotsikely. Slightly different data were obtained by Reuning on another supposed betafite from Madagascar. Bjørlykke (1931) obtained 5.148 or 10.296 on the titanian variety (anal. 6, 7, 8). This latter value is similar to the microlite-pyrochlore cell dimensions.
7. Larsen (46, 130, 1921).
8. Machatschki, *Chem. Erde*, **7**, 72 (1932), gives a tentative formula for betafite. See also Niggli and Faesy, *Zs. Kr.*, **61**, 366 (1925), who suggest the grouping of betafite, samiresite, and blomstrandite as variants of one species, as here done. Reuning, *Chem. Erde*, **8**, 211 (1933), discusses the relation of betafite to pyrochlore-microl te. The supposed betafite from Ambatofotsikely examined by Reuning deviates most markedly from all the others in its formula. Bjørlykke (1931) finds that the powder pattern of the titanian-rich material (anal. 6, 7, 8) differs from that of betafite from Madagascar.
9. An analysis of supposed betafite from Ambatolampikely by Pisani in Lacroix (1, 384, 1922) yields a formula $(Ca,U)_2(Cb,Ti)_3O_{10}$, not in conformity with the other betafites. See further under *betafite Pisani*, p. 773.
10. Pisani anal. in Lacroix, *Bull. soc. min.*, **35**, 84 (1912).
11. Chernik, *Bull. soc. min.*, **50**, 485 (1927).
12. Pisani anal. in Lacroix (1, 384, 1922).
13. Bjørlykke, *Norsk Geol. Tidskr.*, **12**, 73 (1931).

842   **Djalmaite** $[(U,Ca,Pb,Bi,Fe)(Ta,Cb,Ti,Zr)_3O_9 \cdot nH_2O]$.   *Guimarães* (*Ann. Ac. Brasil. Sc.*, **9**, 347, 1939; *Am. Min.*, **26**, 343, 1941).

Isometric. Octahedrons modified by {113}.

P h y s. Fracture irregular. H. $5\frac{1}{2}$. G. 5.75–5.88. Color yellowish brown, greenish brown, or brownish black. Transparent in thin splinters, with a yellowish brown color. *n* 1.97.

C h e m. Essentially an oxide of tantalum and uranium, with titanium and other metals in small amounts. The formula is uncertain, perhaps $(U,Ca,Pb,Bi,Fe)(Ta,Cb,Ti,Zr)_3O_9 \cdot nH_2O$. Analysis gave: CaO 3.40, PbO 1.10, MgO 0.24, FeO 0.56, UO_2 2.17, UO_3 9.38, SnO_2 tr., TiO_2 2.54, ZrO_2 0.80, Bi_2O_3 0.98, WO_3 0.18, Ta_2O_5 72.27, Cb_2O_5 1.41, H_2O 4.62, total 99.65.

O c c u r. Found in granite pegmatite on Posse farm, Conçeicão County, Minas Geraes, Brazil. Associated with columbite, magnetite, samarskite, garnet, beryl, tourmaline, and bismuth minerals.

N a m e. After the Brazilian mineralogist and petrologist, Dr. Djalma Guimarães.

Possibly the tantalum equivalent of betafite.

843   **Ampangabeite** $[(Y,Er,U,Ca,Th)_2(Cb,Ta,Fe,Ti)_7O_{18}$?].   Ampangabéite *Lacroix (Bull. soc. min.*, **35**, 194, 1912; *C.R.*, **154**, 1040, 1912).   Hydroeuxenite *Sabot* (Inaug. Diss., Geneva, 50, 1914 — in Hintze [27, 1936]).

C r y s t.   Probably orthorhombic.   In short rectangular prisms.[1] Crystals sometimes large, and usually indistinctly developed or rounded. In radial prismatic aggregates.

P h y s.   Fracture irregular to conchoidal.   H. 4.   G. 3.36–4.64, increasing as the color becomes darker.   Luster horny or fatty.   Color light yellow-brown to deep brown and brownish black.   In thin splinters transparent.

O p t.   In transmitted light red-brown in color and isotropic (metamict). Color zones are sometimes seen. n 2.13 $\pm$ 0.03 (Ampangabé[2]).

Ch em.   Essentially an oxide of columbium, rare earths, and uranium, with the uncertain general formula varying between $A_2B_7O_{18}$ and AB_6O_{14}, according to the reported analyses.[3] A = Y, Er, U, Ca, Th; B = Cb, Ta, Fe[3], Ti.   The considerable water content is presumably due to alteration. Marked radioactivity has been observed.[4]

Anal.

	1	2	3	4	5
CaO	1.50	1.83	.....	0.87	0.36
MnO	.....	1.53	.....	.....	.....
(Y,Er)$_2$O$_3$	4.00	1.35	.....	4.71	2.18
CeO$_2$	.....	5.75	.....	.....	.....
(Ce,La,Di)$_2$O$_3$	0.60	2.10	5.10	0.67	1.45
UO$_2$	19.40	.....	14.35	11.98	6.72
U$_3$O$_8$	.....	12.50	.....	.....	.....
ThO$_2$	2.00	1.30	1.50	1.65	2.09
SnO$_2$	0.80	0.30	1.44	0.27	0.56
Al$_2$O$_3$	2.10	1.20	.....	trace	.....
Fe$_2$O$_3$	8.60	7.20	8.33	10.03	6.43
TiO$_2$	4.90	2.10	0.12	5.22	19.14
Cb$_2$O$_5$	34.80	}50.60	44.36	50.78	31.53
Ta$_2$O$_5$	8.90		1.76	1.80	12.61
H$_2$O	.....	.....	6.00	11.04	15.91
Ign. loss	12.40	11.55	.....	.....	.....
Rem.	.....	1.75	.....	.....	1.81
Total	100.50	101.06	82.96	99.02	100.79
G.	3.97–4.29	3.75	4.64	4.45	4.49

1. Ampangabé.[5]   2. Ambatofotsikely.   WO$_3$ in SnO$_2$.   Rem. is SiO$_2$.[6]   3. Ambatofotsikely.   Partial analysis.[7]   4. Ambatofotsikely.[8]   5. Unnamed mineral.   Divino de Ubá, Brazil.   Rem. is PbO 1.54, MgO 0.27, UO$_3$ as given.[10]

Tests.   Fuses to a black slag (more readily in the lighter-colored specimens).   More or less decomposed by acids; in HCl leaves a white residue and affords a golden-colored solution.

O c c u r.   In potash-rich pegmatites in Madagascar, associated with columbite, beryl, microcline, euxenite, strueverite, monazite, garnet, and muscovite.   The pegmatites are deeply weathered, and the contained minerals usually are more or less decomposed and associated with bismuth ochres and other secondary products.   Oriented growths of ampangabeite upon columbite, with the crystal axes (?) of the two minerals parallel, are common.

Originally from Ampangabé, near Miandrarivo, about 100 km. southwest of Tanarive, Madagascar. Also at Ambatofotsikely, northwest of Antsirabe, and reported from Sahamandrevo, southwest of Ampangabé, and from Andreba and Makonjovato, in Madagascar.

N a m e. From the locality, Ampangabé.

The species validity of ampangabeite is uncertain; it may be an inhomogeneous alteration product.[9]

UNNAMED. *Guimarães (Bol. Inst. Brasil Sc.*, **2**, 56, 1926).

In parallel and divergent groups of orthorhombic crystals, resembling eschynite in habit. Forms: {100}, {010}, and {101}, with (101) $\wedge$ ($\overline{1}$01) about 75°. Fracture subconchoidal. H. $5\frac{1}{2}$. G. 4.49. Luster resinous. Color on fracture dark chocolate to clear maroon.

C h e m. Similar to ampangabeite, with a possible formula AB_3O_8 (or $A_3B_{10}O_{26}$) with A = (Y,Er), U, Th, $Fe^3(?)$[10]; B = Ti, Cb, Ta. (See anal. 5 above.) Slightly attacked by H_2SO_4 and completely by HF. Found with samarskite, columbite, and monazite in pegmatite at Divino de Ubá, Minas Geraes, Brazil.

Ref.

1. Ungemach, *Bull. Soc. Min.*, **39**, 25 (1912), lists the forms {010}, {100}, {110}, and {201}, and states that the angles are approximately the same as euxenite but gives no measurements. Sabot (1914) gives {001}, {010}, and {100}, states that the angles vary somewhat from columbite and euxenite.

2. Larsen (39, 1921). Sabot (1914) gives n = 1.55, a value inconsistent with the supposed composition of the mineral. He also gives data on the absorption spectra.

3. The variation in the formula may be in part due to impurities in the analyzed material and in part to oxidation of the iron through alteration; in the latter case, some of the iron may have been erroneously assigned to the B part of the formula, and the formula may then approach that of betafite (Berman, 1941).

4. See Sabot (1914) and Lacroix (**2**, 131, 1922).

5. Pisani anal. in Lacroix (1912).

6. Duparc, Sabot, and Wunder, *Bull. soc. min.*, **36**, 15 (1913).

7. Sabot (1914).

8. Chernik, *Bull. soc. min.*, **49**, 129 (1926).

9. A crystallographic resemblance to euxenite was remarked by Ungemach, *Bull. soc. min.*, **39**, 25 (1916), and the mineral was held by Sabot (1914) to be an altered euxenite. Lacroix (**1**, 376, 1922); *Bull. soc. min.*, **35**, 194 (1912), however, does not support this view. The variation in the proportions of the constituents is a strong indication that the material is not homogeneous.

10. The Fe_2O_3 reported in the analysis normally would go into the B part of the formula, but the analysis material may well have been an altered and oxidized sample; the Fe may have been originally divalent and therefore probably belonging to the A part of the formula.

PISEKITE. *Krejčí* (*Časopis Min. Geol. Prague*, **1**, 2, 1923).

Found as fibro-lamellar aggregates and as supposedly monoclinic crystals with a habit similar to monazite.[1] Crystals elongated [010] and flattened {100}. Qualitative tests indicate the material to be essentially a columbate-tantalate-titanate of uranium and rare earths, with Th and Sn. Fracture conchoidal. H. $5\frac{1}{2}$–6. G. 4.032. Luster vitreous to resinous. Color yellowish brown to black. Streak gray. Metamict.[2]

Found with beryl, tourmaline, monazite, strueverite and garnet in pegmatite at Pisek, Bohemia. Originally considered to be a pseudomorph after monazite, but later denied and suggested to be related to ampangabeite.[3]

Ref.

1. Krejčí (1923) gives the observed forms {100}, {110}, {101}, {10$\bar{1}$} and angles close to the ratio 0.9659 : 1 : 0.9004 with β = 103°28′ (monazite).
2. Ježek, *Časopis Min. Geol. Prague*, **1**, 69 (1923), by Laue study.
3. Nováček, *Věda Přírodin Jahrg.*, **17**, 1 (1936) — *Min. Abs.*, **6**, 507 (1937).

844   **DELORENZITE** [(Y,U,Fe^2)(Ti,Sn ?)$_3$O$_8$?].   *Zambonini* (*Zs. Kr.*, **45**, 76, 1908; *Acc. Napoli, Rend.*, **14**, 113, 1908).

Cryst. Orthorhombic; dipyramidal — $2/m\ 2/m\ 2/m$.

$a : b : c = 0.3375 : 1 : 0.3412;$ $p_0 : q_0 : r_0 = 1.0109 : 0.3412 : 1$

$q_1 : r_1 : p_1 = 0.3375 : 0.9892 : 1;$ $r_2 : p_2 : q_2 = 2.9308 : 2.9628 : 1$

Forms:[1]

		ϕ	$\rho = C$	ϕ_1	$\rho_1 = A$	ϕ_2	$\rho_2 = B$
b	010	0°00′	90°00′	90°00′	90°00′	.....	0°00′
a	100	90 00	90 00	.....	0 00	0°00′	90 00
m	110	71 21	90 00	90 00	18 39	0 00	71 21
d	201	90 00	63 41	0 00	28 19	26 19	90 00
s	111	71 21	46 51$\frac{1}{2}$	18 50$\frac{1}{2}$	46 16	44$\cdot$41$\frac{1}{2}$	76 30$\frac{1}{2}$

Habit. Elongated [001] and tabular to lath-shaped {010}. {100} and {110} striated [001]. Usually in subparallel growths.

Craveggia, Piedmont.

Phys. Fracture subconchoidal. Brittle. H. 5$\frac{1}{2}$–6. G. 4.7±. Luster resinous. Color black. Transparent in thin splinters. Radioactive.

Opt. In transmitted light, chestnut brown in color. Metamict and isotropic.

Chem. An oxide of titanium, yttrium, uranium, iron, and tin, with a possible formula of AB_3O_8; B = Ti, Sn(?).[2] Analysis gave: FeO 4.25, Y$_2$O$_3$ 14.63, UO$_2$ 9.87, SnO$_2$ 4.33, TiO$_2$ 66.03, total 99.11. The true state of oxidation of the U and Fe is unknown.

Occur. Found with strueverite, columbite, ilmenite, tourmaline, spessartite and beryl in pegmatite at Craveggia, Val Vigesso, Piedmont, Italy.

Name. After G. De Lorenzo (1871–   ), Italian geologist.

Ref.

1. Uncertain form: g{130}.
2. Zambonini (1908) gives 2FeO·UO$_2$·2Y$_2$O$_3$·24TiO$_2$, but the constitution must remain uncertain in lack of adequate analytical data.

INDEX

Names of numbered and accepted species are printed in bold-face type.

Aarite, 236
Acanthite, 191
Acerdèse, 646
Acerilla, 203
Achondrites, 121
Acicular Bismuth, 412
Aciculite, 412
Acide antimonieux, 547, 595
　arsénieux, 543
　arsénieux prismatique, 545
　boracique, 662
　sélénieux, 595
Acido arsenioso, 543
Acidum boracis, 662
Acqua, 494
Adamantine Spar, 520, 523
Adamas, 146
Adamas Siderites, 520
Adelfolite; Adelpholite, 762, 778
Adlerstein, 681
Aerolites, 119, 121
Aerosit, 362
Aeschynite, 793
Aes caldarium rubro-fuscum, 491
Aes Cyprium, 99
Aes rude plumbei coloris, 187
Aethiops mineral, 215
Aguilarite, 178
Aikinite, 412
Aimant, 698
Ainalite, 577
Aithalite, 566
Akanthit, 191
Akontit, 322
Alabandine, 207
Alabandite, 200, 207
Alaite; alaïte, 603
Alaskaite, 475
Alcohol, 270
Aleación de plata con bismuto, 167
Alexandrite, 718, 720
Alexandrite-sapphire, 523
Algodonite, 170, 171
Alisonite, 200
Alkali-spinel, 689
Al-kohl, 270

Allcharite, 486
Allemontite, 128, 130
Alloclase; Alloclasite, Alloklas, 322, 324
Allopalladium, 106, 113
Allophytin, 567
Almandine; almandine-spinel, 692
Aloite, 603
Alquifoux, 203
Altaite, 200, 205
Aluminate of Glucina, 718
Alumine hydratée de Beaux, 667
Alumisches Eisenerz, 692
Alumochromite, 709
Alumogel, 667
Alundum, 525
Amalgam; Amalgama, 97
Amalgam, 103
Amalgam natif, 97
Amianthoid Magnesite, 636
Amianthus, 636
Amoibit, 298
Amorphous sulfur, 144
Ampangabeite, 806
Anatase, 583
Andorite, 457
Anglarite, 481
Anhydrous Binoxyd of Manganese, 562
Animikite, 97
Ännerödite, Aanerödite, 797
Annivite, 379
Anomalite, 566, 569
Antamokite, 187
Antimoine natif, 132
　natif arsenifère, 130
　oxydé, 547
　oxydé octaédrique, 544
　oxydé sulfuré, 279
　sulfuré, 270
　sulfuré capillaire, 452
　sulfuré nickelifère, 301
　sulfuré plumbocuprifère, 406
Antimon-Arsen, 130
Antimon-Arseniknickelglanz, 301
Antimonarsennickel, 236
Antimonbleiblende, 420
Antimonbleikupferblende, 406

809

Marceline, 551
Marchasita, 282
Marcylite, 508
Marignacite, 748, 755
Marmatite, 212
Marrite, 487
Mars, 114
Marsh Ore, 685
Martite, 532
Martourite, 481
Massicot, 516
Massicottite, 516
Matildite, 429
Maucherite, 192
Meadow Ore, 685
Melaconite; Melaconisa, 508
Melanglanz, 358
Melangraphite, 152
Melanochalcite, 508, 509
Melanosiderite, 687
Melnikovite; Melnikowit, 288
Melnokowit-Pyrit, 288
Melonite, 341
Menaccanite, 537
Menachanite; Menakanite, 534
Mendelejevite, 803
Mendeleyevite; Mendelyeevite, 803
Meneghinite, 402
Mengite, 780
Mennige, 517
Merasmolite, 210
Mercure argental, 97
  natif, 103
Mercurio; Mercurius, 103
Mercury, 103
Merkur-Blende, 251
Merkurfahlerz, 379
Merkur-Glanz, 216
Mesabite, 680
Metabrucite, 638
Metacinnabar, 209, 215
  selenian, 216
  zincian, 216
Metacinnabarite, 215
Metal escrito, 338
Metallum problematicum, 138
Metaperovskite, 730
Metasimpsonite, 748, 755
Metastibnite, 275, 454
Metazinnober, 215
Meteoric Iron, 115
  Nickel-Iron, 118
Meteorin, 119
Meteorites, 119
Meymacite, 606
Miargyrite, 424

Miargyrite, arsenian, 426
Micaceous hematite, 530
  Iron Ore, 527
Mica des Peintres; Mica pictoria nigra, 152
Micaultite, 562
Microlite, 748
Miedziankite, 379
Millerite, 231, 239
Minasite, 680
Mindigite, 652
Mine d'antimoine au plumes, 452
  d'Antimoine en plumes, 279
  d'antimoine grise tenant argent, 416
  d'argent rouge, 362
  de bismuth calciforme, 599
  de Cobalt arsenicale, 342
  de cobalt arsen. tenant cuivre, 236
  de Cobalt arsenico-sulfureuse, 296
  de Cobalt blanche, 296
  de Cobalt gris, 342
  de Cobalt sulfureuse, 262
  de cuivre grise, 374
  de cuivre vitreuse rouge, 491
  de fer limoneuse, 685
  d'Etain, 574
  rouge de cuivre, 491
Minera Antimonii, 270
  Ant. colorata, 279
  antimonii plumosa, 452
  argenti alba, 379
  argenti grisea, 374
  argenti nigra spongiosa, 358
  argenti rubra nigrescens, 362
  argenti rubra opaca, 362
  argenti rubra pellucida, 366
  argenti vitrea, 176
  Cobalti cinerea, 342
  Cupri Hepatica, 195
  Cupri Lazurea, 195
  cupri calc. . . . colore rubro, 491
  Ferri attractoria, 698
  Ferri lacustris var. palustris, 685
  ferri nigracans, magneti amica, 698
  ferri specularis, 527
  Ferri subaquosa, 685
  hepatica, 231
Minerale Cobalti terrea fuliginea, 566
Minio, 517
Minium, 517
Minium nativum; Minium, 251
Mispickel; Mistpuckel, 316
Mitchellite, 692
Mock-Lead, 210
Modderite, 242
Modumite, 342